List of the Elements with Their Atomic Symbols and Atomic Weights

Name	Symbol	Atomic Number	Atomic Weight	Name	Symbol	Atomic Number	Atomic Weight
Actinium	Ac	89	227.028	Mendelevium	Md	101	(258)
Aluminum	Al	13	26.9815	Mercury	Hg	80	200.59
Americium	Am	95	(243)	Molybdenum	Mo	42	95.94
Antimony	Sb	51	121.76	Neodymium	Nd	60	144.24
Argon	Ar	18	39.948	Neon	Ne	10	20.1797
Arsenic	As	33	74.9216	Neptunium	Np	93	237.048
Astatine	At	85	(210)	Nickel	Ni	28	58.693
Barium	Ba	56	137.327	Niobium	Nb	41	92.9064
Berkelium	Bk	97	(247)	Nitrogen	N	7	14.0067
Beryllium	Be	4	9.01218	Nobelium	No	102	(259)
Bismuth	Bi	83	208.980	Osmium	Os	76	190.23
Bohrium	Bh	107	(264)	Oxygen	O	8	15.9994
Boron	B	5	10.811	Palladium	Pd	46	106.42
Bromine	Br	35	79.904	Phosphorus	P	15	30.9738
Cadmium	Cd	48	112.411	Platinum	Pt	78	195.08
Calcium	Ca	20	40.078	Plutonium	Pu	94	(244)
Californium	Cf	98	(251)	Polonium	Po	84	(209)
Carbon	C	6	12.011	Potassium	K	19	39.0983
Cerium	Ce	58	140.115	Praseodymium	Pr	59	140.908
Cesium	Cs	55	132.905	Promethium	Pm	61	(145)
Chlorine	Cl	17	35.4527	Protactinium	Pa	91	231.036
Chromium	Cr	24	51.9961	Radium	Ra	88	226.025
Cobalt	Co	27	58.9332	Radon	Rn	86	(222)
Copper	Cu	29	63.546	Rhenium	Re	75	186.207
Curium	Cm	96	(247)	Rhodium	Rh	45	102.906
Darmstadtium	Ds	110	(271)	Roentgenium	Rg	111	(272)
Dubnium	Db	105	(262)	Rubidium	Rb	37	85.4678
Dysprosium	Dy	66	162.50	Ruthenium	Ru	44	101.07
Einsteinium	Es	99	(252)	Rutherfordium	Rf	104	(261)
Erbium	Er	68	167.26	Samarium	Sm	62	150.36
Europium	Eu	63	151.965	Scandium	Sc	21	44.9559
Fermium	Fm	100	(257)	Seaborgium	Sg	106	(266)
Fluorine	F	9	18.9984	Selenium	Se	34	78.96
Francium	Fr	87	(223)	Silicon	Si	14	28.0855
Gadolinium	Gd	64	157.25	Silver	Ag	47	107.868
Gallium	Ga	31	69.723	Sodium	Na	11	22.9898
Germanium	Ge	32	72.61	Strontium	Sr	38	87.62
Gold	Au	79	196.967	Sulfur	S	16	32.066
Hafnium	Hf	72	178.49	Tantalum	Ta	73	180.948
Hassium	Hs	108	(269)	Technetium	Tc	43	(98)
Helium	He	2	4.00260	Tellurium	Te	52	127.60
Holmium	Ho	67	164.930	Terbium	Tb	65	158.925
Hydrogen	H	1	1.00794	Thallium	Tl	81	204.383
Indium	In	49	114.818	Thorium	Th	90	232.038
Iodine	I	53	126.904	Thulium	Tm	69	168.934
Iridium	Ir	77	192.22	Tin	Sn	50	118.710
Iron	Fe	26	55.847	Titanium	Ti	22	47.88
Krypton	Kr	36	83.80	Tungsten	W	74	183.84
Lanthanum	La	57	138.906	Uranium	U	92	238.029
Lawrencium	Lr	103	(260)	Vanadium	V	23	50.9415
Lead	Pb	82	207.2	Xenon	Xe	54	131.29
Lithium	Li	3	6.941	Ytterbium	Yb	70	173.04
Lutetium	Lu	71	174.967	Yttrium	Y	39	88.9059
Magnesium	Mg	12	24.3050	Zinc	Zn	30	65.39
Manganese	Mn	25	54.9381	Zirconium	Zr	40	91.224
Meitnerium	Mt	109	(268)				

Chemistry 101: Fundamentals of General, Organic, and Biological Chemistry with Solutions Manual

CUSTOM EDITION FOR BUCKS COUNTY COMMUNITY COLLEGE

Taken from:

Fundamentals of General, Organic, and Biological Chemistry, Sixth Edition
by John McMurry, Mary Castellion, David S. Ballantine, Carl A. Hoeger, and Virginia E. Peterson

Study Guide and Full Solutions Manual for *Fundamentals of General, Organic, and Biological Chemistry,* Sixth Edition
by Susan E. McMurry

Learning Solutions

New York   Boston   San Francisco
London   Toronto   Sydney   Tokyo   Singapore   Madrid
Mexico City   Munich   Paris   Cape Town   Hong Kong   Montreal

Cover Art: Courtesy of PhotoDisc/GettyImages.

Taken from:

Fundamentals of General, Organic, and Biological Chemistry, Sixth Edition
by John McMurry, Mary Castellion, David S. Ballantine, Carl A. Hoeger, and Virginia E. Peterson
Copyright © 2010, 2007, 2003, 1999, 1996, 1992 by Pearson Education, Inc.
Published by Prentice Hall
Upper Saddle River, New Jersey 07458

Study Guide and Full Solutions Manual for *Fundamentals of General, Organic, and Biological Chemistry,* Sixth Edition
by Susan E. McMurry
Copyright © 2010 by Pearson Education, Inc.
Published by Prentice Hall
Upper Saddle River, New Jersey 07458

This special edition published in cooperation with Pearson Learning Solutions.

All trademarks, service marks, registered trademarks, and registered service marks are the property of their respective owners and are used herein for identification purposes only.

Pearson Learning Solutions, 501 Boylston Street, Suite 900, Boston, MA 02116
A Pearson Education Company
www.pearsoned.com

Printed in United States of America

1 2 3 4 5 6 7 8 9 10 V011 15 14 13 12 11 10

000200010270649540

JL

ISBN 10: 0-558-91270-2
ISBN 13: 978-0-558-91270-3

About the Authors

John McMurry, educated at Harvard and Columbia, has taught approximately 17,000 students in general and organic chemistry over a 30-year period. A Professor of Chemistry at Cornell University since 1980, Dr. McMurry previously spent 13 years on the faculty at the University of California at Santa Cruz. He has received numerous awards, including the Alfred P. Sloan Fellowship (1969–71), the National Institute of Health Career Development Award (1975–80), the Alexander von Humboldt Senior Scientist Award (1986–87), and the Max Planck Research Award (1991).

David S. Ballantine received his B.S. in Chemistry in 1977 from the College of William and Mary in Williamsburg, VA, and his Ph.D. in Chemistry in 1983 from the University of Maryland at College Park. After several years as a researcher at the Naval Research Labs in Washington, DC, he joined the faculty in the Department of Chemistry and Biochemistry of Northern Illinois University, where he has been a professor for the past twenty years. He was awarded the Excellence in Undergraduate Teaching Award in 1998 and was recently named the departmental Director of Undergraduate Studies. In addition, he is the faculty advisor to the NIU Chemistry Club, an American Chemical Society Student Affiliate program.

Carl A. Hoeger received his B.S. in Chemistry from San Diego State University and his Ph.D. in Organic Chemistry from the University of Wisconsin, Madison in 1983. After a postdoctoral stint at the University of California, Riverside, he joined the Peptide Biology Laboratory at the Salk Institute in 1985 where he ran the NIH Peptide Facility while doing basic research in the development of peptide agonists and antagonists. During this time he also taught general, organic, and biochemistry at San Diego City College, Palomar College, and Miramar College. He joined the teaching faculty at University of Califiornia, San Diego in 1998. Dr. Hoeger has been teaching chemistry to undergraduates for over 20 years, where he continues to explore the use of technology in the classroom. In 2004 he won the Paul and Barbara Saltman Distinguished Teaching Award from UCSD. He is currently the General Chemistry coordinator at UCSD, where he is also responsible for the training and guidance of over 100 teaching assistants in the Chemistry and Biochemistry departments.

Virginia E. Peterson received her B.S. in Chemistry in 1967 from the University of Washington in Seattle, and her Ph.D. in Biochemistry in 1980 from the University of Maryland at College Park. Between her undergraduate and graduate years she worked in lipid, diabetes, and heart disease research at Stanford University. Following her Ph.D. she took a position in the Biochemistry Department at the University of Missouri in Columbia and is now an Associate Professor. Currently she is the Director of Undergraduate Advising for the department and teaches both senior capstone classes and biochemistry classes for nonscience majors. Awards include both the college level and the university-wide Excellence in Teaching Award and, in 2006, the University's Outstanding Advisor Award and the State of Missouri Outstanding University Advisor Award. Dr. Peterson believes in public service and in 2003 received the Silver Beaver Award for service from the Boy Scouts of America.

Brief Contents

Contents

7   Chemical Reactions: Energy, Rates, and Equilibrium   182

5   Molecular Compounds   106

8   Gases, Liquids, and Solids   214

6   Chemical Reactions: Classification and Mass Relationships   142

Applications

ix

Preface

This textbook is primarily designed to provide students in the allied health sciences with an appropriate background in chemistry and biochemistry. But it also provides a general context for many of the chemical concepts so that students in other disciplines will gain a better appreciation of the importance of chemistry in everyday life. The coverage in this sixth edition includes sufficient breadth and depth to ensure adequate context and to provide students with opportunities to expand their knowledge.

To teach chemistry all the way from "What is an atom?" to "How do we get energy from glucose?" is a challenge. Throughout our general chemistry and organic chemistry coverage, the focus is on concepts fundamental to the chemistry of living things and everyday life. In our biochemistry coverage we strive to meet the further challenge of providing a context for the application of those concepts in biological systems. Our goal is to provide enough detail for thorough understanding while avoiding so much detail that students are overwhelmed. Many practical and relevant examples are included to illustrate the concepts and enhance student learning.

The material covered is ample for a two-term introduction to general, organic, and biological chemistry. While the general and early organic chapters contain concepts that are fundamental to understanding the material in biochemistry, the later chapters can be covered individually and in an order that can be adjusted to meet the needs of the students and the duration of the course.

The writing style is clear and concise and punctuated with practical and familiar examples from students' personal experience. Art work, diagrams, and molecular models are used extensively to provide graphical illustration of concepts to enhance student understanding. Since the true test of knowledge is the ability to apply that knowledge appropriately, we include numerous worked examples that incorporate consistent problem-solving strategies.

Regardless of their career paths, all students will be citizens in an increasingly technological society. When they recognize the principles of chemistry at work not just in their careers but in their daily lives, they are prepared to make informed decisions on scientific issues based on a firm understanding of the underlying concepts.

Organization

GENERAL CHEMISTRY: CHAPTERS 1–11 The introduction to elements, atoms, the periodic table, and the quantitative nature of chemistry (Chapters 1–3) is followed by chapters that individually highlight the nature of ionic and molecular compounds (Chapters 4 and 5). The next two chapters discuss chemical reactions and their stoichiometry, energies, rates, and equilibria (Chapters 6 and 7). Topics relevant to the chemistry of life follow: Gases, Liquids, and Solids (Chapter 8); Solutions (Chapter 9); and Acids and Bases (Chapter 10). Nuclear Chemistry (Chapter 11) closes the general chemistry sequence.

ORGANIC CHEMISTRY: CHAPTERS 12–17 These chapters concisely focus on what students must know in order to understand biochemistry. The introduction to hydrocarbons (Chapters 12 and 13) includes the basics of nomenclature, which is thereafter kept to a minimum. Discussion of functional groups with single bonds to oxygen, sulfur, or a halogen (Chapter 14) is followed by a short chapter on amines, which are so important to the chemistry of living things and drugs (Chapter 15). After introducing aldehydes and ketones (Chapter 16), the chemistry of carboxylic acids and their derivatives (including amides) is covered (Chapter 17), with a focus on similarities among the derivatives.

BIOLOGICAL CHEMISTRY: CHAPTERS 18–29　Rather than proceed through the complexities of protein, carbohydrate, lipid, and nucleic acid structure before getting to the roles of these compounds in the body, structure and function are integrated in this text. Protein structure (Chapter 18) is followed by enzyme and coenzyme chemistry (Chapter 19). After that we cover the function of hormones and neurotransmitters, and the action of drugs (Chapter 20). With enzymes introduced, the central pathways and themes of biochemical energy production can be described (Chapter 21). If the time you have available to cover biochemistry is limited, stop with Chapter 21 and your students will have an excellent preparation in the essentials of metabolism. The following chapters cover carbohydrate chemistry (Chapters 22 and 23), then lipid chemistry (Chapters 24 and 25). Next we discuss nucleic acids and protein synthesis (Chapter 26) and genomics (Chapter 27). The last two chapters cover protein and amino acid metabolism (Chapter 28) and provide an overview of the chemistry of body fluids (Chapter 29).

Changes to This Edition

COVERAGE OF GENERAL CHEMISTRY

Once again, there is a major emphasis in this edition on problem-solving strategies. This is reflected in expanded solutions in the Worked Example problems and the addition of more Key Concept Problems that focus on conceptual understanding. The most significant change in the Worked Example problems is the addition of a Ballpark Estimate at the beginning of many problems. The Ballpark Estimate provides an opportunity for students to evaluate the relationships involved in the problem and allows them to use an intuitive approach to arrive at a first approximation of the final answer. The ability to think through a problem before attempting a mathematical solution is a skill that will be particularly useful on exams, or when solving "real world" problems.

Other specific changes to chapters are provided below:

Chapter 1

- The Scientific Method is introduced in the text and reinforced in Applications presented in the chapter.

Chapter 3

- Discussion of the critical experiments of Thomson, Millikan, and Rutherford are included in the Application "Are Atoms Real" to provide historical perspective on the development of our understanding of atomic structure.
- Electron dot structures are introduced in Chapter 3 to emphasize the importance of the valence shell electronic configurations with respect to chemical behavior of the elements.

Chapter 4

- Electron dot structures are used to reinforce the role of valence shell electronic configurations in explaining periodic behavior and the formation of ions.

Chapter 5

- The two methods for drawing Lewis dot structures (the "general" method and the streamlined method for molecules containing C, N, O, X, and H) are discussed back-to-back to highlight the underlying principle of the octet rule common to both methods.

Chapter 6

- The concept of limiting reagents is incorporated in Section 6.7 in the discussion of reaction stoichiometry and percent yields.

Chapter 7

- The discussion of free energy and entropy in Section 7.4 has been revised to help students develop a more intuitive understanding of the role of entropy in spontaneous processes.
- Section 7.8 includes more discussion of how the equilibrium constant is calculated and what it tells us about the extent of reaction.

Chapter 8

- Sections 8.3–8.10 include more emphasis on use of the kinetic molecular theory to understand the behavior of gases described by the gas laws.
- Section 8.15 includes more discussion on the energetics of phase changes to help students understand the difference between heat transfer associated with a temperature change and heat transfer associated with the phase change of a substance.

Chapter 9

- Discussion of equivalents in Section 9.10 has been revised to emphasize the relationship between ionic charge and equivalents of ionic compounds.
- Discussion of osmotic pressure (Section 9.12) now includes the osmotic pressure equation and emphasizes the similarity with the ideal gas law.

Chapter 10

- Both the algebraic and logarithmic forms of K_w are presented in Section 10.8 to give students another approach to solving pH problems.
- The discussion of buffer systems now introduces the Henderson-Hasselbalch equation. This relationship makes it easier to identify the factors that affect the pH of a buffer system and is particularly useful in biochemical applications in later chapters.
- Discussion of common acid-base reactions has been moved back in the chapter to provide a more logical segue into titrations in Section 10.15.

Chapter 11

- Treatment of half-life in Section 11.5 now includes a generic equation to allow students to determine the fraction of isotope remaining after an integral or non-integral number of half-lives, which is more consistent with "real world" applications.
- The Applications in this chapter have been expanded to include discussion of new technologies such as Boron Neutron-Capture Therapy (BNCT), or to clear up misconceptions about current methods such as MRI.

COVERAGE OF ORGANIC CHEMISTRY

A major emphasis in this edition was placed on making the fundamental reactions organic molecules undergo much clearer to the reader, with particular vision toward those reactions encountered again in biochemical transformations. Also new to this edition is the expanded use and evaluation of line-angle structure for organic molecules, which are so important when discussing biomolecules. Most of the Applications have been updated to reflect current understanding and research.
    Other specific changes to chapters are provided below:

Chapter 12

- This chapter has been significantly rewritten to provide the student with a stronger foundation for the organic chemistry chapters that follow.
- A clearer description of what a functional group is, as well as a more systematic approach to drawing alkane isomers have been made.

- The topic of how to draw and interpret line structures for organic molecules has been added, along with worked examples of such.
- The discussion of conformations has been expanded.

Chapter 13

- A more general discussion of cis and trans isomers has been added.
- The discussion of organic reaction types, particularly rearrangement reactions, have been simplified.

Chapter 14

- The topic of oxidation in organic molecules has been clarified.

Chapter 15

- The role of NO in human biology has been updated to reflect current research.

Chapter 16

- A more detailed discussion of what is meant by toxic or poisonous has been added.

Chapter 17

- A discussion of ibuprofen has been added.

COVERAGE OF BIOLOGICAL CHEMISTRY

New topics, such as the use of anabolic steroids in sports, have been added to many of these chapters to highlight the relevance of biochemistry in modern society. In this text, nutrition is not treated as a separate subject but is integrated with the discussion of each type of biomolecule.

Chapter 18

- The discussion of sickle cell anemia has been expanded and the role of an amino acid substitution on hemoglobin structure clarified.
- The Application *Prions—Proteins That Cause Disease* has been updated to reflect current research.

Chapter 19

- Incorporated the information about lead poisoning into the discussion of enzyme inhibition.

Chapter 20

- The discussion of anabolic steroids has been updated.
- The discussion of drugs and their interaction with the neurotransmitter acetylcholine has been expanded.

Chapter 21

- The discussion of ATP energy production has been revised.

Chapter 22

- An explanation of the chair conformation of glucose has been included to enhance understanding of the shape of cyclic sugars.
- The Application *Chirality and Drugs* has been updated.
- The Application *Cell Surface Carbohydrates and Blood Type* has been revised.

Chapter 23

- The explanation of substrate level phosphorylation has been expanded for clarity.
- The emerging medical condition referred to as Metabolic Syndrome has been added to the text discussion of diabetes.
- The Application *Diagnosis and Monitoring of Diabetes* has been updated to include metabolic syndrome.
- Section 23.11 now contains an expanded discussion of gluconeogenesis.
- The discussion of polysaccharides has been updated.

Chapter 24

- The description of the cell membrane has been expanded.
- A discussion of some inhibitors of Cox 1 and Cox 2 enzymes, important in inflammation, has been added.

Chapter 25

- The discussion of triacylglycerol synthesis has been expanded.
- The discussion of ketone body formation has been expanded.
- A thorough explanation of the biosynthesis of fatty acids has been added.

Chapter 26

- The Application *Viruses and AIDS* has been updated.
- Information about the 1918 influenza pandemic was included in the Application *"Bird Flu": The Next Epidemic?*

Chapter 27

- A discussion of the problems associated with using recombinant DNA for commercial protein manufacture has been added.
- In Section 27.5, new bioethical issues are pointed out to reflect modern concerns.
- The discussion of recombinant DNA and polymerase chain reactions has been moved to this chapter from Chapter 26.

Focus on Learning

WORKED EXAMPLES   Most Worked Examples, both quantitative and not quantitative, include an Analysis section that precedes the Solution. The Analysis lays out the approach to solving a problem of the given type. When appropriate, a "Ballpark Estimate" gives students an overview of the relationships needed to solve the problem, and provides an intuitive approach to arrive at a rough estimate of the answer. The Solution presents the worked-out example using the strategy laid out in the Analysis and, in many cases, includes expanded discussion to enhance student understanding. The use of the two-column format introduced in the fifth edition for quantitative problems has been applied to more Worked Examples throughout the text. Following the Solution there is a Ballpark Check that compares the calculated answer to the Ballpark Estimate, when appropriate, and verifies that the answer makes chemical and physical sense.

KEY CONCEPT PROBLEMS are integrated throughout the chapters to focus attention on the use of essential concepts, as do the ***Understanding Key Concepts*** problems at the end of each chapter. Understanding Key Concepts problems are designed to test students' mastery of the core principles developed in the chapter. Students thus have an opportunity to ask "Did I get it?" before they proceed. Most of these Key Concept Problems use graphics or molecular-level art to illustrate the core principles and will be particularly useful to visual learners.

PROBLEMS   The problems within the chapters, for which brief answers are given in an appendix, cover every skill and topic to be understood. One or more problems, many of which are *new* to this edition, follow each Worked Example and others stand alone at the ends of sections.

MORE COLOR-KEYED, LABELED EQUATIONS   It is entirely too easy to skip looking at a chemical equation while reading. We have extensively used color to call attention to the aspects of chemical equations and structures under discussion, a continuing feature of this book that has been judged very helpful.

MOLECULAR MODELS   Additional computer-generated molecular models have been introduced, including the use of *electrostatic-potential maps for molecular models*.

KEY WORDS   Every key term is boldfaced on its first use, fully defined in the margin adjacent to that use, and listed at the end of the chapter. These are the terms students must understand to get on with the subject at hand. Definitions of all Key Words are collected in the Glossary.

END-OF-CHAPTER SUMMARIES   Here, the answers to the questions posed at the beginning of the chapter provide a summary of what is covered in that chapter. Where appropriate, the types of chemical reactions in a chapter are also summarized.

Focus on Relevancy

Chemistry is often considered to be a difficult and tedious subject. But when students make a connection between a concept in class and an application in their daily lives the chemistry comes alive, and they get excited about the subject. The applications in this book strive to capture student interest and emphasize the relevance of the scientific concepts. The use of relevant applications makes the concepts more accessible and increases understanding.

- **Applications** are both integrated into the discussions in the text and set off from the text in Application boxes. Each boxed application provides sufficient information for reasonable understanding and, in many cases, extends the concepts discussed in the text in new ways. The boxes end with a cross-reference to end-of-chapter problems that can be assigned by the instructor. Some well-received Applications from previous editions that have been retained include *Breathing and Oxygen Transport, Buffers in the Body, Prions, Protein Analysis by Electrophoresis, The Biochemistry of Running*, and *DNA Fingerprinting*.

- **New Applications in this edition** include *Aspirin—A Case Study, Temperature-Sensitive Materials, Anemia—A Limiting Reagent Problem, GERD: Too Much Acid or Not Enough*, and *It's a Ribozyme!*

FOCUS ON MAKING CONNECTIONS AMONG GENERAL, ORGANIC, AND BIOLOGICAL CHEMISTRY   This can be a difficult course to teach. Much of what students are interested in lies in the last part of the course, but the material they need to understand the biochemistry is found in the first two-thirds. It is easy to lose sight of the connections among general, organic, and biological chemistry so we use a feature, **Concepts to Review**, to call attention to these connections. From Chapter 4 on, the Concepts to Review section at the beginning of the chapter lists topics covered in earlier chapters that form the basis for what is discussed in the current chapter.

We have also retained the successful concept link icons and Looking Ahead notes.

- **Concept link icons** ⬭ are used extensively to indicate places where previously covered material is relevant to the discussion at hand. These links provide for cross-references and also serve to highlight important chemical themes as they are revisited.
- **Looking Ahead notes** call attention to connections between just-covered material and discussions in forthcoming chapters. These notes are designed to illustrate to the students why what they are learning will be useful in what lies ahead.

Making It Easier to Teach: Supplements for Instructors

MasteringChemistry™ **(www.masteringchemistry.com)** MasteringChemistry is the first adaptive-learning online homework system. It provides selected end-of-chapter problems from the text, as well as hundreds of tutorials with automatic grading, immediate answer-specific feedback, and simpler questions on request. Based on extensive research of precise concepts students struggle with, MasteringChemistry uniquely responds to your immediate needs, thereby optimizing your study time.

Instructor Resource Manual (0-32-161241-8) Features lecture outlines with presentation suggestions, teaching tips, suggested in-class demonstrations, and topics for classroom discussion.

Test Item File (0-32-161514-X) Updated to reflect the revisions in this text and contains questions in a bank of more than 2,000 multiple-choice questions.

Transparency Pack (0-32-161513-1) More than 225 full-color transparencies chosen from the text put principles into visual perspective and save you time while you are preparing for your lectures.

Instructor Resource Center on CD/DVD (0-32-161242-6) This CD/DVD provides an intergrated collection of resources designed to help you make efficient and effective use of your time. This CD/DVD features most art from the text, including figures and tables in PDF format for high-resolution printing, as well as four pre-built PowerPoint™ presentations. The first presentation contains the images/figures/tables embedded within the PowerPoint slides, while the second includes a complete modifiable lecture outline. The final two presentations contain worked "in chapter" sample exercises and questions to be used with Classroom Response Systems. This CD/DVD also contains movies and animations, as well as the TestGen version of the Test Item File, which allows you to create and tailor exams to your needs.

BlackBoard® and WebCT®—Practice and assessment materials are available upon request in these course management platforms.

Making It Easier to Learn: Supplements for Students

Study Guide and Full Solutions Manual (0-32-161238-8) and **Study Guide and Selected Solutions Manual (0-32-161239-6)**, both by Susan McMurry. The selected version provides solutions only to those problems that have a short answer in the text's Selected Answer Appendix (problems numbered in blue in the text). Both versions explain in detail how the answers to the in-text and end-of-chapter problems are obtained. They also contain chapter summaries, study hints, and self-tests for each chapter.

For the Laboratory

Exploring Chemistry: Laboratory Experiments in General, Organic and Biological Chemistry, 2nd Edition (0-13-047714-1) by Julie R. Peller of Indiana University. Written specifically to accompany Fundamentals of General, Organic and Biological Chemistry, this manual contains 34 fresh and accessible experiments specifically for GOB students.

Catalyst: The Prentice Hall Custom Laboratory Program for Chemistry. This program allows you to custom-build a chemistry lab manual that matches your content needs and course organization. You can either write your own labs using the Lab Authoring Kit tool, or select from the hundreds of labs available at www.prenhall.com/catalyst. This program also allows you to add your own course notes, syllabi, or other materials.

Acknowledgments

From conception to completion, the development of a modern textbook requires both a focused attention on the goals and the coordinated efforts of a diverse team. We have been most fortunate to have had the services of many talented and dedicated individuals whose efforts have contributed greatly to the overall quality of this text.

First and foremost, we are grateful to Kent Porter Hamann who, as senior editor of this text through many past revisions, provided exemplary leadership and encouragement to the team in the early stages of this project. Very special appreciation goes to Ray Mullaney, editor in chief of book development, who mentored the new team members and managed to coordinate the many and varied details. Irene Nunes, our developmental editor, worked closely with the authors to ensure accuracy and consistency. We also are grateful for the services of Wendy Perez, project manager; Laurie Varites, assistant editor; Lia Tarabokjia, and Jill Traut and Robert Walters, production project managers. Finally, special thanks also to Susan McMurry and Margaret Trombley, whose efforts on the Solutions Manuals and MasteringChemistry tutorial software, respectively, have added value to the overall package.

Finally, many instructors and students who have used the fifth edition have provided valuable insights and feedback and improved the accuracy of the current edition. We gratefully acknowledge the following reviewers for their contributions to the sixth edition:

Sheikh Ahmed, *West Virginia University*
Stanley Bajue, *CUNY-Medgar Evers College*
Daniel Bender, *Sacramento City College*
Dianne A. Bennett, *Sacramento City College*
Alfredo Castro, *Felician College*
Gezahegn Chaka, *Louisiana State University, Alexandria*
Michael Columbia, *Indiana University-Purdue University, Fort Wayne*
Rajeev B. Dabke, *Columbus State University*
Danae R. Quirk-Dorr, *Minnesota State University, Mankato*
Pamela S. Doyle, *Essex County College*
Marie E. Dunstan, *York College of Pennsylvania*

Karen L. Ericson, *Indiana University-Purdue University, Fort Wayne*
Charles P. Gibson, *University of Wisconsin, Oshkosh*
Clifford Gottlieb, *Shasta College*
Mildred V. Hall, *Clark State Community College*
Meg Hausman, *University of Southern Maine*
Ronald Hirko, *South Dakota State University*
L. Jaye Hopkins, *Spokane Community College*
Margaret Isbell, *Sacramento City College*
James T. Johnson, *Sinclair Community College*
Margaret G. Kimble, *Indiana University-Purdue University Fort Wayne*

Grace Lasker, *Lake Washington Technical College*
Ashley Mahoney, *Bethel University*
Matthew G. Marmorino, *Indiana University, South Bend*
Diann Marten, *South Central College, Mankato*
Barbara D. Mowery, *York College of Pennsylvania*
Tracey Arnold Murray, *Capital University*
Andrew M. Napper, *Shawnee State University*
Lisa Nichols, *Butte Community College*
Glenn S. Nomura, *Georgia Perimeter College*

Douglas E. Raynie, *South Dakota State University*
Paul D. Root, *Henry Ford Community College*
Victor V. Ryzhov, *Northern Illinois University*
Karen Sanchez, *Florida Community College, Jacksonville-South*
Mir Shamsuddin, *Loyola University, Chicago*
Jeanne A. Stuckey, *University of Michigan*
John Sullivan, *Highland Community College*
Deborah E. Swain, *North Carolina Central University*
Susan T. Thomas, *University of Texas, San Antonio*
Yakov Woldman, *Valdosta State University*

The authors are committed to maintaining the highest quality and accuracy and look forward to comments from students and instructors regarding any aspect of this text and supporting materials. Questions or comments should be directed to the lead co-author.

David S. Ballantine
dballant@niu.edu

Concise, Accessible, and Unique

QUANTITATIVE AND CONCEPTUAL

Worked Examples
These examples have been modified to emphasize both problem-solving strategies and conceptual understanding.

Analysis
Most Worked Examples include an Analysis section that precedes the solution. The Analysis lays out the approach to solving a problem of the given type.

NEW! Ballpark Estimates
Ballpark Estimates help students arrive at a rough estimate of the final answer based on an intuitive approach to the problem.

Solution
The Solution shows students how to apply the appropriate problem-solving strategy and guides them through the steps to follow in obtaining the answer.

Ballpark Check
Many of the Worked Examples culminate with a Ballpark Check that helps students quickly check whether the answer they have calculated in numerical Worked Examples is reasonable.

WORKED EXAMPLE **8.4** Using Boyle's Law: Finding Volume at a Given Pressure

In a typical automobile engine, the fuel/air mixture in a cylinder is compressed from 1.0 atm to 9.5 atm. If the uncompressed volume of the cylinder is 750 mL, what is the volume when fully compressed?

ANALYSIS This is a Boyle's law problem because the volume and pressure in the cylinder change but the amount of gas and the temperature remain constant. According to Boyle's law, the pressure of the gas times its volume is constant:

$$P_1V_1 = P_2V_2$$

Knowing three of the four variables in this equation, we can solve for the unknown.

◄ A cut-away diagram of internal combustion engine shows movement of pistons during expansion and compression cycles.

BALLPARK ESTIMATE Since the pressure *increases* approximately tenfold (from 1.0 atm to 9.5 atm), the volume must *decrease* to approximately one-tenth, from 750 mL to about 75 mL.

SOLUTION

STEP 1: Identify known information. Of the four variables in Boyle's law, we know $P_1, V_1,$ and P_2.

$P_1 = 1.0$ atm
$V_1 = 750$ mL
$P_2 = 9.5$ atm

STEP 2: Identify answer and units.

$V_2 = ??$ mL

STEP 3: Identify equation. In this case, we simply substitute the known variables into Boyle's law and rearrange to isolate the unknown.

$$P_1V_1 = P_2V_2 \implies V_2 = \frac{P_1V_1}{P_2}$$

STEP 4: Solve. Substitute the known information into the equation. Make sure units cancel so that the answer is given in the units of the unknown variable.

$$V_2 = \frac{P_1V_1}{P_2} = \frac{(1.0\ \text{atm})(750\ \text{mL})}{(9.5\ \text{atm})} = 79\ \text{mL}$$

BALLPARK CHECK Our estimate was 75 mL.

KEY CONCEPT PROBLEM 8.17

Assume that you have a mixture of He (MW = 4 amu) and Xe (MW = 131 amu) at 300 K. Which of the drawings (a)-(c) best represents the mixture (blue = He; green = Xe)?

(a) (b) (c)

8.11 Intermolecular Forces

What determines whether a substance is a gas [...] perature? Why does rubbing alcohol evapor[...] Why do molecular compounds have lower m[...] To answer these and a great many other such [...] nature of **intermolecular forces**—the forces tha[...] than within an individual molecule.

In gases, the intermolecular forces are neg[...] pendently of one another. In liquids and solid[...] strong enough to hold the molecules in close c[...] the intermolecular forces in a substance, the m[...] ecules, and the higher the melting and boiling [...]

There are three major types of intermolecu[...] sion, and *hydrogen bonding*. We will discuss ea[...]

Dipole–Dipole Forces

Recall from Sections 5.8 and 5.9 that many mo[...] and may therefore have a net molecular polari[...] the positive and negative ends of different m[...] by what is called a **dipole–dipole force**. (Figur[...]

Dipole–dipole forces are weak, with stren[...] pared to the 70–100 kcal/mol typically found for the strength of a covalent bond. Nevertheless, the effects of dipole–dipole forces are important, as can be seen by looking at the difference in boiling points between polar and nonpolar molecules. Butane, for instance, is a nonpolar molecule with a molecular weight of 58 amu and a boiling point of −0.5 °C, whereas acetone has the same molecular weight yet boils 57 °C higher because it is polar. (Recall from Section 5.8 how molecular polarities can be visualized using electrostatic potential maps. ([⬡], p. 000)

A summary and comparison of the various kinds of intermolecular forces is shown in Table 8.3.

TABLE 8.3 A Comparison of Intermolecular Forces

FORCE	STRENGTH	CHARACTERISTICS
Dipole–dipole	Weak (1 kcal/mol)	Occurs between polar molecules
London dispersion	Weak (0.5–2.5 kcal/mol)	Occurs between all molecules; strength depends on size
Hydrogen bond	Moderate (2–10 kcal/mol)	Occurs between molecules with O—H, N—H, and F—H bonds

Looking Ahead

Dipole–dipole forces, London dispersion forces, and hydrogen bonds are traditionally called "intermolecular forces" because of their influence on the properties of molecular compounds. But these same forces can also operate between different parts of a very large molecule. In this context, they are often referred to as "noncovalent interactions." In later chapters, we will see how noncovalent interactions determine the shapes of biologically important molecules such as proteins and nucleic acids. [⬡]

[...] polar molecules of similar size.

Dipole–dipole force The attractive force between positive and negative ends of polar molecules.

δ−   δ+   δ−   δ+

(a)   (b)

Key Concept Problems
These problems are integrated within the chapter, appearing at the end of a Worked Example or after the discussion of an important concept. These problems immediately focus students' attention on essential concepts and help them to test their understanding.

Looking Ahead
Looking Ahead Notes provide students with a preview of how the material being presented connects to the discussion in forthcoming chapters.

Concept Links
These links indicate where concepts in the text build on material from earlier chapters. This chain link icon provides a quick visual reminder that new material being discussed relates to a concept introduced previously.

This best-selling text showcases the hallmark strengths of the McMurry author team—a concise writing style, a unique approach to explaining the quantitative aspects of chemistry, and deep insight into chemical principles. The elements on each page—text, worked examples, figures, molecular structures and models, and the various learning aids described below—were designed to work together to help students develop an understanding to the quantitative and conceptual side of chemistry.

APPLICATION ▶ Greenhouse Gases and Global Warming

The mantle of gases surrounding the earth is far from the uniform mixture you might expect, consisting of layers that vary in composition and properties at different altitudes. The ability of the gases in these layers to absorb radiation is responsible for life on earth as we know it.

The *stratosphere*—the layer extending from about 12 km up to 50 km altitude—contains the ozone layer that is responsible for absorbing harmful UV radiation. The *troposphere* is the layer extending from the surface up to about 12 km altitude. It should not surprise you to learn that the troposphere is the layer most easily disturbed by human activities and that this layer has the greatest impact on the earth's surface conditions. Among those impacts, a process called the *greenhouse effect* is much in the news today.

The greenhouse effect refers to the warming that occurs in the troposphere as gases absorb radiant energy. Much of the radiant energy reaching the earth's surface from the sun is reflected back into space, but some is absorbed by atmospheric gases—particularly those referred to as—*greenhouse gases* (GHGs)—water vapor, carbon dioxide, and methane. This absorbed radiation warms the atmosphere and acts to maintain a relatively stable temperature of 15 °C (59 °F) at the earth's surface. Without the greenhouse effect, the average surface temperature would be about −18 °C (0 °F)—a temperature so low that Earth would be frozen and unable to sustain life.

The basis for concern about the greenhouse effect is the fear that human activities over the past century have disturbed the earth's delicate thermal balance. Should increasing amounts of radiation be absorbed, increased atmospheric heating will result, and global temperatures will continue to rise.

Measurements show that the concentration of atmospheric CO_2 has been rising in the last 150 years, largely because of the increased use of fossil fuels, from an estimated 290 parts per million (ppm) in 1850 to current levels approaching 380 ppm. The increase in CO_2 levels correlates with a concurrent increase in average global temperatures, with the 11 years between 1995 and 2006 ranking among the 12-highest since recording of global temperatures began in 1850. The latest report of the Intergovernmental Panel on Climate Change published in November 2007 concluded that "Warming of the climate system is unequivocal, as is now evident from observations of increases in global average air and ocean temperatures, widespread melting of snow and ice and rising global average sea level. . . . Continued GHG emissions at or above current rates would cause further warming and induce many changes in the global climate system during the 21st century that would *very likely* be larger than those observed during the 20th century."

See Additional Problems 8.101 and 8.102 at the end of the chapter.

▲ **Concentrations of atmospheric** ... age temperatures have increased d... 150 years because of increased fo... serious changes in earth's climate s...
© Crown copyright 2006 data provided by t...

Applications

These boxed Application essays connect the chemical concepts within each chapter to topics that are drawn from everyday life, clinical practice, health and nutrition, ecology, biotechnology, and chemical research.

Molecular Models

These computer-generated molecular models promote students' understanding of chemistry on a molecular level with electrostatic potential maps.

CH_3CH_2OH
Ethyl alcohol

OH

Phenol

$CH_3CH_2OCH_2CH_3$
Diethyl ether

6.5 Mole Relationships and Chemical Equations

In a typical recipe, the amount of ingredients needed are specified using a variety of units: The amount of flour, for example, is usually specified in cups, whereas the amount of salt or vanilla flavoring might be indicated in teaspoons. In chemical reactions, the appropriate unit to specify the relationship between reactants and products is the mole.

The coefficients in a balanced chemical equation tell how many *molecules*, and thus how many *moles*, of each reactant are needed and how many molecules, and thus moles, of each product are formed. You can then use molar mass to calculate reactant and product masses. If, for example, you saw the following balanced equation for the industrial synthesis of ammonia, you would know that 3 mol of H_2 (3 mol × 2.0 g/mol = 6.0 g) are required for reaction with 1 mol of N_2 (28.0 g) to yield 2 mol of NH_3 (2 mol × 17.0 g/mol = 34.0 g).

This number of moles of hydrogen . . . . . . reacts with this number of moles of nitrogen . . . to yield this number of moles of ammonia.

$$3\,H_2 + 1\,N_2 \longrightarrow 2\,NH_3$$

The coefficients can be put in the form of *mole ratios*, which act as conversion factors when setting up factor-label calculations. In the ammonia synthesis, for example, the mole ratio of H_2 to N_2 is 3:1, the mole ratio of H_2 to NH_3 is 3:2, and the mole ratio of N_2 to NH_3 is 1:2:

$$\frac{3\ \text{mol } H_2}{1\ \text{mol } N_2} \quad \frac{3\ \text{mol } H_2}{2\ \text{mol } NH_3} \quad \frac{1\ \text{mol } N_2}{2\ \text{mol } NH_3}$$

Worked Example 6.9 shows how to set up and use mole ratios.

Color and Labeling Equations

Color has been extensively used to call attention to the aspects of chemical equations and structures under discussion. The number of explanatory labels set in balloons that focus on the important details in chemical equations and structures have also been increased.

A Balanced Approach to General, Organic, and Biological Chemistry

UNDERSTANDING CORE PRINCIPLES

Summary: Revisiting the Chapter Goals

The chapter summary revisits the chapter goals that open the chapter. Each of the questions posed at the start of the chapter is answered by a summary of the essential information needed to attain the corresponding goal.

Key Words

All of the chapter's boldface terms are listed in alphabetical order and are cross-referenced to the page where it appears in the text.

PROBLEM 5.25

A white crystalline solid has a melting point of 128 °C. It is soluble in water, but the resulting solution does not conduct electricity. Is the substance ionic or molecular? Explain.

PROBLEM 5.26

Aluminum chloride ($AlCl_3$) has a melting point of 190 °C, whereas aluminum oxide (Al_2O_3) has a melting point of 2070 °C. Explain.

KEY WORDS

Binary compound, *p. 90*
Bond angle, *p. 91*
Bond length, *p. 92*
Condensed structure, *p. 102*
Coordinate covalent bond, *p. 103*
Covalent bond, *p. 105*
Double bond, *p. 109*
Electronegativity, *p. 110*
Lewis structure, *p. 110*
Lone pair, *p. 114*
Molecular compound, *p. 120*
Molecular formula, *p. 120*
Molecule, *p. 122*
Polar covalent bond, *p. 125*
Regular tetrahedron, *p. 126*
Single bond, *p. 130*
Structural formula, *p. 131*
Triple bond, *p. 132*
Valence-shell electron-pair repulsion (VSEPR) model, *p. 132*

SUMMARY: REVISITING THE CHAPTER GOALS

1. **What is a covalent bond?** A *covalent bond* is formed by the sharing of electrons between atoms rather than by the complete transfer of electrons from one atom to another. Atoms that share two electrons are joined by a *single bond* (such as C—C), atoms that share four electrons are joined by a *double bond* (such as C=C), and atoms that share six electrons are joined by a *triple bond* (such as C≡C). The group of atoms held together by covalent bonds is called a *molecule*.
   Electron sharing typically occurs when a singly occupied valence orbital on one atom *overlaps* a singly occupied valence orbital on another atom. The two electrons occupy both overlapping orbitals and belong to both atoms, thereby bonding the atoms together. Alternatively, electron sharing can occur when a filled orbital containing an unshared, *lone pair* of electrons on one atom overlaps a vacant orbital on another atom to form a *coordinate covalent bond*.

2. **How does the octet rule apply to covalent bond formation?** Depending on the number of valence electrons, different atoms form different numbers of covalent bonds. In general, an atom shares enough electrons to reach a noble gas configuration. Hydrogen, for instance, forms one covalent bond because it needs to share one more electron to achieve the helium configuration ($1s^2$). Carbon and other group 4A elements form four covalent bonds because they need to share four more electrons to reach an octet. In the same way, nitrogen and other group 5A elements form three covalent bonds, oxygen and other group 6A elements form two covalent bonds, and halogens (group 7A elements) form one covalent bond.

3. **How are molecular compounds represented?** Formulas such as H_2O, NH_3, and CH_4, which show the numbers and kinds of atoms in a molecule, are called *molecular formulas*. More useful are *Lewis structures*, which show how atoms are connected in molecules. Covalent bonds are indicated as lines between atoms, and valence electron lone pairs are shown as dots. Lewis structures are drawn by counting the total number of valence electrons in a molecule or polyatomic ion and then placing shared pairs (bonding) and lone pairs (nonbonding) so that all electrons are accounted for.

4. **What is the influence of valence-shell electrons on molecular shape?** Molecules have specific shapes that depend on the number of electron charge clouds (bonds and lone pairs) surrounding the various atoms. These shapes can often be predicted using the *valence-shell electron-pair repulsion* (*VSEPR*) model. Atoms with two electron charge clouds adopt linear geometry, atoms with three charge clouds adopt planar triangular geometry, and atoms with four charge clouds adopt tetrahedral geometry.

5. **When are bonds and molecules polar?** Bonds between atoms are *polar covalent* if the bonding electrons are not shared equally between the atoms. The ability of an atom to attract electrons in a covalent bond is the atom's *electronegativity* and is highest for reactive nonmetal elements on the upper right of the periodic table and lowest for metals on the lower left. Comparing electronegativities allows a prediction of whether a given bond is covalent, polar covalent, or ionic. Just as individual bonds can be polar, entire molecules can be polar if electrons are attracted more strongly to one part of the molecule than to another. Molecular polarity is due to the sum of all individual bond polarities and lone-pair contributions in the molecule.

6. **What are the major differences between ionic and molecular compounds?** *Molecular compounds* can be gases, liquids, or low-melting solids. They usually have lower melting points and boiling points than ionic compounds, many are water insoluble, and they do not conduct electricity when melted or dissolved.

Demanding, yet logical, this text sets itself apart by requiring students to master problem-solving strategies and conceptual understanding before moving on to the next concept.

Understanding Key Concepts

These problems at the end of each chapter allow students to test their mastery of the core principles developed in the chapter. Students have an opportunity to ask "Did I get it?" before they proceed.

UNDERSTANDING KEY CONCEPTS

5.27 Which of the drawings shown here is more likely to represent an ionic compound and which a covalent compound?

(a)   (b)

5.28 If yellow spheres represent sulfur atoms and red spheres represent oxygen atoms, which of the following drawings depicts a collection of sulfur dioxide molecules?

(a)   (b)

(c)   (d)

5.29 What is the geometry around the central atom in the following molecular models? (There are no "hidden" atoms; all atoms in each model are visible.)

(a)   (b)

(c)

...he following molecular models have a tetrahe-...al atom, and one does not. Which is the odd ...e: All peripheral atoms are visible.)

(a)   (b)

(c)

5.31 The ball-and-stick molecular model shown here is a representation of acetaminophen, the active ingredient in such over-the-counter headache remedies as Tylenol. The lines indicate only the connections between atoms, not whether the bonds are single, double, or triple (red = O, gray = C, blue = N, ivory = H).

(a) What is the molecular formula of acetaminophen?
(b) Indicate the positions of the multiple bonds in acetaminophen.
(c) What is the geometry around each carbon and each nitrogen?

Acetaminophen

5.32 The atom-to-atom connections in vitamin C (ascorbic acid) are as shown here. Convert this skeletal drawing to a Lewis electron-dot structure for vitamin C by showing the positions of any multiple bonds and lone pairs of electrons.

Vitamin C

5.33 The ball-and-stick molecular model shown here is a representation of thalidomide, a drug that causes terrible birth defects when taken by expectant mothers but has been approved for treating leprosy. The lines indicate only the connections between atoms, not whether the bonds are single, double, or triple (red = O, gray = C, blue = N, ivory = H).

(a) What is the molecular formula of thalidomide?
(b) Indicate the positions of the multiple bonds in thalidomide.

---

140 CHAPTER 5 Molecular Compounds

5.72 Predict the three-dimensional shape of the following molecules:
(a) SiF_4
(b) CF_2Cl_2
(c) SO_3
(d) BBr_3
(e) NF_3

5.73 Predict the geometry around each carbon atom in the amino acid alanine.

$$CH_3CHCOOH$$
$$NH_2$$
Alanine

5.74 Predict the geometry around each carbon atom in vinyl acetate, a precursor of the poly(vinyl alcohol) polymer used in automobile safety glass.

$$H_2C=CH-O-C-CH_3$$
Vinyl acetate

POLARITY OF BONDS AND MOLECULES

5.75 Where in the periodic table are the most electronegative elements found, and where are the least electronegative elements found?

5.76 Predict the electronegativity of the yet undiscovered element with $Z = 119$.

5.77 Look at the periodic table, and then order the following elements according to increasing electronegativity: Li, K, Br, C, Cl.

5.78 Look at the periodic table, and then order the following elements according to decreasing electronegativity: C, Ca, Cs, Cl, Cu.

5.79 Which of the following bonds are polar? Identify the negative and positive ends of each bond by using $\delta-$ and $\delta+$.
(a) I—Br
(b) O—H
(c) C—F
(d) N—C
(e) C—C

5.80 Which of the following bonds are polar? Identify the negative and positive ends of each bond by using $\delta-$ and $\delta+$.
(a) O—Br
(b) N—H
(c) P—O
(d) C—S
(e) C—Li

5.81 Based on electronegativity differences, would you expect bonds between the following pairs of atoms to be largely ionic or largely covalent?
(a) Be and F
(b) Ca and Cl
(c) O and H
(d) Be and Br

5.82 Arrange the following molecules in order of the increasing polarity of their bonds:
(a) HCl
(b) PH_3
(c) H_2O
(d) CF_4

5.83 Ammonia, NH_3, and phosphorus trihydride, PH_3, both have a trigonal pyramid geometry. Which one is more polar? Explain.

5.84 Decide whether each of the compounds listed in Problem 5.82 is polar, and show the direction of polarity.

5.85 Carbon dioxide is a nonpolar molecule, whereas sulfur dioxide is polar. Draw Lewis structures for each of these molecules to explain this observation.

5.86 Water (H_2O) is more polar than hydrogen sulfide (H_2S). Explain.

NAMES AND FORMULAS OF MOLECULAR COMPOUNDS

5.87 Name the following binary compounds:
(a) NO_2
(b) SF_6
(c) BrI_5
(d) N_2O_3
(e) NI_3
(f) IF_7

5.88 Name the following compounds:
(a) $SiCl_4$
(b) NaH
(c) SbF_5
(d) OsO_4

5.89 Write formulas for the following compounds:
(a) Phosphorus triiodide
(b) Arsenic trichloride
(c) Tetraphosphorus trisulfide
(d) Dialuminum hexafluoride
(e) Dinitrogen tetroxide
(f) Arsenic pentachloride

5.90 Write formulas for the following compounds:
(a) Selenium dioxide
(b) Xenon tetroxide
(c) Dinitrogen pentasulfide
(d) Triphosphorus tetraselenide

Applications

5.91 Draw electron-dot structures for CO and NO. Why are these molecules so reactive? [*CO and NO: Pollutants or Miracle Molecules?*, p. 116]

5.92 What is a vasodilator, and why would it be useful in treating hypertension (high blood pressure)? [*CO and NO: Pollutants or Miracle Molecules?*, p. 116]

5.93 How is a polymer formed? [*VERY Big Molecules*, p. 127]

5.94 Do any polymers exist in nature? Explain. [*VERY Big Molecules*, p. 127]

5.95 Why are many chemical names so complex? [*Damascenone by Any Other Name*, p. 135]

5.96 Can you tell from the name whether a chemical is natural or synthetic? [*Damascenone by Any Other Name*, p. 135]

General Questions and Problems

5.97 The discovery in the 1960s that xenon and fluorine react to form a molecular compound was a surprise to most chemists, because it had been thought that noble gases could not form bonds.
(a) Why was it thought that noble gases could not form bonds?
(b) Draw a Lewis structure of XeF_4.

Application Problems

Each boxed application essay throughout the text ends with a cross-reference to end-of-chapter problems. These problems help students test their understanding of the material and, more importantly, help students see the connection between chemistry and the world around them.

General Questions and Problems

These problems are cumulative, pulling together topics from various parts of the chapter and previous chapters. These help students synthesize the material just learned while helping them review topics from previous chapters.

Three Steps to Make Learning Part of the Grade

MasteringChemistry™ emulates the instructor's office-hour environment, coaching students on problem-solving techniques by asking questions that reveal gaps in understanding, giving them the power to answer questions on their own. It tutors them individually—with feedback specific to their errors, offering optional simpler steps.

1. Submit an answer and receive immediate, error-specific feedback.

MasteringChemistry is the only system to provide instantaneous feedback specific to the most-common wrong answers, accumulated over eight years of capturing and researching student errors.

2. Show help specific to your needs.

Simpler sub-problems—"hints"—are provided upon request. From these, students can pick and choose only the help they need. These hints are built on data of key steps and concepts that students are found to struggle with nationally.

3. Partial credit means motivation for method.

MasteringChemistry is uniquely able to provide partial credit for the student's method (based on the simpler subproblems requested and errors made). Credit is at the heart of student motivation and so MasteringChemistry encourages students to focus on their method as well as their final answer.-

www.masteringchemistry.com

Incorporate Dynamic Homework into Your Course with Automatic Grading

Homework Assignments of Ideal Difficulty and Duration

MasteringChemistry™ is unique in providing instructors with national data on difficulty and duration of every problem and tutorial. This allows you to quickly build homework assignments uniquely tailored to the ability of your students and goals of your course. Alternately, you can customize or choose pre-built weekly assignments to your needs.

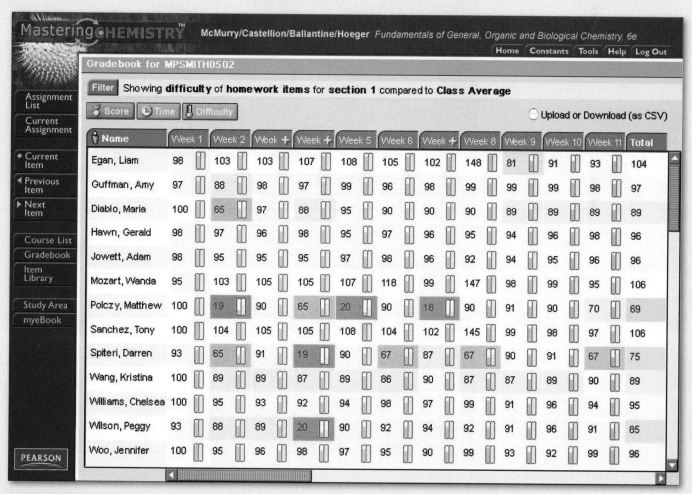

Unmatched Gradebook Capability

By capturing more detailed work of every student than any other homework system, MasteringChemistry provides the most powerful gradebook and diagnostics available. Spot students in trouble at a glance with the color-coded gradebook, effortlessly identify the most difficult problem (and step within that problem) in your last assignment, or critique the detailed work of any one student who needs more help. Compare results on any problem and any step with a previous class, or the national average.

CHAPTER 1

Matter and Life

▲ The variety of exotic colors and aromas featured in this marketplace is due to the chemical and physical properties of chemicals.

CONTENTS

CHAPTER GOALS

We will begin in this chapter by looking at the following topics:

1. What is matter?

THE GOAL: Be able to discuss the properties of matter and describe the three states of matter.

2. How is matter classified?

THE GOAL: Be able to distinguish between mixtures and pure substances, and between elements and compounds.

3. What kinds of properties does matter have?

THE GOAL: Be able to distinguish between chemical and physical properties.

4. How are chemical elements represented?

THE GOAL: Be able to name and give the symbols of common elements.

Look around you. Everything you see, touch, taste, and smell is made of chemicals. Many of these chemicals—those in rocks, trees, and your own body—occur naturally, but others are synthetic. Many of the plastics, fibers, and medicines that are so important a part of modern life do not occur in nature but have been created in the chemical laboratory.

Just as everything you see is made of chemicals, many of the natural changes you see taking place around you are the result of *chemical reactions*—the change of one chemical into another. The crackling fire of a log burning in the fireplace, the color change of a leaf in the fall, and the changes that a human body undergoes as it grows and ages are all the results of chemical reactions. To understand these and all other natural processes, you must have a basic understanding of chemistry.

As you might expect, the chemistry of living organisms is complex and it is not possible to jump right into it. Thus, the general plan of this book is to increase gradually in complexity, beginning in the first eleven chapters with a grounding in the scientific fundamentals that govern all of chemistry. In the next six chapters we look at the nature of the carbon-containing substances, or *organic chemicals*, that compose all living things. In the final twelve chapters we apply what we have learned to biological chemistry.

1.1 Chemistry: The Central Science

Chemistry is often referred to as "the central science" because it is crucial to all other sciences. In fact, as more and more is learned, the historical dividing lines between chemistry, biology, and physics are fading and current research is becoming more interdisciplinary. Figure 1.1 diagrams the relationship of chemistry and biological chemistry to some other fields of scientific study. Whatever the discipline in which you are most interested, the study of chemistry builds the necessary foundation.

Chemistry is the study of matter—its nature, properties, and transformations. **Matter**, in turn, is a catchall word used to describe anything physically real—anything you can see, touch, taste, or smell. In more scientific terms, matter is anything that has mass and volume. As with our knowledge of all the other sciences, our knowledge of chemistry has developed by application of a process called the **scientific method**. Starting with observations of the physical world, we form hypotheses to explain what we have observed. These hypotheses can then be tested by experiments to improve our understanding.

How might we describe different kinds of matter more specifically? Any characteristic that can be used to describe or identify something is called a **property**; size, color, and temperature are all familiar examples. Less familiar properties include *chemical composition*, which describes what matter is made of, and *chemical reactivity*, which describes how matter behaves. Rather than focus on the properties themselves, however, it is often more useful to think about *changes* in properties. Changes are of two types: *physical* and *chemical*. A **physical change** is one that does not alter the chemical makeup of a substance, whereas a **chemical change** is one that *does* alter a substance's chemical makeup. The melting of solid ice to give liquid water, for instance, is a physical change because the water changes only in form but not in chemical makeup. The rusting of an iron bicycle left in the rain, however, is

Chemistry The study of the nature, properties, and transformations of matter.

Matter The physical material that makes up the universe; anything that has mass and occupies space.

Scientific Method The systematic process of observation, hypothesis, and experimentation used to expand and refine a body of knowledge.

Property A characteristic useful for identifying a substance or object.

Physical change A change that does not affect the chemical makeup of a substance or object.

Chemical change A change in the chemical makeup of a substance.

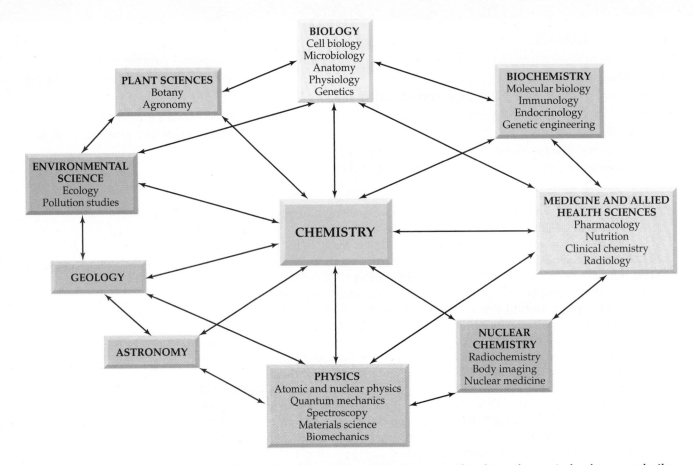

▲ **FIGURE 1.1 Some relationships between chemistry, the central science, and other scientific and health-related disciplines.**

a chemical change because iron combines with oxygen and moisture from the air to give a new substance, rust.

Figure 1.2 shows several familiar substances—water, table sugar (sucrose), and baking soda (sodium bicarbonate)—and Table 1.1 lists their composition and some

▲ **FIGURE 1.2 Samples of the pure substances water, sugar, and baking soda.**

TABLE 1.1   Some Properties of Water, Sugar, and Baking Soda

WATER	SUGAR (SUCROSE)	BAKING SODA (SODIUM BICARBONATE)
Physical properties		
Colorless liquid	White crystals	White powder
Odorless	Odorless	Odorless
Melting point: 0 °C	Begins to decompose at 160 °C, turning black and giving off water.	Decomposes at 270 °C, Giving off water and carbon dioxide.
Boiling point: 100 °C	—	—
Chemical properties		
Composition:*	Composition:*	Composition:*
11.2% hydrogen	6.4% hydrogen	27.4% sodium
88.8% oxygen	42.1% carbon	1.2% hydrogen
	51.5% oxygen	14.3% carbon
		57.1% oxygen
Does not burn.	Burns in air.	Does not burn.

Compositions are given by mass percent.

properties. Note in Table 1.1 that the changes occurring when sugar and baking soda are heated are chemical changes because new substances are produced.

PROBLEM 1.1

Which of the following are made of chemicals? Which might consist of "natural" chemicals and which of "synthetic" chemicals?

(a) Apple juice   **(b)** Laundry bleach

(c) Glass   **(d)** Coffee beans

PROBLEM 1.2

Identify each of the following as a physical change or a chemical change:

(a) A metal surface being ground   **(b)** Fruit ripening

(c) Wood burning   **(d)** A rain puddle evaporating

▲ Burning of potassium in water is an example of a chemical change.

1.2 States of Matter

Matter exists in three forms: solid, liquid, and gas. A **solid** has a definite volume and a definite shape that does not change regardless of the container in which it is placed; for example, a wooden block, marbles, or a cube of ice. A **liquid**, by contrast, has a definite volume but an indefinite shape. The volume of a liquid, such as water, does not change when it is poured into a different container, but its shape does. A **gas** is different still, having neither a definite volume nor a definite shape. A gas expands to fill the volume and take the shape of any container it is placed in, such as the helium in a balloon, or steam formed by boiling water (Figure 1.3).

Solid A substance that has a definite shape and volume.

Liquid A substance that has a definite volume but assumes the shape of its container.

Gas A substance that has neither a definite volume nor a definite shape.

(a) Ice: A solid has a definite volume and a definite shape independent of its container.

(b) Water: A liquid has a definite volume but a variable shape that depends on its container.

(c) Steam: A gas has both variable volume and shape that depend on its container.

◀ **FIGURE 1.3 The three states of matter—solid, liquid, and gas.**

Many substances, such as water, can exist in all three phases, or **states of matter**—the solid state, the liquid state, and the gaseous state—depending on the temperature. The conversion of a substance from one state to another is known as a **change of state** and is a common occurrence. The melting of a solid, the freezing or boiling of a liquid, and the condensing of a gas to a liquid are familiar to everyone.

State of matter The physical state of a substance as a solid, liquid, or gas.

Change of state The conversion of a substance from one state to another—for example, from liquid to gas.

WORKED EXAMPLE **1.1**

Formaldehyde is a disinfectant, a preservative, and a raw material for plastics manufacture. Its melting point is −92 °C, and its boiling point is −19.5 °C. Is formaldehyde a gas, a liquid, or a solid at room temperature (25 °C)? (The symbol °C means degrees Celsius.)

ANALYSIS The state of matter of any substance depends on its temperature. How do the melting point and boiling point of formaldehyde compare with room temperature?

SOLUTION
At room temperature (25 °C), the formaldehyde temperature is above the boiling point and so the formaldehyde is a gas.

PROBLEM 1.3

Acetic acid, which gives the sour taste to vinegar, has a melting point of 16.7 °C and a boiling point of 118 °C. Does a bottle of acetic acid contain a solid or a liquid on a chilly morning with the window open and the laboratory at 10 °C?

Pure substance A substance that has a uniform chemical composition throughout.

Mixture A blend of two or more substances, each of which retains its chemical identity.

Element A fundamental substance that cannot be broken down chemically into any simpler substance.

Chemical compound A pure substance that can be broken down into simpler substances by chemical reactions.

Reactant A starting substance that undergoes change during a chemical reaction.

Product A substance formed as the result of a chemical reaction.

Chemical reaction A process in which the identity and composition of one or more substances are changed.

1.3 Classification of Matter

The first question a chemist asks about an unknown substance is whether it is a pure substance or a mixture. Every sample of matter is one or the other. Water and sugar alone are pure substances, but stirring some sugar into a glass of water creates a *mixture*.

What is the difference between a pure substance and a mixture? One difference is that a **pure substance** is uniform in its chemical composition and its properties all the way down to the microscopic level. Every sample of water, sugar, or baking soda, regardless of source, has the composition and properties listed in Table 1.1. A **mixture**, however, can vary in both composition and properties, depending on how it is made (, Section 9.1). The amount of sugar dissolved in a glass of water will determine the sweetness, boiling point, and other properties of the mixture. Note that you often cannot distinguish between a pure substance and a mixture just by looking. The sugar–water mixture *looks* just like pure water but differs on a molecular level.

Another difference between a pure substance and a mixture is that the components of a mixture can be separated without changing their chemical identities. Water can be separated from a sugar–water mixture, for example, by boiling the mixture to drive off the steam and then condensing the steam to recover the pure water. Pure sugar is left behind in the container.

Pure substances are themselves classified into two groups: those that can undergo a chemical breakdown to yield simpler substances and those that cannot. A pure substance that cannot be broken down chemically into simpler substances is called an **element** (, Section 1.5). Examples include hydrogen, oxygen, aluminum, gold, and sulfur. At the time this book was printed, 117 elements had been identified, and all the millions of other substances in the universe are derived from them.

Any pure material that *can* be broken down into simpler substances by a chemical change is called a **chemical compound**. The term *compound* implies "more than one" (think "compound fracture"). A chemical compound, therefore, is formed by combining two or more elements to make a new substance. Water, sugar, baking soda, and millions of other substances are examples. Water, for example, can be chemically changed by passing an electric current through it to produce hydrogen and oxygen. In writing this chemical change, the **reactant** (water) is written on the left, the **products** (hydrogen and oxygen) are written on the right, and an arrow connects the two parts to indicate a chemical change, or **chemical reaction**. The conditions necessary to bring about the reaction are written above and below the arrow.

▲ Individually, sugar and water are pure substances. Honey, however, is a mixture composed mostly of sugar and water.

Reactant

Products

$$\text{A chemical reaction} \quad \text{Water} \xrightarrow[\text{current}]{\text{Electric}} \text{Hydrogen} + \text{Oxygen}$$

The classification of matter into mixtures, pure compounds, and elements is summarized in Figure 1.4.

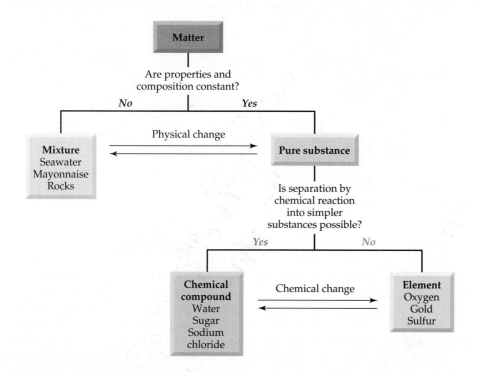

◀ **FIGURE 1.4 A scheme for the classification of matter.**

WORKED EXAMPLE 1.2 Classifying Matter

Classify each of the following as a mixture or a pure substance:

(a) Vanilla ice cream   (b) Sugar

ANALYSIS Refer to the definitions of pure substances and mixtures. Is the substance composed of more than one kind of matter?

SOLUTION

(a) Vanilla ice cream is composed of more than one substance—cream, sugar, and vanilla flavoring. This is a mixture.

(b) Sugar is composed of only one kind of matter—pure sugar. This is a pure substance.

PROBLEM 1.4

Classify each of the following as a mixture or a pure substance:

(a) Concrete   (b) The helium in a balloon
(c) A lead weight   (d) Wood

PROBLEM 1.5

Classify each of the following as a physical change or a chemical change:

(a) Dissolving sugar in water.

(b) Producing carbon dioxide gas and solid lime by heating limestone

(c) Frying an egg

▲ **The reactants.** The flat dish contains pieces of nickel, an element that is a typical, lustrous metal. The bottle contains hydrochloric acid, a solution of the chemical compound hydrogen chloride in water. These reactants are about to be combined in the test tube.

▲ **The reaction** As the chemical reaction occurs, the colorless solution turns green when water-insoluble nickel metal slowly changes into the water-soluble chemical compound nickel chloride. Gas bubbles of the element hydrogen are produced and rise slowly through the green solution.

▶ **The product** Hydrogen gas can be collected as it bubbles from the solution. Removal of water from the solution leaves behind the other product, a solid green chemical compound known as nickel chloride.

◖● KEY CONCEPT PROBLEM 1.6

Identify the process illustrated in the figure below as a chemical change or a physical change. Explain.

1.4 An Example of a Chemical Reaction

If we take a quick look at an example of a chemical reaction, we can reinforce some of the ideas discussed in the previous section. The element *nickel* is a hard, shiny metal, and the compound *hydrogen chloride* is a colorless gas that dissolves in water to give a solution called *hydrochloric acid*. When pieces of nickel are added to hydrochloric acid in a test tube, the nickel is slowly eaten away, the colorless solution turns green, and a gas bubbles out of the test tube. The change in color, the dissolving of the nickel, and the appearance of gas bubbles are indications that a chemical reaction is taking place.

Overall, the reaction of nickel with hydrochloric acid can be either written in words or represented in a shorthand notation using symbols, as shown below in brackets. We will explain the meaning of these symbols in the next section.

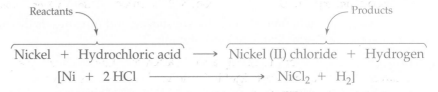

Reactants ⌐ Products ⌐

$$\text{Nickel} + \text{Hydrochloric acid} \longrightarrow \text{Nickel (II) chloride} + \text{Hydrogen}$$
$$[Ni + 2 HCl \longrightarrow NiCl_2 + H_2]$$

1.5 Chemical Elements and Symbols

As of the date this book was printed, 117 chemical elements had been identified. Some are certainly familiar to you—oxygen, helium, iron, aluminum, copper, and gold, for example—but many others are probably unfamiliar—rhenium, niobium, thulium, and promethium. Rather than write out the full names of elements, chemists use a shorthand notation in which elements are referred to by one- or two-letter symbols. The names and symbols of some common elements are listed in Table 1.2, and a complete alphabetical list is given inside the front cover of this book.

Note that all two-letter symbols have only their first letter capitalized, whereas the second letter is always lowercase. The symbols of most common elements are the first one or two letters of the elements' commonly used names, such as

APPLICATION ▶ Aspirin—A Case Study

Acetylsalicylic acid, more commonly known as aspirin, is perhaps the first true wonder drug. It is used as an analgesic to reduce fevers and to relieve headaches and body pains. It possesses anticoagulant properties, which in low doses can help prevent heart attacks and minimize the damage caused by strokes. But how was it discovered, and how does it work? The "discovery" of aspirin is a combination of serendipity and the scientific method.

The origins of aspirin can be traced back to the ancient Greek physician Hippocrates in 400 B.C., who prescribed the bark and leaves of the willow tree to relieve pain and fever. In 1828 scientists isolated from willow bark a bitter-tasting yellow extract, called salicin, that was identified as the active ingredient responsible for the observed medical effects. Salicin could be easily converted to salicylic acid (SA), which by the late 1800s was being mass-produced and marketed. SA had an unpleasant taste, however, and often caused stomach irritation and indigestion.

The discovery of acetylsalicylic acid (ASA) has often been attributed to Felix Hoffman, a chemist working for the Bayer pharmaceutical labs, but the first synthesis of ASA was reported by a French chemist, Charles Gerhardt, in 1853. Nevertheless, Hoffman obtained a patent for ASA in 1900, and Bayer marketed the new drug, now called aspirin, in water-soluble tablets.

How does aspirin work? In 1971 the British pharmacologist John Vane discovered that aspirin suppresses the body's production of prostaglandins (⊂⊃, Section 24.9), which are

▲ **Hippocrates.** The ancient Greek physician, prescribed a precursor of aspirin found in willowbark to relieve pain.

responsible for the pain and swelling that accompany inflammation. This discovery of this mechanism led to the development of new analgesic drugs.

Research continues to explore aspirin's potential for preventing colon cancer, cancer of the esophagus, and other diseases.

See Additional Problem 1.52 at the end of the chapter.

H (hydrogen) and Al (aluminum). Pay special attention, however, to the elements grouped in the last column to the right in Table 1.2. The symbols for these elements are derived from their original Latin names, such as Na for sodium, once known as *natrium*. The only way to learn these symbols is to memorize them; fortunately they are few in number.

Only 90 of the elements occur naturally; the remaining elements have been produced artificially by chemists and physicists. Each element has its own distinctive

TABLE 1.2 Names and Symbols for Some Common Elements

ELEMENTS WITH SYMBOLS BASED ON MODERN NAMES						ELEMENTS WITH SYMBOLS BASED ON LATIN NAMES	
Al	Aluminum	Co	Cobalt	N	Nitrogen	Cu	Copper (*cuprum*)
Ar	Argon	F	Fluorine	O	Oxygen	Au	Gold (*aurum*)
Ba	Barium	He	Helium	P	Phosphorus	Fe	Iron (*ferrum*)
Bi	Bismuth	H	Hydrogen	Pt	Platinum	Pb	Lead (*plumbum*)
B	Boron	I	Iodine	Rn	Radon	Hg	Mercury (*hydrargyrum*)
Br	Bromine	Li	Lithium	Si	Silicon	K	Potassium (*kalium*)
Ca	Calcium	Mg	Magnesium	S	Sulfur	Ag	Silver (*argentum*)
C	Carbon	Mn	Manganese	Ti	Titanium	Na	Sodium (*natrium*)
Cl	Chlorine	Ni	Nickel	Zn	Zinc	Sn	Tin (*stannum*)

TABLE 1.3 Elemental Composition of the Earth's Crust and the Human Body*

EARTH'S CRUST		HUMAN BODY	
Oxygen	46.1%	Oxygen	61%
Silicon	28.2%	Carbon	23%
Aluminum	8.2%	Hydrogen	10%
Iron	5.6%	Nitrogen	2.6%
Calcium	4.1%	Calcium	1.4%
Sodium	2.4%	Phosphorus	1.1%
Magnesium	2.3%	Sulfur	0.20%
Potassium	2.1%	Potassium	0.20%
Titanium	0.57%	Sodium	0.14%
Hydrogen	0.14%	Chlorine	0.12%

Mass percent values are given.

Chemical formula A notation for a chemical compound using element symbols and subscripts to show how many atoms of each element are present.

properties, and just about all of the first 95 elements have been put to use in some way that takes advantage of those properties. As indicated in Table 1.3, which shows the approximate elemental composition of the earth's crust and the human body, the naturally occurring elements are not equally abundant. Oxygen and silicon together account for nearly 75% of the mass in the earth's crust; oxygen, carbon, and hydrogen account for nearly all the mass of a human body.

Just as elements combine to form chemical compounds, symbols are combined to produce **chemical formulas**, which show by subscripts how many *atoms* (the smallest fundamental units) of different elements are in a given chemical compound. For example, the formula H_2O represents water, which contains 2 hydrogen atoms combined with 1 oxygen atom. Similarly, the formula CH_4 represents methane (natural gas), and the formula $C_{12}H_{22}O_{11}$ represents table sugar (sucrose). When no subscript is given for an element, as for carbon in the formula CH_4, a subscript of "1" is understood.

H_2O	CH_4	$C_{12}H_{22}O_{11}$
2 H atoms	1 C atom	12 C atoms
1 O atom	4 H atoms	22 H atoms
		11 O atoms

PROBLEM 1.7

Look at the alphabetical list inside the front cover of this book and find the symbols for the following elements:

(a) Sodium, a major component in table salt

(b) Titanium, used in artificial hip and knee replacement joints

(c) Strontium, used to produce brilliant red colors in fireworks

(d) Yttrium, used in many lasers

(e) Fluorine, added to municipal water supplies to strengthen tooth enamel

(f) Hydrogen, used in fuel cells

PROBLEM 1.8

What elements do the following symbols represent?

(a) U   (b) Ca   (c) Nd
(d) K   (e) W   (f) Sn

PROBLEM 1.9

Identify the elements represented in each of the following chemical formulas, and tell the number of atoms of each element:

(a) NH_3 (ammonia)

(b) $NaHCO_3$ (sodium bicarbonate)

(c) C_8H_{18} (octane, a component of gasoline)

(d) $C_6H_8O_6$ (vitamin C)

1.6 Elements and the Periodic Table

The symbols of the known elements are normally presented in a tabular format called the **periodic table**, as shown in Figure 1.5 and the inside front cover of this book. We will have much more to say about the periodic table and how it is numbered in Sections 3.4–3.8 but will note for now that it is the most important organizing principle in chemistry. An enormous amount of information is embedded in the periodic table, information that gives chemists the ability to explain known chemical behavior of elements and to predict new behavior. The elements can be roughly divided into three groups: *metals*, *nonmetals*, and *metalloids* (sometimes called *semimetals*).

Periodic table A tabular format listing all known elements.

Metals   Metalloids   Nonmetals

FIGURE 1.5 The periodic table of the elements. Metals appear on the left, nonmetals on the right, and metalloids in a zigzag band between metals and nonmetals. The numbering system is explained in Section 3.4.

Ninety of the currently known elements are metals—aluminum, gold, copper, and zinc, for example. **Metals** are solid at room temperature (except for mercury), usually have a lustrous appearance when freshly cut, are good conductors of heat and electricity, and are malleable rather than brittle. That is, a metal can be pounded into a different shape rather than shattering when struck. Note that metals occur on the left side of the periodic table.

Metal A malleable element with a lustrous appearance that is a good conductor of heat and electricity.

(a)

 (b)

 (c)

▲ **Metals: Gold, zinc, and copper.** (a) Known for its beauty, gold is very unreactive and is used primarily in jewelry and in electronic components. (b) Zinc, an essential trace element in our diets, has industrial uses ranging from the manufacture of brass, to roofing materials, to batteries. (c) Copper is widely used in electrical wiring, in water pipes, and in coins.

Nonmetal An element that is a poor conductor of heat and electricity.

Seventeen elements are **nonmetals**. All are poor conductors of heat and electricity, eleven are gases at room temperature, five are brittle solids, and one is a liquid. Oxygen and nitrogen, for example, are gases present in air; sulfur is a solid found in large underground deposits. Bromine is the only liquid nonmetal. Note that nonmetals occur on the right side of the periodic table.

 (a)

 (b)

 (c)

▲ **Nonmetals: Nitrogen, sulfur, and iodine.** (a) Nitrogen, (b) sulfur, and (c) iodine are essential to all living things. Pure nitrogen, which constitutes almost 80% of air, is a gas at room temperature and does not condense to a liquid until it is cooled to −328 °F. Sulfur, a yellow solid, is found in large underground deposits in Texas and Louisiana. Iodine is a dark violet, crystalline solid first isolated from seaweed.

Metalloid An element whose properties are intermediate between those of a metal and a nonmetal.

Only seven elements are **metalloids**, so-named because their properties are intermediate between those of metals and nonmetals. Boron, silicon, and arsenic are examples. Pure silicon has a lustrous or shiny surface, like a metal. But it is brittle, like a nonmetal, and its electrical conductivity lies between that of metals and nonmetals. Note that metalloids occur in a zigzag band between metals on the left and nonmetals on the right side of the periodic table.

Those elements essential for human life are listed in Table 1.4. In addition to the well-known elements carbon, hydrogen, oxygen, and nitrogen, less familiar elements such as molybdenum and selenium are also important.

⊂⊃ Looking Ahead

The elements listed in Table 1.4 are not present in our bodies in their free forms, of course. Instead, they are combined into many thousands of different chemical compounds. We will talk about some compounds formed by metals in Chapter 4 and compounds formed by nonmetals in Chapter 5. ⊂⊃

TABLE 1.4 Elements Essential for Human Life*

ELEMENT	SYMBOL	FUNCTION
Carbon	C	These four elements are present in all living organisms
Hydrogen	H	
Oxygen	O	
Nitrogen	N	
Arsenic	As	May affect cell growth and heart function
Boron	B	Aids in the use of Ca, P, and Mg
Calcium*	Ca	Necessary for growth of teeth and bones
Chlorine*	Cl	Necessary for maintaining salt balance in body fluids
Chromium	Cr	Aids in carbohydrate metabolism
Cobalt	Co	Component of vitamin B_{12}
Copper	Cu	Necessary to maintain blood chemistry
Fluorine	F	Aids in the development of teeth and bones
Iodine	I	Necessary for thyroid function
Iron	Fe	Necessary for oxygen-carrying ability of blood
Magnesium*	Mg	Necessary for bones, teeth, and muscle and nerve action
Manganese	Mn	Necessary for carbohydrate metabolism and bone formation
Molybdenum	Mo	Component of enzymes necessary for metabolism
Nickel	Ni	Aids in the use of Fe and Cu
Phosphorus*	P	Necessary for growth of bones and teeth; present in DNA/RNA
Potassium*	K	Component of body fluids; necessary for nerve action
Selenium	Se	Aids vitamin E action and fat metabolism
Silicon	Si	Helps form connective tissue and bone
Sodium*	Na	Component of body fluids; necessary for nerve and muscle action
Sulfur*	S	Component of proteins; necessary for blood clotting
Zinc	Zn	Necessary for growth, healing, and overall health

C, H, O, and N are present in all foods. Other elements listed vary in their distribution in different foods. Those marked with an asterisk are macronutrients, essential in the diet at more than 100 mg/day; the rest, other than C, H, O, and N, are micronutrients, essential at 15 mg or less per day.

(a)

(b)

◀ **Metalloids: Boron and silicon.** (a) Boron is a strong, hard metalloid used in making the composite materials found in military aircraft. (b) Silicon is well known for its use in making computer chips.

PROBLEM 1.10

Look at the periodic table inside the front cover, locate the following elements and identify them as metals or nonmetals:

(a) Cr, chromium

(b) K, potassium

(c) S, sulfur

(d) Rn, radon

PROBLEM 1.11

The seven metalloids are boron (B), silicon (Si), germanium (Ge), arsenic (As), antimony (Sb), tellurium (Te), and astatine (At). Locate them in the periodic table, and tell where they appear with respect to metals and nonmetals.

APPLICATION ▶ Mercury and Mercury Poisoning

Mercury, the only metallic element that is liquid at room temperature, has fascinated people for millennia. Egyptian kings were buried in their pyramids along with containers of mercury, alchemists during the Middle Ages used mercury to dissolve gold, and Spanish galleons carried loads of mercury to the New World in the 1600s for use in gold and silver mining. Even its symbol, Hg, from the Latin *hydrargyrum,* meaning "liquid silver," hints at mercury's uniqueness.

Much of the recent interest in mercury has concerned its toxicity, but there are some surprises. For example, the mercury compound Hg_2Cl_2 (called *calomel*) is nontoxic and has a long history of medical use as a laxative, yet it is also used as a fungicide and rat poison. Dental amalgam, a solid alloy of approximately 50% elemental mercury, 35% silver, 13% tin, 1% copper, and trace amounts of zinc, has been used by dentists for many years to fill tooth cavities. Yet exposure to elemental mercury *vapor* for long periods leads to mood swings, headaches, tremors, and loss of hair and teeth. The widespread use of mercuric nitrate, a mercury compound to make the felt used in hats, exposed many hatters of the eighteenth and nineteenth centuries to toxic levels of mercury. The eccentric behavior displayed by hatters suffering from mercury poisoning led to the phrase "mad as a hatter"—the Mad Hatter from Lewis Carroll's *Alice in Wonderland* is a parody of this stereotype.

Why is mercury toxic in some forms but not in others? It turns out that the toxicity of mercury and its compounds is related to solubility. Only soluble mercury compounds are toxic, because they can be transported through the bloodstream to all parts of the body where they react with different enzymes and interfere with various biological processes. Elemental mercury and insoluble mercury compounds become toxic only when converted into soluble compounds, reactions that are extremely slow in the body. Calomel, for example, is an insoluble mercury compound that passes

▲ The Mad Hatter's erratic behavior was a parody of the symptoms commonly associated with mercury poisoning.

through the body long before it is converted into any soluble compounds. Mercury alloys were considered safe for dental use because mercury does not evaporate readily from the alloys and it neither reacts with nor dissolves in saliva. Mercury vapor, however, remains in the lungs when breathed, until it is slowly converted into soluble compounds.

Of particular concern with regard to mercury toxicity is the environmental danger posed by pollution from both natural and industrial sources. Microorganisms present in lakes and streams are able to convert many mercury-containing wastes into a soluble and highly toxic compound called *methylmercury*. Methylmercury is concentrated to high levels in fish, particularly in shark and swordfish, which are then hazardous when eaten. Although the commercial fishing catch is now monitored carefully, more than 50 deaths from eating contaminated fish were recorded in Minimata, Japan, during the 1950s before the cause of the problem was realized.

See Additional Problem 1.53 at the end of the chapter.

SUMMARY: REVISITING THE CHAPTER GOALS

1. **What is matter?** *Matter* is anything that has mass and occupies volume—that is, anything physically real. Matter can be classified by its physical state as *solid*, *liquid*, or *gas*. A solid has a definite volume and shape, a liquid has a definite volume but indefinite shape, and a gas has neither a definite volume nor shape.

2. **How is matter classified?** A substance can be characterized as being either *pure* or a *mixture*. A pure substance is uniform in its composition and properties, but a mixture can vary in both composition and properties, depending on how it was made. Every pure substance is either an *element* or a *chemical compound*. Elements are fundamental substances that cannot be chemically changed into anything simpler. A chemical compound, by contrast, can be broken down by chemical change into simpler substances.

3. **What kinds of properties does matter have?** A *property* is any characteristic that can be used to describe or identify something. A *physical property* can be seen or measured without changing the chemical identity of the substance, (that is, color, melting point). A *chemical property* can only be seen or measured when the substance undergoes a *chemical change*, such as a chemical reaction.

4. **How are chemical elements represented?** Elements are represented by one- or two-letter symbols, such as H for hydrogen, Ca for calcium, Al for aluminum, and so on. Most symbols are the first one or two letters of the element name, but some symbols are derived from Latin names—Na (sodium), for example. All the known elements are commonly organized into a form called the *periodic table*. Most elements are *metals*, 17 are *nonmetals*, and 7 are *metalloids*.

KEY WORDS

Change of state, *p. 5*

Chemical change, *p. 3*

Chemical compound, *p. 6*

Chemical formula, *p. 10*

Chemical reaction, *p. 6*

Chemistry, *p. 3*

Element, *p. 6*

Gas, *p. 5*

Liquid, *p. 5*

Matter, *p. 3*

Metal, *p. 11*

Metalloid, *p. 12*

Mixture, *p. 6*

Nonmetal, *p. 12*

Periodic table, *p. 11*

Physical change, *p. 3*

Pure substance, *p. 6*

Product, *p. 6*

Property, *p. 3*

Reactant, *p. 6*

Scientific Method, *p. 3*

Solid, *p. 5*

State of matter, *p. 5*

UNDERSTANDING KEY CONCEPTS

The problems in this section are intended as a bridge between the Chapter Summary and the Additional Problems that follow. Primarily visual in nature, they are designed to help you test your grasp of the chapter's most important principles before attempting to solve quantitative problems. Answers to all Key Concept problems are at the end of the book following the appendixes.

1.12 Six of the elements at the far right of the periodic table are gases at room temperature. Identify them using the periodic table inside the front cover of this book.

1.13 The so-called "coinage metals" are located near the middle of the periodic table. Identify them using the periodic table inside the front cover of this book.

1.14 Identify the three elements indicated on the following periodic table and tell which is a metal, which is a nonmetal, and which is a metalloid.

1.15 The radioactive element indicated on the following periodic table is used in smoke detectors. Identify it, and tell whether it is a metal, a nonmetal, or a metalloid.

ADDITIONAL PROBLEMS

These exercises are divided into sections by topic. Each section begins with review and conceptual questions, followed by numerical problems of varying levels of difficulty. The problems are presented in pairs, with each even-numbered problem followed by an odd-numbered one requiring similar skills. The final section consists of unpaired General Questions and Problems that draw on various parts of the chapter and, in future chapters, may even require the use of concepts from previous chapters. Answers to all even-numbered problems are given at the end of the book following the appendixes.

CHEMISTRY AND THE PROPERTIES OF MATTER

1.16 What is chemistry?

1.17 Identify the following chemicals as natural or synthetic.

(a) The nylon used in stockings
(b) The substances that give roses their fragrance
(c) The yeast used in bread dough

1.18 Which of the following is a physical change and which is a chemical change?

(a) Boiling water
(b) Decomposing water by passing an electric current through it
(c) Dissolving sugar in water
(d) Exploding of potassium metal when placed in water
(e) Breaking of glass

1.19 Which of the following is a physical change and which is a chemical change?

(a) Steam condensing
(b) Milk souring
(c) Ignition of matches
(d) Breaking of a dinner plate
(e) Nickel sticking to a magnet
(f) Exploding of nitroglycerin

STATES AND CLASSIFICATION OF MATTER

1.20 Name and describe the three states of matter.

1.21 Name two changes of state, and describe what causes each to occur.

1.22 Sulfur dioxide is a compound produced when sulfur burns in air. It has a melting point of $-72.7\ ^{\circ}C$ and a boiling point of $-10\ ^{\circ}C$. In what state does it exist at room temperature $(25\ ^{\circ}C)$? (The symbol $^{\circ}C$ means degrees Celsius.)

1.23 Menthol, a chemical compound obtained from peppermint or other mint oils, melts at $45\ ^{\circ}C$ and boils at $212\ ^{\circ}C$. In what state is it found at:

(a) Room temperature $(25\ ^{\circ}C)$? (b) $60\ ^{\circ}C$? (c) $260\ ^{\circ}C$?

1.24 Classify each of the following as a mixture or a pure substance:

(a) Pea soup   (b) Seawater
(c) The contents of a propane tank
(d) Urine   (e) Lead
(f) A multivitamin tablet

1.25 Classify each of the following as a mixture or a pure substance. If it is a pure substance, classify it as an element or a compound:

(a) Blood   (b) Silicon
(c) Dishwashing liquid (d) Toothpaste
(e) Gold   (f) Gaseous ammonia

1.26 Classify each of the following as an element, a compound, or a mixture:

(a) Aluminum foil (b) Table salt (c) Water
(d) Air   (e) A banana   (f) Notebook paper

1.27 Which of these terms, (i) mixture, (ii) solid, (iii) liquid, (iv) gas, (v) chemical element, (vi) chemical compound, applies to the following substances at room temperature?

(a) Gasoline   (b) Iodine   (c) Water
(d) Air   (e) Sodium bicarbonate

1.28 Hydrogen peroxide, often used in solutions to cleanse cuts and scrapes, breaks down to yield water and oxygen:

$$\text{Hydrogen peroxide} \longrightarrow \text{Water} + \text{Oxygen}$$

(a) Identify the reactants and products.
(b) Which of the substances are chemical compounds, and which are elements?

1.29 When sodium metal is placed in water, the following change occurs:

$$\text{Sodium} + \text{Water} \longrightarrow \text{Hydrogen} + \text{Sodium hydroxide}$$

(a) Identify the reactants and products.
(b) Which of the substances are elements, and which are chemical compounds?

ELEMENTS AND THEIR SYMBOLS

1.30 How many elements are presently known? About how many occur naturally?

1.31 Where in the periodic table are the metallic elements found? The nonmetallic elements? The metalloid elements?

1.32 Describe the general properties of metals, nonmetals, and metalloids.

1.33 What is the most abundant element in the earth's crust? In the human body? List the name and symbol for each.

1.34 What are the symbols for the following elements?

(a) Gadolinium (used in color TV screens)
(b) Germanium (used in semiconductors)
(c) Technetium (used in biomedical imaging)
(d) Arsenic (used in pesticides)
(e) Cadmium (used in rechargeable batteries)

1.35 What are the symbols for the following elements?

(a) Tungsten   (b) Mercury   (c) Boron
(d) Gold   (e) Silicon   (f) Argon
(g) Silver   (h) Magnesium

1.36 Give the names corresponding to the following symbols:

(a) N   (b) K   (c) Cl
(d) Ca (e) P   (f) Mn

1.37 Give the names corresponding to the following symbols:

(a) Te (b) Re (c) Be
(d) Cr (e) Pu (f) Mn

1.38 The symbol CO stands for carbon monoxide, a chemical compound, but the symbol Co stands for cobalt, an element. Explain how you can tell them apart.

1.39 Explain why the symbol for sulfur is S, but the symbol for sodium is Na.

1.40 What is wrong with the following statements? Correct them.

(a) The symbol for bromine is BR.
(b) The symbol for manganese is Mg.
(c) The symbol for carbon is Ca.
(d) The symbol for potassium is Po.

1.41 What is wrong with the following statements? Correct them.

(a) Carbon dioxide has the formula CO2.
(b) Carbon dioxide has the formula Co_2.
(c) Table salt, NaCl, is composed of nitrogen and chlorine.

1.42 What is wrong with the following statements? Correct them.

(a) "Fool's gold" is a mixture of iron and sulfur with the formula IrS_2.
(b) "Laughing gas" is a compound of nitrogen and oxygen with the formula NiO.

1.43 What is wrong with the following statements? Correct them.

(a) Soldering compound is an alloy of tin and lead with the formula TiPb.
(b) White gold is an alloy of gold and nickel with the formula GdNI.

1.44 Name the elements combined in the chemical compounds represented by the following formulas:

(a) $MgSO_4$ (b) $FeBr_2$ (c) CoP
(d) AsH_3 (e) $CaCr_2O_7$

1.45 How many atoms of what elements are represented by the following formulas?

(a) Propane (LP gas), C_3H_8
(b) Sulfuric acid, H_2SO_4
(c) Aspirin, $C_9H_8O_4$
(d) Rubbing alcohol, C_3H_8O

1.46 The amino acid glycine has the formula $C_2H_5NO_2$. What elements are present in glycine? What is the total number of atoms represented by the formula?

1.47 Benzyl salicylate, a chemical compound sometimes used as a sunscreen, has the formula $C_{14}H_{12}O_3$. What is the total number of atoms represented by the formula? How many are carbon?

1.48 What is the formula for ibuprofen: 13 carbons, 18 hydrogens, and 2 oxygens.

1.49 What is the formula for penicillin V: 16 carbons, 18 hydrogens, 2 nitrogens, 5 oxygens, and 1 sulfur.

1.50 Which of the following two elements is a metal, and which is a nonmetal?

(a) Osmium, a hard, shiny, very dense solid that conducts electricity
(b) Xenon, a colorless, odorless gas

1.51 Which of the following elements is likely to be a metal and which a metalloid?

(a) Tantalum, a hard, shiny solid that conducts electricity
(b) Germanium, a brittle, gray solid that conducts electricity poorly

Applications

1.52 The active ingredient in aspirin, acetylsalicylic acid (ASA), has the formula $C_9H_8O_4$ and melts at 140 °C.

Identify the elements and how many atoms of each are present in ASA. Is it a solid or a liquid at room temperature? [*Aspirin—A Case Study, p. 9*]

1.53 Why is Hg_2Cl_2 harmless when swallowed, yet elemental mercury is toxic when breathed? [*Mercury and Mercury Poisoning, p. 14*]

General Questions and Problems

1.54 Distinguish between the following:

(a) Physical changes and chemical changes
(b) Melting point and boiling point
(c) Elements, compounds, and mixtures
(d) Chemical symbols and chemical formulas
(e) Reactants and products
(f) Metals and nonmetals

1.55 Are the following statements true or false? If false, explain why.

(a) The combination of sodium and chlorine to produce sodium chloride is a chemical reaction.
(b) The addition of heat to solid sodium chloride until it melts is a chemical reaction.
(c) The formula for a chemical compound that contains lead and oxygen is LiO.
(d) By stirring together salt and pepper we can create a new chemical compound to be used for seasoning food.
(e) Heating sugar to make caramel is a physical change.

1.56 Which of the following are chemical compounds, and which are elements?

(a) H_2O_2 (b) Al   (c) CO
(d) N_2 (e) $NaHCO_3$

1.57 A white solid with a melting point of 730 °C is melted. When electricity is passed through the resultant liquid, a brown gas and a molten metal are produced. Neither the metal nor the gas can be broken down into anything simpler by chemical means. Classify each—the white solid, the molten metal, and the brown gas—as a mixture, a compound, or an element.

1.58 As a clear red liquid sits at room temperature, evaporation occurs until only a red solid remains. Was the original liquid an element, a compound, or a mixture?

1.59 Describe how you could physically separate a mixture of iron filings, table salt, and white sand.

1.60 Small amounts of the following elements in our diets are essential for good health. What is the chemical symbol for each?

(a) Iron   (b) Copper   (c) Cobalt
(d) Molybdenum   (e) Chromium   (f) Fluorine
(g) Sulfur

1.61 Obtain a bottle of multivitamins from your local drug store or pharmacy and identify as many of the essential elements from Table 1.4 as you can. How many of them are listed as elements, and how many are included as part of chemical compounds?

1.62 Consider the recently discovered or as yet undiscovered elements with atomic numbers 115, 117, and 119. Is element 115 likely to be a metal or a nonmetal? What about element 117? Element 119?

1.63 How high would the atomic number of a new element need to be to appear under uranium in the periodic table?

CHAPTER 2

Measurements in Chemistry

▲ The success of many endeavors, such as NASA's Deep Impact comet probe, depends on both the accuracy and the precision of measurements.

CONTENTS

CHAPTER GOALS

In this chapter we will deal with the following questions about measurement:

1. How are measurements made, and what units are used?

THE GOAL: Be able to name and use the metric and SI units of measure for mass, length, volume, and temperature.

2. How good are the reported measurements?

THE GOAL: Be able to interpret the number of significant figures in a measurement and round off numbers in calculations involving measurements.

3. How are large and small numbers best represented?

THE GOAL: Be able to interpret prefixes for units of measure and express numbers in scientific notation.

4. How can a quantity be converted from one unit of measure to another?

THE GOAL: Be able to convert quantities from one unit to another using conversion factors.

5. What techniques are used to solve problems?

THE GOAL: Be able to analyze a problem, use the factor-label method to solve the problem, and check the result to ensure that it makes sense chemically and physically.

6. What are temperature, specific heat, density, and specific gravity?

THE GOAL: Be able to define these quantities and use them in calculations.

How often do you make an observation or perform an action that involves measurement? Whenever you check the temperature outside, make a pitcher of lemonade, or add detergent to the laundry, you are making a measurement. Likewise, whenever you use chemical compounds—whether you are adding salt to your cooking, putting antifreeze in your car radiator, or choosing a dosage of medicine—quantities of substances must be measured. A mistake in measuring the quantities could ruin the dinner, damage the engine, or harm the patient.

2.1 Physical Quantities

Height, volume, temperature, and other physical properties that can be measured are called **physical quantities** and are described by both a number and a **unit** of defined size:

Number   Unit

61.2 kilograms

Physical quantity A physical property that can be measured.

Unit A defined quantity used as a standard of measurement.

The number alone is not much good without a unit. If you asked how much blood an accident victim had lost, the answer "three" would not tell you much. Three drops? Three milliliters? Three pints? Three liters? (By the way, an adult human has only 5–6 liters of blood.)

Any physical quantity can be measured in many different units. For example, a person's height might be measured in inches, feet, yards, centimeters, or many other units. To avoid confusion, scientists from around the world have agreed on a system of standard units, called by the French name *Système International d'Unites* (International System of Units), abbreviated *SI*. **SI units** for some common physical quantities are given in Table 2.1. Mass is measured in *kilograms* (kg), length is measured in *meters* (m), volume is measured in *cubic meters* (m^3), temperature is measured in *kelvins* (K), and time is measured in *seconds* (s, not sec).

SI units Units of measurement defined by the International System of Units.

SI units are closely related to the more familiar *metric units* used in all industrialized nations of the world except the United States. If you compare the SI and metric units shown in Table 2.1, you will find that the basic metric unit of mass is the *gram* (g) rather than the kilogram (1 g = 1/1000 kg), the metric unit of volume is the *liter* (L) rather than the cubic meter (1 L = 1/1000 m^3), and the metric unit of temperature is the *Celsius degree* (°C) rather than the kelvin. The meter is the unit of

TABLE 2.1 Some SI and Metric Units and Their Equivalents

QUANTITY	SI UNIT (SYMBOL)	METRIC UNIT (SYMBOL)	EQUIVALENTS
Mass	Kilogram (kg)	Gram (g)	1 kg = 1000 g = 2.205 lb
Length	Meter (m)	Meter (m)	1 m = 3.280 ft
Volume	Cubic meter (m^3)	Liter (L)	$1 m^3$ = 1000 L = 264.2 gal
Temperature	Kelvin (K)	Celsius degree (°C)	See Section 2.9
Time	Second (s)	Second (s)	—

length and the second is the unit of time in both systems. Although SI units are now preferred in scientific research, metric units are still used in some fields. You will probably find yourself working with both.

In addition to the units listed in Table 2.1, many other widely used units are derived from them. For instance, units of *meters per second* (m/s) are often used for *speed*—the distance covered in a given time. Similarly, units of *grams per cubic centimeter* (g/cm^3) are often used for *density*—the mass of substance in a given volume. We will see other such derived units in future chapters.

One problem with any system of measurement is that the sizes of the units often turn out to be inconveniently large or small for the problem at hand. A biologist describing the diameter of a red blood cell (0.000 006 m) would find the meter to be an inconveniently large unit, but an astronomer measuring the average distance from the earth to the sun (150,000,000,000 m) would find the meter to be inconveniently small. For this reason, metric and SI units can be modified by prefixes to refer to either smaller or larger quantities. For instance, the SI unit for mass—the kilogram—differs by the prefix *kilo-* from the metric unit gram. *Kilo-* indicates that a kilogram is 1000 times as large as a gram:

$$1 \text{ kg} = (1000)(1 \text{ g}) = 1000 \text{ g}$$

Small quantities of active ingredients in medications are often reported in *milligrams* (mg). The prefix *milli-* shows that the unit gram has been divided by 1000, which is the same as multiplying by 0.001:

$$1 \text{ mg} = \left(\frac{1}{1000}\right)(1 \text{ g}) = (0.001)(1 \text{ g}) = 0.001 \text{ g}$$

A list of prefixes is given in Table 2.2, with the most common ones displayed in color. Note that the exponents are multiples of 3 for *mega-* (10^6), *kilo-* (10^3), *milli-* (10^{-3}), *micro-* (10^{-6}), *nano-* (10^{-9}), and *pico-* (10^{-12}). (The use of exponents is reviewed in Section 2.5.) The prefixes *centi-*, meaning 1/100, and *deci-*, meaning 1/10, indicate exponents that are not multiples of 3. *Centi-* is seen most often in the length unit *centimeter* (1 cm = 0.01 m), and *deci-* is used most often in clinical chemistry, where the concentrations of blood components are given in milligrams per deciliter (1 dL = 0.1 L). These prefixes allow us to compare the magnitudes of different numbers by noting how the prefixes modify a common unit. For example,

$$1 \text{ meter} = 10 \text{ dm} = 100 \text{ cm} = 1000 \text{ mm} = 1,000,000 \text{ } \mu m$$

Such comparisons will be useful when we start performing calculations involving units in Section 2.7. Note also in Table 2.2 that numbers having five or more digits to the right of the decimal point are shown with thin spaces every three digits for convenience—0.000 001, for example. This manner of writing numbers is becoming more common and will be used throughout this book.

▲ The HIV-1 virus particles (in green) budding from the surface of a lymphocyte have an approximate diameter of 0.000 000 120 m.

TABLE 2.2   Some Prefixes for Multiples of Metric and SI Units

PREFIX	SYMBOL	BASE UNIT MULTIPLIED BY*	EXAMPLE
mega	M	$1,000,000 = 10^6$	1 megameter (Mm) = 10^6 m
kilo	k	$1000 = 10^3$	1 kilogram (kg) = 10^3 g
hecto	h	$100 = 10^2$	1 hectogram (hg) = 100 g
deka	da	$10 = 10^1$	1 dekaliter (daL) = 10 L
deci	d	$0.1 = 10^{-1}$	1 deciliter (dL) = 0.1 L
centi	c	$0.01 = 10^{-2}$	1 centimeter (cm) = 0.01 m
milli	m	$0.001 = 10^{-3}$	1 milligram (mg) = 0.001 g
micro	μ	$0.000\ 001 = 10^{-6}$	1 micrometer (μm) = 10^{-6} m
nano	n	$0.000\ 000\ 001 = 10^{-9}$	1 nanogram (ng) = 10^{-9} g
pico	p	$0.000\ 000\ 000\ 001 = 10^{-12}$	1 picogram (pg) = 10^{-12} g
femto	f	$0.000\ 000\ 000\ 000\ 001 = 10^{-15}$	1 femtogram = 10^{-15} g

*The scientific notation method of writing large and small numbers (for example, 10^6 for 1,000,000) is explained in Section 2.5.

PROBLEM 2.1

Give the full name of the following units:

(a) dL   (b) mg   (c) ns   (d) km   (e) μg

PROBLEM 2.2

Write the symbol for the following units:

(a) liter   (b) kilogram   (c) nanometer   (d) megameter

PROBLEM 2.3

Express the following quantities in terms of the basic unit (for example, 1 mL = 0.001 L):

(a) 1 nm   (b) 1 dg   (c) 1 km   (d) 1 μs   (e) 1 ng

2.2 Measuring Mass

The terms *mass* and *weight*, though often used interchangeably, really have quite different meanings. **Mass** is a measure of the amount of matter in an object, whereas **weight** is a measure of the gravitational pull that the earth, moon, or other large body exerts on an object. Clearly, the amount of matter in an object does not depend on location. Whether you are standing on the earth or standing on the moon, the mass of your body is the same. On the other hand, the weight of an object *does* depend on location. Your weight on earth might be 140 lb, but it would only be 23 lb on the moon because the pull of gravity there is only about one-sixth as great.

At the same location, two objects with identical masses have identical weights; that is, gravity pulls equally on both. Thus, the *mass* of an object can be determined by comparing the *weight* of the object to the weight of a known reference standard. Much of the confusion between mass and weight is simply due to a language problem: We speak of "weighing" when we really mean that we are measuring mass by

Mass   A measure of the amount of matter in an object.

Weight   A measure of the gravitational force that the earth or other large body exerts on an object.

(a)   **(b)**

▶ **FIGURE 2.1** (a) The single-pan balance has a sliding counterweight that is adjusted until the weight of the object on the pan is just balanced. (b) A modern electronic balance.

comparing two weights. Figure 2.1 shows two types of balances used for measuring mass in the laboratory.

One kilogram, the SI unit for mass, is equal to 2.205 lb—too large a quantity for many purposes in chemistry and medicine. Thus, smaller units of mass such as the gram, milligram (mg), and microgram (μg), are more commonly used. Table 2.3 shows the relationships between metric and common units for mass.

▲ This pile of 400 pennies has a mass of about 1 kg.

TABLE 2.3   Units of Mass

UNIT	EQUIVALENT	UNIT	EQUIVALENT
1 kilogram (kg)	= 1000 grams = 2.205 pounds	1 ton	= 2000 pounds = 907.03 kilograms
1 gram (g)	= 0.001 kilogram = 1000 milligrams = 0.035 27 ounce	1 pound (lb)	= 16 ounces = 0.454 kilogram = 454 grams
1 milligram (mg)	= 0.001 gram = 1000 micrograms	1 ounce (oz)	= 0.028 35 kilogram = 28.35 grams
1 microgram (μg)	= 0.000 001 gram = 0.001 milligram		= 28,350 milligrams

2.3 Measuring Length and Volume

The meter is the standard measure of length, or distance, in both the SI and metric systems. One meter is 39.37 inches (about 10% longer than a yard), a length that is much too large for most measurements in chemistry and medicine. Other, more commonly used measures of length are the *centimeter* (cm; 1/100 m) and the *millimeter* (mm; 1/1000 m). One centimeter is a bit less than half an inch—0.3937 inch to be exact. A millimeter, in turn, is 0.03937 inch, or about the thickness of a dime. Table 2.4 lists the relationships of these units.

Volume is the amount of space occupied by an object. The SI unit for volume—the cubic meter, m^3—is so large that the liter (1 L = 0.001 m^3 = 1 dm^3) is much more commonly used in chemistry and medicine. One liter has the volume of a cube 10 cm (1 dm) on edge and is a bit larger than one U.S. quart. Each liter is further divided into 1000 *milliliters* (mL), with 1 mL being the size of a cube 1 cm on edge, or 1 cm^3. In fact, the milliliter is often called a *cubic centimeter* (cm^3, or cc) in medical work. Figure 2.2 shows the divisions of a cubic meter, and Table 2.5 shows the relationships among units of volume.

TABLE 2.4   Units of Length

UNIT	EQUIVALENT	UNIT	EQUIVALENT
1 kilometer (km)	= 1000 meters = 0.6214 mile	1 mile (mi)	= 1.609 kilometers = 1609 meters
1 meter (m)	= 100 centimeters = 1000 millimeters = 1.0936 yards = 39.37 inches	1 yard (yd)	= 0.9144 meter = 91.44 centimeters
		1 foot (ft)	= 0.3048 meter = 30.48 centimeters
1 centimeter (cm)	= 0.01 meter = 10 millimeters = 0.3937 inch	1 inch (in.)	= 2.54 centimeters = 25.4 millimeters
1 millimeter (mm)	= 0.001 meter = 0.1 centimeter		

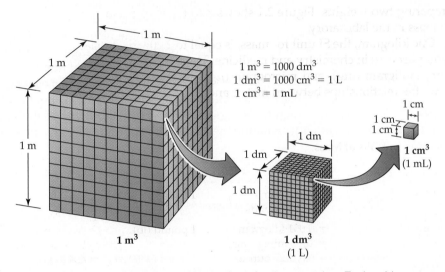

$1 m^3 = 1000 dm^3$
$1 dm^3 = 1000 cm^3 = 1 L$
$1 cm^3 = 1 mL$

▲ **FIGURE 2.2**   A cubic meter is the volume of a cube 1 m on edge. Each cubic meter contains 1000 cubic decimeters (liters), and each cubic decimeter contains 1000 cubic centimeters (milliliters). Thus, there are 1000 mL in a liter and 1000 L in a cubic meter.

TABLE 2.5   Units of Volume

UNIT	EQUIVALENT
1 cubic meter (m^3)	= 1000 liters = 264.2 gallons
1 liter (L)	= 0.001 cubic meter = 1000 milliliters = 1.057 quarts
1 deciliter (dL)	= 0.1 liter = 100 milliliters
1 milliliter (mL)	= 0.001 liter = 1000 microliters
1 microliter (μL)	= 0.001 milliliter
1 gallon (gal)	= 3.7854 liters
1 quart (qt)	= 0.9464 liter = 946.4 milliliters
1 fluid ounce (fl oz)	= 29.57 milliliters

▲ The tennis ball weighs 54.07 g on this common laboratory balance, which is capable of determining mass to about 0.01 g.

Significant figures The number of meaningful digits used to express a value.

17._?_ mL

▲ **FIGURE 2.3** What is the volume of liquid in this graduated cylinder?

2.4 Measurement and Significant Figures

How much does a tennis ball weigh? If you put a tennis ball on an ordinary bathroom scale, the scale would probably register 0 lb (or 0 kg if you have a metric scale). If you placed the same tennis ball on a common laboratory balance, however, you might get a reading of 54.07 g. Trying again by placing the ball on an expensive analytical balance like those found in clinical and research laboratories, you might find a weight of 54.071 38 g. Clearly, the precision of your answer depends on the equipment used for the measurement.

Every experimental measurement, no matter how precise, has a degree of uncertainty to it because there is always a limit to the number of digits that can be determined. An analytical balance, for example, might reach its limit in measuring mass to the fifth decimal place, and weighing the tennis ball several times might produce slightly different readings, such as 54.071 39 g, 54.071 38 g, and 54.071 37 g. Also, different people making the same measurement might come up with slightly different answers. How, for instance, would you record the volume of the liquid shown in Figure 2.3? It is clear that the volume of liquid lies between 17.0 and 18.0 mL, but the exact value of the last digit must be estimated.

To indicate the precision of a measurement, the value recorded should use all the digits known with certainty, plus one additional estimated digit that is usually considered uncertain by plus or minus 1 (written as ±1). The total number of digits used to express such a measurement is called the number of **significant figures**. Thus, the quantity 54.07 g has four significant figures (5, 4, 0, and 7), and the quantity 54.071 38 g has seven significant figures. *Remember*: All but one of the significant figures are known with certainty; the last significant figure is only an estimate accurate to ±1.

Uncertain digit

54.07 g   A mass between 54.06 g and 54.08 g (±0.01 g)

Uncertain digit

54.071 38 g   A mass between 54.071 37 g and 54.071 39 g (±0.000 01 g)

Deciding the number of significant figures in a given measurement is usually simple, but can be troublesome when zeros are involved. Depending on the circumstances, a zero might be significant or might be just a space-filler to locate the decimal point. For example, how many significant figures does each of the following measurements have?

94.072 g	Five significant figures (9, 4, 0, 7, 2)
0.0834 cm	Three significant figures (8, 3, 4)
0.029 07 mL	Four significant figures (2, 9, 0, 7)
138.200 m	Six significant figures (1, 3, 8, 2, 0, 0)
23,000 kg	*Anywhere* from two (2, 3) to five (2, 3, 0, 0, 0) significant figures

The following rules are helpful for determining the number of significant figures when zeros are present:

RULE 1. Zeros in the middle of a number are like any other digit; they are always significant. Thus, 94.072 g has five significant figures.

RULE 2. Zeros at the beginning of a number are not significant; they act only to locate the decimal point. Thus, 0.0834 cm has three significant figures, and 0.029 07 mL has four.

RULE 3. Zeros at the end of a number and *after* the decimal point are significant. It is assumed that these zeros would not be shown unless they were significant. Thus, 138.200 m has six significant figures. If the value were known to only four significant figures, we would write 138.2 m.

RULE 4. Zeros at the end of a number and *before* an implied decimal point may or may not be significant. We cannot tell whether they are part of the measurement or whether they act only to locate the unwritten but implied decimal point. Thus, 23,000 kg may have two, three, four, or five significant figures. Adding a decimal point at the end would indicate that all five numbers are significant.

Often, however, a little common sense is useful. A temperature reading of 20 °C probably has two significant figures rather than one, because one significant figure would imply a temperature anywhere from 10 °C to 30 °C and would be of little use. Similarly, a volume given as 300 mL probably has three significant figures. On the other hand, a figure of 150,000,000 km for the distance between the earth and the sun has only two or three significant figures because the distance is variable. We will see a better way to deal with this problem in the next section.

One final point about significant figures: Some numbers, such as those obtained when counting objects and those that are part of a definition, are *exact* and effectively have an unlimited number of significant figures. Thus, a class might have *exactly* 32 students (not 31.9, 32.0, or 32.1), and 1 foot is defined to have *exactly* 12 inches.

▲ How many CDs are in this stack? (Answer: *exactly* 29.)

WORKED EXAMPLE **2.1** Significant Figures of Measurements

How many significant figures do the following measurements have?

   (a) 2730.78 m   (b) 0.0076 mL   (c) 3400 kg   (d) 3400.0 m²

ANALYSIS All nonzero numbers are significant; the number of significant figures will then depend on the status of the zeros in each case. (Hint: which rule applies in each case?)

SOLUTION

   (a) Six (rule 1)   (b) Two (rule 2)
   (c) Two, three, or four (rule 4)   (d) Five (rule 3)

PROBLEM 2.4

How many significant figures do the following measurements have?

(a) 3.45 m   (b) 0.1400 kg
(c) 10.003 L   (d) 35 cents

◁● KEY CONCEPT PROBLEM 2.5

What is the temperature reading on the following Celsius thermometer? How many significant figures do you have in your answer?

2.5 Scientific Notation

Scientific notation A number expressed as the product of a number between 1 and 10, times the number 10 raised to a power.

Rather than write very large or very small numbers in their entirety, it is more convenient to express them using *scientific notation*. A number is written in **scientific notation** as the product of a number between 1 and 10, times the number 10 raised to a power. Thus, 215 is written in scientific notation as 2.15×10^2:

$$215 = 2.15 \times 100 = 2.15 \times (10 \times 10) = 2.15 \times 10^2$$

Notice that in this case, where the number is *larger* than 1, the decimal point has been moved *to the left* until it follows the first digit. The exponent on the 10 tells how many places we had to move the decimal point to position it just after the first digit:

$$215. = 2.15 \times 10^2$$

Decimal point is moved two places to the left, so exponent is 2.

To express a number *smaller* than 1 in scientific notation, we have to move the decimal point *to the right* until it follows the first digit. The number of places moved is the negative exponent of 10. For example, the number 0.002 15 can be rewritten as 2.15×10^{-3}:

$$0.002\ 15 = 2.15 \times \frac{1}{1000} = 2.15 \times \frac{1}{10 \times 10 \times 10} = 2.15 \times \frac{1}{10^3} = 2.15 \times 10^{-3}$$

$$0.002\ 15 = 2.15 \times 10^{-3}$$

Decimal point is moved three places to the right, so exponent is −3.

To convert a number written in scientific notation to standard notation, the process is reversed. For a number with a *positive* exponent, the decimal point is moved to the *right* a number of places equal to the exponent:

$$3.7962 \times 10^4 = 37,962$$

Positive exponent of 4, so decimal point is moved to the right four places.

For a number with a *negative* exponent, the decimal point is moved to the *left* a number of places equal to the exponent:

$$1.56 \times 10^{-8} = 0.000\ 000\ 015\ 6$$

Negative exponent of −8, so decimal point is moved to the left eight places.

Scientific notation is particularly helpful for indicating how many significant figures are present in a number that has zeros at the end but to the left of a decimal point. If we read, for instance, that the distance from the earth to the sun is 150,000,000 km, we do not really know how many significant figures are indicated. Some of the zeros might be significant, or they might merely act to locate the decimal point. Using scientific notation, however, we can indicate how many of the zeros are significant. Rewriting 150,000,000 as 1.5×10^8 indicates two significant figures, whereas writing it as 1.500×10^8 indicates four significant figures.

Scientific notation is not ordinarily used for numbers that are easily written, such as 10 or 175, although it is sometimes helpful in doing arithmetic. Rules for doing arithmetic with numbers written in scientific notation are reviewed in Appendix A.

WORKED EXAMPLE **2.2** Significant Figures and Scientific Notation

There are 1,760,000,000,000,000,000,000 molecules of sucrose (table sugar) in 1 g. Use scientific notation to express this number with four significant figures.

ANALYSIS Because the number is larger than 1, the exponent will be positive. You will have to move the decimal point 21 places to the left.

SOLUTION
The first four digits—1, 7, 6, and 0—are significant, meaning that only the first of the 19 zeros is significant. Because we have to move the decimal point 21 places to the left to put it after the first significant digit, the answer is 1.760×10^{21}.

▲ How many molecules are in this 1 g pile of table sugar?

WORKED EXAMPLE **2.3** Scientific Notation

The rhinovirus responsible for the common cold has a diameter of 20 nm, or 0.000 000 020 m (See Application on p. 28). Express this number in scientific notation.

ANALYSIS The number is smaller than 1, and so the exponent will be negative. You will have to move the decimal point eight places to the right.

SOLUTION
There are only two significant figures, because zeros at the beginning of a number are not significant. We have to move the decimal point 8 places to the right to place it after the first digit, so the answer is 2.0×10^{-8} m.

WORKED EXAMPLE **2.4** Scientific Notation and Unit Conversions

A clinical laboratory found that a blood sample contained 0.0026 g of phosphorus and 0.000 101 g of iron.

(a) Give these quantities in scientific notation.
(b) Give these quantities in the units normally used to report them—milligrams for phosphorus and micrograms for iron.

ANALYSIS Is the number larger or smaller than 1? How many places do you have to move the decimal point?

SOLUTION

(a) 0.0026 g phosphorus $= 2.6 \times 10^{-3}$ g phosphorus

$0.000\ 101$ g iron $= 1.01 \times 10^{-4}$ g iron

(b) We know that 1 mg $= 1 \times 10^{-3}$ g, where the exponent is -3. Expressing the amount of phosphorus in milligrams is straightforward because the amount in grams (2.6×10^{-3} g) already has an exponent of -3. Thus, 2.6×10^{-3} g $= 2.6$ mg of phosphorus.

$$(2.6 \times 10^{-3}\ \cancel{g})\left(\frac{1\ \text{mg}}{1 \times 10^{-3}\ \cancel{g}}\right) = 2.6\ \text{mg}$$

We know that 1 μg $= 1 \times 10^{-6}$ g, where the exponent is -6. Expressing the amount of iron in micrograms thus requires that we restate the amount in grams so that the exponent is -6. We can do this by moving the decimal point six places to the right:

$$0.000\ 101 \text{ g iron} = 101 \times 10^{-6} \text{ g iron} = 101\ \mu\text{g iron}$$

APPLICATION ▶ Powers of 10

It is not easy to grasp the enormous differences in size represented by powers of 10 (scientific notation). A sodium atom has a diameter of 388 pm (3.88×10^{-10} m), a typical rhinovirus may have a diameter of 20 nm (2.0×10^{-8} m), and a single bacteria cell may be 3 μm long (3×10^{-6} m). Even though none of these objects can be seen with the naked eye, scientists know that the size of an atom relative to the size of a bacterium would be like comparing the size of a bowling ball with that of a baseball stadium. So how do scientists know the relative sizes of these items if we can not see them?

To study the miniature world of bacteria and viruses requires special tools. Optical light microscopes, for example, can magnify an object up to 1500 (1.5×10^3) times,

enabling us to study objects as small as 0.2 μm, such as bacteria. To study smaller objects, such as viruses, requires even higher magnification. Electron microscopy, which uses a beam of electrons instead of light, can achieve magnifications of 1×10^5 for scanning electron microscopy (SEM), and the ability to distinguish features on the order of 0.1 nm in length are possible with scanning tunneling microscopes (STM).

The change in magnification needed to distinguish features from 1 mm to 1 nm may not seem great, but it represents a million-fold (10^6) increase—enough to open a whole new world. Powers of 10 are powerful indeed.

See Additional Problems 2.78 and 2.79 at the end of the chapter.

(a)   (b)   (c)

▲ (a) A light microscope image of bacteria; (b) a color-enhanced SEM image showing a T-lymphocyte white blood cell (in orange) with HIV particles (in blue) budding on the surface of the cell membrane; (c) an STM image of a "blue nickel" surface showing the orientation of individual metal atoms.

PROBLEM 2.6

Convert the following values to scientific notation:

(a) 0.058 g   **(b)** 46,792 m   **(c)** 0.006 072 cm   **(d)** 345.3 kg

PROBLEM 2.7

Convert the following values from scientific notation to standard notation:

(a) 4.885×10^4 mg   **(b)** 8.3×10^{-6} m   **(c)** 4.00×10^{-2} m

PROBLEM 2.8

Rewrite the following numbers in scientific notation as indicated:

(a) 630,000 with five significant figures

(b) 1300 with three significant figures

(c) 794,200,000,000 with four significant figures

PROBLEM 2.9

Ordinary table salt, or sodium chloride, is made up of small particles called *ions*, which we will discuss in Chapter 4. If the distance between a sodium ion and a chloride ion is 0.000 000 000 278 m, what is the distance in scientific notation? How many picometers is this?

2.6 Rounding Off Numbers

It often happens, particularly when doing arithmetic on a pocket calculator, that a quantity appears to have more significant figures than are really justified. For example, you might calculate the gas mileage of your car by finding that it takes 11.70 gallons of gasoline to drive 278 miles:

$$\text{Mileage} = \frac{\text{Miles}}{\text{Gallons}} = \frac{278 \text{ mi}}{11.70 \text{ gal}} = 23.760\,684 \text{ mi/gal (mpg)}$$

Although the answer on a pocket calculator has eight digits, your measurement is really not as precise as it appears. In fact, as we will see below, your answer is good to only three significant figures and should be **rounded off** to 23.8 mi/gal.

How do you decide how many digits to keep? The full answer to this question is a bit complex and involves a mathematical treatment called *error analysis*, but for many purposes, a simplified procedure using just two rules is sufficient:

Rounding off A procedure used for deleting nonsignificant figures.

RULE 1. In carrying out a multiplication or division, the answer cannot have more significant figures than either of the original numbers. This is just a common-sense rule if you think about it. After all, if you do not know the number of miles you drove to better than three significant figures (278 could mean 277, 278, or 279), you certainly cannot calculate your mileage to more than the same number of significant figures.

▲ Calculators often display more digits than are justified by the precision of the data.

Three significant figures

Three significant figures

$$\frac{278 \text{ mi}}{11.70 \text{ gal}} = 23.8 \text{ mi/gal}$$

Four significant figures

RULE 2. In carrying out an addition or subtraction, the answer cannot have more digits after the decimal point than either of the original numbers. For example, if you have 3.18 L of water and you add 0.013 15 L more, you now have 3.19 L. Again, this rule is just common sense. If you do not know the volume you started with past the second decimal place (it could be 3.17, 3.18, or 3.19), you cannot know the total of the combined volumes past the same decimal place.

Volume of water at start ⟶ 3.18? ?? L ⟵ Two digits after decimal point
Volume of water added ⟶ + 0.013 15 L ⟵ Five digits after decimal point
Total volume of water ⟶ 3.19? ?? L ⟵ Two digits after decimal point

If a calculation has several steps, it is generally best to round off at the end after all the steps have been carried out, keeping the number of significant figures determined by the least precise number in your calculations. Once you decide how many digits to retain for your answer, the rules for rounding off numbers are straightforward:

RULE 1. If the first digit you remove is 4 or less, drop it and all following digits. Thus, 2.4271 becomes 2.4 when rounded off to two significant figures because the first of the dropped digits (a 2) is 4 or less.

RULE 2. If the first digit you remove is 5 or greater, round the number up by adding a 1 to the digit to the left of the one you drop. Thus, 4.5832 becomes 4.6 when rounded off to two significant figures because the first of the dropped digits (an 8) is 5 or greater.

WORKED EXAMPLE 2.5 Significant Figures and Calculations: Addition/Subtraction

Suppose that you weigh 124 lb before dinner. How much will you weigh after dinner if you eat 1.884 lb of food?

ANALYSIS When performing addition or subtraction, the number of significant figures you report in the final answer is determined by the number of digits in the least precise number in the calculation.

SOLUTION
Your after-dinner weight is found by adding your original weight to the weight of the food consumed:

$$
\begin{array}{r}
124 \quad \text{lb} \\
\underline{1.884\ \text{lb}} \\
125.884\ \text{lb} \quad \text{(Unrounded)}
\end{array}
$$

Because the value of your original weight has no significant figures after the decimal point, your after-dinner weight also must have no significant figures after the decimal point. Thus, 125.884 lb must be rounded off to 126 lb.

WORKED EXAMPLE 2.6 Significant Figures and Calculations: Multiplication/Division

To make currant jelly, 13.75 cups of sugar was added to 18 cups of currant juice. How much sugar was added per cup of juice?

ANALYSIS For calculations involving multiplication or division, the final answer cannot have more significant figures than either of the original numbers.

SOLUTION
The quantity of sugar must be divided by the quantity of juice:

$$
\frac{13.75\ \text{cups sugar}}{18\ \text{cups juice}} = 0.763\ 888\ 89\ \frac{\text{cup sugar}}{\text{cup juice}}\text{(Unrounded)}
$$

The number of significant figures in the answer is limited to two by the quantity 18 cups in the calculation and must be rounded to 0.76 cup of sugar per cup of juice.

PROBLEM 2.10

Round off the following quantities to the indicated number of significant figures:

(a) 2.304 g (three significant figures)
(b) 188.3784 mL (five significant figures)
(c) 0.008 87 L (one significant figure)
(d) 1.000 39 kg (four significant figures)

PROBLEM 2.11

Carry out the following calculations, rounding each result to the correct number of significant figures:

(a) 4.87 mL + 46.0 mL   (b) 3.4 × 0.023 g
(c) 19.333 m − 7.4 m   (d) 55 mg − 4.671 mg + 0.894 mg
(e) 62,911 ÷ 611

2.7 Problem Solving: Converting a Quantity from One Unit to Another

Many activities in the laboratory and in medicine—measuring, weighing, preparing solutions, and so forth—require converting a quantity from one unit to another. For example: "These pills contain 1.3 grains of aspirin, but I need 200 mg. Is one pill enough?" Converting between units is not mysterious; we all do it every day. If you run 9 laps around a 400 meter track, for instance, you have to convert between the distance unit "lap" and the distance unit "meter" to find that you have run 3600 m (9 laps times 400 m/lap). If you want to find how many miles that is, you have to convert again to find that 3600 m = 2.237 mi.

The simplest way to carry out calculations involving different units is to use the **factor-label method**. In this method, a quantity in one unit is converted into an equivalent quantity in a different unit by using a **conversion factor** that expresses the relationship between units:

Starting quantity × Conversion factor = Equivalent quantity

As an example, we said in Section 2.3 that 1 km = 0.6214 mi. Writing this relationship as a fraction restates it in the form of a conversion factor, either kilometers per mile or miles per kilometer.

Since 1 km = 0.6214 mi, then:

Conversion factors between kilometers and miles
$$\frac{1 \text{ km}}{0.6214 \text{ mi}} = 1 \quad \text{or} \quad \frac{0.6214 \text{ mi}}{1 \text{ km}} = 1$$

Note that this and all other conversion factors are numerically equal to 1 because the value of the quantity above the division line (the numerator) is equal in value to the quantity below the division line (the denominator). Thus, multiplying by a conversion factor is equivalent to multiplying by 1 and so does not change the value of the quantity being multiplied:

These two quantities are the same.
$$\frac{1 \text{ km}}{0.6214 \text{ mi}} \quad \text{or} \quad \frac{0.6214 \text{ mi}}{1 \text{ km}}$$
These two quantities are the same.

The key to the factor-label method of problem solving is that units are treated like numbers and can thus be multiplied and divided (though not added or subtracted) just as numbers can. When solving a problem, the idea is to set up an equation so that all unwanted units cancel, leaving only the desired units. Usually, it is best to start by writing what you know and then manipulating that known quantity. For example, if you know there are 26.22 mi in a marathon and want to find how many kilometers that is, you could write the distance in miles and multiply by the conversion factor in kilometers per mile. The unit "mi" cancels because it appears both above and below the division line, leaving "km" as the only remaining unit.

$$26.22 \text{ mi} \times \frac{1 \text{ km}}{0.6214 \text{ mi}} = 42.20 \text{ km}$$

Starting quantity   Conversion factor   Equivalent quantity

The factor-label method gives the right answer only if the equation is set up so that the unwanted unit (or units) cancel. If the equation is set up in any other way, the units will not cancel and you will not get the right answer. Thus, if you selected the incorrect conversion factor (miles per kilometer) for the above problem,

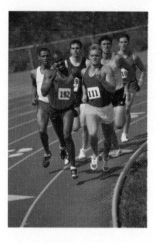

▲ These runners have to convert from laps to meters to find out how far they have run.

Factor-label method A problem-solving procedure in which equations are set up so that unwanted units cancel and only the desired units remain.

Conversion factor An expression of the numerical relationship between two units.

you would end up with an incorrect answer expressed in meaningless units:

$$\text{Incorrect } 26.22 \text{ mi} \times \frac{0.6214 \text{ mi}}{1 \text{ km}} = 16.29 \frac{\text{mi}^2}{\text{km}} \text{ Incorrect}$$

WORKED EXAMPLE **2.7** Factor Labels: Unit Conversions

Write conversion factors for the following pairs of units (use Tables 2.3–2.5):

(a) Deciliters and milliliters

(b) Pounds and grams

ANALYSIS Start with the appropriate equivalency relationship and rearrange to form conversion factors.

SOLUTION

(a) Since 1 dL = 0.1 L and 1 mL = 0.001L, then

$$1 \text{ dL} = (0.1 \text{ L}) \left(\frac{1 \text{ mL}}{0.001 \text{L}} \right) = 100 \text{ mL. The conversion factors are}$$

$$\frac{1 \text{ dL}}{100 \text{ mL}} \quad \text{and} \quad \frac{100 \text{ mL}}{1 \text{ dL}}$$

(b) $\dfrac{1 \text{ lb}}{454 \text{ g}}$ and $\dfrac{454 \text{ g}}{1 \text{ lb}}$

WORKED EXAMPLE **2.8** Factor Labels: Unit Conversions

(a) Convert 0.75 lb to grams.

(b) Convert 0.50 qt to deciliters.

ANALYSIS Start with conversion factors and set up equations so that units cancel appropriately.

SOLUTION

(a) Select the conversion factor from Worked Example 2.7(b) so that the "lb" units cancel and "g" remains:

$$0.75 \text{ lb} \times \frac{454 \text{ g}}{1 \text{ lb}} = 340 \text{ g}$$

(b) In this, as in many problems, it is convenient to use more than one conversion factor. As long as the unwanted units cancel correctly, two or more conversion factors can be strung together in the same calculation. In this case, we can convert first between quarts and milliliters, and then between milliliters and deciliters:

$$0.50 \text{ qt} \times \frac{946.4 \text{ mL}}{1 \text{ qt}} \times \frac{1 \text{ dL}}{100 \text{ mL}} = 4.7 \text{ dL}$$

PROBLEM 2.12

Write conversion factors for the following pairs of units:

(a) liters and milliliters   (b) grams and ounces

(c) liters and quarts

> **PROBLEM 2.13**
>
> Carry out the following conversions:
>
> **(a)** 16.0 oz = ? g   **(b)** 2500 mL = ? L   **(c)** 99.0 L = ? qt
>
> **PROBLEM 2.14**
>
> Convert 0.840 qt to milliliters in a single calculation using more than one conversion factor.
>
> **PROBLEM 2.15**
>
> One international nautical mile is defined as exactly 6076.1155 ft, and a speed of 1 knot is defined as one international nautical mile per hour. What is the speed in meters per second of a boat traveling at a speed of 14.3 knots?

2.8 Problem Solving: Estimating Answers

The main drawback to using the factor-label method is that it is possible to get an answer without really understanding what you are doing. It is therefore best when solving a problem to first think through a rough estimate, or *ballpark estimate*, as a check on your work. If your ballpark estimate is not close to the final calculated solution, there is a misunderstanding somewhere and you should think the problem through again. If, for example, you came up with the answer 5.3 cm^3 when calculating the volume of a human cell, you should realize that such an answer could not possibly be right. Cells are too tiny to be distinguished with the naked eye, but a volume of 5.3 cm^3 is about the size of a walnut. The Worked Examples at the end of this section show how to estimate the answers to simple unit-conversion problems.

The factor-label method and the use of ballpark estimates are techniques that will help you solve problems of many kinds, not just unit conversions. Problems sometimes seem complicated, but you can usually sort out the complications by analyzing the problem properly:

STEP 1: Identify the information given, including units.

STEP 2: Identify the information needed in the answer, including units.

STEP 3: Find the relationship(s) between the known information and unknown answer, and plan a series of steps, including conversion factors, for getting from one to the other.

STEP 4: Solve the problem.

BALLPARK CHECK: Make a ballpark estimate at the beginning and check it against your final answer to be sure the value and the units of your calculated answer are reasonable.

Worked Examples 2.9, 2.10 and 2.11 illustrate how to use the analysis steps and ballpark checks as an aid in dosage calculations.

▲ What is the volume of a red blood cell?

WORKED EXAMPLE   **2.9** Factor Labels: Unit Conversions

A child is 21.5 in. long at birth. How long is this in centimeters?

ANALYSIS This problem calls for converting from inches to centimeters, so we will need to know how many cm are in an inch, and how to use this information as a conversion factor.

BALLPARK ESTIMATE It takes about 2.5 cm to make 1 in., and so it should take 2.5 times as many centimeters to make a distance equal to approximately 20 in., or about 20 in. × 2.5 = 50 cm.

SOLUTION

STEP 1: Identify given information.   Length = 21.5 in.

STEP 2: Identify answer and units.   Length = ?? cm

STEP 3: Identify conversion factor.   1 in. = 2.54 cm ⟶ $\dfrac{2.54 \text{ cm}}{1 \text{ in.}}$

STEP 4: Solve Multiply the known length (in inches) by the conversion factor so that units cancel, providing the answer (in cm).

$$21.5 \text{ in.} \times \dfrac{2.54 \text{ cm}}{1 \text{ in.}} = 54.6 \text{ cm (Rounded off from 54.61)}$$

BALLPARK CHECK How does this value compare with the ballpark estimate we made at the beginning? Are the final units correct?

WORKED EXAMPLE   **2.10** Factor Labels: Concentration to Mass

A patient requires injection of 0.012 g of a pain killer available as a 15 mg/mL solution. How many milliliters should be administered?

ANALYSIS Knowing the amount of pain killer in 1 mL allows us to use the concentration as a conversion factor to determine the volume of solution that would contain the desired amount.

BALLPARK ESTIMATE One milliliter contains 15 mg of the pain killer, or 0.015 g. Since only 0.012 g is needed, a little less than 1.0 mL should be administered.

▲ How many milliliters should be injected?

SOLUTION

STEP 1: Identify known information.

Dosage = 0.012 g
Concentration = 15 mg/mL

STEP 2: Identify answer and units.

Volume to administer = ?? mL

STEP 3: Identify conversion factors. Two conversion factors are needed. First, g must be converted to mg. Once we have the mass in mg, then we can calculate mL using the conversion factor of mL/mg.

$$1 \text{ mg} = .001 \text{ g} \Rightarrow \dfrac{1 \text{ mg}}{0.001 \text{g}}$$

$$15 \text{ mg/mL} \Rightarrow \dfrac{1 \text{ mL}}{15 \text{ mg}}$$

STEP 4: Solve. Starting from the desired dosage, we use the conversion factors to cancel units, obtaining the final answer in mL.

$$(0.012 \text{ g})\left(\dfrac{1 \text{ mg}}{0.001 \text{ g}}\right)\left(\dfrac{1 \text{ mL}}{15 \text{ mg}}\right) = 0.80 \text{ mL}$$

BALLPARK CHECK Consistent with our initial estimate of a little less than 1 mL.

WORKED EXAMPLE   **2.11** Factor Labels: Multiple Conversion Calculations

Administration of digitalis to control atrial fibrillation in heart patients must be carefully regulated because even a modest overdose can be fatal. To take differences between patients into account, dosages are sometimes prescribed in micrograms per kilogram of body weight (μg/kg). Thus, two people may differ greatly in weight, but both will receive the proper dosage. At a dosage of 20 μg/kg body weight, how many milligrams of digitalis should a 160 lb patient receive?

ANALYSIS Knowing the patient's body weight (in kg) and the recommended dosage (in μg/kg), we can calculate the appropriate amount of digitalis.

BALLPARK ESTIMATE Since a kilogram is roughly equal to 2 lb, a 160 lb patient has a mass of about 80 kg. At a dosage of 20 μg/kg, an 80 kg patient should receive 80 × 20 μg, or about 1600 μg of digitalis, or 1.6 mg.

SOLUTION

STEP 1: Identify known information.

STEP 2: Identify answer and units.

STEP 3: Identify conversion factors. Two conversions are needed. First, convert the patient's weight in pounds to weight in kg. The correct dose can then be determined based on μg digitalis/kg of body weight. Finally the dosage in μg is converted to mg.

STEP 4: Solve. Use the known information and the conversion factors so that units cancel, obtaining the answer in mg.

BALLPARK CHECK Close to our estimate of 1.6 mg.

Patient weight = 160 lb

Prescribed dosage = 20 μg digitalis/kg body weight

Delivered dosage = ?? mg digitalis

$$1 \text{ kg} = 2.205 \text{ lb} \rightarrow \frac{1 \text{ kg}}{2.205 \text{ lb}}$$

$$1 \text{ mg} = (0.001 \text{ g})\left(\frac{1 \mu g}{10^{-6} g}\right) = 1000 \ \mu g$$

$$160 \ \cancel{lb} \times \frac{1 \ \cancel{kg}}{2.205 \ \cancel{lb}} \times \frac{20 \ \cancel{\mu g} \text{ digitalis}}{1 \ \cancel{kg}} \times \frac{1 \text{ mg}}{1000 \ \cancel{\mu g}}$$

$$= 1.5 \text{ mg digitalis (Rounded off)}$$

PROBLEM 2.16

(a) How many kilograms does a 7.5 lb infant weigh?

(b) How many milliliters are in a 4.0 fl oz bottle of cough medicine?

PROBLEM 2.17

Calculate the dosage in milligrams per kilogram body weight for a 135 lb adult who takes two aspirin tablets containing 0.324 g of aspirin each. Calculate the dosage for a 40 lb child who also takes two aspirin tablets.

2.9 Measuring Temperature

Temperature, the measure of how hot or cold an object is, is commonly reported either in Fahrenheit (°F) or Celsius (°C) units. The SI unit for reporting temperature, however, is the *kelvin* (K). (Note that we say only "kelvin," not "kelvin degree.")

The kelvin and the Celsius degree are the same size—both are 1/100 of the interval between the freezing point of water and the boiling point of water at atmospheric pressure. Thus, a change in temperature of 1 °C is equal to a change of 1 K. The only difference between the Kelvin and Celsius temperature scales is that they have different zero points. The Celsius scale assigns a value of 0 °C to the freezing point of water, but the Kelvin scale assigns a value of 0 K to the coldest possible temperature, sometimes called *absolute zero*, which is equal to −273.15 °C. Thus, 0 K = −273.15 °C, and +273.15 K = 0 °C. For example, a warm spring day with a temperature of 25 °C has a Kelvin temperature of 25 + 273.15 = 298 K (for most purposes, rounding off to 273 is sufficient):

Temperature in K = Temperature in °C + 273.15

Temperature in °C = Temperature in K − 273.15

For practical applications in medicine and clinical chemistry, the Fahrenheit and Celsius scales are used almost exclusively. The Fahrenheit scale defines the freezing point of water as 32 °F and the boiling point of water as 212 °F, whereas 0 °C and 100 °C are the freezing and boiling points of water on the Celsius scale. Thus, it takes 180 Fahrenheit degrees to cover the same range encompassed by only 100 Celsius degrees, and a Celsius degree is therefore exactly 180/100 = 9/5 = 1.8

Temperature The measure of how hot or cold an object is.

▲ Gold metal is a liquid at temperatures above 1064.4 °C?

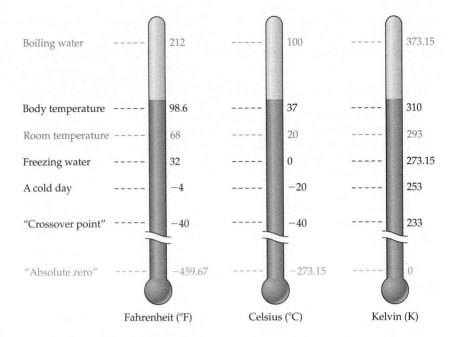

	Fahrenheit (°F)	Celsius (°C)	Kelvin (K)
Boiling water	212	100	373.15
Body temperature	98.6	37	310
Room temperature	68	20	293
Freezing water	32	0	273.15
A cold day	−4	−20	253
"Crossover point"	−40	−40	233
"Absolute zero"	−459.67	−273.15	0

▶ **FIGURE 2.4 A comparison of the Fahrenheit, Celsius, and Kelvin temperature scales.** One Fahrenheit degree is 5/9 the size of a kelvin or a Celsius degree.

times as large as a Fahrenheit degree. In other words, a change in temperature of 1.0 °C is equal to a change of 1.8 °F. Figure 2.4 gives a comparison of all three scales.

Converting between the Fahrenheit and Celsius scales is similar to converting between different units of length or volume, but is a bit more complex because two corrections need to be made—one to adjust for the difference in degree size and one to adjust for the different zero points. The size correction is made by using the relationship 1 °C = (9/5) °F and 1 °F = (5/9) °C. The zero-point correction is made by

APPLICATION ▶ **Temperature–Sensitive Materials**

Wouldn't it be nice to be able to tell if the baby's formula bottle is too hot? Or if the package of chicken you are buying for dinner has been stored appropriately? Temperature-sensitive materials are being used in these and other applications.

A class of materials called thermochromic materials change color as their temperature increases and they change from the liquid phase to a semicrystalline ordered state. These "liquid crystals" can be incorporated into plastics or paints, and can be used to monitor the temperature of the products or packages in which they are incorporated. For example, some meat packaging now includes a temperature strip that darkens when the meat is stored above a certain temperature, making the meat unsafe to eat. Hospitals and other medical facilities now routinely use temperature strips that, when placed under the tongue or applied to the forehead, change color to indicate the patient's body temperature. There are even clothes that change color based on the air temperature.

Can't decide what color bathing suit to wear to the beach? Pick one that will change color to fit your mood!

See Additional Problems 2.80 and 2.81 at the end of the chapter.

remembering that the freezing point is higher by 32 on the Fahrenheit scale than on the Celsius scale. Thus, if you want to convert from Celsius to Fahrenheit, you do a size adjustment (multiply °C by 9/5) and then a zero-point adjustment (add 32); if you want to convert from Fahrenheit to Celsius, you find out how many Fahrenheit degrees there are above freezing (by subtracting 32) and then do a size adjustment (multiply °C by 5/9). The following formulas show the conversion methods:

Celsius to Fahrenheit:

$$°F = \left(\frac{9 \, °F}{5 \, °\cancel{C}} \times °\cancel{C} \right) + 32 \, °F$$

Fahrenheit to Celsius:

$$°C = \frac{5 \, °C}{9 \, °\cancel{F}} \times (°\cancel{F} - 32 \, °\cancel{F})$$

WORKED EXAMPLE **2.12** Temperature Conversions: Fahrenheit to Celsius

A body temperature above 107 °F can be fatal. What does 107 °F correspond to on the Celsius scale?

ANALYSIS Using the temperature (in °F) and the appropriate temperature conversion equation we can convert from the Fahrenheit scale to the Celsius scale.

BALLPARK ESTIMATE Note in Figure 2.4 that normal body temperature is 98.6 °F or 37 °C. A temperature of 107 °F is approximately 8 °F above normal; since 1 °C is nearly 2 °F, then 8 °F is about 4 °C. Thus, the 107 °F body temperature is 41 °C.

SOLUTION

STEP 1: Identify known information.

Temperature = 107 °F

STEP 2: Identify answer and units.

Temperature = ?? °C

STEP 3: Identify conversion factors.
We can convert from °F to °C using this equation.

$$°C = \frac{5 \, °C}{9 \, °F} \times (°F - 32 \, °F)$$

STEP 4: Solve. Substitute the known temperature (in °F) into the equation.

$$°C = \frac{5 \, °C}{9 \, °\cancel{F}} \times (107 \, °\cancel{F} - 32 \, °\cancel{F}) = 42 \, °C^*$$

BALLPARK CHECK Close to our estimate of 41 °C. (Rounded off from 41.666 667 °C)

*It is worth noting that the 5/9 conversion factor in the equation is an exact conversion, and so does not impact the number of significant figures in the final answer.

PROBLEM 2.18

The highest land temperature ever recorded was 136 °F in Al Aziziyah, Libya, on September 13, 1922. What is this temperature on the Celsius scale?

PROBLEM 2.19

The use of mercury thermometers is limited by the fact that mercury freezes at −38.9 °C. To what temperature does this correspond on the Fahrenheit scale? On the Kelvin scale?

2.10 Energy and Heat

All chemical reactions are accompanied by a change in **energy**, which is defined in scientific terms as *the capacity to do work or supply heat* (Figure 2.5). Detailed discussion of the various kinds of energy will be included in Chapter 7, but for now we will look at the various units used to describe energy, and the way heat energy can be gained or lost by matter.

Energy is measured in SI units by the unit *joule* (J; pronounced "jool"), but the metric unit *calorie* (cal) is still widely used in medicine. One calorie is the amount of heat necessary to raise the temperature of 1 g of water by 1 °C. A *kilocalorie* (kcal), often called a *large calorie (Cal)* or *food calorie* by nutritionists, equals 1000 cal:

$$1000 \text{ cal} = 1 \text{ kcal} \qquad 1000 \text{ J} = 1 \text{ kJ}$$
$$1 \text{ cal} = 4.184 \text{ J} \qquad 1 \text{ kcal} = 4.184 \text{ kJ}$$

Not all substances have their temperatures raised to the same extent when equal amounts of heat energy are added. One calorie raises the temperature of 1 g of water by 1 °C but raises the temperature of 1 g of iron by 10 °C. The amount of heat needed to raise the temperature of 1 g of a substance by 1 °C is called the **specific heat** of the substance. It is measured in units of cal/(g·°C).

$$\text{Specific heat} = \frac{\text{Calories}}{\text{Grams} \times °C}$$

Specific heats vary greatly from one substance to another, as shown in Table 2.6. The specific heat of water, 1.00 cal/(g·°C), is higher than that of most other substances, which means that a large transfer of heat is required to change the temperature of a given amount of water by a given number of degrees. One consequence is that the human body, which is about 60% water, is able to withstand changing outside conditions.

▲ FIGURE 2.5 The reaction of aluminum with bromine releases energy in the form of heat. When the reaction is complete, the products undergo no further change.

Energy The capacity to do work or supply heat.

Specific heat The amount of heat that will raise the temperature of 1 g of a substance by 1 °C.

TABLE 2.6 Specific Heats of Some Common Substances

SUBSTANCE	SPECIFIC HEAT [cal/(g · °C)]
Ethanol	0.59
Gold	0.031
Iron	0.106
Mercury	0.033
Sodium	0.293
Water	1.00

Knowing the mass and specific heat of a substance makes it possible to calculate how much heat must be added or removed to accomplish a given temperature change, as shown in Worked Example 2.13.

$$\text{Heat (cal)} = \text{Mass } (g) \times \text{Temperature change } (°C) \times \text{Specific heat}\left(\frac{\text{cal}}{g \cdot °C}\right)$$

WORKED EXAMPLE 2.13 Specific Heat: Mass, Temperature, and Energy

Taking a bath might use about 95 kg of water. How much energy (in calories) is needed to heat the water from a cold 15 °C to a warm 40 °C?

ANALYSIS From the amount of water being heated (95 kg) and the amount of the temperature change (40 °C − 15 °C = 25 °C), the total amount of energy needed can be calculated by using specific heat [1.00 cal/(g·°C)] as a conversion factor.

BALLPARK ESTIMATE The water is being heated 25 °C (from 15 °C to 40 °C), and it therefore takes 25 cal to heat each gram. The tub contains nearly 100,000 g (95 kg is 95,000 g), and so it takes about 25 × 100,000 cal, or 2,500,000 cal, to heat all the water in the tub.

SOLUTION

STEP 1: **Identify known information.**

STEP 2: **Identify answer and units.**

STEP 3: **Identify conversion factors.** The amount of energy (in cal) can be calculated using the specific heat of water (cal/g · °C), and will depend on both the mass of water (in g) to be heated and the total temperature change (in °C). In order for the units in specific heat to cancel correctly, the mass of water must first be converted from kg to g.

STEP 4: **Solve.** Starting with the known information, use the conversion factors to cancel unwanted units.

Mass of water = 95 kg

Temperature change = 40 °C − 15 °C = 25 °C

Heat = ?? cal

$$\text{Specific heat} = \frac{1.0 \text{ cal}}{g \cdot °C}$$

$$1 \text{ kg} = 1000 \text{ g} \rightarrow \frac{1000 \text{ g}}{1 \text{ kg}}$$

$$95 \text{ kg} \times \frac{1000 \text{ g}}{\text{kg}} \times \frac{1.00 \text{ cal}}{g \cdot °C} \times 25 °C = 2,400,000 \text{ cal}$$

$$= 2.4 \times 10^6 \text{ cal}$$

BALLPARK CHECK Close to our estimate of 2.5 × 10⁶ cal.

PROBLEM 2.20

Assuming that Coca-Cola has the same specific heat as water, how much energy in calories is removed when 350 g of Coke (about the contents of one 12 oz can) is cooled from room temperature (25 °C) to refrigerator temperature (3 °C)?

PROBLEM 2.21

What is the specific heat of aluminum if it takes 161 cal to raise the temperature of a 75 g aluminum bar by 10.0 °C?

2.11 Density

One further physical quantity that we will take up in this chapter is **density**, which relates the mass of an object to its volume. Density is usually expressed in units of grams per cubic centimeter (g/cm³) for solids and grams per milliliter (g/mL) for liquids. Thus, if we know the density of a substance, we know both the mass of a given volume and the volume of a given mass. The densities of some common materials are listed in Table 2.7.

$$\text{Density} = \frac{\text{Mass (g)}}{\text{Volume (mL or cm}^3)}$$

Most substances change their volume by expanding or contracting when heated or cooled, and densities are therefore temperature-dependent. For example, at 3.98 °C a 1 mL container holds exactly 1.0000 g of water (density = 1.0000 g/mL). As the temperature rises, however, the volume occupied by the water expands so that only 0.9584 g fits in the 1 mL container at 100 °C (density = 0.9584 g/mL). When reporting a density, the temperature must also be specified.

Although most substances contract when cooled and expand when heated, water behaves differently. Water contracts when cooled from 100 °C to 3.98 °C, but

Density The physical property that relates the mass of an object to its volume; mass per unit volume.

▲ Which has the greater mass, the pillow or the brass cylinder? In fact, they have similar masses, but the brass cylinder has a higher *density* because of its smaller volume.

TABLE 2.7 Densities of Some Common Materials at 25 °C

SUBSTANCE	DENSITY*	SUBSTANCE	DENSITY*
Gases		Solids	
Helium	0.000 194	Ice (0 °C)	0.917
Air	0.001 185	Gold	19.3
Liquids		Human fat	0.94
Water (3.98 °C)	1.0000	Cork	0.22–0.26
Urine	1.003–1.030	Table sugar	1.59
Blood plasma	1.027	Balsa wood	0.12
		Earth	5.54

Densities are in g/cm³ for solids and g/mL for liquids and gases.

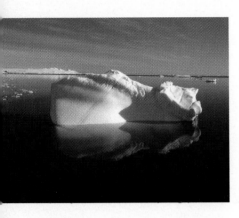

▲ Ice floats because its density is less than that of water.

below this temperature it begins to *expand* again. The density of liquid water is at its maximum of 1.0000 g/mL at 3.98 °C but decreases to 0.999 87 g/mL at 0 °C. When freezing occurs, the density drops still further to a value of 0.917 g/cm³ for ice at 0 °C. Since a less dense substance will float on top of a more dense fluid, ice and any other substance with a density less than that of water will float. Conversely, any substance with a density greater than that of water will sink.

Knowing the density of a liquid is useful because it is often easier to measure a liquid's volume rather than its mass. Suppose, for example, that you need 1.50 g of ethanol. Rather than use a dropper to weigh out exactly the right amount, it would be much easier to look up the density of ethanol (0.7893 g/mL at 20 °C) and measure the correct volume (1.90 mL) with a syringe or graduated cylinder. Thus, density acts as a conversion factor between mass (g) and volume (mL).

$$1.50 \text{ g ethanol} \times \frac{1 \text{ mL ethanol}}{0.7893 \text{ g ethanol}} = 1.90 \text{ mL ethanol}$$

WORKED EXAMPLE **2.14** Density: Mass-to-Volume Conversion.

What volume of isopropyl alcohol (rubbing alcohol) would you use if you needed 25.0 g? The density of isopropyl alcohol is 0.7855 g/mL at 20 °C.

ANALYSIS The known information is the mass of isopropyl alcohol needed (25.0 g). The density (0.7855 g/mL) acts as a conversion factor between mass and the unknown volume of isopropyl alcohol.

BALLPARK ESTIMATE Because 1 mL of isopropyl alcohol contains only 0.7885 g of the alcohol, obtaining 1 g of alcohol would require almost 20% more than 1 mL, or about 1.2 mL. Therefore, a volume of about 25 × 1.2 mL = 30 mL is needed to obtain 25 g of alcohol.

SOLUTION

STEP 1: **Identify known information.**

STEP 2: **Identify answer and units.**

STEP 3: **Identify conversion factors.** Starting with the mass of isopropyl alcohol (in g), the corresponding volume (in mL) can be calculated using density (g/mL) as the conversion factor.

STEP 4: **Solve.** Starting with the known information, set up the equation with conversion factors so that unwanted units cancel.

Mass of rubbing alcohol = 25.0 g

Density of rubbing alcohol = 0.7855 g/mL

Volume of rubbing alcohol = ?? mL

Density = g/mL → 1/density = mL/g

$$25.0 \text{ g alcohol} \times \frac{1 \text{ mL alcohol}}{0.7855 \text{ g alcohol}} = 31.8 \text{ mL alcohol}$$

BALLPARK CHECK Our estimate was 30 mL.

APPLICATION ▶ Obesity and Body Fat

According to the U.S. Center for Disease Control, the U.S. population is suffering from a fat epidemic. Over the last 25 years, the percentage of adults (20 years or older) identified as obese increased from 15% in the late 1970s to nearly 33% in 2004. Even children and adolescents are gaining too much weight: the number of overweight children in all age groups increased by nearly a factor of 3, with the biggest increase seen among teenagers (from 5% to 17.4%). How do we define obesity, however, and how is it measured?

Obesity is defined by reference to *body mass index* (BMI), which is equal to a person's mass in kilograms divided by the square of his or her height in meters. Alternatively, a person's weight in pounds divided by the square of her or his height in inches is multiplied by 703 to give the BMI. For instance, someone 5 ft 7 in. (67 inches; 1.70 m) tall weighing 147 lb (66.7 kg) has a BMI of 23:

$$BMI = \frac{weight\ (kg)}{[height\ (m)]^2}, \quad or \quad \frac{weight\ (lb)}{[height\ (in.)]^2} \times 703$$

A BMI of 25 or above is considered overweight, and a BMI of 30 or above is obese. By these standards, approximately 61% of the U.S. population is overweight.

Health professionals are concerned by the rapid rise in obesity in the United States because of the link between BMI and health problems. Many reports have documented the correlation between health and BMI, including a recent study on more than one million adults. The lowest death risk from any cause, including cancer and heart disease, is associated with a BMI between 22 and 24. Risk increases steadily as BMI increases, more than doubling for a BMI above 29.

Fat is not the enemy, however, because having some body fat is not just good, it is necessary! The layer of adipose tissue (body fat) lying just beneath our skin acts as a shock absorber and as a thermal insulator to maintain body temperature. It also serves as a long-term energy storehouse (see Section 25.6). A typical adult body contains about 50% muscles and other cellular material, 24% blood and other fluids, 7% bone, and 19% body fat. Overweight sedentary individuals

▲ A person's percentage body fat can be estimated by measuring the thickness of the fat layer under the skin.

have a higher fat percentage, whereas some world-class athletes have as little as 3% body fat. The problem occurs when the percentage of body fat is excessive.

An individual's percentage of body fat is most easily measured by the skinfold thickness method. The skin at several locations on the arm, shoulder, and waist is pinched, and the thickness of the fat layer beneath the skin is measured with calipers. Comparing the measured results to those in a standard table gives an estimation of percentage body fat.

As an alternative to skinfold measurement, a more accurate assessment of body fat can be made by underwater immersion. The person's underwater body weight is less than her weight on land because water gives the body buoyancy. The higher the percentage of body fat, the more buoyant the person and the greater the difference between land weight and underwater body weight. Checking the observed buoyancy on a standard table then gives an estimation of body fat.

See Additional Problems 2.82 and 2.83 at the end of the chapter.

Weight (lb)

Height	110	115	120	125	130	135	140	145	150	155	160	165	170	175	180	185	190	195	200
5′0″	21	22	23	24	25	26	27	28	29	30	31	32	33	34	35	36	37	38	39
5′2″	20	21	22	23	24	25	26	27	27	28	29	30	31	32	33	34	35	36	37
5′4″	19	20	21	21	22	23	24	25	26	27	27	28	29	30	31	32	33	33	34
5′6″	18	19	19	20	21	22	23	23	24	25	26	27	27	28	29	30	31	31	32
5′8″	17	17	18	19	20	21	21	22	23	24	24	25	26	27	27	28	29	30	30
5′10″	16	17	17	18	19	19	20	21	22	22	23	24	24	25	26	27	27	28	29
6′0″	15	16	16	17	18	18	19	20	20	21	22	22	23	24	24	25	26	26	27
6′2″	14	15	15	16	17	17	18	19	19	20	21	21	22	22	23	24	24	25	26
6′4″	13	14	15	15	16	16	17	18	18	19	19	20	21	21	22	23	23	24	24

Body Mass Index (numbers in boxes)

PROBLEM 2.22

Which of the solids whose densities are given in Table 2.7 will float on water, and which will sink?

PROBLEM 2.23

Chloroform, once used as an anesthetic agent, has a density of 1.474 g/mL. What volume would you use if you needed 12.37 g?

PROBLEM 2.24

A glass stopper that has a mass of 16.8 g has a volume of 7.60 cm^3. What is the density of the glass?

2.12 Specific Gravity

Specific gravity The density of a substance divided by the density of water at the same temperature.

For many purposes, ranging from winemaking to medicine, it is more convenient to use *specific gravity* than density. The **specific gravity** (sp gr) of a substance (usually a liquid) is simply the density of the substance divided by the density of water at the same temperature. Because all units cancel, specific gravity is unitless:

$$\text{Specific gravity} = \frac{\text{Density of substance (g/mL)}}{\text{Density of water at the same temperature (g/mL)}}$$

At normal temperatures, the density of water is very close to 1 g/mL. Thus, the specific gravity of a substance is numerically equal to its density and is used in the same way.

The specific gravity of a liquid can be measured using an instrument called a *hydrometer*, which consists of a weighted bulb on the end of a calibrated glass tube, as shown in Figure 2.6. The depth to which the hydrometer sinks when placed in a fluid indicates the fluid's specific gravity: The lower the bulb sinks, the lower the specific gravity of the fluid.

Water that contains dissolved substances can have a specific gravity either higher or lower than 1.00. In winemaking, for instance, the amount of fermentation taking place is gauged by observing the change in specific gravity on going from grape juice, which contains 20% dissolved sugar and has a specific gravity of 1.082, to dry wine, which contains 12% alcohol and has a specific gravity of 0.984. (Pure alcohol has a specific gravity of 0.789.)

In medicine, a hydrometer called a *urinometer* is used to indicate the amount of solids dissolved in urine. Although the specific gravity of normal urine is about 1.003–1.030, conditions such as diabetes mellitus or a high fever cause an abnormally high urine specific gravity, indicating either excessive elimination of solids or decreased elimination of water. Abnormally low specific gravity is found in individuals using diuretics—drugs that increase water elimination.

▲ **FIGURE 2.6   A hydrometer for measuring specific gravity.** The instrument has a weighted bulb at the end of a calibrated glass tube. The depth to which the hydrometer sinks in a liquid indicates the liquid's specific gravity.

PROBLEM 2.25

The sulfuric acid solution in an automobile battery typically has a specific gravity of about 1.27. Is battery acid more dense or less dense than pure water?

▲ The amount of fermentation that has taken place in the wine can be measured with a hydrometer.

SUMMARY: REVISITING THE CHAPTER GOALS

1. **How are measurements made, and what units are used?** A property that can be measured is called a *physical quantity* and is described by both a number and a label, or *unit*. The preferred units are either those of the International System of Units (*SI units*) or the *metric system*. Mass, the amount of matter an object contains, is measured in *kilograms* (kg) or *grams* (g). Length is measured in *meters* (m). Volume is measured in *cubic meters* (m³) in the SI system and in *liters* (L) or *milliliters* (mL) in the metric system. Temperature is measured in *kelvins* (K) in the SI system and in *degrees Celsius* (°C) in the metric system.

2. **How good are the reported measurements?** When measuring physical quantities or using them in calculations, it is important to indicate the exactness of the measurement by *rounding off* the final answer using the correct number of *significant figures*. All but one of the significant figures in a number is known with certainty; the final digit is estimated to ±1.

3. **How are large and small numbers best represented?** Measurements of small and large quantities are usually written in *scientific notation* as the product of a number between 1 and 10, times a power of 10. Numbers greater than 10 have a positive exponent, and numbers less than 1 have a negative exponent. For example, $3562 = 3.562 \times 10^3$, and $0.003\,91 = 3.91 \times 10^{-3}$.

4. **How can a quantity be converted from one unit of measure to another?** A measurement in one unit can be converted to another unit by multiplying by a *conversion factor* that expresses the exact relationship between the units.

5. **What techniques are used to solve problems?** Problems are best solved by applying the *factor-label method*, in which units can be multiplied and divided just as numbers can. The idea is to set up an equation so that all unwanted units cancel, leaving only the desired units. Usually it is best to start by identifying the known and needed information, then

KEY WORDS

Conversion factor, *p. 31*

Density, *p. 39*

Energy, *p. 38*

Factor-label method, *p. 31*

Mass, *p. 21*

Physical quantity, *p. 19*

Rounding off, *p. 29*

Scientific notation, *p. 26*

SI units, *p. 19*

Significant figures, *p. 24*

Specific gravity, *p. 42*

Specific heat, *p. 38*

Temperature, *p. 35*

Unit, *p. 19*

Weight, *p. 21*

decide how to convert the known information to the answer, and finally check to make sure the answer is reasonable both chemically and physically.

6. **What are temperature, specific heat, density, and specific gravity?** *Temperature* is a measure of how hot or cold an object is. The *specific heat* of a substance is the amount of heat necessary to raise the temperature of 1 g of the substance by 1 °C. Water has an unusually high specific heat, which helps our bodies to maintain an even temperature. *Density*, the physical property that relates mass to volume, is expressed in units of grams per milliliter (g/mL) for a liquid or grams per cubic centimeter (g/cm³) for a solid. The *specific gravity* of a liquid is the density of the liquid divided by the density of water at the same temperature. Because the density of water is approximately 1 g/mL, specific gravity and density have the same numerical value.

UNDERSTANDING KEY CONCEPTS

2.26 How many milliliters of water does the graduated cylinder in (a) contain, and how tall in centimeters is the paper clip in (b)? How many significant figures do you have in each answer?

(a)   (b)

2.27 Using a metric ruler, measure the following objects:
  (a) Length of your calculator
  (b) Width of a page in this text book
  (c) Height and diameter of a 12 ounce can

2.28 **(a)** What is the specific gravity of the following solution?
  (b) How many significant figures does your answer have?
  (c) Is the solution more dense or less dense than water?

2.29 Assume that you have two graduated cylinders, one with a capacity of 5 mL (a) and the other with a capacity of 50 mL (b). Draw a line in each showing how much liquid you would add if you needed to measure 2.64 mL of water. Which cylinder do you think is more precise? Explain.

(a)   (b)

2.30 State the length of the pencil depicted in the accompanying figure in both inches and cm.

2.31 Assume that you are delivering a solution sample from a pipette. Figures (a) and (b) show the volume level before and after dispensing the sample, respectively. State the liquid level (in mL) before and after dispensing the sample, and calculate the volume of the sample.

(a)   (b)

2.32 **(a)** Pour the contents of a 12 ounce can into a measuring cup. Record the volume in both fluid ounces and in cups. Which measurement is more precise?

(b) Pour the contents of a 12 ounce can into a 400 mL beaker. What is the volume in mL?

2.33 Assume that identical hydrometers are placed in ethanol (sp gr 0.7893) and in chloroform (sp gr 1.4832). In which liquid will the hydrometer float higher? Explain.

ADDITIONAL PROBLEMS

DEFINITIONS AND UNITS

2.34 What is the difference between a physical quantity and a number?

2.35 What is the difference between mass and weight?

2.36 What are the units used in the SI system to measure mass, volume, length, and temperature?

2.37 What are the units used in the metric system to measure mass, volume, length, and temperature?

2.38 What is the difference between a cubic decimeter (SI) and a liter (metric)?

2.39 What is the difference between a kelvin (SI) and a Celsius degree (metric)?

2.40 Give the full name of the following units:

(a) cL   **(b)** dm   **(c)** mm
(d) nL   **(e)** mg   **(f)** m^3
(g) cc

2.41 Write the symbol for the following units:

(a) nanogram   **(b)** centimeter   **(c)** microlliter
(d) micrometer   **(e)** milligram

2.42 How many picograms are in 1 mg? In 35 ng?

2.43 How many microliters are in 1 L? In 20 mL?

SCIENTIFIC NOTATION AND SIGNIFICANT FIGURES

2.44 Express the following numbers in scientific notation:

(a) 9457   **(b)** 0.000 07
(c) 20,000,000,000 (four significant figures)
(d) 0.012 345   **(e)** 652.38

2.45 Convert the following numbers from scientific notation to standard notation:

(a) 5.28×10^3 **(b)** 8.205×10^{-2}
(c) 1.84×10^{-5} **(d)** 6.37×10^4

2.46 How many significant figures does each of the following numbers have?

(a) 237,401   **(b)** 0.300   **(c)** 3.01
(d) 244.4   **(e)** 50,000   **(f)** 660

2.47 How many significant figures are there in each of the following quantities?

(a) Distance from New York City to Wellington, New Zealand, 14,397 km
(b) Average body temperature of a crocodile, 25.6 °C
(c) Melting point of gold, 1064 °C
(d) Diameter of an influenza virus, 0.000 01 mm
(e) Radius of a phosphorus atom, 0.110 nm

2.48 The diameter of the earth at the equator is 7926.381 mi.

(a) Round off the earth's diameter to four significant figures, to two significant figures, and to six significant figures.
(b) Express the earth's diameter in scientific notation.

2.49 Round off each of the numbers in Problem 2.46 to two significant figures, and express them in scientific notation.

2.50 Carry out the following calculations, express each answer to the correct number of significant figures, and include units in the answers.

(a) 9.02 g + 3.1 g
(b) 88.80 cm + 7.391 cm
(c) 362 mL − 99.5 mL
(d) 12.4 mg + 6.378 mg + 2.089 mg

2.51 Carry out the following calculations, express the answers to the correct numbers of significant figures, and include units in the answers.

(a) $5{,}280 \dfrac{\text{ft}}{\text{mi}} \times 6.2 \text{ mi}$

(b) $4.5 \text{ m} \times 3.25 \text{ m}$

(c) $2.50 \text{ g} \div 8.3\dfrac{\text{g}}{\text{cm}^3}$

(d) $4.70 \text{ cm} \times 6.8 \text{ cm} \times 2.54 \text{ cm}$

UNIT CONVERSIONS AND PROBLEM SOLVING

2.52 Carry out the following conversions:

(a) 3.614 mg to centigrams
(b) 12.0 kL to megaliters
(c) 14.4 μm to millimeters
(d) 6.03×10^{-6} cg to nanograms
(e) 174.5 mL to deciliters
(f) 1.5×10^{-2} km to centimeters

2.53 Carry out the following conversions. Consult Tables 2.3–2.5 as needed.

(a) 56.4 mi to kilometers and to megameters
(b) 2.0 L to to quarts and to fluid ounces
(c) 7 ft 2.0 in. to centimeters and to meters
(d) 1.35 lb to kilograms and to decigrams

2.54 Express the following quantities in more convenient units by using SI unit prefixes:

(a) 9.78×10^4 g   **(b)** 1.33×10^{-4} L
(c) 0.000 000 000 46 g   **(d)** 2.99×10^8 cm

2.55 Which SI unit prefix corresponds to each of the following multipliers?

(a) 10^3 **(b)** 10^{-3}
(c) 10^6 **(d)** 10^{-6}

2.56 The speed limit in Canada is 100 km/h.

(a) How many miles per hour is this?
(b) How many feet per second?

2.57 The muzzle velocity of a projectile fired from a 9 mm handgun is 1200 ft/s.

(a) How many miles per hour is this?
(b) How many meters per second?

2.58 The diameter of a red blood cell is 6×10^{-6} m. How many red blood cells are needed to make a line 1 in. long?

2.59 The Sears Tower in Chicago has an approximate floor area of 418,000 m^2. How many square feet of floor is this?

2.60 A normal value for blood cholesterol is 200 mg/dL of blood. If a normal adult has a total blood volume of 5 L, how much total cholesterol is present?

2.61 One bottle of aspirin holds 50 tablets, each containing 250 mg of aspirin, and sells for $1.95. Another bottle holds 100 tablets, each containing 200 mg of aspirin, and sells for $3.75. For each bottle, calculate the value in milligrams of aspirin per dollar. Which bottle is the better bargain?

2.62 The white blood cell concentration in normal blood is approximately 12,000 cells/mm^3 of blood. How many white blood cells does a normal adult with 5 L of blood have? Express the answer in scientific notation.

2.63 The recommended daily dose of calcium for an 18-year-old male is 1200 mg. If 1.0 cup of whole milk contains 290 mg of calcium and milk is his only calcium source, how much milk should an 18-year-old male drink each day?

ENERGY, HEAT, AND TEMPERATURE

2.64 What is the normal temperature of the human body (98.6 °F) in degrees Celsius? In kelvins?

2.65 The boiling point of liquid nitrogen, used in the removal of warts and in other surgical applications, is −195.8 °C. What is this temperature in kelvins and in degrees Fahrenheit?

2.66 Diethyl ether, a substance once used as a general anesthetic, has a specific heat of 0.895 cal/(g·°C). How many calories and how many kilocalories of heat are needed to raise the temperature of 30.0 g of diethyl ether from 10.0 °C to 30.0 °C?

2.67 Copper has a specific heat of 0.092 cal/(g·°C). When 52.7 cal of heat is added to a piece of copper, the temperature increases from 22.4 °C to 38.6 °C. What is the mass of the piece of copper?

2.68 Calculate the specific heat of copper if it takes 23 cal to heat a 5.0 g sample from 25 °C to 75 °C.

2.69 The specific heat of fat is 0.45 cal/(g·°C), and the density of fat is 0.94 g/cm^3. How much energy (in calories) is needed to heat 10 cm^3 of fat from room temperature (25 °C) to its melting point (35 °C)?

2.70 A 150 g sample of mercury and a 150 g sample of iron are at an initial temperature of 25.0 °C. If 250 cal of heat is applied to each sample, what is the final temperature of each? (See Table 2.6.)

2.71 When 100 cal of heat is applied to a 125 g sample, the temperature increases by 28 °C. Calculate the specific heat of the sample and compare your answer to the values in Table 2.6. What is the identity of the sample?

DENSITY AND SPECIFIC GRAVITY

2.72 Aspirin has a density of 1.40 g/cm^3. What is the volume in cubic centimeters of a tablet weighing 250 mg?

2.73 Gaseous hydrogen has a density of 0.0899 g/L at 0 °C. How many liters would you need if you wanted 1.0078 g of hydrogen?

2.74 What is the density of lead (in g/cm^3) if a rectangular bar measuring 0.500 cm in height, 1.55 cm in width, and 25.00 cm in length has a mass of 220.9 g?

2.75 What is the density of lithium metal (in g/cm^3) if a cube measuring 0.82 cm $\times$ 1.45 cm $\times$ 1.25 cm has a mass of 0.794 g?

2.76 What is the density of isopropyl alcohol (rubbing alcohol) in grams per milliliter if a 5.000 mL sample has a mass of 3.928 g at room temperature? What is the specific gravity of isopropyl alcohol?

2.77 Ethylene glycol, commonly used as automobile antifreeze, has a specific gravity of 1.1088 at room temperature. What is the volume of 1.00 kg of ethylene glycol? What is the volume of 2.00 lb of ethylene glycol?

Applications

2.78 The typical rhinovirus has a diameter of 20 nm, or 2.0×10^{-8} m
(a) What is the length in centimeters?
(b) How many rhinoviruses would need to be laid end to end to make a chain 1 in. long?
[*Powers of 10, p. 28*]

2.79 Blood cells have a mean cell volume of 90 fL, or 9.0×10^{-14} L
(a) Convert this volume to cubic centimeters.
(b) The formula for the volume of a sphere is $V = 4\pi r^2/3$. Assuming a spherical shape, calculate the mean diameter of a blood cell in centimeters.
[*Powers of 10, p. 28*]

2.80 A thermochromic plastic chip included in a shipping container for beef undergoes an irreversible color change if the storage temperature exceeds 28 °F. What is this temperature on the Celsius and Kelvin scales?
[*Temperature-Sensitive Materials, p. 36*]

2.81 A temperature-sensitive bath toy undergoes several color changes in the temperature range from 37 °C to 47 °C. What is the corresponding temperature range on the Fahrenheit scale?
[*Temperature-Sensitive Materials, p. 36*]

2.82 Calculate the BMI for an individual who is:
(a) 5 ft 1 in. tall and weighs 155 lb
(b) 5 ft 11 in. tall and weigh 170 lb
(c) 6 ft 3 in. tall and weigh 195 lb
Which of these individuals is likely to have increased health risks?
[*Obesity and Body Fat, p. 41*]

2.83 Liposuction is a technique for removing fat deposits from various areas of the body. How many liters of fat would have to be removed to result in a 5.0 lb weight loss? The density of human fat is 0.94 g/mL.
[*Measuring Body Fat, p.41*]

General Questions and Problems

2.84 Refer to the pencil in Problem 2.30. Using the equivalent values in Table 2.4 as conversion factors, convert the length measured in inches to centimeters. Compare the calculated length in centimeters to the length in centimeters measured using the metric ruler. How do the two values compare? Explain any differences.

2.85 Gemstones are weighed in carats, where 1 carat = 200 mg exactly. What is the mass in grams of the Hope diamond, the world's largest blue diamond, at 44.4 carats?

2.86 If you were cooking in an oven calibrated in Celsius degrees, what temperature would you use if the recipe called for 350 °F?

2.87 What dosage in grams per kilogram of body weight does a 130 lb woman receive if she takes two 250 mg tablets of penicillin? How many 125 mg tablets should a 40 lb child take to receive the same dosage?

2.88 A clinical report gave the following data from a blood analysis: iron, 39 mg/dL; calcium, 8.3 mg/dL; cholesterol, 224 mg/dL. Express each of these quantities in grams per deciliter, writing the answers in scientific notation.

2.89 The density of air at room temperature is 1.3 g/L. What is the mass of the air **(a)** in grams and **(b)** in pounds in a room that is 4.0 m long, 3.0 m wide, and 2.5 m high?

2.90 Approximately 75 mL of blood is pumped by a normal human heart at each beat. Assuming an average pulse of 72 beats per minute, how many milliliters of blood are pumped in one day?

2.91 A doctor has ordered that a patient be given 15 g of glucose, which is available in a concentration of 50.00 g glucose/1000.0 mL of solution. What volume of solution should be given to the patient?

2.92 Reconsider the volume of the sample dispensed by pipette in Problem 2.31. Assuming that the solution in the pipette has a density of 0.963 g/mL, calculate the mass of solution dispensed in the problem to the correct number of significant figures.

2.93 Today thermometers containing mercury are used less frequently than in the past because of concerns regarding the toxicity of mercury and because of its relatively high melting point (−39 °C), which means that mercury thermometers cannot be used in very cold environments because the mercury is a solid under such conditions. Alcohol thermometers, however, can be used over a temperature range from −115 °C (the melting point of alcohol) to 78.5 °C (the boiling point of alcohol).

(a) What is the effective temperature range of the alcohol thermometer in °F?

(b) The densities of alcohol and mercury are 0.79 g/mL and 13.6 g/mL, respectively. If the volume of liquid in a typical laboratory thermometer is 1.0 mL, what mass of alcohol is contained in the thermometer? What mass of mercury?

2.94 In a typical person, the level of glucose (also known as blood sugar) is about 85 mg/100 mL of blood. If an average body contains about 11 pints of blood, how many grams and how many pounds of glucose are present in the blood?

2.95 A patient is receiving 3000 mL/day of a solution that contains 5 g of dextrose (glucose) per 100 mL of solution. If glucose provides 4 kcal/g of energy, how many kilocalories per day is the patient receiving from the glucose?

2.96 A rough guide to fluid requirements based on body weight is 100 mL/kg for the first 10 kg of body weight, 50 mL/kg for the next 10 kg, and 20 mL/kg for weight over 20 kg. What volume of fluid per day is needed by a 55 kg woman? Give the answer with two significant figures.

2.97 Chloral hydrate, a sedative and sleep-inducing drug, is available as a solution labeled 10.0 gr/fluidram. What volume in milliliters should be administered to a patient who is meant to receive 7.5 gr per dose? (1 gr = 64.8 mg; 1 fluidram = 3.72 mL)

2.98 When 1.0 tablespoon of butter is burned or used by our body, it releases 100 kcal (100 food calories) of energy. If we could use all the energy provided, how many tablespoons of butter would have to be burned to raise the temperature of 3.00 L of water from 18.0 °C to 90.0 °C?

2.99 An archeologist finds a 1.62 kg goblet that she believes to be made of pure gold. When 1350 cal of heat is added to the goblet, its temperature increases by 7.8 °C. Calculate the specific heat of the goblet. Is it made of gold? Explain.

2.100 In another test, the archeologist in Problem 2.99 determines that the volume of the goblet is 205 mL. Calculate the density of the goblet and compare it with the density of gold (19.3 g/mL), lead (11.4 g/mL), and iron (7.86 g/mL). What is the goblet probably made of?

2.101 The density of sulfuric acid, H_2SO_4, is 1.83 g/mL. What volume of sulfuric acid is needed to obtain 98.0 g of H_2SO_4?

2.102 Sulfuric acid (Problem 2.101) is produced in larger amounts than any other chemical: 2.01×10^{11} lb worldwide in 2004. What is the volume of this amount in liters?

2.103 The caliber of a gun is expressed by measuring the diameter of the gun barrel in hundredths of an inch. A "22" rifle, for example, has a barrel diameter of 0.22 in. What is the barrel diameter of a .22 rifle in millimeters?

2.104 Amounts of substances dissolved in solution are often expressed as mass per unit volume. For example, normal human blood has a cholesterol concentration of about 200 mg of cholesterol/100 mL of blood. Express this concentration in the following units:

(a) milligrams per liter **(b)** micrograms per liter
(c) grams per liter **(d)** nanograms per microliter

2.105 The element gallium (Ga) has the second largest liquid range of any element, melting at 29.8 °C and boiling at 2204 °C at atmospheric pressure.

(a) Is gallium a metal, a nonmetal, or a metalloid?
(b) What is the density of gallium in grams per cubic centimeter at 25 °C if a 1.00 in. cube has a mass of 0.2133 lb?

2.106 A sample of water at 293.2 K was heated for 8 min and 25 s, and the heating was carried out so that the temperature increased at a constant rate of 3.0 °F/min. What is the final temperature of the water in degrees Celsius?

2.107 At a certain point, the Celsius and Fahrenheit scales "cross," and at this point the numerical value of the Celsius temperature is the same as the numerical value of the Fahrenheit temperature. At what temperature does this crossover occur?

2.108 Imagine that you place a piece of cork measuring 1.30 cm × 5.50 cm × 3.00 cm in a pan of water and that on top of the cork you place a small cube of lead measuring 1.15 cm on each edge. The density of cork is 0.235 g/cm³, and the density of lead is 11.35 g/cm³. Will the combination of cork plus lead float or sink?

CHAPTER 3

Atoms and the Periodic Table

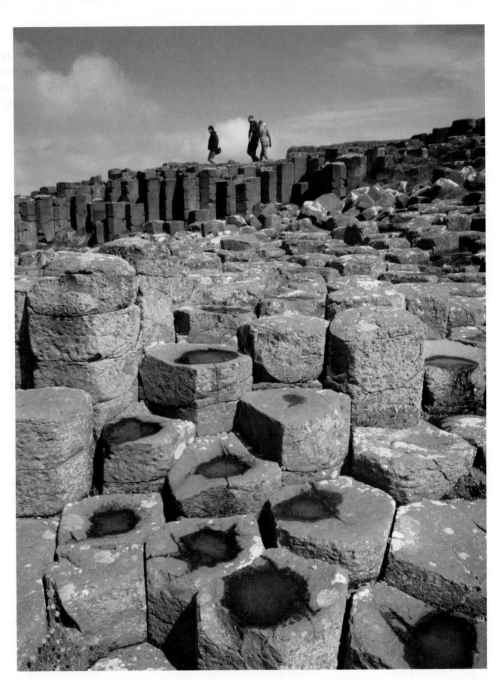

▲ The mineral formations of the Giant's Causeway in Northern Ireland are an example of periodicity—the presence of regularly repeating patterns—found throughout nature.

CONTENTS

CHAPTER GOALS

We will take up the following questions about atoms and atomic theory:

1. What is the modern theory of atomic structure?

THE GOAL: Be able to explain the major assumptions of atomic theory.

2. How do atoms of different elements differ?

THE GOAL: Be able to explain the composition of different atoms according to the number of protons, neutrons, and electrons they contain.

3. What are isotopes, and what is atomic weight?

THE GOAL: Be able to explain what isotopes are and how they affect an element's atomic weight.

4. How is the periodic table arranged?

THE GOAL: Be able to describe how elements are arranged in the periodic table, name the subdivisions of the periodic table, and relate the position of an element in the periodic table to its electronic structure.

5. How are electrons arranged in atoms?

THE GOAL: Be able to explain how electrons are distributed in shells and subshells around the nucleus of an atom, how valence electrons can be represented as electron-dot symbols, and how the electron configurations can help explain the chemical properties of the elements.

Chemistry must be studied on two levels. In the past two chapters we have dealt with chemistry on the large-scale, or *macroscopic*, level, looking at the properties and transformations of matter that we can see and measure. Now we are ready to look at the sub-microscopic, or atomic level, studying the behavior and properties of individual atoms. Although scientists have long been convinced of their existence, only within the past twenty years have powerful new instruments made it possible to see individual atoms themselves. In this chapter we will look at modern atomic theory and at how the structure of atoms influences macroscopic properties.

3.1 Atomic Theory

Take a piece of aluminum foil and cut it in two. Then take one of the pieces and cut *it* in two, and so on. Assuming that you have extremely small scissors and extraordinary dexterity, how long can you keep dividing the foil? Is there a limit, or is matter infinitely divisible into ever smaller and smaller pieces? Historically, this argument can be traced as far back as the ancient Greek philosophers. Aristotle believed that matter could be divided infinitely, while Democritus argued (correctly) that there is a limit. The smallest and simplest bit that aluminum (or any other element) can be divided into and still be identifiable as aluminum is called an **atom**, a word derived from the Greek *atomos*, meaning "indivisible."

Chemistry is founded on four fundamental assumptions about atoms and matter, which together make up modern **atomic theory**:

- All matter is composed of atoms.

- The atoms of a given element differ from the atoms of all other elements.

- Chemical compounds consist of atoms combined in specific ratios. That is, only whole atoms can combine—one A atom with one B atom, or one A atom with two B atoms, and so on. The enormous diversity in the substances we see around us is based on the vast number of ways that atoms can combine with one another.

- Chemical reactions change only the way that atoms are combined in compounds. The atoms themselves are unchanged.

Atoms are extremely small, ranging from about 7.4×10^{-11} m in diameter for a hydrogen atom to 5.24×10^{-10} m for a cesium atom. In mass, atoms vary from 1.67×10^{-24} g for hydrogen to 3.95×10^{-22} g for uranium, one of the heaviest naturally occurring atoms. It is difficult to appreciate just how small atoms are, although it might help if you realize that a fine pencil line is about 3 *million* atoms across, and that even the smallest speck of dust contains about 10^{16} atoms.

Atom The smallest and simplest particle of an element.

Atomic theory A set of assumptions proposed by the English scientist John Dalton to explain the chemical behavior of matter.

▲ How small can a piece of aluminum foil be cut?

▶ Atoms are so small that the radius of this circle is about three million atoms wide.

Subatomic particles Three kinds of fundamental particles from which atoms are made: protons, neutrons, and electrons.

Proton A positively charged subatomic particle.

Neutron An electrically neutral subatomic particle.

Electron A negatively charged subatomic particle.

Atomic mass unit (amu) A convenient unit for describing the mass of an atom; 1 amu = $\frac{1}{12}$ the mass of a carbon-12 atom.

Nucleus The dense, central core of an atom that contains protons and neutrons.

▲ The relative size of a nucleus in an atom is the same as that of a pea in the middle of this stadium.

Atoms are composed of tiny **subatomic particles** called *protons, neutrons,* and *electrons.* A **proton** has a mass of $1.672\ 622 \times 10^{-24}$ g and carries a positive (+) electrical charge; a **neutron** has a mass similar to that of a proton ($1.674\ 927 \times 10^{-24}$ g) but is electrically neutral; and an **electron** has a mass that is only 1/1836 that of a proton ($9.109\ 328 \times 10^{-28}$ g) and carries a negative (−) electrical charge. In fact, electrons are so much lighter than protons and neutrons that their mass is usually ignored. Table 3.1 compares the properties of the three fundamental subatomic particles.

TABLE 3.1 A Comparison of Subatomic Particles

NAME	SYMBOL	MASS (GRAMS)	MASS (AMU)	CHARGE (CHARGE UNITS)
Proton	p	$1.672\ 622 \times 10^{-24}$	1.007 276	+1
Neutron	n	$1.674\ 927 \times 10^{-24}$	1.008 665	0
Electron	e^-	$9.109\ 328 \times 10^{-28}$	$5.485\ 799 \times 10^{-4}$	−1

The masses of atoms and their constituent subatomic particles are so small when measured in grams that it is more convenient to express them on a *relative* mass scale. That is, one atom is assigned a mass, and all others are measured relative to it. The process is like deciding that a golf ball (46.0 g) will be assigned a mass of 1. A baseball (149 g), which is 149/46.0 = 3.24 times heavier than a golf ball, would then have a mass of about 3.24, a volleyball (270 g) would have a mass of 270/46.0 = 5.87, and so on.

The basis for the relative atomic mass scale is an atom of carbon that contains 6 protons and 6 neutrons. Such an atom is assigned a mass of exactly 12 **atomic mass units** (**amu**; also called a *dalton* in honor of the English scientist John Dalton, who proposed most of atomic theory as we know it), where 1 amu = $1.660\ 539 \times 10^{-24}$ g. Thus, for all practical purposes, both a proton and a neutron have a mass of 1 amu (Table 3.1). Hydrogen atoms are only about one-twelfth as heavy as carbon atoms and have a mass close to 1 amu, magnesium atoms are about twice as heavy as carbon atoms and have a mass close to 24 amu, and so forth.

Subatomic particles are not distributed at random throughout an atom. Rather, the protons and neutrons are packed closely together in a dense core called the **nucleus.** Surrounding the nucleus, the electrons move about rapidly through a large, mostly empty volume of space (Figure 3.1). Measurements show that the diameter of a nucleus is only about 10^{-15} m, whereas that of the atom itself is about 10^{-10} m. For comparison, if an atom were the size of a large domed stadium, the nucleus would be approximately the size of a small pea in the center of the playing field.

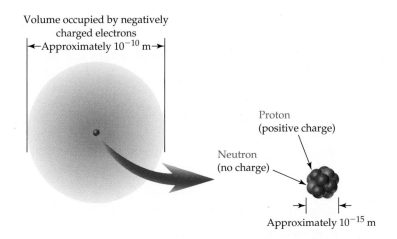

Volume occupied by negatively
charged electrons
←Approximately 10^{-10} m→

Proton
(positive charge)

Neutron
(no charge)

Approximately 10^{-15} m

◄ **FIGURE 3.1 The structure of an atom.** Protons and neutrons are packed together in the nucleus, whereas electrons move about in the large surrounding volume. Virtually all the mass of an atom is concentrated in the nucleus.

The structure of the atom is determined by an interplay of different attractive and repulsive forces. Because unlike charges attract one another, the negatively charged electrons are held near the positively charged nucleus. But because like charges repel one another, the negatively charged electrons try to get as far away from one another as possible, accounting for the relatively large volume they occupy. The positively charged protons in the nucleus also repel one another, but are nevertheless held together by a unique attraction called the *nuclear strong force*, which is beyond the scope of this text.

Electrons repel
one another

Protons repel
one another

Protons and electrons
attract one another

WORKED EXAMPLE   **3.1** Atomic Mass Units: Gram-to-Atom Conversions

How many atoms are in a small piece of aluminum foil with a mass of 0.100 g? The mass of an atom of aluminum is 27.0 amu.

ANALYSIS We know the sample mass in grams and the mass of one atom in atomic mass units. To find the number of atoms in the sample, two conversions are needed, the first between grams and atomic mass units and the second between atomic mass units and the number of atoms. The conversion factor between atomic mass units and grams is 1 amu = $1.660\,539 \times 10^{-24}$ g.

BALLPARK ESTIMATE An atom of aluminum has a mass of 27.0 amu; since 1 amu $\sim 10^{-24}$ g, the mass of a single aluminum atom is very small ($\approx 10^{-23}$ g). A very *large* number of atoms, therefore (10^{22} ?), is needed to obtain a mass of 0.100 g.

SOLUTION

STEP 1: Identify known information.

Mass of aluminum foil = 0.100 g

1 Al atom = 27.0 amu

STEP 2: Identify unknown answer and units.

Number of Al atoms = ?

STEP 3: Identify needed conversion factors.
Knowing the mass of foil (in g) and the mass of individual atoms (in amu) we need to convert from amu/atom to g/atom.

1 amu = $1.660\,539 \times 10^{-24}$ g

$$\rightarrow \frac{1\ \text{amu}}{1.660\,539 \times 10^{-24}\ \text{g}}$$

STEP 4: Solve. Set up an equation using known information and conversion factors so that unwanted units cancel.

$$(0.100\ \cancel{g})\left(\frac{1\ \cancel{\text{amu}}}{1.660\,539 \times 10^{-24}\ \cancel{g}}\right)\left(\frac{1\ \text{Al atom}}{27.0\ \cancel{\text{amu}}}\right)$$

$$= 2.23 \times 10^{21}\ \text{Al atoms}$$

BALLPARK CHECK: Our estimate was 10^{22}, which is within a factor of 10.

PROBLEM 3.1

What is the mass in atomic mass units of a nitrogen atom weighing 2.33×10^{-23} g?

PROBLEM 3.2

What is the mass in grams of 150×10^{12} iron atoms, each having a mass of 56 amu?

PROBLEM 3.3

How many atoms are in each of the following?

(a) 1.0 g of hydrogen atoms, each of mass 1.0 amu

(b) 12.0 g of carbon atoms, each of mass 12.0 amu

(c) 23.0 g of sodium atoms, each of mass 23.0 amu

PROBLEM 3.4

What pattern do you see in your answers to Problem 3.3? (We will return to this very important pattern in Chapter 6.)

APPLICATION ▶ Are Atoms Real?

Chemistry rests on the premise that matter is composed of the tiny particles we call atoms. Every chemical reaction and every physical law that governs the behavior of matter are explained by chemists in terms of atomic theory. But how do we know that atoms are real and not just an imaginary concept? And how do we know the structure of the atom? Our understanding of atomic structure is another example of the scientific method at work.

Dalton's atomic theory was originally published in 1808, but many prominent scientists dismissed it. Over the next century, however, several unrelated experiments provided insight into the nature of matter and the structure of the atom. Nineteenth-century investigations into electricity, for example, demonstrated that matter was composed of charged particles—rubbing a glass rod with a silk cloth would generate "static electricity," the same phenomenon that shocks you when you walk across a carpet and then touch a metal surface. It was also known that passing electricity through certain substances, such as water, decomposed the compounds into their constituent elements.

In 1897, J. J. Thomson used magnetic fields to deflect a beam of particles emitted from a cathode ray tube, demonstrating that these particles had a negative charge and were 1000 times lighter than the lightest charged particles found in aqueous solution (H^+). (⬤▭ Section 6.10 and Chapter 10) This result implied that atoms were *not* the smallest particles of matter but could be divided into even smaller particles. In 1909, Robert Millikan studied the behavior of oil droplets in a

▲ Colored scanning tunneling micrograph of the surface of graphite, a form of the element carbon. The hexagonal pattern is related to an identical arrangement of the carbon atoms.

chamber containing electrically charged plates. When Millikan bombarded the atmosphere in the chamber with x-rays, the droplets acquired a negative charge. Millikan observed that by varying the strength of the electric field associated with the charged plates he could alter the rate of descent of the droplets or even suspend them in midair! From these results he was able to calculate the charge associated with the electron (16×10^{-19} coulombs). Finally, in 1910 Ernest Rutherford bombarded a gold foil with positively charged "alpha" particles emitted from radium during radioactive decay. The majority of these particles passed straight through the foil, but a small fraction of them were deflected, and a few even bounced backward. From these results Rutherford deduced that an atom consists mostly of empty space (occupied by the negatively charged electrons) and that most of the mass and all of the positive charge are contained in a relatively small, dense region that he called the nucleus.

We can now actually "see" and manipulate individual atoms through the use of a device called a *scanning tunneling microscope*, or STM (⬭⬭ see Application on p. 28). With the STM, invented in 1981 by a research team at the IBM Corporation, magnifications of up to ten million have been achieved, allowing chemists to look directly at atoms. The accompanying photograph shows a computer-enhanced representation of carbon atoms in graphite that have been deposited on a copper surface.

Most present uses of the STM involve studies of surface chemistry, such as the events accompanying the corrosion of metals and the ordering of large molecules in polymers. Work is also under way using the STM to determine the structures of complex biological molecules.

See Additional Problems 3.90 and 3.91 at the end of the chapter.

3.2 Elements and Atomic Number

Atoms of different elements differ from one another according to how many protons they contain, a value called the element's **atomic number (Z)**. Thus, if we know the number of protons in an atom, we can identify the element. Any atom with 6 protons, for example, is a carbon atom because carbon has $Z = 6$.

Atoms are neutral overall and have no net charge because the number of positively charged protons in an atom is the same as the number of negatively charged electrons. Thus, the atomic number also equals the number of electrons in every atom of a given element. Hydrogen, $Z = 1$, has only 1 proton and 1 electron; carbon, $Z = 6$, has 6 protons and 6 electrons; sodium, $Z = 11$, has 11 protons and 11 electrons; and so on up to the newly discovered element with $Z = 118$. In a periodic table, elements are listed in order of increasing atomic number, beginning at the upper left and ending at the lower right.

Atomic number (Z)   The number of protons in atoms of a given element; the number of electrons in atoms of a given element

The sum of the protons and neutrons in an atom is called the atom's **mass number (A)**. Hydrogen atoms with 1 proton and no neutrons have mass number 1; carbon atoms with 6 protons and 6 neutrons have mass number 12; sodium atoms with 11 protons and 12 neutrons have mass number 23; and so on. Except for hydrogen, atoms generally contain at least as many neutrons as protons, and frequently contain more. There is no simple way to predict how many neutrons a given atom will have.

Mass number (A)   The total number of protons and neutrons in an atom

WORKED EXAMPLE   **3.2** Atomic Structure: Protons, Neutrons, and Electrons

Phosphorus has atomic number $Z = 15$. How many protons, electrons, and neutrons are there in phosphorus atoms, which have mass number $A = 31$?

ANALYSIS The atomic number gives the number of protons, which is the same as the number of electrons, and the mass number gives the total number of protons plus neutrons.

SOLUTION

Phosphorus atoms, with $Z = 15$, have 15 protons and 15 electrons. To find the number of neutrons, subtract the atomic number from the mass number:

Mass number
(sum of protons and neutrons)

Atomic number
(number of protons)

$$31 - 15 = 16 \text{ neutrons}$$

WORKED EXAMPLE **3.3** Atomic Structure: Atomic Number and Atomic Mass

An atom contains 28 protons and has $A = 60$. Give the number of electrons and neutrons in the atom, and identify the element.

ANALYSIS The number of protons and the number of electrons are the same and are equal to the atomic number Z, 28 in this case. Subtracting the number of protons (28) from the total number of protons plus neutrons (60) gives the number of neutrons.

SOLUTION

The atom has 28 electrons and $60 - 28 = 32$ neutrons. Looking at the list of elements inside the front cover shows that the element with atomic number 28 is nickel (Ni).

PROBLEM 3.5

Use the list inside the front cover to identify elements with the following atomic numbers:

(a) $Z = 75$

(b) $Z = 20$

(c) $Z = 52$

PROBLEM 3.6

The cobalt used in cancer treatments has $Z = 27$ and $A = 60$. How many protons, neutrons, and electrons are in these cobalt atoms?

PROBLEM 3.7

A certain atom has $A = 98$ and contains 55 neutrons. Identify the element.

3.3 Isotopes and Atomic Weight

All atoms of a given element have the same number of protons—the atomic number Z characteristic of that element—but different atoms of an element can have different numbers of neutrons and therefore different mass numbers. Atoms with identical atomic numbers but different mass numbers are called **isotopes**. Hydrogen, for example, has three isotopes. The most abundant hydrogen isotope, called *protium*, has no neutrons and thus has a mass number of 1. A second hydrogen isotope, called *deuterium*, has one neutron and a mass number of 2; and a third isotope, called *tritium*, has two neutrons and a mass number of 3. Tritium is unstable and does not occur naturally in significant amounts, although it can be made in nuclear reactors (⬤, see Section 11.11).

Isotopes Atoms with identical atomic numbers but different mass numbers.

Protium—one proton
( ) and no neutrons;
mass number = 1

Deuterium—one proton
( ) and one neutron ( );
mass number = 2

Tritium—one proton
( ) and two neutrons ( );
mass number = 3

A specific isotope is represented by showing its mass number (A) as a superscript and its atomic number (Z) as a subscript in front of the atomic symbol, for example, ${}^{A}_{Z}X$, where X represents the symbol for the element. Thus, protium is ${}^{1}_{1}H$, deuterium is ${}^{2}_{1}H$, and tritium is ${}^{3}_{1}H$.

Mass number
(sum of protons and neutrons)

${}^{3}_{1}H$ ⟵ Symbol of element

Atomic number
(number of protons)

Unlike the three isotopes of hydrogen, the isotopes of most elements do not have distinctive names. Instead, the mass number of the isotope is given after the name of the element. The ${}^{235}_{92}U$ isotope used in nuclear reactors, for example, is usually referred to as uranium-235, or U-235.

Most naturally occurring elements are mixtures of isotopes. In a large sample of naturally occurring hydrogen atoms, for example, 99.985% have mass number $A = 1$ (protium) and 0.015% have mass number $A = 2$ (deuterium). It is therefore useful to know the *average* mass of the atoms in a large sample, a value called the element's **atomic weight**. For hydrogen, the atomic weight is 1.008 amu. Atomic weights for all elements are given inside the front cover of this book.

Atomic weight The weighted average mass of an element's atoms.

To calculate the atomic weight of an element, the individual masses of the naturally occurring isotopes and the percentage of each must be known. The atomic weight can then be calculated as the sum of the masses of the individual isotopes for that element, or

$$\text{Atomic weight} = \Sigma(\text{isotopic abundance}) \times (\text{isotopic mass})$$

where the Greek symbol Σ indicates the mathematical summing of terms.

Chlorine, for example, occurs on earth as a mixture of 75.77% Cl-35 atoms (mass = 34.97 amu) and 24.23% Cl-37 atoms (mass = 36.97 amu). The atomic weight is found by calculating the percentage of the mass contributed by each isotope. For chlorine, the calculation is done in the following way (to four significant figures), giving an atomic weight of 35.45 amu:

Contribution from ${}^{35}Cl$: (0.7577)(34.97 amu) = 26.4968 amu

Contribution from ${}^{37}Cl$: (0.2423)(36.97 amu) = 8.9578 amu

Atomic weight = 35.4546 = 35.45 amu
(rounded to four significant figures)

The final number of significant figures in this case (four) was determined by the atomic masses. Note that the final rounding to four significant figures was not done until *after* the final answer was obtained.

WORKED EXAMPLE **3.4** Average Atomic Mass: Weighted-Average Calculation

Gallium is a metal with a very low melting point—it will melt in the palm of your hand. It has two naturally occurring isotopes: 60.4% is Ga-69, (mass = 68.9257 amu), and 39.6% is Ga-71, (mass = 70.9248 amu). Calculate the average atomic weight for gallium.

ANALYSIS We can calculate the average atomic mass for the element by summing up the contributions from each of the naturally occurring isotopes.

BALLPARK ESTIMATE The masses of the two naturally occurring isotopes of gallium differ by 2 amu (68.9 and 70.9 amu). Since slightly more than half of the Ga atoms are the lighter isotope (Ga-69), the average mass will be slightly less than halfway between the two isotopic masses; estimate = 69.8 amu.

SOLUTION

STEP 1: Identify known information.	Ga-69 (60.4% at 68.9257 amu)
	Ga-71 (39.6% at 70.9248 amu)
STEP 2: Identify the unknown answer and units.	Average atomic weight for Ga (in amu) = ?
STEP 3: Identify conversion factors or equations. This equation calculates the average atomic weight as a weighted average of all naturally occurring isotopes.	Atomic weight = $\sum$(isotopic abundance) × (isotopic mass)
STEP 4: Solve. Substitute known information and solve.	Atomic weight = (0.604) × (68.9257 amu) = 41.6311 amu
	+ (0.396) × (70.9248 amu) = 28.0862 amu
	Atomic weight = 69.7 amu
	(3 significant figures)

BALLPARK CHECK: Our estimate (69.8 amu) is close!

WORKED EXAMPLE **3.5** Identifying Isotopes from Atomic Mass and Atomic Number

Identify element X in the symbol $^{194}_{78}$X and give its atomic number, mass number, number of protons, number of electrons, and number of neutrons.

ANALYSIS The identity of the atom corresponds to the atomic number—78.

SOLUTION

Element X has Z = 78, which shows that it is platinum. (Look inside the front cover for the list of elements.) The isotope $^{194}_{78}$Pt has a mass number of 194, and we can subtract the atomic number from the mass number to get the number of neutrons. This platinum isotope therefore has 78 protons, 78 electrons, and 194 − 78 = 116 neutrons.

PROBLEM 3.8

Potassium (K) has two naturally occurring isotopes: K-39 (93.12%; mass = 38.9637 amu), and K-41 (6.88%; 40.9618 amu). Calculate the atomic weight for potassium. How does your answer compare with the atomic mass given in the list inside the front cover of this book?

PROBLEM 3.9

Bromine, an element present in compounds used as sanitizers and fumigants (for example, ethylene bromide), has two naturally occurring isotopes, with mass numbers 79 and 81. Write the symbols for both, including their atomic numbers and mass numbers.

PROBLEM 3.10

Complete the following isotope symbols:

(a) $^{11}_{5}?$ (b) $^{56}_{?}\text{Fe}$ (c) $^{37}_{17}?$

3.4 The Periodic Table

Ten elements have been known since the beginning of recorded history: antimony (Sb), carbon (C), copper (Cu), gold (Au), iron (Fe), lead (Pb), mercury (Hg), silver (Ag), sulfur (S), and tin (Sn). It is worth noting that the symbols for many of these elements are derived from their Latin names, a reminder that they have been known since the time when Latin was the language used for all scholarly work. The first "new" element to be found in several thousand years was arsenic (As), discovered in about 1250. In fact, only 24 elements were known up to the time of the American Revolution in 1776.

As the pace of discovery quickened in the late 1700s and early 1800s, chemists began to look for similarities among elements that might make it possible to draw general conclusions. Particularly important was Johann Döbereiner's observation in 1829 that there were several *triads*, or groups of three elements, that appeared to have similar chemical and physical properties. For example, lithium, sodium, and potassium were all known to be silvery metals that react violently with water; chlorine, bromine, and iodine were all known to be colored nonmetals with pungent odors.

Numerous attempts were made in the mid-1800s to account for the similarities among groups of elements, but the great breakthrough came in 1869 when the Russian chemist Dmitri Mendeleev organized the elements into a forerunner of the modern periodic table, introduced previously in Section 1.6 and shown again in Figure 3.2. The table has boxes for each element that give the symbol, atomic number, and atomic weight of the element:

▲ Samples of chlorine, bromine, and iodine, one of Döbereiner's triads of elements with similar chemical properties.

6 ◀────── Atomic number
C ◀────── Symbol
12.011 ◀────── Atomic weight

Beginning at the upper left corner of the periodic table, elements are arranged by increasing atomic number into seven horizontal rows, called **periods**, and 18 vertical columns, called **groups**. When organized in this way, *the elements in a given group have similar chemical properties.* Lithium, sodium, potassium, and the other elements in group 1A behave similarly. Chlorine, bromine, iodine, and the other elements in group 7A behave similarly, and so on throughout the table.

Note that different periods (rows) contain different numbers of elements. The first period contains only 2 elements, hydrogen and helium; the second and third periods each contain 8 elements; the fourth and fifth periods each contain 18; the sixth period contains 32; and the seventh period (incomplete as yet) contains 31 elements. Note also that the 14 elements following lanthanum (the *lanthanides*) and the 14 following actinium (the *actinides*) are pulled out and shown below the others.

Groups are numbered in two ways, both shown in Figure 3.2. The two large groups on the far left and the six on the far right are called the **main group elements** and are numbered 1A through 8A. The ten smaller groups in the middle of the table are called the **transition metal elements** and are numbered 1B through 8B. Alternatively, all 18 groups are numbered sequentially from 1 to 18. The 14 groups shown separately at the bottom of the table are called the **inner transition metal elements** and are not numbered.

Period One of the 7 horizontal rows of elements in the periodic table.

Group One of the 18 vertical columns of elements in the periodic table.

Main group element An element in one of the two groups on the left or the six groups on the right of the periodic table.

Transition metal element An element in one of the 10 smaller groups near the middle of the periodic table.

Inner transition metal element An element in one of the 14 groups shown separately at the bottom of the periodic table.

▲ **FIGURE 3.2** **The periodic table of the elements.** Each element is identified by a one- or two-letter symbol and is characterized by an *atomic number*. The table begins with hydrogen (H, atomic number 1) in the upper left-hand corner and continues to the yet unnamed element with atomic number 118. The 14 elements following lanthanum (La, atomic number 57) and the 14 elements following actinium (Ac, atomic number 89) are pulled out and shown below the others.

Elements are organized into 18 vertical columns, or *groups*, and 7 horizontal rows, or *periods*. The two groups on the left and the six on the right are the *main groups*; the ten in the middle are the *transition metal groups*. The 14 elements following lanthanum are the *lanthanides*, and the 14 elements following actinium are the *actinides*; together these are known as the *inner transition metals*. Two systems for numbering the groups are explained in the text.

Those elements (except hydrogen) on the left-hand side of the zigzag line running from boron (B) to astatine (At) are *metals*, those elements to the right of the line are *nonmetals*, and most elements abutting the line are *metalloids*.

▲ Sodium, an alkali metal, reacts violently with water to yield hydrogen gas and an alkaline (basic) solution.

PROBLEM 3.11

Locate aluminum in the periodic table, and give its group number and period number.

PROBLEM 3.12

Identify the group 1B element in period 5 and the group 2A element in period 4.

PROBLEM 3.13

There are five elements in group 5A of the periodic table. Identify them, and give the period of each.

3.5 Some Characteristics of Different Groups

To see why the periodic table has the name it does, look at the graph of atomic radius versus atomic number in Figure 3.3. The graph shows an obvious *periodicity*—a repeating, rise-and-fall pattern. Beginning on the left with atomic number 1 (hydrogen), the sizes of the atoms increase to a maximum at atomic number 3 (lithium), then decrease to a minimum, then increase again to a maximum at atomic number 11 (sodium), then decrease, and so on. It turns out that the maxima occur for atoms of group 1A elements—Li, Na, K, Rb, Cs, and Fr—and the minima occur for atoms of the group 7A elements.

▲ **FIGURE 3.3   A graph of atomic radius in picometers (pm) versus atomic number shows a periodic rise-and-fall pattern.**   The maxima occur for atoms of the group 1A elements (Li, Na, K, Rb, Cs, Fr); the minima occur for atoms of the group 7A elements. Accurate data are not available for the group 8A elements.

There is nothing unique about the periodicity of atomic radii shown in Figure 3.3. The melting points of the first 100 elements, for example, exhibit similar periodic behavior, as shown in Figure 3.4. Many other physical and chemical properties can be plotted in a similar way with similar results. In fact, the various elements in a given group of the periodic table usually show remarkable similarities

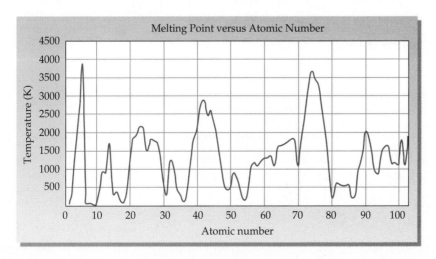

▲ **FIGURE 3.4   A graph of melting point versus atomic number shows periodic properties similar to the trend in Figure 3.3.**   While the maxima and minima are not as sharp as in Figure 3.3, the change in melting points of the elements still shows the same periodic trend.

Alkali metal An element in group 1A of the periodic table.

Alkaline earth metal An element in group 2A of the periodic table.

Halogen An element in group 7A of the periodic table.

Noble gas An element in group 8A of the periodic table.

▲ Magnesium, an alkaline earth metal, burns in air. Magnesium alloys are often used in welding rods.

▲ Chlorine, a halogen, is a toxic, corrosive green gas.

▲ Neon and other noble gases are used in neon lights, signs, and works of art.

in many of their chemical and physical properties. Look at the following four groups, for example:

- **Group 1A—Alkali metals:** Lithium (Li), sodium (Na), potassium (K), rubidium (Rb), cesium (Cs), and francium (Fr) are shiny, soft metals with low melting points. All react rapidly (often violently) with water to form products that are highly alkaline, or basic—hence the name *alkali metals*. Because of their high reactivity, the alkali metals are never found in nature in the pure state but only in combination with other elements.

- **Group 2A—Alkaline earth metals:** Beryllium (Be), magnesium (Mg), calcium (Ca), strontium (Sr), barium (Ba), and radium (Ra) are also lustrous, silvery metals, but are less reactive than their neighbors in group 1A. Like the alkali metals, the alkaline earths are never found in nature in the pure state.

- **Group 7A—Halogens:** Fluorine (F), chlorine (Cl), bromine (Br), iodine (I), and astatine (At) are colorful and corrosive nonmetals. All are found in nature only in combination with other elements, such as with sodium in table salt (sodium chloride, NaCl). In fact, the group name *halogen* is taken from the Greek word *hals*, meaning salt.

- **Group 8A—Noble gases:** Helium (He), neon (Ne), argon (Ar), krypton (Kr), xenon (Xe), and radon (Rn) are colorless gases. The elements in this group were labeled the "noble" gases because of their lack of chemical reactivity—helium, neon, and argon don't combine with any other elements, whereas krypton and xenon combine with very few.

Although the resemblances are not as pronounced as they are within a single group, *neighboring* elements often behave similarly as well. Thus, as noted in Section 1.6 and indicated in Figure 3.2, the periodic table can be divided into three major classes of elements—*metals*, *nonmetals*, and *metalloids* (metal-like). Metals, the largest category of elements, are found on the left side of the periodic table, bounded on the right by a zigzag line running from boron (B) at the top to astatine (At) at the bottom. Nonmetals are found on the right side of the periodic table, and seven of the elements adjacent to the zigzag boundary between metals and nonmetals are metalloids.

⊂⊃ Looking Ahead

Carbon, the element on which life is based, is a group 4A nonmetal near the top right of the periodic table. Clustered near carbon are other elements often found in living organisms, including oxygen, nitrogen, phosphorus, and sulfur. We will look at the subject of *organic chemistry*—the chemistry of carbon compounds—in Chapters 12–17, and move on to *biochemistry*—the chemistry of living things—in Chapters 18–29. ⊂⊃

PROBLEM 3.14

Identify the following elements as metals, nonmetals, or metalloids:

(a) Ti   **(b)** Te   **(c)** Se

(d) Sc   **(e)** At   **(f)** Ar

PROBLEM 3.15

Locate **(a)** krypton, **(b)** strontium, **(c)** nitrogen, and **(d)** cobalt in the periodic table. Indicate which categories apply to each: (i) metal, (ii) nonmetal, (iii) transition element, (iv) main group element, (v) noble gas.

APPLICATION ▶ The Origin of Chemical Elements

Astronomers believe that the universe began some 15 billion years ago in an extraordinary moment they call the "big bang." Initially, the temperature must have been inconceivably high, but after 1 second, it had dropped to about 10^{10} K and subatomic particles began to form: protons, neutrons, and electrons. After 3 minutes, the temperature had dropped to 10^9 K, and protons began fusing with neutrons to form helium nuclei, ^4_2He.

Matter remained in this form for many millions of years until the expanding universe had cooled to about 10,000 K and electrons were then able to bind to protons and to helium nuclei, forming stable hydrogen and helium atoms.

The attractive force of gravity acting on regions of higher-than-average density slowly produced massive local concentrations of matter and ultimately formed billions of galaxies, each with many billions of stars. As the gas clouds of hydrogen and helium condensed under gravitational attraction and stars formed, their temperatures reached 10^7 K, and their densities reached 100 g/cm^3. Protons and neutrons again fused to yield helium nuclei, generating vast amounts of heat and light.

Most of these early stars probably burned out after a few billion years, but a few were so massive that, as their nuclear fuel diminished, gravitational attraction caused a rapid contraction leading to still higher core temperatures and higher densities—up to 5×10^8 K and 5×10^5 g/cm^3. Under such extreme conditions, larger nuclei were formed, including carbon, oxygen, silicon, magnesium, and iron. Ultimately, the

▲ The stars in the Milky Way galaxy condensed from gas clouds under gravitational attraction.

stars underwent a gravitational collapse resulting in the synthesis of still heavier elements and an explosion visible throughout the universe as a *supernova*.

Matter from exploding supernovas was blown throughout the galaxy, forming a new generation of stars and planets. Our own sun and solar system formed about 4.5 billion years ago from matter released by former supernovas. Except for hydrogen and helium, all the atoms in our bodies and our entire solar system were created more than five billion years ago in exploding stars. We and our world are made from the ashes of dying stars.

See Additional Problems 3.92 and 3.93 at the end of this chapter.

▬● KEY CONCEPT PROBLEM 3.16

Identify the elements shown in red and in blue on the following periodic table. For each, tell its group number, its period number, and whether it is a metal, nonmetal, or metalloid.

3.6 Electronic Structure of Atoms

Why does the periodic table have the shape it does, with periods of different length? Why are periodic variations observed in atomic radii and in so many other characteristics of the elements? And why do elements in a given group of the periodic table show similar chemical behavior? These questions occupied the thoughts of chemists for more than 50 years after Mendeleev, and it was not until well into the 1920s that the answers were established. Today, we know that *the properties of the elements are determined by the arrangement of electrons in their atoms.*

Our current understanding of the electronic structure of atoms is based on the now accepted *quantum mechanical model*, developed by Austrian physicist Erwin Schrödinger in 1926. Although a detailed discussion of the model is beyond the scope of this text, one of the fundamental assumptions of the model is that electrons have both particle-like and wave-like properties, and that the behavior of electrons can be described using a mathematical equation called a wave function. One consequence of this assumption is that electrons are not perfectly free to move about in an atom. Instead, each electron is restricted to moving about in only a certain region of space within the atom, depending on the energy level of the electron. Different electrons have different amounts of energy and thus occupy different regions within the atom. Furthermore, the energies of electrons are *quantized*, or restricted to having only certain values.

To understand the idea of quantization, think about the difference between stairs and a ramp. A ramp is *not* quantized because it changes height continuously. Stairs, by contrast, *are* quantized because they change height only by a fixed amount. You can climb one stair or two stairs, but you cannot climb 1.5 stairs. In the same way, the energy values available to electrons in an atom change only in steps rather than continuously.

▲ Stairs are *quantized* because they change height in discrete amounts. A ramp, by contrast, is not quantized because it changes height continuously.

The wave functions derived from the quantum mechanical model also provide important information about the location of electrons in an atom. Just as a person can be found by giving his or her address within a state, an electron can be found by giving its "address" within an atom. Furthermore, just as a person's address is composed of several successively narrower categories—city, street, and house number—an electron's address is also composed of successively narrower categories—*shell, subshell,* and *orbital,* which are defined by the quantum mechanical model.

Shell (electron) A grouping of electrons in an atom according to energy.

The electrons in an atom are grouped around the nucleus into **shells**, roughly like the layers in an onion, according to the energy of the electrons. The farther a shell is from the nucleus, the larger it is, the more electrons it can hold, and the higher the energies of those electrons. The first shell (the one nearest the nucleus) can hold only 2 electrons, the second shell can hold 8, the third shell can hold 18, and the fourth shell can hold 32 electrons.

Shell number:	1	2	3	4
Electron capacity:	2	8	18	32

Subshell (electron) A grouping of electrons in a shell according to the shape of the region of space they occupy.

Within shells, electrons are further grouped into **subshells** of four different types, identified in order of increasing energy by the letters *s, p, d,* and *f.* The first shell has only an *s* subshell; the second shell has an *s* and a *p* subshell; the third shell has an *s,* a *p,* and a *d* subshell; and the fourth shell has an *s,* a *p,* a *d,* and an *f* subshell. Of the four types, we will be concerned mainly with *s* and *p* subshells because most of the elements found in living organisms use only these. A specific subshell is symbolized by writing the number of the shell, followed by the letter for the subshell. For example, the designation 3*p* refers to the *p* subshell in the third shell.

Shell number:	1	2	3	4
Subshell designation:	*s*	*s , p*	*s , p , d*	*s , p , d , f*

Note that the number of subshells in a given shell is equal to the shell number. For example, shell number 3 has 3 subshells.

Orbital A region of space within an atom where an electron in a given subshell can be found.

Finally, within each subshell, electrons are grouped into **orbitals**, regions of space within an atom where the specific electrons are most likely to be found. There are different numbers of orbitals within the different kinds of subshells. A given *s* subshell has only 1 orbital, a *p* subshell has 3 orbitals, a *d* subshell has 5 orbitals, and an *f* subshell has 7 orbitals. Each orbital can hold only two electrons, which differ in a property known as *spin*. If one electron in an orbital has a clockwise spin, the other electron in the same orbital must have a counterclockwise spin.

Shell number:	1	2	3	4
Subshell designation:	*s*	*s* , *p*	*s* , *p* , *d*	*s* , *p* , *d* , *f*
Number of orbitals:	1	1 , 3	1 , 3 , 5	1 , 3 , 5 , 7

Different orbitals have different shapes and orientations, which are described by the quantum mechanical model. Orbitals in *s* subshells are spherical regions centered about the nucleus, whereas orbitals in *p* subshells are roughly dumbbell-shaped regions (Figure 3.5). As shown in Figure 3.5(b), the three *p* orbitals in a given subshell are oriented at right angles to one another.

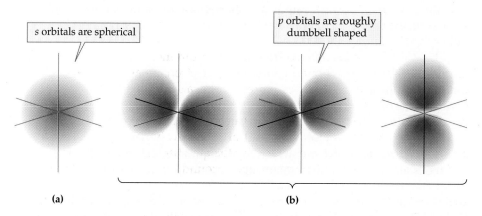

s orbitals are spherical

p orbitals are roughly dumbbell shaped

(a)   (b)

▲ **FIGURE 3.5 The shapes of *s* and *p* orbitals.** (a) The *s* orbitals and (b) the *p* orbitals. The three *p* orbitals in a given subshell are oriented at right angles to one another. Each orbital can hold only two electrons.

The overall electron distribution within an atom is summarized in Table 3.2 and in the following list:

- The first shell holds only 2 electrons. The 2 electrons have different spins and are in a single 1*s* orbital.
- The second shell holds 8 electrons. Two are in a 2*s* orbital, and 6 are in the three different 2*p* orbitals (two per 2*p* orbital).
- The third shell holds 18 electrons. Two are in a 3*s* orbital, 6 are in three 3*p* orbitals, and 10 are in five 3*d* orbitals.
- The fourth shell holds 32 electrons. Two are in a 4*s* orbital, 6 are in three 4*p* orbitals, 10 are in five 4*d* orbitals, and 14 are in seven 4*f* orbitals.

TABLE 3.2 Electron Distribution in Atoms

SHELL NUMBER:	1	2	3	4
Subshell designation:	*s*	*s* , *p*	*s* , *p* , *d*	*s* , *p* , *d* , *f*
Number of orbitals:	1	1 , 3	1 , 3 , 5	1 , 3 , 5 , 7
Number of electrons:	2	2 , 6	2 , 6 , 10	2 , 6 , 10 , 14
Total electron capacity:	2	8	18	32

WORKED EXAMPLE **3.6** Atomic Structure: Electron Shells

How many electrons are present in an atom that has its first and second shells filled and has 4 electrons in its third shell? Name the element.

ANALYSIS The number of electrons in the atom is calculated by adding the total electrons in each shell. We can identify the element from the number of protons in the nucleus, which is equal to the number of electrons in the atom.

SOLUTION
The first shell of an atom holds 2 electrons in its $1s$ orbital, and the second shell holds 8 electrons (2 in a $2s$ orbital and 6 in three $2p$ orbitals). Thus, the atom has a total of $2 + 8 + 4 = 14$ electrons and must be silicon (Si).

PROBLEM 3.17

What is the maximum number of electrons that can occupy the following subshells?

(a) $3p$ subshell

(b) $2s$ subshell

(c) $2p$ subshell

PROBLEM 3.18

How many electrons are present in an atom in which the $1s$, $2s$, and $2p$ subshells are filled? Name the element.

PROBLEM 3.19

How many electrons are present in an atom in which the first and second shells and the $3s$ subshell are filled? Name the element.

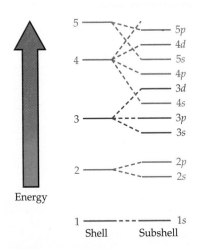

▲ Following the energy level diagram for the electronic orbitals, the orbital filling order can be predicted as indicated in this figure.

Electron configuration The specific arrangement of electrons in an atom's shells and subshells.

3.7 Electron Configurations

The exact arrangement of electrons in an atom's shells and subshells is called the atom's **electron configuration** and can be predicted by applying three rules:

RULE 1. **Electrons occupy the lowest-energy orbitals available, beginning with $1s$ and continuing in the order shown in Figure 3.6.** Within each shell, the orbital energies increase in the order s, p, d, f. The overall ordering is complicated, however, by the fact that some "crossover" of energies occurs between orbitals in different shells above the $3p$ level. The $4s$ orbital is lower in energy than the $3d$ orbitals, for example, and is therefore filled first.

Mg (atomic number 12): $1s^2\ 2s^2\ 2p^6\ 3s^2$

RULE 2. **Each orbital can hold only two electrons, which must be of opposite spin.**

RULE 3. **Two or more orbitals with the same energy—the three p orbitals or the five d orbitals in a given shell, for example—are each half filled by one electron before any one orbital is completely filled by addition of the second electron.**

▲ **FIGURE 3.6 Order of orbital energy levels.** Above the $3p$ level, there is some crossover of energies among orbitals in different shells.

TABLE 3.3 Electron Configurations of the First 20 Elements

	ELEMENT	ATOMIC NUMBER	ELECTRON CONFIGURATION
H	Hydrogen	1	$1s^1$
He	Helium	2	$1s^2$
Li	Lithium	3	$1s^2\,2s^1$
Be	Beryllium	4	$1s^2\,2s^2$
B	Boron	5	$1s^2\,2s^2\,2p^1$
C	Carbon	6	$1s^2\,2s^2\,2p^2$
N	Nitrogen	7	$1s^2\,2s^2\,2p^3$
O	Oxygen	8	$1s^2\,2s^2\,2p^4$
F	Fluorine	9	$1s^2\,2s^2\,2p^5$
Ne	Neon	10	$1s^2\,2s^2\,2p^6$
Na	Sodium	11	$1s^2\,2s^2\,2p^6\,3s^1$
Mg	Magnesium	12	$1s^2\,2s^2\,2p^6\,3s^2$
Al	Aluminum	13	$1s^2\,2s^2\,2p^6\,3s^2\,3p^1$
Si	Silicon	14	$1s^2\,2s^2\,2p^6\,3s^2\,3p^2$
P	Phosphorus	15	$1s^2\,2s^2\,2p^6\,3s^2\,3p^3$
S	Sulfur	16	$1s^2\,2s^2\,2p^6\,3s^2\,3p^4$
Cl	Chlorine	17	$1s^2\,2s^2\,2p^6\,3s^2\,3p^5$
Ar	Argon	18	$1s^2\,2s^2\,2p^6\,3s^2\,3p^6$
K	Potassium	19	$1s^2\,2s^2\,2p^6\,3s^2\,3p^6\,4s^1$
Ca	Calcium	20	$1s^2\,2s^2\,2p^6\,3s^2\,3p^6\,4s^2$

Electron configurations of the first 20 elements are shown in Table 3.3. Notice that the number of electrons in each subshell is indicated by a superscript. For example, the notation $1s^2\,2s^2\,2p^6\,3s^2$ for magnesium means that magnesium atoms have 2 electrons in the first shell, 8 electrons in the second shell, and 2 electrons in the third shell.

As you read through the following electron configurations, check the atomic number and the location of each element in the periodic table (Figure 3.2). See if you can detect the relationship between electron configuration and position in the table.

- **Hydrogen ($Z = 1$):** The single electron in a hydrogen atom is in the lowest-energy, $1s$ level. The configuration can be represented in either of two ways:

$$\mathbf{H}\quad 1s^1 \quad\text{or}\quad \frac{\uparrow}{1s^1}$$

In the written representation, the superscript in the notation $1s^1$ means that the $1s$ orbital is occupied by one electron. In the graphic representation, the $1s$ orbital is indicated by a line and the single electron in this orbital is shown by an up arrow ($\uparrow$). A single electron in an orbital is often referred to as being *unpaired*.

- **Helium ($Z = 2$):** The two electrons in helium are both in the lowest-energy, $1s$ orbital, and their spins are *paired*, as represented by up and down arrows ($\uparrow\downarrow$):

$$\mathbf{He}\quad 1s^2 \quad\text{or}\quad \frac{\uparrow\downarrow}{1s^2}$$

- **Lithium ($Z = 3$):** With the first shell full, the second shell begins to fill. The third electron goes into the $2s$ orbital:

$$\mathbf{Li}\quad 1s^2\,2s^1 \quad\text{or}\quad \frac{\uparrow\downarrow}{1s^2}\ \frac{\uparrow}{2s^1}$$

Because [He] has the configuration of a filled $1s^2$ orbital, it is sometimes substituted for the $1s^2$ orbital in depictions of electron pairing. Using this alternative shorthand notation, the electron configuration for Li is written [He] $2s^1$.

- **Beryllium (Z = 4):** An electron next pairs up to fill the 2s orbital:

$$\textbf{Be} \quad 1s^2\,2s^2 \quad \text{or} \quad \underset{1s^2}{\uparrow\downarrow}\ \underset{2s^2}{\uparrow\downarrow} \quad \text{or} \quad [\text{He}]\,2s^2$$

- **Boron (Z = 5), Carbon (Z = 6), Nitrogen (Z = 7):** The next three electrons enter the three 2p orbitals, one at a time. Note that representing the configurations with lines and arrows gives more information than the alternative written notation because the filling and pairing of electrons in individual orbitals within the p subshell is shown.

$$\textbf{B} \quad 1s^2\,2s^2\,2p^1 \quad \text{or} \quad \underset{1s^2}{\uparrow\downarrow}\ \underset{2s^2}{\uparrow\downarrow}\ \underset{2p^1}{\underbrace{\uparrow\ \_\ \_}} \quad \text{or} \quad [\text{He}]\,2s^2\,2p^1$$

$$\textbf{C} \quad 1s^2\,2s^2\,2p^2 \quad \text{or} \quad \underset{1s^2}{\uparrow\downarrow}\ \underset{2s^2}{\uparrow\downarrow}\ \underset{2p^2}{\underbrace{\uparrow\ \uparrow\ \_}} \quad \text{or} \quad [\text{He}]\,2s^2\,2p^2$$

$$\textbf{N} \quad 1s^2\,2s^2\,2p^3 \quad \text{or} \quad \underset{1s^2}{\uparrow\downarrow}\ \underset{2s^2}{\uparrow\downarrow}\ \underset{2p^3}{\underbrace{\uparrow\ \uparrow\ \uparrow}} \quad \text{or} \quad [\text{He}]\,2s^2\,2p^3$$

- **Oxygen (Z = 8), Fluorine (Z = 9), Neon (Z = 10):** Electrons now pair up one by one to fill the three 2p orbitals and fully occupy the second shell:

$$\textbf{O} \quad 1s^2\,2s^2\,2p^4 \quad \text{or} \quad \underset{1s^2}{\uparrow\downarrow}\ \underset{2s^2}{\uparrow\downarrow}\ \underset{2p^4}{\underbrace{\uparrow\downarrow\ \uparrow\ \uparrow}} \quad \text{or} \quad [\text{He}]\,2s^2\,2p^4$$

$$\textbf{F} \quad 1s^2\,2s^2\,2p^5 \quad \text{or} \quad \underset{1s^2}{\uparrow\downarrow}\ \underset{2s^2}{\uparrow\downarrow}\ \underset{2p^5}{\underbrace{\uparrow\downarrow\ \uparrow\downarrow\ \uparrow}} \quad \text{or} \quad [\text{He}]\,2s^2\,2p^5$$

$$\textbf{Ne} \quad 1s^2\,2s^2\,2p^6 \quad \text{or} \quad \underset{1s^2}{\uparrow\downarrow}\ \underset{2s^2}{\uparrow\downarrow}\ \underset{2p^6}{\underbrace{\uparrow\downarrow\ \uparrow\downarrow\ \uparrow\downarrow}}$$

At this point we may use the shorthand notation [Ne] to represent the electron configuration for a completely filled set of orbitals in the second shell.

- **Sodium to Calcium (Z = 11 − 20):** The pattern seen for lithium through neon is seen again for sodium (Z = 11) through argon (Z = 18) as the 3s and 3p subshells fill up. For elements having a third filled shell, we may use [Ar] to represent a completely filled third shell. After argon, however, the first crossover in subshell energies occurs. As indicated in Figure 3.6, the 4s subshell is lower in energy than the 3d subshell and is filled first. Potassium (Z = 19) and calcium (Z = 20) therefore have the following electron configurations:

$$\textbf{K} \quad 1s^2\,2s^2\,2p^6\,3s^2\,3p^6\,4s^1 \ \text{or}\ [\text{Ar}]\,4s^1 \quad \textbf{Ca} \quad 1s^2\,2s^2\,2p^6\,3s^2\,3p^6\,4s^2 \ \text{or}\ [\text{Ar}]\,4s^2$$

WORKED EXAMPLE **3.7** Atomic Structure: Electron Configurations

Show how the electron configuration of magnesium can be assigned.

ANALYSIS Magnesium, Z = 12, has 12 electrons to be placed in specific orbitals. Assignments are made by putting 2 electrons in each orbital, according to the order shown in Figure 3.6.

- The first 2 electrons are placed in the $1s$ orbital ($1s^2$).
- The next 2 electrons are placed in the $2s$ orbital ($2s^2$).
- The next 6 electrons are placed in the three available $2p$ orbitals ($2p^6$).
- The remaining 2 electrons are both put in the $3s$ orbital ($3s^2$).

SOLUTION

Magnesium has the configuration $1s^2\ 2s^2\ 2p^6\ 3s^2$ or [Ne] $3s^2$.

WORKED EXAMPLE **3.8** Electron Configurations: Orbital-Filling Diagrams

Write the electron configuration of phosphorus, $Z = 15$, using up and down arrows to show how the electrons in each orbital are paired.

ANALYSIS Phosphorus has 15 electrons, which occupy orbitals according to the order shown in Figure 3.6.

- The first 2 are paired and fill the first shell ($1s^2$).
- The next 8 fill the second shell ($2s^2\ 2p^6$). All electrons are paired.
- The remaining 5 electrons enter the third shell, where 2 fill the $3s$ orbital ($3s^2$) and 3 occupy the $3p$ subshell, one in each of the three p orbitals.

SOLUTION

P $\quad \underset{1s^2}{\uparrow\downarrow} \quad \underset{2s^2}{\uparrow\downarrow} \quad \underbrace{\underset{}{\uparrow\downarrow\ \uparrow\downarrow\ \uparrow\downarrow}}_{2p^6} \quad \underset{3s^2}{\uparrow\downarrow} \quad \underbrace{\uparrow\ \uparrow\ \uparrow}_{3p^3}$

PROBLEM 3.20

Write electron configurations for the following elements. (You can check your answers in Table 3.3.)

(a) C   (b) P   (c) Cl   (d) K

PROBLEM 3.21

Write electron configurations for the elements with atomic numbers 14 and 36.

PROBLEM 3.22

For an atom containing 33 electrons, identify the incompletely filled subshell, and show the paired and/or unpaired electrons in this subshell using up and down arrows.

━● KEY CONCEPT PROBLEM 3.23

Identify the atom with the following orbital-filling diagram.

$1s^2\ 2s^2\ 2p^6\ 3s^2\ 3p^6 \quad \underset{4s}{\updownarrow} \quad \underset{}{\updownarrow}\ \underset{}{\updownarrow}\ \underset{3d}{\updownarrow}\ \underset{}{\updownarrow}\ \underset{}{\updownarrow} \quad \underset{}{\uparrow}\ \underline{\ \ }\ \underset{4p}{\underline{\ \ }}$

3.8 Electron Configurations and the Periodic Table

How is an atom's electron configuration related to its chemical behavior, and why do elements with similar behavior occur in the same group of the periodic table? As shown in Figure 3.7, the periodic table can be divided into four regions, or *blocks*, of elements according to the electron shells and subshells occupied by *the subshell filled last*.

s-Block element A main group element that results from the filling of an *s* orbital.

p-Block element A main group element that results from the filling of *p* orbitals.

d-Block element A transition metal element that results from the filling of *d* orbitals.

f-Block element An inner transition metal element that results from the filling of *f* orbitals.

- The main group 1A and 2A elements on the left side of the table (plus He) are called the **s-block elements** because an *s* subshell is filled last in these elements.
- The main group 3A–8A elements on the right side of the table (except He) are the **p-block elements** because a *p* subshell is filled last in these elements.
- The transition metals in the middle of the table are the **d-block elements** because a *d* subshell is filled last in these elements.
- The inner transition metals detached at the bottom of the table are the **f-block elements** because an *f* subshell is filled last in these elements.

Thinking of the periodic table as outlined in Figure 3.7 provides a simple way to remember the order of orbital filling shown previously in Figure 3.6. Beginning at the top left corner of the periodic table, the first row contains only two elements (H and He) because only two electrons are required to fill the *s* orbital in the first shell, $1s^2$. The second row begins with two *s*-block elements (Li and Be) and continues with six *p*-block elements (B through Ne), so electrons fill the next available *s* orbital (2*s*) and then the first available *p* orbitals (2*p*). The third row is similar to the second row, so the 3*s* and 3*p* orbitals are filled next. The fourth row again starts with two *s*-block elements (K and Ca) but is then followed by ten *d*-block elements (Sc through Zn) and six *p*-block elements (Ga through Kr). Thus, the order of orbital filling is 4*s* followed by the first available *d* orbitals (3*d*) followed by 4*p*. Continuing through successive rows of the periodic table gives the entire filling order, identical to that shown in Figure 3.6.

$$1s \rightarrow 2s \rightarrow 2p \rightarrow 3s \rightarrow 3p \rightarrow 4s \rightarrow 3d \rightarrow 4p \rightarrow 5s \rightarrow$$
$$4d \rightarrow 5p \rightarrow 6s \rightarrow 4f \rightarrow 5d \rightarrow 6p \rightarrow 7s \rightarrow 5f \rightarrow 6d$$

But why do the elements in a given group of the periodic table have similar properties? The answer emerges when you look at Table 3.4, which gives electron

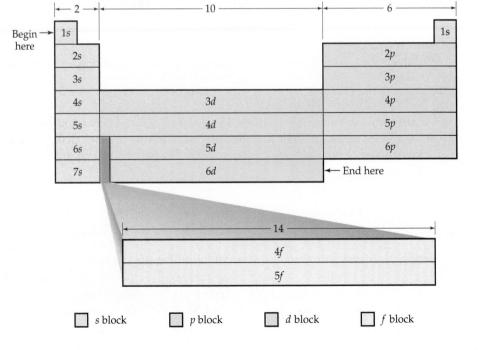

▶ **FIGURE 3.7 The blocks of elements in the periodic table correspond to filling the different types of subshells.** Beginning at the top left and going across successive rows of the periodic table provides a method for remembering the order of orbital filling: $1s \rightarrow 2s \rightarrow 2p \rightarrow 3s \rightarrow 3p \rightarrow 4s \rightarrow 3d \rightarrow 4p$, and so on.

TABLE 3.4   Valence-Shell Electron Configurations for Group 1A, 2A, 7A, and 8A Elements

GROUP	ELEMENT	ATOMIC NUMBER	VALENCE-SHELL ELECTRON CONFIGURATION
1A	Li (lithium)	3	$2s^1$
	Na (sodium)	11	$3s^1$
	K (potassium)	19	$4s^1$
	Rb (rubidium)	37	$5s^1$
	Cs (cesium)	55	$6s^1$
2A	Be (beryllium)	4	$2s^2$
	Mg (magnesium)	12	$3s^2$
	Ca (calcium)	20	$4s^2$
	Sr (strontium)	38	$5s^2$
	Ba (barium)	56	$6s^2$
7A	F (fluorine)	9	$2s^2\ 2p^5$
	Cl (chlorine)	17	$3s^2\ 3p^5$
	Br (bromine)	35	$4s^2\ 4p^5$
	I (iodine)	53	$5s^2\ 5p^5$
8A	He (helium)	2	$1s^2$
	Ne (neon)	10	$2s^2\ 2p^6$
	Ar (argon)	18	$3s^2\ 3p^6$
	Kr (krypton)	36	$4s^2\ 4p^6$
	Xe (xenon)	54	$5s^2\ 5p^6$

configurations for elements in the main groups 1A, 2A, 7A, and 8A. Focusing only on the electrons in the outermost shell, or **valence shell**, *elements in the same group of the periodic table have similar electron configurations in their valence shells*. The group 1A elements, for example, all have one **valence electron**, ns^1 (where n represents the number of the valence shell: $n = 2$ for Li; $n = 3$ for Na; $n = 4$ for K; and so on). The group 2A elements have two valence electrons (ns^2); the group 7A elements have seven valence electrons ($ns^2\ np^5$); and the group 8A elements (except He) have eight valence electrons ($ns^2\ np^6$). You might also notice that the group numbers from 1A through 8A give the numbers of valence electrons for the elements in each main group.

What is true for the main group elements is also true for the other groups in the periodic table: Atoms within a given group have the same number of valence electrons and have similar electron configurations. *Because the valence electrons are the most loosely held, they are the most important in determining an element's properties.* Similar electron configurations thus explain why the elements in a given group of the periodic table have similar chemical behavior.

Valence shell The outermost electron shell of an atom.

Valence electron An electron in the valence shell of an atom.

⊂⊃⊃ Looking Ahead

We have seen that elements in a given group have similar chemical behavior because they have similar valence electron configurations, and that many chemical properties exhibit periodic trends across the periodic table. The *chemical* behavior of nearly all the elements can be predicted based on their position in the periodic table, and will be examined in more detail in Chapters 4–6. Similarly, the *nuclear* behavior of the different isotopes of a given element is related to the configuration of the nucleus (that is, the number of neutrons and protons), and will be examined in Chapter 11.   ⊂⊃⊃

WORKED EXAMPLE 3.9 Electron Configurations: Valence Electrons

Write the electron configuration for the following elements, using both the complete and the shorthand notations. Indicate which electrons are the valence electrons.

(a) Na **(b)** Cl **(c)** Zr

ANALYSIS Locate the row and the block in which each of the elements is found in Figure 3.7. The location can be used to determine the complete electron configuration and to identify the valence electrons.

SOLUTION

(a) Na (sodium) is located in the third row, and in the first column of the s-block. Therefore, all orbitals up to the $3s$ are completely filled, and there is one electron in the $3s$ orbital.

$$\textbf{Na:}\ 1s^2\ 2s^2\ 2p^6\ \underline{3s^1}\quad \text{or}\quad [\text{Ne}]\ \underline{3s^1}\quad \text{(valence electrons are underlined)}$$

(b) Cl (chlorine) is located in the third row, and in the fifth column of the p-block.

$$\textbf{Cl:}\quad 1s^2\ 2s^2\ 2p^6\ \underline{3s^2\ 3p^5}\quad \text{or}\quad [\text{Ne}]\ \underline{3s^2\ 3p^5}$$

(c) Zr (zirconium) is located in the fifth row, and in the second column of the d-block. All orbitals up to the $4d$ are completely filled, and there are 2 electrons in the $4d$ orbitals. Note that the $4d$ orbitals are filled after the $5s$ orbitals in both Figures 3.6 and 3.7.

$$\textbf{Zr:}\quad 1s^2\ 2s^2\ 2p^6\ 3s^1\ 3p^6\ 4s^2\ 3d^{10}\ 4p^6\ \underline{5s^2}\ 4d^2\quad \text{or}\quad [\text{Kr}]\ \underline{5s^2}\ 4d^2$$

WORKED EXAMPLE 3.10 Electron Configurations: Valence-Shell Configurations

Using n to represent the number of the valence shell, write a general valence-shell configuration for the elements in group 6A.

ANALYSIS The elements in group 6A have 6 valence electrons. In each element, the first two of these electrons are in the valence s subshell, giving ns^2, and the next four electrons are in the valence p subshell, giving np^4.

SOLUTION
For group 6A, the general valence-shell configuration is $ns^2\ np^4$.

WORKED EXAMPLE 3.11 Electron Configurations: Inner Shells versus Valence Shell

How many electrons are in a tin atom? Give the number of electrons in each shell. How many valence electrons are there in a tin atom? Write the valence-shell configuration for tin.

ANALYSIS The total number of electrons will be the same as the atomic number for tin ($Z = 50$). The number of valence electrons will equal the number of electrons in the valence shell.

SOLUTION

Checking the periodic table shows that tin has atomic number 50 and is in group 4A. The number of electrons in each shell is

Shell number:	1	2	3	4	5
Number of electrons:	2	8	18	18	4

As expected from the group number, tin has 4 valence electrons. They are in the $5s$ and $5p$ subshells and have the configuration $5s^2\, 5p^2$.

PROBLEM 3.24

Write the electron configuration for the following elements, using both the complete and the shorthand notations. Indicate which electrons are the valence electrons.

(a) F **(b)** Al **(c)** As

PROBLEM 3.25

Identify the group in which all elements have the valence-shell configuration ns^2.

PROBLEM 3.26

For chlorine, identify the group number, give the number of electrons in each occupied shell, and write its valence-shell configuration.

KEY CONCEPT PROBLEM 3.27

Identify the group number, and write the general valence-shell configuration (for example, ns^1 for group 1A elements) for the elements indicated in red in the following periodic table.

3.9 Electron-Dot Symbols

Valence electrons play such an important role in the behavior of atoms that it is useful to have a method for including them with atomic symbols. In an **electron-dot symbol**, dots are placed around the atomic symbol to indicate the number of valence electrons present. A group 1A atom, such as sodium, has a single dot; a group 2A atom, such as magnesium, has two dots; a group 3A atom, such as boron, has three dots; and so on.

Table 3.5 gives electron-dot symbols for atoms of the first few elements in each main group. As shown, the dots are distributed around the four sides of the element symbol, singly at first until each of the four sides has one dot. As more electron dots

Electron-dot symbol An atomic symbol with dots placed around it to indicate the number of valence electrons.

TABLE 3.5 Electron-Dot Symbols for Some Main Group Elements

1A	2A	3A	4A	5A	6A	7A	NOBLE GASES
H·							He:
Li·	·Be·	·Ḃ·	·Ċ·	·N̈:	·Ö:	·F̈:	:N̈e:
Na·	·Mg·	·Äl·	·S̈i·	·P̈:	·S̈:	·C̈l:	:Är:
K·	·Ca·	·Ġa·	·Ġe·	·Äs:	·S̈e:	·B̈r:	:K̈r:

are added they will form pairs, with no more than two dots on a side. Note that helium differs from other noble gases in having only two valence electrons rather than eight. Nevertheless, helium is considered a member of group 8A because its properties resemble those of the other noble gases and because its highest occupied subshell is filled ($1s^2$).

WORKED EXAMPLE **3.12** Electron Configurations: Electron-Dot Symbols

Write the electron-dot symbol for any element X in group 5A.

ANALYSIS The group number, 5A, indicates 5 valence electrons. The first four are distributed singly around the four sides of the element symbol, and any additional are placed to form electron pairs.

SOLUTION

·Ẍ:   (5 electrons)

PROBLEM 3.28

Write the electron-dot symbol for any element X in group 3A.

PROBLEM 3.29

Write electron-dot symbols for radon, lead, xenon, and radium.

APPLICATION ▶ Atoms and Light

What we see as *light* is really a wave of energy moving through space. The shorter the length of the wave (the *wavelength*), the higher the energy; the longer the wavelength, the lower the energy.

Shorter wavelength
(higher energy)

Longer wavelength
(lower energy)

Visible light has wavelengths in the range 400–800 nm, but that is just one small part of the overall *electromagnetic spectrum*, shown in the accompanying figure. Although we cannot see the other wavelengths of electromagnetic energy, we use them for many purposes and their names may be familiar to you: gamma rays, X rays, ultraviolet (UV) rays, infrared (IR) rays, microwaves, and radio waves, for example.

What happens when a beam of electromagnetic energy collides with an atom? Remember that electrons are located in orbitals based on their energy levels. An atom with its electrons in their usual, lowest-energy locations is said to be in its *ground state*. If the amount of electromagnetic energy is just right, an electron can be kicked up from its usual energy level to a higher one. Energy from an electrical discharge or in the form of heat can have the same effect. With one of its electrons promoted to a higher energy, an atom is said to be *excited*. The excited state does not last long, though, because the electron quickly drops back to its more stable, ground-state energy level, releasing its extra energy in the process. If the released energy falls in the range of visible light, we can see the result. Many practical applications, from neon lights to fireworks, are the result of this phenomenon.

In "neon" lights, noble gas atoms are excited by an electric discharge, giving rise to a variety of colors that depend on the gas—red from neon, white from krypton, and blue from argon. Similarly, mercury or sodium atoms excited by electrical energy are responsible for the intense bluish or yellowish light, respectively, provided by some street lamps. In the same manner, metal atoms excited by heat are responsible for the spectacular colors of fireworks—red from strontium, green from barium, and blue from copper, for example.

The concentration of certain metals in body fluids is measured by sensitive instruments relying on the same principle of electron excitation that we see in fireworks. These instruments determine the intensity of the flame color produced by lithium (red), sodium (yellow), and potassium (violet),

▲ The brilliant colors of fireworks are due to the release of energy from excited atoms as electrons fall from higher to lower energy levels.

yielding the concentrations of these metals given in most clinical lab reports. Calcium, magnesium, copper, and zinc concentrations are also found by measuring the energies of excited atoms.

See Additional Problems 3.94 and 3.95 at the end of the chapter.

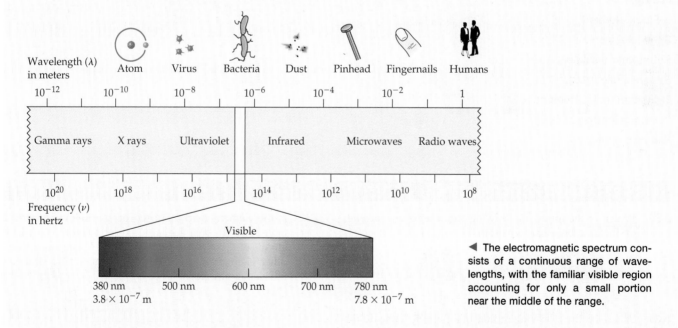

◀ The electromagnetic spectrum consists of a continuous range of wavelengths, with the familiar visible region accounting for only a small portion near the middle of the range.

SUMMARY: REVISITING THE CHAPTER GOALS

1. What is the modern theory of atomic structure? All matter is composed of *atoms*. An atom is the smallest and simplest unit into which a sample of an element can be divided while maintaining the properties of the element. Atoms are made up of subatomic particles called *protons, neutrons,* and *electrons*. Protons have a positive electrical charge, neutrons are electrically neutral, and electrons have a negative electrical charge. The protons and neutrons in an atom are present in a dense, positively charged central region called

KEY WORDS

Alkali metal, *p. 60*

Alkaline earth metal, *p. 60*

Atom, *p. 49*

Atomic mass unit (amu), *p. 50*

the *nucleus*. Electrons are situated a relatively large distance away from the nucleus, leaving most of the atom as empty space.

2. **How do atoms of different elements differ?** Elements differ according to the number of protons their atoms contain, a value called the element's *atomic number* (*Z*). All atoms of a given element have the same number of protons and an equal number of electrons. The number of neutrons in an atom is not predictable but is generally as great or greater than the number of protons. The total number of protons plus neutrons in an atom is called the atom's *mass number* (*A*).

3. **What are isotopes, and what is atomic weight?** Atoms with identical numbers of protons and electrons but different numbers of neutrons are called *isotopes*. The atomic weight of an element is the weighted average mass of atoms of the element's naturally occurring isotopes measured in *atomic mass units* (amu).

4. **How is the periodic table arranged?** Elements are organized into the *periodic table*, consisting of 7 rows, or *periods*, and 18 columns, or *groups*. The two groups on the left side of the table and the six groups on the right are called the *main group elements*. The ten groups in the middle are the *transition metal groups*, and the 14 groups pulled out and displayed below the main part of the table are called the *inner transition metal groups*. Within a given group in the table, elements have the same number of valence electrons in their valence shell and similar electron configurations.

5. **How are electrons arranged in atoms?** The electrons surrounding an atom are grouped into layers, or *shells*. Within each shell, electrons are grouped into *subshells*, and within each subshell into *orbitals*—regions of space in which electrons are most likely to be found. The *s* orbitals are spherical, and the *p* orbitals are dumbbell-shaped.

Each shell can hold a specific number of electrons. The first shell can hold 2 electrons in an *s* orbital ($1s^2$); the second shell can hold 8 electrons in one *s* and three *p* orbitals ($2s^2\ 2p^6$); the third shell can hold 18 electrons in one *s*, three *p*, and five *d* orbitals ($3s^2\ 3p^6\ 3d^{10}$); and so on. The *electron configuration* of an element is predicted by assigning the element's electrons into orbitals, beginning with the lowest-energy orbital. The electrons in the outermost shell, or *valence shell*, can be represented using electron-dot symbols.

UNDERSTANDING KEY CONCEPTS

3.30 Which of the following drawings represents an *s* orbital, and which represents a *p* orbital?

(a)   (b)

3.31 Where on the following outline of a periodic table do the indicated elements or groups of elements appear?

(a) Alkali metals   (b) Halogens
(c) Alkaline earth metals   (d) Transition metals
(e) Hydrogen   (f) Helium   (g) Metalloids

3.32 Is the element marked in red on the following periodic table likely to be a gas, a liquid, or a solid? What is the atomic number of the element in blue? Name at least one other element that is likely to be chemically similar to the element in green.

3.33 Use the blank periodic table at the top of the next page to show where elements matching the following descriptions appear.

(a) Elements with the valence-shell electron configuration $ns^2\ np^5$

(b) An element whose third shell contains two p electrons

(c) Elements with a completely filled valence shell

3.34 What atom has the following orbital-filling diagram?

$1s^2\ 2s^2\ 2p^6\ 3s^2\ 3p^6$ $\boxed{\uparrow\downarrow}$ $\quad$ $\boxed{\uparrow\downarrow}$ $\boxed{\uparrow\downarrow}$ $\boxed{\uparrow\downarrow}$ $\boxed{\uparrow\downarrow}$ $\boxed{\uparrow\downarrow}$ $\quad$ $\boxed{\uparrow\downarrow}$ $\boxed{\downarrow}$ $\boxed{\downarrow}$

$4s$ $\qquad\qquad$ $3d$ $\qquad\qquad$ $4p$

3.35 Use the orbital-filling diagram below to show the electron configuration for As:

$1s^2\ 2s^2\ 2p^6\ 3s^2\ 3p^6$ $\underline{\quad}$ $\quad$ $\underline{\quad}$ $\underline{\quad}$ $\underline{\quad}$ $\underline{\quad}$ $\underline{\quad}$ $\quad$ $\underline{\quad}$ $\underline{\quad}$ $\underline{\quad}$

$4s$ $\qquad\qquad$ $3d$ $\qquad\qquad$ $4p$

ADDITIONAL PROBLEMS

ATOMIC THEORY AND THE COMPOSITION OF ATOMS

3.36 What four fundamental assumptions about atoms and matter make up modern atomic theory?

3.37 How do atoms of different elements differ?

3.38 Find the mass in grams of one atom of the following elements:

(a) Bi, atomic weight 208.9804 amu
(b) Xe, atomic weight 131.29 amu
(c) He, atomic weight 4.0026 amu

3.39 Find the mass in atomic mass units of the following:

(a) 1 O atom, with a mass of 2.66×10^{-23} g
(b) 1 Br atom, with a mass of 1.31×10^{-22} g

3.40 What is the mass in grams of 6.022×10^{23} N atoms of mass 14.01 amu?

3.41 What is the mass in grams of 6.022×10^{23} O atoms of mass 16.00 amu?

3.42 How many O atoms of mass 15.99 amu are in 15.99 g of oxygen?

3.43 How many C atoms of mass 12.00 amu are in 12.00 g of carbon?

3.44 What are the names of the three subatomic particles? What are their approximate masses in atomic mass units, and what electrical charge does each have?

3.45 Where within an atom are the three types of subatomic particles located?

3.46 Identify the following atoms:

(a) Contains 19 protons
(b) Contains 50 protons
(c) Has $Z = 30$

3.47 Identify the following atoms:

(a) Contains 15 electrons
(b) Contains 41 protons
(c) Has $Z = 27$

3.48 Give the number of neutrons in each naturally occurring isotope of argon: argon-36, argon-38, argon-40.

3.49 Give the number of protons, neutrons, and electrons in the following isotopes:

(a) Al-27 $\qquad\qquad$ **(b)** $^{28}_{14}\text{Si}$
(c) B-11 $\qquad\qquad$ **(d)** $^{115}_{47}\text{Ag}$

3.50 Which of the following symbols represent isotopes of the same element?

(a) $^{19}_{9}\text{X}$ $\qquad\qquad$ **(b)** $^{19}_{10}\text{X}$
(c) $^{21}_{9}\text{X}$ $\qquad\qquad$ **(d)** $^{21}_{12}\text{X}$

3.51 Complete the following isotope symbols:

(a) $^{206}_{?}\text{Po}$ $\qquad\qquad$ **(b)** $^{224}_{88}\text{?}$
(c) $^{197}_{79}\text{?}$ $\qquad\qquad$ **(d)** $^{84}_{?}\text{Kr}$

3.52 Name the isotope represented by each symbol in Problem 3.50.

3.53 Give the number of neutrons in each isotope listed in Problem 3.51.

3.54 Write the symbols for the following isotopes:

(a) Its atoms contain 6 protons and 8 neutrons.
(b) Its atoms have mass number 39 and contain 19 protons.
(c) Its atoms have mass number 20 and contain 10 electrons.

3.55 Write the symbols for the following isotopes:

(a) Its atoms contain 9 electrons and 10 neutrons.
(b) Its atoms have $A = 79$ and $Z = 35$.
(c) Its atoms have $A = 51$ and contain 23 electrons.

3.56 There are three naturally occurring isotopes of carbon, with mass numbers of 12, 13, and 14. How many neutrons does each have? Write the symbol for each isotope, indicating its atomic number and mass number.

3.57 The isotope of iodine with mass number 131 is often used in medicine as a radioactive tracer. Write the symbol for this isotope, indicating both mass number and atomic number.

3.58 Naturally occurring copper is a mixture of 69.17% ^{63}Cu with a mass of 62.93 amu and 30.83% ^{65}Cu with a mass of 64.93 amu. What is the atomic weight of copper?

3.59 Naturally occurring lithium is a mixture of 92.58% ^{7}Li with a mass of 7.016 amu and 7.42% ^{6}Li with a mass of 6.015 amu. What is the atomic weight of lithium?

THE PERIODIC TABLE

3.60 Why does the third period in the periodic table contain eight elements?

3.61 Why does the fourth period in the periodic table contain 18 elements?

3.62 Americium, atomic number 95, is used in household smoke detectors. What is the symbol for americium? Is americium a metal, a nonmetal, or a metalloid?

3.63 Antimony, $Z = 51$, is alloyed with lead for use in automobile batteries. What is the symbol for antimony? Is antimony a metal, a nonmetal, or a metalloid?

3.64 Answer the following questions for the elements from scandium through zinc:

(a) Are they metals or nonmetals?
(b) To what general class of elements do they belong?
(c) What subshell is being filled by electrons in these elements?

3.65 Answer the following questions for the elements from cerium through lutetium:

(a) Are they metals or nonmetals?
(b) To what general class of elements do they belong?
(c) What subshell is being filled by electrons in these elements?

3.66 For (a) rubidium (b) tungsten, (c) germanium, and (d) krypton, which of the following terms apply? (i) metal, (ii) nonmetal, (iii) metalloid (iv) transition element, (v) main group element, (vi) noble gas, (vii) alkali metal, (viii) alkaline earth metal

3.67 For (a) calcium, (b) palladium, (c) carbon, and (d) radon, which of the following terms apply? (i) metal, (ii) nonmetal, (iii) metalloid (iv) transition element, (v) main group element, (vi) noble gas, (vii) alkali metal, (viii) alkaline earth metal

3.68 Name an element in the periodic table that you would expect to be chemically similar to sulfur.

3.69 Name an element in the periodic table that you would expect to be chemically similar to magnesium

3.70 What elements in addition to lithium make up the alkali metal family?

3.71 What elements in addition to fluorine make up the halogen family?

ELECTRON CONFIGURATIONS

3.72 What is the maximum number of electrons that can go into an orbital?

3.73 What are the shapes and locations within an atom of s and p orbitals?

3.74 What is the maximum number of electrons that can go into the first shell? The second shell? The third shell?

3.75 What is the total number of orbitals in the third shell? The fourth shell?

3.76 How many subshells are there in the third shell? The fourth shell? The fifth shell?

3.77 How many orbitals would you expect to find in the last subshell of the fifth shell? How many electrons would you need to fill this subshell?

3.78 How many electrons are present in an atom with its $1s$, $2s$, and $2p$ subshells filled? What is this element?

3.79 How many electrons are present in an atom with its $1s$, $2s$, $2p$, and $3s$ subshells filled and with two electrons in the $3p$ subshell? What is this element?

3.80 Use arrows to show electron pairing in the valence p subshell of:

(a) Sulfur
(b) Bromine
(c) Silicon

3.81 Use arrows to show electron pairing in the $5s$ and $4d$ orbitals of:

(a) Strontium
(b) Technetium
(c) Palladium

3.82 Determine the number of unpaired electrons for each of the atoms in Problems 3.80 and 3.81.

3.83 Without looking back in the text, write the electron configurations for the following:

(a) Calcium, $Z = 20$
(b) Sulfur, $Z = 16$
(c) Fluorine, $Z = 9$
(d) Cadmium, $Z = 48$

3.84 How many electrons does the element with $Z = 12$ have in its valence shell? Write the electron-dot symbol for this element.

3.85 How many valence electrons do group 4A elements have? Explain. Write a generic electron-dot symbol for elements in this group.

3.86 Identify the valence subshell occupied by electrons in beryllium and arsenic atoms.

3.87 What group in the periodic table has the valence-shell configuration $ns^2 np^3$?

3.88 Give the number of valence electrons and draw electron-dot symbols for atoms of the following elements:

(a) Kr   (b) C
(c) Ca   (d) K
(e) B   (f) Cl

3.89 Using n for the number of the valence shell, write a general valence-shell configuration for the elements in group 7A and in group 1A.

Applications

3.90 What is the advantage of using a scanning tunneling microscope rather than a normal light microscope? [*Are Atoms Real? p. 52*]

3.91 Before Rutherford's experiments, atomic structure was represented using a *"plum pudding" model* proposed by Thomson, in which negatively charged electrons were embedded in diffuse, positively charged matter like raisins in plum pudding. How might Rutherford's experimental results have been different if this model were correct? [*Are Atoms Real? p. 52*]

3.92 What are the first two elements that are made in stars? [*The Origin of Chemical Elements, p. 61*]

3.93 How are elements heavier than iron made? [*The Origin of Chemical Elements, p. 61*]

3.94 Which type of electromagnetic energy in the following pairs is of higher energy? [*Atoms and Light, p. 72*]

(a) Infrared, ultraviolet
(b) Gamma waves, microwaves
(c) Visible light, X rays

3.95 Why do you suppose ultraviolet rays from the sun are more damaging to the skin than visible light? [*Atoms and Light, p. 72*]

General Questions and Problems

3.96 What elements in addition to helium make up the noble gas family?

3.97 Hydrogen is placed in group 1A on many periodic charts, even though it is not an alkali metal. On other periodic charts, however, hydrogen is included with group 7A even though it is not a halogen. Explain. (Hint: draw electron-dot symbols for H and for the 1A and 7A elements.)

3.98 Tellurium ($Z = 52$) has a *lower* atomic number than iodine ($Z = 53$), yet it has a *higher* atomic weight (127.60 amu for Te versus 126.90 amu for I). How is this possible?

3.99 What is the atomic number of the yet undiscovered element directly below francium (Fr) in the periodic table?

3.100 Give the number of electrons in each shell for lead.

3.101 Identify the highest-energy occupied subshell in atoms of the following elements:

(a) Argon
(b) Magnesium
(c) Technetium
(d) Iron

3.102 What is the atomic weight of naturally occurring bromine, which contains 50.69% Br-79 of mass 78.92 amu and 49.31% Br-81 of mass 80.91 amu?

3.103 Naturally occurring magnesium consists of three isotopes: 78.99% ^{24}Mg with a mass of 23.99 amu, 10.00% ^{25}Mg with a mass of 24.99 amu, and 11.01% ^{26}Mg with a mass of 25.98 amu. Calculate the atomic weight of magnesium.

3.104 If you had one atom of hydrogen and one atom of carbon, which would weigh more? Explain.

3.105 If you had a pile of 10^{23} hydrogen atoms and another pile of 10^{23} carbon atoms, which of the two piles would weigh more? (See Problem 3.104.)

3.106 If your pile of hydrogen atoms in Problem 3.105 weighed about 1 gram, how much would your pile of carbon atoms weigh?

3.107 Based on your answer to Problem 3.106, how much would you expect a pile of 10^{23} sodium atoms to weigh?

3.108 An unidentified element is found to have an electron configuration by shell of 2 8 18 8 2. To what group and period does this element belong? Is the element a metal or a nonmetal? How many protons does an atom of the element have? What is the name of the element? Write its electron-dot symbol.

3.109 Germanium, atomic number 32, is used in building semiconductors for microelectronic devices. If germanium, has an electron configuration by shell of 2 8 18 4, in what orbital are the valence electrons?

3.110 Tin, atomic number 50, is directly beneath germanium (Problem 3.109) in the periodic table. What electron configuration by shell would you expect tin to have? Is tin a metal or a nonmetal?

3.111 A blood sample is found to contain 8.6 mg/dL of Ca. How many atoms of Ca are present in 8.6 mg? The atomic weight of Ca is 40.08 amu.

3.112 What is wrong with the following electron configurations?

(a) Ni $1s^2\ 2s^2\ 2p^6\ 3s^2\ 3p^6\ 3d^{10}$
(b) N $1s^2\ 2p^5$
(c) Si $1s^2\ 2s^2\ 2p\ \underset{}{\uparrow\downarrow}\ \underline{}\ \underline{}$
(d) Mg $1s^2\ 2s^2\ 2p^6\ 3s\ \underset{}{\uparrow\uparrow}$

3.113 Not all elements follow exactly the electron-filling order described in Figure 3.7. Atoms of which elements are represented by the following electron configurations? (Hint: count the total number of electrons!)

(a) $1s^2\ 2s^2\ 2p^6\ 3s^2\ 3p^6\ 3d^5\ 4s^1$
(b) $1s^2\ 2s^2\ 2p^6\ 3s^2\ 3p^6\ 3d^{10}\ 4s^1$
(c) $1s^2\ 2s^2\ 2p^6\ 3s^2\ 3p^6\ 3d^{10}\ 4s^2\ 4p^6\ 4d^5\ 5s^1$
(d) $1s^2\ 2s^2\ 2p^6\ 3s^2\ 3p^6\ 3d^{10}\ 4s^2\ 4p^6\ 4d^{10}\ 5s^1$

3.114 What similarities do you see in the electron configurations for the atoms in Problem 3.113? How might these similarities explain their anomalous electron configurations?

3.115 What orbital is filled last in the yet undiscovered element 117?

CHAPTER 4

Ionic Compounds

CONCEPTS TO REVIEW

The Periodic Table
(Sections 3.4 and 3.5)

Electron Configurations
(Sections 3.7 and 3.8)

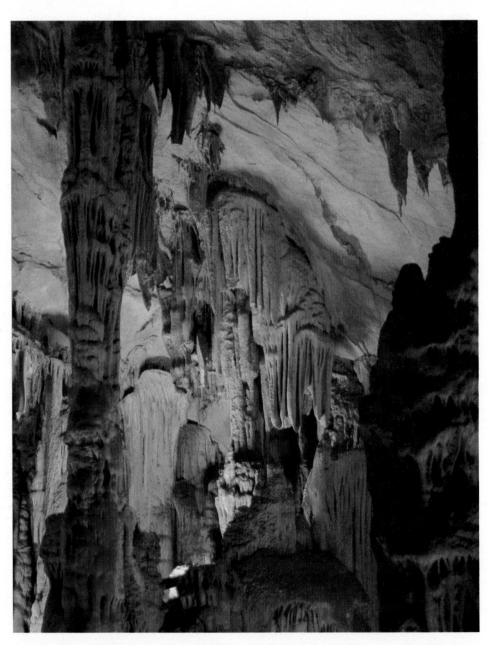

▲ Stalagmites and stalactites, such as these in a cave in the Nangu Stone Forest in China, are composed of the ionic compounds calcium carbonate, $CaCO_3$, and magnesium carbonate, $MgCO_3$.

CONTENTS

CHAPTER GOALS

We will answer the following questions in this chapter:

1. **What is an ion, what is an ionic bond, and what are the general characteristics of ionic compounds?**

   THE GOAL: Be able to describe ions and ionic bonds, and give the general properties of compounds that contain ionic bonds.

2. **What is the octet rule, and how does it apply to ions?**

   THE GOAL: Be able to state the octet rule and use it to predict the electron configurations of ions of main group elements.

3. **What is the relationship between an element's position in the periodic table and the formation of its ion?**

   THE GOAL: Be able to predict what ions are likely to be formed by atoms of a given element.

4. **What determines the chemical formula of an ionic compound?**

   THE GOAL: Be able to write formulas for ionic compounds, given the identities of the ions.

5. **How are ionic compounds named?**

   THE GOAL: Be able to name an ionic compound from its formula or give the formula of a compound from its name.

6. **What are acids and bases?**

   THE GOAL: Be able to recognize common acids and bases.

There are more than 19 million known chemical compounds, ranging in size from small *diatomic* (two-atom) substances like carbon monoxide, CO, to deoxyribonucleic acid (DNA), which can contain several *billion* atoms linked together in a precise way. Clearly, there must be some force that holds atoms together in compounds; otherwise, the atoms would simply drift apart and no compounds could exist. The forces that hold atoms together are called *chemical bonds* and are of two major types: *ionic bonds* and *covalent bonds*. In this chapter, we look at ionic bonds and at the substances formed by them. In the next chapter, we will look at covalent bonds.

All chemical bonds result from the electrical attraction between opposite charges—between positively charged nuclei and negatively charged electrons. As a result, the way in which different elements form bonds is related to their different electron configurations.

4.1 Ions

A general rule noted by early chemists is that metals, on the left side of the periodic table, tend to form compounds with nonmetals, on the right side of the table. The alkali metals of group 1A, for instance, react with the halogens of group 7A to form a variety of compounds. Sodium chloride (table salt), formed by the reaction of sodium with chlorine, is a familiar example. The names and chemical formulas of some other compounds containing elements from groups 1A and 7A include:

Potassium iodide, KI	Added to table salt to provide iodide ion needed by the thyroid gland
Sodium fluoride, NaF	Added to many municipal water supplies to provide fluoride ion for the prevention of tooth decay
Sodium iodide, NaI	Used in laboratory scintillation counters to detect radiation (See Section 11.8)

Both the compositions and the properties of these alkali metal–halogen compounds are similar. For instance, the two elements always combine in a 1:1 ratio: one alkali metal atom for every halogen atom. Each compound has a high melting point (all are over 500 °C); each is a stable, white, crystalline solid; and each is soluble in water. Furthermore, the water solution of each compound conducts electricity, a property that gives a clue to the kind of chemical bond holding the atoms together.

Electricity can flow only through a medium containing charged particles that are free to move. The electrical conductivity of metals, for example, results from the

▲ A solution of sodium chloride in water conducts electricity, allowing the bulb to light.

movement of negatively charged electrons through the metal. But what charged particles might be present in the water solutions of alkali metal–halogen compounds? To answer this question, think about the composition of atoms. Atoms are electrically neutral because they contain equal numbers of protons and electrons. By gaining or losing one or more electrons, however, an atom can be converted into a charged particle called an **ion**.

The *loss* of one or more electrons from a neutral atom gives a *positively* charged ion called a **cation** (**cat**-ion). As we saw in Section 3.8, sodium and other alkali metal atoms have a single electron in their valence shell and an electron configuration symbolized as ns^1, where n represents the shell number. By losing this electron, an alkali metal is converted to a cation.

Ion An electrically charged atom or group of atoms.

Cation A positively charged ion.

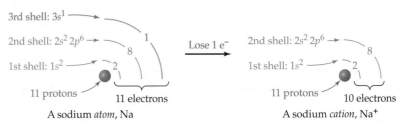

Conversely, the *gain* of one or more electrons by a neutral atom gives a *negatively* charged ion called an **anion** (**an**-ion). Chlorine and other halogen atoms have $ns^2\,np^5$ valence electrons and can easily gain an additional electron to fill out their valence subshell, thereby forming anions.

Anion A negatively charged ion.

The symbol for a cation is written by adding the positive charge as a superscript to the symbol for the element; an anion symbol is written by adding the negative charge as a superscript. If one electron is lost or gained, the charge is $+1$ or -1 but the number 1 is omitted in the notation, as in Na^+ and Cl^-. If two or more electrons are lost or gained, however, the charge is ±2 or greater and the number *is* used, as in Ca^{2+} and N^{3-}.

PROBLEM 4.1

Magnesium atoms lose two electrons when they react. Write the symbol of the ion that results. Is it a cation or an anion?

PROBLEM 4.2

Sulfur atoms gain two electrons when they react. Write the symbol of the ion that results. Is it a cation or an anion?

◖◦ KEY CONCEPT PROBLEM 4.3

Write the symbol for the ion depicted here. Is it a cation or an anion?

4.2 Periodic Properties and Ion Formation

The ease with which an atom loses an electron to form a positively charged cation is measured by a property called the atom's **ionization energy**, defined as the energy required to remove one electron from a single atom in the gaseous state. Conversely, the ease with which an atom *gains* an electron to form a negatively charged anion is measured by a property called **electron affinity**, defined as the energy released on adding an electron to a single atom in the gaseous state.

Ionization energy (energy is added)

$$\text{Atom} + \text{Energy} \longrightarrow \text{Cation} + \text{Electron}$$

Electron affinity (energy is released)

$$\text{Atom} + \text{Electron} \longrightarrow \text{Anion} + \text{Energy}$$

Ionization energy The energy required to remove one electron from a single atom in the gaseous state.

Electron affinity The energy released on adding an electron to a single atom in the gaseous state.

The relative magnitudes of ionization energies and electron affinities for elements in the first four rows of the periodic table are shown in Figure 4.1. Because ionization energy measures the amount of energy that must be *added* to pull an electron away from a neutral atom, the small values shown in Figure 4.1 for alkali metals (Li, Na, K) and other elements on the left side of the periodic table mean that these elements lose an electron easily. Conversely, the large values shown for halogens (F, Cl, Br) and noble gases (He, Ne, Ar, Kr) on the right side of the periodic table mean that these elements do not lose an electron easily. Electron affinities, however, measure the amount of energy *released* when an atom gains an electron. Although electron affinities are small compared to ionization energies, the halogens nevertheless have the largest values and therefore gain an electron most easily, whereas metals have the smallest values and do not gain an electron easily:

Alkali metal { Small ionization energy—-electron easily lost
Small electron affinity—-electron not easily gained
Net result: Cation formation is favored.

Halogen { Large ionization energy—-electron not easily lost
Large electron affinity—-electron easily gained
Net result: Anion formation is favored.

▲ **FIGURE 4.1** **Relative ionization energies (red) and electron affinities (blue) for elements in the first four rows of the periodic table.** Those elements having a value of zero for electron affinity do not accept an electron. Note that the alkali metals (Li, Na, K) have the lowest ionization energies and lose an electron most easily, whereas the halogens (F, Cl, Br) have the highest electron affinities and gain an electron most easily. The noble gases (He, Ne, Ar, Kr) neither gain nor lose an electron easily.

You might also note in Figure 4.1 that main group elements near the *middle* of the periodic table—boron (Z = 5), carbon (Z = 6, group 4A), and nitrogen (Z = 7, group 5A)—neither lose nor gain electrons easily and thus do not form ions easily. In the next chapter, we will see that these elements tend not to form ionic bonds but form covalent bonds instead.

Because alkali metals such as sodium tend to lose an electron, and halogens such as chlorine tend to gain an electron, these two elements (sodium and chlorine) will react with each other by transfer of an electron from the metal to the halogen (Figure 4.2). The product that results—sodium chloride (NaCl)—is electrically neutral because the positive charge of each Na^+ ion is balanced by the negative charge of each Cl^- ion.

(a)   (b)

▶ **FIGURE 4.2** (a) Chlorine is a toxic green gas, sodium is a reactive metal, and sodium chloride is a harmless white solid. (b) Sodium metal burns with an intense yellow flame when immersed in chlorine gas, yielding white sodium chloride "smoke."

WORKED EXAMPLE **4.1** Periodic Trends: Ionization Energy

Look at the periodic trends in Figure 4.1, and predict where the ionization energy of rubidium is likely to fall on the chart.

ANALYSIS Identify the group number of rubidium (group 1A), and find where other members of the group appear in Figure 4.1.

SOLUTION
Rubidium (Rb) is the alkali metal below potassium (K) in the periodic table. Since the alkali metals Li, Na, and K all have ionization energies near the bottom of the chart, the ionization energy of rubidium is probably similar.

WORKED EXAMPLE **4.2** Periodic Trends: Formation of Anions and Cations

Which element is likely to lose an electron more easily, Mg or S?

ANALYSIS Identify the group numbers of the elements, and find where members of those groups appear in Figure 4.1.

SOLUTION
Magnesium, a group 2A element on the left side of the periodic table, has a relatively low ionization energy, and loses an electron easily. Sulfur, a group 6A element on the right side of the table, has a higher ionization energy, and loses an electron less easily.

PROBLEM 4.4

Look at the periodic trends in Figure 4.1, and predict approximately where the ionization energy of xenon is likely to fall.

PROBLEM 4.5

Which element in the following pairs is likely to lose an electron more easily?

(a) Be or B   **(b)** Ca or Co   **(c)** Sc or Se

PROBLEM 4.6

Which element in the following pairs is likely to gain an electron more easily?

(a) H or He   **(b)** S or Si   **(c)** Cr or Mn

4.3 Ionic Bonds

When sodium reacts with chlorine, the product is sodium chloride, a compound completely unlike either of the elements from which it is formed. Sodium is a soft, silvery metal that reacts violently with water, and chlorine is a corrosive, poisonous, green gas (Figure 4.2a). When chemically combined, however, they produce our familiar table salt containing Na^+ ions and Cl^- ions. Because opposite electrical charges attract each other, the positive Na^+ ion and negative Cl^- ion are said to be held together by an **ionic bond.**

When a vast number of sodium atoms transfer electrons to an equally vast number of chlorine atoms, a visible crystal of sodium chloride results. In this crystal, equal numbers of Na^+ and Cl^- ions are packed together in a regular arrangement. Each positively charged Na^+ ion is surrounded by six negatively charged Cl^- ions, and each Cl^- ion is surrounded by six Na^+ ions (Figure 4.3). This packing arrangement allows each ion to be stabilized by the attraction of unlike charges on its six nearest-neighbor ions, while being as far as possible from ions of like charge.

Because of the three-dimensional arrangement of ions in a sodium chloride crystal, we cannot speak of specific ionic bonds between specific pairs of ions. Rather, there are many ions attracted by ionic bonds to their nearest neighbors. We therefore speak of the whole NaCl crystal as being an **ionic solid** and of such compounds as being **ionic compounds**. The same is true of all compounds composed of ions.

Ionic bond The electrical attractions between ions of opposite charge in a crystal.

Ionic solid A crystalline solid held together by ionic bonds.

Ionic compound A compound that contains ionic bonds.

◀ **FIGURE 4.3 The arrangement of Na^+ and Cl^- ions in a sodium chloride crystal.** Each positively charged Na^+ ion is surrounded by six negatively charged Cl^- ions, and each Cl^- ion is surrounded by six Na^+ ions. The crystal is held together by ionic bonds—the attraction between oppositely charged ions.

▲ The melting point of sodium chloride is 801 °C.

4.4 Some Properties of Ionic Compounds

Like sodium chloride, ionic compounds are usually crystalline solids. Different ions vary in size and charge, however, and therefore are packed together in crystals in different ways. The ions in each compound settle into a pattern that efficiently fills space and maximizes ionic bonding.

Because the ions in an ionic solid are held rigidly in place by attraction to their neighbors, they cannot move about. Once an ionic solid is dissolved in water, however, the ions can move freely, thereby accounting for the electrical conductivity of these compounds in solution.

The high melting points and boiling points observed for ionic compounds are also accounted for by ionic bonding. The attractive force between oppositely charged particles is extremely strong, and the ions need to gain a large amount of energy by being heated to high temperatures for them to loosen their grip on one another. Sodium chloride, for example, melts at 801 °C and boils at 1413 °C; potassium iodide melts at 681 °C and boils at 1330 °C.

Despite the strength of ionic bonds, ionic solids shatter if struck sharply. A blow disrupts the orderly arrangement of cations and anions, and the electrical repulsion between ions of like charge that have been pushed together helps to split apart the crystal.

Ionic compounds dissolve in water if the attraction between water and the ions overcomes the attraction of the ions for one another. Compounds like sodium chloride are very soluble and can be dissolved to make solutions of high concentration. Do not be misled, however, by the ease with which sodium chloride and other familiar ionic compounds dissolve in water. Many other ionic compounds are not water-soluble, because water is unable to overcome the ionic forces in many crystals.

4.5 Ions and the Octet Rule

We have seen that alkali metal atoms have a single valence-shell electron, ns^1. The electron-dot symbol $X\cdot$ is consistent with this valence electron configuration. Halogens, having seven valence electrons, ns^2np^5, can be represented using $:\ddot{X}\cdot$ as the electron-dot symbol. Noble gases can be represented as $:\ddot{X}:$, since they have eight valence electrons, ns^2np^6. Both the alkali metals and the halogens are extremely reactive, undergoing many chemical reactions and forming many compounds. The noble gases, however, are quite different. They are the least reactive of all elements.

Now look at sodium chloride and similar ionic compounds. When sodium or any other alkali metal reacts with chlorine or any other halogen, the metal transfers an electron from its valence shell to the valence shell of the halogen. Sodium thereby changes its valence-shell electron configuration from $2s^22p^63s^1$ in the atom to $2s^22p^6(3s^0)$ in the Na^+ ion, and chlorine changes from $3s^23p^5$ in the atom to $3s^23p^6$ in the Cl^- ion. *In so doing, both sodium and chlorine gain noble gas electron configurations, with 8 valence electrons.* The Na^+ ion has 8 electrons in the $n = 2$ shell, matching the electron configuration of neon. The Cl^- ion has 8 electrons in the $n = 3$ shell, matching the electron configuration of argon.

$$Na \quad + \quad Cl \quad \longrightarrow \quad Na^+ \quad + \quad Cl^-$$
$$1s^2\,2s^2\,2p^6\,3s^1 \qquad 1s^2\,2s^2\,2p^6\,3s^2\,3p^5 \qquad \underbrace{1s^2\,2s^2\,2p^63s^0}_{\text{Neon configuration}} \qquad \underbrace{1s^2\,2s^2\,2p^6\,3s^2\,3p^6}_{\text{Argon configuration}}$$

$$Na\cdot \quad + \quad \cdot\ddot{\underset{..}{Cl}}: \quad \longrightarrow \quad Na \quad + \quad :\ddot{\underset{..}{Cl}}:$$

Evidently there is something special about having 8 valence electrons (filled s and p subshells) that leads to stability and lack of chemical reactivity. In fact,

APPLICATION ▶ Minerals and Gems

I f you are wearing a sapphire, ruby, emerald, or zircon ring, you have a crystalline ionic compound on your finger. The gem came from the earth's crust, the source of most of our chemical raw materials. These gemstones are *minerals*, which to a geologist means that they are naturally occurring, crystalline chemical compounds. (To a nutritionist, by contrast, a "mineral" is one of the metal ions essential to human health.)

Sapphire and ruby are forms of the mineral *corundum*, or aluminum oxide (Al_2O_3). The blue of sapphire is due to traces of iron and titanium ions also present in the crystal, and the red of ruby is due to traces of chromium ions. Many minerals are *silicates*, meaning that their anions contain silicon and

oxygen combined in a variety of ways. Zircon is zirconium silicate ($ZrSiO_4$), and emerald is a form of the mineral beryl, $Be_3Al_2(Si_6O_{18})$, which is composed of Al^{3+}, Be^{2+}, and silicate rings.

Many minerals not sufficiently beautiful for use in jewelry are valuable as sources for the exotic metals so essential to our industrial civilization. Extraction of the metals from these minerals requires energy and a series of chemical reactions to convert the metal ions into free elements—the reverse of ion formation from atoms.

See Additional Problem 4.82 at the end of the chapter.

(a)

(b)

(c)

▲ Many minerals are silicates, which are compounds made up of polyatomic anions of silicon and oxygen. Their colors are determined largely by the cations they contain. (a) A crystal of tourmaline, a complex silicate of boron, aluminum, and other elements. (b) Dioptase from Namibia and (c) epidote from Pakistan.

observations of a great many chemical compounds have shown that main group elements frequently combine in such a way that each winds up with 8 valence electrons, a so-called *electron octet*. This conclusion is summarized in a statement called the **octet rule**:

Octet rule   Main group elements tend to undergo reactions that leave them with 8 valence electrons.

Put another way, main group *metals* tend to lose electrons when they react so that they attain an electron configuration like that of the noble gas just *before* them in the periodic table, and reactive main group *nonmetals* tend to gain electrons when they react so that they attain an electron configuration like that of the noble gas just *after* them in the periodic table. In both cases, the product ions have filled *s* and *p* subshells in their valence electron shell.

WORKED EXAMPLE | **4.3** Electron Configurations: Octet Rule for Cations

Write the electron configuration of magnesium ($Z = 12$). Show how many electrons a magnesium atom must lose to form an ion with a valence octet, and write the configuration of the ion. Explain the reason for the ion's charge, and write the ion's symbol.

ANALYSIS Write the electron configuration of magnesium as described in Section 3.7 and count the number of electrons in the valence shell.

SOLUTION

Magnesium has the electron configuration $1s^2 2s^2 2p^6 3s^2$. Since the second shell contains an octet of electrons ($2s^2 2p^6$) whereas the third shell is only partially filled ($3s^2$), magnesium can achieve a valence-shell octet by losing the two electrons in the $3s$ subshell. The result is formation of a doubly charged cation, Mg^{2+} with the neon configuration:

$$Mg^{2+} \qquad 1s^2 2s^2 2p^6 \quad \text{(Neon configuration)(or [Ne])}$$

A neutral magnesium atom has 12 protons and 12 electrons. With the loss of 2 electrons, there is an excess of 2 protons, accounting for the +2 charge of the ion, Mg^{2+}.

WORKED EXAMPLE | **4.4** Electron Configurations: Octet Rule for Anions

How many electrons must a nitrogen atom, $Z = 7$, gain to attain a noble gas configuration? Write the electron-dot and ion symbols for the ion formed.

ANALYSIS Write the electron configuration of nitrogen, and see how many more electrons are needed to reach a noble gas configuration.

SOLUTION

Nitrogen, a group 5A element, has the electron configuration $1s^2 2s^2 2p^3$. The second shell contains 5 electrons ($2s^2 2p^3$) and needs 3 more to reach an octet. The result is formation of a triply charged anion, N^{3-}, with 8 valence electrons, matching the neon configuration:

$$N^{3-} \qquad 1s^2 2s^2 2p^6 \quad \text{(Neon configuration)} \quad :\overset{..}{\underset{..}{N}}:^{3-}$$

PROBLEM 4.7

Write the electron configuration of potassium, $Z = 19$, and show how a potassium atom can attain a noble gas configuration.

PROBLEM 4.8

How many electrons must an aluminum atom, $Z = 13$, lose to attain a noble gas configuration? Write the symbol for the ion formed.

KEY CONCEPT PROBLEM 4.9

Which atom in the reaction depicted here gains electrons, and which loses electrons? Draw the electron-dot symbols for the resulting ions.

$$X: + \cdot \overset{..}{Y} \cdot \rightarrow \ ?$$

4.6 Ions of Some Common Elements

The periodic table is the key to understanding and remembering which elements form ions and which do not. As shown in Figure 4.4, atoms of elements in the same group tend to form ions of the same charge. The metals of groups 1A and 2A, for example, form only +1 and +2 ions, respectively. The ions of these elements all have noble gas configurations as a result of electron loss from their valence s sub-shells. (Note in the following equations that the electrons being lost are shown as products.)

Group 1A: $M \cdot \rightarrow M^+ + e^-$
              (M = Li, Na, K, Rb, or Cs)

Group 2A: $M: \rightarrow M^{2+} + 2e^-$
              (M = Be, Mg, Ca, Sr, Ba, or Ra)

Four of these ions, Na^+, K^+, Mg^{2+}, and Ca^{2+}, are present in body fluids, where they play extremely important roles in biochemical processes.

The only group 3A element commonly encountered in ionic compounds is aluminum, which forms Al^{3+} by loss of three electrons from its valence s and p sub-shells. Aluminum is not thought to be an essential element in the human diet, although it is known to be present in some organisms.

The first three elements in groups 4A (C, Si, Ge) and 5A (N, P, As) do not ordinarily form cations or anions, because either too much energy is required to remove an electron or not enough energy is released by adding an electron to make the process energetically favorable. The bonding of these elements is largely covalent and will be described in the next chapter. Carbon, in particular, is the key element on which life is based. Together with hydrogen, nitrogen, phosphorus, and oxygen, carbon is present in all the essential biological compounds that we will be describing throughout the latter half of this book.

The group 6A elements oxygen and sulfur form large numbers of compounds, some of which are ionic and some of which are covalent. Their ions have noble gas configurations, achieved by gaining two electrons:

Group 6A: $\cdot \ddot{\text{O}} \cdot \; + \; 2\,e^- \longrightarrow \; :\ddot{\text{O}}:^{2-}$

              $\cdot \ddot{\text{S}} \cdot \; + \; 2\,e^- \longrightarrow \; :\ddot{\text{S}}:^{2-}$

The halogens are present in many compounds as −1 ions, formed by gaining one electron:

Group 7A: $\cdot \ddot{\text{X}}: \; + \; e^- \longrightarrow \; :\ddot{\text{X}}:^-$
              (X = F, Cl, Br, I)

Transition metals lose electrons to form cations, some of which are present in the human body. The charges of transition metal cations are not as predictable as those of main group elements, however, because many transition metal atoms can lose one or more d electrons in addition to losing valence s electrons. For example, iron $(\ldots 3s^2 3p^6 3d^6 4s^2)$ forms Fe^{2+} by losing two electrons from the $4s$ subshell and also forms Fe^{3+} by losing an additional electron from the $3d$ subshell. Looking at the iron configuration shows why the octet rule is limited to main group elements: Transition metal cations generally do not have noble gas configurations because they would have to lose *all* their d electrons.

Important Points about Ion Formation and the Periodic Table:

- Metals form cations by losing one or more electrons.
  - Group 1A and 2A metals form $+1$ and $+2$ ions, respectively (for example, Li^+ and Mg^{2+}) to achieve a noble gas configuration.
  - Transition metals can form cations of more than one charge (for example, Fe^{2+} and Fe^{3+}) by losing a combination of valence-shell s electrons and inner-shell d electrons.
- Reactive nonmetals form anions by gaining one or more electrons to achieve a noble gas configuration.
  - Group 6A nonmetals oxygen and sulfur form the anions O^{2-} and S^{2-}.
  - Group 7A elements (the halogens) form -1 ions; for example, F^- and Cl^-.
- Group 8A elements (the noble gases) are unreactive.
- Ionic charges of main group elements can be predicted using the group number and the octet rule.
  - For 1A and 2A metals, cation charge = group number
  - For nonmetals in groups 5A, 6A, and 7A, anion charge = 8 − (group number)

WORKED EXAMPLE　**4.5** Formation of Ions: Gain/Loss of Valence Electrons

Which of the following ions is likely to form?

　(a) S^{3-}　　　　(b) Si^{2+}　　　　(c) Sr^{2+}

ANALYSIS Count the number of valence electrons in each ion. For main group elements, only ions with a valence octet of electrons are likely to form.

SOLUTION

　(a) Sulfur is in group 6A, has 6 valence electrons, and needs only two more to reach an octet. Gaining two electrons gives an S^{2-} ion with a noble gas configuration, but gaining three electrons does not. The S^{3-} ion is therefore unlikely to form.

　(b) Silicon is a nonmetal in group 4A. Like carbon, it does not form ions because it would have to gain or lose too many (4) electrons to reach a noble gas electron configuration. The Si^{2+} ion does not have an octet and will not form.

　(c) Strontium is a metal in group 2A, has only 2 outer-shell electrons, and can lose both to reach a noble gas configuration. The Sr^{2+} ion has an octet and therefore forms easily.

PROBLEM 4.10

Is molybdenum more likely to form a cation or an anion? Why?

PROBLEM 4.11

Which of the following elements can form more than one cation?

　(a) Strontium　　　　(b) Chromium　　　　(c) Bromine

PROBLEM 4.12

Write symbols, both with and without electron dots, for the ions formed by the following processes:

(a) Gain of two electrons by selenium

(b) Loss of two electrons by barium

(c) Gain of one electron by bromine

APPLICATION ▶ Salt

If you are like most people, you feel a little guilty about reaching for the salt shaker at mealtime. The notion that high salt intake and high blood pressure go hand in hand is surely among the most highly publicized pieces of nutritional lore ever to appear.

Salt has not always been held in such disrepute. Historically, salt has been prized since the earliest recorded times as a seasoning and a food preservative. Words and phrases in many languages reflect the importance of salt as a life-giving and life-sustaining substance. We refer to a kind and generous person as "the salt of the earth," for instance, and we speak of being "worth one's salt." In Roman times, soldiers were paid in salt; the English word "salary" is derived from the Latin word for paying salt wages (*salarium*).

Salt is perhaps the easiest of all minerals to obtain and purify. The simplest method, used for thousands of years throughout the world in coastal climates where sunshine is abundant and rainfall is scarce, is to evaporate seawater. Though the exact amount varies depending on the source, seawater contains an average of about 3.5% by mass of dissolved substances, most of which is sodium chloride. It has been estimated that evaporation of all the world's oceans would yield approximately *4.5 million cubic miles* of NaCl.

Only about 10% of current world salt production comes from evaporation of seawater. Most salt is obtained by mining the vast deposits of *halite*, or *rock salt*, formed by evaporation of ancient inland seas. These salt beds vary in thickness up to hundreds of meters and vary in depth from a few meters to thousands of meters below the earth's surface. Salt mining has gone on for at least 3400 years, and the Wieliczka mine in Galicia, Poland, has been worked continuously from A.D. 1000 to the present.

Now, back to the dinner table. What about the link between dietary salt intake and high blood pressure? There is no doubt that most people in industrialized nations have a relatively high salt intake, and also that high blood pressure among industrialized populations is on the rise. How closely, though, are the two observations related?

In a study called the DASH-Sodium study published in 2001, a strong correlation was found between a change in salt intake and a change in blood pressure. When volunteers cut back their salt intake from 8.3 g per day—roughly what Americans typically consume—to 3.8 g per day, significant

▲ In many areas of the world salt is still harvested by evaporation of ocean or tidal waters.

drops in blood pressure were found. The largest reduction in blood pressure was seen in people already diagnosed with hypertension, but subjects with normal blood pressure also lowered their readings by several percent.

What should an individual do? The best answer, as in so many things, is to use moderation and common sense. People with hypertension should make a strong effort to lower their sodium intake; others might be well advised to choose unsalted snacks, use less salt in preparing food, and read nutrition labels for sodium content.

See Additional Problems 4.83 and 4.84 at the end of this chapter.

4.7 Naming Ions

Main group metal cations in groups 1A, 2A, and 3A are named by identifying the metal, followed by the word "ion," as in the following examples:

$$K^+ \qquad\qquad Mg^{2+} \qquad\qquad Al^{3+}$$

Potassium ion   Magnesium ion   Aluminum ion

It is sometimes a little confusing to use the same name for both a metal and its ion, and you may occasionally have to stop and think about what is meant. For example, it is common practice in nutrition and health-related fields to talk about sodium or potassium in the bloodstream. Because both sodium and potassium *metals* react violently with water, however, they cannot possibly be present in blood. The references are to dissolved sodium and potassium *ions*.

For transition metals, such as iron or chromium, which can form more than one type of cation, a method is needed to differentiate these ions. Two systems are used. The first is an old system that gives the ion with the smaller charge the word ending -*ous* and the ion with the larger charge the ending -*ic*.

The second is a newer system in which the charge on the ion is given as a Roman numeral in parentheses right after the metal name. For example:

$$Cr^{2+} \qquad\qquad Cr^{3+}$$

Old name:	Chrom*ous* ion	Chrom*ic* ion
New name:	Chromium(II) ion	Chromium(III) ion

We will generally emphasize the new system in this book, but it is important to understand both because the old system is often found on labels of commercially supplied chemicals. The small differences between the names in either system illustrate the importance of reading a name very carefully before using a chemical. There are significant differences between compounds consisting of the same two elements but having different charges on the cation. In treating iron-deficiency anemia, for example, iron(II) compounds are preferable because the body absorbs them considerably better than iron(III) compounds.

The names of some common transition metal cations are listed in Table 4.1. Notice that the old names of the copper, iron, and tin ions are derived from their Latin names (*cuprum*, *ferrum*, and *stannum*).

Anions are named by replacing the ending of the element name with -*ide*, followed by the word "ion" (Table 4.2). For example, the anion formed by fluor*ine* is the fluor*ide* ion, and the anion formed by sul*fur* is the sul*fide* ion.

TABLE 4.1   Names of Some Transition Metal Cations

ELEMENT	SYMBOL	OLD NAME	NEW NAME
Chromium	Cr^{2+}	Chromous	Chromium(II)
	Cr^{3+}	Chromic	Chromium(III)
Copper	Cu^+	Cuprous	Copper(I)
	Cu^{2+}	Cupric	Copper(II)
Iron	Fe^{2+}	Ferrous	Iron(II)
	Fe^{3+}	Ferric	Iron(III)
Mercury	$*Hg_2^{2+}$	Mercurous	Mercury(I)
	Hg^{2+}	Mercuric	Mercury(II)
Tin	Sn^{2+}	Stannous	Tin(II)
	Sn^{4+}	Stannic	Tin(IV)

*This cation is composed of two mercury atoms, each of which has an average charge of +1.

TABLE 4.2   Names of Some Common Anions

ELEMENT	SYMBOL	NAME
Bromine	Br^-	Bromide ion
Chlorine	Cl^-	Chloride ion
Fluorine	F^-	Fluoride ion
Iodine	I^-	Iodide ion
Oxygen	O^{2-}	Oxide ion
Sulfur	S^{2-}	Sulfide ion

PROBLEM 4.13

Name the following ions:

(a) Cu^{2+} (b) F^- (c) Mg^{2+} (d) S^{2-}

PROBLEM 4.14

Write the symbols for the following ions:

(a) Silver(I) ion   (b) Iron(II) ion   (c) Cuprous ion   (d) Telluride ion

PROBLEM 4.15

Ringer's solution, which is used intravenously to adjust ion concentrations in body fluids, contains the ions of sodium, potassium, calcium, and chlorine. Give the names and symbols of these ions.

4.8 Polyatomic Ions

Ions that are composed of more than one atom are called **polyatomic ions**. Most polyatomic ions contain oxygen and another element, and their chemical formulas show by subscripts how many of each type of atom are combined. Sulfate ion, for example, is composed of one sulfur atom and four oxygen atoms, and has a -2 charge: SO_4^{2-}. The atoms in a polyatomic ion are held together by covalent bonds, of the sort discussed in the next chapter, and the entire group of atoms acts as a single unit. A polyatomic ion is charged because it contains a total number of electrons different from the total number of protons in the combined atoms.

The most common polyatomic ions are listed in Table 4.3. Note that the ammonium ion, NH_4^+, and the hydronium ion, H_3O^+, are the only cations; all the others

Polyatomic ion An ion that is composed of more than one atom.

TABLE 4.3   Some Common Polyatomic Ions

NAME	FORMULA	NAME	FORMULA
Hydronium ion	H_3O^+	Nitrate ion	NO_3^-
Ammonium ion	NH_4^+	Nitrite ion	NO_2^-
Acetate ion	$CH_3CO_2^-$	Oxalate ion	$C_2O_4^{2-}$
Carbonate ion	CO_3^{2-}	Permanganate ion	MnO_4^-
Hydrogen carbonate ion (bicarbonate ion)	HCO_3^-	Phosphate ion	PO_4^{3-}
		Hydrogen phosphate ion	HPO_4^{2-}
Chromate ion	CrO_4^{2-}	Dihydrogen phosphate ion	$H_2PO_4^-$
Dichromate ion	$Cr_2O_7^{2-}$	Sulfate ion	SO_4^{2-}
Cyanide ion	CN^-	Hydrogen sulfate ion (bisulfate ion)	HSO_4^-
Hydroxide ion	OH^-		
Hypochlorite ion	OCl^-	Sulfite ion	SO_3^{2-}

▲ The brilliant blue mineral chalcanthite consists of the hydrated ionic compound copper sulfate, $CuSO_4$ $5H_2O$.

APPLICATION ▶ Biologically Important Ions

The human body requires many different ions for proper functioning. Several of these ions, such as Ca^{2+}, Mg^{2+}, and HPO_4^{2-}, are used as structural materials in bones and teeth in addition to having other essential functions. Although 99% of Ca^{2+} is contained in bones and teeth, small amounts in body fluids play a vital role in transmission of nerve impulses. Other ions, including essential transition metal ions such as Fe^{2+}, are required for specific chemical reactions in the body. And still others, such as K^+, Na^+, and Cl^-, are present in fluids throughout the body.

Solutions containing ions must have overall neutrality, and several polyatomic anions, especially HCO_3^- and HPO_4^{2-}, are present in body fluids where they help balance the cation charges. Some of the most important ions and their functions are shown in the accompanying table.

See Additional Problems 4.85, 4.86, and 4.87 at the end of the chapter.

Some Biologically Important Ions

ION	LOCATION	FUNCTION	DIETARY SOURCE
Ca^{2+}	Outside cell; 99% of Ca^{2+} is in bones and teeth as $Ca_3(PO_4)_2$ and $CaCO_3$	Bone and tooth structure; necessary for blood clotting, muscle contraction, and transmission of nerve impulses	Milk, whole grains, leafy vegetables
Fe^{2+}	Blood hemoglobin	Transports oxygen from lungs to cells	Liver, red meat, leafy green vegetables
K^+	Fluids inside cells	Maintain ion concentrations in cells; regulate insulin release and heartbeat	Milk, oranges, bananas, meat
Na^+	Fluids outside cells	Protect against fluid loss; necessary for muscle contraction and transmission of nerve impulses	Table salt, seafood
Mg^{2+}	Fluids inside cells; bone	Present in many enzymes; needed for energy generation and muscle contraction	Leafy green plants, seafood, nuts
Cl^-	Fluids outside cells; gastric juice	Maintain fluid balance in cells; help transfer CO_2 from blood to lungs	Table salt, seafood
HCO_3^-	Fluids outside cells	Control acid–base balance in blood	By-product of food metabolism
HPO_4^{2-}	Fluids inside cells; bones and teeth	Control acid–base balance in cells	Fish, poultry, milk

are anions. These ions are encountered so frequently in chemistry, biology, and medicine that there is no alternative but to memorize their names and formulas. Fortunately, there are only a few of them.

Note in Table 4.3 that several pairs of ions— CO_3^{2-} and HCO_3^-, for example— are related by the presence or absence of a hydrogen ion, H^+. In such instances, the ion with the hydrogen is sometimes named using the prefix *bi-*. Thus, CO_3^{2-} is the carbonate ion and HCO_3^- is the bicarbonate ion; similarly, SO_4^{2-} is the sulfate ion and HSO_4^- is the bisulfate ion.

PROBLEM 4.16

Name the following ions:

(a) NO_3^- **(b)** CN^- **(c)** OH^- **(d)** HPO_4^{2-}

PROBLEM 4.17

Write the formulas of the following ions:

(a) Bicarbonate ion
(b) Ammonium ion
(c) Phosphate ion
(d) Permanganate ion

4.9 Formulas of Ionic Compounds

Since all chemical compounds are neutral, it is relatively easy to figure out the formulas of ionic compounds. Once the ions are identified, all we need to do is decide how many ions of each type give a total charge of zero. Thus, the chemical formula of an ionic compound tells the ratio of anions and cations.

If the ions have the same charge, only one of each ion is needed:

$$K^+ \quad \text{and} \quad F^- \quad \text{form} \quad KF$$
$$Ca^{2+} \quad \text{and} \quad O^{2-} \quad \text{form} \quad CaO$$

This makes sense when we look at how many electrons must be gained or lost by each atom in order to satisfy the octet rule:

$$K\cdot \; + \; \cdot\ddot{\underset{..}{F}}\text{:} \; \rightarrow \; K^+ \; + \; \text{:}\ddot{\underset{..}{F}}\text{:}^-$$
$$Ca\text{:} \; + \; \cdot\ddot{\underset{..}{O}}\cdot \; \rightarrow \; Ca^{2+} \; + \; \text{:}\ddot{\underset{..}{O}}\text{:}^{2-}$$

If the ions have different charges, however, unequal numbers of anions and cations must combine in order to have a net charge of zero. When potassium and oxygen combine, for example, it takes two K^+ ions to balance the -2 charge of the O^{2-} ion. Put another way, it takes two K atoms to provide the two electrons needed in order to complete the octet for the O atom:

$$2\,K\cdot \; + \; \cdot\ddot{\underset{..}{O}}\cdot \; \rightarrow \; 2\,K^+ \; + \; \text{:}\ddot{\underset{..}{O}}\text{:}^{2-}$$
$$2\,K^+ \quad \text{and} \quad O^{2-} \quad \text{form} \quad K_2O$$

The situation is reversed when a Ca^{2+} ion reacts with a Cl^- ion. One Ca atom can provide two electrons; each Cl atom requires only one electron to achieve a complete octet. Thus, there is one Ca^{2+} cation for every two Cl^- anions:

$$Ca\text{:} \; + \; 2\cdot\ddot{\underset{..}{Cl}}\text{:} \; \rightarrow \; Ca^{2+} \; + \; 2\;\text{:}\ddot{\underset{..}{Cl}}\text{:}^-$$
$$Ca^{2+} \quad \text{and} \quad 2\,Cl^- \quad \text{form} \quad CaCl_2$$

It sometimes helps when writing the formulas for an ionic compound to remember that, when the two ions have different charges, the number of one ion is equal to the charge on the other ion. In magnesium phosphate, for example, the charge on the magnesium ion is $+2$ and the charge on the polyatomic phosphate ion is -3. Thus, there must be 3 magnesium ions with a total charge of $3 \times (+2) = +6$ and 2 phosphate ions with a total charge of $2 \times (-3) = -6$ for overall neutrality:

The charge on this ion (-3) $PO_4{}^{3-}$ Mg^{2+} The charge on this ion ($+2$)

is the same as the $Mg_3(PO_4)_2$ is the same as the
number of the other ion (3).   number of the other ion (2).

Magnesium phosphate

The formula of an ionic compound shows the lowest possible ratio of atoms in the compound and is thus known as a *simplest formula*. Because there is no such

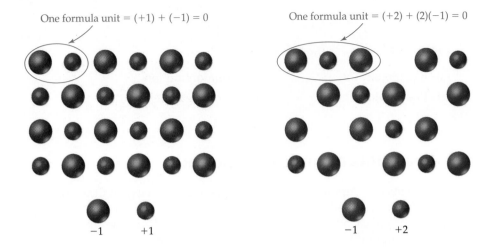

One formula unit = (+1) + (−1) = 0   One formula unit = (+2) + (2)(−1) = 0

−1   +1   −1   +2

► **FIGURE 4.5 Formula units of ionic compounds.** The sum of charges on the ions in a formula unit equals zero.

Formula unit The formula that identifies the smallest neutral unit of an ionic compound.

thing as a single neutral *particle* of an ionic compound, however, we use the term **formula unit** to identify the smallest possible neutral *unit* (Figure 4.5). For NaCl, the formula unit is one Na^+ ion and one Cl^- ion; for K_2SO_4, the formula unit is two K^+ ions and one SO_4^{2-} ion; for CaF_2, the formula unit is one Ca^{2+} ion and two F^- ions; and so on.

Once the numbers and kinds of ions in a compound are known, the formula is written using the following rules:

- List the cation first and the anion second; for example, NaCl rather than ClNa.
- Do not write the charges of the ions; for example, KF rather than K^+F^-.
- Use parentheses around a polyatomic ion formula if it has a subscript; for example, $Al_2(SO_4)_3$ rather than Al_2SO_{43}.

WORKED EXAMPLE **4.6** Ionic Compounds: Writing Formulas

Write the formula for the compound formed by calcium ions and nitrate ions.

ANALYSIS Knowing the formula and charges on the cation and anion (Table 4.4), we determine how many of each are needed to yield a neutral formula for the ionic compound.

SOLUTION
The two ions are Ca^{2+} and NO_3^-. Two nitrate ions, each with a −1 charge, will balance the +2 charge of the calcium ion.

Ca^{2+} Charge = 1 × (+2) = +2
$2 NO_3^-$ Charge = 2 × (−1) = −2

Since there are two nitrate ions, the nitrate formula must be enclosed in parentheses:

$Ca(NO_3)_2$ Calcium nitrate

PROBLEM 4.18

Write the formulas for the ionic compounds that silver(I) forms with each of the following:

(a) Iodide ion

(b) Oxide ion

(c) Phosphate ion

PROBLEM 4.19

Write the formulas for the ionic compounds that sulfate ion forms with the following:

(a) Sodium ion   **(b)** Iron(II) ion   **(c)** Chromium(III) ion

PROBLEM 4.20

The ionic compound containing ammonium ion and carbonate ion gives off the odor of ammonia, a property put to use in smelling salts for reviving someone who has fainted. Write the formula for this compound.

PROBLEM 4.21

An *astringent* is a compound that causes proteins in blood, sweat, and other body fluids to coagulate, a property put to use in deodorants. Two safe and effective astringents are the ionic compounds of aluminum with sulfate ion and with acetate ion. Write the formulas of both.

KEY CONCEPT PROBLEM 4.22

Three ionic compounds are represented on this periodic table—red cation with red anion, blue cation with blue anion, and green cation with green anion. Give a likely formula for each compound.

KEY CONCEPT PROBLEM 4.23

The ionic compound calcium nitride is represented here. What is the formula for calcium nitride, and what are the charges on the calcium and nitride ions?

4.10 Naming Ionic Compounds

Just as in writing formulas for ionic compounds, these compounds are named by citing first the cation and then the anion, with a space between words. There are two kinds of ionic compounds, and the rules for naming them are slightly different.

Type I: Ionic compounds containing cations of main group elements (1A, 2A, aluminum). Since the charges on these cations do not vary, we do not need to specify the charge on the cation as discussed in Section 4.7.

Type II: Ionic compounds containing metals that can exhibit more than one charge. Since some metals, including the transition metals, often form more than one ion, we need to specify the charge on the cation in these compounds. Either the old (-ous, -ic) or the new (Roman numerals) system described in Section 4.7 can be used. Thus, $FeCl_2$ is called iron(II) chloride (or ferrous chloride), and $FeCl_3$ is called iron(III) chloride (or ferric chloride). Note that we do *not* name these compounds iron *di*chloride or iron *tri*chloride—once the charge on the metal is known, the number of anions needed to yield a neutral compound is also known and does not need to be included as part of the compound name. Ions of elements that form only one type of ion, such as Na^+ and Ca^{2+}, do not need Roman numerals. Table 4.4 lists some common ionic compounds and their uses.

Looking Ahead

Because the formula unit for an ionic compound must be neutral, we can unambiguously write the formula from the name of the compound, and vice versa. As we shall see in Chapter 5, covalent bonding between atoms can produce a much greater variety of compounds. The rules for naming covalent compounds must be able to accommodate multiple combinations of elements (for example, CO and CO_2).

TABLE 4.4 Some Common Ionic Compounds and Their Applications

CHEMICAL NAME (COMMON NAME)	FORMULA	APPLICATIONS
Ammonium carbonate	$(NH_4)_2CO_3$	Smelling salts
Calcium hydroxide (hydrated lime)	$Ca(OH)_2$	Mortar, plaster, whitewash
Calcium oxide (lime)	CaO	Lawn treatment, industrial chemical
Lithium carbonate ("lithium")	Li_2CO_3	Treatment of manic depression
Magnesium hydroxide (milk of magnesia)	$Mg(OH)_2$	Antacid
Magnesium sulfate (Epsom salts)	$MgSO_4$	Laxative, anticonvulsant
Potassium permanganate	$KMnO_4$	Antiseptic, disinfectant*
Potassium nitrate (saltpeter)	KNO_3	Fireworks, matches, and desensitizer for teeth
Silver nitrate	$AgNO_3$	Antiseptic, germicide
Sodium bicarbonate (baking soda)	$NaHCO_3$	Baking powder, antacid, mouthwash, deodorizer
Sodium hypochlorite	$NaOCl$	Disinfectant; active ingredient in household bleach
Zinc oxide	ZnO	Skin protection, in calamine lotion

*An antiseptic kills or inhibits growth of harmful microorganisms on the skin or in the body; a disinfectant kills harmful microorganisms but is generally not used on living tissue.

WORKED EXAMPLE **4.7** Ionic Compounds: Formulas Involving Polyatomic Ions

Magnesium carbonate is used as an ingredient in Bufferin tablets. Write its formula.

ANALYSIS Since magnesium is a main group metal, we can determine its ionic compound formula by identifying the charges and formulas for the anion and the cation, remembering that the overall formula must be neutral.

SOLUTION
Look at the cation and the anion parts of the name separately. Magnesium, a group 2A element, forms the doubly positive Mg^{2+} cation; carbonate anion is doubly negative, CO_3^{2-}. Because the charges on the anion and cation are equal, a formula of $MgCO_3$ will be neutral.

WORKED EXAMPLE **4.8** Ionic Compounds: Formulas and Ionic Charges

Sodium and calcium both form a wide variety of ionic compounds. Write formulas for the following compounds:

    (a) Sodium bromide and calcium bromide

    (b) Sodium sulfide and calcium sulfide

    (c) Sodium phosphate and calcium phosphate

ANALYSIS Using the formulas and charges for the cations and the anions (from Tables 4.2 and 4.3) we determine how many of each cation and anion are needed to yield a formula that is neutral.

SOLUTION

    (a) Cations = Na^+ and Ca^{2+}; anion = Br^-: $NaBr$ and $CaBr_2$

    (b) Cations = Na^+ and Ca^{2+}; anion = S^{2-}: Na_2S and CaS

    (c) Cations = Na^+ and Ca^{2+}; anion = PO_4^{3-}: Na_3PO_4 and $Ca_3(PO_4)_2$

WORKED EXAMPLE **4.9** Naming Ionic Compounds

Name the following compounds, using Roman numerals to indicate the charges on the cations where necessary:

    (a) KF   **(b)** $MgCl_2$ **(c)** $AuCl_3$ **(d)** Fe_2O_3

ANALYSIS For main group metals, the charge is determined from the group number and no Roman numerals are necessary. For transition metals, the charge on the metal can be determined from the total charge(s) on the anion(s).

SOLUTION

    (a) Potassium fluoride. No Roman numeral is necessary because a group 1A metal forms only one cation.

    (b) Magnesium chloride. No Roman numeral is necessary because magnesium (group 2A) forms only Mg^{2+}.

    (c) Gold(III) chloride. The three Cl^- ions require a +3 charge on the gold for a neutral formula. Since gold is a transition metal that can form other ions, the Roman numeral is necessary to specify the +3 charge.

    (d) Iron(III) oxide. Because the three oxide anions (O^{2-}) have a total negative charge of −6, the two iron cations must have a total charge of +6. Thus, each is Fe^{3+}, and the charge on each is indicated by the Roman numeral (III).

PROBLEM 4.24

Barium sulfate is an ionic compound swallowed by patients before having an X-ray of their gastrointestinal tract. Write its formula.

PROBLEM 4.25

The compound Ag_2S is responsible for much of the tarnish found on silverware. Name this compound, and give the charge on the silver ion.

▲ A barium sulfate "cocktail" is given to patients prior to an X-ray to help make the gastrointestinal tract visible on the film.

PROBLEM 4.26

Name the following compounds:

(a) SnO_2 (b) $Ca(CN)_2$ (c) Na_2CO_3

(d) Cu_2SO_4 (e) $Ba(OH)_2$ (f) $Fe(NO_3)_2$

PROBLEM 4.27

Write formulas for the following compounds:

(a) Lithium phosphate

(b) Copper(II) carbonate

(c) Aluminum sulfite

(d) Cuprous fluoride

(e) Ferric sulfate

(f) Ammonium chloride

KEY CONCEPT PROBLEM 4.28

The ionic compound formed between chromium and oxygen is shown here. Name the compound and write its formula.

4.11 H^+ and OH^- Ions: An Introduction to Acids and Bases

Two of the most important ions we will be discussing in the remainder of this book are the hydrogen cation (H^+) and the hydroxide anion (OH^-). Since a hydrogen *atom* contains one proton and one electron, a hydrogen *cation* is simply a proton. When an acid dissolves in water, the proton typically attaches to a molecule of water to form the hydronium ion (H_3O^+), but chemists routinely use the H^+ and H_3O^+ ions interchangeably. A hydroxide anion, by contrast, is a polyatomic ion in which an oxygen atom is covalently bonded to a hydrogen atom. Although much of Chapter 10 is devoted to the chemistry of H^+ and OH^- ions, it is worth taking a preliminary look now.

The importance of the H^+ cation and the OH^- anion is that they are fundamental to the concepts of *acids* and *bases*. In fact, one definition of an **acid** is a substance

that provides H⁺ ions when dissolved in water, and one definition of a **base** is a substance that provides OH⁻ ions when dissolved in water.

Acid   A substance that provides H⁺ ions in water; for example, HCl, HNO_3, H_2SO_4, H_3PO_4

Base   A substance that provides OH⁻ ions in water; for example, NaOH, KOH, $Ba(OH)_2$

Hydrochloric acid (HCl), nitric acid (HNO_3), sulfuric acid (H_2SO_4), and phosphoric acid (H_3PO_4) are among the most common acids. When any of these substances is dissolved in water, H⁺ ions are formed along with the corresponding anion (Table 4.5).

TABLE 4.5   Some Common Acids and Ions Derived from Them

ACIDS		IONS	
Acetic acid	CH_3COOH	Acetate ion	*CH_3COO^-
Carbonic acid	H_2CO_3	Hydrogen carbonate ion (bicarbonate ion)	HCO_3^-
		Carbonate ion	CO_3^{2-}
Hydrochloric acid	HCl	Chloride ion	Cl^-
Nitric acid	HNO_3	Nitrate ion	NO_3^-
Nitrous acid	HNO_2	Nitrite ion	NO_2^-
Phosphoric acid	H_3PO_4	Dihydrogen phosphate ion	$H_2PO_4^-$
		Hydrogen phosphate ion	HPO_4^{2-}
		Phosphate ion	PO_4^{3-}
Sulfuric acid	H_2SO_4	Hydrogen sulfate ion	HSO_4^-
		Sulfate ion	SO_4^{2-}

*Sometimes written $C_2H_3O_2^-$ or as $CH_3CO_2^-$.

Different acids can provide different numbers of H⁺ ions per acid molecule. Hydrochloric acid, for instance, provides one H⁺ ion per acid molecule; sulfuric acid can provide two H⁺ ions per acid molecule; and phosphoric acid can provide three H⁺ ions per acid molecule.

Sodium hydroxide (NaOH; also known as *lye* or *caustic soda*), potassium hydroxide (KOH; also known as *caustic potash*), and barium hydroxide [$Ba(OH)_2$] are examples of bases. When any of these compounds dissolves in water, OH⁻ anions go into solution along with the corresponding metal cation. Sodium hydroxide and potassium hydroxide provide one OH⁻ ion per formula unit; barium hydroxide provides two OH⁻ ions per formula unit, as indicated by its formula, $Ba(OH)_2$.

PROBLEM 4.29

Which of the following compounds are acids, and which are bases? Explain.

(a) HF

(b) $Ca(OH)_2$

(c) LiOH

(d) HCN

⚬ KEY CONCEPT PROBLEM 4.30

One of these pictures represents a solution of HCl, and one represents a solution of H_2SO_4. Which is which?

(a)

(b)

APPLICATION ▶ Osteoporosis

Bone consists primarily of two components, one mineral and one organic. About 70% of bone is the ionic compound *hydroxyapatite*, $Ca_{10}(PO_4)_6(OH)_2$, called the *trabecular*, or spongy, bone. This mineral component is intermingled in a complex matrix with about 30% by mass of fibers of the protein *collagen*, called the *cortical*, or compact, bone. Hydroxyapatite gives bone its hardness and strength, whereas collagen fibers add flexibility and resistance to breaking.

Total bone mass in the body increases from birth until reaching a maximum in the mid 30s. By the early 40s, however, an age-related decline in bone mass begins to occur in both sexes. Should this thinning of bones become too great and the bones become too porous and brittle, a clinical condition called *osteoporosis* can result. Osteoporosis is, in fact, the most common of all bone diseases, affecting approximately 25 million people in the United States. Approximately 1.5 million bone fractures each year are caused by osteoporosis at an estimated health-care cost of $14 billion.

Although both sexes are affected by osteoporosis, the condition is particularly common in postmenopausal women, who undergo cortical bone loss at a rate of 2–3% per year over and above that of the normal age-related loss. The cumulative lifetime bone loss, in fact, may approach 40–50% in women versus 20–30% in men. It has been estimated that half of all women over age 50 will have an osteoporosis-related bone fracture at some point in their life. Other risk factors in addition to sex include being thin, being sedentary, having a family history of osteoporosis, smoking, and having a diet low in calcium.

No cure yet exists for osteoporosis, but treatment for its prevention and management includes estrogen replacement therapy for postmenopausal women as well as several approved medications called *bisphosphonates* to prevent further bone loss. Calcium supplements are also recommended, as is appropriate weight-bearing exercise. In addition, treatment with sodium fluoride is under active investigation and shows considerable promise. Fluoride ion reacts with hydroxyapatite to give *fluorapatite*, in which OH^- ions are replaced by F^-, increasing both bone strength and density.

$$Ca_{10}(PO_4)_6(OH)_2 + 2\ F^- \longrightarrow Ca_{10}(PO_4)_6F_2$$

Hydroxyapatite Fluorapatite

See Additional Problems 4.88 and 4.89 at the end of the chapter.

▲ Normal bone is strong and dense; a bone affected by osteoporosis is weak and spongy in appearance.

SUMMARY: REVISITING THE CHAPTER GOALS

1. **What is an ion, what is an ionic bond, and what are the general characteristics of ionic compounds?** Atoms are converted into *cations* by the loss of one or more electrons and into *anions* by the gain of one or more electrons. Ionic compounds are composed of cations and anions held together by *ionic bonds*, which result from the attraction between opposite electrical charges. Ionic compounds conduct electricity when dissolved in water, and they are generally crystalline solids with high melting points and high boiling points.

2. **What is the octet rule, and how does it apply to ions?** A valence-shell electron configuration of 8 electrons in filled *s* and *p* subshells leads to stability and lack of reactivity, as typified by the noble gases in group 8A. According to the *octet rule*, atoms of main group elements tend to form ions in which they have gained or lost the appropriate number of electrons to reach a noble gas configuration.

3. **What is the relationship between an element's position in the periodic table and the formation of its ion?** Periodic variations in *ionization energy*, the amount of energy that must be supplied to remove an electron from an atom, show that metals lose electrons more easily than nonmetals. As a result, metals usually form cations. Similar periodic variations in *electron affinity*, the amount of energy released on adding an electron to an atom, show that reactive nonmetals gain electrons more easily than metals. As a result, reactive nonmetals usually form anions. The ionic charge can be predicted from the group number and the octet rule. For main group metals, the charge on the cation is equal to the group number. For nonmetals, the charge on the anion is equal to 8 − (group number).

4. **What determines the chemical formula of an ionic compound?** Ionic compounds contain appropriate numbers of anions and cations to maintain overall neutrality, thereby providing a means of determining their chemical formulas.

5. **How are ionic compounds named?** Cations have the same name as the metal from which they are derived. Monatomic anions have the name ending *-ide*. For metals that form more than one ion, a Roman numeral equal to the charge on the ion is added to the name of the cation. Alternatively, the ending *-ous* is added to the name of the cation with the lesser charge and the ending *-ic* is added to the name of the cation with the greater charge. To name an ionic compound, the cation name is given first, with the charge of the metal ion indicated if necessary, and the anion name is given second.

6. **What are acids and bases?** The hydrogen ion (H^+) and the hydroxide ion (OH^-) are among the most important ions in chemistry because they are fundamental to the idea of acids and bases. According to one common definition, an *acid* is a substance that yields H^+ ions when dissolved in water, and a *base* is a substance that yields OH^- ions when dissolved in water.

KEY WORDS

Acid, *p. 99*

Anion, *p. 80*

Base, *p. 99*

Cation, *p. 80*

Electron affinity, *p. 81*

Formula unit, *p. 94*

Ion, *p. 80*

Ionic bond, *p. 83*

Ionic compound, *p. 83*

Ionic solid, *p. 83*

Ionization energy, *p. 81*

Octet rule, *p. 85*

Polyatomic ion, *p. 91*

UNDERSTANDING KEY CONCEPTS

4.31 Where on the blank outline of the periodic table are the following elements found?

(a) Elements that commonly form only one type of cation

(b) Elements that commonly form anions

(c) Elements that can form more than one type of cation

(d) Elements that do not readily form either anions or cations

4.32 Where on the blank outline of the periodic table are the following elements found?

(a) Elements that commonly form +2 ions

(b) Elements that commonly form −2 ions

(c) An element that forms a +3 ion

4.33 Which of these drawings represents a Ca atom, which an Na$^+$ ion, and which an O^{2-} ion?

4.34 One of these drawings represents an Na atom, and one represents an Na$^+$ ion. Tell which is which, and explain why there is a difference in size.

4.35 One of these drawings represents a Cl atom, and one represents a Cl$^-$ ion. Tell which is which, and explain why there is a difference in size.

4.36 Three ionic compounds are represented in this outline of the periodic table—red cation with red anion, blue cation with blue anion, and green cation with green anion. Give a likely formula for each compound, and tell the name of each.

4.37 Each of these drawings (a)–(d) represents one of the following ionic compounds: PbBr$_2$, ZnS, CrF$_3$, Al$_2$O$_3$. Which is which?

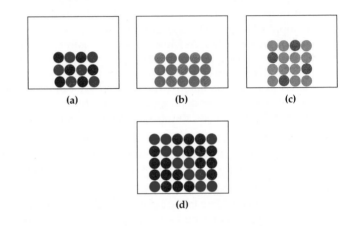

ADDITIONAL PROBLEMS

IONS AND IONIC BONDING

4.38 Write electron-dot symbols for the following atoms:

(a) Beryllium
(b) Neon
(c) Strontium
(d) Aluminum

4.39 Write electron-dot symbols for the following atoms:

(a) Nitrogen
(b) Selenium
(c) Iodine
(d) Strontium

4.40 Write equations for loss or gain of electrons by atoms that result in formation of the following ions from the corresponding atoms:

(a) Ca^{2+}
(b) Au$^+$
(c) F$^-$
(d) Cr^{3+}

4.41 Write symbols for the ions formed by the following:

(a) Gain of 3 electrons by phosphorus
(b) Loss of 1 electron by lithium
(c) Loss of 2 electrons by cobalt
(d) Loss of 3 electrons by thallium

4.42 Tell whether each statement about ions is true or false:

(a) A cation is formed by addition of one or more electrons to an atom.
(b) Group 4A elements tend to lose 4 electrons to yield ions with a +4 charge.
(c) Group 4A elements tend to gain 4 electrons to yield ions with a −4 charge.
(d) The individual atoms in a polyatomic ion are held together by covalent bonds.

4.43 Tell whether each statement about ionic solids is true or false:

(a) Ions are randomly arranged in ionic solids.
(b) All ions are the same size in ionic solids.
(c) Ionic solids can often be shattered by a sharp blow.
(d) Ionic solids have low boiling points.

IONS AND THE OCTET RULE

4.44 What is the *octet rule*?

4.45 Why do H and He not obey the octet rule?

4.46 What is the charge of an ion that contains 34 protons and 36 electrons?

4.47 What is the charge of an ion that contains 20 protons and 18 electrons?

4.48 Identify the element X in the following ions, and tell which noble gas has the same electron configuration.

(a) X^{2+}, a cation with 36 electrons

(b) X^-, an anion with 36 electrons

4.49 Element Z forms an ion Z^{3+}, which contains 31 protons. What is the identity of Z, and how many electrons does Z^{3+} have?

4.50 Write the electron configuration for the following ions:

(a) Rb^+

(b) Br^-

(c) S^{2-}

(d) Ba^{2+}

(e) Al^{3+}

4.51 The following ions have a noble gas configuration. Identify the noble gas.

(a) Ca^{2+}

(b) Li^+

(c) O^{2-}

(d) F^-

(e) Mg^{2+}

PERIODIC PROPERTIES AND ION FORMATION

4.52 Looking only at the periodic table, tell which member of each pair of atoms has the larger ionization energy and thus loses an electron less easily:

(a) Li and O

(b) Li and Cs

(c) K and Zn

(d) Mg and N

4.53 Looking only at the periodic table, tell which member of each pair of atoms has the larger electron affinity and thus gains an electron more easily:

(a) Li and S

(b) Ba and I

(c) Ca and Br

4.54 Which of the following ions are likely to form? Explain.

(a) Li^{2+}

(b) K^-

(c) Mn^{3+}

(d) Zn^{4+}

(e) Ne^+

4.55 Which of the following elements are likely to form more than one cation?

(a) Magnesium

(b) Silicon

(c) Manganese

4.56 Write the electron configurations of Cr^{2+} and Cr^{3+}.

4.57 Write the electron configurations of Co, Co^{2+}, and Co^{3+}.

4.58 Would you expect the ionization energy of Li^+ to be less than, greater than, or the same as the ionization energy of Li? Explain.

4.59 (a) Write equations for the loss of an electron by a K atom and the gain of an electron by a K^+ ion.

(b) What is the relationship between the equations?

(c) What is the relationship between the ionization energy of a K atom and the electron affinity of a K^+ ion?

SYMBOLS, FORMULAS, AND NAMES FOR IONS

4.60 Name the following ions:

(a) S^{2-}

(b) Sn^{2+}

(c) Sr^{2+}

(d) Mg^{2+}

(e) Au^+

4.61 Name the following ions in both the old and the new systems:

(a) Cu^{2+}

(b) Fe^{2+}

(c) Hg_2^{2+}

4.62 Write symbols for the following ions:

(a) Selenide ion

(b) Oxide ion

(c) Silver(I) ion

4.63 Write symbols for the following ions:

(a) Ferric ion

(b) Cobalt(II) ion

(c) Lead (IV) ion

4.64 Write formulas for the following ions:

(a) Hydroxide ion

(b) Bisulfate ion

(c) Acetate ion

(d) Permanganate ion

(e) Hypochlorite ion

(f) Nitrate ion

(g) Carbonate ion

(h) Dichromate ion

4.65 Name the following ions:

(a) SO_3^{2-}

(b) CN^-

(c) H_3O^+

(d) $PO_4{}^{3-}$

NAMES AND FORMULAS FOR IONIC COMPOUNDS

4.66 Write formulas for the compounds formed by the sulfate ion with the following cations:

(a) Aluminum

(b) Silver(I)

(c) Zinc

(d) Barium

4.67 Write formulas for the compounds formed by the carbonate ion with the following cations:

(a) Strontium

(b) Fe(III)

(c) Ammonium

(d) Sn(IV)

4.68 Write the formula for the following substances:

(a) Sodium bicarbonate (baking soda)

(b) Potassium nitrate (a backache remedy)

(c) Calcium carbonate (an antacid)

(d) Ammonium nitrate (first aid cold packs)

4.69 Write the formula for the following compounds:

(a) Calcium hypochlorite, used as a swimming pool disinfectant

(b) Copper(II) sulfate, used to kill algae in swimming pools

(c) Sodium phosphate, used in detergents to enhance cleaning action

4.70 Complete the table by writing in the formula of the compound formed by each pair of ions:

	S^{2-}	Cl^-	$PO_4{}^{3-}$	$CO_3{}^{2-}$
Copper(II)	CuS			
Ca^{2+}				
$NH_4{}^+$				
Ferric ion				

4.71 Complete the table by writing in the formula of the compound formed by each pair of ions:

	O^{2-}	$HSO_4{}^-$	$HPO_4{}^{2-}$	$C_2O_4{}^{2-}$
Na^+	Na_2O			
Zn^{2+}				
$NH_4{}^+$				
Ferrous ion				

4.72 Write the name of each compound in the table for Problem 4.70.

4.73 Write the name of each compound in the table for Problem 4.71.

4.74 Name the following substances:

(a) $MgCO_3$
(b) $Ca(CH_3CO_2)_2$
(c) $AgCN$
(d) $Na_2Cr_2O_7$

4.75 Name the following substances:

(a) $Fe(OH)_2$
(b) $KMnO_4$
(c) Na_2CrO_4
(d) $Ba_3(PO_4)_2$

4.76 Which of the following formulas is most likely to be correct for calcium phosphate?

(a) Ca_2PO_4
(b) $CaPO_4$
(c) $Ca_2(PO_4)_3$
(d) $Ca_3(PO_4)_2$

4.77 Fill in the missing information to give the correct formula for each compound:

(a) $Na_?SO_4$
(b) $Ba_?(PO_4)_?$
(c) $Ga_?(SO_4)_?$

ACIDS AND BASES

4.78 What is the difference between an acid and a base?

4.79 Identify the following substances as either an acid or a base:

(a) H_2CO_3
(b) HCN

(c) $Mg(OH)_2$
(d) KOH

4.80 Write equations to show how the substances listed in Problem 4.79 give ions when dissolved in water.

4.81 Name the anions that result when the acids in Problem 4.79 are dissolved in water.

Applications

4.82 What is the difference between a geologist's and a nutritionist's definition of a mineral? [*Minerals and Gems, p. 85*]

4.83 How is salt obtained? [*Salt, p. 89*]

4.84 What is the effect of normal dietary salt on most people? [*Salt, p. 89*]

4.85 Where are most of the calcium ions found in the body? [*Biologically Important Ions, p. 92*]

4.86 Excess sodium ion is considered hazardous, but a certain amount is necessary for normal body functions. What is the purpose of sodium in the body? [*Biologically Important Ions, p. 92*]

4.87 Before a person is allowed to donate blood, a drop of the blood is tested to be sure that it contains a sufficient amount of iron (men, 41 μg/dL; women, 38 μg/dL). Why is this required? [*Biologically Important Ions, p. 92*]

4.88 Name each ion in hydroxyapatite, $Ca_{10}(PO_4)_6(OH)_2$; give its charge; and show that the formula represents a neutral compound. [*Osteoporosis, p. 100*]

4.89 Sodium fluoride reacts with hydroxyapatite to give fluorapatite. What is the formula of fluorapatite? [*Osteoporosis, p. 100*]

General Questions and Problems

4.90 Explain why the hydride ion, H^-, has a noble gas configuration.

4.91 The H^- ion (Problem 4.90) is stable, but the Li^- ion is not. Explain.

4.92 Many compounds containing a metal and a nonmetal are not ionic, yet they are named using the Roman numeral system for ionic compounds described in Section 4.7. Write the chemical formulas for the following such compounds.

(a) Chromium(VI) oxide
(b) Vanadium(V) chloride
(c) Manganese(IV) oxide
(d) Molybdenum(IV) sulfide

4.93 The arsenate ion has the formula $AsO_4{}^{3-}$. Write the formula of lead(II) arsenate, used as an insecticide.

4.94 One commercially available calcium supplement contains calcium gluconate, a compound that is also used as an anticaking agent in instant coffee.

(a) If this compound contains one calcium ion for every two gluconate ions, what is the charge on a gluconate ion?

(b) What is the ratio of iron ions to gluconate ions in iron(III) gluconate, a commercial iron supplement?

4.95 The names given for the following compounds are incorrect. Write the correct name for each compound.

(a) Cu_3PO_4, copper(III) phosphate
(b) Na_2SO_4, sodium sulfide
(c) MnO_2, manganese(II) oxide
(d) $AuCl_3$, gold chloride
(e) $Pb(CO_3)_2$, lead(II) acetate
(f) Ni_2S_3, nickel(II) sulfide

4.96 The formulas given for the following compounds are incorrect. Write the correct formula for each compound.

(a) Cobalt(II) cyanide, $CoCN_2$
(b) Uranium(VI) oxide, UO_6
(c) Tin(II) sulfate, $Ti(SO_4)_2$
(d) Manganese(IV) oxide; MnO_4
(e) Potassium phosphate, K_2PO_4
(f) Calcium phosphide, CaP
(g) Lithium bisulfate, $Li(SO_4)_2$
(h) Aluminum hydroxide; $Al_2(OH)_3$

4.97 How many protons, electrons, and neutrons are in each of these following ions?

(a) $^{16}O^{2-}$
(b) $^{89}Y^{3+}$
(c) $^{133}Cs^+$
(d) $^{81}Br^-$

4.98 Element X reacts with element Y to give a product containing X^{3+} ions and Y^{2-} ions.

(a) Is element X likely to be a metal or a nonmetal?
(b) Is element Y likely to be a metal or a nonmetal?
(c) What is the formula of the product?
(d) What groups of the periodic table are elements X and Y likely to be in?

4.99 Identify each of the ions having the following charges and electron configurations:

(a) X^{3+}; $[Ar]\ 4s^03d^5$
(b) X^{2+}; $[Ar]\ 4s^03d^8$
(c) X^{6+}; $[Ar]\ 4s^03d^0$

CHAPTER 5

Molecular Compounds

CONCEPTS TO REVIEW

The Periodic Table
(Sections 3.4 and 3.5)

Electron Configurations
(Sections 3.7 and 3.8)

The Octet Rule
(Section 4.5)

Electron-Dot Symbols
(Section 3.9)

▲ In living systems, as in this print by the Dutch artist M. C. Escher (1898–1972), the shapes of the component parts determine their contribution to the whole.

CHAPTER GOALS

In this chapter, we will explore the following questions about molecules and covalent bonds:

1. **What is a covalent bond?**

THE GOAL: Be able to describe the nature of covalent bonds and how they are formed.

2. **How does the octet rule apply to covalent bond formation?**

THE GOAL: Be able to use the octet rule to predict the numbers of covalent bonds formed by common main group elements.

3. **How are molecular compounds represented?**

THE GOAL: Be able to interpret molecular formulas and draw Lewis structures for molecules.

4. **What is the influence of valence-shell electrons on molecular shape?**

THE GOAL: Be able to use Lewis structures to predict molecular geometry.

5. **When are bonds and molecules polar?**

THE GOAL: Be able to use electronegativity and molecular geometry to predict bond and molecular polarity.

6. **What are the major differences between ionic and molecular compounds?**

THE GOAL: Be able to compare the structures, compositions, and properties of ionic and molecular compounds.

We saw in the preceding chapter that ionic compounds are crystalline solids composed of positively and negatively charged ions. Not all substances, however, are ionic. In fact, with the exception of table salt (NaCl), baking soda ($NaHCO_3$), lime for the garden (CaO), and a few others, most of the compounds around us are *not* crystalline, brittle, high-melting ionic solids. We are much more likely to encounter gases (like those in air), liquids (such as water), low-melting solids (such as butter), and flexible solids like plastics. All these materials are composed of *molecules* rather than ions, all contain *covalent* bonds rather than ionic bonds, and all consist primarily of nonmetal atoms rather than metals.

5.1 Covalent Bonds

How do we describe the bonding in carbon dioxide, water, polyethylene, and the many millions of nonionic compounds that make up our bodies and much of the world around us? Simply put, the bonds in such compounds are formed by the *sharing* of electrons between atoms (in contrast to ionic bonds, which involve the complete transfer of electrons from one atom to another). The bond formed when atoms share electrons is called a **covalent bond**, and the group of atoms held together by covalent bonds is called a **molecule**. A single molecule of water, for example, contains two hydrogen atoms and one oxygen atom covalently bonded to one another. We might visualize a water molecule using a space-filling model as shown here:

Covalent bond A bond formed by sharing electrons between atoms.

Molecule A group of atoms held together by covalent bonds.

Two hydrogen atoms   One oxygen atom   Combine to give   One water molecule (H_2O)

Recall that according to the *octet rule* (Section 4.5), main group elements tend to undergo reactions that leave them with completed outer subshells with eight valence electrons (or two for hydrogen), so that they have a noble gas electron configuration. (⊂⊃ , p. 85) Although metals and reactive nonmetals can achieve an electron octet by gaining or losing an appropriate number of electrons to form ions, the nonmetals can also achieve an electron octet by *sharing* an appropriate number of electrons in covalent bonds.

As an example of how covalent bond formation occurs, let us look first at the bond between two hydrogen atoms in a hydrogen molecule, H_2. Recall that a hydrogen *atom* consists of a positively charged nucleus and a single, negatively charged $1s$ valence electron, which we represent as H· using the electron-dot symbols. When two hydrogen atoms come together, electrical interactions occur. Some of these interactions are repulsive—the two positively charged nuclei repel each other and the two negatively charged electrons repel each other. Other interactions, however, are attractive—each nucleus attracts both electrons and each electron attracts both nuclei (Figure 5.1). Because the attractive forces are stronger than the repulsive forces, a covalent bond is formed and the hydrogen atoms stay together.

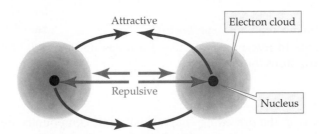

▲ **FIGURE 5.1 A covalent H—H bond is the net result of attractive and repulsive forces.** The nucleus–electron attractions (blue arrows) are greater than the nucleus–nucleus and electron–electron repulsions (red arrows), resulting in a net attractive force that holds the atoms together to form an H_2 molecule.

In essence, the electrons act as a kind of "glue" to bind the two nuclei together into an H_2 molecule. Both nuclei are simultaneously attracted to the same electrons and are therefore held together, much as two tug-of-war teams pulling on the same rope are held together.

▶ The two teams are joined together because both are holding onto the same rope. In a similar way, two atoms are bonded together when both hold onto the same electrons.

Covalent bond formation in the H—H molecule can be visualized by imagining that the spherical $1s$ orbitals from the two individual atoms blend together and *overlap* to give an egg-shaped region in the H_2 molecule. The two electrons in the H—H covalent bond occupy the central region between the nuclei, giving both atoms a share in two valence electrons and the $1s^2$ electron configuration of the noble gas helium. For simplicity, the shared pair of electrons in a covalent bond is often represented as a line between atoms. Thus, the symbols H—H, H:H, and H_2 all represent a hydrogen molecule.

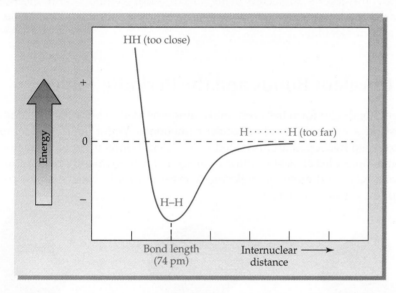

Two hydrogen atoms   A hydrogen molecule

As you might imagine, the magnitudes of the various attractive and repulsive forces between nuclei and electrons in a covalent bond depend on how close the atoms are to each other. If the atoms are too far apart, the attractive forces are small and no bond exists. If the atoms are too close, the repulsive interaction between nuclei is so strong that it pushes the atoms apart. Thus, there is an optimum point where net attractive forces are maximized and where the H_2 molecule is most stable. This optimum distance between nuclei is called the **bond length** and is 74 pm (7.4×10^{-11} m) in the H_2 molecule. On a graph of energy versus internuclear distance, the bond length corresponds to the minimum-energy, most stable arrangement (Figure 5.2).

Bond length The optimum distance between nuclei in a covalent bond.

◄ **FIGURE 5.2 A graph of potential energy versus internuclear distance for the H_2 molecule.** If the hydrogen atoms are too far apart, attractions are weak and no bonding occurs. If the atoms are too close, strong repulsions occur. When the atoms are optimally separated, the energy is at a minimum. The distance between nuclei at this minimum-energy point is called the *bond length*.

As another example of covalent bond formation, look at the chlorine molecule, Cl_2. An individual chlorine atom has seven valence electrons and the valence-shell electron configuration $3s^2\,3p^5$. Using the electron-dot symbols for the valence electrons, each Cl atom can be represented as :C̈l·. The $3s$ orbital and two of the three $3p$ orbitals are filled by two electrons each, but the third $3p$ orbital holds only one electron. When two chlorine atoms approach each other, the unpaired $3p$ electrons are shared by both atoms in a covalent bond. Each chlorine atom in the resultant Cl_2 molecule now "owns" six outer-shell electrons and "shares" two more, giving each a valence-shell octet like that of the noble gas argon. We can represent the formation of a covalent bond between chlorine atoms as

$$:\!\ddot{C}l\cdot\ +\ \cdot\ddot{C}l\!: \ \longrightarrow\ :\!\ddot{C}l\!:\!\ddot{C}l\!:$$

Such bond formation can also be pictured as the overlap of the $3p$ orbitals containing the single electrons, with resultant formation of a region of high electron density between the nuclei:

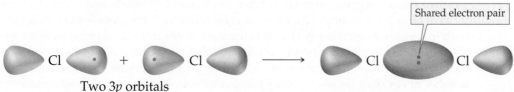

Two $3p$ orbitals

In addition to H_2 and Cl_2, five other elements always exist as *diatomic* (two-atom) molecules (Figure 5.3): Nitrogen (N_2) and oxygen (O_2) are colorless, odorless, nontoxic gases

► **FIGURE 5.3 Diatomic elements in the periodic table.**

present in air; fluorine (F_2) is a pale yellow, highly reactive gas; bromine (Br_2) is a dark red, toxic liquid; and iodine (I_2) is a violet, crystalline solid.

PROBLEM 5.1

Draw the iodine molecule using electron-dot symbols, and indicate the shared electron pair. What noble gas configuration do the iodine atoms have in an I_2 molecule?

5.2 Covalent Bonds and the Periodic Table

Molecular compound A compound that consists of molecules rather than ions.

Covalent bonds can form between unlike atoms as well as between like atoms, making possible a vast number of **molecular compounds**. Water molecules, for example, consist of two hydrogen atoms joined by covalent bonds to an oxygen atom, H_2O; ammonia molecules consist of three hydrogen atoms covalently bonded to a nitrogen atom, NH_3; and methane molecules consist of four hydrogen atoms covalently bonded to a carbon atom, CH_4.

H—O—H
Water, H_2O

Oxygen bonds to 2 hydrogen atoms.

H—N—H
|
H
Ammonia, NH_3

Nitrogen bonds to 3 hydrogen atoms.

H
|
H—C—H
|
H
Methane, CH_4

Carbon bonds to 4 hydrogen atoms.

Note that in all these examples, each atom shares enough electrons to achieve a noble gas configuration: two electrons for hydrogen, and octets for oxygen, nitrogen, and carbon. Hydrogen, with one valence electron (H·), needs one more electron to achieve a noble gas configuration (that of helium, $1s^2$) and thus forms one covalent bond. Oxygen, with six valence electrons (·Ö·), needs two more electrons to have an octet; this happens when oxygen forms two covalent bonds. Nitrogen, with five valence electrons (·N̈·), needs three more electrons to achieve an octet and thus forms three covalent bonds. Carbon, with four valence electrons (·Ċ·), needs four more electrons and thus forms four covalent bonds. Figure 5.4 summarizes the number of covalent bonds typically formed by common main group elements.

The octet rule is a useful guideline, but it has numerous exceptions. Boron, for example, has only three valence electrons it can share (·Ḃ·) and thus forms

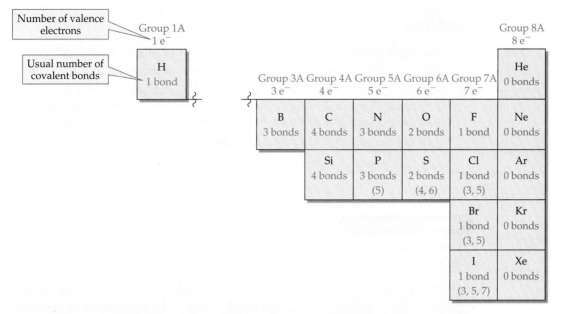

▲ **FIGURE 5.4** **Numbers of covalent bonds typically formed by main group elements to achieve octet configurations.** For P, S, Cl, and other elements in the third period and below, the number of covalent bonds may vary. Numbers in parentheses indicate other possible numbers of bonds that result in exceptions to the octet rule as explained in the text.

compounds in which it has only 3 covalent bonds and 6 electrons, such as BF_3. Exceptions to the octet rule are also seen with elements in the third row and below in the periodic table because these elements have vacant d orbitals that can be used for bonding. Phosphorus, for example, sometimes forms 5 covalent bonds (using 10 bonding electrons); sulfur sometimes forms 4 or 6 covalent bonds (using 8 and 12 bonding electrons, respectively); and chlorine, bromine, and iodine sometimes form 3, 5, or 7 covalent bonds. Phosphorus and sulfur, for example, form molecules such as PCl_5, SF_4, and SF_6.

BF_3
Boron trifluoride
(6 valence electrons on B)

PCl_5
Phosphorus pentachloride
(10 valence electrons on P)

SF_6
Sulfur hexafluoride
(12 valence electrons on S)

WORKED EXAMPLE **5.1** Molecular Compounds: Octet Rule and Covalent Bonds

Look at Figure 5.4 and tell whether the following molecules are likely to exist.

ANALYSIS Count the number of covalent bonds formed by each element and see if the numbers correspond to those shown in Figure 5.4.

SOLUTION

   (a) No. Carbon needs four covalent bonds but has only three in CBr_3.

   (b) Yes. Both iodine and chlorine have one covalent bond in ICl.

   (c) No. Fluorine only needs one covalent bond to achieve an octet. It cannot form more than one covalent bond because it is in the second period and does not have valence d orbitals to use for bonding.

   (d) Yes. Sulfur, which is in group 6A like oxygen, often forms two covalent bonds.

WORKED EXAMPLE   **5.2** Molecular Compounds: Electron-Dot Symbols

Using electron-dot symbols, show the reaction between a hydrogen atom and a fluorine atom.

ANALYSIS The electron-dot symbols show the valence electrons for the hydrogen and fluorine atoms. A covalent bond is formed by the sharing of unpaired valence electrons between the two atoms.

SOLUTION
Draw the electron-dot symbols for the H and F atoms, showing the covalent bond as a shared electron pair.

$$H\cdot + \cdot \ddot{\underset{\cdot\cdot}{F}}: \longrightarrow H\!:\!\ddot{\underset{\cdot\cdot}{F}}:$$

WORKED EXAMPLE   **5.3** Molecular Compounds: Predicting Number of Bonds

What are likely formulas for the following molecules?

   (a) $SiH_2Cl_?$ **(b)** $HBr_?$ **(c)** $PBr_?$

ANALYSIS The numbers of covalent bonds formed by each element should be those shown in Figure 5.4.

SOLUTION

   (a) Silicon typically forms 4 bonds: SiH_2Cl_2

   (b) Hydrogen forms only 1 bond: HBr

   (c) Phosphorus typically forms 3 bonds: PBr_3

PROBLEM 5.2

How many covalent bonds are formed by each atom in the following molecules? Draw molecules using the electron-dot symbols and lines to show the covalent bonds.

(a) PH_3 **(b)** H_2Se **(c)** HCl   **(d)** SiF_4

PROBLEM 5.3

Lead forms both ionic and molecular compounds. Using Figure 5.4 and the periodic table, predict whether a molecular compound containing lead and chlorine is more likely to be $PbCl_4$ or $PbCl_5$.

PROBLEM 5.4

What are likely formulas for the following molecules?

(a) $CH_2Cl_?$ **(b)** $BH_?$ **(c)** $NI_?$ **(d)** $SiCl_?$

5.3 Multiple Covalent Bonds

The bonding in some molecules cannot be explained by the sharing of only two electrons between atoms. For example, the carbon and oxygen atoms in carbon dioxide (CO_2) and the nitrogen atoms in the N_2 molecule cannot have electron octets if only two electrons are shared:

$$\cdot\ddot{O}\cdot + \cdot\dot{C}\cdot + \cdot\ddot{O}\cdot \qquad\qquad \cdot\ddot{N}\cdot + \cdot\ddot{N}\cdot$$

$$\underbrace{} \qquad\qquad \underbrace{}$$

$$\cdot\ddot{O}:\dot{C}:\ddot{O}\cdot \qquad\qquad \cdot\ddot{N}:\ddot{N}\cdot$$

UNSTABLE—Carbon has only   UNSTABLE—Each nitrogen
6 electrons; each oxygen has only 7.   has only 6 electrons.

The only way the atoms in CO_2 and N_2 can have outer-shell electron octets is by sharing *more* than two electrons, resulting in the formation of *multiple* covalent bonds. Only if the carbon atom shares four electrons with each oxygen atom do all atoms in CO_2 have electron octets, and only if the two nitrogen atoms share six electrons do both have electron octets. A bond formed by sharing two electrons (one pair) is a **single bond**, a bond formed by sharing four electrons (two pairs) is a **double bond**, and a bond formed by sharing six electrons (three pairs) is a **triple bond**. Just as a single bond is represented by a single line between atoms, a double bond is represented by two lines between atoms and a triple bond by three lines:

Single bond A covalent bond formed by sharing one electron pair.

Double bond A covalent bond formed by sharing two electron pairs.

Triple bond A covalent bond formed by sharing three electron pairs.

Double bonds

$:\ddot{O}::C::\ddot{O}:$ *or* $:\ddot{O}=C=\ddot{O}:$

A triple bond

$:N:::N:$ *or* $:N\equiv N:$

Each atom has 8 electrons:
    C: 2 double bonds (4 e^- each) = 8 e^-
  Each O: 1 double bond (4 e^-) + 4 lone pair e^- = 8 e^-

Each N: triple bond (6 e^-) + 2 lone pair e^- = 8 e^-

Carbon, nitrogen, and oxygen are the elements most often present in multiple bonds. Carbon and nitrogen form both double and triple bonds; oxygen forms double bonds. Multiple covalent bonding is particularly common in *organic* molecules, which consist predominantly of the element carbon. For example, ethylene, a simple compound used commercially to induce ripening in fruit, has the formula C_2H_4. The only way for the two carbon atoms to have octets is for them to share four electrons in a carbon—carbon double bond:

Ethylene—the carbon atoms share
4 electrons in a double bond.

As another example, acetylene, the gas used in welding, has the formula C_2H_2. To achieve octets, the two acetylene carbons share six electrons in a carbon—carbon triple bond:

$$H : C :: C : H \quad or \quad H—C≡C—H$$

Acetylene—the carbon atoms share
6 electrons in a triple bond.

Note that in compounds with multiple bonds like ethylene and acetylene, each carbon atom still forms a total of 4 covalent bonds.

▲ Acetylene is frequently used for welding metal because it burns with such a hot flame.

WORKED EXAMPLE **5.4** Molecular Compounds: Multiple Bonds

The compound 1-butene contains a multiple bond. In the following representation, however, only the connections between atoms are shown; the multiple bond is not specifically indicated. Identify the position of the multiple bond.

```
       H   H   H   H
       |   |   |   |
   H—C—C—C—C—H
       |       |   |
       H       H   H
```
1-Butene

ANALYSIS Look for two adjacent atoms that appear to have fewer than the typical number of covalent bonds, and connect those atoms by a double or triple bond. Refer to Figure 5.4 to see how many bonds will typically be formed by hydrogen and carbon atoms.

SOLUTION

```
[    H   H   H   H   ]         H   H   H   H
     |   |   |   |             |   |   |   |
 H—C—C—C—C—H           H—C=C—C—C—H
     |       |   |                     |   |
     H       H   H                     H   H
```
Only 3 bonds here   Double bond here

WORKED EXAMPLE **5.5** Multiple Bonds: Electron-Dot and Line Structures

Draw the oxygen molecule (a) using the electron-dot symbols, and (b) using lines rather than dots to indicate covalent bonds.

ANALYSIS Each oxygen atom has six valence electrons, and will tend to form two covalent bonds to reach an octet. Thus, each oxygen will need to share four electrons to form a double bond.

SOLUTION

$$:Ö::Ö: \quad or \quad :Ö=Ö:$$

PROBLEM 5.5

Acetic acid, the organic constituent of vinegar, can be drawn using electron-dot symbols as shown below. How many outer-shell electrons are associated with each atom? Draw the structure using lines rather than dots to indicate covalent bonds.

$$
\begin{array}{c}
H\ \ \ \ddot{O}: \\
H:\ddot{C}:\ddot{C}:\ddot{O}:H \\
\ddot{H}
\end{array}
$$

PROBLEM 5.6

Identify the position of the double bond in methyl ethyl ketone, a common industrial solvent with the following connections among atoms.

$$
\begin{array}{ccccc}
 & H & O & H & H \\
 & | & | & | & | \\
H- & C- & C- & C- & C-H \\
 & | & & | & | \\
 & H & & H & H
\end{array}
$$

Methyl ethyl ketone

5.4 Coordinate Covalent Bonds

In the covalent bonds we have seen thus far, the shared electrons have come from different atoms. That is, the bonds result from the overlap of two singly occupied valence orbitals, one from each atom. Sometimes, though, a bond is formed by the overlap of a filled orbital on one atom with a vacant orbital on another atom so that both electrons come from the *same* atom. The bond that results in this case is called a **coordinate covalent bond**.

Coordinate covalent bond The covalent bond that forms when both electrons are donated by the same atom.

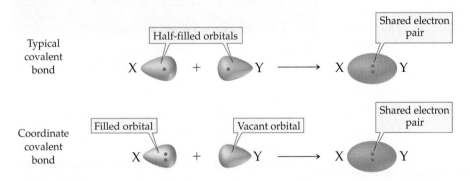

The ammonium ion, NH_4^+, is an example of a species with a coordinate covalent bond. When ammonia reacts in water solution with a hydrogen ion, H^+, the nitrogen atom donates two electrons from a filled valence orbital to form a coordinate covalent bond to the hydrogen ion, which has a vacant $1s$ orbital.

$$
H^+ \ + \ H-\underset{\underset{\displaystyle H}{|}}{\overset{\overset{\displaystyle H}{|}}{\underset{..}{N}}}-H \longrightarrow \left[\ H-\underset{\underset{\displaystyle H}{|}}{\overset{\overset{\displaystyle H}{|}}{N}}-H\ \right]^{+}
$$

Once formed, a coordinate covalent bond contains two shared electrons and is no different from any other covalent bond. All four covalent bonds in NH_4^+ are identical, for example. Note, however, that formation of a coordinate covalent bond results in unusual bonding patterns, such as an N atom with four covalent bonds rather than the usual three.

APPLICATION ▶ CO and NO: Pollutants or Miracle Molecules?

Carbon monoxide (CO) is a killer; everyone knows that. It is to blame for an estimated 3500 accidental deaths and suicides each year in the United States and is the number one cause of all deaths by poisoning. Nitric oxide (NO) is formed in combustion engines and reacts with oxygen to form nitrogen dioxide (NO_2), the reddish-brown gas associated with urban smog. What most people do not know, however, is that our bodies cannot function *without* these molecules. A startling discovery made in 1992 showed that CO and NO are key chemical messengers in the body, used by cells to regulate critical metabolic processes.

The toxicity of CO in moderate concentration is due to its ability to bind to hemoglobin molecules in the blood, thereby preventing the hemoglobin from carrying oxygen to tissues. The high reactivity of NO leads to the formation of compounds that are toxic irritants. At the same time, though, low concentrations of CO and NO are produced in cells throughout the body. Both CO and NO are highly soluble in water and can diffuse from one cell to another, where they stimulate production of a substance called *guanylyl cyclase*. Guanylyl cyclase, in turn, controls the production of another substance called *cyclic GMP*, which regulates many cellular functions.

Levels of CO production are particularly high in certain regions of the brain, including those associated with long-term memory. Evidence from experiments with rat brains suggests that a special kind of cell in the brain's hippocampus is signaled by transfer of a molecular messenger from a neighboring cell. The receiving cell responds back to the signaling cell by releasing CO, which causes still more messenger molecules to be sent. After several rounds of this back-and-forth communication, the receiving cell undergoes some sort of change that serves as a memory. When CO production is blocked, long-term memories are no longer stored, and those memories that previously existed are erased. When CO production is stimulated, however, memories are again laid down.

NO controls a seemingly limitless range of functions in the body. The immune system uses NO to fight infections and tumors. It also is used to transmit messages between nerve cells and is associated with the processes involved in learning and memory, sleeping, and depression. Its most advertised role, however, is as a *vasodilator*, a substance that allows blood vessels to relax and dilate. This discovery led to

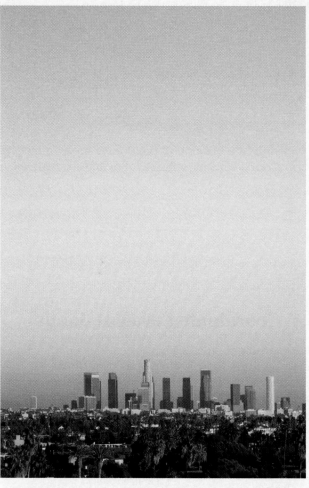

▲ Los Angeles at sunset. Carbon monoxide is a major component of photochemical smog, but it also functions as an essential chemical messenger in our bodies.

the development of a new class of drugs that stimulate production of enzymes called nitric oxide synthases (NOS). These drugs can be used to treat conditions from erectile dysfunction (Viagra) to hypertension. Given the importance of NO in the fields of neuroscience, physiology, and immunology, it is not surprising that it was named "Molecule of the Year" in 1992.

See Additional Problems 5.91 and 5.92 at the end of the chapter.

⊂◯⊃ Looking Ahead

An entire class of substances is based on the ability of transition metals to form coordinate covalent bonds with nonmetals. Called *coordination compounds*, many of these substances have important roles in living organisms. For example, toxic metals can be removed from the bloodstream by forming water-soluble coordination compounds. As another example, we will see in Chapter 19 that essential metal ions are held in enzyme molecules by coordinate covalent bonds. ⊂◯⊃

5.5 Molecular Formulas and Lewis Structures

Formulas such as H_2O, NH_3, and CH_4, which show the numbers and kinds of atoms in one molecule of a compound, are called **molecular formulas**. Though important, molecular formulas are limited in their use because they do not provide information about how the atoms in a given molecule are connected.

Much more useful are **structural formulas**, which use lines to show how atoms are connected, and **Lewis structures**, which show both the connections among atoms and the placement of unshared valence electrons. In a water molecule, for instance, the oxygen atom shares two electron pairs in covalent bonds with two hydrogen atoms and has two other pairs of valence electrons that are not shared in bonds. Such unshared pairs of valence electrons are called **lone pairs**. In an ammonia molecule, three electron pairs are used in bonding and there is one lone pair. In methane, all four electron pairs are bonding.

Molecular formula A formula that shows the numbers and kinds of atoms in one molecule of a compound.

Structural formula A molecular representation that shows the connections among atoms by using lines to represent covalent bonds.

Lewis structure A molecular representation that shows both the connections among atoms and the locations of lone-pair valence electrons.

Lone pair A pair of electrons that is not used for bonding.

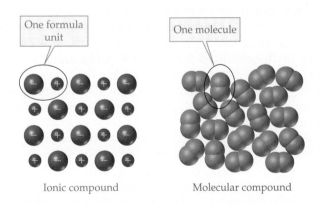

Note how a molecular formula differs from an ionic formula, described previously in Section 4.10. A *molecular* formula gives the number of atoms that are combined in one molecule of a compound, whereas an *ionic* formula gives only a ratio of ions (Figure 5.5). The formula C_2H_4 for ethylene, for example, says that every ethylene molecule consists of two carbon atoms and four hydrogen atoms. The formula NaCl for sodium chloride, however, says only that there are equal numbers of Na^+ and Cl^- ions in the crystal; the formula says nothing about how the ions interact with one another.

▲ Ammonia is used as a fertilizer to supply nitrogen to growing plants.

◀ **FIGURE 5.5 The distinction between ionic and molecular compounds.** In ionic compounds, the smallest particle is an ion. In molecular compounds, the smallest particle is a molecule.

5.6 Drawing Lewis Structures

To draw a Lewis structure, you first need to know the connections among atoms. Sometimes the connections are obvious. Water, for example, can only be H—O—H because only oxygen can be in the middle and form two covalent bonds. Other times, you will have to be told how the atoms are connected.

Two approaches are used for drawing Lewis structures once the connections are known. The first is particularly useful for organic molecules like those found in living organisms because common bonding patterns are followed by the atoms. The second approach is a more general, stepwise procedure that works for all molecules.

Lewis Structures for Molecules Containing C, N, O, X (Halogen), and H

As summarized in Figure 5.4, carbon, nitrogen, oxygen, halogen, and hydrogen atoms usually maintain consistent bonding patterns:

- H forms one covalent bond.
- C forms four covalent bonds and often bonds to other carbon atoms.
- N forms three covalent bonds and has one lone pair of electrons.
- O forms two covalent bonds and has two lone pairs of electrons.
- Halogens (X = F, Cl, Br, I) form one covalent bond and have three lone pairs of electrons.

| Carbon 4 bonds | Nitrogen 3 bonds | Oxygen 2 bonds | Halogen 1 bond | Hydrogen 1 bond |

Relying on these common bonding patterns simplifies writing Lewis structures. In ethane (C_2H_6), a constituent of natural gas, for example, three of the four covalent bonds of each carbon atom are used in bonds to hydrogen, and the fourth is a carbon—carbon bond. There is no other arrangement in which all eight atoms can have their usual bonding patterns. In acetaldehyde (C_2H_4O), a substance used in manufacturing perfumes, dyes, and plastics, one carbon has three bonds to hydrogen, while the other has one bond to hydrogen and a double bond to oxygen.

Ethane, CH_3CH_3 Acetaldehyde, CH_3CHO

Condensed structure A molecular representation in which bonds are understood by the order in which they are written rather than specifically shown.

Because Lewis structures are awkward for larger organic molecules, ethane is more frequently written as a **condensed structure** in which the bonds are not specifically shown. In its condensed form, ethane is CH_3CH_3, meaning that each carbon atom has three hydrogen atoms bonded to it (CH_3) and the two CH_3 units are bonded to each other. In the same way, acetaldehyde can be written as CH_3CHO. Note that neither the lone-pair electrons nor the C=O double bond in acetaldehyde are shown explicitly. You will get a lot more practice with such condensed structures in later chapters.

Many of the computer-generated pictures we will be using from now on will be *ball-and-stick models* rather than the space-filling models used previously. Space-filling models are more realistic, but ball-and-stick models do a better job of showing connections and molecular geometry. All models, regardless of type, use a consistent color code in which C is dark gray or black, H is white or ivory, O is red, N is blue, S is yellow, P is dark blue, F is light green, Cl is greenish yellow, Br is brownish red, and I is purple.

Space-filling

Ball-and-stick

A General Method for Drawing Lewis Structures

A Lewis structure can be drawn for any molecule or polyatomic ion by following a five-step procedure. Take PCl_3, for example, a substance in which three chlorine atoms surround the central phosphorus atom.

STEP 1: Find the total number of valence electrons of all atoms in the molecule or ion. For a polyatomic ion, add one electron for each negative charge or subtract one for each positive charge. In PCl_3, for example, phosphorus (group 5A) has 5 valence electrons and chlorine (group 7A) has 7 valence electrons, giving a total of 26:

$$P + (3 \times Cl) = PCl_3$$
$$5e^- + (3 \times 7e^-) = 26e^-$$

In OH^-, the total is 8 electrons (6 from oxygen, 1 from hydrogen, plus 1 for the negative charge). In NH_4^+, the total is 8 (5 from nitrogen, 1 from each of 4 hydrogens, minus 1 for the positive charge).

STEP 2: Draw a line between each pair of connected atoms to represent the two electrons in a covalent bond. Remember that elements in the second row of the periodic table form the number of bonds discussed earlier in this section, whereas elements in the third row or lower can use more than 8 electrons and form more than the "usual" number of bonds (Figure 5.4). A particularly common pattern is that an atom in the third row or lower occurs as the central atom in a cluster. In PCl_3, for example, the phosphorus atom is in the center with the three chlorine atoms bonded to it:

$$
\begin{array}{c}
Cl \\
| \\
Cl-P-Cl
\end{array}
$$

STEP 3: Add lone pairs so that each atom connected to the central atom (except H) gets an octet. In PCl_3, each Cl atom needs three lone pairs:

$$
\begin{array}{c}
:\ddot{C}l: \\
| \\
:\ddot{C}l-P-\ddot{C}l:
\end{array}
$$

STEP 4: Place all remaining electrons in lone pairs on the central atom. In PCl_3, we have used 24 of the 26 available electrons—6 in three single bonds and 18 in the three lone pairs on each chlorine atom. This leaves 2 electrons for one lone pair on phosphorus:

$$
\begin{array}{c}
:\ddot{C}l: \\
| \\
:\ddot{C}l-\ddot{P}-\ddot{C}l:
\end{array}
$$

STEP 5: If the central atom does not yet have an octet after all electrons have been assigned, take a lone pair from a neighboring atom and form a multiple bond to the central atom. In PCl_3, each atom has an octet, all 26 available electrons have been used, and the Lewis structure is finished.

Worked Examples 5.6–5.8 shows how to deal with cases where this fifth step is needed.

WORKED EXAMPLE | 5.6 Multiple Bonds: Electron Dots and
Valence Electrons

Draw a Lewis structure for the toxic gas hydrogen cyanide, HCN. The atoms are connected in the order shown in the preceding sentence.

ANALYSIS Follow the procedure outlined in the text.

SOLUTION

STEP 1: Find the total number of valence electrons:

H = 1, C = 4, N = 5   Total number of valence electrons = 10

STEP 2: Draw a line between each pair of connected atoms to represent bonding electron pairs:

H—C—N   two bonds = 4 electrons; 6 electrons remaining

STEP 3: Add lone pairs so that each atom (except H) has a complete octet:

H—C—N̈:

STEP 4: All valence electrons have been used, and so step 4 is not needed. H and N have filled valence shells, but C does not.

STEP 5: If central atom (C in this case) does not yet have an octet, use lone pairs from a neighboring atom (N) to form multiple bonds. This results in a triple bond between the C and N atoms, as shown n the electron dot and ball-and stick representations below:

H—C≡N:

We can check the structure by noting that all 10 valence electrons have been used (in four covalent bonds and one lone pair) and that each atom has the expected number of bonds (one bond for H, three for N, and four for C).

WORKED EXAMPLE | 5.7 Lewis Structures: Location of Multiple Bonds

Draw a Lewis structure for vinyl chloride, C_2H_3Cl, a substance used in making poly(vinyl chloride), or PVC, plastic.

ANALYSIS Since H and Cl form only one bond each, the carbon atoms must be bonded to each other, with the remaining atoms bonded to the carbons. With only four atoms available to bond with them, the carbon atoms cannot have four covalent bonds each unless they are joined by a double bond.

SOLUTION

STEP 1: The total number of valence electrons is 18; 4 from each of the two C atoms, 1 from each of the three H atoms, and 7 from the Cl atom.

STEP 2: Place the two C atoms in the center and divide the other four other atoms between them:

```
    H      Cl
     \    /
      C—C
     /    \
    H      H
```

The five bonds account for 10 valence electrons, with 8 remaining.

STEP 3: Place 6 of the remaining valence electrons around the Cl atom so that it has a complete octet, and the remaining 2 valence electrons on one of the C atoms (either C, it does not matter):

$$
\begin{array}{cc}
\text{H} & :\overset{..}{\underset{..}{\text{Cl}}}: \\
\diagdown & \diagup \\
\text{C} & \!\!\!-\!\!\! \text{C}: \\
\diagup & \diagdown \\
\text{H} & \text{H}
\end{array}
$$

When all the valence electrons are distributed, the C atoms still do not have a complete octet; they each need 4 bonds but have only 3.

STEP 5: The lone pair of electrons on the C atom can be used to form a double bond between the C atoms, giving each a total of four bonds (8 electrons). Placement of the double bond yields the Lewis structure and ball-an-stick model for vinyl chloride shown below:

$$
\begin{array}{cc}
\text{H} & :\overset{..}{\underset{..}{\text{Cl}}}: \\
\diagdown & \diagup \\
\text{C} & \!\!\!=\!\!\! \text{C} \\
\diagup & \diagdown \\
\text{H} & \text{H}
\end{array}
$$

All 18 valence electrons are accounted for in six covalent bonds and three lone pairs, and each atom has the expected number of bonds.

WORKED EXAMPLE **5.8** Lewis Structures: Octet Rule and Multiple Bonds

Draw a Lewis structure for sulfur dioxide, SO_2. The connections are O—S—O.

ANALYSIS Follow the procedure outlined in the text.

SOLUTION

STEP 1: The total number of valence electrons is 18, 6 from each atom:

$$S + (2 \times O) = SO_2$$
$$6e^- + (2 \times 6e^-) = 18e^-$$

STEP 2: O—S—O Two covalent bonds use 4 valence electrons.

STEP 3: $:\overset{..}{\text{O}}$—S—$\overset{..}{\text{O}}:$ Adding three lone pairs to each oxygen to give each an octet uses 12 additional valence electrons.

STEP 4: $:\overset{..}{\text{O}}$—$\underset{..}{\text{S}}$—$\overset{..}{\text{O}}:$ The remaining 2 valence electrons are placed on sulfur, but sulfur still does not have an octet.

STEP 5: Moving one lone pair from a neighboring oxygen to form a double bond with the central sulfur gives sulfur an octet (it does not matter on which side the S=O bond is written):

$$:\overset{..}{\underset{..}{\text{O}}}\!\!-\!\!\underset{..}{\text{S}}\!\!=\!\!\overset{..}{\text{O}}:$$

PROBLEM 5.7

Methylamine, CH_5N, is responsible for the characteristic odor of decaying fish. Draw a Lewis structure of methylamine.

PROBLEM 5.8

Add lone pairs where appropriate to the following structures:

(a)
$$\begin{array}{c} H \\ | \\ H-C-O-H \\ | \\ H \end{array}$$

(b)
$$\begin{array}{c} H \\ | \\ N\equiv C-C-H \\ | \\ H \end{array}$$

(c)
$$\begin{array}{c} Cl \\ | \\ N-Cl \\ | \\ Cl \end{array}$$

PROBLEM 5.9

Draw Lewis structures for the following:

(a) Phosgene, $COCl_2$, a poisonous gas
(b) Hypochlorite ion, OCl^-, present in many swimming pool chemicals
(c) Hydrogen peroxide, H_2O_2
(d) Sulfur dichloride, SCl_2

PROBLEM 5.10

Draw a Lewis structure for nitric acid, HNO_3. The nitrogen atom is in the center, and the hydrogen atom is bonded to an oxygen atom.

KEY CONCEPT PROBLEM 5.11

The molecular model shown here is a representation of methyl methacrylate, a starting material used to prepare Lucite plastic. Only the connections between atoms are shown; multiple bonds are not indicated.

(a) What is the molecular formula of methyl methacrylate?
(b) Indicate the positions of the multiple bonds and lone pairs in methyl methacrylate.

5.7 The Shapes of Molecules

Look back at the computer-generated drawings of molecules in the preceding section and you will find that the molecules are shown with specific shapes. Acetylene is *linear*, water is *bent*, ammonia is *pyramid-shaped*, methane is *tetrahedral*, and ethylene is flat, or *planar*. What determines such shapes? Why, for example, are the three atoms in water connected at an angle of 104.5° rather than in a straight line? Like so many properties, molecular shapes are related to the numbers and locations of the valence electrons around atoms.

Molecular shapes can be predicted by noting how many bonds and electron pairs surround individual atoms and applying what is called the **valence-shell electron-pair repulsion (VSEPR) model**. The basic idea of the VSEPR model is that the constantly moving valence electrons in bonds and lone pairs make up negatively

Valence-shell electron-pair repulsion (VSEPR) model A method for predicting molecular shape by noting how many electron charge clouds surround atoms and assuming that the clouds orient as far away from one another as possible.

charged clouds of electrons, which electrically repel one another. The clouds therefore tend to keep as far apart as possible, causing molecules to assume specific shapes. There are three steps to applying the VSEPR model:

STEP 1: Draw a Lewis structure of the molecule, and identify the atom whose geometry is of interest. In a simple molecule like PCl_3 or CO_2, this is usually the central atom.

STEP 2: Count the number of electron charge clouds surrounding the atom of interest. The number of charge clouds is simply the total number of lone pairs plus connections to other atoms. It does not matter whether a connection is a single bond or a multiple bond because we are interested only in the *number* of charge clouds, not in how many electrons each cloud contains. The carbon atom in carbon dioxide, for instance, has two double bonds to oxygen (O=C=O), and thus has two charge clouds.

STEP 3: Predict molecular shape by assuming that the charge clouds orient in space so that they are as far away from one another as possible. How they achieve this favorable orientation depends on their number, as summarized in Table 5.1.

TABLE 5.1 Molecular Geometry Around Atoms with 2, 3, and 4 Charge Clouds

NUMBER OF BONDS	NUMBER OF LONE PAIRS	TOTAL NUMBER OF CHARGE CLOUDS	MOLECULAR GEOMETRY		EXAMPLE
2	0	2		Linear	O=C=O
3	0	3		Planar triangular	H⋯C=O / H
2	1			Bent	O⋯S / O
4	0	4		Tetrahedral	H—C—H, H, H
3	1			Pyramidal	H⋯N—H / H
2	2			Bent	H⋯O / H

If there are only two charge clouds, as occurs on the central atom of CO_2 (two double bonds) and HCN (one single bond and one triple bond), the clouds are farthest apart when they point in opposite directions. Thus, both HCN and CO_2 are linear molecules, with **bond angles** of 180°:

Bond angle The angle formed by three adjacent atoms in a molecule.

$$H-C\equiv N\colon \quad 180°$$

These molecules are linear, with bond angles of 180°.

$$\ddot{O}=C=\ddot{O} \quad 180°$$

When there are three charge clouds, as occurs on the central atom in formaldehyde (two single bonds and one double bond) and SO_2 (one single bond, one double bond, and one lone pair), the clouds will be farthest apart if they lie in a plane and point to the corners of an equilateral triangle. Thus, a formaldehyde molecule is planar triangular, with all bond angles near 120°. In the same way, an SO_2 molecule has a planar triangular arrangement of its three electron clouds, but one point of the triangle is occupied by a lone pair. The relationship of the three atoms themselves is therefore bent rather than linear, with an O—S—O bond angle of approximately 120°:

A formaldehyde molecule is planar triangular, with bond angles of roughly 120°. Note: solid wedges and dashed lines indicate bonds projecting out from and into the plane of the page, respectively.

Top view

Side view

An SO_2 molecule is bent, with a bond angle of approximately 120°.

Top view

Side view

When there are four charge clouds, as occurs on the central atom in CH_4 (four single bonds), NH_3 (three single bonds and one lone pair), and H_2O (two single bonds and two lone pairs), the clouds can be farthest apart when they extend to the corners of a *regular tetrahedron*. As illustrated in Figure 5.6, a **regular tetrahedron** is a geometric solid whose four identical faces are equilateral triangles. The central atom is at the center of the tetrahedron, the charge clouds point to the corners, and the angle between lines drawn from the center to any two corners is 109.5°.

Regular tetrahedron A geometric figure with four identical triangular faces.

▲ The tetrahedral arrangement of atoms at the corners of a trigonal pyramid is clearly seen in this model.

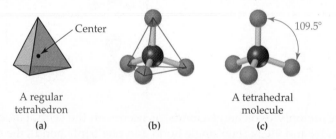

A regular tetrahedron

(a)

A tetrahedral molecule

(b)   (c)

109.5°

Center

▲ **FIGURE 5.6 The tetrahedral geometry of an atom surrounded by four charge clouds.** The atom is located at the center of the regular tetrahedron, and the four charge clouds point toward the corners. The bond angle between the center and any two corners is 109.5°.

Because valence-shell electron octets are so common, a great many molecules have geometries based on the tetrahedron. In methane (CH_4), for example, the carbon atom has tetrahedral geometry with H—C—H bond angles of exactly 109.5°. In ammonia (NH_3), the nitrogen atom has a tetrahedral arrangement of its four charge clouds, but one corner of the tetrahedron is occupied by a lone pair, resulting in an overall pyramidal shape for the molecule. Similarly, water, which has two corners of the tetrahedron occupied by lone pairs, has an overall bent shape.

A methane molecule is tetrahedral, with bond angles of 109.5°.

An ammonia molecule is pyramidal, with bond angles of 107°.

A water molecule is bent, with a bond angle of 104.5°.

Note how the three-dimensional shapes of molecules like methane, ammonia, and water are shown. Solid lines are assumed to be in the plane of the paper; a dashed line recedes behind the plane of the paper away from the viewer; and a dark wedged line protrudes out of the paper toward the viewer. This standard method for showing three-dimensionality will be used throughout the rest of the book. Note also that the H—N—H bond angle in ammonia (107°) and the H—O—H bond angle in water (104.5°) are close to, but not exactly equal to, the ideal 109.5° tetrahedral value. The angles are diminished somewhat from their ideal value because the lone-pair charge clouds repel other electron clouds strongly and compress the rest of the molecule.

The geometry around atoms in larger molecules also derives from the shapes shown in Table 5.1. For example, each of the two carbon atoms in ethylene ($H_2C{=}CH_2$) has three charge clouds, giving rise to planar triangular geometry. It turns out that the molecule as a whole is also planar, with H—C—C and H—C—H bond angles of approximately 120°:

The ethylene molecule is planar, with bond angles of 120°.

Top view

Side view

Carbon atoms bonded to four other atoms are each at the center of a tetrahedron, as shown here for ethane, $H_3C{-}CH_3$:

The ethane molecule has tetrahedral carbon atoms, with bond angles of 109.5°.

WORKED EXAMPLE **5.9** Lewis Structures: Molecular Shape

What shape do you expect for the hydronium ion, H_3O^+?

ANALYSIS Draw the Lewis structure for the molecular ion and count the number of charge clouds around the central oxygen atom; imagine the clouds orienting as far away from one another as possible.

SOLUTION
The Lewis structure for the hydronium ion shows that the oxygen atom has four charge clouds (three single bonds and one lone pair). The hydronium ion is therefore pyramidal with bond angles of approximately 109.5°:

WORKED EXAMPLE **5.10** Lewis Structures: Charge Cloud Geometry

Predict the geometry around each of the carbon atoms in an acetaldehyde molecule, CH_3CHO.

ANALYSIS Draw the Lewis structure and identify the number of charge clouds around each of the central carbon atoms.

SOLUTION
The Lewis structure of acetaldehyde shows that the CH_3 carbon has four charge clouds (four single bonds) and the CHO carbon atom has three charge clouds (two single bonds, one double bond). Table 5.1 indicates that the CH_3 carbon is tetrahedral, but the CHO carbon is planar triangular.

PROBLEM 5.12

Boron typically only forms three covalent bonds because it only has three valence electrons, but can form coordinate covalent bonds. Draw the Lewis structure for BF_4^- and predict the molecular shape of the ion.

PROBLEM 5.13

Predict shapes for the organic molecules chloroform, $CHCl_3$, and dichloroethylene, $Cl_2C=CH_2$.

PROBLEM 5.14

Electron-pair repulsion influences the shapes of polyatomic *ions* in the same way it influences neutral molecules. Draw electron-dot symbols and predict the shape of the ammonium ion, NH_4^+, and the sulfate ion, SO_4^{2-}.

APPLICATION ▶ VERY Big Molecules

How big can a molecule be? The answer is very, *very* big. The really big molecules in our bodies and in many items we buy are all *polymers*. Like a string of beads, a polymer is formed of many repeating units connected in a long chain. Each "bead" in the chain comes from a simple molecule that has formed chemical bonds at both ends, linking it to other molecules. The repeating units can be the same:

–a–a–a–a–a–a–a–a–a–a–a–a–a–

or they can be different. If different, they can be connected in an ordered pattern:

–a–b–a–b–a–b–a–b–a–b–a–b–

or in a random pattern:

–a–b–b–a–b–a–a–a–b–a–b–b–

Furthermore, the polymer chains can have branches, and the branches can have either the same repeating unit as the main chain or a different one:

```
        a
        |
        a–a–a–a–
        |
        a
        |
        a
        |
        a–a–a–a–
        |
        a
        |
        a–a–a–a–
        |
        a
        |
```

or

```
        a
        |
        a–b–b–b–
        |
        a
        |
        a
        |
        a
        |
        a–b–b–b–
        |
        a
        |
        a
        |
        a–b–b–b–
        |
        a
        |
```

Still other possible variations include complex, three-dimensional networks of "cross-linked" chains. The rubber used in tires, for example, contains polymer chains connected by cross-linking atoms of sulfur to impart greater rigidity.

We all use synthetic polymers every day—we usually call them "plastics." Common synthetic polymers are made by connecting up to several hundred thousand smaller molecules together, producing giant polymer molecules with masses up to several million atomic mass units. Polyethylene, for example, is made by combining as many as 50,000 ethylene molecules ($H_2C \!=\! CH_2$) to give a polymer with repeating $-CH_2CH_2-$ units:

Many $H_2C \!=\! CH_2 \longrightarrow -CH_2CH_2CH_2CH_2CH_2CH_2-$
Ethylene   Polyethlene

The product is used in such items as chairs, toys, drain pipes, milk bottles, and packaging films.

Nature began to exploit the extraordinary variety of polymer properties long before humans did. In fact, despite great progress in recent years, there is still much to be learned about the polymers in living things. Carbohydrates and proteins are polymers, as are the giant molecules of deoxyribonucleic acid (DNA) that govern the reproduction of viruses, bacteria, plants, and all living creatures. Nature's polymer molecules, though, are larger and more complex than any that chemists have yet created. We will see the structures of these natural polymers in later chapters.

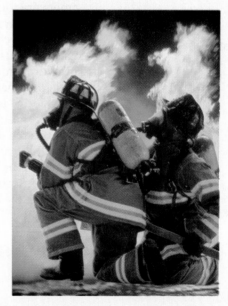

▲ The protective gear used by these firefighters is composed of advanced materials based on polymers.

See Additional Problems 5.93 and 5.94 at the end of the chapter.

PROBLEM 5.15

Hydrogen selenide (H_2Se) resembles hydrogen sulfide (H_2S) in that both compounds have terrible odors and are poisonous. What are their shapes?

KEY CONCEPT PROBLEM 5.16

Draw a structure corresponding to the molecular model of the amino acid methionine shown here and describe the geometry around the indicated atoms. (Remember the color key discussed in Section 5.6: black = carbon; white = hydrogen; red = oxygen; blue = nitrogen; yellow = sulfur.)

Methionine

5.8 Polar Covalent Bonds and Electronegativity

Electrons in a covalent bond occupy the region between the bonded atoms. If the atoms are identical, as in H_2 and Cl_2, the electrons are attracted equally to both atoms and are shared equally. If the atoms are *not* identical, however, as in HCl, the bonding electrons may be attracted more strongly by one atom than by the other and may thus be shared unequally. Such bonds are said to be **polar covalent bonds**. In hydrogen chloride, for example, electrons spend more time near the chlorine atom than near the hydrogen atom. Although the molecule as a whole is neutral, the chlorine is more negative than the hydrogen, resulting in *partial* charges on the atoms. These partial charges are represented by placing a $\delta-$ (Greek lowercase *delta*) on the more negative atom and a $\delta +$ on the more positive atom.

A particularly helpful way of visualizing this unequal distribution of bonding electrons is to look at what is called an *electrostatic potential map*, which uses color to portray the calculated electron distribution in a molecule. In HCl, for example, the electron-poor hydrogen is blue, and the electron-rich chlorine is reddish-yellow:

Polar covalent bond A bond in which the electrons are attracted more strongly by one atom than by the other.

This end of the molecule is electron-poor and has a partial positive charge ($\delta+$).

This end of the molecule is electron-rich and has a partial negative charge ($\delta-$).

$$\overset{\delta+}{H}-\overset{\delta-}{Cl}$$

The ability of an atom to attract electrons in a covalent bond is called the atom's **electronegativity**. Fluorine, the most electronegative element, is assigned a value of 4, and less electronegative atoms are assigned lower values, as shown in Figure 5.7. Metallic elements on the left side of the periodic table attract electrons only weakly and have lower electronegativities, whereas the halogens and other reactive non-metal elements on the upper right side of the table attract electrons strongly and have higher electronegativities. Note also in Figure 5.7 that electronegativity generally decreases going down the periodic table within a group.

Electronegativity The ability of an atom to attract electrons in a covalent bond.

▲ **FIGURE 5.7   Electronegativities of several main-group and transition-metal elements.** Reactive nonmetals at the top right of the periodic table are most electronegative, and metals at the lower left are least electronegative. The noble gases are not assigned values.

Comparing the electronegativities of bonded atoms makes it possible to compare the polarities of bonds and to predict the occurrence of ionic bonding. Both oxygen (electronegativity 3.5) and nitrogen (3.0), for instance, are more electronegative than carbon (2.5). As a result, both C—O and C—N bonds are polar, with carbon at the positive end. The larger difference in electronegativity values shows that the C—O bond is the more polar of the two:

Less polar

$\delta+C—N\delta-$

Electronegativity difference: 3.0 − 2.5 = 0.5

More polar

$\delta+C—O\delta-$

Electronegativity difference: 3.5 − 2.5 = 1.0

As a rule of thumb, electronegativity differences of less than 0.5 result in non-polar covalent bonds, differences up to 1.9 indicate increasingly polar covalent bonds, and differences of 2 or more indicate substantially ionic bonds. The electronegativity differences show, for example, that the bond between carbon and fluorine is highly polar covalent, the bond between sodium and chlorine is largely ionic, and the bond between rubidium and fluorine is almost completely ionic:

E.N difference		Type of bond
0 — 0.4	~	Covalent
0.5 — 1.9	~	Polar covalent
2.0 and above	~	Ionic

$\delta+C—F\delta-$ Na^+Cl^- Rb^+F^-

Electronegativity difference: 1.5   2.1   3.2

Note, though, that there is no sharp dividing line between covalent and ionic bonds; most bonds fall somewhere between two extremes.

◁◁◁ Looking Ahead

The values given in Figure 5.7 indicate that carbon and hydrogen have similar electronegativities. As a result, C—H bonds are nonpolar. We will see in Chapters 12–25 how this fact helps explain the properties of organic and biological compounds, all of which have carbon and hydrogen as their principal constituents. ◁▷

| **WORKED EXAMPLE** | **5.11** Electronegativity: Ionic, Nonpolar, and Polar Covalent Bonds |

Predict whether each of the bonds between the following atoms would be ionic, polar covalent, or nonpolar covalent. If polar covalent, which atom would carry the partial positive and negative charges?

(a) C and Br   (b) Li and Cl   (c) N and H   (d) Si and I

ANALYSIS Compare the electronegativity values for the atoms and classify the nature of the bonding based on the electronegativity difference.

SOLUTION

(a) The electronegativity for C is 2.5, and for Br is 2.8; the difference is 0.3, indicating nonpolar covalent bonding would occur between these atoms.

(b) The electronegativity for Li is 1.0, and for Cl is 3.0; the difference is 2.0, indicating ionic bonding would occur between these atoms.

(c) The electronegativity for N is 3.0, and for H is 2.5; the difference is 0.5. Bonding would be polar covalent, with N $= \delta^-$, and H $= \delta^+$.

(d) The electronegativity for Si is 1.8, and for I is 2.5; the difference is 0.7. Bonding would be polar covalent, with I $= \delta^-$, and Si $= \delta^+$.

PROBLEM 5.17

Arrange the elements commonly bonded to carbon in organic compounds, H, N, O, P, and S, in order of increasing electronegativity.

PROBLEM 5.18

Use electronegativity differences to classify bonds between the following pairs of atoms as ionic, nonpolar covalent, or polar covalent:

(a) I and Cl   (b) Li and O   (c) Br and Br   (d) P and Br

PROBLEM 5.19

Use the symbols $\delta+$ and $\delta-$ to identify the location of the partial charges on the polar covalent bonds formed between the following:

(a) Fluorine and sulfur

(b) Phosphorus and oxygen

(c) Arsenic and chlorine

5.9 Polar Molecules

Just as individual bonds can be polar, entire *molecules* can be polar if electrons are attracted more strongly to one part of the molecule than to another. Molecular polarity is due to the sum of all individual bond polarities and lone-pair contributions in the molecule and is often represented by an arrow pointing in the direction that electrons are displaced. The arrow is pointed at the negative end and is crossed at the positive end to resemble a plus sign, $(\delta+) \longmapsto (\delta-)$.

Molecular polarity depends on the shape of the molecule as well as the presence of polar covalent bonds and lone pairs. In water, for example, electrons are displaced away from the less electronegative hydrogen atoms toward the more electronegative oxygen atom so that the net polarity points between the two O—H bonds. In chloromethane, CH_3Cl, electrons are attracted from the carbon/hydrogen part of the molecule toward the electronegative chlorine atom so that the net polarity points along the C—Cl bond. Electrostatic potential maps show these polarities clearly, with electron-poor regions in blue and electron-rich regions in red.

Water, H_2O Chloromethane, CH_3Cl

Furthermore, just because a molecule has polar covalent bonds does not mean that the molecule is necessarily polar overall. Carbon dioxide (CO_2) and tetrachloromethane (CCl_4) molecules, for instance, have no net polarity because their symmetrical shapes cause the individual C=O and C—Cl bond polarities to cancel.

Zero net polarity   Zero net polarity

Polarity has a dramatic effect on the physical properties of molecules, particularly on melting points, boiling points, and solubilities. We will see numerous examples of such effects in subsequent chapters.

WORKED EXAMPLE   **5.12** Electronegativity: Polar Bonds and Polar Molecules

Look at the structures of (a) hydrogen cyanide (HCN) and (b) vinyl chloride (H_2C=CHCl) described in Worked Examples 5.6 and 5.7, decide whether the molecules are polar, and show the direction of net polarity in each.

ANALYSIS Draw a Lewis structure for each molecule to find its shape, and identify any polar bonds using the electronegativity values in Figure 5.7. Then decide on net polarity by adding the individual contributions.

SOLUTION

(a) The carbon atom in hydrogen cyanide has two charge clouds, making HCN a linear molecule. The C—H bond is relatively nonpolar, but the C≡N bonding electrons are pulled toward the electronegative nitrogen atom. In addition, a lone pair protrudes from nitrogen. Thus, the molecule has a net polarity:

(b) Vinyl chloride, like ethylene, is a planar molecule. The C—H and C=C bonds are nonpolar, but the C—Cl bonding electrons are displaced toward the electronegative chlorine. Thus, the molecule has a net polarity:

PROBLEM 5.20

Look at the molecular shape of formaldehyde (CH_2O) described on page 124, decide whether the molecule is polar, and show the direction of net polarity.

PROBLEM 5.21

Draw a Lewis structure for dimethyl ether (CH_3OCH_3), predict its shape, and tell whether the molecule is polar.

KEY CONCEPT PROBLEM 5.22

From this electrostatic potential map of methyllithium, identify the direction of net polarity in the molecule. Explain this polarity based on electronegativity values.

Methyllithium

5.10 Naming Binary Molecular Compounds

Binary compound A compound formed by combination of two different elements.

When two different elements combine, they form what is called a **binary compound**. The formulas of binary molecular compounds are usually written with the less electronegative element first. Thus, metals are always written before nonmetals,

Periodic Table of the Elements

Main-group elements

Transition elements

Main-group elements

Legend:
- Metals
- Nonmetals
- Metalloids
- Noble gases

Period	1A (1)	2A (2)	3B (3)	4B (4)	5B (5)	6B (6)	7B (7)	8B (8)	8B (9)	8B (10)	1B (11)	2B (12)	3A (13)	4A (14)	5A (15)	6A (16)	7A (17)	8A (18)
1	1 **H** 1.00794																	2 **He** 4.00260
2	3 **Li** 6.941	4 **Be** 9.01218											5 **B** 10.811	6 **C** 12.011	7 **N** 14.0067	8 **O** 15.9994	9 **F** 18.9984	10 **Ne** 20.1797
3	11 **Na** 22.9898	12 **Mg** 24.3050											13 **Al** 26.9815	14 **Si** 28.0855	15 **P** 30.9738	16 **S** 32.066	17 **Cl** 35.4527	18 **Ar** 39.948
4	19 **K** 39.0983	20 **Ca** 40.078	21 **Sc** 44.9559	22 **Ti** 47.88	23 **V** 50.9415	24 **Cr** 51.9961	25 **Mn** 54.9381	26 **Fe** 55.847	27 **Co** 58.9332	28 **Ni** 58.693	29 **Cu** 63.546	30 **Zn** 65.39	31 **Ga** 69.723	32 **Ge** 72.61	33 **As** 74.9216	34 **Se** 78.96	35 **Br** 79.904	36 **Kr** 83.80
5	37 **Rb** 85.4678	38 **Sr** 87.62	39 **Y** 88.9059	40 **Zr** 91.224	41 **Nb** 92.9064	42 **Mo** 95.94	43 **Tc** (98)	44 **Ru** 101.07	45 **Rh** 102.906	46 **Pd** 106.42	47 **Ag** 107.868	48 **Cd** 112.411	49 **In** 114.818	50 **Sn** 118.710	51 **Sb** 121.76	52 **Te** 127.60	53 **I** 126.904	54 **Xe** 131.29
6	55 **Cs** 132.905	56 **Ba** 137.327	57 ***La** 138.906	72 **Hf** 178.49	73 **Ta** 180.948	74 **W** 183.84	75 **Re** 186.207	76 **Os** 190.23	77 **Ir** 192.22	78 **Pt** 195.08	79 **Au** 196.967	80 **Hg** 200.59	81 **Tl** 204.383	82 **Pb** 207.2	83 **Bi** 208.980	84 **Po** (209)	85 **At** (210)	86 **Rn** (222)
7	87 **Fr** (223)	88 **Ra** 226.025	89 **†Ac** 227.028	104 **Rf** (261)	105 **Db** (262)	106 **Sg** (266)	107 **Bh** (264)	108 **Hs** (269)	109 **Mt** (268)	110 **Ds** (271)	111 **Rg** (272)	112 ** ** (285)	113 ** ** (284)	114 ** ** (284)	115 ** ** (288)	116 ** ** (292)	** **	118 ** ** (294)

*Lanthanide series

58 **Ce** 140.115	59 **Pr** 140.908	60 **Nd** 144.24	61 **Pm** (145)	62 **Sm** 150.36	63 **Eu** 151.965	64 **Gd** 157.25	65 **Tb** 158.925	66 **Dy** 162.50	67 **Ho** 164.930	68 **Er** 167.26	69 **Tm** 168.934	70 **Yb** 173.04	71 **Lu** 174.967

†Actinide series

90 **Th** 232.038	91 **Pa** 231.036	92 **U** 238.029	93 **Np** 237.048	94 **Pu** (244)	95 **Am** (243)	96 **Cm** (247)	97 **Bk** (247)	98 **Cf** (251)	99 **Es** (252)	100 **Fm** (257)	101 **Md** (258)	102 **No** (259)	103 **Lr** (260)

** Not yet named

FAMILY NAME	FUNCTIONAL GROUP STRUCTURE*	SIMPLE EXAMPLE	NAME ENDING
Alkane	Contains only C—H and C—C single bonds	CH_3CH_3 Ethane	-ane
Alkene		$H_2C{=}CH_2$ Ethylene	-ene
Alkyne	—C≡C—	H—C≡C—H Acetylene (Ethyne)	-yne
Aromatic		Benzene	None
Alkyl halide	(X=F, Cl, Br, I)	CH_3—Cl Methyl chloride	None
Alcohol		CH_3—OH Methyl alcohol (Methanol)	-ol
Ether		CH_3—O—CH_3 Dimethyl ether	None
Amine		CH_3—NH_2 Methylamine	-amine
Aldehyde		Acetaldehyde (Ethanal)	-al
Ketone		Acetone	-one
Carboxylic acid		Acetic acid	-ic acid
Anhydride		Acetic anhydride	None
Ester		Methyl acetate	-ate
Amide		Acetamide	-amide

*The bonds whose connections are not specified are assumed to be attached to carbon or hydrogen atoms in the rest of the molecule.

and a nonmetal farther left on the periodic table generally comes before a nonmetal farther right. For example,

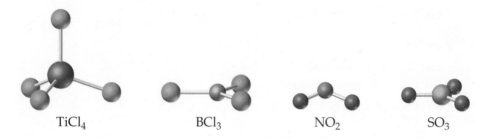

$TiCl_4$ BCl_3 NO_2 SO_3

As we learned in Section 4.10, the formulas of ionic compounds indicate the number of anions and cations necessary for a neutral formula unit, which depends on the charge on each of the ions. With molecular compounds, however, many combinations of atoms are possible since nonmetals are capable of forming multiple covalent bonds. When naming binary molecular compounds, therefore, we must identify exactly how many atoms of each element are included in the molecular formula. The names of binary molecular compounds are assigned in two steps, using the prefixes listed in Table 5.2 to indicate the number of atoms of each element combined.

TABLE 5.2   Numerical Prefixes Used in Chemical Names

NUMBER	PREFIX
1	mono-
2	di-
3	tri-
4	tetra-
5	penta-
6	hexa-
7	hepta-
8	octa-
9	nona-
10	deca-

STEP 1: Name the first element in the formula, using a prefix if needed to indicate the number of atoms.

STEP 2: Name the second element in the formula, using an *-ide* ending as for anions (Section 4.8), along with a prefix if needed.

The prefix *mono-*, meaning one, is omitted except where needed to distinguish between two different compounds with the same elements. For example, the two oxides of carbon are named carbon *mon*oxide for CO and carbon *di*oxide for CO_2. (Note that we say *mon*oxide rather than *mono*oxide.) Some other examples are

N_2O_5 BBr_3 SO_3 SF_6
*Di*nitrogen   Boron   Sulfur   Sulfur
*pent*oxide   *tri*bromide   *tri*oxide   *hexa*fluoride

WORKED EXAMPLE   **5.13** Naming Molecular Compounds

Name the following compounds:

(a) N_2O_3 (b) $GeCl_4$ (c) PCl_5

SOLUTION

(a) Dinitrogen trioxide

(b) Germanium tetrachloride

(c) Phosphorus pentachloride

WORKED EXAMPLE   **5.14** Writing Formulas for Molecular Compounds

Write molecular formulas for the following compounds:

(a) Nitrogen triiodide

(b) Silicon tetrachloride

(c) Carbon disulfide

SOLUTION

(a) NI_3 (b) $SiCl_4$ (c) CS_2

PROBLEM 5.23

Name the following compounds:

(a) S_2Cl_2 (b) ICl (c) ICl_3

PROBLEM 5.24

Write formulas for the following compounds:

(a) Selenium tetrafluoride

(b) Diphosphorus pentoxide

(c) Bromine trifluoride

5.11 Characteristics of Molecular Compounds

We saw in Section 4.4 that ionic compounds have high melting and boiling points because the attractive forces between oppositely charged ions are so strong that the ions are held tightly together. *Molecules*, however, are neutral, so there is no strong electrical attraction between different molecules to hold them together. There are, however, several weaker forces between molecules, called *intermolecular forces*, that we will look at in more detail in Chapter 8.

When intermolecular forces are very weak, molecules of a substance are so weakly attracted to one another that the substance is a gas at ordinary temperatures. If the forces are somewhat stronger, the molecules are pulled together into a liquid; and if the forces are still stronger, the substance becomes a molecular solid. Even so, the melting points and boiling points of molecular solids are usually lower than those of ionic solids.

In addition to having lower melting points and boiling points, molecular compounds differ from ionic compounds in other ways. Most molecular compounds are insoluble in water, for instance, because they have little attraction to strongly polar water molecules. In addition, they do not conduct electricity when melted because they have no charged particles. Table 5.3 provides a comparison of the properties of ionic and molecular compounds.

APPLICATION ▶ Damascenone by Any Other Name Would Smell as Sweet

What's in a name? According to Shakespeare's *Romeo and Juliet*, a rose by any other name would smell as sweet. Chemical names, however, often provoke less favorable responses: "It's unpronounceable." "It's too complicated." "It must be something bad."

Regarding pronunciation, chemical names are usually pronounced using every possible syllable. *Phenylpropanolamine*, for instance, a substance used in over-the-counter decongestants, is spoken with seven syllables: phen-yl-pro-pa-**nol**-a-mine.

Regarding complexity, the reason is obvious once you realize that there are more than 19 *million* known chemical compounds: The full name of a chemical compound has to include enough information to tell chemists the composition and structure of the compound. It is as if every person on earth had to have his or her own unique name that described height, hair color, and other identifying characteristics.

But does it really follow that a chemical with a really complicated name must be bad? These days, it seems that a different chemical gets into the news every week, often in a story describing some threat to health or the environment. The unfortunate result is that people sometimes conclude that everything with a chemical name is unnatural and dangerous. Neither is true, though. Acetaldehyde, for instance, is present naturally in most tart, ripe fruits and is often added in small amounts to artificial flavorings. When *pure*, however, acetaldehyde is also a flammable gas that is toxic and explosive in high concentrations.

Similar comparisons of desirable and harmful properties can be made for almost all chemicals, including water, sugar, and salt. The properties of a substance and the conditions surrounding its use must be evaluated before judgments are made. And damascenone, by the way, is the chemical largely responsible for the wonderful odor of roses.

▲ The scent of these roses contains the following: β-damascenone, β-ionone, citronellol, geraniol, nerol, eugenol, methyl eugenol, β-phenylethyl, alcohol, farnesol, linalool, terpineol, rose oxide, carvone, and many other natural substances.

See Additional Problems 5.95 and 5.96 at the end of the chapter.

TABLE 5.3 A Comparison of Ionic and Molecular Compounds

IONIC COMPOUNDS	MOLECULAR COMPOUNDS
Smallest components are ions (e.g., Na^+, Cl^-)	Smallest components are molecules (e.g., CO_2, H_2O)
Usually composed of metals combined with nonmetals	Usually composed of nonmetals with nonmetals
Crystalline solids	Gases, liquids, or low-melting solids
High melting points (e.g., NaCl = 801 °C)	Low melting points (H_2O = 0.0 °C)
High boiling points (above 700 °C) (e.g., NaCl = 1413 °C)	Low boiling points (e.g. H_2O = 100 °C; CH_3CH_2OH = 76 °C)
Conduct electricity when molten or dissolved in water	Do not conduct electricity
Many are water-soluble	Relatively few are water-soluble
Not soluble in organic liquids	Many are soluble in organic liquids

PROBLEM 5.25

A white crystalline solid has a melting point of 128 °C. It is soluble in water, but the resulting solution does not conduct electricity. Is the substance ionic or molecular? Explain.

PROBLEM 5.26

Aluminum chloride ($AlCl_3$) has a melting point of 190 °C, whereas aluminum oxide (Al_2O_3) has a melting point of 2070 °C. Explain.

SUMMARY: REVISITING THE CHAPTER GOALS

1. **What is a covalent bond?** A *covalent bond* is formed by the sharing of electrons between atoms rather than by the complete transfer of electrons from one atom to another. Atoms that share two electrons are joined by a *single bond* (such as C—C), atoms that share four electrons are joined by a *double bond* (such as C=C), and atoms that share six electrons are joined by a *triple bond* (such as C≡C). The group of atoms held together by covalent bonds is called a *molecule*.

   Electron sharing typically occurs when a singly occupied valence orbital on one atom *overlaps* a singly occupied valence orbital on another atom. The two electrons occupy both overlapping orbitals and belong to both atoms, thereby bonding the atoms together. Alternatively, electron sharing can occur when a filled orbital containing an unshared, *lone pair* of electrons on one atom overlaps a vacant orbital on another atom to form a *coordinate covalent bond*.

2. **How does the octet rule apply to covalent bond formation?** Depending on the number of valence electrons, different atoms form different numbers of covalent bonds. In general, an atom shares enough electrons to reach a noble gas configuration. Hydrogen, for instance, forms one covalent bond because it needs to share one more electron to achieve the helium configuration ($1s^2$). Carbon and other group 4A elements form four covalent bonds because they need to share four more electrons to reach an octet. In the same way, nitrogen and other group 5A elements form three covalent bonds, oxygen and other group 6A elements form two covalent bonds, and halogens (group 7A elements) form one covalent bond.

3. **How are molecular compounds represented?** Formulas such as H_2O, NH_3, and CH_4, which show the numbers and kinds of atoms in a molecule, are called *molecular formulas*. More useful are *Lewis structures*, which show how atoms are connected in molecules. Covalent bonds are indicated as lines between atoms, and valence electron lone pairs are shown as dots. Lewis structures are drawn by counting the total number of valence electrons in a molecule or polyatomic ion and then placing shared pairs (bonding) and lone pairs (nonbonding) so that all electrons are accounted for.

4. **What is the influence of valence-shell electrons on molecular shape?** Molecules have specific shapes that depend on the number of electron charge clouds (bonds and lone pairs) surrounding the various atoms. These shapes can often be predicted using the *valence-shell electron-pair repulsion (VSEPR)* model. Atoms with two electron charge clouds adopt linear geometry, atoms with three charge clouds adopt planar triangular geometry, and atoms with four charge clouds adopt tetrahedral geometry.

5. **When are bonds and molecules polar?** Bonds between atoms are *polar covalent* if the bonding electrons are not shared equally between the atoms. The ability of an atom to attract electrons in a covalent bond is the atom's *electronegativity* and is highest for reactive nonmetal elements on the upper right of the periodic table and lowest for metals on the lower left. Comparing electronegativities allows a prediction of whether a given bond is covalent, polar covalent, or ionic. Just as individual bonds can be polar, entire molecules can be polar if electrons are attracted more strongly to one part of the molecule than to another. Molecular polarity is due to the sum of all individual bond polarities and lone-pair contributions in the molecule.

6. **What are the major differences between ionic and molecular compounds?** *Molecular compounds* can be gases, liquids, or low-melting solids. They usually have lower melting points and boiling points than ionic compounds, many are water insoluble, and they do not conduct electricity when melted or dissolved.

UNDERSTANDING KEY CONCEPTS

5.27 Which of the drawings shown here is more likely to represent an ionic compound and which a covalent compound?

(a)   (b)

5.28 If yellow spheres represent sulfur atoms and red spheres represent oxygen atoms, which of the following drawings depicts a collection of sulfur dioxide molecules?

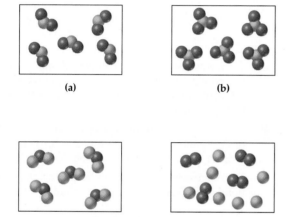

(a)   (b)

(c)   (d)

5.29 What is the geometry around the central atom in the following molecular models? (There are no "hidden" atoms; all atoms in each model are visible.)

(a)   (b)

(c)

5.30 Three of the following molecular models have a tetrahedral central atom, and one does not. Which is the odd one?

(a)   (b)

(c)   (d)

5.31 The ball-and-stick molecular model shown here is a representation of acetaminophen, the active ingredient in such over-the-counter headache remedies as Tylenol. The lines indicate only the connections between atoms, not whether the bonds are single, double, or triple (red = O, gray = C, blue = N, ivory = H).

(a) What is the molecular formula of acetaminophen?

(b) Indicate the positions of the multiple bonds in acetaminophen.

(c) What is the geometry around each carbon and each nitrogen?

Acetaminophen

5.32 The atom-to-atom connections in vitamin C (ascorbic acid) are as shown here. Convert this skeletal drawing to a Lewis electron-dot structure for vitamin C by showing the positions of any multiple bonds and lone pairs of electrons.

Vitamin C

5.33 The ball-and-stick molecular model shown here is a representation of thalidomide, a drug that causes terrible birth defects when taken by expectant mothers but has been approved for treating leprosy. The lines indicate only the connections between atoms, not whether the bonds are single, double, or triple (red = O, gray = C, blue = N, ivory = H).

(a) What is the molecular formula of thalidomide?

(b) Indicate the positions of the multiple bonds in thalidomide.

(c) What is the geometry around each carbon and each nitrogen?

Thalidomide

5.34 Show the position of any electron lone pairs in this structure of acetamide, and indicate the electron-rich and electron-poor regions.

Acetamide

ADDITIONAL PROBLEMS

COVALENT BONDS

5.35 What is a covalent bond, and how does it differ from an ionic bond?

5.36 What is a coordinate covalent bond and how does it differ from a covalent bond?

5.37 Which of the following elements would you expect to form (i) diatomic molecules, (ii) mainly covalent bonds, (iii) mainly ionic bonds, (iv) both covalent and ionic bonds? (More than one answer may apply.)

(a) Oxygen
(b) Potassium
(c) Phosphorus
(d) Iodine
(e) Hydrogen
(f) Cesium

5.38 Identify the bonds formed between the following pairs of atoms as either covalent or ionic.

(a) Aluminum and bromine
(b) Carbon and fluorine
(c) Cesium and iodine
(d) Zinc and fluorine
(e) Lithium and chlorine

5.39 Write electron-dot symbols to show the number of covalent bonds in the molecules that are formed by reactions between the atoms in Problem 5.38.

5.40 Look up tellurium ($Z = 52$) in the periodic table and predict how many covalent bonds it is likely to form. Explain.

5.41 Germanium (atomic number 32) is an element used in the manufacture of transistors. Judging from its position in the periodic table, how many covalent bonds does it usually form?

5.42 Which of the following contains a coordinate covalent bond?

(a) $PbCl_2$ **(b)** $Cu(NH_3)_4{}^{2+}$ **(c)** $NH_4{}^+$

5.43 Which of the following contain a coordinate covalent bond?

(a) H_2O **(b)** $BF_4{}^-$ **(c)** H_3O^+

5.44 Tin forms both an ionic compound and a covalent compound with chlorine. The ionic compound is $SnCl_2$. Is the covalent compound more likely to be $SnCl_3$, $SnCl_4$, or $SnCl_5$? Explain.

5.45 A compound of gallium with chlorine has a melting point of 77 °C and a boiling point of 201 °C. Is the compound ionic or covalent? What is a likely formula?

5.46 Nitrous oxide, N_2O, has the following structure. Which bond in N_2O is a coordinate covalent bond?

$$:N\equiv N-\ddot{O}:$$

Nitrous oxide

5.47 Thionyl chloride, $SOCl_2$, has the following structure. Which bond in $SOCl_2$ is a coordinate covalent bond?

Thionyl chloride

STRUCTURAL FORMULAS

5.48 Distinguish between the following:

(a) A molecular formula and a structural formula
(b) A structural formula and a condensed structure
(c) A lone pair and a shared pair of electrons

5.49 Assume that you are given samples of two white, crystalline compounds, one of them ionic and one covalent. Describe how you might tell which is which.

5.50 Give the total number of valence electrons in the following molecules:

(a) N_2 **(b)** CO
(c) CH_3CH_2CHO **(d)** OF_2

5.51 Add lone pairs where appropriate to the following structures:

(a) $C\equiv O$ **(b)** CH_3SH

(c) $H-\overset{\overset{\displaystyle H}{|}}{O}{}^+-H$ **(d)** $H_3C-\overset{\overset{\displaystyle H}{|}}{N}-CH_3$

5.52 If a research paper appeared reporting the structure of a new molecule with formula C_2H_8, most chemists would be highly skeptical. Why?

5.53 Which of these possible structural formulas for $C_3H_6O_2$ is correct? Explain.

(a)
$$
\begin{array}{c}
\text{H} \quad \text{H} \quad \text{O} \\
| \quad\quad | \quad\quad \| \\
\text{H}-\text{C}-\text{C}-\text{C}-\text{OH} \\
| \quad\quad | \\
\text{H} \quad \text{H}
\end{array}
$$

(b)
$$
\begin{array}{c}
\text{H} \quad\quad \text{OH} \\
| \quad\quad\quad | \\
\text{H}-\text{C}-\text{C}-\text{C}-\text{H} \\
| \quad\quad | \\
\text{H} \quad \text{OH}
\end{array}
$$

(c)
$$
\begin{array}{c}
\text{H} \quad\quad \text{H} \\
| \quad\quad\quad | \\
\text{H}-\text{C}-\text{O}-\text{C}-\text{C}=\text{O} \\
| \quad\quad | \\
\text{H} \quad \text{H} \quad \text{H}
\end{array}
$$

5.54 Convert the following Lewis structures into structural formulas in which lines replace the bonding electrons. Include the lone pairs.

(a) H:Ö:N::Ö: (b)
$$
\begin{array}{c}
\text{H} \\
\text{H:C:C:::N:} \\
\text{H}
\end{array}
$$
 (c) H:F̈:

5.55 Convert the following Lewis structure for the nitrate ion into a line structure that includes the lone pairs. Why does the nitrate ion have a −1 charge?

$$\left[\begin{array}{c} :\text{O}: \\ :\text{Ö}:\text{N}:\text{Ö}: \end{array} \right]^{-}$$

5.56 Convert the following structural formulas into condensed structures.

(a)
$$
\begin{array}{c}
\text{H} \quad \text{H} \quad \text{H} \\
| \quad\quad | \quad\quad | \\
\text{H}-\text{C}-\text{C}-\text{C}-\text{H} \\
| \quad\quad | \quad\quad | \\
\text{H} \quad \text{H} \quad \text{H}
\end{array}
$$

(b)
$$
\begin{array}{c}
\text{H} \quad\quad \text{H} \\
\text{H} \quad \backslash \quad / \quad \text{C} \\
\backslash \quad\quad \quad\quad | \\
\text{C}=\text{C} \quad\quad \text{H} \\
/ \quad\quad \backslash \\
\text{H} \quad\quad \text{H}
\end{array}
$$

(c)
$$
\begin{array}{c}
\text{H} \quad \text{H} \\
| \quad\quad | \\
\text{H}-\text{C}-\text{C}-\text{Cl} \\
| \quad\quad | \\
\text{H} \quad \text{H}
\end{array}
$$

5.57 Expand the following condensed structures into the correct structural formulas.

(a) $CH_3COCH_2CH_3$
(b) CH_3CH_2COOH
(c) $CH_3CH_2OCH_3$

5.58 Acetic acid is the major organic constituent of vinegar. Convert the following structural formula of acetic acid into a condensed structure.

$$
\begin{array}{c}
\text{H} \quad \text{O} \\
| \quad\quad \| \\
\text{H}-\text{C}-\text{C}-\text{O}-\text{H} \\
| \\
\text{H}
\end{array}
$$

DRAWING LEWIS STRUCTURES

5.59 Draw a Lewis structure for the following molecules:
(a) SiF_4
(b) $AlCl_3$
(c) CH_2O
(d) SO_2
(e) BBr_3
(f) NF_3

5.60 Draw a Lewis structure for the following molecules:
(a) Nitrous acid, HNO_2 (H is bonded to an O atom)
(b) Ozone, O_3
(c) Acetaldehyde, CH_3CHO

5.61 Ethanol, or "grain alcohol," has the formula C_2H_6O and contains an O—H bond. Propose a structure for ethanol that is consistent with common bonding patterns.

5.62 Dimethyl ether has the same molecular formula as ethanol (Problem 5.61) but very different properties. Propose a structure for dimethyl ether in which the oxygen is bonded to two carbons.

5.63 Hydrazine, a substance used to make rocket fuel, has the formula N_2H_4. Propose a structure for hydrazine.

5.64 Tetrachloroethylene, C_2Cl_4, is used commercially as a dry cleaning solvent. Propose a structure for tetrachloroethylene based on the common bonding patterns expected in organic molecules. What kind of carbon–carbon bond is present?

5.65 Draw a Lewis structure for carbon disulfide, CS_2, a foul-smelling liquid used as a solvent for fats. What kind of carbon–sulfur bonds are present?

5.66 Draw a Lewis structure for hydroxylamine, NH_2OH.

5.67 The nitrate ion, NO_3^-, contains a double bond. Draw a Lewis structure for the ion and show why it has a negative charge.

5.68 Draw a Lewis structure for the following polyatomic ions:
(a) Formate, HCO_2^-
(b) Carbonate, CO_3^{2-}
(c) Sulfite, SO_3^{2-}
(d) Thiocyanate, SCN^-
(e) Phosphate, PO_4^{3-}
(f) Chlorite, ClO_2^- (chloride is the central atom)

MOLECULAR GEOMETRY

5.69 Predict the geometry and bond angles around atom A for molecules with the general formulas AB_3 and AB_2E, where B represents another atom and E represents an electron pair.

5.70 Predict the geometry and bond angles around atom A for molecules with the general formulas AB_4, AB_3E, and AB_2E_2, where B represents another atom and E represents an electron pair.

5.71 Sketch the three-dimensional shape of the following molecules:
(a) Chloroform, $CHCl_3$
(b) Hydrogen sulfide, H_2S
(c) Ozone, O_3
(d) Nitrogen triiodide, NI_3
(e) Chlorous acid, $HClO_2$

5.72 Predict the three-dimensional shape of the following molecules:

(a) SiF_4
(b) CF_2Cl_2
(c) SO_3
(d) BBr_3
(e) NF_3

5.73 Predict the geometry around each carbon atom in the amino acid alanine.

$$CH_3CHCOH$$

with O double-bonded above the C, and NH_2 below the CH

Alanine

5.74 Predict the geometry around each carbon atom in vinyl acetate, a precursor of the poly(vinyl alcohol) polymer used in automobile safety glass.

$$H_2C=CH-O-C-CH_3$$

with O double-bonded above the second C

Vinyl acetate

POLARITY OF BONDS AND MOLECULES

5.75 Where in the periodic table are the most electronegative elements found, and where are the least electronegative elements found?

5.76 Predict the electronegativity of the yet undiscovered element with $Z = 119$.

5.77 Look at the periodic table, and then order the following elements according to increasing electronegativity: Li, K, Br, C, Cl.

5.78 Look at the periodic table, and then order the following elements according to decreasing electronegativity: C, Ca, Cs, Cl, Cu.

5.79 Which of the following bonds are polar? Identify the negative and positive ends of each bond by using $\delta-$ and $\delta+$.

(a) I—Br
(b) O—H
(c) C—F
(d) N—C
(e) C—C

5.80 Which of the following bonds are polar? Identify the negative and positive ends of each bond by using $\delta-$ and $\delta+$.

(a) O—Br
(b) N—H
(c) P—O
(d) C—S
(e) C—Li

5.81 Based on electronegativity differences, would you expect bonds between the following pairs of atoms to be largely ionic or largely covalent?

(a) Be and F
(b) Ca and Cl
(c) O and H
(d) Be and Br

5.82 Arrange the following molecules in order of the increasing polarity of their bonds:

(a) HCl
(b) PH_3
(c) H_2O
(d) CF_4

5.83 Ammonia, NH_3, and phosphorus trihydride, PH_3, both have a trigonal pyramid geometry. Which one is more polar? Explain.

5.84 Decide whether each of the compounds listed in Problem 5.82 is polar, and show the direction of polarity.

5.85 Carbon dioxide is a nonpolar molecule, whereas sulfur dioxide is polar. Draw Lewis structures for each of these molecules to explain this observation.

5.86 Water (H_2O) is more polar than hydrogen sulfide (H_2S). Explain.

NAMES AND FORMULAS OF MOLECULAR COMPOUNDS

5.87 Name the following binary compounds:

(a) NO_2
(b) SF_6
(c) BrI_5
(d) N_2O_3
(e) NI_3
(f) IF_7

5.88 Name the following compounds:

(a) $SiCl_4$
(b) NaH
(c) SbF_5
(d) OsO_4

5.89 Write formulas for the following compounds:

(a) Phosphorus triiodide
(b) Arsenic trichloride
(c) Tetraphosphorus trisulfide
(d) Dialuminum hexafluoride
(e) Dinitrogen tetroxide
(f) Arsenic pentachloride

5.90 Write formulas for the following compounds:

(a) Selenium dioxide
(b) Xenon tetroxide
(c) Dinitrogen pentasulfide
(d) Triphosphorus tetraselenide

Applications

5.91 Draw electron-dot structures for CO and NO. Why are these molecules so reactive? [*CO and NO: Pollutants or Miracle Molecules?, p. 116*]

5.92 What is a vasodilator, and why would it be useful in treating hypertension (high blood pressure)? [*CO and NO: Pollutants or Miracle Molecules?, p. 116*]

5.93 How is a polymer formed? [*VERY Big Molecules, p. 127*]

5.94 Do any polymers exist in nature? Explain. [*VERY Big Molecules, p. 127*]

5.95 Why are many chemical names so complex? [*Damascenone by Any Other Name, p. 135*]

5.96 Can you tell from the name whether a chemical is natural or synthetic? [*Damascenone by Any Other Name, p. 135*]

General Questions and Problems

5.97 The discovery in the 1960s that xenon and fluorine react to form a molecular compound was a surprise to most chemists, because it had been thought that noble gases could not form bonds.

(a) Why was it thought that noble gases could not form bonds?
(b) Draw a Lewis structure of XeF_4.

5.98 Acetone, a common solvent used in some nail polish removers, has the molecular formula C_3H_6O and contains a carbon—oxygen double bond.

   (a) Propose two Lewis structures for acetone.

   (b) What is the geometry around the carbon atoms in each of the structures?

   (c) Which of the bonds in each structure are polar?

5.99 Draw the structural formulas for two compounds having the molecular formula C_2H_4O. What is the molecular geometry around the carbon atoms in each of these molecules? Would these molecules be polar or nonpolar? (Hint: there is one double bond.)

5.100 The following formulas are unlikely to be correct. What is wrong with each?

   (a) CCl_3 **(b)** N_2H_5

   (c) H_3S **(d)** C_2OS

5.101 Which of the compounds (a) through (d) contain one or more of the following: (i) ionic bonds, (ii) covalent bonds, (iii) coordinate covalent bonds?

   (a) $BaCl_2$ **(b)** $Ca(NO_3)_2$

   (c) BCl_4^- **(d)** $TiBr_4$

5.102 The phosphonium ion, PH_4^+, is formed by reaction of phosphine, PH_3, with an acid.

   (a) Draw the Lewis structure of the phosphonium ion.

   (b) Predict its molecular geometry.

   (c) Describe how a fourth hydrogen can be added to PH_3.

   (d) Explain why the ion has a +1 charge.

5.103 Compare the trend in electronegativity seen in Figure 5.7 (p. 129) with the trend in electron affinity shown in Figure 4.1 (p. 81). What similarities do you see? What differences? Explain.

5.104 Name the following compounds. Be sure to determine whether the compound is ionic or covalent so that you use the proper rules.

   (a) $CaCl_2$ **(b)** $TeCl_2$ **(c)** BF_3

   (d) $MgSO_4$ **(e)** K_2O **(f)** FeF_3

   (g) PF_3

5.105 Titanium forms both molecular and ionic compounds with nonmetals, as, for example, $TiBr_4$ and TiO_2. One of these compounds has a melting point of 39 °C, and the other has a melting point of 1825 °C. Which is ionic and which is molecular? Explain your answer in terms of electronegativities of the atoms involved in each compound.

5.106 Draw a Lewis structure for chloral hydrate, known in detective novels as "knockout drops." Indicate all lone pairs.

Chloral hydrate

5.107 The dichromate ion, $Cr_2O_7^{2-}$, has neither Cr—Cr nor O—O bonds. Write a Lewis structure.

5.108 Oxalic acid, $H_2C_2O_4$, is a poisonous substance found in uncooked spinach leaves. If oxalic acid has a C—C single bond, draw its Lewis structure.

5.109 Identify the elements in the fourth row of the periodic table that form the following compounds.

5.110 Write Lewis structures for molecules with the following connections, showing the positions of any multiple bonds and lone pairs of electrons.

CHAPTER 6

Chemical Reactions: Classification and Mass Relationships

CONCEPTS TO REVIEW

Problem Solving: Converting a Quantity from One Unit to Another
(Section 2.7)

Periodic Properties and Ion Formation
(Section 4.2)

H^+ and OH^- Ions: An Introduction to Acids and Bases
(Section 4.11)

▲ The A320 Airbus shown on the assembly line in Toulouse, France. Commercial air transport relies on oxidation-reduction reactions, from the production of lightweight materials used for construction to the generation of energy required for flight.

CONTENTS

CHAPTER GOALS

Among the questions we will answer are the following:

1. How are chemical reactions written?

THE GOAL: Given the identities of reactants and products, be able to write a balanced chemical equation or net ionic equation.

2. What is the mole, and why is it useful in chemistry?

THE GOAL: Be able to explain the meaning and uses of the mole and Avogadro's number.

3. How are molar quantities and mass quantities related?

THE GOAL: Be able to convert between molar and mass quantities of an element or compound.

4. What are the limiting reagent, theoretical yield, and percent yield of a reaction?

THE GOAL: Be able to take the amount of product actually formed in a reaction, calculate the amount that could form theoretically, and express the results as a percent yield.

5. How are chemical reactions of ionic compounds classified?

THE GOAL: Be able to recognize precipitation, acid–base neutralization, and redox reactions.

6. What are oxidation numbers, and how are they used?

THE GOAL: Be able to assign oxidation numbers to atoms in compounds and identify the substances oxidized and reduced in a given reaction.

A log burns in the fireplace, an oyster makes a pearl, a seed grows into a plant—these and almost all other changes you see taking place around you are the result of *chemical reactions*. The study of how and why chemical reactions happen is a major part of chemistry, providing information that is both fascinating and practical. In this chapter, we will begin to look at chemical reactions, starting with a discussion of how to represent them in writing. Next we will describe the mass relationships among substances involved in chemical reactions, and then introduce a few easily recognized classes of chemical reactions.

6.1 Chemical Equations

One way to view chemical reactions is to think of them as "recipes." Like recipes, all the "ingredients" in a chemical equation and their relative amounts are given, as well as the amount of product that would be obtained. Take, for example, a recipe for making s'mores, a concoction of chocolate, marshmallows, and graham crackers, which could be written as

Graham crackers + Roasted marshmallows + Chocolate bars $\longrightarrow$ S'mores

This recipe, however, is simply a list of ingredients and gives no indication of the relative amounts of each ingredient, or how many s'mores we would obtain. A more detailed recipe would be

2 Graham crackers + 1 Roasted marshmallow + $\frac{1}{4}$ Chocolate bar $\longrightarrow$ 1 S'more

In this case, the relative amounts of each ingredient are given, as well as the amount of the final product.

Let us extend this analogy to a typical chemical reaction. When sodium bicarbonate is heated in the range 50–100 °C, sodium carbonate, water, and carbon dioxide are produced. In words, we might write the reaction as

Sodium bicarbonate $\xrightarrow{\text{Heat}}$ Sodium carbonate + Water + Carbon dioxide

Just as in the recipe, the starting materials and final products are listed. Replacing the chemical names with formulas converts the word description of this reaction into a **chemical equation**:

$$2\,\underbrace{NaHCO_3}_{\text{Reactant}} \xrightarrow{\text{Heat}} \underbrace{Na_2CO_3 + H_2O + CO_2}_{\text{Products}}$$

Chemical equation An expression in which symbols and formulas are used to represent a chemical reaction.

Reactant A substance that undergoes change in a chemical reaction and is written on the left side of the reaction arrow in a chemical equation.

Product A substance that is formed in a chemical reaction and is written on the right side of the reaction arrow in a chemical equation.

Balanced equation A chemical equation in which the numbers and kinds of atoms are the same on both sides of the reaction arrow.

Coefficient A number placed in front of a formula to balance a chemical equation.

Look at how this equation is written. The **reactants** are written on the left, the **products** are written on the right, and an arrow is placed between them to indicate a chemical change. Conditions necessary for the reaction to occur—heat in this particular instance—are often specified above the arrow.

Why is the number 2 placed before $NaHCO_3$ in the equation? The 2 is necessary because of a fundamental law of nature called the *law of conservation of mass*:

Law of conservation of mass   Matter is neither created nor destroyed in chemical reactions.

The bonds between atoms in the reactants are rearranged to form new compounds in chemical reactions, but none of the atoms disappear and no new ones are formed. As a consequence, chemical equations must be **balanced**, meaning that *the numbers and kinds of atoms must be the same on both sides of the reaction arrow.*

The numbers placed in front of formulas to balance equations are called **coefficients**, and they multiply all the atoms in a formula. Thus, the symbol "$2 NaHCO_3$" indicates two units of sodium bicarbonate, which contain 2 Na atoms, 2 H atoms, 2 C atoms, and 6 O atoms ($2 \times 3 = 6$, the coefficient times the subscript for O). Count the numbers of atoms on the right side of the equation to convince yourself that it is indeed balanced.

The substances that take part in chemical reactions may be solids, liquids, or gases, or they may be dissolved in a solvent. Ionic compounds, in particular, frequently undergo reaction in *aqueous solution*— that is, dissolved in water. Sometimes this information is added to an equation by placing the appropriate symbols after the formulas:

$$
\begin{array}{cccc}
(s) & (l) & (g) & (aq) \\
\text{Solid} & \text{Liquid} & \text{Gas} & \text{Aqueous solution}
\end{array}
$$

Thus, the decomposition of solid sodium bicarbonate can be written as

$$2\,NaHCO_3(s) \xrightarrow{\text{Heat}} Na_2CO_3(s) + H_2O(l) + CO_2(g)$$

WORKED EXAMPLE   **6.1** Balancing Chemical Reactions

Interpret in words the following equation for the reaction used in extracting lead metal from its ores. Show that the equation is balanced.

$$2\,PbS(s) + 3\,O_2(g) \longrightarrow 2\,PbO(s) + 2\,SO_2(g)$$

SOLUTION

The equation can be read as, "Solid lead(II) sulfide plus gaseous oxygen yields solid lead(II) oxide plus gaseous sulfur dioxide."

To show that the equation is balanced, count the atoms of each element on each side of the arrow:

On the left:	2 Pb	2 S	$(3 \times 2)\,O = 6\,O$
On the right:	2 Pb	2 S	$2\,O + (2 \times 2)\,O = 6\,O$

From 2 PbO   From 2 SO$_2$

The numbers of atoms of each element are the same in the reactants and products, so the equation is balanced.

PROBLEM 6.1

Interpret the following equations in words:

(a) $CoCl_2(s) + 2\,HF(g) \longrightarrow CoF_2(s) + 2\,HCl(g)$

(b) $Pb(NO_3)_2(aq) + 2\,KI(aq) \longrightarrow PbI_2(s) + 2\,KNO_3(aq)$

PROBLEM 6.2

Which of the following equations are balanced?

(a) $HCl + KOH \longrightarrow H_2O + KCl$

(b) $CH_4 + Cl_2 \longrightarrow CH_2Cl_2 + HCl$

(c) $H_2O + MgO \longrightarrow Mg(OH)_2$

(d) $Al(OH)_3 + H_3PO_4 \longrightarrow AlPO_4 + 2\,H_2O$

6.2 Balancing Chemical Equations

Just as a recipe indicates the appropriate amounts of each ingredient needed to make a given product, a balanced chemical equation indicates the appropriate amounts of reactants needed to generate a given amount of product. Balancing chemical equations can often be done using a mixture of common sense and trial-and-error. There are four steps:

STEP 1: Write an unbalanced equation, using the correct formulas for all reactants and products. For example, hydrogen and oxygen must be written as H_2 and O_2, rather than as H and O, since we know that both elements exist as diatomic molecules. Remember that *the subscripts in chemical formulas cannot be changed in balancing an equation because doing so would change the identity of the substances in the reaction.*

STEP 2: Add appropriate coefficients to balance the numbers of atoms of each element. It helps to begin with elements that appear in only one formula on each side of the equation, which usually means leaving oxygen and hydrogen until last. For example, in the reaction of sulfuric acid with sodium hydroxide to give sodium sulfate and water, we might balance first for sodium. We could do this by adding a coefficient of 2 for NaOH:

$$H_2SO_4 + NaOH \longrightarrow Na_2SO_4 + H_2O \quad \text{(Unbalanced)}$$

$$H_2SO_4 + 2\,NaOH \longrightarrow Na_2SO_4 + H_2O \quad \text{(Balanced for Na)}$$

Add this coefficient . . .   . . . to balance these 2 Na.

If a polyatomic ion appears on both sides of an equation, it is treated as a single unit. For example, the sulfate ion (SO_4^{2-}) in our example is balanced because there is one on the left and one on the right:

$$H_2SO_4 + 2\,NaOH \longrightarrow Na_2SO_4 + H_2O \quad \text{(Balanced for Na and sulfate)}$$

One sulfate here . . .   . . . and one here.

At this point, the equation can be balanced for H and O by adding a coefficient of 2 for H_2O

$$H_2SO_4 + 2\,NaOH \longrightarrow Na_2SO_4 + 2\,H_2O \quad \text{(Completely balanced)}$$

4 H and 2 O here.   4 H and 2 O here.

STEP 3: Check the equation to make sure the numbers and kinds of atoms on both sides of the equation are the same.

STEP 4: Make sure the coefficients are reduced to their lowest whole-number values. For example, the equation

$$2\,H_2SO_4 + 4\,NaOH \longrightarrow 2\,Na_2SO_4 + 4\,H_2O$$

is balanced but can be simplified by dividing all coefficients by 2:

$$H_2SO_4 + 2\,NaOH \longrightarrow Na_2SO_4 + 2\,H_2O$$

WORKED EXAMPLE **6.2** Balancing Chemical Equations

Write a balanced chemical equation for the Haber process, an important industrial reaction in which elemental nitrogen and hydrogen combine to form ammonia according to the following unbalanced reaction:

$$N_2(g) + H_2(g) \longrightarrow NH_3(g)$$

SOLUTION

STEP 1: Write an unbalanced equation, using the correct formulas for all reactants and products. The unbalanced equation is provided above. By examination, we see that only two elements, N and H, need to be balanced. Both these elements exist in nature as diatomic gases, as indicated on the reactant side of the unbalanced equation.

STEP 2: Add appropriate coefficients to balance the numbers of atoms of each element. Remember that the subscript 2 in N_2 and H_2 indicates that these are diatomic molecules (that is, two N atoms or two H atoms per molecule). Since there are two nitrogen atoms on the left, we must add a coefficient of 2 in front of the NH_3 on the right side of the equation to balance the equation with respect to N:

$$N_2(g) + H_2(g) \longrightarrow 2\,NH_3(g)$$

Now we see that there are two H atoms on the left, but six H atoms on the right. We can balance the equation with respect to hydrogen by adding a coefficient of 3 in front of the $H_2(g)$ on the left side:

$$N_2(g) + 3\,H_2(g) \longrightarrow 2\,NH_3(g)$$

STEP 3: Check the equation to make sure the numbers and kinds of atoms on both sides of the equation are the same.

On the left: $(1 \times 2)\,N = 2\,N$ $(3 \times 2)\,H = 6\,H$

On the right: $(2 \times 1)\,N = 2\,N$ $(2 \times 3)\,H = 6\,H$

STEP 4: Make sure the coefficients are reduced to their lowest whole-number values. In this case, the coefficients already represent the lowest whole-number ratios.

WORKED EXAMPLE **6.3** Balancing Chemical Equations

Natural gas (methane, CH_4) burns in oxygen to yield water and carbon dioxide (CO_2). Write a balanced equation for the reaction.

SOLUTION

STEP 1: Write the unbalanced equation, using correct formulas for all substances:

$$CH_4 + O_2 \longrightarrow CO_2 + H_2O \text{ (Unbalanced)}$$

STEP 2: Since carbon appears in one formula on each side of the arrow, let us begin with that element. In fact, there is only one carbon atom in each formula, so the equation is already balanced for that element. Next, note that there are four hydrogen atoms on the left (in CH_4) and only two on the right (in H_2O). Placing a coefficient of 2 before H_2O gives the same number of hydrogen atoms on both sides:

$$CH_4 + O_2 \longrightarrow CO_2 + 2\,H_2O \text{ (Balanced for C and H)}$$

Finally, look at the number of oxygen atoms. There are two on the left (in O_2) but four on the right (two in CO_2 and one in each H_2O). If we place a 2 before the O_2, the number of oxygen atoms will be the same on both sides, but the numbers of other elements will not change:

$$CH_4 + 2\,O_2 \longrightarrow CO_2 + 2\,H_2O \text{ (Balanced for C, H, and O)}$$

STEP 3: Check to be sure the numbers of atoms on both sides are the same.

On the left:	1 C	4 H	$(2 \times 2)\,O = 4\,O$
On the right:	1 C	$(2 \times 2)\,H = 4\,H$	$2\,O + 2\,O = 4\,O$

From CO_2 From $2\,H_2O$

STEP 4: Make sure the coefficients are reduced to their lowest whole-number values. In this case, the answer is already correct.

WORKED EXAMPLE   **6.4** Balancing Chemical Equations

Sodium chlorate ($NaClO_3$) decomposes when heated to yield sodium chloride and oxygen, a reaction used to provide oxygen for the emergency breathing masks in airliners. Write a balanced equation for this reaction.

SOLUTION

STEP 1: The unbalanced equation is

$$NaClO_3 \longrightarrow NaCl + O_2$$

STEP 2: Both the Na and the Cl are already balanced, with only one atom of each on the left and right sides of the equation. There are three O atoms on the left, but only two on the right. The O atoms can be balanced by placing a coefficient of 1½ in front of O_2 on the right side of the equation:

$$NaClO_3 \longrightarrow NaCl + 1^1/_2\,O_2$$

STEP 3: Checking to make sure the same number of atoms of each type occurs on both sides of the equation, we see one atom of Na and Cl on both sides, and three O atoms on both sides.

STEP 4: In this case, obtaining all coefficients in their smallest whole-number values requires that we multiply all coefficients by 2 to obtain

$$2\,NaClO_3 \longrightarrow 2\,NaCl + 3\,O_2$$

Checking gives

On the left:	2 Na 2 Cl $(2 \times 3)\,O = 6\,O$
On the right:	2 Na 2 Cl $(3 \times 2)\,O = 6\,O$

▲ The oxygen in emergency breathing masks comes from heating sodium chlorate.

PROBLEM 6.3

Ozone (O_3) is formed in the earth's upper atmosphere by the action of solar radiation on oxygen molecules (O_2). Write a balanced equation for the formation of ozone from oxygen.

PROBLEM 6.4

Balance the following equations:

(a) $Ca(OH)_2 + HCl \longrightarrow CaCl_2 + H_2O$

(b) $Al + O_2 \longrightarrow Al_2O_3$

(c) $CH_3CH_3 + O_2 \longrightarrow CO_2 + H_2O$

(d) $AgNO_3 + MgCl_2 \longrightarrow AgCl + Mg(NO_3)_2$

KEY CONCEPT PROBLEM 6.5

The following diagram represents the reaction of A (red spheres) with B_2 (blue spheres). Write a balanced equation for the reaction.

6.3 Avogadro's Number and the Mole

The balanced chemical equation indicates what is happening at the molecular level. Now let us imagine a laboratory experiment: the reaction of ethylene (C_2H_4) with hydrogen chloride (HCl) to prepare ethyl chloride (C_2H_5Cl), a colorless, low-boiling liquid used by doctors and athletic trainers as a spray-on anesthetic. The reaction is represented as

$$C_2H_4(g) + HCl(g) \rightarrow C_2H_5Cl(g)$$

In this reaction, one molecule of ethylene reacts with one molecule of hydrogen chloride to produce one molecule of ethyl chloride.

How, though, can you be sure you have a 1 to 1 ratio of reactant molecules in your reaction flask? Since it is impossible to hand-count the number of molecules correctly, you must weigh them instead. (This is a common method for dealing with all kinds of small objects: Nails, nuts, and grains of rice are all weighed rather than counted.) But the weighing approach leads to another problem. How many molecules are there in one gram of ethylene, hydrogen chloride, or any other substance? The answer depends on the identity of the substance because different molecules have different masses.

To determine how many molecules of a given substance are in a certain mass, it is helpful to define a quantity called *molecular weight*. Just as the *atomic* weight of an element is the average mass of the element's *atoms* (Section 3.3), the **molecular weight (MW)** of a molecule is the average mass of a substance's *molecules*. (, p. 55) Numerically, a substance's molecular weight (or **formula weight** for an ionic compound) is equal to the sum of the atomic weights for all the atoms in the molecule or formula unit.

▲ Ethyl chloride is often used as a spray-on anesthetic for athletic injuries.

| Molecular weight | The sum of atomic weights of all atoms in a molecule |
| Formula weight | The sum of atomic weights of all atoms in one formula unit of any compound, whether molecular or ionic |

For example, the molecular weight of ethylene (C_2H_4) is 28.0 amu, the molecular weight of HCl is 36.5 amu, and the molecular weight of ethyl chloride (C_2H_5Cl) is 64.5 amu. (The actual values are known more precisely but are rounded off here for convenience.)

For ethylene, C_2H_4:

Atomic weight of 2 C = 2 × 12.0 amu = 24.0 amu

Atomic weight of 4 H = 4 × 1.0 amu = 4.0 amu

MW of C_2H_4 = 28.0 amu

For hydrogen chloride, HCl:

$$\begin{aligned}
\text{Atomic weight of H} &= 1.0 \text{ amu} \\
\underline{\text{Atomic weight of Cl}} &= \underline{35.5 \text{ amu}} \\
\text{MW of HCl} &= 36.5 \text{ amu}
\end{aligned}$$

For ethyl chloride, C_2H_5Cl:

$$\begin{aligned}
\text{Atomic weight of 2 C} &= 2 \times 12.0 \text{ amu} = 24.0 \text{ amu} \\
\text{Atomic weight of 5 H} &= 5 \times 1.0 \text{ amu} = 5.0 \text{ amu} \\
\underline{\text{Atomic weight of Cl}} &\phantom{= 5 \times 1.0 \text{ amu}} = \underline{35.5 \text{ amu}} \\
\text{MW of } C_2H_5Cl &\phantom{= 5 \times 1.0 \text{ amu}} = 64.5 \text{ amu}
\end{aligned}$$

How are molecular weights used? Since the mass ratio of *one* ethylene molecule to *one* HCl molecule is 28.0 to 36.5, the mass ratio of *any* given number of ethylene molecules to the same number of HCl molecules is also 28.0 to 36.5. In other words, a 28.0 to 36.5 *mass* ratio of ethylene and HCl always guarantees a 1 to 1 *number* ratio. *Samples of different substances always contain the same number of molecules or formula units whenever their mass ratio is the same as their molecular or formula weight ratio* (Figure 6.1).

 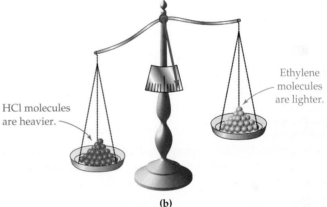

| (a) | (b) |

▲ **FIGURE 6.1** (a) Because one gumdrop weighs more than one jellybean, you cannot get equal numbers by taking equal weights. The same is true for atoms or molecules of different substances. (b) Equal numbers of ethylene and HCL molecules always have a mass ratio equal to the ratio of their molecular weights, 28.0 to 36.5.

A particularly convenient way to use this mass/number relationship for molecules is to measure amounts in grams that are numerically equal to molecular weights. If, for instance, you were to carry out your experiment with 28.0 g of ethylene and 36.5 g of HCl, you could be certain that you would have a 1 to 1 ratio of reactant molecules.

◄ These samples of water, sulfur, table sugar, mercury, and copper each contain 1 mol. Do they all weigh the same?

When referring to the vast numbers of molecules or formula units that take part in a visible chemical reaction, it is convenient to use a counting unit called a **mole**, abbreviated *mol*. One mole of any substance is the amount whose mass in grams—its *molar mass*—is numerically equal to its molecular or formula weight. One mole of ethylene has a mass of 28.0 g, one mole of HCl has a mass of 36.5 g, and one mole of ethyl chloride has a mass of 64.5 g.

> **Mole** The amount of a substance whose mass in grams is numerically equal to its molecular or formula weight.

Avogadro's number (N_A) The number of units in 1 mol of anything; 6.022×10^{23}.

Just how many molecules are there in a mole? Experiments show that one mole of any substance contains 6.022×10^{23} formula units, a value called **Avogadro's number** (abbreviated N_A) after the Italian scientist who first recognized the importance of the mass/number relationship in molecules. Avogadro's number of formula units of any substance—that is, one mole—has a mass in grams numerically equal to the molecular weight of the substance.

$$1 \text{ mol HCl} = 6.022 \times 10^{23} \text{ HCl molecules} = 36.5 \text{ g HCl}$$

$$1 \text{ mol C}_2\text{H}_4 = 6.022 \times 10^{23} \text{ C}_2\text{H}_4 \text{ molecules} = 28.0 \text{ g C}_2\text{H}_4$$

$$1 \text{ mol C}_2\text{H}_5\text{Cl} = 6.022 \times 10^{23} \text{ C}_2\text{H}_5\text{Cl molecules} = 64.5 \text{ g C}_2\text{H}_5\text{Cl}$$

How big is Avogadro's number? Our minds cannot really conceive of the magnitude of a number like 6.022×10^{23}, but the following comparisons will give you a sense of the scale:

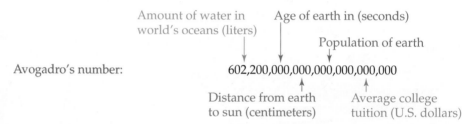

WORKED EXAMPLE **6.5** Molar Mass and Avogadro's Number: Number of Molecules

Pseudoephedrine hydrochloride ($C_{10}H_{16}ClNO$) is a nasal decongestant commonly found in cold medication. (a) What is the molar mass of pseudoephedrine hydrochloride? (b) How many molecules of pseudoephedrine hydrochloride are in a tablet that contains 30.0 mg of this decongestant ?

ANALYSIS We are given a mass and need to convert to a number of molecules. This is most easily accomplished by using the molecular weight of pseudoephedrine hydrochloride calculated in part (a) as the conversion factor from mass to moles and realizing that this mass (in grams) contains Avogadro's number of molecules (6.022×10^{23}).

BALLPARK ESTIMATE The formula for pseudoephedrine contains ten carbon atoms (each one of atomic weight 12.0 amu), so the molecular weight is greater than 120 amu, probably near 200 amu. Thus the molar mass should be near 200 g/mol. The mass of 30 mg of pseudoepinephrine HCl is less than the mass of 1 mol of this compound by a factor of roughly 10^4 (0.03 g versus 200 g), which means the number of molecules should also be smaller by a factor of 10^4 (on the order of 10^{19} in the tablet versus 10^{23} in 1 mol).

SOLUTION

(a) The molecular weight of pseudoephedrine is found by summing the atomic weights of all atoms in the molecule:

Atomic Weight of 10 atoms of C:	10×12.011 amu	$= 120.11$ amu
16 atoms of H:	16×1.00794 amu $=$	16.127 amu
1 atom of Cl:	1×35.4527 amu $=$	35.4527 amu
1 atom of N:	1×14.0067 amu $=$	14.0067 amu
1 atom of O:	1×15.9994 amu $=$	15.9994 amu

MW of $C_{10}H_{16}ClNO$ $= 201.6958$ amu $\rightarrow 201.70$ g/mol

Remember that atomic mass in amu converts directly to molecular weight in g/mol. Also, following the rules for significant figures from Section 2.6, our final answer is rounded to the second decimal place.

(b) Since this problem involves unit conversions, we can use the step-wise solution introduced in Chapter 2.

STEP 1: Identify known information. We are given the mass of pseudoephedrine hydrochloride (in mg).

30.0 mg pseudoephedrine hydrochloride

STEP 2: Identify answer and units. We are looking for the number of molecules of pseudoephedrine hydrochloride in a 30 mg tablet.

?? = molecules

STEP 3: Identify conversion factors. Since the molecular weight of pseudoephedrine hydrochloride is 201.70 amu, 201.70 g contains 6.022×10^{23} molecules. We can use this ratio as a conversion factor to convert from mass to molecules. We will also need to convert from mg to g.

$$\frac{6.022 \times 10^{23} \text{ molecules}}{201.70 \text{ g}}$$

$$\frac{.001 \text{ g}}{1 \text{ mg}}$$

STEP 4: Solve. Set up an equation so that unwanted units cancel.

$$(30.0 \text{ mg pseudoephedrine hydrochloride}) \times \left(\frac{.001 \text{ g}}{1 \text{ mg}}\right) \times$$

$$\left(\frac{6.022 \times 10^{23} \text{ molecules}}{201.70 \text{ g}}\right)$$

$$= 8.96 \times 10^{19} \text{ molecules of pseudoephedrine hydrochloride}$$

BALLPARK CHECK: Our estimate for the number of molecules was on the order of 10^{19}, which is consistent with the calculated answer.

WORKED EXAMPLE **6.6** Avogadro's Number: Atom to Mass Conversions

A tiny pencil mark just visible to the naked eye contains about 3×10^{17} atoms of carbon. What is the mass of this pencil mark in grams?

ANALYSIS We are given a number of atoms and need to convert to mass. The conversion factor can be obtained by realizing that the atomic weight of carbon in grams contains Avogadro's number of atoms (6.022×10^{23}).

BALLPARK ESTIMATE Since we are given a number of atoms that is six orders of magnitude less than Avogadro's number, we should get a corresponding mass that is six orders of magnitude less than the molar mass of carbon, which means a mass for the pencil mark of about 10^{-6} g.

SOLUTION

STEP 1: Identify known information. We know the number of carbon atoms in the pencil mark.

3×10^{17} atoms of carbon

STEP 2: Identify answer and units.

Mass of carbon = ?? g

STEP 3: Identify conversion factors. The atomic weight of carbon is 12.01 amu, so 12.01 g of carbon contains 6.022×10^{23} atoms.

$$\frac{12.01 \text{ g carbon}}{6.022 \times 10^{23} \text{ atoms}}$$

STEP 4: Solve. Set up an equation using the conversion factors so that unwanted units cancel.

$$(3 \times 10^{17} \text{ atoms})\left(\frac{12.01 \text{ g carbon}}{6.022 \times 10^{23} \text{ atoms}}\right) = 6 \times 10^{-6} \text{ g carbon}$$

BALLPARK CHECK: The answer is of the same magnitude as our estimate and makes physical sense.

PROBLEM 6.6

Calculate the molecular weight of the following substances:

(a) Ibuprofen, $C_{13}H_{18}O_2$
(b) Phenobarbital, $C_{12}H_{12}N_2O_3$

PROBLEM 6.7

How many molecules of ascorbic acid (vitamin C, $C_6H_8O_6$) are in a 500 mg tablet?

PROBLEM 6.8

What is the mass in grams of 5.0×10^{20} molecules of aspirin ($C_9H_8O_4$)?

◄─◯ KEY CONCEPT PROBLEM 6.9

What is the molecular weight of cytosine, a component of DNA (deoxyribonucleic acid)? (Gray = C, blue = N, red = O, ivory = H.)

Cytosine

6.4 Gram–Mole Conversions

To ensure that we have the correct molecule to molecule (or mole to mole) relationship between reactants as specified by the balanced chemical equation, we can take advantage of the constant mass ratio between reactants, as indicated previously. The mass in grams of 1 mol of any substance (that is, Avogadro's number of molecules or formula units) is called the **molar mass** of the substance.

Molar mass The mass in grams of 1 mol of a substance, numerically equal to molecular weight.

Molar mass = Mass of 1 mol of substance

= Mass of 6.022×10^{23} molecules (formula units) of substance

= Molecular (formula) weight of substance in grams

In effect, molar mass serves as a conversion factor between numbers of moles and mass. If you know how many moles you have, you can calculate their mass; if you know the mass of a sample, you can calculate the number of moles. Suppose, for example, we need to know how much 0.25 mol of water weighs. The molecular weight of H_2O is $(2 \times 1.0 \text{ amu}) + 16.0 \text{ amu} = 18.0 \text{ amu}$, so the molar mass of water is 18.0 g. Thus, the conversion factor between moles of water and mass of water is 18.0 g/mol:

Molar mass used as conversion factor

$$0.25 \text{ mol } H_2O \times \frac{18.0 \text{ g } H_2O}{1 \text{ mol } H_2O} = 4.5 \text{ g } H_2O$$

APPLICATION ▶ Did Ben Franklin Have Avogadro's Number? A Ballpark Calculation

At length being at Clapham, where there is on the common a large pond . . . I fetched out a cruet of oil and dropped a little of it on the water. I saw it spread itself with surprising swiftness upon the surface. The oil, though not more than a teaspoonful, produced an instant calm over a space several yards square which spread amazingly and extended itself gradually . . . making all that quarter of the pond, perhaps half an acre, as smooth as a looking glass. *Excerpt from a letter of Benjamin Franklin to William Brownrigg, 1773.*

▲ **What did these two have in common? [Benjamin Franklin (left), Amedeo Avogadro (right)]**

Benjamin Franklin, author and renowned statesman, was also an inventor and a scientist. Every schoolchild knows of Franklin's experiment with a kite and a key, demonstrating that lightning is electricity. Less well known is that his measurement of the extent to which oil spreads on water makes possible a simple estimate of molecular size and Avogadro's number.

The calculation goes like this: Avogadro's number is the number of molecules in 1 mol of any substance. So if we can estimate both the number of molecules and the number of moles in Franklin's teaspoon of oil, we can calculate Avogadro's number. Let us start by calculating the number of molecules in the oil.

1. The volume (V) of oil Franklin used was 1 tsp = 4.9 cm^3, and the area (A) covered by the oil was 1/2 acre = 2.0×10^7 cm^2. We will assume that the oil molecules are tiny cubes that pack closely together and form a layer only one molecule thick. As shown in the accompanying figure, the volume of the oil is equal to the surface area of the layer times the length (l) of the side of one molecule: $V = A \times l$. Rearranging this equation to find the length then gives us an estimate of molecular size:

$$l = \frac{V}{A} = \frac{4.9 \text{ cm}^3}{2.0 \times 10^7 \text{ cm}^2} = 2.5 \times 10^{-7} \text{ cm}$$

Area = A

2. The area of the oil layer is the area of the side of one molecule (l^2) times the number of molecules (N) of oil: $A = l^2 \times N$. Rearranging this equation gives us the number of molecules:

$$N = \frac{A}{l^2} = \frac{2 \times 10^7 \text{ cm}^2}{(2.5 \times 10^{-7} \text{ cm})^2} = 3.2 \times 10^{20} \text{ molecules}$$

3. To calculate the number of moles, we first need to know the mass (M) of the oil. This could have been determined by weighing the oil, but Franklin neglected to do so. Let us therefore estimate the mass by multiplying the volume (V) of the oil by the density (D) of a typical oil, 0.95 g/cm^3. (Since oil floats on water, it is not surprising that the density of oil is a bit less than the density of water, which is 1.00 g/cm^3.)

$$M = V \times D = 4.9 \text{ cm}^3 \times 0.95 \frac{\text{g}}{\text{cm}^3} = 4.7 \text{ g}$$

4. We now have to make one final assumption about the molecular weight of the oil before we complete the calculation. Assuming that a typical oil has MW = 200, then the mass of 1 mol of oil is 200 g. Dividing the mass of the oil (M) by the mass of 1 mol gives the number of moles of oil:

$$\text{Moles of oil} = \frac{4.7 \text{ g}}{200 \text{ g/mol}} = 0.024 \text{ mol}$$

5. Finally, the number of molecules per mole—Avogadro's number—can be obtained:

$$\text{Avogadro's number} = \frac{3.2 \times 10^{20} \text{ molecules}}{0.024 \text{ mol}} = 1.3 \times 10^{22}$$

The calculation is not very accurate, of course, but Ben was not really intending for us to calculate Avogadro's number when he made a rough estimate of how much his oil spread out. Nevertheless, the result is not too bad for such a simple experiment.

See Additional Problem 6.93 at the end of the chapter.

Alternatively, suppose we need to know how many moles of water are in 27 g of water. The conversion factor is 1 mol/18.0 g:

> Molar mass used as conversion factor

$$27 \text{ g } H_2O \times \frac{1 \text{ mol } H_2O}{18.0 \text{ g } H_2O} = 1.5 \text{ mol } H_2O$$

Worked Examples 6.7 and 6.8 give more practice in gram–mole conversions.

WORKED EXAMPLE 6.7 Molar Mass: Mole to Gram Conversion

The nonprescription pain relievers Advil and Nuprin contain ibuprofen ($C_{13}H_{18}O_2$), whose molecular weight is 206.3 amu (Problem 6.6a). If all the tablets in a bottle of pain reliever together contain 0.082 mol of ibuprofen, what is the number of grams of ibuprofen in the bottle?

ANALYSIS We are given a number of moles and asked to find the mass. Molar mass is the conversion factor between the two.

BALLPARK ESTIMATE Since 1 mol of ibuprofen has a mass of about 200 g, 0.08 mol has a mass of about $0.08 \times 200 \text{ g} = 16 \text{ g}$.

SOLUTION

STEP 1: Identify known information.	0.082 mol ibuprofen in bottle
STEP 2: Identify answer and units.	mass ibuprofen in bottle = ?? g
STEP 3: Identify conversion factor. We use the molecular weight of ibuprofen to convert from moles to grams.	1 mol ibuprofen = 206.3 g $$\frac{206.3 \text{ g ibuprofen}}{1 \text{ mol ibuprofen}}$$
STEP 4: Solve. Set up an equation using the known information and conversion factor so that unwanted units cancel.	$$0.082 \text{ mol } C_{13}H_{18}O_2 \times \frac{206.3 \text{ g ibuprofen}}{1 \text{ mol ibuprofen}} = 17 \text{ g } C_{13}H_{18}O_2$$

BALLPARK CHECK: The calculated answer is consistent with our estimate of 16 g.

WORKED EXAMPLE 6.8 Molar Mass: Gram to Mole Conversion

The maximum dose of sodium hydrogen phosphate (Na_2HPO_4, MW = 142.0 g/mol) that should be taken in one day for use as a laxative is 3.8 g. How many moles of sodium hydrogen phosphate, how many moles of Na^+ ions, and how many total moles of ions are in this dose?

ANALYSIS Molar mass is the conversion factor between mass and number of moles. The chemical formula Na_2HPO_4 shows that each formula unit contains 2 Na^+ ions and 1 HPO_4^{2-} ion.

BALLPARK ESTIMATE The maximum dose is about two orders of magnitude smaller than the molecular weight (approximately 4 g compared to 142 g). Thus, the number of moles of sodium hydrogen phosphate in 3.8 g should be about two orders of magnitude less than one mole. The number of moles of $NaHPO_4$ and total moles of ions, then, should be on the order of 10^{-2}.

SOLUTION

STEP 1: Identify known information. We are given the mass and molecular weight of Na_2HPO_4.	3.8 g Na_2HPO_4; MW = 142.0 amu
STEP 2: Identify answer and units. We need to find the number of moles of Na_2HPO_4, and the total number of moles of ions.	Moles of Na_2HPO_4 = ?? mol Moles of Na^+ ions = ?? mol Total moles of ions = ?? mol

STEP 3: Identify conversion factor. We can use the molecular weight of Na_2HPO_4 to convert from grams to moles.

$$\frac{1 \text{ mol } Na_2HPO_4}{142.0 \text{ g } Na_2HPO_4}$$

STEP 4: Solve. We use the known information and conversion factor to obtain moles of Na_2HPO_4; since 1 mol of Na_2HPO_4 contains 2 mol of Na^+ ions and 1 mol of HPO_4^{2-} ions, we multiply these values by the number of moles in the sample.

$$3.8 \text{ g } \cancel{Na_2HPO_4} \times \frac{1 \text{ mol } Na_2HPO_4}{142.0 \text{ g } \cancel{Na_2HPO_4}} = 0.027 \text{ mol } Na_2HPO_4$$

$$\frac{2 \text{ mol } Na^+}{1 \text{ mol } \cancel{Na_2HPO_4}} \times 0.027 \text{ mol } \cancel{Na_2HPO_4} = 0.054 \text{ mol } Na^+$$

$$\frac{3 \text{ mol ions}}{1 \text{ mol } \cancel{Na_2HPO_4}} \times 0.027 \text{ mol } \cancel{Na_2HPO_4} = 0.081 \text{ mol ions}$$

BALLPARK CHECK: The calculated answers (0.027 mol Na_2HPO_4, 0.081 mol ions) are on the order of 10^{-2}, consistent with our estimate.

PROBLEM 6.10

How many moles of ethyl alcohol, C_2H_6O, are in a 10.0 g sample? How many grams are in a 0.10 mol sample of ethyl alcohol?

PROBLEM 6.11

Which weighs more, 5.00 g or 0.0225 mol of acetaminophen ($C_8H_9NO_2$)?

6.5 Mole Relationships and Chemical Equations

In a typical recipe, the amount of ingredients needed are specified using a variety of units: The amount of flour, for example, is usually specified in cups, whereas the amount of salt or vanilla flavoring might be indicated in teaspoons. In chemical reactions, the appropriate unit to specify the relationship between reactants and products is the mole.

The coefficients in a balanced chemical equation tell how many *molecules*, and thus how many *moles*, of each reactant are needed and how many molecules, and thus moles, of each product are formed. You can then use molar mass to calculate reactant and product masses. If, for example, you saw the following balanced equation for the industrial synthesis of ammonia, you would know that 3 mol of H_2 (3 mol $\times$ 2.0 g/mol = 6.0 g) are required for reaction with 1 mol of N_2 (28.0 g) to yield 2 mol of NH_3 (2 mol $\times$ 17.0 g/mol = 34.0 g).

This number of moles of hydrogen . . .   . . . reacts with this number of moles of nitrogen . . .   to yield this number of moles of ammonia.

$$3 \text{ H}_2 \;+\; 1 \text{ N}_2 \longrightarrow 2 \text{ NH}_3$$

The coefficients can be put in the form of *mole ratios*, which act as conversion factors when setting up factor-label calculations. In the ammonia synthesis, for example, the mole ratio of H_2 to N_2 is 3:1, the mole ratio of H_2 to NH_3 is 3:2, and the mole ratio of N_2 to NH_3 is 1:2:

$$\frac{3 \text{ mol H}_2}{1 \text{ mol N}_2} \quad \frac{3 \text{ mol H}_2}{2 \text{ mol NH}_3} \quad \frac{1 \text{ mol N}_2}{2 \text{ mol NH}_3}$$

Worked Example 6.9 shows how to set up and use mole ratios.

WORKED EXAMPLE **6.9** Balanced Chemical Equations: Mole Ratios

Rusting involves the reaction of iron with oxygen to form iron(III) oxide, Fe_2O_3:

$$4\ Fe(s) + 3\ O_2(g) \longrightarrow 2\ Fe_2O_3(s)$$

(a) What are the mole ratios of the product to each reactant and of the reactants to each other?

(b) How many moles of iron(III) oxide are formed by the complete oxidation of 6.2 mol of iron?

ANALYSIS AND SOLUTION

(a) The coefficients of a balanced equation represent the mole ratios:

$$\frac{2\ mol\ Fe_2O_3}{4\ mol\ Fe} \qquad \frac{2\ mol\ Fe_2O_3}{3\ mol\ O_2} \qquad \frac{4\ mol\ Fe}{3\ mol\ O_2}$$

(b) To find how many moles of Fe_2O_3 are formed, write down the known information—6.2 mol of iron—and select the mole ratio that allows the quantities to cancel, leaving the desired quantity:

$$6.2\ \cancel{mol\ Fe} \times \frac{2\ mol\ Fe_2O_3}{4\ \cancel{mol\ Fe}} = 3.1\ mol\ Fe_2O_3$$

Note that mole ratios are exact numbers and therefore do not limit the number of significant figures in the result of a calculation.

PROBLEM 6.12

(a) Balance the following equation, and tell how many moles of nickel will react with 9.81 mol of hydrochloric acid.

$$Ni(s) + HCl(aq) \longrightarrow NiCl_2(aq) + H_2(g)$$

(b) How many moles of $NiCl_2$ can be formed in the reaction of 6.00 mol of Ni and 12.0 mol of HCl?

PROBLEM 6.13

Plants convert carbon dioxide and water to glucose ($C_6H_{12}O_6$) and oxygen in the process of photosynthesis. Write a balanced equation for this reaction, and determine how many moles of CO_2 are required to produce 15.0 mol of glucose.

6.6 Mass Relationships and Chemical Equations

It is important to remember that the coefficients in a balanced chemical equation represent molecule to molecule (or mole to mole) relationships between reactants and products. Mole ratios make it possible to calculate the molar amounts of reactants and products, but actual amounts of substances used in the laboratory are weighed out in grams. Regardless of what units we use to specify the amount of reactants and/or products (mass, volume, number of molecules, and so on), the reaction always takes place on a mole to mole basis. Thus, we need to be able to carry out three kinds of conversions when doing chemical arithmetic:

- **Mole to mole conversions** are carried out using *mole ratios* as conversion factors. Worked Example 6.9 at the end of the preceding section is an example of this kind of calculation.

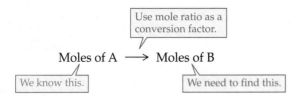

- **Mole to mass and mass to mole conversions** are carried out using *molar mass* as a conversion factor. Worked Examples 6.7 and 6.8 at the end of Section 6.4 are examples of this kind of calculation.

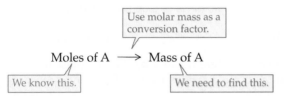

- **Mass to mass conversions** are frequently needed but cannot be carried out directly. If you know the mass of substance A and need to find the mass of substance B, you must first convert the mass of A into moles of A, then carry out a mole to mole conversion to find moles of B, and then convert moles of B into the mass of B (Figure 6.2).

Overall, there are four steps for determining mass relationships among reactants and products:

STEP 1: Write the balanced chemical equation.

STEP 2: Choose molar masses and mole ratios to convert the known information into the needed information.

STEP 3: Set up the factor-label expression and calculate the answer.

STEP 4: Check the answer against the ballpark estimate you made before you began your calculations.

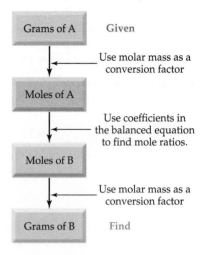

▲ **FIGURE 6.2 A summary of conversions between moles and grams for substances in a chemical reaction.** The numbers of moles tell how many molecules of each substance are needed, as given by the coefficients in the balanced equation; the numbers of grams tell what mass of each substance is needed.

| **WORKED EXAMPLE** | **6.10** Mole Ratios: Mole to Mass Conversions |

In the atmosphere, nitrogen dioxide reacts with water to produce NO and nitric acid, which contributes to pollution by acid rain:

$$3\,NO_2(g) + H_2O(l) \longrightarrow 2\,HNO_3(aq) + NO(g)$$

How many grams of HNO_3 are produced for every 1.0 mol of NO_2 that reacts? The molecular weight of HNO_3 is 63.0 amu.

ANALYSIS We are given the number of moles of a reactant and are asked to find the mass of a product. Problems of this sort always require working in moles and then converting to mass, as outlined in Figure 6.2.

BALLPARK ESTIMATE The molar mass of nitric acid is approximately 60 g/mol, and the coefficients in the balanced equation say that 2 mol of HNO_3 are formed for each 3 mol of NO_2 that undergo reaction. Thus, 1 mol of NO_2 should give about 2/3 mol HNO_3, or 2/3 mol × 60 g/mol = 40 g.

SOLUTION

STEP 1: Write balanced equation.

$3\,NO_2(g) + H_2O(l) \longrightarrow 2\,HNO_3(aq) + NO(g)$

STEP 2: Identify conversion factors. We need a mole to mole conversion to find the number of moles of product, and then a mole to mass conversion to find the mass of product. For the first conversion we use the mole ratio of NO_2 to HNO_3 as a conversion factor, and for the mole to mass calculation we use the molar mass of HNO_3 (63.0 g) as a conversion factor.

$\dfrac{2\ mol\ HNO_3}{3\ mol\ NO_2}$

$\dfrac{63.0\ g\ HNO_3}{1\ mol\ HNO_3}$

STEP 3: Set up factor labels. Identify appropriate mole-ratio factor labels to convert moles NO_2 to moles HNO_3, and moles HNO_3 to grams.

$$1.0 \text{ mol } NO_2 \times \frac{2 \text{ mol } HNO_3}{3 \text{ mol } NO_2} \times \frac{63.0 \text{ g } HNO_3}{1 \text{ mol } HNO_3} = 42 \text{ g } HNO_3$$

STEP 4: BALLPARK CHECK

Our estimate was 40 g!

WORKED EXAMPLE   **6.11** Mole Ratios: Mass to Mole/Mole to Mass Conversions

The following reaction produced 0.022 g of calcium oxalate (CaC_2O_4). What mass of calcium chloride was used as reactant? (The molar mass of CaC_2O_4 is 128.1 g, and the molar mass of $CaCl_2$ is 111.0 g.)

$$CaCl_2(aq) + Na_2C_2O_4(aq) \longrightarrow CaC_2O_4(s) + 2 NaCl(aq)$$

ANALYSIS Both the known information and that to be found are masses, so this is a mass to mass conversion problem. The mass of CaC_2O_4 is first converted into moles, a mole ratio is used to find moles of $CaCl_2$, and the number of moles of $CaCl_2$ is converted into mass.

BALLPARK ESTIMATE The balanced equation says that 1 mol of CaC_2O_4 is formed for each mole of $CaCl_2$ that reacts. Because the formula weights of the two substances are similar, it should take about 0.02 g of $CaCl_2$ to form 0.02 g of CaC_2O_4.

SOLUTION

STEP 1: Write the balanced equation.

$$CaCl_2(aq) + Na_2C_2O_4(aq) \longrightarrow CaC_2O_4(s) + 2 NaCl(aq)$$

STEP 2: Identify conversion factors. Convert the mass of CaC_2O_4 into moles, use a mole ratio to find moles of $CaCl_2$, and convert the number of moles of $CaCl_2$ to mass. We will need three conversion factors.

mass CaC_2O_4 to moles: $\dfrac{1 \text{ mol } CaC_2O_4}{128.1 \text{ g}}$

moles $Ca\ C_2O_4$ to moles $CaCl_2$: $\dfrac{1 \text{ mol } CaCl_2}{1 \text{ mol } CaC_2O_4}$

moles $CaCl_2$ to mass: $\dfrac{111.0 \ CaCl_2}{1 \text{ mol } CaCl_2}$

STEP 3: Set up factor-labels. We will need to perform gram to mole and mole to mole conversions to get from grams CaC_2O_4 to grams $CaCl_2$.

$$0.022 \text{ g } CaC_2O_4 \times \frac{1 \text{ mol } CaC_2O_4}{128.1 \text{ g } CaC_2O_4} \times$$

$$\frac{1 \text{ mol } CaCl_2}{1 \text{ mol } CaC_2O_4} \times \frac{111.0 \text{ g } CaCl_2}{1 \text{ mol } CaCl_2} = 0.019 \text{ g } CaCl_2$$

STEP 4: BALLPARK CHECK

The calculated answer (0.019 g) is consistent with our estimate (0.02 g).

▲ The floral pattern on this glass was created by *etching*, a process based on the reaction of HF with glass.

PROBLEM 6.14

Hydrogen fluoride is one of the few substances that react with glass (which is made of silicon dioxide, SiO_2).

$$4 HF(g) + SiO_2(s) \longrightarrow SiF_4(g) + 2 H_2O(l)$$

(a) How many moles of HF will react completely with 9.90 mol of SiO_2?

(b) What mass of water (in grams) is produced by the reaction of 23.0 g of SiO_2?

PROBLEM 6.15

The tungsten metal used for filaments in light bulbs is made by reaction of tungsten trioxide with hydrogen:

$$WO_3(s) + 3 H_2(g) \longrightarrow W(s) + 3 H_2O(g)$$

How many grams of tungsten trioxide and how many grams of hydrogen must you start with to prepare 5.00 g of tungsten? (For WO_3, MW = 231.8 amu.)

6.7 Limiting Reagent and Percent Yield

All the calculations we have done in the last several sections have assumed that 100% of the reactants are converted to products. Only rarely is this the case in practice, though. Let us return to the recipe for s'mores presented previously:

2 Graham crackers + 1 Roasted marshmallow + $\frac{1}{4}$ Chocolate bar $\longrightarrow$ 1 S'more

When you check your supplies, you find that you have 20 graham crackers, 8 marshmallows, and 3 chocolate bars. How many s'mores can you make? (Answer = 8!) You have enough graham crackers and chocolate bars to make more, but you will run out of marshmallows after you have made eight s'mores. In a similar way, when running a chemical reaction we don't always have the exact amounts of reagents to allow all of them to react completely. The reactant that is exhausted first in such a reaction is called the **limiting reagent.** The amount of product you obtain if the limiting reagent is completely consumed is called the **theoretical yield** of the reaction.

Suppose that, while you are making s'mores, one of your eight marshmallows gets burned to a crisp. If this happens, the actual number of s'mores produced will be less than what you predicted based on the amount of starting materials. Similarly, chemical reactions do not always yield the exact amount of product predicted by the initial amount of reactants. More frequently, a majority of the reactant molecules behave as written but other processes, called *side reactions*, also occur. In addition, some of the product may be lost in handling. As a result, the amount of product actually formed—the reaction's **actual yield**—is somewhat less than the theoretical yield. The amount of product actually obtained in a reaction is usually expressed as a **percent yield**:

$$\text{Percent yield} = \frac{\text{Actual yield}}{\text{Theoretical yield}} \times 100\%$$

A reaction's actual yield is found by weighing the amount of product obtained. The theoretical yield is found by using the amount of limiting reagent in a mass to mass calculation like those illustrated in the preceding section (see Worked Example 6.11). Worked Examples 6.12–6.14 involve limiting reagent, percent yield, actual yield, and theoretical yield calculations.

Limiting reagent The reactant that runs out first.

Theoretical yield The amount of product formed assuming complete reaction of the limiting reagent.

Actual yield The amount of product actually formed in a reaction.

Percent yield The percent of the theoretical yield actually obtained from a chemical reaction.

WORKED EXAMPLE **6.12** Percent Yield

The combustion of acetylene gas (C_2H_2) produces carbon dioxide and water as indicated in the following reaction:

$$2\,C_2H_2(g) + 5\,O_2(g) \longrightarrow 4\,CO_2(g) + 2\,H_2O(g)$$

When 26.0 g of acetylene is burned in sufficient oxygen for complete reaction, the theoretical yield of CO_2 is 88.0 g. Calculate the percent yield for this reaction if the actual yield is only 72.4 g CO_2.

ANALYSIS The percent yield is calculated by dividing the actual yield by the theoretical yield and multiplying by 100.

BALLPARK ESTIMATE The theoretical yield (88.0 g) is close to 100 g. The actual yield (72.4 g) is about 15 g less than the theoretical yield. The actual yield is thus about 15% less than the theoretical yield, so the percent yield is about 85%.

SOLUTION

$$\text{Percent yield} = \frac{\text{Actual yield}}{\text{Theoretical yield}} \times 100 = \frac{72.4 \text{ g } CO_2}{88.0 \text{ g } CO_2} \times 100 = 82.3\%$$

BALLPARK CHECK The calculated percent yield agrees very well with our estimate of 85%.

WORKED EXAMPLE **6.13** Mass to Mole Conversions: Limiting Reagent and Theoretical Yield

The element boron is produced commercially by the reaction of boric oxide with magnesium at high temperature:

$$B_2O_3(l) + 3\,Mg(s) \longrightarrow 2\,B(s) + 3\,MgO(s)$$

What is the theoretical yield of boron when 2350 g of boric oxide is reacted with 3580 g of magnesium? The molar masses of boric oxide and magnesium are 69.6 g/mol and 24.3 g/mol, respectively.

ANALYSIS To calculate theoretical yield, we first have to identify the limiting reagent. The theoretical yield in grams is then calculated from the amount of limiting reagent used in the reaction. The calculation involves the mass to mole and mole to mass conversions discussed in the preceding section.

SOLUTION

STEP 1: **Identify known information.** We have the masses and molar masses of the reagents.

2350 g B_2O_3, molar mass 69.6 g/mol
3580 g Mg, molar mass 24.3 g/mol

STEP 2: **Identify answer and units.** We are solving for the theoretical yield of boron.

Theoretical mass of B = ?? g

STEP 3: **Identify conversion factors.** We can use the molar masses to convert from masses to moles of reactants (B_2O_3, Mg). From moles of reactants, we can use mole ratios from the balanced chemical equation to find the number of moles of B produced. B_2O_3 is the limiting reagent, since complete reaction of this reagent yields less product (B).

$$(2350 \text{ g } B_2O_3) \times \frac{1 \text{ mol } B_2O_3}{69.6 \text{ g } B_2O_3} = 33.8 \text{ mol } B_2O_3$$

$$(3580 \text{ g Mg}) \times \frac{1 \text{ mol Mg}}{24.3 \text{ g Mg}} = 147 \text{ mol Mg}$$

$$33.8 \text{ mol } B_2O_3 \times \frac{2 \text{ mol B}}{1 \text{ mol } B_2O_3} = 67.6 \text{ mol B*}$$

$$147 \text{ mol Mg} \times \frac{2 \text{ mol B}}{3 \text{ mol Mg}} = 98.0 \text{ mol B}$$

(*limiting reagent!)

STEP 4: **Solve.** Once the limiting reagent has been identified (B_2O_3), the theoretical amount of B that should be formed can be calculated using a mole to mass conversion.

$$67.6 \text{ mol B} \times \frac{10.8 \text{ g B}}{1 \text{ mol B}} = 730 \text{ g B}$$

WORKED EXAMPLE **6.14** Mass to Mole Conversion: Percent Yield

The reaction of ethylene with water to give ethyl alcohol (CH_3CH_2OH) occurs in 78.5% actual yield. How many grams of ethyl alcohol are formed by reaction of 25.0 g of ethylene? (For ethylene, MW = 28.0 amu; for ethyl alcohol, MW = 46.0 amu.)

$$H_2C{=}CH_2 + H_2O \longrightarrow CH_3CH_2OH$$

ANALYSIS Treat this as a typical mass relationship problem to find the amount of ethyl alcohol that can theoretically be formed from 25.0 g of ethylene, and then multiply the answer by 78.5% to find the amount actually formed.

BALLPARK ESTIMATE The 25.0 g of ethylene is a bit less than 1 mol; since the percent yield is about 78%, a bit less than 0.78 mol of ethyl alcohol will form—perhaps about 3/4 mol, or $3/4 \times 46$ g = 34 g.

SOLUTION
The theoretical yield of ethyl alcohol is

$$25.0 \text{ g ethylene} \times \frac{1 \text{ mol ethylene}}{28.0 \text{ g ethylene}} \times \frac{1 \text{ mol ethyl alc.}}{1 \text{ mol ethylene}} \times \frac{46.0 \text{ g ethyl alc.}}{1 \text{ mol ethyl alc.}} = 41.1 \text{ g ethyl alcohol}$$

and so the actual yield is

$$41.1 \text{ g ethyl alc.} \times 0.785 = 32.3 \text{ g ethyl alcohol}$$

BALLPARK CHECK The calculated result (32.3 g) is close to our estimate (34 g).

APPLICATION ▶ Gout and Kidney Stones: Problems in Solubility

One of the major pathways in the body for the breakdown of the nucleic acids DNA and RNA is by conversion to a substance called *uric acid*, $C_5H_4N_4O_3$, so named because it was first isolated in 1776 from urine. Most people excrete about 0.5 g of uric acid every day in the form of sodium urate, the salt that results from an acid–base reaction of uric acid. Unfortunately, the amount of sodium urate that dissolves in water (or urine) is fairly low—only about 0.07 mg/mL at the normal body temperature of 37 °C. When too much sodium urate is produced or mechanisms for its elimination fail, its concentration in blood and urine rises, and the excess sometimes precipitates in the joints and kidneys.

Gout is a disorder of nucleic acid metabolism that primarily affects middle-aged men (only 5% of gout patients are women). It is characterized by an increased sodium urate concentration in blood, leading to the deposit of sodium urate crystals in soft tissue around the joints, particularly in the hands and at the base of the big toe. Deposits of the sharp, needlelike crystals cause an extremely painful inflammation that can lead ultimately to arthritis and even to bone destruction.

Just as increased sodium urate concentration in blood can lead to gout, increased concentration in urine can result in the formation of one kind of *kidney stones*, small crystals that precipitate in the kidney. Although often quite small, kidney stones cause excruciating pain when they pass through the ureter, the duct that carries urine from the kidney to the bladder. In some cases, complete blockage of the ureter occurs.

The GOUT.

▲ This old cartoon leaves little doubt about how painful gout can be.

Treatment of excessive sodium urate production involves both dietary modification and drug therapy. Foods such as liver, sardines, and asparagus should be avoided, and drugs such as allopurinol can be taken to lower production of sodium urate. Allopurinol functions by inhibiting the action of an enzyme called *xanthine oxidase*, thereby blocking a step in nucleic acid metabolism.

See Additional Problem 6.95 at the end of the chapter.

PROBLEM 6.21

Predict whether a precipitation reaction will occur in the following situations:

(a) $NiCl_2(aq) + (NH_4)_2S(aq) \longrightarrow$

(b) $AgNO_3(aq) + CaBr_2(aq) \longrightarrow$

6.10 Acids, Bases, and Neutralization Reactions

When acids and bases are mixed in the correct proportion, both acidic and basic properties disappear because of a **neutralization reaction**. The most common kind of neutralization reaction occurs between an acid (generalized as HA), and a metal hydroxide (generalized as MOH), to yield water and a salt. The H^+ ion from the acid combines with the OH^- ion from the base to give neutral H_2O, whereas the anion from the acid (A^-) combines with the cation from the base (M^+) to give the salt:

Neutralization reaction The reaction of an acid with a base.

A neutralization reaction: $HA(aq) + MOH(aq) \longrightarrow H_2O(l) + MA(aq)$
                                     Acid   Base   Water   A salt

The reaction of hydrochloric acid with potassium hydroxide to produce potassium chloride is an example:

$$HCl(aq) + KOH(aq) \longrightarrow H_2O(l) + KCl(aq)$$

Another kind of neutralization reaction occurs between an acid and a carbonate (or bicarbonate) to yield water, a salt, and carbon dioxide. Hydrochloric acid reacts with potassium carbonate, for example, to give H_2O, KCl, and CO_2:

$$2\,HCl(aq) + K_2CO_3(aq) \longrightarrow H_2O(l) + 2\,KCl(aq) + CO_2(g)$$

The reaction occurs because the carbonate ion (CO_3^{2-}) reacts initially with H^+ to yield H_2CO_3, which is unstable and immediately decomposes to give CO_2 plus H_2O.

We will defer a more complete discussion of carbonates as bases until Chapter 10, but note for now that they yield OH^- ions when dissolved in water just as KOH and other bases do.

$$K_2CO_3(s) + H_2O(l) \xrightarrow{\text{Dissolve in water}} 2K^+(aq) + HCO_3^-(aq) + OH^-(aq)$$

Looking Ahead

Acids and bases are enormously important in biological chemistry. We will see in Chapter 18, for instance, how acids and bases affect the structure and properties of proteins.

WORKED EXAMPLE **6.17** Chemical Reactions: Acid–Base Neutralization

Write an equation for the neutralization reaction of aqueous HBr and aqueous $Ba(OH)_2$.

SOLUTION

The reaction of HBr with $Ba(OH)_2$ involves the combination of a proton (H^+) from the acid with OH^- from the base to yield water and a salt ($BaBr_2$).

$$2\,HBr(aq) + Ba(OH)_2(aq) \longrightarrow 2\,H_2O(l) + BaBr_2(aq)$$

PROBLEM 6.22

Write and balance equations for the following acid–base neutralization reactions:

(a) $CsOH(aq) + H_2SO_4(aq) \longrightarrow$

(b) $Ca(OH)_2(aq) + CH_3CO_2H(aq) \longrightarrow$

(c) $NaHCO_3(aq) + HBr(aq) \longrightarrow$

6.11 Redox Reactions

Oxidation-reduction (redox) reactions, the third and final category of reactions that we will discuss, are more complex than precipitation and neutralization reactions. Look, for instance, at the following examples and see if you can tell what they have in common. Copper metal reacts with aqueous silver nitrate to form silver metal and aqueous copper(II) nitrate; iron rusts in air to form iron(III) oxide; the zinc metal container on the outside of a battery reacts with manganese dioxide and ammonium chloride inside the battery to generate electricity and give aqueous zinc chloride plus manganese(III) oxide. Although these and many thousands of other reactions appear unrelated, all are examples of redox reactions.

$$Cu(s) + 2\,AgNO_3(aq) \longrightarrow 2\,Ag(s) + Cu(NO_3)_2(aq)$$
$$2\,Fe(s) + 3\,O_2(g) \longrightarrow Fe_2O_3(s)$$
$$Zn(s) + 2\,MnO_2(s) + 2\,NH_4Cl(s) \longrightarrow$$
$$ZnCl_2(aq) + Mn_2O_3(s) + 2\,NH_3(aq) + H_2O(l)$$

Historically, the word *oxidation* referred to the combination of an element with oxygen to yield an oxide, and the word *reduction* referred to the removal of oxygen from an oxide to yield the element. Today, though, the words have taken on a much broader meaning. An **oxidation** is now defined as the loss of one or more electrons by an atom, and a **reduction** is the gain of one or more electrons. Thus, an oxidation–reduction reaction, or redox reaction, is one in which *electrons are transferred from one atom to another.*

Oxidation The loss of one or more electrons by an atom.

Reduction The gain of one or more electrons by an atom.

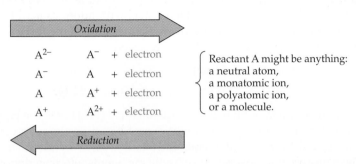

Reactant A might be anything: a neutral atom, a monatomic ion, a polyatomic ion, or a molecule.

▲ The copper wire reacts with aqueous Ag^+ ion and becomes coated with metallic silver. At the same time, copper(II) ions go into solutions, producing the blue color.

Take the reaction of copper with aqueous Ag^+ as an example. Copper metal gives an electron to each of two Ag^+ ions, forming Cu^{2+} and silver metal. Copper is oxidized in the process, and Ag^+ is reduced. You can follow the transfer of the electrons by noting that the charge on the copper increases from 0 to +2 when it loses two electrons, whereas the charge on Ag^+ decreases from +1 to 0 when it gains an electron.

Similarly, in the reaction of aqueous iodide ion with bromine, iodide ion gives an electron to bromine, forming iodine and bromide ion. Iodide ion is oxidized as its charge increases from −1 to 0, and bromine is reduced as its charge decreases from 0 to −1.

As these examples show, oxidation and reduction always occur together. Whenever one substance loses an electron (is oxidized), another substance must gain that electron (be reduced). The substance that gives up an electron and causes the reduction—the copper atom in the reaction of Cu with Ag^+ and the iodide ion in the reaction of I^- with Br_2—is called a **reducing agent**. The substance that gains an electron and causes the oxidation—the silver ion in the reaction of Cu with Ag^+ and the bromine molecule in the reaction of I^- with Br_2—is called an **oxidizing agent**. The charge on the reducing agent increases during the reaction, and the charge on the oxidizing agent decreases.

Reducing agent A reactant that causes a reduction by giving up electrons to another reactant.

Oxidizing agent A reactant that causes an oxidation by taking electrons from another reactant.

Reducing agent Loses one or more electrons
Causes reduction
Undergoes oxidation
Becomes more positive (or less negative)

Oxidizing agent   Gains one or more electrons
Causes oxidation
Undergoes reduction
Becomes more negative (or less positive)

Among the simplest of redox processes is the reaction of an element, usually a metal, with an aqueous cation to yield a different element and a different ion. Iron metal reacts with aqueous copper(II) ion, for example, to give iron(II) ion and copper metal. Similarly, magnesium metal reacts with aqueous acid to yield magnesium ion and hydrogen gas. In both cases, the reactant element (Fe or Mg) is oxidized, and the reactant ion (Cu^{2+} or H^+) is reduced.

$$Fe(s) + Cu^{2+}(aq) \longrightarrow Fe^{2+}(aq) + Cu(s)$$
$$Mg(s) + 2\,H^+(aq) \longrightarrow Mg^{2+}(aq) + H_2(g)$$

The reaction of a metal with water or aqueous acid (H^+) to release H_2 gas is a particularly important process. As you might expect based on the periodic properties discussed in Section 4.2, the alkali metals and alkaline earth metals (on the left side of the periodic table) are the most powerful reducing agents (electron donors), so powerful that they even react with pure water, in which the concentration of H^+ is very low. Ionization energy, which is a measure of how easily an element will lose an electron, tends to decrease as we move to the left and down in the periodic table. In contrast, metals toward the middle of the periodic table, such as iron and chromium, do not lose electrons as readily; they react only with aqueous acids but not with water. Those metals near the bottom right of the periodic table, such as platinum and gold, react with neither aqueous acid nor water. At the other extreme, the reactive nonmetals at the top right of the periodic table are extremely weak reducing agents and instead are powerful oxidizing agents (electron acceptors). This is, again, predictable based on the periodic property of electron affinity (, Section 4.2) which becomes more energetically favored as we move up and to the right in the periodic table.

We can make a few generalizations about the redox behavior of metals and nonmetals.

1. In reactions involving metals and nonmetals, metals tend to lose electrons while nonmetals tend to gain electrons. The number of electrons lost or gained can often be predicted based on the position of the element in the periodic table. (, Section 4.5)

2. In reactions involving nonmetals, the "more metallic" element (farther down and/or to the left in the periodic table) tends to lose electrons, and the "less metallic" element (up and/or to the right) tends to gain electrons.

Redox reactions involve almost every element in the periodic table, and they occur in a vast number of processes throughout nature, biology, and industry. Here are just a few examples:

▲ Magnesium metal reacts with aqueous acid to give hydrogen gas and Mg^{2+} ion.

- **Corrosion** is the deterioration of a metal by oxidation, such as the rusting of iron in moist air. The economic consequences of rusting are enormous: It has been estimated that up to one-fourth of the iron produced in the United States is used to replace bridges, buildings, and other structures that have been destroyed by corrosion. (The raised dot in the formula $Fe_2O_3 \cdot H_2O$ for rust indicates that one water molecule is associated with each Fe_2O_3 in an undefined way.)

- **Combustion** is the burning of a fuel by rapid oxidation with oxygen in air. Gasoline, fuel oil, natural gas, wood, paper, and other organic substances of carbon and hydrogen are the most common fuels that burn in air. Even some metals, though, will burn in air. Magnesium and calcium are examples.

$$CH_4(g) + 2\,O_2(g) \longrightarrow CO_2(g) + 2\,H_2O(l)$$
Methane
(natural gas)

$$2\,Mg(s) + O_2(g) \longrightarrow 2\,MgO(s)$$

- **Respiration** is the process of breathing and using oxygen for the many biological redox reactions that provide the energy that living organisms need. We will see in Chapters 21–22 that energy is released from food molecules slowly and in complex, multistep pathways, but the overall result of respiration is similar to that of combustion reactions. For example, the simple sugar glucose ($C_6H_{12}O_6$) reacts with O_2 to give CO_2 and H_2O according to the following equation:

$$C_6H_{12}O_6 + 6\,O_2 \longrightarrow 6\,CO_2 + 6\,H_2O + \text{Energy}$$
Glucose
(a carbohydrate)

- **Bleaching** makes use of redox reactions to decolorize or lighten colored materials. Dark hair is bleached to turn it blond, clothes are bleached to remove stains, wood pulp is bleached to make white paper, and so on. The oxidizing agent used depends on the situation: hydrogen peroxide (H_2O_2) is used for hair, sodium hypochlorite (NaOCl) for clothes, and elemental chlorine for wood pulp, but the principle is always the same. In all cases, colored organic materials are destroyed by reaction with strong oxidizing agents.
- **Metallurgy,** the science of extracting and purifying metals from their ores, makes use of numerous redox processes. Worldwide, approximately 800 million tons of iron is produced each year by reduction of the mineral hematite, Fe_2O_3, with carbon monoxide.

$$Fe_2O_3(s) + 3\,CO(g) \longrightarrow 2\,Fe(s) + 3\,CO_2(g)$$

WORKED EXAMPLE **6.18** Chemical Reactions: Redox Reactions

For the following reactions, indicate which atom is oxidized and which is reduced, based on the definitions provided in this section. Identify the oxidizing and reducing agents.

(a) $Cu(s) + Pt^{2+}(aq) \rightarrow Cu^{2+}(aq) + 2\,Pt(s)$

(b) $2\,Mg(s) + CO_2(g) \rightarrow 2\,MgO(s) + C(s)$

ANALYSIS The definitions for oxidation include a loss of electrons, an increase in charge, and a gain of oxygen atoms; reduction is defined as a gain of electrons, a decrease in charge, or a loss of oxygen atoms.

SOLUTION

(a) In this reaction, the charge on the Cu atom increases from 0 to 2+. This corresponds to a loss of 2 electrons. The Cu is therefore oxidized, and acts as the reducing agent. Conversely, each Pt^{2+} ion undergoes a decrease in charge from 2+ to 0, corresponding to a gain of 2 electrons per Pt^{2+} ion. The Pt^{2+} is reduced, and acts as the oxidizing agent.

(b) In this case, the gain or loss of oxygen atoms is the easiest way to identify which atoms are oxidized and reduced. The Mg atom is gaining oxygen to form MgO; therefore, the Mg is being oxidized and acts as the reducing agent. The C atom in CO_2 is losing oxygen. Therefore, the C atom is being reduced and acts as the oxidizing agent.

WORKED EXAMPLE **6.19** Chemical Reactions: Identifying Oxidizing/ Reducing Agents

For the respiration and metallurgy examples discussed above, identify the atoms being oxidized and reduced, and label the oxidizing and reducing agents.

ANALYSIS Again, using the definitions of oxidation and reduction provided in this section, we can determine which atom(s) are gaining/losing electrons or gaining/losing oxygen atoms.

SOLUTION

$$\textit{Respiration:} \quad C_6H_{12}O_6 + 6\,O_2 \longrightarrow 6\,CO_2 + 6\,H_2O$$

Since the charge associated with the individual atoms is not evident, we will use the definition of oxidation/reduction as the gaining/losing of oxygen atoms. In this reaction, there is only one reactant besides oxygen ($C_6H_{12}O_6$), so we must determine *which* atom in the compound is changing. The ratio of carbon to oxygen in $C_6H_{12}O_6$ is 1:1, while the ratio in CO_2 is 1:2. Therefore, the C atoms are gaining oxygen and are oxidized; the C is the reducing agent. The O_2 is the oxidizing agent. Note that the ratio of hydrogen to oxygen in $C_6H_{12}O_6$ and in H_2O is 2:1. The H atoms are neither oxidized nor reduced.

$$\textit{Metallurgy:} \quad Fe_2O_3(s) + 3\,CO(g) \longrightarrow 2\,Fe(s) + 3\,CO_2(g)$$

The Fe_2O_3 is losing oxygen to form Fe(s); it is being reduced, and acts as the oxidizing agent. In contrast, the CO is gaining oxygen to form CO_2; it is being oxidized and acts as the reducing agent.

WORKED EXAMPLE **6.20** Chemical Reactions: Identifying Redox Reactions

For the following reactions, identify the atom(s) being oxidized and reduced:

    (a) $2\,Al(s) + 3\,Cl_2(g) \longrightarrow 2\,AlCl_3(s)$

    (b) $C(s) + 2\,Cl_2(g) \longrightarrow CCl_4(l)$

ANALYSIS Again, there is no obvious increase or decrease in charge to indicate a gain or loss of electrons. Also, the reactions do not involve a gain or loss of oxygen. We can, however, evaluate the reactions in terms of the typical behavior of metals and nonmetals in reactions.

SOLUTION

    (a) In this case, we have the reaction of a metal (Al) with a nonmetal (Cl_2). Since metals tend to lose electrons and nonmetals tend to gain electrons, we can assume that the Al atom is oxidized (loss of electrons), and the Cl_2 is reduced (gains electrons).

    (b) In this case, we have a reaction involving two nonmetals. The carbon is the more metallic element (farther to the left) and is more likely to lose electrons (oxidized). The less metallic element (Cl) will tend to gain electrons and be reduced.

PROBLEM 6.23

Identify the oxidized reactant, the reduced reactant, the oxidizing agent, and the reducing agent in the following reactions:

(a) $Fe(s) + Cu^{2+}(aq) \longrightarrow Fe^{2+}(aq) + Cu(s)$

(b) $Mg(s) + Cl_2(g) \longrightarrow MgCl_2(s)$

(c) $2\,Al(s) + Cr_2O_3(s) \longrightarrow 2\,Cr(s) + Al_2O_3(s)$

PROBLEM 6.24

Potassium, a silvery metal, reacts with bromine, a corrosive, reddish liquid, to yield potassium bromide, a white solid. Write the balanced equation, and identify the oxidizing and reducing agents.

APPLICATION ▶ Batteries

Imagine life without batteries: no cars (they do not start very easily without their batteries!), no heart pacemakers, no flashlights, no hearing aids, no portable computers, radios, cellular phones, or thousands of other things. Modern society cannot exist without batteries.

Although they come in many types and sizes, all batteries are based on redox reactions. In a typical redox reaction carried out in the laboratory—say, the reaction of zinc metal with Ag^+ to yield Zn^{2+} and silver metal—the reactants are simply mixed in a flask and electrons are transferred by direct contact between the reactants. In a battery, however, the two reactants are kept in separate compartments and the electrons are transferred through a wire running between them.

▲ Think of all the devices we use every day–laptop computers, cell phones, iPods—that depend on batteries.

The common household battery used for flashlights and radios is the *dry-cell*, developed in 1866. One reactant is a can of zinc metal, and the other is a paste of solid manganese dioxide. A graphite rod sticks into the MnO_2 paste to provide electrical contact, and a moist paste of ammonium chloride separates the two reactants. When the zinc can and the graphite rod are connected by a wire, zinc sends electrons flowing through the wire toward the MnO_2 in a redox reaction. The resultant electrical current can then be used to light a bulb or power a radio. The accompanying figure shows a cutaway view of a dry-cell battery.

$$Zn(s) + 2\ MnO_2(s) + 2\ NH_4Cl(s) \longrightarrow$$
$$ZnCl_2(aq) + Mn_2O_3(s) + 2\ NH_3(aq) + H_2O(l)$$

Closely related to the dry-cell battery is the familiar *alkaline* battery, in which the ammonium chloride paste is replaced by an alkaline, or basic, paste of NaOH or KOH. The alkaline battery has a longer life than the standard dry-cell battery because the zinc container corrodes less easily under basic conditions. The redox reaction is

$$Zn(s) + 2\ MnO_2(s) \longrightarrow ZnO(aq) + Mn_2O_3(s)$$

The batteries used in implanted medical devices such as pacemakers must be small, corrosion-resistant, reliable, and able to last up to 10 years. Nearly all pacemakers being implanted today—about 750,000 each year—use titanium-encased, lithium-iodine batteries, whose redox reaction is

$$2\ Li(s) + I_2(s) \longrightarrow 2\ LiI(aq)$$

See Additional Problem 6.96 at the end of the chapter.

▲ A dry-cell battery. The cutaway view shows the two reactants that make up the redox reaction.

▲ Sulfur burns in air to yield SO_2. Is this a redox reaction?

Oxidation number A number that indicates whether an atom is neutral, electron-rich, or electron-poor.

6.12 Recognizing Redox Reactions

How can you tell when a redox reaction is taking place? When ions are involved, it is simply a matter of determining whether there is a change in the charges. For reactions involving metals and nonmetals, we can predict gain or loss of electrons as discussed previously. When molecular substances are involved, though, it is not as obvious. Is the combining of sulfur with oxygen a redox reaction? If so, which partner is the oxidizing agent and which is the reducing agent?

$$S(s) + O_2(g) \longrightarrow SO_2(g)$$

One way to evaluate this reaction is in terms of the oxygen gain by sulfur, indicating that S atoms are oxidized and O atoms are reduced. But can we also look at this reaction in terms of the gain or loss of electrons by the S and O atoms? Because oxygen is more electronegative than sulfur (Section 5.8), the oxygen atoms in SO_2 attract the electrons in the S—O bonds more strongly than sulfur does, giving the oxygen atoms a larger share of the electrons than sulfur. (, p. 129) By extending the ideas of oxidation and reduction to an increase or decrease in electron *sharing* instead of complete electron *transfer*, we can say that the sulfur atom is oxidized in its reaction with oxygen because it loses a share in some electrons, whereas the oxygen atoms are reduced because they gain a share in some electrons.

A formal system has been devised for keeping track of changes in electron sharing, and thus for determining whether atoms are oxidized or reduced in reactions. To each atom in a substance, we assign a value called an **oxidation number** (or *oxidation state*), which indicates whether the atom is neutral, electron-rich, or electron-poor. By comparing the oxidation number of an atom before and after reaction, we can tell whether the atom has gained or lost shares in electrons. Note that *oxidation numbers do not necessarily imply ionic charges*. They are simply a convenient device for keeping track of electrons in redox reactions.

The rules for assigning oxidation numbers are straightforward:

- **An atom in its elemental state has an oxidation number of 0.**

Elements in natural elemental state have oxidation number = 0

Na H_2 Br_2

- **A monatomic ion has an oxidation number equal to its charge.**

Oxidation number +1   Oxidation number +2   Oxidation number −1   Oxidation number −2

Na^+ Ca^{2+} Cl^- O^{2-}

- **In a molecular compound, an atom usually has the same oxidation number it would have if it were a monatomic ion.** Recall from Chapters 4 and 5 that the less electronegative elements (hydrogen and metals) on the left side of the periodic table tend to form cations, and the more electronegative elements (oxygen, nitrogen, and the halogens) near the top right of the periodic table tend to form anions. (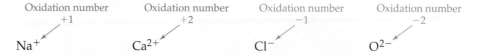, p. 88) Hydrogen and metals therefore have positive oxidation numbers in most compounds, whereas reactive nonmetals generally have negative oxidation numbers. Hydrogen is usually +1, oxygen is usually −2, nitrogen is usually −3, and halogens are usually −1:

+1 −1   +1 −2 +1   +1 −3 +1

H—Cl   H—O—H   H—N—H
                               |
                              H ← +1

For compounds with more than one nonmetal element, such as SO_2, NO, or CO_2, the more electronegative element—oxygen in these examples—has a negative oxidation number and the less electronegative element has a positive oxidation number. Thus, in answer to the question posed at the beginning of this section, combining sulfur with oxygen to form SO_2 is a redox reaction because the oxidation number of sulfur increases from 0 to +4 and that of oxygen decreases from 0 to −2.

$$\overset{-2}{O}-\overset{+4}{S}=\overset{-2}{O} \qquad \overset{+2}{N}=\overset{-2}{O} \qquad \overset{-2}{O}=\overset{+4}{C}=\overset{-2}{O}$$

- **The sum of the oxidation numbers in a neutral compound is 0.** Using this rule, the oxidation number of any atom in a compound can be found if the oxidation numbers of the other atoms are known. In the SO_2 example just mentioned, each of the two O atoms has an oxidation number of −2, so the S atom must have an oxidation number of +4. In HNO_3, the H atom has an oxidation number of +1 and the strongly electronegative O atom has an oxidation number of −2, so the N atom must have an oxidation number of +5. In a polyatomic ion, the sum of the oxidation numbers equals the charge on the ion.

$$\overset{+1}{H}-\overset{-2}{O}-\overset{+5}{N}=\overset{-2}{O} \qquad \text{Total } = 1 + 5 + 3(-2) = 0$$
$$\underset{\overset{|}{O}\,{}^{-2}}{}$$

Worked Examples 6.21 and 6.22 show further instances of assigning and using oxidation numbers.

WORKED EXAMPLE **6.21** Redox Reactions: Oxidation Numbers

What is the oxidation number of the titanium atom in $TiCl_4$? Name the compound using a Roman numeral (Section 4.11).

SOLUTION
Chlorine, a reactive nonmetal, is more electronegative than titanium and has an oxidation number of −1. Because there are four chlorine atoms in $TiCl_4$, the oxidation number of titanium must be +4. The compound is named titanium(IV) chloride. Note that the Roman numeral IV in the name of this molecular compound refers to the oxidation number +4 rather than to a true ionic charge.

WORKED EXAMPLE **6.22** Redox Reactions: Identifying Redox Reactions

Use oxidation numbers to show that the production of iron metal from its ore (Fe_2O_3) by reaction with charcoal (C) is a redox reaction. Which reactant has been oxidized, and which has been reduced? Which reactant is the oxidizing agent, and which is the reducing agent?

$$2\,Fe_2O_3(s) + 3\,C(s) \longrightarrow 4\,Fe(s) + 3\,CO_2(g)$$

SOLUTION
The idea is to assign oxidation numbers to both reactants and products, and see if there has been a change. In the production of iron from Fe_2O_3, the oxidation number of Fe changes from +3 to 0, and the oxidation number of C changes from 0 to +4. Iron has thus been reduced (decrease in oxidation number), and carbon has been oxidized (increase in oxidation number). Oxygen is neither oxidized nor reduced because its oxidation number does not change. Carbon is the reducing agent and Fe_2O_3 is the oxidizing agent.

$$2\,\overset{+3}{Fe_2}\overset{-2}{O_3} + 3\,\overset{0}{C} \longrightarrow 4\,\overset{0}{Fe} + 3\,\overset{+4}{C}\overset{-2}{O_2}$$

PROBLEM 6.25

What are the oxidation numbers of the metal atoms in the following compounds? Name each, using the oxidation number as a Roman numeral.

(a) VCl_3 **(b)** $SnCl_4$ **(c)** CrO_3 **(d)** $Cu(NO_3)_2$ **(e)** $NiSO_4$

PROBLEM 6.26

Assign an oxidation number to each atom in the reactants and products shown here to determine which of the following reactions are redox reactions:

(a) $Na_2S(aq) + NiCl_2(aq) \longrightarrow 2\,NaCl(aq) + NiS(s)$
(b) $2\,Na(s) + 2\,H_2O(l) \longrightarrow 2\,NaOH(aq) + H_2(g)$
(c) $C(s) + O_2(g) \longrightarrow CO_2(g)$
(d) $CuO(s) + 2\,HCl(aq) \longrightarrow CuCl_2(aq) + H_2O(l)$
(e) $2\,MnO_4^-(aq) + 5\,SO_2(g) + 2\,H_2O(l) \longrightarrow 2\,Mn^{2+}(aq) + 5\,SO_4^{2-}(aq) +$
    $4\,H^+(aq)$

6.13 Net Ionic Equations

In the equations we have been writing up to this point, all the substances involved in reactions have been written using their full formulas. In the precipitation reaction of lead(II) nitrate with potassium iodide mentioned in Section 6.8, for example, only the parenthetical (*aq*) indicated that the reaction actually takes place in aqueous solution, and nowhere was it explicitly indicated that ions are involved:

$$Pb(NO_3)_2(aq) + 2\,KI(aq) \longrightarrow 2\,KNO_3(aq) + PbI_2(s)$$

In fact, lead(II) nitrate, potassium iodide, and potassium nitrate dissolve in water to yield solutions of ions. Thus, it is more accurate to write the reaction as an **ionic equation**, in which all the ions are explicitly shown:

Ionic equation An equation in which ions are explicitly shown.

An ionic equation: $Pb^{2+}(aq) + 2\,NO_3^-(aq) + 2\,K^+(aq) + 2\,I^-(aq) \longrightarrow$
$$2\,K^+(aq) + 2\,NO_3^-(aq) + PbI_2(s)$$

A look at this ionic equation shows that the NO_3^- and K^+ ions undergo no change during the reaction. They appear on both sides of the reaction arrow and act merely as **spectator ions**, that is, they are present but play no role. The actual reaction, when stripped to its essentials, can be described more simply by writing a **net ionic equation**, which includes only the ions that undergo change and ignores all spectator ions:

Spectator ion An ion that appears unchanged on both sides of a reaction arrow.

Net ionic equation An equation that does not include spectator ions.

Ionic equation: $Pb^{2+}(aq) + 2\,\cancel{NO_3^-}(aq) + 2\,\cancel{K^+}(aq) + 2\,I^-(aq) \longrightarrow$
$$2\,\cancel{K^+}(aq) + 2\,\cancel{NO_3^-}(aq) + PbI_2(s)$$

Net Ionic equation: $Pb^{2+}(aq) + 2\,I^-(aq) \rightarrow PbI_2(s)$

Note that a net ionic equation, like all chemical equations, must be balanced both for atoms and for charge, with all coefficients reduced to their lowest whole numbers. Note also that all compounds that do *not* give ions in solution—all insoluble compounds and all molecular compounds—are represented by their full formulas.

We can apply the concept of ionic equations to acid–base neutralization reactions and redox reactions as well. Consider the neutralization reaction between KOH and HNO_3:

$$KOH(aq) + HNO_3(aq) \longrightarrow H_2O(l) + KNO_3(aq)$$

Since acids and bases are identified based on the ions they form when dissolved in aqueous solutions, we can write an ionic equation for this reaction:

Ionic equation: $\cancel{K^+(aq)} + OH^-(aq) + H^+(aq) + \cancel{NO_3^-(aq)} \longrightarrow$

$$H_2O(l) + \cancel{K^+(aq)} + \cancel{NO_3^-(aq)}$$

Eliminating the spectator ions (K^+ and NO_3^-) we obtain the net ionic equation for the neutralization reaction:

Net ionic equation: $OH^-(aq) + H^+(aq) \longrightarrow H_2O(l)$

The net ionic equation confirms the basis of the acid–base neutralization; the OH^- from the base and the H^+ from the acid neutralize each other to form water.

Similarly, many redox reactions can be viewed in terms of ionic equations. Consider the reaction between $Cu(s)$ and $AgNO_3$ from Section 6.11:

$$Cu(s) + 2\,AgNO_3(aq) \longrightarrow 2\,Ag^+(aq) + Cu(NO_3)_2(aq)$$

The aqueous products and reactants can be written as dissolved ions:

Ionic equation: $Cu(s) + 2\,Ag^+(aq) + 2\,\cancel{NO_3^-(aq)} \longrightarrow$

$$2\,Ag(s) + Cu^{2+}(aq) + 2\,\cancel{NO_3^-(aq)}$$

Again, eliminating the spectator ions (NO_3^-), we obtain the net ionic equation for this redox reaction:

Net ionic equation: $Cu(s) + 2\,Ag^+(aq) \longrightarrow 2\,Ag(s) + Cu^{2+}(aq)$

It is now clear that the $Cu(s)$ loses two electrons and is oxidized, whereas each Ag^+ ion gains an electron and is reduced.

WORKED EXAMPLE   **6.23** Chemical Reactions: Net Ionic Reactions

Write balanced net ionic equations for the following reactions:

(a) $AgNO_3(aq) + ZnCl_2(aq) \longrightarrow$
(b) $HCl(aq) + Ca(OH)_2(aq) \longrightarrow$
(c) $6\,HCl(aq) + 2\,Al(s) \longrightarrow 2\,AlCl_3(aq) + 3\,H_2(g)$

SOLUTION

(a) The solubility guidelines discussed in Section 6.9 predict that a precipitate of insoluble AgCl forms when aqueous solutions of Ag^+ and Cl^- are mixed. Writing all the ions separately gives an ionic equation, and eliminating spectator ions Zn^{2+} and NO_3^- gives the net ionic equation.

Ionic equation: $2\,Ag^+(aq) + \cancel{2\,NO_3^-(aq)} + \cancel{Zn^{2+}(aq)} + 2\,Cl^-(aq) \longrightarrow$

$$2\,AgCl(s) + \cancel{Zn^{2+}(aq)} + \cancel{2\,NO_3^-(aq)}$$

Net ionic equation: $2\,Ag^+(aq) + 2\,Cl^-(aq) \longrightarrow 2\,AgCl(s)$

The coefficients can all be divided by 2 to give

Net ionic equation: $Ag^+(aq) + Cl^-(aq) \longrightarrow AgCl(s)$

A check shows that the equation is balanced for atoms and charge (zero on each side).

(b) Allowing the acid HCl to react with the base $Ca(OH)_2$ leads to a neutralization reaction. Writing the ions separately, and remembering to write a complete formula for water, gives an ionic equation. Then eliminating the spectator ions and dividing the coefficients by 2 gives the net ionic equation.

Ionic equation: $2 H^+(aq) + \cancel{2 Cl^-(aq)} + \cancel{Ca^{2+}(aq)} + 2 OH^-(aq) \longrightarrow$
$$2 H_2O(l) + \cancel{Ca^{2+}(aq)} + \cancel{2 Cl^-(aq)}$$

Net ionic equation: $H^+(aq) + OH^-(aq) \longrightarrow H_2O(l)$

A check shows that atoms and charges are the same on both sides of the equation.

(c) The reaction of Al metal with acid (HCl) is a redox reaction. The Al is oxidized, since the oxidation number increases from $0 \rightarrow +3$, whereas the H in HCl is reduced from $+1 \rightarrow 0$. We write the ionic equation by showing the ions that are formed for each aqueous ionic species. Eliminating the spectator ions yields the net ionic equation.

Ionic equation: $6 H^+(aq) + \cancel{6 Cl^-(aq)} + 2 Al(s) \longrightarrow$
$$2 Al^{3+}(aq) + \cancel{6 Cl^-(aq)} + 3 H_2(g)$$

Net ionic equation: $6 H^+(aq) + 2 Al(s) \longrightarrow 2 Al^{3+}(aq) + 3 H_2(g)$

A check shows that atoms and charges are the same on both sides of the equation.

PROBLEM 6.27

Write net ionic equations for the following reactions:

(a) $Zn(s) + Pb(NO_3)_2(aq) \longrightarrow Zn(NO_3)_2(aq) + Pb(s)$

(b) $2 KOH(aq) + H_2SO_4(aq) \longrightarrow K_2SO_4(aq) + 2 H_2O(l)$

(c) $2 FeCl_3(aq) + SnCl_2(aq) \longrightarrow 2 FeCl_2(aq) + SnCl_4(aq)$

KEY WORDS

Actual yield, *p. 159*

Avogadro's number (N_A), *p. 150*

Balanced equation, *p. 144*

Chemical equation, *p. 143*

Coefficient, *p. 144*

Formula weight, *p. 148*

Ionic equation, *p. 174*

Law of conservation of mass, *p. 144*

Limiting reagent, *p. 159*

Molar mass, *p. 152*

Mole, *p. 150*

Molecular weight (MW), *p. 148*

Net ionic equation, *p. 174*

Neutralization reaction, *p. 165*

SUMMARY: REVISITING THE CHAPTER GOALS

1. **How are chemical reactions written?** Chemical equations must be *balanced*; that is, the numbers and kinds of atoms must be the same in both the reactants and the products. To balance an equation, *coefficients* are placed before formulas but the formulas themselves cannot be changed.

2. **What is the mole, and why is it useful in chemistry?** A *mole* refers to *Avogadro's number* (6.022×10^{23}) of formula units of a substance. One mole of any substance has a mass (a *molar mass*) equal to the molecular or formula weight of the substance in grams. Because equal numbers of moles contain equal numbers of formula units, molar masses act as conversion factors between numbers of molecules and masses in grams.

3. **How are molar quantities and mass quantities related?** The coefficients in a balanced chemical equation represent the numbers of moles of reactants and products in a reaction. Thus, the ratios of coefficients act as *mole ratios* that relate amounts of reactants and/or products. By using molar masses and mole ratios in factor-label calculations, unknown masses or molar amounts can be found from known masses or molar amounts.

4. **What are the limiting reagent, theoretical yield, and percent yield of a reaction?** The *limiting reagent* is the reactant that runs out first. The *theoretical yield* is the amount of product that would be formed based on the amount of the limiting reagent. The *actual yield* of a reaction is the amount of product obtained. The *percent yield* is the amount of product obtained divided by the amount theoretically possible and multiplied by 100%.

5. How are chemical reactions of ionic compounds classified? There are three common types of reactions of ionic compounds: *Precipitation reactions* are processes in which an insoluble solid called a *precipitate* is formed. Most precipitations take place when the anions and cations of two ionic compounds change partners. Solubility guidelines for ionic compounds are used to predict when precipitation will occur.

Acid–base neutralization reactions are processes in which an acid reacts with a base to yield water plus an ionic compound called a *salt*. Since acids produce H^+ ions and bases produce OH^- ions when dissolved in water, a neutralization reaction removes H^+ and OH^- ions from solution and yields neutral H_2O.

Oxidation–reduction (redox) reactions are processes in which one or more electrons are transferred between reaction partners. An *oxidation* is defined as the loss of one or more electrons by an atom, and a *reduction* is the gain of one or more electrons. An *oxidizing agent* causes the oxidation of another reactant by accepting electrons, and a *reducing agent* causes the reduction of another reactant by donating electrons.

6. What are oxidation numbers, and how are they used? *Oxidation numbers* are assigned to atoms in reactants and products to provide a measure of whether an atom is neutral, electron-rich, or electron-poor. By comparing the oxidation number of an atom before and after reaction, we can tell whether the atom has gained or lost shares in electrons and thus whether a redox reaction has occurred.

Oxidation, *p. 167*

Oxidation number, *p. 172*

Oxidation–reduction (redox) reaction, *p. 162*

Oxidizing agent, *p. 167*

Percent yield, *p. 159*

Precipitate, *p. 161*

Product, *p. 144*

Reactant, *p. 144*

Reducing agent, *p. 167*

Reduction, *p. 167*

Salt, *p. 162*

Solubility, *p. 163*

Spectator ion, *p. 174*

Theoretical yield, *p. 159*

UNDERSTANDING KEY CONCEPTS

6.28 Assume that the mixture of substances in drawing (a) undergoes a reaction. Which of the drawings (b)–(d) represents a product mixture consistent with the law of conservation of mass?

(a)

(b)   **(c)**   **(d)**

6.29 Reaction of A (green spheres) with B (blue spheres) is shown in the following diagram:

Which equation best describes the reaction?

(a) $A_2 + 2B \longrightarrow A_2B_2$ **(b)** $10A + 5B_2 \longrightarrow 5A_2B_2$
(c) $2A + B_2 \longrightarrow A_2B_2$ **(d)** $5A + 5B_2 \longrightarrow 5A_2B_2$

6.30 If blue spheres represent nitrogen atoms and red spheres represent oxygen atoms in the following diagrams, which box represents reactants and which represents products for the reaction $2NO(g) + O_2(g) \longrightarrow 2NO_2(g)$?

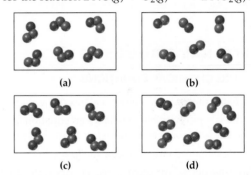

(a)   **(b)**

(c)   **(d)**

6.31 Methionine, an amino acid used by organisms to make proteins, can be represented by the following ball-and-stick molecular model. Write the formula for methionine, and give its molecular weight (red = O, gray = C, blue = N, yellow = S, ivory = H).

Methionine

6.32 The following diagram represents the reaction of A_2 (red spheres) with B_2 (blue spheres):

(a) Write a balanced equation for the reaction.

(b) How many moles of product can be made from 1.0 mol of A_2? From 1.0 mol of B_2?

6.33 Assume that an aqueous solution of a cation (represented as red spheres in the diagram) is allowed to mix with a solution of an anion (represented as yellow spheres). Three possible outcomes are represented by boxes (1)–(3):

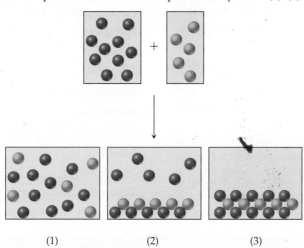

(1)   (2)   (3)

Which outcome corresponds to each of the following reactions?

(a) $2\,Na^+(aq) + CO_3{}^{2-}(aq) \longrightarrow$

(b) $Ba^{2+}(aq) + CrO_4{}^{2-}(aq) \longrightarrow$

(c) $2\,Ag^+(aq) + SO_3{}^{2-}(aq) \longrightarrow$

6.34 An aqueous solution of a cation (represented as blue spheres in the diagram) is allowed to mix with a solution of an anion (represented as green spheres) and the following result is obtained:

Which combinations of cation and anion, chosen from the following lists, are compatible with the observed results? Explain.

Cations: $Na^+, Ca^{2+}, Ag^+, Ni^{2+}$

Anions: $Cl^-, CO_3{}^{2-}, CrO_4{}^{2-}, NO_3{}^-$

6.35 The following drawing represents the reaction of ethylene oxide with water to give ethylene glycol, a compound used as automobile antifreeze. What mass in grams of ethylene oxide is needed to react with 9.0 g of water, and what mass in grams of ethylene glycol is formed?

Ethylene oxide

Ethylene glycol

ADDITIONAL PROBLEMS

BALANCING CHEMICAL EQUATIONS

6.36 What is meant by the term "balanced equation"?

6.37 Why is it not possible to balance an equation by changing the subscript on a substance, say from H_2O to H_2O_2?

6.38 Write balanced equations for the following reactions:

(a) Gaseous sulfur dioxide reacts with water to form aqueous sulfurous acid (H_2SO_3).

(b) Liquid bromine reacts with solid potassium metal to form solid potassium bromide.

(c) Gaseous propane (C_3H_8) burns in oxygen to form gaseous carbon dioxide and water vapor.

6.39 Balance the following equation for the synthesis of hydrazine, N_2H_4, a substance used as rocket fuel.

$$NH_3(g) + Cl_2(g) \longrightarrow N_2H_4(l) + NH_4Cl(s)$$

6.40 Which of the following equations are balanced? Balance those that need it.

(a) $2\,C_2H_6(g) + 5\,O_2(g) \longrightarrow 2\,CO_2(g) + 6\,H_2O(l)$

(b) $3\,Ca(OH)_2(aq) + 2\,H_3PO_4(aq) \longrightarrow$
$$Ca_3(PO_4)_2(aq) + 6\,H_2O(l)$$

(c) $Mg(s) + O_2(g) \longrightarrow 2\,MgO(s)$

(d) $K(s) + H_2O(l) \longrightarrow KOH(aq) + H_2(g)$

6.41 Which of the following equations are balanced? Balance those that need it.

(a) $CaC_2 + 2\,H_2O \longrightarrow Ca(OH)_2 + C_2H_2$

(b) $C_2H_8N_2 + 2\,N_2O_4 \longrightarrow 2\,N_2 + 2\,CO_2 + 4\,H_2O$

(c) $3\,MgO + 2\,Fe \longrightarrow Fe_2O_3 + 3\,Mg$

(d) $N_2O \longrightarrow N_2 + O_2$

6.42 Balance the following equations:

(a) $Hg(NO_3)_2(aq) + LiI(aq) \longrightarrow LiNO_3(aq) + HgI_2(s)$

(b) $I_2(s) + Cl_2(g) \longrightarrow ICl_5(s)$

(c) $Al(s) + O_2(g) \longrightarrow Al_2O_3(s)$

(d) $CuSO_4(aq) + AgNO_3(aq) \longrightarrow$
$$Ag_2SO_4(s) + Cu(NO_3)_2(aq)$$

(e) $Mn(NO_3)_3(aq) + Na_2S(aq) \longrightarrow$
$$Mn_2S_3(s) + NaNO_3(aq)$$

(f) $NO_2(g) + O_2(g) \longrightarrow N_2O_5(g)$

(g) $P_4O_{10}(s) + H_2O(l) \longrightarrow H_3PO_4(aq)$

6.43 Write a balanced equation for the reaction of aqueous sodium carbonate (Na_2CO_3) with aqueous nitric acid (HNO_3) to yield CO_2, $NaNO_3$, and H_2O.

6.44 When organic compounds are burned, they react with oxygen to form CO_2 and H_2O. Write balanced equations for the combustion of the following:

(a) C_4H_{10} (butane, used in lighters)

(b) C_2H_6O (ethyl alcohol, used in gasohol and as race car fuel)

(c) C_8H_{18} (octane, a component of gasoline)

MOLAR MASSES AND MOLES

6.45 What is a mole of a substance? How many molecules are in 1 mol of a molecular compound?

6.46 What is the difference between molecular weight and formula weight? Between molecular weight and molar mass?

6.47 How many Na^+ ions are in a mole of Na_2SO_4? How many SO_4^{2-} ions?

6.48 How many moles of ions are in 1.75 mol of K_2SO_4?

6.49 How many calcium atoms are in 16.2 g of calcium?

6.50 What is the mass in grams of 2.68×10^{22} atoms of uranium?

6.51 Calculate the molar mass of each of the following compounds:

(a) Calcium carbonate, $CaCO_3$
(b) Urea, $CO(NH_2)_2$
(c) Ethylene glycol, $C_2H_6O_2$

6.52 How many moles of carbon atoms are there in 1 mol of each compound in Problem 6.51?

6.53 How many atoms of carbon and how many grams of carbon are there in 1 mol of each compound in Problem 6.51?

6.54 Caffeine has the formula $C_8H_{10}N_4O_2$. If an average cup of coffee contains approximately 125 mg of caffeine, how many moles of caffeine are in one cup?

6.55 How many moles of aspirin, $C_9H_8O_4$, are in a 500 mg tablet?

6.56 What is the molar mass of diazepam (Valium), $C_{16}H_{13}ClN_2O$?

6.57 Calculate the molar masses of the following substances:

(a) Aluminum sulfate, $Al_2(SO_4)_3$
(b) Sodium bicarbonate, $NaHCO_3$
(c) Diethyl ether, $(C_2H_5)_2O$
(d) Penicillin V, $C_{16}H_{18}N_2O_5S$

6.58 How many moles are present in a 4.50 g sample of each compound listed in Problem 6.57?

6.59 The recommended daily dietary intake of calcium for adult men and pre-menopausal women is 1000 mg/day. Calcium citrate , $Ca_3(C_6H_5O_7)_2$ (MW = 498.5 g/mol), is a common dietary supplement. What mass of calcium citrate would be needed to provide the recommended daily intake of calcium?

6.60 What is the mass in grams of 0.0015 mol of aspirin, $C_9H_8O_4$? How many aspirin molecules are there in this 0.0015 mol sample?

6.61 How many grams are present in a 0.075 mol sample of each compound listed in Problem 6.57?

6.62 The principal component of many kidney stones is calcium oxalate, CaC_2O_4. A kidney stone recovered from a typical patient contains 8.5×10^{20} formula units of calcium oxalate. How many moles of CaC_2O_4 are present in this kidney stone? What is the mass of the kidney stone in grams?

MOLE AND MASS RELATIONSHIPS FROM CHEMICAL EQUATIONS

6.63 At elevated temperatures in an automobile engine, N_2 and O_2 can react to yield NO, an important cause of air pollution.

(a) Write a balanced equation for the reaction.
(b) How many moles of N_2 are needed to react with 7.50 mol of O_2?
(c) How many moles of NO can be formed when 3.81 mol of N_2 reacts?

(d) How many moles of O_2 must react to produce 0.250 mol of NO?

6.64 Ethyl acetate reacts with H_2 in the presence of a catalyst to yield ethyl alcohol:

$$C_4H_8O_2(l) + H_2(g) \longrightarrow C_2H_6O(l)$$

(a) Write a balanced equation for the reaction.
(b) How many moles of ethyl alcohol are produced by reaction of 1.5 mol of ethyl acetate?
(c) How many grams of ethyl alcohol are produced by reaction of 1.5 mol of ethyl acetate with H_2?
(d) How many grams of ethyl alcohol are produced by reaction of 12.0 g of ethyl acetate with H_2?
(e) How many grams of H_2 are needed to react with 12.0 g of ethyl acetate?

6.65 The active ingredient in Milk of Magnesia (an antacid) is magnesium hydroxide, $Mg(OH)_2$. A typical dose (one tablespoon) contains 1.2 g of $Mg(OH)_2$. Calculate (a) the molar mass of magnesium hydroxide, and (b) the amount of magnesium hydroxide (in moles) in one teaspoon.

6.66 Ammonia, NH_3, is prepared for use as a fertilizer by reacting N_2 with H_2.

(a) Write a balanced equation for the reaction.
(b) How many moles of N_2 are needed for reaction to make 16.0 g of NH_3?
(c) How many grams of H_2 are needed to react with 75.0 g of N_2?

6.67 Hydrazine, N_2H_4, a substance used as rocket fuel, reacts with oxygen as follows:

$$N_2H_4(l) + O_2(g) \longrightarrow NO_2(g) + H_2O(g)$$

(a) Balance the equation.
(b) How many moles of oxygen are needed to react with 165 g of hydrazine?
(c) How many grams of oxygen are needed to react with 165 g of hydrazine?

6.68 One method for preparing pure iron from Fe_2O_3 is by reaction with carbon monoxide:

$$Fe_2O_3(s) + CO(g) \longrightarrow Fe(s) + CO_2(g)$$

(a) Balance the equation.
(b) How many grams of CO are needed to react with 3.02 g of Fe_2O_3?
(c) How many grams of CO are needed to react with 1.68 mol of Fe_2O_3?

6.69 Magnesium metal burns in oxygen to form magnesium oxide, MgO.

(a) Write a balanced equation for the reaction.
(b) How many grams of oxygen are needed to react with 25.0 g of Mg? How many grams of MgO will result?
(c) How many grams of Mg are needed to react with 25.0 g of O_2? How many grams of MgO will result?

6.70 Titanium metal is obtained from the mineral rutile, TiO_2. How many kilograms of rutile are needed to produce 95 kg of Ti?

6.71 In the preparation of iron from hematite (Problem 6.68) how many moles of carbon monoxide are needed to react completely with 105 kg of Fe_2O_3.

LIMITING REAGENT AND PERCENT YIELD

6.72 Once made by heating wood in the absence of air, methanol (CH_3OH) is now made by reacting carbon monoxide and hydrogen at high pressure:

$$CO(g) + 2\,H_2(g) \longrightarrow CH_3OH(l)$$

(a) If 25.0 g of CO is reacted with 6.00 g of H_2, which is the limiting reagent?

(b) How many grams of CH_3OH can be made from 10.0 g of CO if it all reacts?

(c) If 9.55 g of CH_3OH is recovered when the amounts in part (b) are used, what is the percent yield?

6.73 In Problem 6.67 hydrazine reacted with oxygen according to the (unbalanced) equation:

$$N_2H_4(l) + O_2(g) \longrightarrow NO_2(g) + H_2O(g)$$

(a) If 75.0 kg of hydrazine are reacted with 75.0 kg of oxygen, which is the limiting reagent?

(b) How many kilograms of NO_2 are produced from the reaction of 75.0 kg of the limiting reagent?

(c) If 59.3 kg of NO_2 are obtained from the reaction in part (a), what is the percent yield?

6.74 Dichloromethane, CH_2Cl_2, the solvent used to decaffeinate coffee beans, is prepared by reaction of CH_4 with Cl_2.

(a) Write the balanced equation. (HCl is also formed.)

(b) How many grams of Cl_2 are needed to react with 50.0 g of CH_4?

(c) How many grams of dichloromethane are formed from 50.0 g of CH_4 if the percent yield for the reaction is 76%?

6.75 Cisplatin $[Pt(NH_3)_2Cl_2]$, a compound used in cancer treatment, is prepared by reaction of ammonia with potassium tetrachloroplatinate:

$$K_2PtCl_4 + 2\,NH_3 \longrightarrow 2\,KCl + Pt(NH_3)_2Cl_2$$

(a) How many grams of NH_3 are needed to react with 55.8 g of K_2PtCl_4?

(b) How many grams of cisplatin are formed from 55.8 g of K_2PtCl_4 if the percent yield for the reaction is 95%?

TYPES OF CHEMICAL REACTIONS

6.76 Identify the following reactions as a precipitation, neutralization, or redox reaction:

(a) $Mg(s) + 2\,HCl(aq) \longrightarrow MgCl_2(aq) + H_2(g)$

(b) $KOH(aq) + HNO_3(aq) \longrightarrow KNO_3(aq) + H_2O(l)$

(c) $Pb(NO_3)_2(aq) + 2\,HBr(aq) \longrightarrow$ $PbBr_2(s) + 2\,HNO_3(aq)$

(d) $Ca(OH)_2(aq) + 2\,HCl(aq) \longrightarrow 2\,H_2O(l) + CaCl_2(aq)$

6.77 Write balanced ionic equations and net ionic equations for the following reactions:

(a) Aqueous sulfuric acid is neutralized by aqueous potassium hydroxide.

(b) Aqueous magnesium hydroxide is neutralized by aqueous hydrochloric acid.

6.78 Write balanced ionic equations and net ionic equations for the following reactions:

(a) A precipitate of barium sulfate forms when aqueous solutions of barium nitrate and potassium sulfate are mixed.

(b) Zinc ion and hydrogen gas form when zinc metal reacts with aqueous sulfuric acid.

6.79 Which of the following substances are likely to be soluble in water?

(a) $ZnSO_4$ **(b)** $NiCO_3$
(c) $PbCl_2$ **(d)** $Ca_3(PO_4)_2$

6.80 Which of the following substances are likely to be soluble in water?

(a) Ag_2O **(b)** $Ba(NO_3)_2$
(c) $SnCO_3$ **(d)** Al_2S_3

6.81 Use the solubility guidelines in Section 6.9 to predict whether a precipitation reaction will occur when aqueous solutions of the following substances are mixed.

(a) $NaOH + HClO_4$ **(b)** $FeCl_2 + KOH$
(c) $(NH_4)_2SO_4 + NiCl_2$

6.82 Use the solubility guidelines in Section 6.9 to predict whether precipitation reactions will occur between the listed pairs of reactants. Write balanced equations for those reactions that should occur.

(a) NaBr and $Hg_2(NO_3)_2$ **(b)** $CuCl_2$ and K_2SO_4
(c) $LiNO_3$ and $Ca(CH_3CO_2)_2$ **(d)** $(NH_4)_2CO_3$ and $CaCl_2$
(e) KOH and $MnBr_2$ **(f)** Na_2S and $Al(NO_3)_3$

6.83 Write net ionic equations for the following reactions:

(a) $Mg(s) + CuCl_2(aq) \longrightarrow MgCl_2(aq) + Cu(s)$

(b) $2\,KCl(aq) + Pb(NO_3)_2(aq) \longrightarrow$ $PbCl_2(s) + 2\,KNO_3(aq)$

(c) $2\,Cr(NO_3)_3(aq) + 3\,Na_2S(aq) \longrightarrow$ $Cr_2S_3(s) + 6\,NaNO_3(aq)$

6.84 Write net ionic equations for the following reactions:

(a) $2\,AuCl_3(aq) + 3\,Sn(s) \longrightarrow 3\,SnCl_2(aq) + 2\,Au(s)$

(b) $2\,NaI(aq) + Br_2(l) \longrightarrow 2\,NaBr(aq) + I_2(s)$

(c) $2\,AgNO_3(aq) + Fe(s) \longrightarrow Fe(NO_3)_2(aq) + 2\,Ag(s)$

REDOX REACTIONS AND OXIDATION NUMBERS

6.85 Where in the periodic table are the best reducing agents found? The best oxidizing agents?

6.86 Where in the periodic table are the most easily reduced elements found? The most easily oxidized?

6.87 In each of the following, tell whether the substance gains electrons or loses electrons in a redox reaction:

(a) An oxidizing agent

(b) A reducing agent

(c) A substance undergoing oxidation

(d) A substance undergoing reduction

6.88 For the following substances, tell whether the oxidation number increases or decreases in a redox reaction:

(a) An oxidizing agent

(b) A reducing agent

(c) A substance undergoing oxidation

(d) A substance undergoing reduction

6.89 Assign an oxidation number to each element in the following compounds or ions:

(a) N_2O_5 **(b)** SO_3^{2-}
(c) CH_2O **(d)** $HClO_3$

6.90 Assign an oxidation number to the metal in the following compounds:

(a) $CoCl_3$ **(b)** $FeSO_4$ **(c)** UO_3
(d) CuF_2 **(e)** TiO_2 **(f)** SnS

6.91 Which element is oxidized and which is reduced in the following reactions?

(a) $Si(s) + 2\,Cl_2(g) \longrightarrow SiCl_4(l)$
(b) $Cl_2(g) + 2\,NaBr(aq) \longrightarrow Br_2(aq) + 2\,NaCl(aq)$
(c) $SbCl_3(s) + Cl_2(g) \longrightarrow SbCl_5(s)$

6.92 Which element is oxidized and which is reduced in the following reactions?

(a) $2\,SO_2(g) + O_2(g) \longrightarrow 2\,SO_3(g)$
(b) $2\,Na(s) + Cl_2(g) \longrightarrow 2\,NaCl(s)$
(c) $CuCl_2(aq) + Zn(s) \longrightarrow ZnCl_2(aq) + Cu(s)$
(d) $2\,NaCl(aq) + F_2(g) \longrightarrow 2\,NaF(aq) + Cl_2(g)$

Applications

6.93 What do you think are some of the errors involved in calculating Avogadro's number by spreading oil on a pond? [*Did Ben Franklin Have Avogadro's Number?*, p. 153]

6.94 Ferrous sulfate is one dietary supplement used to treat iron-deficiency anemia. What are the molecular formula and molecular weight of this compound? How many milligrams of iron are in 250 mg of ferrous sulfate? [*Anemia— A Limiting Reagent Problem?*, p. 162]

6.95 Sodium urate, the principal constituent of some kidney stones, has the formula $NaC_5H_3N_4O_3$. In aqueous solution, the solubility of sodium urate is only 0.067 g/L. How many moles of sodium urate dissolve in 1.00 L of water? [*Gout and Kidney Stones*, p. 165]

6.96 Identify the oxidizing and reducing agents in a typical dry-cell battery. [*Batteries*, p. 171]

General Questions and Problems

6.97 Zinc metal reacts with hydrochloric acid (HCl) according to the equation:

$$Zn(s) + 2\,HCl(aq) \longrightarrow ZnCl_2(aq) + H_2(g)$$

(a) How many grams of hydrogen are produced if 15.0 g of zinc reacts?
(b) Is this a redox reaction? If so, tell what is reduced, what is oxidized, and reducing and oxidizing agents.

6.98 Lithium oxide is used aboard the space shuttle to remove water from the atmosphere according to the equation

$$Li_2O(s) + H_2O(g) \longrightarrow 2\,LiOH(s)$$

(a) How many grams of Li_2O must be carried on board to remove 80.0 kg of water?
(b) Is this a redox reaction? Why or why not?

6.99 Balance the following equations.

(a) The thermite reaction, used in welding:

$$Al(s) + Fe_2O_3(s) \longrightarrow Al_2O_3(l) + Fe(l)$$

(b) The explosion of ammonium nitrate:

$$NH_4NO_3(s) \longrightarrow N_2(g) + O_2(g) + H_2O(g)$$

6.100 Batrachotoxin, $C_{31}H_{42}N_2O_6$, an active component of South American arrow poison, is so toxic that 0.05 μg can kill a person. How many molecules is this?

6.101 Look at the solubility guidelines in Section 6.9 and predict whether a precipitate forms when $CuCl_2(aq)$ and $Na_2CO_3(aq)$ are mixed. If so, write both the balanced equation and the net ionic equation for the process.

6.102 When table sugar (sucrose, $C_{12}H_{22}O_{11}$) is heated, it decomposes to form C and H_2O.

(a) Write a balanced equation for the process.
(b) How many grams of carbon are formed by the breakdown of 60.0 g of sucrose?
(c) How many grams of water are formed when 6.50 g of carbon are formed?

6.103 Although Cu is not sufficiently active to react with acids, it can be dissolved by concentrated nitric acid, which functions as an oxidizing agent according to the following equation:

$$Cu(s) + 4\,HNO_3(aq) \longrightarrow$$
$$Cu(NO_3)_2(aq) + 2\,NO_2(g) + 2\,H_2O(l)$$

(a) Write the net ionic equation for this process.
(b) Is 35.0 g of HNO_3 sufficient to dissolve 5.00 g of copper?

6.104 The net ionic equation for the Breathalyzer test used to indicate alcohol concentration in the body is

$$16\,H^+(aq) + 2\,Cr_2O_7{}^{2-}(aq) + 3\,C_2H_6O(aq) \longrightarrow$$
$$3\,C_2H_4O_2(aq) + 4\,Cr^{3+}(aq) + 11\,H_2O(l)$$

(a) How many grams of $K_2Cr_2O_7$ must be used to consume 1.50 g of C_2H_6O?
(b) How many grams of $C_2H_4O_2$ can be produced from 80.0 g of C_2H_6O?

6.105 Ethyl alcohol is formed by enzyme action on sugars and starches during fermentation:

$$C_6H_{12}O_6 \longrightarrow 2\,CO_2 + 2\,C_2H_6O$$

If the density of ethyl alcohol is 0.789 g/mL, how many quarts can be produced by the fermentation of 100.0 lb of sugar?

6.106 Balance the following equations:

(a) $Al(OH)_3(aq) + HNO_3(aq) \longrightarrow$
$Al(NO_3)_3(aq) + H_2O(l)$
(b) $AgNO_3(aq) + FeCl_3(aq) \longrightarrow$
$AgCl(s) + Fe(NO_3)_3(aq)$
(c) $(NH_4)_2Cr_2O_7(s) \longrightarrow Cr_2O_3(s) + H_2O(g) + N_2(g)$
(d) $Mn_2(CO_3)_3(s) \longrightarrow Mn_2O_3(s) + CO_2(g)$

6.107 White phosphorus (P_4) is a highly reactive form of elemental phosphorus that reacts with oxygen to form a variety of molecular compounds, including diphosphorus pentoxide.

(a) Write the balanced chemical equation for this reaction.
(b) Calculate the oxidation number for P and O on both sides of the reaction, and identify the oxidizing and reducing agents.

6.108 The combustion of fossil fuels containing sulfur contributes to the phenomenon known as acid rain. The combustion process releases sulfur in the form of sulfur dioxide, which is converted to sulfuric acid in a process involving two reactions.

(a) In the first reaction, sulfur dioxide reacts with molecular oxygen to form sulfur trioxide. Write the balanced chemical equation for this reaction.
(b) In the second reaction, sulfur trioxide reacts with water in the atmosphere to form sulfuric acid. Write the balanced chemical equation for this reaction.
(c) Calculate the oxidation number for the S atom in each compound in these reactions.

CHAPTER 7

Chemical Reactions: Energy, Rates, and Equilibrium

CONCEPTS TO REVIEW

Energy and Heat
(Section 2.10)

Ionic Bonds
(Section 4.3)

Covalent Bonds
(Section 5.1)

Chemical Equations
(Section 6.1)

▲ Many spontaneous chemical reactions are accompanied by the release of energy, in some cases explosively.

CONTENTS

CHAPTER GOALS

In this chapter, we will look more closely at chemical reactions and answer the following questions:

1. What energy changes take place during reactions?

THE GOAL: Be able to explain the factors that influence energy changes in chemical reactions.

2. What is "free energy," and what is the criterion for spontaneity in chemistry?

THE GOAL: Be able to define enthalpy, entropy, and free-energy changes, and explain how the values of these quantities affect chemical reactions.

3. What determines the rate of a chemical reaction?

THE GOAL: Be able to explain activation energy and other factors that determine reaction rate.

4. What is chemical equilibrium?

THE GOAL: Be able to describe what occurs in a reaction at equilibrium and write the equilibrium equation for a given reaction.

5. What is Le Châtelier's principle?

THE GOAL: Be able to state Le Châtelier's principle and use it to predict the effect of changes in temperature, pressure, and concentration on reactions.

We have yet to answer many questions about reactions. Why, for instance, do reactions occur? Just because a balanced equation can be written does not mean it will take place. We can write a balanced equation for the reaction of gold with water, for example, but the reaction does not occur in practice, so your gold jewelry is safe in the shower.

Balanced, but does not occur $2 Au(s) + 3 H_2O(l) \longrightarrow Au_2O_3(s) + 3 H_2(g)$

To describe reactions more completely, several fundamental questions are commonly asked: Is energy released or absorbed when a reaction occurs? Is a given reaction fast or slow? Does a reaction continue until all reactants are converted to products or is there a point beyond which no additional product forms?

7.1 Energy and Chemical Bonds

There are two fundamental and interconvertible kinds of energy: *potential* and *kinetic*. **Potential energy** is stored energy. The water in a reservoir behind a dam, an automobile poised to coast downhill, and a coiled spring have potential energy waiting to be released. **Kinetic energy**, by contrast, is the energy of motion. When the water falls over the dam and turns a turbine, when the car rolls downhill, or when the spring uncoils and makes the hands on a clock move, the potential energy in each is converted to kinetic energy. Of course, once all the potential energy is converted, nothing further occurs. The water at the bottom of the dam, the car at the bottom of the hill, and the uncoiled spring no longer have potential energy and thus undergo no further change.

In chemical compounds, the attractive forces between ions (ionic bonds) or atoms (covalent bonds) are a form of potential energy. In many chemical reactions, this potential energy is often converted into **heat**—the kinetic energy of the moving particles that make up the compound. Because the reaction products have less potential energy than the reactants, we say that the products are *more stable* than the reactants. The term "stable" is used in chemistry to describe a substance that has little remaining potential energy and consequently little tendency to undergo further change. Whether a reaction occurs, and how much energy or heat is associated with the reaction, depends on the amount of potential energy contained in the reactants and products.

Potential energy   Stored energy.

Kinetic energy   The energy of an object in motion.

Heat   A measure of the transfer of thermal energy.

7.2 Heat Changes during Chemical Reactions

Why does chlorine react so easily with many elements and compounds but nitrogen does not? What difference between Cl_2 molecules and N_2 molecules accounts for their different reactivities? The answer is that the nitrogen–nitrogen triple bond

Bond dissociation energy The amount of energy that must be supplied to break a bond and separate the atoms in an isolated gaseous molecule.

is much *stronger* than the chlorine–chlorine single bond and cannot be broken as easily in chemical reactions.

The strength of a covalent bond is measured by its **bond dissociation energy**, defined as the amount of energy that must be supplied to break the bond and separate the atoms in an isolated gaseous molecule. The triple bond in N_2, for example, has a bond dissociation energy of 226 kcal/mol, whereas the single bond in chlorine has a bond dissociation energy of only 58 kcal/mol:

$$:N:::N: \xrightarrow{\text{226 kcal/mol}} :\dot{N}\cdot + \cdot\dot{N}: \qquad N_2 \text{ bond dissociation energy } = 226 \text{ kcal/mol}$$

$$:\ddot{C}l:\ddot{C}l: \xrightarrow{\text{58 kcal/mol}} :\ddot{C}l\cdot + \cdot\ddot{C}l: \qquad Cl_2 \text{ bond dissociation energy } = 58 \text{ kcal/mol}$$

Endothermic A process or reaction that absorbs heat and has a positive ΔH.

Exothermic A process or reaction that releases heat and has a negative ΔH.

A chemical change like bond breaking that absorbs heat is said to be **endothermic**, from the Greek words *endon* (within) and *therme* (heat), meaning that *heat* is put *in*. The reverse of bond breaking is bond formation, a process that *releases* heat and is described as **exothermic**, from the Greek *exo* (outside), meaning that heat goes *out*. The amount of energy released in forming a bond is numerically the same as that absorbed in breaking it. When nitrogen atoms combine to give N_2, 226 kcal/mol of heat is released. Similarly, when Cl_2 molecules are pulled apart into atoms, 58 kcal/mol of heat is absorbed; when chlorine atoms combine to give Cl_2, 58 kcal/mol of heat is released.

$$:\dot{N}\cdot + \cdot\dot{N}: \longrightarrow :N:::N: + 226 \text{ kcal/mol heat released}$$

$$:\ddot{C}l\cdot + \cdot\ddot{C}l: \longrightarrow :\ddot{C}l:\ddot{C}l: + 58 \text{ kcal/mol heat released}$$

The same energy relationships that govern bond breaking and bond formation apply to every physical or chemical change. That is, the amount of heat transferred during a change in one direction is numerically equal to the amount of heat transferred during the change in the opposite direction. Only the *direction* of the heat transfer is different. This relationship reflects a fundamental law of nature called the *law of conservation of energy:*

Law of conservation of energy Energy can be neither created nor destroyed in any physical or chemical change.

If more energy could be released by an exothermic reaction than was consumed in its reverse, the law would be violated and we could "manufacture" energy out of nowhere by cycling back and forth between forward and reverse reactions—a clear impossibility.

In every chemical reaction, some bonds in the reactants are broken and new bonds are formed in the products. The difference between the energy absorbed in breaking bonds and the energy released in forming bonds is called the **heat of reaction** and is a quantity that we can measure. Heats of reaction that are measured when a reaction is held at constant pressure are represented by the abbreviation ΔH, where Δ (the Greek capital letter delta) is a general symbol used to indicate "a change in" and *H* is a quantity called **enthalpy**. Thus, the value of ΔH represents the **enthalpy change** that occurs during a reaction. The terms *enthalpy change* and *heat of reaction* are often used interchangeably, but we will generally use the latter term in this book.

Enthalpy (*H*) A measure of the amount of energy associated with substances involved in a reaction.

Heat of reaction ΔH = Energy of bonds formed in products minus
(Enthalpy change) energy of bonds broken in reactants

7.3 Exothermic and Endothermic Reactions

When the total strength of the bonds formed in the products is *greater* than the total strength of the bonds broken in the reactants, energy is released and a reaction is exothermic. All combustion reactions are exothermic; for example, burning 1 mol of methane releases 213 kcal of energy in the form of heat. The heat released in an exothermic reaction can be thought of as a reaction product, and ΔH is assigned a *negative* value because heat *leaves*.

An exothermic reaction—negative ΔH

Heat is a product.

$$CH_4(g) + 2\,O_2(g) \longrightarrow CO_2(g) + 2\,H_2O(l) + 213\,kcal$$

or

$$CH_4(g) + 2\,O_2(g) \longrightarrow CO_2(g) + 2\,H_2O(l) \qquad \Delta H = -213\,kcal/mol$$

Note that ΔH is given in units of kilocalories per mole, where "per mole" means the reaction of *molar amounts of products and reactants as represented by the coefficients of the balanced equation.* Thus, the value $\Delta H = -213$ kcal/mol refers to the amount of heat released when 1 mol (16.0 g) of methane reacts with O_2 to give 1 mol of CO_2 gas and 2 mol of liquid H_2O. If we were to double the amount of methane from 1 mol to 2 mol, the amount of heat released would also double.

The quantities of heat released in the combustion of several fuels, including natural gas (which is primarily methane), are compared in Table 7.1. The values are given in kilocalories per gram to make comparisons easier. You can see from the table why there is interest in the potential of hydrogen as a fuel.

TABLE 7.1   Energy Values of Some Common Fuels

FUEL	ENERGY VALUE (kcal/g)
Wood (pine)	4.3
Ethyl alcohol	7.1
Coal (anthracite)	7.4
Crude oil (Texas)	10.5
Gasoline	11.5
Natural gas	11.7
Hydrogen	34.0

▲ The reaction between aluminum metal and iron(III) oxide, called the *thermite reaction*, is so strongly exothermic that it melts iron.

When the total energy of the bonds formed in the products is *less* than the total energy of the bonds broken in the reactants, energy is absorbed and a reaction is endothermic. The combination of nitrogen and oxygen to give nitrogen oxide (also known as nitric oxide), a gas present in automobile exhaust, is such a reaction. The heat added in an endothermic reaction is like a reactant, and ΔH is assigned a *positive* value because heat is *added*.

An endothermic reaction—positive ΔH

Heat is a reactant.

$$N_2(g) + O_2(g) + 43\,kcal \longrightarrow 2\,NO(g)$$

or

$$N_2(g) + O_2(g) \longrightarrow 2\,NO(g) \qquad \Delta H = +43\,kcal/mol$$

Important points about heat transfers and chemical reactions

- An exothermic reaction releases heat to the surroundings; ΔH is negative.
- An endothermic reaction absorbs heat from the surroundings; ΔH is positive.

- The reverse of an exothermic reaction is endothermic.
- The reverse of an endothermic reaction is exothermic.
- The amount of heat absorbed or released in the reverse of a reaction is equal to that released or absorbed in the forward reaction, but ΔH has the opposite sign.

Worked Examples 7.1-7.3 show how to calculate the amount of heat absorbed or released for reaction of a given amount of reactant. All that is needed is the balanced equation and its accompanying ΔH. Mole ratios and molar masses are used to convert between masses and moles of reactants or products, as discussed in Sections 6.5 and 6.6.

▲ Methane produced from rotting refuse is trapped and used for energy production to ease the energy crisis in California.

WORKED EXAMPLE **7.1** Heat of Reaction

Methane undergoes combustion with O_2 according to the following equation:

$$CH_4(g) + 2\,O_2(g) \longrightarrow CO_2(g) + 2\,H_2O(l) \quad \Delta H = -213\frac{kcal}{mol\ CH_4}$$

How much heat is released during the combustion of 0.35 mol of methane?

ANALYSIS Since the value of ΔH for the reaction (213 kcal/mol) is negative, it indicates the amount of heat released when 1 mol of methane reacts with O_2. We need to find the amount of heat released when an amount other than 1 mol reacts, using appropriate factor-label calculations to convert from our known or given units to kilocalories.

BALLPARK ESTIMATE Since 213 kcal is released for each mole of methane that reacts, 0.35 mol of methane should release about one-third of 213 kcal, or about 70 kcal.

SOLUTION
To find the amount of heat released (in kilocalories) by combustion of 0.35 mol of methane, we use a conversion factor of kcal/mol:

$$0.35\ \cancel{mol\ CH_4} \times \frac{-213\ kcal}{1\ \cancel{mol\ CH_4}} = -75\ kcal$$

The negative sign indicates that the 75 kcal of heat is released.

BALLPARK CHECK The calculated answer is consistent with our estimate (70 kcal).

WORKED EXAMPLE **7.2** Heat of Reaction: Mass to Mole Conversion

How much heat is released during the combustion of 7.50 g of methane (MW = 16.0 g/mol)?

$$CH_4(g) + 2\,O_2(g) \longrightarrow CO_2(g) + 2\,H_2O(l) \quad \Delta H = -213\frac{kcal}{mol\ CH_4}$$

ANALYSIS We can find the moles of methane involved in the reaction by using the molecular weight in a mass to mole conversion, and then use ΔH to find the heat released.

BALLPARK ESTIMATE Since 1 mol of methane (MW = 16.0 g/mol) has a mass of 16.0 g, 7.50 g of methane is a little less than 0.5 mol. Thus, less than half of 213 kcal, or about 100 kcal, is released from combustion of 7.50 g.

SOLUTION
Going from a given mass of methane to the amount of heat released in a reaction requires that we first find the number of moles of methane by including

molar mass (in mol/g) in the calculation and then converting moles to kilocalories:

$$7.50 \text{ g } \cancel{CH_4} \times \frac{1 \text{ mol } \cancel{CH_4}}{16.0 \text{ g } \cancel{CH_4}} \times \frac{-213 \text{ kcal}}{1 \text{ mol } \cancel{CH_4}} = -99.8 \text{ kcal}$$

The negative sign indicates that the 99.8 kcal of heat is released.

BALLPARK CHECK Our estimate was –100 kcal!

WORKED EXAMPLE **7.3** Heat of Reaction: Mole Ratio Calculations

How much heat is released when 2.50 mol of O_2 reacts completely with methane?

$$CH_4(g) + 2 O_2(g) \longrightarrow CO_2(g) + 2 H_2O(l) \quad \Delta H = -213 \frac{\text{kcal}}{\text{mol } CH_4}$$

ANALYSIS Since the ΔH for the reaction is based on the combustion of 1 mol of methane, we will need to perform a mole ratio calculation.

BALLPARK ESTIMATE The balanced equation shows that 213 kcal is released for each 2 mol of oxygen that reacts. Thus, 2.50 mol of oxygen should release a bit more than 213 kcal, perhaps about 250 kcal.

SOLUTION
To find the amount of heat released by combustion of 2.50 mol of oxygen, we include in our calculation a mole ratio based on the balanced chemical equation:

$$2.50 \text{ mol } \cancel{O_2} \times \frac{1 \text{ mol } \cancel{CH_4}}{2 \text{ mol } \cancel{O_2}} \times \frac{-213 \text{ kcal}}{1 \text{ mol } \cancel{CH_4}} = -266 \text{ kcal}$$

The negative sign indicates that the 266 kcal of heat is released.

BALLPARK CHECK The calculated answer is close to our estimate (250 kcal).

PROBLEM 7.1

In photosynthesis, green plants convert carbon dioxide and water into glucose ($C_6H_{12}O_6$) according to the following equation:

$$6 CO_2(g) + 6 H_2O(l) + 678 \text{ kcal} \longrightarrow C_6H_{12}O_6(aq) + 6 O_2(g)$$

(a) Is the reaction exothermic or endothermic?
(b) What is the value of ΔH for the reaction?
(c) Write the equation for the reverse of the reaction, including heat as a reactant or product.

PROBLEM 7.2

The following equation shows the conversion of aluminum oxide (from the ore bauxite) to aluminum:

$$2 Al_2O_3(s) \longrightarrow 4 Al(s) + 3 O_2(g) \quad \Delta H = +801 \text{ kcal/mol}$$

(a) Is the reaction exothermic or endothermic?
(b) How many kilocalories are required to produce 1.00 mol of aluminum?
(c) How many kilocalories are required to produce 10.0 g of aluminum?

> **PROBLEM 7.3**
>
> How much heat is absorbed during production of 127 g of NO by the combination of nitrogen and oxygen?
>
> $$N_2(g) + O_2(g) \longrightarrow 2\,NO(g) \quad \Delta H = +43\ \text{kcal/mol}$$

▲ Events that lead to lower energy tend to occur spontaneously. Thus, water always flows *down* a waterfall, not up.

Spontaneous process A process or reaction that, once started, proceeds on its own without any external influence.

Entropy (S) A measure of the amount of molecular disorder in a system.

7.4 Why Do Chemical Reactions Occur? Free Energy

Events that lead to lower energy tend to occur spontaneously. Water falls downhill, for instance, releasing its stored (potential) energy and reaching a lower-energy, more stable position. Similarly, a wound-up spring uncoils when set free. Applying this lesson to chemistry, the obvious conclusion is that exothermic processes—those that release heat energy—should be spontaneous. A log burning in a fireplace is just one example of a spontaneous reaction that releases heat. At the same time, endothermic processes, which absorb heat energy, should not be spontaneous. Often, these conclusions are correct, but not always. Many, but not all, exothermic processes take place spontaneously, and many, but not all, endothermic processes are nonspontaneous.

Before exploring the situation further, it is important to understand what the word "spontaneous" means in chemistry, which is not quite the same as in everyday language. A **spontaneous process** is one that, once started, proceeds on its own without any external influence. The change does not necessarily happen quickly, like a spring suddenly uncoiling or a car coasting downhill. It can also happen slowly, like the gradual rusting away of an abandoned bicycle. A *nonspontaneous process*, by contrast, takes place only in the presence of a continuous external influence: Energy must be continually expended to rewind a spring or push a car uphill. The reverse of a spontaneous process is always nonspontaneous.

As an example of a process that takes place spontaneously yet absorbs heat, think about what happens when you take an ice cube out of the refrigerator. The ice spontaneously melts to give liquid water above 0 °C, even though it *absorbs* heat energy from the surroundings. What this and other spontaneous processes that absorb heat energy have in common is *an increase in molecular disorder, or randomness*. When the solid ice melts, the H_2O molecules are no longer locked in position but are now free to move around randomly in the liquid water.

The amount of disorder in a system is called the system's **entropy**, symbolized S and expressed in units of calories per mole-kelvin [cal/(mol·K)]. The greater the disorder, or randomness, of the particles in a substance or mixture, the larger the value of S (Figure 7.1). Gases have more disorder and therefore higher entropy than liquids because particles in the gas move around more freely than particles in the liquid. Similarly, liquids have higher entropy than solids. In chemical reactions, entropy increases when, for example, a gas is produced from a solid or when 2 mol of reactants split into 4 mol of products.

Lower entropy { Solid $\longrightarrow$ Liquid $\longrightarrow$ Gas } Higher entropy

{ Fewer moles of reactants $\longrightarrow$ More moles of products }

The entropy *change* for a process, ΔS, has a *positive* value if disorder increases because the process adds disorder to the system. The melting of ice to give water is an example. Conversely, ΔS has a *negative* value if the disorder of a system decreases. The freezing of water to give ice is an example.

It thus appears that two factors determine the spontaneity of a chemical or physical change: the release or absorption of heat, ΔH, and the increase or decrease in entropy, ΔS. *To decide whether a process is spontaneous, both the enthalpy change and*

APPLICATION ▶   Energy from Food

Any serious effort to lose weight usually leads to studying the caloric values of foods. Have you ever wondered how the numbers quoted on food labels are obtained?

Food is "burned" in the body to yield H_2O, CO_2, and energy, just as natural gas is burned in furnaces to yield the same products. In fact, the "caloric value" of a food is just the heat of reaction for complete combustion of the food (minus a small correction factor). The value is the same whether the food is burned in the body or in the laboratory. One gram of protein releases 4 kcal, 1 g of table sugar (a carbohydrate) releases 4 kcal, and 1 g of fat releases 9 kcal (see Table).

The caloric value of a food is usually given in "Calories" (note the capital C), where 1 Cal = 1000 cal = 1 kcal. To determine these values experimentally, a carefully dried and weighed food sample is placed together with oxygen into an instrument called a *calorimeter*, the food is ignited, the temperature change is measured, and the amount of heat given off is calculated from the temperature change. In the calorimeter, the heat from the food is released very quickly and the temperature rises dramatically. Clearly, though, something a bit different goes on when food is burned in the body, otherwise we would burst into flames after a meal!

It is a fundamental principle of chemistry that the total heat released or absorbed in going from reactants to products is the same, no matter how many reactions are involved.

Caloric Values of Some Foods

SUBSTANCE, SAMPLE SIZE	CALORIC VALUE (kcal)
Protein, 1 g	4
Carbohydrate, 1 g	4
Fat, 1 g	9
Alcohol, 1 g	7.1
Cola drink, 12 fl oz (369 g)	160
Apple, one medium (138 g)	80
Iceberg lettuce, 1 cup shredded (55 g)	5
White bread, 1 slice (25 g)	65
Hamburger patty, 3 oz (85 g)	245
Pizza, 1 slice (120 g)	290
Vanilla ice cream, 1 cup (133 g)	270

The body applies this principle by withdrawing energy from food a bit at a time in a long series of interconnected reactions rather than all at once in a single reaction. These and other reactions continually taking place in the body—called the body's *metabolism*—will be examined in later chapters.

See Additional Problems 7.70 and 7.71 at the end of the chapter.

▲ Eating this dessert gives your body 550 Calories. Burning the dessert in a calorimeter releases 550 kcal as heat.

▶ **FIGURE 7.1 Entropy and values of S.** The mixture on the right has more disorder and a higher entropy than the mixture on the left, and has a higher value of S. The value of the entropy change, Δ*S*, for converting the mixture on the left to that on the right is positive because entropy increases.

the entropy change must be taken into account. We have already seen that a negative ΔH favors spontaneity, but what about Δ*S*? The answer is that an increase in molecular disorder (Δ*S* positive) favors spontaneity. A good analogy is the bedroom or office that seems to spontaneously become more messy over time (increase in disorder means increase in entropy, Δ*S* positive); to clean it up (a decrease in disorder, Δ*S* negative) requires an input of energy, a nonspontaneous process. Using our chemical example, the combustion of a log spontaneously converts large, complex molecules like lignin and cellulose (high molecular order, low entropy) into CO_2 and H_2O (smaller molecules with less molecular order and higher entropy). For this process, the level of disorder increases, and so Δ*S* is positive. The reverse process—turning CO_2 and H_2O back into cellulose—does occur in photosynthesis, but it requires a significant input of energy in the form of sunlight.

When enthalpy and entropy are both favorable (ΔH negative, Δ*S* positive), a process is spontaneous; when both are unfavorable, a process is nonspontaneous. Clearly, however, the two factors do not have to operate in the same direction. It is possible for a process to be *unfavored* by enthalpy (the process absorbs heat and so has a positive ΔH) and yet be *favored* by entropy (there is an increase in disorder and so Δ*S* is positive). The melting of an ice cube above 0 °C, for which ΔH = +1.44 kcal/mol and Δ*S* = +5.26 cal/(mol·K) is just such a process. To take both heat of reaction (ΔH) and change in disorder (Δ*S*) into account when determining the spontaneity of a process, a quantity called the **free-energy change** (ΔG) is needed:

Free-energy change

$$\Delta G = \Delta H - T\Delta S$$

The value of the free-energy change ΔG determines spontaneity. A negative value for ΔG means that free energy is released and the reaction or process is spontaneous. Such events are said to be **exergonic**. A positive value for ΔG means that free energy must be added and the process is nonspontaneous. Such events are said to be **endergonic**.

Exergonic A spontaneous reaction or process that releases free energy and has a negative ΔG.

Endergonic A nonspontaneous reaction or process that absorbs free energy and has a positive ΔG.

Spontaneous process	ΔG is negative; free energy is released; process is exergonic.
Nonspontaneous process	ΔG is positive; free energy is added; process is endergonic.

The equation for the free-energy change shows that spontaneity also depends on temperature (T). At low temperatures, the value of $T\Delta S$ is often small so that ΔH is the dominant factor. At a high enough temperature, however, the value of $T\Delta S$ can become larger than ΔH. Thus, an endothermic process that is nonspontaneous at low temperature can become spontaneous at a higher temperature. An example is the industrial synthesis of hydrogen by reaction of carbon with water:

$$C(s) + H_2O(l) \longrightarrow CO(g) + H_2(g) \qquad \begin{aligned} \Delta H &= +31.3 \text{ kcal/mol} & \text{(Unfavorable)} \\ \Delta S &= +32 \text{ cal/(mol} \cdot \text{K)} & \text{(Favorable)} \end{aligned}$$

The reaction has an unfavorable (positive) ΔH term but a favorable (positive) ΔS term because disorder increases when a solid and a liquid are converted into two gases. No reaction occurs if carbon and water are mixed together at 25 °C (298 K) because the unfavorable ΔH is larger than the favorable $T\,\Delta S$. Above about 700 °C (973 K), however, the favorable $T\,\Delta S$ becomes larger than the unfavorable ΔH, so the reaction becomes spontaneous.

Important points about spontaneity and free energy

- A spontaneous process, once begun, proceeds without any external assistance and is exergonic; that is, it has a negative value of ΔG.

- A nonspontaneous process requires continuous external influence and is endergonic; that is, it has a positive value of ΔG.

- The value of ΔG for the reverse of a reaction is numerically equal to the value of ΔG for the forward reaction, but has the opposite sign.

- Some nonspontaneous processes become spontaneous with a change in temperature.

⫘ Looking Ahead

In later chapters, we will see that a knowledge of free-energy changes is especially important for understanding how metabolic reactions work. Living organisms cannot raise their temperatures to convert nonspontaneous reactions into spontaneous reactions, so they must resort to other strategies, which we will explore in Chapter 21. ⫘

WORKED EXAMPLE   **7.4** Entropy Change of Processes

Does entropy increase or decrease in the following processes?

   (a) Smoke from a cigarette disperses throughout a room rather than remaining in a cloud over the smoker's head.

   (b) Water boils, changing from liquid to vapor.

   (c) A chemical reaction occurs: $3 H_2(g) + N_2(g) \longrightarrow 2 NH_3(g)$

ANALYSIS Entropy is a measure of molecular disorder. Entropy increases when the products are more disordered than the reactants; entropy decreases when the products are less disordered than the reactants.

SOLUTION

   (a) Entropy increases because smoke particles are more disordered when they are randomly distributed in the larger volume.

   (b) Entropy increases because H_2O molecules have more freedom and disorder in the gas phase than in the liquid phase.

   (c) Entropy decreases because 4 mol of reactant gas particles become 2 mol of product gas particles, with a consequent decrease in freedom and disorder.

| WORKED EXAMPLE | **7.5** Spontaneity of Reactions: Enthalpy, Entropy, and Free Energy |

The industrial method for synthesizing hydrogen by reaction of carbon with water has $\Delta H = +31.3$ kcal/mol and $\Delta S = +32$ cal/(mol·K). What is the value of ΔG for the reaction at 27 °C (300 K)? Is the reaction spontaneous or nonspontaneous at this temperature?

$$C(s) + H_2O(l) \longrightarrow CO(g) + H_2(g)$$

ANALYSIS The reaction is endothermic (ΔH positive) and does not favor spontaneity, whereas the ΔS indicates an increase in disorder (ΔS positive), which *does* favor spontaneity. Calculate ΔG to determine spontaneity.

BALLPARK ESTIMATE The unfavorable ΔH (+31.3 kcal/mol) is 1000 times greater than the favorable ΔS (+32 cal/mol·K), so the reaction will be spontaneous (ΔG negative) only when the temperature is high enough to make the $T\Delta S$ term in the equation for ΔG larger than the ΔH term. This happens at $T \geq 1000$ K. Since $T = 300$ K, expect ΔG to be positive and the reaction to be nonspontaneous.

SOLUTION
Use the free-energy equation to determine the value of ΔG at this temperature. (Remember that ΔS has units of *calories* per mole-kelvin, not kilocalories per mole-kelvin.)

$$\Delta G = \Delta H - T\,\Delta S$$
$$= +31.3\,\frac{kcal}{mol} - (300\ K)\left(+32\,\frac{cal}{mol \cdot K}\right)\left(\frac{1\ kcal}{1000\ cal}\right)$$
$$= +21.7\,\frac{kcal}{mol}$$

BALLPARK CHECK Because ΔG is positive, the reaction is nonspontaneous at 300 K, consistent with our estimate.

PROBLEM 7.4

Does entropy increase or decrease in the following processes?

(a) After raking your leaves into a neat pile, a breeze blows them all over your lawn.

(b) Gasoline fumes escape as the fuel is pumped into your car.

(c) $Mg(s) + Cl_2(g) \longrightarrow MgCl_2(s)$

PROBLEM 7.5

Lime (CaO) is prepared by the decomposition of limestone ($CaCO_3$).

$$CaCO_3(s) \longrightarrow CaO(s) + CO_2(g) \quad \Delta G = +31\ kcal/mol\ at\ 25\ ^{\circ}C$$

(a) Does the reaction occur spontaneously at 25 °C?

(b) Does entropy increase or decrease in this reaction?

(c) Would you expect the reaction to be spontaneous at higher temperatures?

PROBLEM 7.6

The melting of solid ice to give liquid water has $\Delta H = 1.44$ kcal/mol and $\Delta S = +5.26$ cal/(mol·K). What is the value of ΔG for the melting process at the following temperatures? Is the melting spontaneous or nonspontaneous at these temperatures?

(a) −10 °C (263 K)

(b) 0 °C (273 K)

(c) +10 °C (283 K)

◖● KEY CONCEPT PROBLEM 7.7

The following diagram portrays a reaction of the type A(s) ⟶ B(s) + C(g), where the different colored spheres represent different molecular structures. Assume that the reaction has $\Delta H = -23.5$ kcal/mol.

(a) What is the sign of ΔS for the reaction?

(b) Is the reaction likely to be spontaneous at all temperatures, nonspontaneous at all temperatures, or spontaneous at some but nonspontaneous at others?

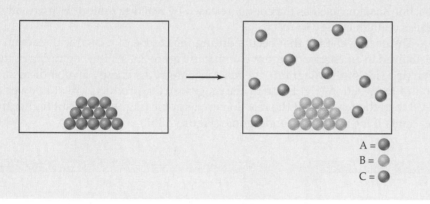

A =
B =
C =

7.5 How Do Chemical Reactions Occur? Reaction Rates

Just because a chemical reaction has a favorable free-energy change does not mean that it occurs rapidly. The value of ΔG tells us only whether a reaction *can* occur; it says nothing about how *fast* the reaction will occur or about the details of the molecular changes that take place during the reaction. It is now time to look into these other matters.

For a chemical reaction to occur, reactant particles must collide, some chemical bonds have to break, and new bonds have to form. Not all collisions lead to products, however. One requirement for a productive collision is that the colliding molecules must approach with the correct orientation so that the atoms about to form new bonds can connect. In the reaction of ozone (O_3) with nitric oxide (NO) to give oxygen (O_2) and nitrogen dioxide (NO_2), for example, the two reactants must collide so that the nitrogen atom of NO strikes a terminal oxygen atom of O_3 (Figure 7.2).

Another requirement for a reaction to occur is that the collision must take place with enough energy to break the appropriate bonds in the reactant. If the reactant particles are moving slowly, collisions might be too gentle to overcome the repulsion between electrons in the different reactants, and the particles will simply bounce apart. Only if the collisions are sufficiently energetic will a reaction ensue.

For this reason, many reactions with a favorable free-energy change do not occur at room temperature. To get such a reaction started, energy (heat) must be

▲ Matches are unreactive at room temperature but burst into flames when struck. The frictional heat produced on striking provides enough energy to start the combustion.

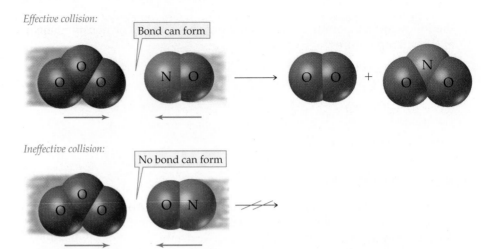

Effective collision:

Bond can form

Ineffective collision:

No bond can form

▶ **FIGURE 7.2 How do chemical reactions occur?** For a collision between NO and O_3 molecules to give O_2 and NO_2, the molecules must collide so that the correct atoms come into contact. No bond forms if the molecules collide with the wrong orientation.

added. The heat causes the reactant particles to move faster, thereby increasing both the frequency and the force of the collisions. We all know that matches burn, for instance, but we also know that they do not burst into flame until struck. The heat of friction provides enough energy for a few molecules to react. Once started, the reaction sustains itself as the energy released by reacting molecules gives other molecules enough energy to react.

The energy change that occurs during the course of a chemical reaction can be visualized in an energy diagram like that in Figure 7.3. At the beginning of the reaction (left side of the diagram), the reactants are at the energy level indicated. At the end of the reaction (right side of the diagram), the products are at a lower energy level than the reactants if the reaction is exergonic (Figure 7.3a) but higher than the reactants if the reaction is endergonic (Figure 7.3b).

(a) An exergonic reaction

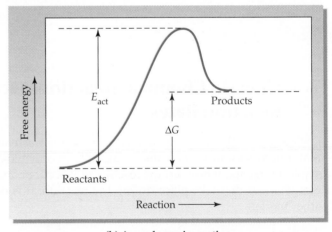

(b) An endergonic reaction

▲ **FIGURE 7.3 Reaction energy diagrams show energy changes during a chemical reaction.** A reaction begins on the left and proceeds to the right. (a) In an exergonic reaction, the product energy level is lower than that of reactants. (b) In an endergonic reaction, the situation is reversed. The height of the barrier between reactant and product energy levels is the activation energy, E_{act}. The difference between reactant and product energy levels is the free-energy change, ΔG.

Activation energy (E_{act}) The amount of energy necessary for reactants to surmount the energy barrier to reaction; determines reaction rate.

Reaction rate A measure of how rapidly a reaction occurs; determined by E_{act}.

Lying between the reactants and the products is an energy "barrier" that must be surmounted. The height of this barrier represents the amount of energy the colliding particles must have for productive collisions to occur, an amount called the **activation energy (E_{act})** of the reaction. The size of the activation energy determines the **reaction rate**, or how fast the reaction occurs. The lower the activation energy, the greater the number of productive collisions in a given amount of time, and the faster the reaction. Conversely, the higher the activation energy, the lower the number of productive collisions, and the slower the reaction.

Note that the size of the activation energy and the size of the free-energy change are unrelated. A reaction with a large E_{act} takes place very slowly even if it has a large negative ΔG. Every reaction is different; each has its own characteristic activation energy and free-energy change.

WORKED EXAMPLE **7.6** Energy of Reactions: Energy Diagrams

Draw an energy diagram for a reaction that is very fast but has a small negative free-energy change.

ANALYSIS A very fast reaction has a small E_{act}. A reaction with a small negative free-energy change is a favorable reaction with a small energy difference between starting materials and products.

SOLUTION

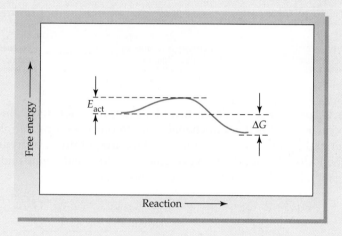

PROBLEM 7.8

Draw an energy diagram for a reaction that is very slow but highly favorable.

PROBLEM 7.9

Draw an energy diagram for a reaction that is slightly unfavorable.

7.6 Effects of Temperature, Concentration, and Catalysts on Reaction Rates

Several things can be done to help reactants over an activation energy barrier and thereby speed up a reaction. Let us look at some possibilities.

Temperature

One way to increase reaction rate is to add energy to the reactants by raising the temperature. With more energy in the system, the reactants move faster, so the frequency of collisions increases. Furthermore, the force with which collisions occur increases, making them more likely to overcome the activation barrier. As a rule of thumb, a 10 °C rise in temperature causes a reaction rate to double.

Concentration

Concentration A measure of the amount of a given substance in a mixture.

A second way to speed up a reaction is to increase the **concentrations** of the reactants. As the concentration increases reactants are crowded together, and collisions between reactant molecules become more frequent. As the frequency of collisions increases, reactions between molecules become more likely. Flammable materials burn more rapidly in pure oxygen than in air, for instance, because the concentration of O_2 molecules is higher (air is approximately 21% oxygen). Hospitals must therefore take extraordinary precautions to ensure that no flames are used near patients receiving oxygen. Although different reactions respond differently to concentration changes, doubling or tripling a reactant concentration often doubles or triples the reaction rate.

Catalysts

Catalyst A substance that speeds up the rate of a chemical reaction but is itself unchanged.

A third way to speed up a reaction is to add a **catalyst**—a substance that accelerates a chemical reaction but is itself unchanged in the process. For example, such metals as nickel, palladium, and platinum catalyze the addition of hydrogen to the carbon–carbon double bonds in vegetable oils to yield semisolid margarine. Without the metal catalyst, the reaction does not occur.

H   H
 \\ /
  C=C   +   H₂   —Ni, Pd, or Pt→   —C—C—
 / \\   catalyst
                                       H H

A double bond in   A single bond
vegetable oil   in margarine

A catalyst does not affect the energy level of either reactants or products. Rather, it increases reaction rate either by letting a reaction take place through an alternative pathway with a lower energy barrier, or by orienting the reacting molecules appropriately. In a reaction energy diagram, the catalyzed reaction has a lower activation energy (Figure 7.4). It is worth noting that the free-energy change

▶ **FIGURE 7.4** **A reaction energy diagram for a reaction in the presence (green curve) and absence (red curve) of a catalyst.** The catalyzed reaction has a lower (E_{act}) because it uses an alternative pathway with a lower energy barrier. The free-energy change ΔG is unaffected by the presence of a catalyst.

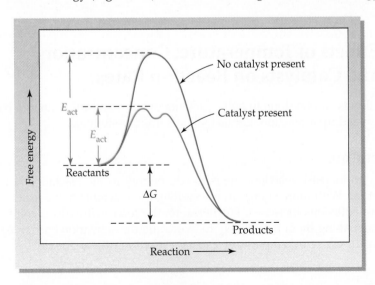

for a reaction depends *only* on the difference in the energy levels of the reactants and products, and *not* on the pathway of the reaction. Therefore, a catalyzed reaction releases (or absorbs) the same amount of energy as an uncatalyzed reaction. It simply occurs more rapidly.

In addition to their widespread use in industry, we also rely on catalysts to reduce the air pollution created by exhaust from automobile engines. The catalytic converters in most automobiles are tubes packed with catalysts of two types (Figure 7.5). One catalyst accelerates the complete combustion of hydrocarbons and CO in the exhaust to give CO_2 and H_2O, and the other decomposes NO to N_2 and O_2.

Exhaust pipe

Catalytic converter

Tailpipe

C_xH_y, CO, NO, O_2 CO_2, H_2O, N_2, O_2

◄ **FIGURE 7.5 A catalytic converter.** The exhaust gases from an automobile pass through a two-stage catalytic converter. In one stage, carbon monoxide and unburned hydrocarbons are converted to CO_2 and H_2O. In the second stage, NO is converted to N_2 and O_2.

Table 7.2 summarizes the effects of changing conditions on reaction rates.

TABLE 7.2   Effects of Changes in Reaction Conditions on Reaction Rate

CHANGE	EFFECT
Concentration	Increase in reactant concentration increases rate.
	Decrease in reactant concentration decreases rate.
Temperature	Increase in temperature increases rate.
	Decrease in temperature decreases rate.
Catalyst added	Increases reaction rate.

⊂⊐⊃ Looking Ahead

The thousands of biochemical reactions continually taking place in our bodies are catalyzed by large protein molecules called *enzymes*, which promote reaction by controlling the orientation of the reacting molecules. Since almost every reaction is catalyzed by its own specific enzyme, the study of enzyme structure, activity, and control is a central part of biochemistry. We will look more closely at enzymes and how they work in Chapters 19 and 20.   ⊂⊐⊃

PROBLEM 7.10

Ammonia is synthesized industrially by reaction of nitrogen and hydrogen in the presence of an iron catalyst according to the equation $3\,H_2(g) + N_2(g) \longrightarrow 2\,NH_3(g)$.

What effect will the following changes have on the reaction rate?

(a) The temperature is raised from 600 K to 700 K.

(b) The iron catalyst is removed.

(c) The concentration of H_2 gas is halved.

7.7 Reversible Reactions and Chemical Equilibrium

Many chemical reactions result in the virtually complete conversion of reactants into products. When sodium metal reacts with chlorine gas, for example, both are entirely consumed. The sodium chloride product is so much more stable than the reactants that, once started, the reaction keeps going until it is complete.

What happens, though, when the reactants and products are of approximately equal stability? This is the case, for example, in the reaction of acetic acid (the main organic constituent of vinegar) with ethyl alcohol to yield ethyl acetate, a solvent used in nail-polish remover and glue.

$$\underset{\text{Acetic acid}}{\text{CH}_3\overset{\overset{\text{O}}{\|}}{\text{C}}\text{OH}} + \underset{\text{Ethyl alcohol}}{\text{HOCH}_2\text{CH}_3} \underset{\text{Or this direction?}}{\overset{\text{This direction?}}{\rightleftarrows}} \underset{\text{Ethyl acetate}}{\text{CH}_3\overset{\overset{\text{O}}{\|}}{\text{C}}\text{OCH}_2\text{CH}_3} + \underset{\text{Water}}{\text{H}_2\text{O}}$$

APPLICATION ▶   Regulation of Body Temperature

Maintaining normal body temperature is crucial. If the body's thermostat is unable to maintain a temperature of 37 °C, the rates of the many thousands of chemical reactions that take place constantly in the body will change accordingly, with potentially disastrous consequences.

If, for example, a skater fell through the ice of a frozen lake, *hypothermia* could soon result. Hypothermia is a dangerous state that occurs when the body is unable to generate enough heat to maintain normal temperature. All chemical reactions in the body slow down because of the lower temperature, energy production drops, and death can result. Slowing the body's reactions can also be used to advantage, however. During open-heart surgery, the heart is stopped and maintained at about 15 °C, while the body, which receives oxygenated blood from an external pump, is cooled to 25–32 °C.

Conversely, a marathon runner on a hot, humid day might become overheated, and *hyperthermia* could result. Hyperthermia, also called *heat stroke*, is an uncontrolled rise in temperature as the result of the body's inability to lose sufficient heat. Chemical reactions in the body are accelerated at higher temperatures, the heart struggles to pump blood faster to supply increased oxygen, and brain damage can result if the body temperature rises above 41 °C.

Body temperature is maintained both by the thyroid gland and by the hypothalamus region of the brain, which act together to regulate metabolic rate. When the body's environment changes, temperature receptors in the skin, spinal cord, and abdomen send signals to the hypothalamus, which contains both heat-sensitive and cold-sensitive neurons.

Stimulation of the heat-sensitive neurons on a hot day causes a variety of effects: Impulses are sent to stimulate the sweat glands, dilate the blood vessels of the skin, decrease muscular activity, and reduce metabolic rate. Sweating cools the body through evaporation; approximately 540 cal is removed by evaporation of 1.0 g of sweat. Dilated blood vessels cool the body by allowing more blood to flow close to

▲ The body is cooled to 25–32 °C by immersion in ice prior to open-heart surgery to slow down metabolism.

the surface of the skin where heat is removed by contact with air. Decreased muscular activity and a reduced metabolic rate cool the body by lowering internal heat production.

Stimulation of the cold-sensitive neurons on a cold day also causes a variety of effects: The hormone epinephrine is released to stimulate metabolic rate; peripheral blood vessels contract to decrease blood flow to the skin and prevent heat loss; and muscular contractions increase to produce more heat, resulting in shivering and "goosebumps."

One further comment: Drinking alcohol to warm up on a cold day actually has the opposite effect. Alcohol causes blood vessels to dilate, resulting in a warm feeling as blood flow to the skin increases. Although the warmth feels good temporarily, body temperature ultimately drops as heat is lost through the skin at an increased rate.

See Problems 7.72 and 7.73 at the end of the chapter.

Imagine the situation if you mix acetic acid and ethyl alcohol. The two begin to form ethyl acetate and water. But as soon as ethyl acetate and water form, they begin to go back to acetic acid and ethyl alcohol. Such a reaction, which easily goes in either direction, is said to be **reversible** and is indicated by a double arrow ($\rightleftharpoons$) in equations. The reaction read from left to right as written is referred to as the *forward reaction*, and the reaction from right to left is referred to as the *reverse reaction*.

Reversible reaction A reaction that can go in either direction, from products to reactants or reactants to products.

Now suppose you mix some ethyl acetate and water. The same thing occurs: As soon as small quantities of acetic acid and ethyl alcohol form, the reaction in the other direction begins to take place. No matter which pair of reactants is mixed together, both reactions occur until ultimately the concentrations of reactants and products reach constant values and undergo no further change. At this point, the reaction vessel contains all four substances—acetic acid, ethyl acetate, ethyl alcohol, and water—and the reaction is said to be in a state of **chemical equilibrium**.

Since the reactant and product concentrations undergo no further change once equilibrium is reached, you might conclude that the forward and reverse reactions have stopped. That is not the case, however. The forward reaction takes place rapidly at the beginning of the reaction but then slows down as reactant concentrations decrease. At the same time, the reverse reaction takes place slowly at the beginning but then speeds up as product concentrations increase (Figure 7.6). Ultimately, the forward and reverse rates become equal and change no further.

Chemical equilibrium A state in which the rates of forward and reverse reactions are the same.

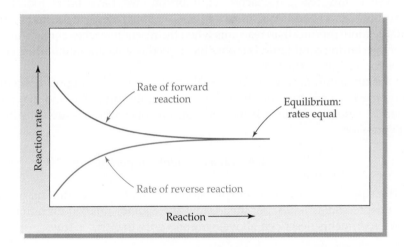

▲ **FIGURE 7.6 Reaction rates in an equilibrium reaction.** The forward rate is large initially but decreases as the concentrations of reactants drop. The reverse rate is small initially but increases as the concentrations of products increase. At equilibrium, the forward and reverse reaction rates are equal.

Chemical equilibrium is an active, dynamic condition. All substances present are continuously being made and unmade at the same rate, so their concentrations are constant at equilibrium. As an analogy, think of two floors of a building connected by up and down escalators. If the number of people moving up is the same as the number of people moving down, the numbers of people on each floor remain constant. *Individual people* are continuously changing from one floor to the other, but the *total populations* of the two floors are in equilibrium.

Note that it is not necessary for the concentrations of reactants and products at equilibrium to be equal (just as it is not necessary for the numbers of people on two floors connected by escalators to be equal). Equilibrium can be reached at any point between pure products and pure reactants. The extent to which the forward or reverse reaction is favored over the other is a characteristic property of a given reaction under given conditions.

▲ When the number of people moving up is the same as the number of people moving down, the number of people on each floor remains constant, and the two populations are in equilibrium.

7.8 Equilibrium Equations and Equilibrium Constants

Remember that the rate of a reaction depends on the number of collisions between molecules (Section 7.5), and that the number of collisions in turn depends on concentration, i.e., the number of molecules in a given volume (Section 7.6). For a reversible reaction, then, the rates of both the forward *and* the reverse reactions must depend on the concentration of reactants and products, respectively. When a reaction reaches equilibrium the rates of the forward and reverse reactions are equal, and the concentration of reactants and products remain constant. We can use this fact to obtain useful information about a reaction.

Let us look at the details of a specific equilibrium reaction. Suppose that you allow various mixtures of sulfur dioxide and oxygen to come to equilibrium with sulfur trioxide at a temperature of 727 °C and then measure the concentrations of all three gases in the mixtures.

$$2\,SO_2(g) + O_2(g) \rightleftharpoons 2\,SO_3(g)$$

In one experiment, we start with only 1.00 mol of SO_2 and 1.00 mol of O_2 in a 1.00 L container. In other words, the initial concentrations of reactants are 1.00 mol/L. When the reaction reaches equilibrium, we have 0.0620 mol/L of SO_2, 0.538 mol/L of O_2, and 0.938 mol/L of SO_3. In another experiment, we start with only 1.00 mol/L of SO_3. When this reaction reaches equilibrium, we have 0.150 mol/L of SO_2, 0.0751 mol/L of O_2, and 0.850 mol/L of SO_3. In both cases, we see that there is substantially more product than reactants when the reaction reaches equilibrium, regardless of the starting conditions. Is it possible to predict what the equilibrium conditions will be for any given reaction?

As it turns out, the answer is YES! No matter what the original concentrations, and no matter what concentrations remain at equilibrium, we find that a constant numerical value is obtained if the equilibrium concentrations are substituted into the expression

$$\frac{[SO_3]^2}{[SO_2]^2[O_2]} = 429 \quad \text{(at a constant temperature of 72 °C)}$$

The square brackets in this expression indicate the concentration of each substance expressed as moles per liter. Using the equilibrium concentrations for each of the experiments described above, we can verify that this is true:

Experiment 1. $\quad \dfrac{[SO_3]^2}{[SO_2]^2[O_2]} = \dfrac{(0.938\ \text{mol/L})^2}{(0.0620\ \text{mol/L})^2(0.538\ \text{mol/L})} = 425$

Experiment 2. $\quad \dfrac{[SO_3]^2}{[SO_2]^2[O_2]} = \dfrac{(0.850\ \text{mol/L})^2}{(0.150\ \text{mol/L})^2(0.0751\ \text{mol/L})} = 428$

Within experimental error, the ratios of product and reactant concentrations at equilibrium yield the same result. Numerous experiments like those just described have led to a general equation that is valid for any reaction. Consider a general reversible reaction:

$$aA + bB + \cdots \rightleftharpoons mM + nN + \cdots$$

where A, B, . . . are reactants; M, N, . . . are products; and $a, b, \ldots, m, n, \ldots$ are coefficients in the balanced equation. At equilibrium, the composition of the reaction mixture obeys the following *equilibrium equation*, where K is the **equilibrium constant**.

Equilibrium equation $\qquad K = \dfrac{[M]^m[N]^n \cdots}{[A]^a[B]^b \cdots}$ ⟶ Product concentrations ⟶ Reactant concentrations

Equilibrium constant

The equilibrium constant K is the number obtained by multiplying the equilibrium concentrations of the products and dividing by the equilibrium concentrations of the reactants, with the concentration of each substance raised to a power equal to its coefficient in the balanced equation. If we take another look at the reaction between sulfur dioxide and oxygen, we can now see how the equilibrium constant was obtained:

$$2\,SO_2\,(g)\;+\;O_2\,(g)\;\rightleftharpoons\;2\,SO_3\,(g)$$

$$K = \frac{[SO_3]^2}{[SO_2]^2\,[O_2]}$$

▲ The hydrogen gas in these soap bubbles reacts completely with oxygen when ignited to form water.

Note that if there is no coefficient for a reactant or product in the reaction equation it is assumed to be 1. The value of K varies with temperature—25 °C is assumed unless otherwise specified—and units are usually omitted.

The value of the equilibrium constant indicates the position of a reaction at equilibrium. If the forward reaction is favored, the product term $[M]^m[N]^n$ is larger than the reactant term $[A]^a[B]^b$, and the value of K is larger than 1. If instead the reverse reaction is favored, $[M]^m[N]^n$ is smaller than $[A]^a[B]^b$ at equilibrium, and the value of K is smaller than 1.

For a reaction such as the combination of hydrogen and oxygen to form water vapor, the equilibrium constant is enormous (3.1×10^{81}), showing how greatly the formation of water is favored. Equilibrium is effectively nonexistent for such reactions, and the reaction is described as *going to completion*.

On the other hand, the equilibrium constant is very small for a reaction such as the combination of nitrogen and oxygen at 25 °C to give NO (4.7×10^{-31}), showing what we know from observation—that N_2 and O_2 in the air do not combine noticeably at room temperature:

$$N_2(g) + O_2(g) \rightleftharpoons 2\,NO(g) \quad K = \frac{[NO]^2}{[N_2][O_2]} = 4.7 \times 10^{-31}$$

When K is close to 1, say between 10^3 and 10^{-3}, significant amounts of both reactants and products are present at equilibrium. An example is the reaction of acetic acid with ethyl alcohol to give ethyl acetate (Section 7.7). For this reaction, $K = 3.4$.

$$CH_3CO_2H + CH_3CH_2OH \rightleftharpoons CH_3CO_2CH_2CH_3 + H_2O$$

$$K = \frac{[CH_3CO_2CH_2CH_3][H_2O]}{[CH_3CO_2H][CH_3CH_2OH]} = 3.4$$

We can summarize the meaning of equilibrium constants in the following way:

| K very small | | K | | K very large |

$$10^{-3} \qquad 1 \qquad 10^3$$

| Reaction goes hardly at all | More reactants than products present | More products than reactants present | Reaction goes to completion |

K much smaller than 0.001 Only reactants are present at equilibrium; essentially no reaction occurs.

K between 0.001 and 1 More reactants than products are present at equilibrium.

K between 1 and 1000	More products than reactants are present at equilibrium.
K much larger than 1000	Only products are present at equilibrium; reaction goes essentially to completion.

WORKED EXAMPLE **7.7** Writing Equilibrium Equations

The first step in the industrial synthesis of hydrogen is the reaction of steam with methane to give carbon monoxide and hydrogen. Write the equilibrium equation for the reaction.

$$H_2O(g) + CH_4(g) \rightleftharpoons CO(g) + 3\,H_2(g)$$

ANALYSIS The equilibrium constant *K* is the number obtained by multiplying the equilibrium concentrations of the products (CO and H_2) and dividing by the equilibrium concentrations of the reactants (H_2O and CH_4), with the concentration of each substance raised to the power of its coefficient in the balanced equation.

SOLUTION

$$K = \frac{[CO][H_2]^3}{[H_2O][CH_4]}$$

WORKED EXAMPLE **7.8** Equilibrium Equations: Calculating *K*

In the reaction of Cl_2 with PCl_3, the concentrations of reactants and products were determined experimentally at equilibrium and found to be 7.2 mol/L for PCl_3, 7.2 mol/L for Cl_2, and 0.050 mol/L for PCl_5.

$$PCl_3(g) + Cl_2(g) \rightleftharpoons PCl_5(g)$$

Write the equilibrium equation, and calculate the equilibrium constant for the reaction. Which reaction is favored, the forward one or the reverse one?

ANALYSIS All the coefficients in the balanced equation are 1, so the equilibrium constant equals the concentration of the product, PCl_5, divided by the product of the concentrations of the two reactants, PCl_3 and Cl_2. Insert the values given for each concentration, and calculate the value of *K*.

BALLPARK ESTIMATE At equilibrium, the concentration of the reactants (7.2 mol/L for each reactant) is higher than the concentration of the product (0.05 mol/L), so we expect a value of *K* less than 1.

SOLUTION

$$K = \frac{[PCl_5]}{[PCl_3][Cl_2]} = \frac{0.050 \text{ mol/L}}{(7.2 \text{ mol/L})(7.2 \text{ mol/L})} = 9.6 \times 10^{-4}$$

The value of *K* is less than 1, so the reverse reaction is favored. Note that units for K are omitted.

BALLPARK CHECK Our calculated value of *K* is just as we predicted: *K* < 1.

PROBLEM 7.11

Write equilibrium equations for the following reactions:

(a) $N_2O_4(g) \rightleftharpoons 2\,NO_2(g)$

(b) $CH_4(g) + Cl_2(g) \rightleftharpoons CH_3Cl(g) + HCl(g)$

(c) $2\,BrF_5(g) \rightleftharpoons Br_2(g) + 5\,F_2(g)$

PROBLEM 7.12

Do the following reactions favor reactants or products at equilibrium?

(a) Sucrose(aq) + H_2O(l) $\rightleftharpoons$ Glucose(aq) + Fructose(aq) $K = 1.4 \times 10^5$

(b) NH_3(aq) + H_2O(l) $\rightleftharpoons$ NH_4^+(aq) + OH^-(aq) $K = 1.6 \times 10^{-5}$

(c) Fe_2O_3(s) + 3 CO(g) $\rightleftharpoons$ 2 Fe(s) + 3 CO_2(g)   K(at 727°C) = 24.2

PROBLEM 7.13

For the reaction H_2(g) + I_2(g) $\rightleftharpoons$ 2 HI(g), equilibrium concentrations at 25 °C are [H_2] = 0.0510 mol/L, [I_2] = 0.174 mol/L, and [HI] = 0.507 mol/L. What is the value of K at 25 °C?

KEY CONCEPT PROBLEM 7.14

The following diagrams represent two similar reactions that have achieved equilibrium:

$A_2 + B_2 \longrightarrow$ 2 AB $C_2 + D_2 \longrightarrow$ 2 CD

Which reaction has the larger equilibrium constant, and which has the smaller equilibrium constant?

7.9 Le Châtelier's Principle: The Effect of Changing Conditions on Equilibria

The effect of a change in reaction conditions on chemical equilibrium is predicted by a general rule called *Le Châtelier's principle*:

Le Châtelier's principle   When a stress is applied to a system at equilibrium, the equilibrium shifts to relieve the stress.

The word "stress" in this context means any change in concentration, pressure, volume, or temperature that disturbs the original equilibrium and causes the rates of the forward and reverse reactions to become temporarily unequal.

We saw in Section 7.6 that reaction rates are affected by changes in temperature and concentration, and by addition of a catalyst. But what about equilibria? Are they similarly affected? The answer is that changes in concentration, temperature, and pressure *do* affect equilibria, but that addition of a catalyst does not (except to reduce the time it takes to reach equilibrium). The change caused by a catalyst affects forward and reverse reactions equally so that equilibrium concentrations are the same in both the presence and the absence of the catalyst.

Effect of Changes in Concentration

Let us look at the effect of a concentration change by considering the reaction of CO with H_2 to form CH_3OH (methanol). Once equilibrium is reached, the concentrations of the reactants and product are constant, and the forward and reverse reaction rates are equal.

$$CO(g) + 2\,H_2(g) \rightleftharpoons CH_3OH(g)$$

What happens if the concentration of CO is increased? To relieve the "stress" of added CO, according to Le Châtelier's principle, the extra CO must be used up. In other words, the rate of the forward reaction must increase to consume CO. Think of the CO added on the left as "pushing" the equilibrium to the right:

$$[CO \longrightarrow]$$
$$CO(g) + 2\,H_2(g) \rightleftharpoons CH_3OH(g)$$

Of course, as soon as more CH_3OH forms, the reverse reaction also speeds up, and so some CH_3OH converts back to CO and H_2. Ultimately, the forward and reverse reaction rates adjust until they are again equal, and equilibrium is reestablished. At this new equilibrium state, the value of $[H_2]$ is lower because some of the H_2 reacted with the added CO and the value of $[CH_3OH]$ is higher because CH_3OH formed as the reaction was driven to the right by the addition of CO. The changes offset each other, however, so that the value of the equilibrium constant K remains constant.

$$CO(g) + 2\,H_2(g) \rightleftharpoons CH_3OH(g)$$

If this increases . . .   . . . then this decreases . . .   . . . and this increases . . .

. . . but this remains constant. $K = \dfrac{[CH_3OH]}{[CO]\,[H_2]^2}$

What happens if CH_3OH is added to the reaction at equilibrium? Some of the methanol reacts to yield CO and H_2, making the values of $[CO]$, $[H_2]$, and $[CH_3OH]$ higher when equilibrium is reestablished. As before, the value of K does not change.

If this increases . . .

$$CO(g) + 2\,H_2(g) \rightleftharpoons CH_3OH(g)$$

. . . then this increases . . .   . . . and this increases . . .

. . . but this remains constant. $K = \dfrac{[CH_3OH]}{[CO]\,[H_2]^2}$

Alternatively, we can view chemical equilibrium as a *balance* between the energy of the reactants (on the left) and the products (on the right). Adding more reactants tips the balance in favor of the reactants. In order to restore the balance, reactants must be converted to products, or the reaction must shift to the right. If, instead, we remove reactants, then the balance is too heavy on the products side and the reaction must shift left, generating more reactants to restore balance.

Finally, what happens if a reactant is continuously supplied or a product is continuously removed? Because the concentrations are continuously changing, equilibrium can never be reached. As a result, it is sometimes possible to force a reaction to produce large quantities of a desirable product even when the equilibrium constant is unfavorable. Take the reaction of acetic acid with ethanol to yield ethyl

Adding reactants
to left side...

...will shift the
reaction to the right.

▲ Equilibrium represents a balance between the energy of reactants and products. Adding reactants (or products) to one side upsets the balance, and the reaction will proceed in a direction to restore the balance.

acetate, for example. As discussed in the preceding section, the equilibrium constant *K* for this reaction is 3.4, meaning that substantial amounts of reactants and products are both present at equilibrium. If, however, the ethyl acetate is removed as soon as it is formed, the production of more and more product is forced to occur, in accord with Le Châtelier's principle.

$$\underset{\text{Acetic acid}}{CH_3\overset{\overset{O}{\|}}{C}OH} + \underset{\text{Ethyl alcohol}}{CH_3CH_2OH} \rightleftharpoons \underset{\text{Ethyl acetate}}{CH_3\overset{\overset{O}{\|}}{C}OCH_2CH_3} + H_2O$$

Continuously removing this product from the reaction forces more of it to be produced.

Metabolic reactions sometimes take advantage of this effect, with one reaction prevented from reaching equilibrium by the continuous consumption of its product in a further reaction.

Effect of Changes in Temperature and Pressure

We noted in Section 7.2 that the reverse of an exothermic reaction is always endothermic. Equilibrium reactions are therefore exothermic in one direction and endothermic in the other. Le Châtelier's principle predicts that an increase in temperature will cause an equilibrium to shift in favor of the endothermic reaction so the additional heat is absorbed. Conversely, a decrease in temperature will cause an equilibrium to shift in favor of the exothermic reaction so additional heat is released. In other words, you can think of heat as a reactant or product whose increase or decrease stresses an equilibrium just as a change in reactant or product concentration does.

Endothermic reaction
(Heat is absorbed) Favored by increase in temperature

Exothermic reaction
(Heat is released) Favored by decrease in temperature

In the exothermic reaction of N_2 with H_2 to form NH_3, for example, raising the temperature favors the reverse reaction, which absorbs the heat:

$$[\longleftarrow \text{Heat}]$$
$$N_2(g) + 3\,H_2(g) \rightleftharpoons 2\,NH_3(g) + \text{Heat}$$

We can also use the balance analogy to predict the effect of temperature on an equilibrium mixture; this time we think of heat as a reactant or product. Increasing the temperature of the reaction is the same as adding heat to the left side (for an endothermic reaction) or to the right side (for an exothermic reaction). The reaction then proceeds in the appropriate direction to restore "balance" to the system.

What about changing the pressure? Pressure influences an equilibrium only if one or more of the substances involved is a gas. As predicted by Le Châtelier's principle, decreasing the volume to increase the pressure in such a reaction shifts the equilibrium in the direction that decreases the number of molecules in the gas phase and thus decreases the pressure. For the ammonia synthesis, decreasing the volume *increases* the concentration of reactants and products, but has a greater effect on the reactant side of the equilibrium since there are more moles of gas phase reactants. Increasing the pressure, therefore, favors the forward reaction because 4 mol of gas is converted to 2 mol of gas.

$$[\text{Pressure} \longrightarrow]$$
$$\underbrace{N_2(g) + 3\,H_2(g)}_{\text{4 mol of gas}} \rightleftharpoons \underbrace{2\,NH_3(g)}_{\text{2 mol of gas}}$$

The effects of changing reaction conditions on equilibria are summarized in Table 7.3.

TABLE 7.3 Effects of Changes in Reaction Conditions on Equilibria

CHANGE	EFFECT
Concentration	Increase in reactant concentration or decrease in product concentration favors forward reaction.
	Increase in product concentration or decrease in reactant concentration favors reverse reaction.
Temperature	Increase in temperature favors endothermic reaction.
	Decrease in temperature favors exothermic reaction.
Pressure	Increase in pressure favors side with fewer moles of gas.
	Decrease in pressure favors side with more moles of gas.
Catalyst added	Equilibrium reached more quickly; value of K unchanged.

⊂⊙⊃ **Looking Ahead**

In Chapter 21, we will see how Le Châtelier's principle is exploited to keep chemical "traffic" moving through the body's metabolic pathways. It often happens that one reaction in a series is prevented from reaching equilibrium because its product is continuously consumed in another reaction. ⊂⊙⊃

APPLICATION ▶ Nitrogen Fixation

All plants and animals need nitrogen—it is present in all proteins and nucleic acids, and is the fourth most abundant element in the human body. Because the triple bond in the N_2 molecule is so strong, however, plants and animals cannot use the free element directly. It is up to nature and the fertilizer industry to convert N_2, which makes up 78% of the atmosphere, into usable nitrogen compounds in a process called *nitrogen fixation*. Plants use ammonia (NH_3), nitrates (NO_3^-), urea (H_2NCONH_2), and other simple, water-soluble compounds as their sources of nitrogen. Animals then get their nitrogen by eating plants or other plant-eating animals. All these processes contribute to the global *nitrogen cycle* (see figure).

Natural Nitrogen Fixation

Because of the very strong triple bond in the N_2 molecule, the rate of conversion of nitrogen to ammonia or nitrate is very slow under normal conditions. However, lightning in the atmosphere supplies sufficient energy to overcome the large activation energy and drive the endothermic reaction between N_2 and O_2 to form NO. Further reactions with O_2 or O_3 ultimately produce water-soluble nitrates that can be used by plants. Lightning produces small amounts of ammonia as well.

Nitrogen fixation also occurs as a result of bacterial activity in the soil. These bacteria are either free-living, such as *cyanobacteria*, or are associated symbiotically with plants, such as the *Rhizobium* found in the root nodules of legumes (peas, beans, and clover). The biological fixation of nitrogen is represented by the following equation:

$$N_2 + 8\,H^+ + 8\,e^- + 16\,ATP \longrightarrow 2\,NH_3 + H_2 + 16\,ADP$$

where ATP and ADP are adenosine triphosphate and adenosine diphosphate respectively, in the reaction that serves as the major source of energy in many organisms (Chapter 21). This reaction is made possible by an enzyme complex called *nitrogenase*, which acts as a catalyst to lower the energy barrier.

Industrial Nitrogen Fixation

Most industrial nitrogen fixation results from fertilizer production utilizing the *Haber process*, the reaction between nitrogen and hydrogen to give ammonia:

The Haber process

$$N_2(g) + 3\,H_2(g) \longrightarrow 2\,NH_3(g)$$

This reaction is performed at high temperatures and pressures in the presence of an iron-based catalyst to increase the rate of reaction and shift the equilibrium in favor of ammonia. Since the reaction is reversible, an equilibrium would quickly be established between products and reactants; by removing ammonia as it forms, the reaction is continuously shifted to the right according to Le Châtelier's principle to maximize ammonia production.

See Additional Problems 7.74 and 7.75 at the end of the chapter.

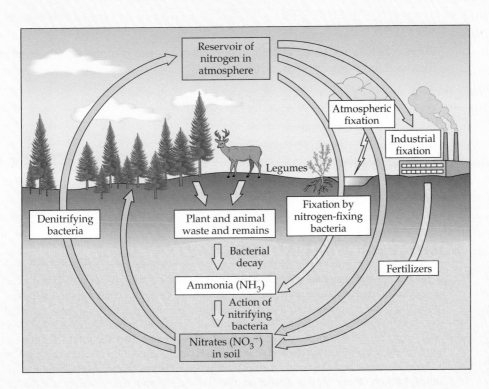

◀ The nitrogen cycle, showing how N_2 in the atmosphere is fixed, used by plants and animals, and then returned to the atmosphere.

WORKED EXAMPLE **7.9** Le Châtelier's Principle and Equilibrium Mixtures

Nitrogen reacts with oxygen to give NO:

$$N_2(g) + O_2(g) \rightleftharpoons 2\,NO(g) \quad \Delta H = +43\,\text{kcal/mol}$$

Explain the effects of the following changes on reactant and product concentrations:

(a) Increasing temperature

(b) Increasing the concentration of NO

(c) Adding a catalyst

SOLUTION

(a) The reaction is endothermic (positive ΔH), so increasing the temperature favors the forward reaction. The concentration of NO will be higher at equilibrium.

(b) Increasing the concentration of NO, a product, favors the reverse reaction. At equilibrium, the concentrations of both N_2 and O_2, as well as that of NO, will be higher.

(c) A catalyst accelerates the rate at which equilibrium is reached, but the concentrations at equilibrium do not change.

PROBLEM 7.15

Is the yield of SO_3 at equilibrium favored by a higher or lower pressure? By a higher or lower temperature?

$$2\,SO_2(g) + O_2(g) \rightleftharpoons 2\,SO_3(g) \quad \Delta H = -47\,\text{kcal/mol}$$

PROBLEM 7.16

What effect do the listed changes have on the position of the equilibrium in the reaction of carbon with hydrogen?

$$C(s) + 2\,H_2(g) \rightleftharpoons CH_4(g) \quad \Delta H = -18\,\text{kcal/mol}$$

(a) Increasing temperature

(b) Increasing pressure by decreasing volume

(c) Allowing CH_4 to escape continuously from the reaction vessel

KEY WORDS

Activation energy (E_{act}) *p. 194*

Bond dissociation energy, *p. 184*

Catalyst, *p. 196*

Chemical equilibrium, *p. 199*

Concentration, *p. 196*

SUMMARY: REVISITING THE CHAPTER GOALS

1. What energy changes take place during reactions? The strength of a covalent bond is measured by its *bond dissociation energy*, the amount of energy that must be supplied to break the bond in an isolated gaseous molecule. For any reaction, the heat released or absorbed by changes in bonding is called the *heat of reaction*, or *enthalpy change* (ΔH). If the total strength of the bonds formed in a reaction is greater than the total strength of the bonds broken, then heat is released (negative ΔH) and the reaction is said to be *exothermic*. If the total strength of the bonds formed in a reaction is less than the total strength of the bonds broken, then heat is absorbed (positive ΔH) and the reaction is said to be *endothermic*.

2. **What is "free energy," and what is the criterion for spontaneity in chemistry?** *Spontaneous reactions* are those that, once started, continue without external influence; nonspontaneous reactions require a continuous external influence. Spontaneity depends on two factors, the amount of heat absorbed or released in a reaction (ΔH) and the *entropy change* (ΔS), which measures the change in molecular disorder in a reaction. Spontaneous reactions are favored by a release of heat (negative ΔH) and an increase in disorder (positive ΔS). The *free-energy change* (ΔG) takes both factors into account, according to the equation $\Delta G = \Delta H - T\Delta S$. A negative value for ΔG indicates spontaneity, and a positive value for ΔG indicates nonspontaneity.

3. **What determines the rate of a chemical reaction?** A chemical reaction occurs when reactant particles collide with proper orientation and sufficient energy. The exact amount of collision energy necessary is called the *activation energy* (E_{act}). A high activation energy results in a slow reaction because few collisions occur with sufficient force, whereas a low activation energy results in a fast reaction. Reaction rates can be increased by raising the temperature, by raising the concentrations of reactants, or by adding a *catalyst*, which accelerates a reaction without itself undergoing any change.

4. **What is chemical equilibrium?** A reaction that can occur in either the forward or reverse direction is *reversible* and will ultimately reach a state of *chemical equilibrium*. At equilibrium, the forward and reverse reactions occur at the same rate, and the concentrations of reactants and products are constant. Every reversible reaction has a characteristic *equilibrium constant* (K), given by an *equilibrium equation*.

For the reaction: $aA + bB + \cdots \rightleftharpoons mM + nN + \cdots$

$$K = \frac{[M]^m[N]^n \cdots}{[A]^a[B]^b \cdots}$$

Product concentrations raised to powers equal to coefficients

Reactant concentrations raised to powers equal to coefficients

If K is larger than 1, the forward reaction is favored; if K is less than 1, the reverse reaction is favored.

5. **What is Le Châtelier's principle?** *Le Châtelier's principle* states that when a stress is applied to a system in equilibrium, the equilibrium shifts so that the stress is relieved. Applying this principle allows prediction of the effects of changes in temperature, pressure, and concentration.

Endergonic, *p. 190*

Endothermic, *p. 184*

Enthalpy (H), *p. 184*

Enthalpy change (ΔH) *p. 184*

Entropy (S), *p. 188*

Equilibrium constant (K), *p. 200*

Exergonic, *p. 190*

Exothermic, *p. 184*

Free-energy change (ΔG) *p. 190*

Heat, *p. 183*

Heat of reaction, *p. 184*

Kinetic energy, *p. 183*

Law of conservation of energy, *p. 184*

Le Châtelier's principle, *p. 203*

Potential energy, *p. 183*

Reaction rate, *p. 194*

Reversible reaction, *p. 199*

Spontaneous process, *p. 188*

UNDERSTANDING KEY CONCEPTS

7.17 What are the signs of ΔH, ΔS, and ΔG for the spontaneous conversion of a crystalline solid into a gas? Explain.

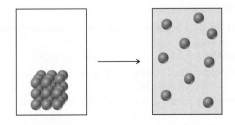

7.18 What are the signs of ΔH, ΔS, and ΔG for the spontaneous condensation of a vapor to a liquid? Explain.

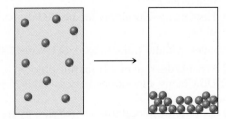

7.19 Consider the following spontaneous reaction of A_2 molecules (red) and B_2 molecules (blue):

   (a) Write a balanced equation for the reaction.
   (b) What are the signs of ΔH, ΔS, and ΔG for the reaction? Explain.

7.20 Two curves are shown in the following energy diagram:

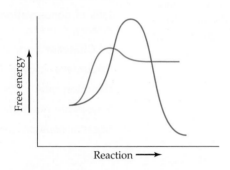

   (a) Which curve represents the faster reaction, and which the slower?
   (b) Which curve represents the spontaneous reaction, and which the nonspontaneous?

7.21 Two curves are shown in the following energy diagram. Which curve represents the catalyzed reaction, and which the uncatalyzed?

7.22 Draw energy diagrams for the following situations:
   (a) A slow reaction with a large negative ΔG
   (b) A fast reaction with a small positive ΔG

7.23 The following diagram portrays a reaction of the type $A(s) \longrightarrow B(g) + C(g)$, where the different colored spheres represent different molecular structures. Assume that the reaction has $\Delta H = +9.1$ kcal/mol.

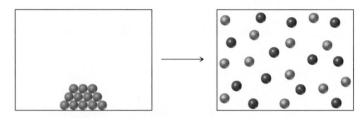

   (a) What is the sign of ΔS for the reaction?
   (b) Is the reaction likely to be spontaneous at all temperatures, nonspontaneous at all temperatures, or spontaneous at some but nonspontaneous at others?

ADDITIONAL PROBLEMS

ENTHALPY AND HEAT OF REACTION

7.24 Is the total enthalpy (H) of the reactants for an endothermic reaction greater than or less than the total enthalpy of the products?

7.25 What is meant by the term *heat of reaction*? What other name is a synonym for this term?

7.26 The vaporization of Br_2 from the liquid to the gas state requires 7.4 kcal/mol.
   (a) What is the sign of ΔH for this process?
   (b) How many kilocalories are needed to vaporize 5.8 mol of Br_2?
   (c) How many kilocalories are needed to evaporate 82 g of Br_2?

7.27 Converting liquid water to solid ice releases 1.44 kcal/mol.
   (a) What is the sign of ΔH for this process?
   (b) How many kilocalories are released by freezing 2.5 mol of H_2O?
   (c) How many kilocalories are released by freezing 32 g of H_2O?
   (d) How many kilocalories are absorbed by melting 1 mol of ice?

7.28 Glucose, also known as "blood sugar," has the formula $C_6H_{12}O_6$.
   (a) Write the equation for the combustion of glucose with O_2 to give CO_2 and H_2O.
   (b) If 3.8 kcal is released by combustion of each gram of glucose, how many kilocalories are released by the combustion of 1.50 mol of glucose?
   (c) What is the minimum amount of energy a plant must absorb to produce 15.0 g of glucose?

7.29 During the combustion of 5.00 g of octane, C_8H_{18}, 239.5 kcal is released.
   (a) Write a balanced equation for the combustion reaction.
   (b) What is the sign of ΔH for this reaction?
   (c) How much energy is released by the combustion of 1.00 mol of C_8H_{18}?
   (d) How many grams and how many moles of octane must be burned to release 450.0 kcal?
   (e) How many kilocalories are released by the combustion of 17.0 g of C_8H_{18}?

ENTROPY AND FREE ENERGY

7.30 Which of the following processes results in an increase in entropy of the system?

(a) A drop of ink spreading out when it is placed in water
(b) Steam condensing into drops on windows
(c) Constructing a building from loose bricks

7.31 For each of the following processes, specify whether entropy increases or decreases. Explain each of your answers.

(a) Assembling a jigsaw puzzle
(b) $I_2(s) + 3 F_2(g) \longrightarrow 2 IF_3(g)$
(c) A precipitate forming when two solutions are mixed
(d) $C_6H_{12}O_6(aq) + 6 O_2(g) \longrightarrow 6 CO_2(g) + 6 H_2O(g)$
(e) $CaCO_3(s) \longrightarrow CaO(s) + CO_2(g)$
(f) $Pb(NO_3)_2(aq) + 2 NaCl(aq) \longrightarrow$
$PbCl_2(s) + 2 NaNO_3(aq)$

7.32 What is meant by a *spontaneous* process?

7.33 How is the sign of the free-energy change related to the spontaneity of a process?

7.34 What two factors affect the spontaneity of a reaction?

7.35 What is the difference between an exothermic reaction and an exergonic reaction?

7.36 Why are most spontaneous reactions exothermic?

7.37 Is it possible for a reaction to be nonspontaneous yet exothermic? Explain.

7.38 For the reaction

$NaCl(s) \xrightarrow{\text{Water}} Na^+(aq) + Cl^-(aq), \quad \Delta H = +1.00 \text{ kcal/mol}$

(a) Is this process endothermic or exothermic?
(b) Does entropy increase or decrease in this process?
(c) Table salt (NaCl) readily dissolves in water. Explain, based on your answers to parts (a) and (b).

7.39 For the reaction $2 Hg(l) + O_2(g) \longrightarrow 2 HgO(s)$,
$\Delta H = -43 \text{ kcal/mol}$.

(a) Does entropy increase or decrease in this process? Explain.
(b) Under what conditions would you expect this process to be spontaneous?

7.40 The reaction of gaseous H_2 and liquid Br_2 to give gaseous HBr has $\Delta H = -17.4 \text{ kcal/mol}$ and $\Delta S = 27.2 \text{ cal/(mol·K)}$.

(a) Write the balanced equation for this reaction.
(b) Does entropy increase or decrease in this process?
(c) Is this process spontaneous at all temperatures? Explain.
(d) What is the value of ΔG for the reaction at 300 K?

7.41 The following reaction is used in the industrial synthesis of PVC polymer:

$Cl_2(g) + H_2C = CH_2(g) \longrightarrow$
$ClCH_2CH_2Cl(l) \quad \Delta H = -52 \text{ kcal/mol}$

(a) Is ΔS positive or negative for this process?
(b) Is this process spontaneous at all temperatures? Explain.

RATES OF CHEMICAL REACTIONS

7.42 What is the activation energy of a reaction?

7.43 Which reaction is faster, one with $E_{act} = +10 \text{ kcal/mol}$ or one with $E_{act} = +5 \text{ kcal/mol}$? Explain.

7.44 Draw energy diagrams for exergonic reactions that meet the following descriptions:

(a) A slow reaction that has a small free-energy change
(b) A fast reaction that has a large free-energy change

7.45 Draw an energy diagram for a reaction whose products have the same free energies as its reactants. What is free-energy change in this case?

7.46 Give two reasons why increasing temperature increases the rate of a reaction.

7.47 Why does increasing concentration generally increase the rate of a reaction?

7.48 What is a catalyst, and what effect does it have on the activation energy of a reaction?

7.49 If a catalyst changes the activation energy of a forward reaction from 28.0 kcal/mol to 23.0 kcal/mol, what effect does it have on the reverse reaction?

7.50 For the reaction $C(s, \text{diamond}) \longrightarrow C(s, \text{graphite})$,
$\Delta G = -0.693 \text{ kcal/mol}$ at 25 °C.

(a) According to this information, do diamonds spontaneously turn into graphite?
(b) In light of your answer to part (a), why can diamonds be kept unchanged for thousands of years?

7.51 The reaction between hydrogen gas and carbon to produce the gas known as ethylene is
$2 H_2(g) + 2 C(s) \longrightarrow H_2C = CH_2(g)$,
$\Delta G = +16.3 \text{ kcal/mol}$ at 25 °C.

(a) Is this reaction spontaneous at 25 °C?
(b) Would it be reasonable to try to develop a catalyst for the reaction run at 25 °C? Explain.

CHEMICAL EQUILIBRIA

7.52 What is meant by the term "chemical equilibrium"? Must amounts of reactants and products be equal at equilibrium?

7.53 Why do catalysts not alter the amounts of reactants and products present at equilibrium?

7.54 Write the equilibrium equations for the following reactions:

(a) $2 CO(g) + O_2(g) \rightleftharpoons 2 CO_2(g)$
(b) $C_2H_6(g) + 2 Cl_2(g) \rightleftharpoons C_2H_4Cl_2(g) + 2 HCl(g)$
(c) $HF(aq) + H_2O(l) \rightleftharpoons H_3O^+(aq) + F^-(aq)$
(d) $3 O_2(g) \rightleftharpoons 2 O_3(g)$

7.55 Write the equilibrium equations for the following reactions, and tell whether reactants or products are favored in each case.

(a) $S_2(g) + 2 H_2(g) \rightleftharpoons 2 H_2S(g) \quad K = 2.8 \times 10^{-21}$
(b) $CO(g) + 2 H_2(g) \rightleftharpoons CH_3OH(g) \quad K = 10.5$
(c) $Br_2(g) + Cl_2(g) \rightleftharpoons 2 BrCl(g) \quad K = 58.0$
(d) $I_2(g) \rightleftharpoons 2I(g) \quad K = 6.8 \times 10^{-3}$

7.56 For the reaction $N_2O_4(g) \rightleftharpoons 2 NO_2(g)$, the equilibrium concentrations at 25 °C are $[NO_2] = 0.0325 \text{ mol/L}$ and $[N_2O_4] = 0.147 \text{ mol/L}$. What is the value of K at 25 °C?

7.57 For the reaction $2 CO(g) + O_2(g) \rightleftharpoons 2 CO_2(g)$, the equilibrium concentrations at a certain temperature are $[CO_2] = 0.11 \text{ mol/L}$, $[O_2] = 0.015 \text{ mol/L}$, $[CO] = 0.025 \text{ mol/L}$.

What is the value of K at this temperature?

7.58 Use your answer from Problem 7.56 to calculate the following:

(a) $[N_2O_4]$ at equilibrium when $[NO_2] = 0.0250$ mol/L

(b) $[NO_2]$ at equilibrium when $[N_2O_4] = 0.0750$ mol/L

7.59 Use your answer from Problem 7.57 to calculate the following:

(a) $[O_2]$ at equilibrium when $[CO_2] = 0.18$ mol/L and $[CO] = 0.0200$ mol/L

(b) $[CO_2]$ at equilibrium when $[CO] = 0.080$ mol/L and $[O_2] = 0.520$ mol/L

7.60 Would you expect to find relatively more reactants or more products for the reaction in Problem 7.56 if the pressure is raised? Explain.

7.61 Would you expect to find relatively more reactants or more products for the reaction in Problem 7.57 if the pressure is lowered?

LE CHÂTELIER'S PRINCIPLE

7.62 Oxygen can be converted into ozone by the action of lightning or electric sparks:

$$3 O_2(g) \rightleftharpoons 2 O_3(g)$$

For this reaction, $\Delta H = +68$ kcal/mol and $K = 2.68 \times 10^{-29}$ at 25 °C.

(a) Is the reaction exothermic or endothermic?

(b) Are the reactants or the products favored at equilibrium?

(c) Explain the effect on the equilibrium of:

   (1) Increasing pressure by decreasing volume

   (2) Increasing the concentration of $O_2(g)$

   (3) Increasing the concentration of $O_3(g)$

   (4) Adding a catalyst

   (5) Increasing the temperature

7.63 Hydrogen chloride can be made from the reaction of chlorine and hydrogen:

$$Cl_2(g) + H_2(g) \longrightarrow 2 HCl(g)$$

For this reaction, $K = 26 \times 10^{33}$ and $\Delta H = -44$ kcal/mol at 25 °C.

(a) Is the reaction endothermic or exothermic?

(b) Are the reactants or the products favored at equilibrium?

(c) Explain the effect on the equilibrium of:

   (1) Increasing pressure by decreasing volume

   (2) Increasing the concentration of $HCl(g)$

   (3) Decreasing the concentration of $Cl_2(g)$

   (4) Increasing the concentration of $H_2(g)$

   (5) Adding a catalyst

7.64 When the following equilibria are disturbed by increasing the pressure, does the concentration of reaction products increase, decrease, or remain the same?

(a) $2 CO_2(g) \rightleftharpoons 2 CO(g) + O_2(g)$

(b) $N_2(g) + O_2(g) \rightleftharpoons 2 NO(g)$

(c) $Si(s) + 2 Cl_2(g) \rightleftharpoons SiCl_4(g)$

7.65 For the following equilibria, use Le Châtelier's principle to predict the direction of the reaction when the pressure is increased by decreasing the volume of the equilibrium mixture.

(a) $C(s) + H_2O(g) \rightleftharpoons CO(g) + H_2(g)$

(b) $2 H_2(g) + O_2(g) \rightleftharpoons 2 H_2O(g)$

(c) $2 Fe(s) + 3 H_2O(g) \rightleftharpoons Fe_2O_3(s) + 3 H_2(g)$

7.66 The reaction $CO(g) + H_2O(g) \rightleftharpoons CO_2(g) + H_2(g)$ has $\Delta H = -9.8$ kcal/mol. Does the amount of H_2 in an equilibrium mixture increase or decrease when the temperature is decreased?

7.67 The reaction $3 O_2(g) \rightleftharpoons 2 O_3(g)$ has $\Delta H = +68$ kcal/mol. Does the equilibrium constant for the reaction increase or decrease when the temperature increases?

7.68 The reaction $H_2(g) + I_2(g) \rightleftharpoons 2 HI(g)$ has $\Delta H = -2.2$ kcal/mol. Will the equilibrium concentration of HI increase or decrease when:

(a) I_2 is added?

(b) H_2 is removed?

(c) A catalyst is added?

(d) The temperature is increased?

7.69 The reaction $Fe^{3+}(aq) + Cl^-(aq) \rightleftharpoons FeCl^{2+}(aq)$ is endothermic. How will the equilibrium concentration of $FeCl^{2+}$ change when:

(a) $Fe(NO_3)_3$ is added?

(b) Cl^- is precipitated by addition of $AgNO_3$?

(c) The temperature is increased?

(d) A catalyst is added?

Applications

7.70 Which provides more energy, 1 g of carbohydrate or 1 g of fat? [*Energy from Food, p. 189*]

7.71 How many Calories (that is, kilocalories) are in a 45.0 g serving of potato chips if we assume that they are essentially 50% carbohydrate, and 50% fats? [*Energy from Food, p. 189*]

7.72 Which body organs help to regulate body temperature? [*Regulation of Body Temperature, p. 198*]

7.73 What is the purpose of blood vessel dilation? [*Regulation of Body Temperature, p. 198*]

7.74 What does it mean to "fix" nitrogen, and what natural processes accomplish nitrogen fixation? [*Nitrogen Fixation, p. 207*]

7.75 The enthalpy change for the production of ammonia from its elements is $\Delta H = -22$ kcal/mol, yet this reaction does not readily occur at room temperature. Give two reasons why this is so. [*Nitrogen Fixation, p. 207*]

General Questions and Problems

7.76 For the unbalanced combustion reaction shown below, 1 mol of ethanol, C_2H_5OH, releases 327 kcal.

$$C_2H_5OH + O_2 \longrightarrow CO_2 + H_2O$$

(a) Write a balanced equation for the combustion reaction.

(b) What is the sign of ΔH for this reaction?

(c) How much heat (in kilocalories) is released from the combustion of 5.00 g of ethanol?

(d) How many grams of C_2H_5OH must be burned to raise the temperature of 500.0 mL of water from 20.0 °C to 100.0 °C? (The specific heat of water is 1.00 cal/g · °C. See Section 2.10)

(e) If the density of ethanol is 0.789 g/mL, calculate the combustion energy of ethanol in kilocalories/milliliter

7.77 For the production of ammonia from its elements, $\Delta H = -22$ kcal/mol.

(a) Is this process endothermic or exothermic?

(b) How many kilocalories are involved in the production of 0.700 mol of NH_3?

7.78 Magnetite, an iron ore with formula Fe_3O_4, can be reduced by treatment with hydrogen to yield iron metal and water vapor.

(a) Write the balanced equation.

(b) This process requires 36 kcal for every 1.00 mol of Fe_3O_4 reduced. How much energy (in kilocalories) is required to produce 55 g of iron?

(c) How many grams of hydrogen are needed to produce 75 g of iron?

(d) This reaction has $K = 2.3 \times 10^{-18}$. Are the reactants or the products favored?

7.79 Hemoglobin (Hb) reacts reversibly with O_2 to form HbO_2, a substance that transfers oxygen to tissues:

$$Hb(aq) + O_2(aq) \rightleftharpoons HbO_2(aq)$$

Carbon monoxide (CO) is attracted to Hb 140 times more strongly than O_2 and establishes another equilibrium.

(a) Explain, using Le Châtelier's principle, why inhalation of CO can cause weakening and eventual death.

(b) Still another equilibrium is established when both O_2 and CO are present:

$$Hb(CO)(aq) + O_2(aq) \rightleftharpoons HbO_2(aq) + CO(aq)$$

Explain, using Le Châtelier's principle, why pure oxygen is often administered to victims of CO poisoning.

7.80 Many hospitals administer glucose intravenously to patients. If 3.8 kcal is provided by each gram of glucose, how many grams must be administered to maintain a person's normal basal metabolic needs of about 1700 kcal/day?

7.81 For the evaporation of water, $H_2O(l) \longrightarrow H_2O(g)$, at 100 °C, $\Delta H = +9.72$ kcal/mol.

(a) How many kilocalories are needed to vaporize 10.0 g of $H_2O(l)$?

(b) How many kilocalories are released when 10.0 g of $H_2O(g)$ is condensed?

7.82 Ammonia reacts slowly in air to produce nitrogen monoxide and water vapor:

$$NH_3(g) + O_2(g) \rightleftharpoons NO(g) + H_2O(g) + Heat$$

(a) Balance the equation.

(b) Write the equilibrium equation.

(c) Explain the effect on the equilibrium of:

(1) Raising the pressure

(2) Adding $NO(g)$

(3) Decreasing the concentration of NH_3

(4) Lowering the temperature

7.83 Methanol, CH_3OH, is used as race car fuel.

(a) Write the balanced equation for the combustion of methanol.

(b) $\Delta H = -174$ kcal/mol methanol for the process. How many kilocalories are released by burning 50.0 g of methanol?

7.84 Sketch an energy diagram for a system in which the forward reaction has $E_{act} = +25$ kcal/mol and the reverse reaction has $E_{act} = +35$ kcal/mol.

(a) Is the forward process endergonic or exergonic?

(b) What is the value of ΔG for the reaction?

7.85 The thermite reaction (photograph, p. 185), in which aluminum metal reacts with iron(III) oxide to produce a spectacular display of sparks, is so exothermic that the product (iron) is in the molten state:

$$2\,Al(s) + Fe_2O_3(s) \longrightarrow 2\,Al_2O_3(s) + 2\,Fe(l)$$
$$\Delta H = -202.9 \text{ kcal/mol}$$

How much heat (in kilocalories) is released when 5.00 g of Al is used in the reaction?

7.86 How much heat (in kilocalories) is evolved or absorbed in the reaction of 1.00 g of Na with H_2O? Is the reaction exothermic or endothermic?

$$2\,Na(s) + 2\,H_2O(l) \longrightarrow 2\,NaOH(aq) + H_2(g)$$
$$\Delta H = -88.0 \text{ kcal/mol}$$

CHAPTER 8

Gases, Liquids, and Solids

CONCEPTS TO REVIEW

Ionic Bonds
(Section 4.3)

Polar Covalent Bonds
and Polar Molecules
(Sections 5.8 and 5.9)

Enthalpy, Entropy, and
Free Energy
(Sections 7.2–7.4)

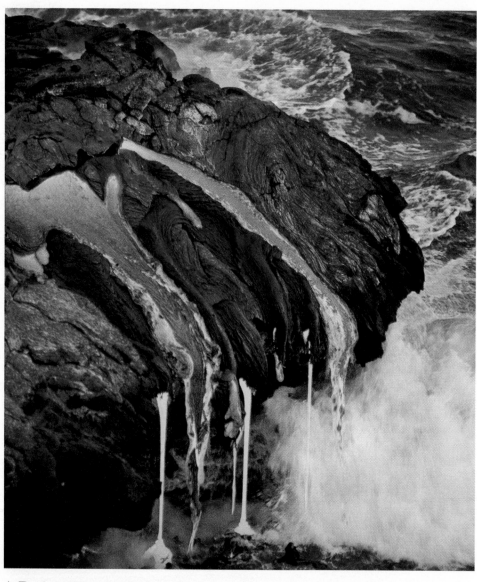

▲ The three states of matter—solid (rock), liquid (lava, water), and gas (steam)—all come together as this lava stream flows into the ocean.

CONTENTS

CHAPTER GOALS

In this chapter, we will answer the following questions:

1. How do scientists explain the behavior of gases?

THE GOAL: Be able to state the assumptions of the kinetic–molecular theory and use these assumptions to explain the behavior of gases.

2. How do gases respond to changes in temperature, pressure, and volume?

THE GOAL: Be able to use Boyle's law, Charles's law, Gay-Lussac's law, and Avogadro's law to explain the effect on gases of a change in pressure, volume, or temperature.

3. What is the ideal gas law?

THE GOAL: Be able to use the ideal gas law to find the pressure, volume, temperature, or molar amount of a gas sample.

4. What is partial pressure?

THE GOAL: Be able to define partial pressure and use Dalton's law of partial pressures.

5. What are the major intermolecular forces, and how do they affect the states of matter?

THE GOAL: Be able to explain dipole–dipole forces, London dispersion forces, and hydrogen bonding, and recognize which of these forces affect a given molecule.

6. What are the various kinds of solids, and how do they differ?

THE GOAL: Be able to recognize the different kinds of solids and describe their characteristics.

7. What factors affect a change of state?

THE GOAL: Be able to apply the concepts of heat change, equilibrium, and vapor pressure to changes of state.

The previous seven chapters dealt with matter at the atomic level. We have seen that all matter is composed of atoms, ions, or molecules; that these particles are in constant motion; that atoms combine to make compounds using chemical bonds; and that physical and chemical changes are accompanied by the release or absorption of energy. Now it is time to look at a different aspect of matter, concentrating not on the properties and small-scale behavior of individual atoms but on the properties and large-scale behavior of visible amounts of matter.

8.1 States of Matter and Their Changes

Matter exists in any of three phases, or *states*—solid, liquid, and gas. The state in which a compound exists under a given set of conditions depends on the relative strength of the attractive forces between particles compared to the kinetic energy of the particles. Kinetic energy (Section 7.1) is energy associated with motion, and is related to the temperature of the substance. In gases, the attractive forces between particles are very weak compared to their kinetic energy, so the particles move about freely, are far apart, and have almost no influence on one another. In liquids, the attractive forces between particles are stronger, pulling the particles close together but still allowing them considerable freedom to move about. In solids, the attractive forces are much stronger than the kinetic energy of the particles, so the atoms, molecules, or ions are held in a specific arrangement and can only wiggle around in place (Figure 8.1).

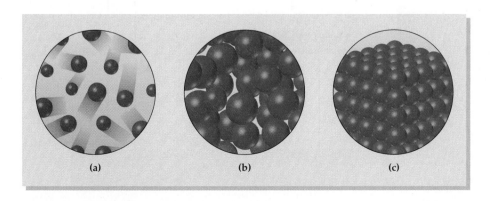

(a)   (b)   (c)

◀ **FIGURE 8.1 A molecular comparison of gases, liquids, and solids.** (a) In gases, the particles feel little attraction for one another and are free to move about randomly. (b) In liquids, the particles are held close together by attractive forces but are free to slide over one another. (c) In solids, the particles still move slightly, but are held in a specific arrangement with respect to one another.

Change of state The change of a substance from one state of matter (gas, liquid, or solid) to another.

The transformation of a substance from one state to another is called a *phase change*, or a **change of state**. Every change of state is reversible and, like all chemical and physical processes, is characterized by a free-energy change, ΔG. A change of state that is spontaneous in one direction (exergonic, negative ΔG) is nonspontaneous in the other direction (endergonic, positive ΔG). As always, the free-energy change ΔG has both an enthalpy term ΔH and a temperature-dependent entropy term ΔS, according to the equation $\Delta G = \Delta H - T\Delta S$. (You might want to reread Section 7.4 to brush up on these ideas.)(, p. 188)

Free-energy change

$$\Delta G = \Delta H - T\Delta S$$

The enthalpy change ΔH is a measure of the heat absorbed or released during a given change of state. In the melting of a solid to a liquid, for example, heat is absorbed and ΔH is positive (endothermic). In the reverse process—the freezing of a liquid to a solid—heat is released and ΔH is negative (exothermic). Look at the change between ice and water for instance:

Melting: $H_2O(s) \longrightarrow H_2O(l)$ $\Delta H = +1.44 \text{ kcal/mol}$

Freezing: $H_2O(l) \longrightarrow H_2O(s)$ $\Delta H = -1.44 \text{ kcal/mol}$

The entropy change ΔS is a measure of the change in molecular disorder or freedom that occurs during a process. In the melting of a solid to a liquid, for example, disorder increases because particles gain freedom of motion, so ΔS is positive. In the reverse process—the freezing of a liquid to a solid—disorder decreases as particles are locked into position, so ΔS is negative. Look at the change between ice and water:

Melting: $H_2O(s) \longrightarrow H_2O(l)$ $\Delta S = +5.26 \text{ cal/(mol·K)}$

Freezing: $H_2O(l) \longrightarrow H_2O(s)$ $\Delta S = -5.26 \text{ cal/(mol·K)}$

As with all processes that are unfavored by one term in the free-energy equation but favored by the other, the sign of ΔG depends on the temperature (Section 7.4). The melting of ice, for instance, is unfavored by a positive ΔH but favored by a positive ΔS. Thus, at a low temperature, the unfavorable ΔH is larger than the favorable

▶ **FIGURE 8.2 Changes of state.** The changes are endothermic from bottom to top and exothermic from top to bottom. Solid and liquid states are in equilibrium at the melting point; liquid and gas states are in equilibrium at the boiling point.

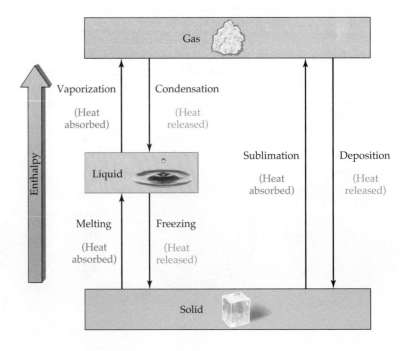

$T\Delta S$ so ΔG is positive and no melting occurs. At a higher temperature, however, $T\Delta S$ becomes larger than ΔH, so ΔG is negative and melting *does* occur. The exact temperature at which the changeover in behavior occurs is called the **melting point (mp)** and represents the temperature at which solid and liquid coexist in equilibrium. In the corresponding change from a liquid to a gas, the two states are in equilibrium at the **boiling point (bp)**.

The names and enthalpy changes associated with the different changes of state are summarized in Figure 8.2. Note a solid can change directly to a gas without going through the liquid state—a process called *sublimation*. Dry ice (solid CO_2) at atmospheric pressure, for example, changes directly to a gas without melting.

Melting point (mp) The temperature at which solid and liquid are in equilibrium.

Boiling point (bp) The temperature at which liquid and gas are in equilibrium.

WORKED EXAMPLE	**8.1** Change of State: Enthalpy, Entropy, and Free Energy

The change of state from liquid to gas for chloroform, formerly used as an anesthetic, has $\Delta H = +6.98$ kcal/mol and a $\Delta S = +20.9$ cal/(mol·K).

(a) Is the change of state from liquid to gas favored or unfavored by ΔH? by ΔS?

(b) Is the change of state from liquid to gas favored or unfavored at 35 °C?

(c) Is this change of state spontaneous at 65 °C?

ANALYSIS A process will be favored if energy is released ($\Delta H = $ negative) and if there is a decrease in disorder ($\Delta S = $ positive). In cases in which one factor is favorable and the other is unfavorable, then we can calculate the free energy change to determine if the process is favored:

$$\Delta G = \Delta H - T\Delta S$$

When ΔG is negative, the process is favored.

SOLUTION

(a) The ΔH does NOT favor this change of state ($\Delta H = $ positive), but the ΔS does favor the process. Since the two factors are not in agreement, we must use the equation for free-energy change to determine if the process is favored at a given temperature.

(b) Substituting the values for ΔH and ΔS into the equation for free energy change we can determine if ΔG is positive or negative at 35 °C (308 K). Note that we must first convert degrees Celsius to kelvins and convert the ΔS from cal to kcal so the units can be added together.

$$\Delta G = \Delta H - T\Delta S = \left(\frac{6.98 \text{ kcal}}{\text{mol}}\right) - (308 \text{ K})\left(\frac{20.9 \text{ cal}}{\text{mol·K}}\right)\left(\frac{1 \text{ kcal}}{1000 \text{ cal}}\right)$$

$$= 6.98\frac{\text{kcal}}{\text{mol}} - 6.44\frac{\text{kcal}}{\text{mol}} = +0.54\frac{\text{kcal}}{\text{mol}}$$

Since the $\Delta G = $ positive, this change of state is not favored at 35 °C.

(c) Repeating the calculation using the equation for free-energy change at 65 °C (338 K):

$$\Delta G = \Delta H - T\Delta S = \left(\frac{6.98 \text{ kcal}}{\text{mol}}\right) - (338 \text{ K})\left(\frac{20.9 \text{ cal}}{\text{mol·K}}\right)\left(\frac{1 \text{ kcal}}{1000 \text{ cal}}\right)$$

$$= 6.98\frac{\text{kcal}}{\text{mol}} - 7.06\frac{\text{kcal}}{\text{mol}} = -0.08\frac{\text{kcal}}{\text{mol}}$$

Because ΔG is negative in this case, the change of state is favored at this temperature.

> **PROBLEM 8.1**
>
> The change of state from liquid H_2O to gaseous H_2O has $\Delta H = +9.72$ kcal/mol and $\Delta S = +26.1$ cal/(mol·K).
>
> **(a)** Is the change from liquid to gaseous H_2O favored or unfavored by ΔH? By ΔS?
>
> **(b)** What is the value of ΔG for the change from liquid to gaseous H_2O at 373 K?
>
> **(c)** What are the values of ΔH and ΔS for the change from gaseous to liquid H_2O?

8.2 Gases and the Kinetic–Molecular Theory

Gases behave quite differently from liquids and solids. Gases, for instance, have low densities and are easily compressed to a smaller volume when placed under pressure, a property that allows them to be stored in large tanks. Liquids and solids, by contrast, are much more dense and much less compressible. Furthermore, gases undergo a far larger expansion or contraction when their temperature is changed than do liquids and solids.

The behavior of gases can be explained by a group of assumptions known as the **kinetic–molecular theory of gases**. We will see in the next several sections how the following assumptions account for the observable properties of gases:

Kinetic–molecular theory of gases A group of assumptions that explain the behavior of gases.

- **A gas consists of many particles, either atoms or molecules, moving about at random with no attractive forces between them.** Because of this random motion, different gases mix together quickly.

- **The amount of space occupied by the gas particles themselves is much smaller than the amount of space between particles.** Most of the volume taken up by gases is empty space, accounting for the ease of compression and low densities of gases.

- **The average kinetic energy of gas particles is proportional to the Kelvin temperature.** Thus, gas particles have more kinetic energy and move faster as the temperature increases. (In fact, gas particles move much faster than you might suspect. The average speed of a helium atom at room temperature and atmospheric pressure is approximately 1.36 km/s, or 3000 mi/hr, nearly that of a rifle bullet.)

- **Collisions of gas particles, either with other particles or with the wall of their container, are elastic; that is, the total kinetic energy of the particles is constant.** The pressure of a gas against the walls of its container is the result of collisions of the gas particles with the walls. The more collisions and the more forceful each collision, the higher the pressure.

Ideal gas A gas that obeys all the assumptions of the kinetic–molecular theory.

A gas that obeys all the assumptions of the kinetic–molecular theory is called an **ideal gas**. In practice, though, there is no such thing as a perfectly ideal gas. All gases behave somewhat differently than predicted when, at very high pressures or very low temperatures, their particles get closer together and interactions between particles become significant. As a rule, however, most real gases display nearly ideal behavior under normal conditions.

8.3 Pressure

We are all familiar with the effects of air pressure. When you fly in an airplane, the change in air pressure against your eardrums as the plane climbs or descends can cause a painful "popping." When you pump up a bicycle tire, you increase the pressure of air against the inside walls of the tire until the tire feels hard.

Pressure (P) The force per unit area pushing against a surface.

In scientific terms, **pressure (P)** is defined as a force (F) per unit area (A) pushing against a surface; that is, $P = F/A$. In the bicycle tire, for example, the pressure you feel is the force of air molecules colliding with the inside walls of the tire. The units you probably use for tire pressure are pounds per square inch (psi), where 1 psi is equal to the pressure exerted by a 1 pound object resting on a 1 square inch surface.

We on earth are under pressure from the atmosphere, the blanket of air pressing down on us (Figure 8.3). Atmospheric pressure is not constant, however; it varies slightly from day to day depending on the weather, and it also varies with altitude. Due to gravitational forces, the density of air is greatest at the earth's surface and decreases with increasing altitude. As a result, air pressure is greatest at the surface: about 14.7 psi at sea level but only about 4.7 psi on the summit of Mt. Everest.

One of the most commonly used units of pressure is the *millimeter of mercury*, abbreviated *mmHg* and often called a *torr* (after the Italian physicist Evangelista Torricelli). This unusual unit dates back to the early 1600s when Torricelli made the first mercury *barometer*. As shown in Figure 8.4, a barometer consists of a long, thin tube that is sealed at one end, filled with mercury, and then inverted into a dish of mercury. Some mercury runs from the tube into the dish until the downward pressure of the mercury in the column is exactly balanced by the outside atmospheric pressure, which presses down on the mercury in the dish and pushes it up into the column. The height of the mercury column varies depending on the altitude and weather conditions, but standard atmospheric pressure at sea level is defined to be exactly 760 mm.

Gas pressure inside a container is often measured using an open-end *manometer*, a simple instrument similar in principle to the mercury barometer. As shown in Figure 8.5, an open-end manometer consists of a U-tube filled with mercury, with one end connected to a gas-filled container and the other end open to the atmosphere. The difference between the heights of the mercury levels in the two arms of the U-tube indicates the difference between the pressure of the gas in the container and the pressure of the atmosphere. If the gas pressure inside the container is less than atmospheric, the mercury level is higher in the arm connected to the container (Figure 8.5a). If the gas pressure inside the container is greater than atmospheric, the mercury level is higher in the arm open to the atmosphere (Figure 8.5b).

Pressure is given in the SI system (Section 2.1) by a unit named the *pascal* (Pa), where 1 Pa = 0.007500 mmHg (or 1 mmHg = 133.32 Pa). Measurements in pascals are becoming more common, and many clinical laboratories have made the

▲ **FIGURE 8.3 Atmospheric pressure.** A column of air weighing 14.7 lb presses down on each square inch of the earth's surface at sea level, resulting in what we call atmospheric pressure.

▲ **FIGURE 8.4 Measuring atmospheric pressure.** A mercury barometer measures atmospheric pressure by determining the height of a mercury column in a sealed glass tube. The downward pressure of the mercury in the column is exactly balanced by the outside atmospheric pressure, which presses down on the mercury in the dish and pushes it up into the column.

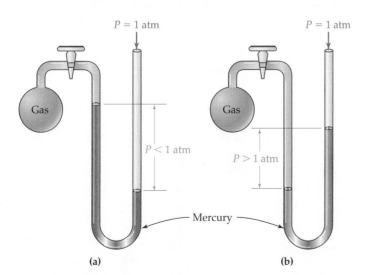

▲ **FIGURE 8.5 Open-end manometers for measuring pressure in a gas-filled bulb.** (a) When the pressure in the gas-filled container is lower than atmospheric, the mercury level is higher in the arm open to the container. (b) When the pressure in the container is higher than atmospheric, the mercury level is higher in the arm open to the atmosphere.

switchover. Higher pressures are often still given in *atmospheres* (atm), where 1 atm = 760 mmHg exactly.

$$\text{Pressure units: } 1 \text{ atm} = 760 \text{ mmHg} = 14.7 \text{ psi} = 101{,}325 \text{ Pa}$$
$$1 \text{ mmHg} = 1 \text{ torr} = 133.32 \text{ Pa}$$

WORKED EXAMPLE **8.2** Unit Conversions (Pressure): psi, Atmospheres, and Pascals

A typical bicycle tire is inflated with air to a pressure of 55 psi. How many atmospheres is this? How many pascals?

ANALYSIS Using the starting pressure in psi, the pressure in atm and pascals can be calculated using the equivalent values in as conversion factors.

SOLUTION

STEP 1: **Identify known information.**

STEP 2: **Identify answer and units.**

STEP 3: **Identify conversion factors.** Using equivalent values in appropriate units, we can obtain conversion factors to convert to atm and pascals.

STEP 4: **Solve.** Use the appropriate conversion factors to set up an equation in which unwanted units cancel.

$$\text{Pressure} = 55 \text{ psi}$$

$$\text{Pressure} = ?? \text{ atm} = ?? \text{ pascals}$$

$$14.7 \text{ psi} = 1 \text{ atm} \rightarrow \frac{1 \text{ atm}}{14.7 \text{ psi}}$$

$$14.7 \text{ psi} = 101{,}325 \text{ Pa} \rightarrow \frac{101{,}325 \text{ Pa}}{14.7 \text{ psi}}$$

$$(55 \text{ psi}) \times \left(\frac{1 \text{ atm}}{14.7 \text{ psi}} \right) = 3.7 \text{ atm}$$

$$(55 \text{ psi}) \times \left(\frac{101{,}325 \text{ Pa}}{14.7 \text{ psi}} \right) = 3.8 \times 10^5 \text{ Pa}$$

WORKED EXAMPLE **8.3** Unit Conversions (Pressure): mmHg to Atmospheres

The pressure in a closed flask is measured using a manometer. If the mercury level in the arm open to the sealed vessel is 23.6 cm higher than the level of mercury in the arm open to the atmosphere, what is the gas pressure (in atm) in the closed flask?

APPLICATION ▶ Blood Pressure

Having your blood pressure measured is a quick and easy way to get an indication of the state of your circulatory system. Although blood pressure varies with age, a normal adult male has a reading near 120/80 mmHg, and a normal adult female has a reading near 110/70 mmHg. Abnormally high values signal an increased risk of heart attack and stroke.

Pressure varies greatly in different types of blood vessels. Usually, though, measurements are carried out on arteries in the upper arm as the heart goes through a full cardiac cycle. *Systolic pressure* is the maximum pressure developed in the artery just after contraction, as the heart forces the maximum amount of blood into the artery. *Diastolic pressure* is the minimum pressure that occurs at the end of the heart cycle.

Blood pressure is most often measured by a *sphygmomanometer*, a device consisting of a squeeze bulb, a flexible cuff, and a mercury manometer. The cuff is placed around the upper arm over the brachial artery and inflated by the squeeze bulb to about 200 mmHg pressure, an amount great enough to squeeze the artery shut and prevent blood flow. Air is then slowly released from the cuff, and pressure drops. As cuff pressure reaches the systolic pressure, blood spurts through the artery, creating a turbulent tapping sound that can be heard through a stethoscope. The pressure registered on the manometer at the moment the first sounds are heard is the systolic blood pressure.

Sounds continue until the pressure in the cuff becomes low enough to allow diastolic blood flow. At this point, blood flow becomes smooth, no sounds are heard, and a diastolic

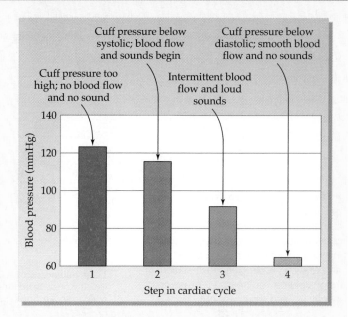

▲ The sequence of events during blood pressure measurement, including the sounds heard.

blood pressure reading is recorded on the manometer. Readings are usually recorded as systolic/diastolic, for example, 120/80. The accompanying Figure shows the sequence of events during measurement.

See Additional Problem 8.100 at the end of the chapter.

Because $P \times V$ is a constant value for a fixed amount of gas at a constant temperature, the starting pressure (P_1) times the starting volume (V_1) must equal the final pressure (P_2) times the final volume (V_2). Thus, Boyle's law can be used to find the final pressure or volume when the starting pressure or volume is changed.

Since $\quad P_1V_1 = k \quad$ and $\quad P_2V_2 = k$

then $\quad P_1V_1 = P_2V_2$

so $\quad P_2 = \dfrac{P_1V_1}{V_2} \quad$ and $\quad V_2 = \dfrac{P_1V_1}{P_2}$

As an example of Boyle's law behavior, think about what happens every time you breathe. Between breaths, the pressure inside your lungs is equal to atmospheric pressure. When inhalation takes place, your diaphragm lowers and the rib cage expands, increasing the volume of the lungs and thereby decreasing the pressure inside them (Figure 8.8). Air must then move into the lungs to equalize their pressure with that of the atmosphere. When exhalation takes place, the diaphragm rises and the rib cage contracts decreasing the volume of the lungs and increasing pressure inside them. Now gases move out of the lungs until pressure is again equalized with the atmosphere.

▲ Air pressure in tires, typically reported in units of pounds per square inch (psi), is another example of Boyle's Law.

Inhalation

Air

Rest position

Exhalation

Air + CO_2

▶ **FIGURE 8.8 Boyle's law in breathing.** During inhalation, the diaphragm moves down and the rib cage moves up and out, thus increasing lung volume, decreasing pressure, and drawing in air. During exhalation, lung volume decreases, pressure increases, and air moves out.

Lung volume increases, causing pressure in lungs to *decrease*. Air flows *in*.

Lung volume decreases, causing pressure in lungs to *increase*. Air flows *out*.

WORKED EXAMPLE **8.4** Using Boyle's Law: Finding Volume at a Given Pressure

In a typical automobile engine, the fuel/air mixture in a cylinder is compressed from 1.0 atm to 9.5 atm. If the uncompressed volume of the cylinder is 750 mL, what is the volume when fully compressed?

ANALYSIS This is a Boyle's law problem because the volume and pressure in the cylinder change but the amount of gas and the temperature remain constant. According to Boyle's law, the pressure of the gas times its volume is constant:

$$P_1V_1 = P_2V_2$$

Knowing three of the four variables in this equation, we can solve for the unknown.

◀ A cut-away diagram of internal combustion engine shows movement of pistons during expansion and compression cycles.

BALLPARK ESTIMATE Since the pressure *increases* approximately tenfold (from 1.0 atm to 9.5 atm), the volume must *decrease* to approximately one-tenth, from 750 mL to about 75 mL.

SOLUTION

STEP 1: **Identify known information.** Of the four variables in Boyle's law, we know P_1, V_1, and P_2.

$P_1 = 1.0$ atm
$V_1 = 750$ mL
$P_2 = 9.5$ atm

STEP 2: **Identify answer and units.**

$V_2 = $?? mL

STEP 3: **Identify equation.** In this case, we simply substitute the known variables into Boyle's law and rearrange to isolate the unknown.

$$P_1V_1 = P_2V_2 \implies V_2 = \frac{P_1V_1}{P_2}$$

STEP 4: **Solve. Substitute the known information into the equation.** Make sure units cancel so that the answer is given in the units of the unknown variable.

$$V_2 = \frac{P_1V_1}{P_2} = \frac{(1.0 \text{ atm})(750 \text{ mL})}{(9.5 \text{ atm})} = 79 \text{ mL}$$

BALLPARK CHECK Our estimate was 75 mL.

PROBLEM 8.4

An oxygen cylinder used for breathing has a volume of 5.0 L at 90 atm pressure. What is the volume of the same amount of oxygen at the same temperature if the pressure is 1.0 atm? (Hint: Would you expect the volume of gas at this pressure to be greater or less than the volume at 90 atm?)

PROBLEM 8.5

A sample of hydrogen gas at 273 K has a volume of 3.2 L at 4.0 atm pressure. What is its pressure if its volume is changed to 10.0 L? To 0.20 L?

8.5 Charles's Law: The Relation between Volume and Temperature

Imagine that you again have a sample of gas inside a cylinder with a plunger at one end. What happens if you double the sample's Kelvin temperature while letting the plunger move freely to keep the pressure constant? The gas particles move with twice as much energy and collide twice as forcefully with the walls. To maintain a constant pressure, the volume of the gas in the cylinder must double (Figure 8.9).

▲ **FIGURE 8.9 Charles's law.** The volume of a gas is directly proportionately to its Kelvin temperature at constant n and P. If the Kelvin temperature of the gas is doubled, its volume doubles.

According to **Charles's law**, the volume of a fixed amount of gas at constant pressure is directly proportional to its Kelvin temperature. Note the difference between *directly* proportional in Charles's law and *inversely* proportional in Boyle's law. Directly proportional quantities change in the same direction: As temperature goes up or down, volume also goes up or down (Figure 8.10).

Charles's law　The volume of a gas is directly proportional to its Kelvin temperature for a fixed amount of gas at a constant pressure. That is, V divided by T is constant when n and P are held constant.

$$V \propto T \quad \text{(In kelvins)}$$

$$\text{or } \frac{V}{T} = k \quad \text{(A constant value)}$$

$$\text{or } \frac{V_1}{T_1} = \frac{V_2}{T_2}$$

This observation is consistent with the kinetic–molecular theory. As temperature increases, the average kinetic energy of the gas molecules increases, as does the

▲ The volume of the gas in the balloon increases as it is heated, causing a decrease in density and allowing the balloon to rise.

▲ **FIGURE 8.10 Charles's law.** Volume is directly proportional to the Kelvin temperature for a fixed amount of gas at a constant pressure. As the temperature goes up, the volume also goes up.

energy of molecular collisions with the interior surface of the container. The volume of the container must increase to maintain a constant pressure. As an example of Charles's law, think about what happens when a hot-air balloon is inflated. Heating causes the air inside to expand and fill the balloon. The air inside the balloon is less dense than the air outside the balloon, creating the buoyancy effect.

WORKED EXAMPLE **8.5** Using Charles's Law: Finding Volume at a Given Temperature

An average adult inhales a volume of 0.50 L of air with each breath. If the air is warmed from room temperature (20 °C = 293 K) to body temperature (37 °C = 310 K) while in the lungs, what is the volume of the air exhaled?

ANALYSIS This is a Charles's law problem because the volume and temperature of the air change while the amount and pressure remain constant. Knowing three of the four variables, we can rearrange Charles's law to solve for the unknown.

BALLPARK ESTIMATE Charles's Law predicts an increase in volume directly proportional to the increase in temperature from 273 K to 310 K. The increase of less than 20 K represents a relatively small change compared to the initial temperature of 273 K. A 10% increase, for example, would be equal to a temperature change of 27 K; so a 20 K change would be less than 10%. We would therefore expect the volume to increase by less than 10%, from 0.50 L to a little less than 0.55 L.

SOLUTION

STEP 1: Identify known information. Of the four variables in Charles's law, we know T_1, V_1, and T_2.

$T_1 = 293$ K
$V_1 = 0.50$ L
$T_2 = 310$ K

STEP 2: Identify answer and units.

$V_2 = ??$ L

STEP 3: Identify equation. Substitute the known variables into Charles's law and rearrange to isolate the unknown.

$$\frac{V_1}{T_1} = \frac{V_2}{T_2} \implies V_2 = \frac{V_1 T_2}{T_1}$$

STEP 4: Solve. Substitute the known information into Charles's law; check to make sure units cancel.

$$V_2 = \frac{V_1 T_2}{T_1} = \frac{(0.50\ \text{L})(310\ \text{K})}{293\ \text{K}} = 0.53\ \text{L}$$

BALLPARK CHECK This is consistent with our estimate!

PROBLEM 8.6

A sample of chlorine gas has a volume of 0.30 L at 273 K and 1 atm pressure. What is its volume at 250 K and 1 atm pressure? At 525 °C and 1 atm?

▲ **FIGURE 8.11 Gay-Lussac's law.** Pressure is directly proportional to the temperature in kelvins for a fixed amount of gas at a constant volume. As the temperature goes up, the pressure also goes up.

8.6 Gay-Lussac's Law: The Relation between Pressure and Temperature

Imagine next that you have a fixed amount of gas in a sealed container whose volume remains constant. What happens if you double the temperature (in kelvins)? The gas particles move with twice as much energy and collide with the walls of the container with twice as much force. Thus, the pressure in the container doubles. According to **Gay-Lussac's law**, the pressure of a fixed amount of gas at constant volume is directly proportional to its Kelvin temperature. As temperature goes up or down, pressure also goes up or down (Figure 8.11).

Gay-Lussac's law The pressure of a gas is directly proportional to its Kelvin temperature for a fixed amount of gas at a constant volume. That is, P divided by T is constant when n and V are held constant.

$$P \propto T \quad \text{(In kelvins)}$$

$$\text{or } \frac{P}{T} = k \quad \text{(A constant value)}$$

$$\text{or } \frac{P_1}{T_1} = \frac{P_2}{T_2}$$

▲ Because of the possibility of explosion (see warning label), aerosol containers cannot be incinerated, requiring disposal in landfills.

According to the kinetic–molecular theory, the kinetic energy of molecules is directly proportional to absolute temperature. As the average kinetic energy of the molecules increases, the energy of collisions with the interior surface of the container increases, causing an increase in pressure. As an example of Gay-Lussac's law, think of what happens when an aerosol can is thrown into an incinerator. As the can gets hotter, pressure builds up inside and the can explodes (hence the warning statement on aerosol cans).

WORKED EXAMPLE   **8.6** Using Gay-Lussac's Law: Finding Pressure at a Given Temperature

What does the inside pressure become if an aerosol can with an initial pressure of 4.5 atm is heated in a fire from room temperature (20 °C) to 600 °C?

ANALYSIS This is a Gay-Lussac's law problem because the pressure and temperature of the gas inside the can change while its amount and volume remain constant. We know three of the four variables in the equation for Gay-Lussac's law, and can find the unknown by substitution and rearrangement.

BALLPARK ESTIMATE Gay-Lussac's law states that pressure is directly proportional to temperature. Since the Kelvin temperature increases approximately threefold (from about 300 K to about 900 K), we expect the pressure to also increase by approximately threefold, from 4.5 atm to about 14 atm.

SOLUTION

STEP 1: Identify known information. Of the four variables in Gay-Lussac's law, we know P_1, T_1 and T_2. (Note that T must be in kelvins.)

$P_1 = 4.5$ atm
$T_1 = 20\ °C = 293$ K
$T_2 = 600\ °C = 873$ K

STEP 2: Identify answer and units.

$P_2 = ??$ atm

STEP 3: Identify equation. Substituting the known variables into Gay-Lussac's law, we rearrange to isolate the unknown.

$$\frac{P_1}{T_1} = \frac{P_2}{T_2} \quad \Rightarrow \quad P_2 = \frac{P_1 T_2}{T_1}$$

STEP 4: Solve. Substitute the known information into Gay-Lussac's law, check to make sure units cancel.

$$P_2 = \frac{P_1 T_2}{T_1} = \frac{(4.5\ \text{atm})(873\ \text{K})}{293\ \text{K}} = 13\ \text{atm}$$

BALLPARK CHECK Our estimate was 14 atm.

PROBLEM 8.7

Driving on a hot day causes tire temperature to rise. What is the pressure inside an automobile tire at 45 °C if the tire has a pressure of 30 psi at 15 °C? Assume that the volume and amount of air in the tire remain constant.

8.7 The Combined Gas Law

Since PV, V/T, and P/T all have constant values for a fixed amount of gas, these relationships can be merged into a **combined gas law**, which holds true whenever the amount of gas is fixed.

COMBINED GAS LAW $\quad \dfrac{PV}{T} = k \quad$ (A constant value)

$$\text{or } \frac{P_1 V_1}{T_1} = \frac{P_2 V_2}{T_2}$$

If any five of the six quantities in this equation are known, the sixth quantity can be calculated. Furthermore, if any of the three variables T, P, or V is constant, that variable drops out of the equation, leaving behind Boyle's law, Charles's law, or Gay-Lussac's law. As a result, *the combined gas law is the only equation you need to remember for a fixed amount of gas.* Worked Example 8.7 gives a sample calculation.

Since $\qquad \dfrac{P_1 V_1}{T_1} = \dfrac{P_2 V_2}{T_2}$

At constant T: $\quad \dfrac{P_1 V_1}{T} = \dfrac{P_2 V_2}{T} \quad$ gives $\quad P_1 V_1 = P_2 V_2 \quad$ (Boyle's law)

At constant P: $\quad \dfrac{P V_1}{T_1} = \dfrac{P V_2}{T_2} \quad$ gives $\quad \dfrac{V_1}{T_1} = \dfrac{V_2}{T_2} \quad$ (Charles's law)

At constant V: $\quad \dfrac{P_1 V}{T_1} = \dfrac{P_2 V}{T_2} \quad$ gives $\quad \dfrac{P_1}{T_1} = \dfrac{P_2}{T_2} \quad$ (Gay-Lussac's law)

WORKED EXAMPLE **8.7** Using the Combined Gas Law: Finding Temperature

A 6.3 L sample of helium gas stored at 25 °C and 1.0 atm pressure is transferred to a 2.0 L tank and maintained at a pressure of 2.8 atm. What temperature is needed to maintain this pressure?

ANALYSIS This is a combined gas law problem because pressure, volume, and temperature change while the amount of helium remains constant. Of the six variables in this equation, we know P_1, V_1, T_1, P_2, and V_2, and we need to find T_2.

BALLPARK ESTIMATE Since the volume goes down by a little more than a factor of about 3 (from 6.3 L to 2.0 L) and the pressure goes up by a little less than a factor of about 3 (from 1.0 atm to 2.8 atm), the two changes roughly offset each other, and so the temperature should not change much. Since the volume-decrease factor (3.2) is slightly greater than the pressure-increase factor (2.8), the temperature will drop slightly ($T \propto V$).

SOLUTION

STEP 1: Identify known information. Of the six variables in combined-gas-law we know P_1, V_1, T_1, P_2, and V_2. (As always, T must be converted from Celsius degrees to kelvins.)

$P_1 = 1.0$ atm, $P_2 = 2.8$ atm
$V_1 = 6.3$ L, $V_2 = 2.0$ L
$T_1 = 25\ °C = 298$ K

STEP 2: Identify answer and units.

$T_2 = $?? kelvin

STEP 3: Identify the equation. Substituting the known variables into the equation for the combined gas law and rearrange to isolate the unknown.

$$\frac{P_1 V_1}{T_1} = \frac{P_2 V_2}{T_2} \implies T_2 = \frac{P_2 V_2 T_1}{P_1 V_1}$$

STEP 4: Solve. Solve the combined gas law equation for T_2; check to make sure units cancel.

$$T_2 = \frac{P_2 V_2 T_1}{P_1 V_1} = \frac{(2.8 \text{ atm})(2.0 \text{ L})(298 \text{ K})}{(1.0 \text{ atm})(6.3 \text{ L})} = 260 \text{ K}(\Delta T = -38\ °C)$$

BALLPARK CHECK The relatively small decrease in temperature (38 °C, or 13% compared to the original temperature) is consistent with our prediction.

PROBLEM 8.8

A weather balloon is filled with helium to a volume of 275 L at 22 °C and 752 mmHg. The balloon ascends to an altitude where the pressure is 480 mmHg, and the temperature is −32 °C. What is the volume of the balloon at this altitude?

KEY CONCEPT PROBLEM 8.9

A balloon is filled under the initial conditions indicated below. If the pressure is then increased to 2 atm while the temperature is increased to 50 °C, which balloon on the right, (a) or (b), represents the new volume of the balloon?

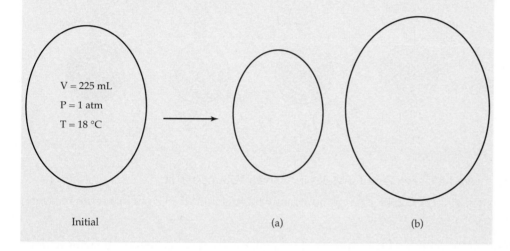

V = 225 mL

P = 1 atm

T = 18 °C

Initial   (a)   (b)

8.8 Avogadro's Law: The Relation between Volume and Molar Amount

Here we look at one final gas law, which takes changes in amount of gas into account. Imagine that you have two different volumes of a gas at the same temperature and pressure. How many moles does each sample contain? According to **Avogadro's law**, the volume of a gas is directly proportional to its molar amount at a constant pressure and temperature (Figure 8.12). A sample that contains twice the molar amount has twice the volume.

Avogadro's law The volume of a gas is directly proportional to its molar amount at a constant pressure and temperature. That is, V divided by n is constant when P and T are held constant.

Volume (V) $\propto$ Number of moles (n)

or $\dfrac{V}{n} = k$ (A constant value; the same for all gases)

or $\dfrac{V_1}{n_1} = \dfrac{V_2}{n_2}$

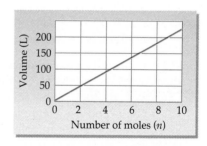

▲ **FIGURE 8.12 Avogadro's law.** Volume is directly proportional to the molar amount, n, at a constant temperature and pressure. As the number of moles goes up, the volume also goes up.

Because the particles in a gas are so tiny compared to the empty space surrounding them, there is no interaction among gas particles as proposed by the kinetic–molecular theory. As a result, the chemical identity of the particles does not matter and the value of the constant k in the equation $V/n = k$ is the same for all gases. It is therefore possible to compare the molar amounts of *any* two gases simply by comparing their volumes at the same temperature and pressure.

Notice that the *values* of temperature and pressure do not matter; it is only necessary that T and P be the same for both gases. To simplify comparisons of gas samples, however, it is convenient to define a set of conditions called **standard temperature and pressure (STP)**:

Standard temperature and pressure (STP) 0 °C (273.15 K); 1 atm (760 mmHg)

At standard temperature and pressure, 1 mol of any gas (6.02×10^{23} particles) has a volume of 22.4 L, a quantity called the **standard molar volume** (Figure 8.13).

Standard molar volume of any ideal gas at STP 22.4 L/mol

▶ **FIGURE 8.13 Avogadro's law.** Each of these 22.4 L bulbs contains 1.00 mol of gas at 0 °C and 1 atm pressure. Note that the volume occupied by 1 mol of gas is the same even though the mass of 1 mol of each gas is different.

O₂ 1.00 mol 32.0 g 22.4 L
He 1.00 mol 4.00 g 22.4 L
F₂ 1.00 mol 38.0 g 22.4 L
Ar 1.00 mol 39.9 g 22.4 L

WORKED EXAMPLE 8.8 Using Avogadro's Law: Finding Moles in a Given Volume at STP

Use the standard molar volume of a gas at STP (22.4 L) to find how many moles of air at STP are in a room measuring 4.11 m wide by 5.36 m long by 2.58 m high.

ANALYSIS We first find the volume of the room and then use standard molar volume as a conversion factor to find the number of moles.

SOLUTION

STEP 1: Identify known information. We are given the room dimensions.

Length = 5.36 m
Width = 4.11 m
Height = 2.58 m

STEP 2: Identify answer and units.

Moles of air = ?? mol

STEP 3: Identify the equation. The volume of the room is the product of its three dimensions. Once we have the volume (in m³), we can convert to liters and use the molar volume at STP as a conversion factor to obtain moles of air.

$$\text{Volume} = (4.11 \text{ m})(5.36 \text{ m})(2.58 \text{ m}) = 56.8 \text{ m}^3$$
$$= 56.8 \text{ m}^3 \times \frac{1000 \text{ L}}{1 \text{ m}^3} = 5.68 \times 10^4 \text{ L}$$
$$1 \text{ mol} = 22.4 \text{ L} \rightarrow \frac{1 \text{ mol}}{22.4 \text{ L}}$$

STEP 4: Solve. Use the room volume and the molar volume at STP to set up an equation, making sure unwanted units cancel.

$$5.68 \times 10^4 \text{ L} \times \frac{1 \text{ mol}}{22.4 \text{ L}} = 2.54 \times 10^3 \text{ mol}$$

PROBLEM 8.10

How many moles of methane gas, CH₄, are in a 1.00×10^5 L storage tank at STP? How many grams of methane is this? How many grams of carbon dioxide gas could the same tank hold?

8.9 The Ideal Gas Law

The relationships among the four variables P, V, T, and n for gases can be combined into a single expression called the **ideal gas law**. If you know the values of any three of the four quantities, you can calculate the value of the fourth.

Ideal gas law $\dfrac{PV}{nT} = R$ (A constant value)

or $PV = nRT$

The constant R in the ideal gas law (instead of the usual k) is called the **gas constant**. Its value depends on the units chosen for pressure, with the two most common values

Gas constant (R) The constant R in the ideal gas law, $PV = nRT$.

For P in atmospheres: $R = 0.0821 \dfrac{\text{L} \cdot \text{atm}}{\text{mol} \cdot \text{K}}$

For P in millimeters Hg: $R = 62.4 \dfrac{\text{L} \cdot \text{mmHg}}{\text{mol} \cdot \text{K}}$

In using the ideal gas law, it is important to choose the value of R having pressure units that are consistent with the problem and, if necessary, to convert volume into liters and temperature into kelvins.

Table 8.1 summarizes the various gas laws, and Worked Example 8.9 shows how to use the ideal gas law.

TABLE 8.1   A Summary of the Gas Laws

	GAS LAW	VARIABLES	CONSTANT
Boyle's law	$P_1V_1 = P_2V_2$	P, V	n, T
Charles's law	$V_1/T_1 = V_2/T_2$	V, T	n, P
Gay-Lussac's law	$P_1/T_1 = P_2/T_2$	P, T	n, V
Combined gas law	$P_1V_1/T_1 = P_2V_2/T_2$	P, V, T	n
Avogadro's law	$V_1/n_1 = V_2/n_2$	V, n	P, T
Ideal gas law	$PV = nRT$	P, V, T, n	R

WORKED EXAMPLE   **8.9** Using Ideal Gas Law: Finding Moles

How many moles of air are in the lungs of an average person with a total lung capacity of 3.8 L? Assume that the person is at 1.0 atm pressure and has a normal body temperature of 37 °C.

ANALYSIS This is an ideal gas law problem because it asks for a value of n when P, V, and T are known: $n = PV/RT$. The volume is given in the correct unit of liters, but temperature must be converted to kelvins.

SOLUTION

STEP 1: Identify known information.
We know three of the four variables in the ideal gas law.

$P = 1.0$ atm
$V = 3.8$ L
$T = 37\ °\text{C} = 310$ K

STEP 2: Identify answer and units.

Moles of air, $n = ??$ mol

STEP 3: Identify the equation. Knowing three of the four variables in the ideal gas law, we can rearrange and solve for the unknown variable, n. (Note: because pressure is given in atm, we use the value of R that is expressed in atm:

$$PV = nRT \implies n = \frac{PV}{RT}$$

$$R = 0.0821 \frac{L \cdot atm}{mol \cdot K}$$

STEP 4: Solve. Substitute the known information and the appropriate value of R into the ideal gas law equation and solve for n.

$$n = \frac{PV}{RT} = \frac{(1.0\ \text{atm})(3.8\ \text{L})}{\left(0.0821\dfrac{\text{L} \cdot \text{atm}}{\text{mol} \cdot \text{K}}\right)(310\ \text{K})} = 0.15\ \text{mol}$$

WORKED EXAMPLE **8.10** Using the Ideal Gas Law: Finding Pressure

Methane gas is sold in steel cylinders with a volume of 43.8 L containing 5.54 kg. What is the pressure in atmospheres inside the cylinder at a temperature of 20.0 °C (293.15 K)? The molar mass of methane (CH_4) is 16.0 g/mol.

ANALYSIS This is an ideal gas law problem because it asks for a value of P when V, T, and n are given. Although not provided directly, enough information is given so that we can calculate the value of n ($n = g/MW$).

SOLUTION

STEP 1: Identify known information. We know two of the four variables in the ideal gas law; V, T, and can calculate the third, n, from the information provided.

$V = 43.8\ \text{L}$
$T = 37\ °C = 310\ \text{K}$

STEP 2: Identify answer and units.

Pressure, $P = ??\ \text{atm}$

STEP 3: Identify equation. First, calculate the number of moles n of methane in the cylinder by using molar mass (16.0 g/mol) as a conversion factor. Then use the ideal gas law to calculate the pressure.

$$n = (5.54\ \text{kg methane})\left(\frac{1000\ \text{g}}{1\ \text{kg}}\right)\left(\frac{1\ \text{mol}}{16.0\ \text{g}}\right) = 346\ \text{mol methane}$$

$$PV = nRT \implies P = \frac{nRT}{V}$$

STEP 4: Solve. Substitute the known information and the appropriate value of R into the ideal gas law equation and solve for P.

$$P = \frac{nRT}{V} = \frac{(346\ \text{mol})\left(0.0821\dfrac{\text{L} \cdot \text{atm}}{\text{mol} \cdot \text{K}}\right)(293\ \text{K})}{43.8\ \text{L}} = 190\ \text{atm}$$

PROBLEM 8.11

An aerosol spray can of deodorant with a volume of 350 mL contains 3.2 g of propane gas (C_3H_8) as propellant. What is the pressure in the can at 20 °C?

PROBLEM 8.12

A helium gas cylinder of the sort used to fill balloons has a volume of 180 L and a pressure of 2200 psi (150 atm) at 25 °C. How many moles of helium are in the tank? How many grams?

KEY CONCEPT PROBLEM 8.13

Show the approximate level of the movable piston in drawings (a) and (b) after the indicated changes have been made to the initial gas sample.

1.0 atm

(initial)
$T = 300\ K$
$n = 0.300\ mol$

(a)
$T = 450\ K$
$n = 0.200\ mol$

(b)
$T = 200\ K$
$n = 0.400\ mol$

8.10 Partial Pressure and Dalton's Law

According to the kinetic–molecular theory, each particle in a gas acts independently of all others because there are no attractive forces between them and they are so far apart. To any individual particle, the chemical identity of its neighbors is irrelevant. Thus, *mixtures* of gases behave the same as pure gases and obey the same laws.

Dry air, for example, is a mixture of about 21% oxygen, 78% nitrogen, and 1% argon by volume, which means that 21% of atmospheric air pressure is caused by O_2 molecules, 78% by N_2 molecules, and 1% by Ar atoms. The contribution of each gas in a mixture to the total pressure of the mixture is called the **partial pressure**. of that gas. According to **Dalton's law**, the total pressure exerted by a gas mixture (P_{total}) is the sum of the partial pressures of the components in the mixture:

> **Partial pressure** The contribution of a given gas in a mixture to the total pressure.

Dalton's law $P_{total} = P_{gas\ 1} + P_{gas\ 2} + \cdots$

In dry air at a total air pressure of 760 mmHg, the partial pressure caused by the contribution of O_2 is $0.21 \times 760\ mmHg = 160\ mmHg$, the partial pressure of N_2 is $0.78 \times 760\ mmHg = 593\ mmHg$, and that of argon is 7 mmHg. *The partial pressure exerted by each gas in a mixture is the same pressure that the gas would exert if it were alone.* Put another way, the pressure exerted by each gas depends on the frequency of collisions of its molecules with the walls of the container. But this frequency does not change when other gases are present because the different molecules have no influence on one another.

To represent the partial pressure of a specific gas, we add the formula of the gas as a subscript to P, the symbol for pressure. You might see the partial pressure of oxygen represented as P_{O_2}, for instance. Moist air inside the lungs at 37 °C and atmospheric pressure has the following average composition at sea level. Note that P_{total} is equal to atmospheric pressure, 760 mmHg.

$$
\begin{aligned}
P_{total} &= \quad P_{N_2} \quad + \quad P_{O_2} \quad + \quad P_{CO_2} \quad + \quad P_{H_2O} \\
&= 573\ mmHg + 100\ mmHg + 40\ mmHg + 47\ mmHg \\
&= 760\ mmHg
\end{aligned}
$$

The composition of air does not change appreciably with altitude, but the total pressure decreases rapidly. The partial pressure of oxygen in air therefore decreases with increasing altitude, and it is this change that leads to difficulty in breathing at high elevations.

WORKED EXAMPLE **8.11** Using Dalton's Law: Finding Partial Pressures

Humid air on a warm summer day is approximately 20% oxygen, 75% nitrogen, 4% water vapor, and 1% argon. What is the partial pressure of each component if the atmospheric pressure is 750 mmHg?

ANALYSIS According to Dalton's law, the partial pressure of any gas in a mixture is equal to the percent concentration of the gas times the total gas pressure (750 mmHg). In this case,

$$P_{total} = P_{O_2} + P_{N_2} + P_{H_2O} + P_{Ar}$$

SOLUTION

Oxygen partial pressure (P_{O_2}):	0.20×750 mmHg $= 150$ mmHg
Nitrogen partial pressure (P_{N_2}):	0.75×750 mmHg $= 560$ mmHg
Water vapor partial pressure (P_{H_2O}):	0.04×750 mmHg $= 30$ mmHg
Argon partial pressure (P_{Ar}):	0.01×750 mmHg $= 8$ mmHg

Total pressure $= 748$ mmHg $\rightarrow 750$ mmHg (rounding to 2 significant figures!)

Note that the sum of the partial pressures must equal the total pressure (within rounding error).

▲ Because of the lack of sufficient oxygen at the top of Mt. Everest, most climbers rely on bottled oxygen supplies.

PROBLEM 8.14

Assuming a total pressure of 9.5 atm, what is the partial pressure of each component in the mixture of 98% helium and 2.0% oxygen breathed by deep-sea divers? How does the partial pressure of oxygen in diving gas compare with its partial pressure in normal air?

PROBLEM 8.15

Determine the percent composition of air in the lungs from the following composition in partial pressures: $P_{N_2} = 573$ mmHg, $P_{O_2} = 100$ mmHg, $P_{CO_2} = 40$ mmHg, $P_{H_2O} = 47$ mmHg; all at 37 °C and 1 atm pressure.

PROBLEM 8.16

The atmospheric pressure on the top of Mt. Everest, an altitude of 29,035 ft, is only 265 mmHg. What is the partial pressure of oxygen in the lungs at this altitude?

🔑 KEY CONCEPT PROBLEM 8.17

Assume that you have a mixture of He (MW = 4 amu) and Xe (MW = 131 amu) at 300 K. Which of the drawings (a)–(c) best represents the mixture (blue = He; green = Xe)?

(a)   (b)   (c)

8.11 Intermolecular Forces

What determines whether a substance is a gas, a liquid, or a solid at a given temperature? Why does rubbing alcohol evaporate much more readily than water? Why do molecular compounds have lower melting points than ionic compounds? To answer these and a great many other such questions, we need to look into the nature of **intermolecular forces**—the forces that act *between different molecules* rather than within an individual molecule.

In gases, the intermolecular forces are negligible, so the gas molecules act independently of one another. In liquids and solids, however, intermolecular forces are strong enough to hold the molecules in close contact. As a general rule, the stronger the intermolecular forces in a substance, the more difficult it is to separate the molecules, and the higher the melting and boiling points of the substance.

There are three major types of intermolecular forces: *dipole–dipole, London dispersion,* and *hydrogen bonding.* We will discuss each in turn.

> **Intermolecular force** A force that acts between molecules and holds molecules close to one another.

Dipole–Dipole Forces

Recall from Sections 5.8 and 5.9 that many molecules contain polar covalent bonds and may therefore have a net molecular polarity. (⬭, pp. 128, 130) In such cases, the positive and negative ends of different molecules are attracted to one another by what is called a **dipole–dipole force**. (Figure 8.14).

> **Dipole–dipole force** The attractive force between positive and negative ends of polar molecules.

▲ **FIGURE 8.14 Dipole–dipole forces.** The positive and negative ends of polar molecules are attracted to one another by dipole–dipole forces. As a result, polar molecules have higher boiling points than nonpolar molecules of similar size.

Dipole–dipole forces are weak, with strengths on the order of 1 kcal/mol compared to the 70–100 kcal/mol typically found for the strength of a covalent bond. Nevertheless, the effects of dipole–dipole forces are important, as can be seen by looking at the difference in boiling points between polar and nonpolar molecules. Butane, for instance, is a nonpolar molecule with a molecular weight of 58 amu and a boiling point of −0.5 °C, whereas acetone has the same molecular weight yet boils 57 °C higher because it is polar. (Recall from Section 5.8 how molecular polarities can be visualized using electrostatic potential maps. (⬭, p. 128)

Butane (C_4H_{10})
Mol wt = 58 amu
bp = −0.5 °C

Acetone (C_3H_6O)
Mol wt = 58 amu
bp = 56.2 °C

APPLICATION ▶   Greenhouse Gases and Global Warming

The mantle of gases surrounding the earth is far from the uniform mixture you might expect, consisting of layers that vary in composition and properties at different altitudes. The ability of the gases in these layers to absorb radiation is responsible for life on earth as we know it.

The *stratosphere*—the layer extending from about 12 km up to 50 km altitude—contains the ozone layer that is responsible for absorbing harmful UV radiation. The *troposphere* is the layer extending from the surface up to about 12 km altitude. It should not surprise you to learn that the troposphere is the layer most easily disturbed by human activities and that this layer has the greatest impact on the earth's surface conditions. Among those impacts, a process called the *greenhouse effect* is much in the news today.

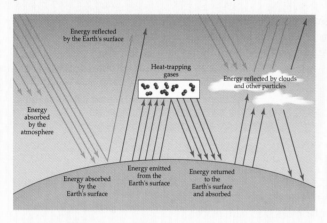

▲ **Greenhouse gases (GHG) trap heat reflected from the earth's surface, resulting in the increase in surface temperatures known as global warming.**

The greenhouse effect refers to the warming that occurs in the troposphere as gases absorb radiant energy. Much of the radiant energy reaching the earth's surface from the sun is reflected back into space, but some is absorbed by atmospheric gases—particularly those referred to as—*greenhouse gases* (GHGs)—water vapor, carbon dioxide, and methane. This absorbed radiation warms the atmosphere and acts to maintain a relatively stable temperature of 15 °C (59 °F) at the earth's surface. Without the greenhouse effect, the average surface temperature would be about −18 °C (0 °F)—a temperature so low that Earth would be frozen and unable to sustain life.

The basis for concern about the greenhouse effect is the fear that human activities over the past century have disturbed the earth's delicate thermal balance. Should increasing amounts of radiation be absorbed, increased atmospheric heating will result, and global temperatures will continue to rise.

Measurements show that the concentration of atmospheric CO_2 has been rising in the last 150 years, largely because of the increased use of fossil fuels, from an estimated 290 parts per million (ppm) in 1850 to current levels approaching 380 ppm. The increase in CO_2 levels correlates with a concurrent increase in average global temperatures, with the 11 years between 1995 and 2006 ranking among the 12-highest since recording of global temperatures began in 1850. The latest report of the Intergovernmental Panel on Climate Change published in November 2007 concluded that "Warming of the climate system is unequivocal, as is now evident from observations of increases in global average air and ocean temperatures, widespread melting of snow and ice and rising global average sea level. . . . Continued GHG emissions at or above current rates would cause further warming and induce many changes in the global climate system during the 21st century that would *very likely* be larger than those observed during the 20th century."

See Additional Problems 8.101 and 8.102 at the end of the chapter.

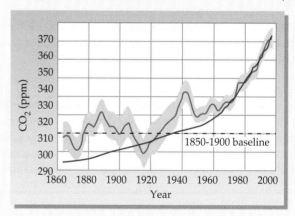

▲ **Concentrations of atmospheric CO_2 and global average temperatures have increased dramatically in the last 150 years because of increased fossil fuel use, causing serious changes in earth's climate system.**

© Crown copyright 2006 data provided by the Met office

London Dispersion Forces

London dispersion force The short-lived attractive force due to the constant motion of electrons within molecules.

Only polar molecules experience dipole–dipole forces, but all molecules, regardless of structure, experience *London dispersion forces*. **London dispersion forces** are caused by the constant motion of electrons within molecules. Take even a simple nonpolar molecule like Br_2, for example. Averaged over time, the distribution of electrons throughout the molecule is uniform, but at any given *instant* there may be more electrons at one end of the molecule than at the other (Figure 8.15). At that instant, the

$\delta-$ $\delta+$ $\delta-$ $\delta+$

(a)   (b)

▲ **FIGURE 8.15** (a) Averaged over time, the electron distribution in a Br_2 molecule is symmetrical. (b) At any given instant, however, the electron distribution may be unsymmetrical, resulting in a temporary polarity that induces a complementary polarity in neighboring molecules.

molecule has a short-lived polarity. Electrons in neighboring molecules are attracted to the positive end of the polarized molecule, resulting in a polarization of the neighbor and creation of an attractive London dispersion force that holds the molecules together. As a result, Br_2 is a liquid at room temperature rather than a gas.

London dispersion forces are weak—in the range 0.5–2.5 kcal/mol—but they increase with molecular weight and amount of surface contact between molecules. The larger the molecular weight, the more electrons there are moving about and the greater the temporary polarization of a molecule. The larger the amount of surface contact, the greater the close interaction between different molecules.

The effect of surface contact on the magnitude of London dispersion forces can be seen by comparing a roughly spherical molecule with a flatter, more linear one having the same molecular weight. Both 2,2-dimethylpropane and pentane, for instance, have the same formula (C_5H_{12}), but the nearly spherical shape of 2,2-dimethylpropane allows for less surface contact with neighboring molecules than does the more linear shape of pentane (Figure 8.16). As a result, London dispersion forces are smaller for 2,2-dimethylpropane, molecules are held together less tightly, and the boiling point is correspondingly lower: 9.5 °C for 2,2-dimethylpropane versus 36 °C for pentane.

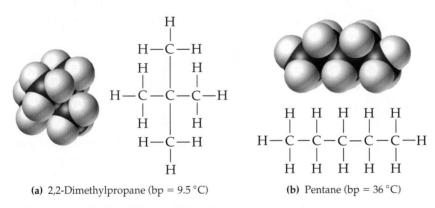

(a) 2,2-Dimethylpropane (bp = 9.5 °C)   (b) Pentane (bp = 36 °C)

▲ **FIGURE 8.16 London dispersion forces.** More compact molecules like 2,2-dimethylpropane have smaller surface areas, weaker London dispersion forces, and lower boiling points. By comparison, flatter, less compact molecules like pentane have larger surface areas, stronger London dispersion forces, and higher boiling points.

Hydrogen Bonds

In many ways, hydrogen bonding is responsible for life on earth. It causes water to be a liquid rather than a gas at ordinary temperatures, and it is the primary intermolecular force that holds huge biomolecules in the shapes needed to play their essential roles in biochemistry. Deoxyribonucleic acid (DNA) and keratin (Figure 8.17), for instance, are long molecular chains that form a coiled structure called an α-helix.

A **hydrogen bond** is an attractive interaction between an unshared electron pair on an electronegative O, N, or F atom and a positively polarized hydrogen atom

Hydrogen bond The attraction between a hydrogen atom bonded to an electronegative O, N, or F atom and another nearby electronegative O, N, or F atom.

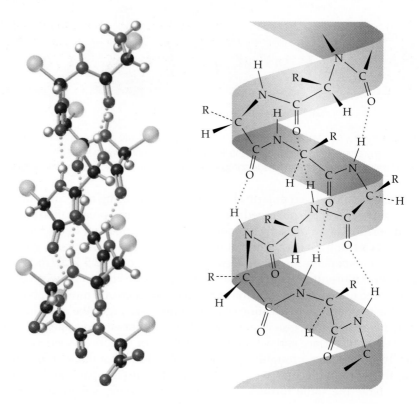

▶ **FIGURE 8.17** The α-helical structure of keratin results from hydrogen bonding along the amino acid backbone of the molecule.

bonded to another electronegative O, N, or F. For example, hydrogen bonds occur in both water and ammonia:

Hydrogen bonding is really just a special kind of dipole–dipole interaction. The O—H, N—H, and F—H bonds are highly polar, with a partial positive charge on the hydrogen and a partial negative charge on the electronegative atom. In addition, the hydrogen atom has no inner-shell electrons to act as a shield around its nucleus, and it is small so it can be approached closely. As a result, the dipole–dipole attractions involving positively polarized hydrogens are unusually strong, and hydrogen bonds result. Water, in particular, is able to form a vast three-dimensional network of hydrogen bonds because each H_2O molecule has two hydrogens and two electron pairs (Figure 8.18).

▶ **FIGURE 8.18 Hydrogen bonding in water.** The intermolecular attraction in water is especially strong because each oxygen atom has two lone pairs and two hydrogen atoms, allowing the formation of as many as four hydrogen bonds per molecule. Individual hydrogen bonds are constantly being formed and broken.

Hydrogen bonds can be quite strong, with energies up to 10 kcal/mol. To see the effect of hydrogen bonding, look at Table 8.2, which compares the boiling points of binary hydrogen compounds of second-row elements with their third-row counterparts. Because NH_3, H_2O, and HF molecules are held tightly together by hydrogen bonds, an unusually large amount of energy must be added to separate them in the boiling process. As a result, the boiling points of NH_3, H_2O, and HF are much higher than the boiling points of their second-row neighbor CH_4 and of related third-row compounds.

TABLE 8.2 Boiling Points for Binary Hydrogen Compounds of Some Second-row and Third-row Elements

COMPOUND	bp (°C)
CH_4	−161.5
NH_3	−33.3
H_2O	100.0
HF	19.5
SiH_4	−111.9
PH_3	−87.7
H_2S	−59.6
HCl	−84.2

A summary and comparison of the various kinds of intermolecular forces is shown in Table 8.3.

TABLE 8.3 A Comparison of Intermolecular Forces

FORCE	STRENGTH	CHARACTERISTICS
Dipole–dipole	Weak (1 kcal/mol)	Occurs between polar molecules
London dispersion	Weak (0.5–2.5 kcal/mol)	Occurs between all molecules; strength depends on size
Hydrogen bond	Moderate (2–10 kcal/mol)	Occurs between molecules with O—H, N—H, and F—H bonds

⊂◯◯⊃ **Looking Ahead**

Dipole–dipole forces, London dispersion forces, and hydrogen bonds are traditionally called "intermolecular forces" because of their influence on the properties of molecular compounds. But these same forces can also operate between different parts of a very large molecule. In this context, they are often referred to as "noncovalent interactions." In later chapters, we will see how noncovalent interactions determine the shapes of biologically important molecules such as proteins and nucleic acids. ⊂◯⊃

WORKED EXAMPLE   **8.12** Identifying Intermolecular Forces:
Polar versus Nonpolar

Identify the intermolecular forces that influence the properties of the following compounds:

(a) Methane, CH_4 **(b)** HCl   **(c)** Acetic acid, CH_3CO_2H

ANALYSIS The intermolecular forces will depend on the molecular structure; what type of bonds are in the molecule (polar or non-polar) and how are they arranged.

SOLUTION

(a) Since methane contains only C—H bonds, it is a nonpolar molecule; it has only London dispersion forces.

(b) The H—Cl bond is polar, so this is a polar molecule; it has both dipole–dipole forces and London dispersion forces.

(c) Acetic acid is a polar molecule with an O—H bond. Thus, it has dipole–dipole forces, London dispersion forces, and hydrogen bonds.

PROBLEM 8.18

Would you expect the boiling points to increase or decrease in the following series? Explain.

(a) Kr, Ar, Ne   (b) Cl_2, Br_2, I_2

PROBLEM 8.19

Which of the following compounds form hydrogen bonds?

Methyl alcohol	Ethylene	Methylamine
(a)	(b)	(c)

PROBLEM 8.20

Identify the intermolecular forces (dipole–dipole, London dispersion, hydrogen bonding) that influence the properties of the following compounds:

(a) Ethane, CH_3CH_3 (b) Ethyl alcohol, CH_3CH_2OH

(c) Ethyl chloride, CH_3CH_2Cl

8.12 Liquids

Molecules are in constant motion in the liquid state, just as they are in gases. If a molecule happens to be near the surface of a liquid, and if it has enough energy, it can break free of the liquid and escape into the gas state, called **vapor**. In an open container, the now gaseous molecule will wander away from the liquid, and the process will continue until all the molecules escape from the container (Figure 8.19a). This, of course, is what happens during *evaporation*. We are all familiar with puddles of water evaporating after a rainstorm.

Vapor The gas molecules in equilibrium with a liquid.

▶ **FIGURE 8.19 The transfer of molecules between liquid and gas states.** (a) Molecules escape from an open container and drift away until the liquid has entirely evaporated. (b) Molecules in a closed container cannot escape. Instead, they reach an equilibrium in which the rates of molecules leaving the liquid and returning to the liquid are equal, and the concentration of molecules in the gas state is constant.

Equilibrium vapor pressure

Mercury-filled manometer

(a)   (b)

If the liquid is in a closed container, the situation is different because the gaseous molecules cannot escape. Thus, the random motion of the molecules occasionally brings them back into the liquid. After the concentration of molecules in the gas state has increased sufficiently, the number of molecules reentering the liquid becomes equal to the number escaping from the liquid (Figure 8.19b). At this point, a dynamic equilibrium exists, exactly as in a chemical reaction at equilibrium. Evaporation and condensation take place at the same rate, and the concentration of vapor in the container is constant as long as the temperature does not change.

Once molecules have escaped from the liquid into the gas state, they are subject to all the gas laws previously discussed. In a closed container at equilibrium, for example, the gas molecules make their own contribution to the total pressure of the gas above the liquid according to Dalton's law (Section 8.10). We call this contribution the **vapor pressure** of the liquid.

Vapor pressure depends on both temperature and the chemical identity of a liquid. As the temperature rises, molecules become more energetic and more likely to escape into the gas state. Thus, vapor pressure rises with increasing temperature until ultimately it becomes equal to the pressure of the atmosphere (Figure 8.20). At this point, bubbles of vapor form under the surface and force their way to the top, giving rise to the violent action observed during a vigorous boil. At an atmospheric pressure of exactly 760 mmHg, boiling occurs at what is called the **normal boiling point**.

▲ Because bromine is colored, it is possible to see its gaseous reddish vapor above the liquid.

Vapor pressure The partial pressure of gas molecules in equilibrium with a liquid.

Normal boiling point The boiling point at a pressure of exactly 1 atmosphere.

▲ **FIGURE 8.20 A plot of the change of vapor pressure with temperature for ethyl ether, ethyl alcohol, and water.** At a liquid's boiling point, its vapor pressure is equal to atmospheric pressure. Commonly reported boiling points are those at 760 mmHg.

If atmospheric pressure is higher or lower than normal, the boiling point of a liquid changes accordingly. At high altitudes, for example, atmospheric pressure is lower than at sea level, and boiling points are also lower. On top of Mt. Everest (29,035 ft; 8850 m), atmospheric pressure is about 245 mmHg and the boiling temperature of water is only 71 °C. If the atmospheric pressure is higher than normal, the boiling point is also higher. This principle is used in strong vessels known as *autoclaves*, in which water at high pressure is heated to the temperatures needed for sterilizing medical and dental instruments (170 °C).

Many familiar properties of liquids can be explained by the intermolecular forces just discussed. We all know, for instance, that some liquids, such as water or gasoline, flow easily when poured, whereas others, such as motor oil or maple syrup, flow sluggishly.

The measure of a liquid's resistance to flow is called its *viscosity*. Not surprisingly, viscosity is related to the ease with which individual molecules move around in the liquid and thus to the intermolecular forces present. Substances such as gasoline, which have small, nonpolar molecules, experience only weak intermolecular

▲ Medical instruments are sterilized in this autoclave by heating them with water at high pressure.

▲ Surface tension allows a water strider to walk on water without penetrating the surface.

forces and have relatively low viscosities, whereas more polar substances such as glycerin [$C_3H_5(OH)_3$] experience stronger intermolecular forces and so have higher viscosities.

Another familiar property of liquids is *surface tension*, the resistance of a liquid to spread out and increase its surface area. The beading-up of water on a newly waxed car and the ability of a water strider to walk on water are both due to surface tension.

Surface tension is caused by the difference between the intermolecular forces experienced by molecules at the surface of the liquid and those experienced by molecules in the interior. Molecules in the interior of a liquid are surrounded and experience maximum intermolecular forces, whereas molecules at the surface have fewer neighbors and feel weaker forces. Surface molecules are therefore less stable, and the liquid acts to minimize their number by minimizing the surface area (Figure 8.21).

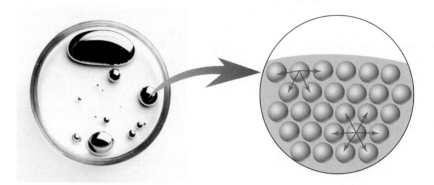

▲ **FIGURE 8.21** **Surface tension.** Surface tension is caused by the different forces experienced by molecules in the interior of a liquid and those on the surface. Molecules on the surface are less stable because they feel fewer attractive forces, so the liquid acts to minimize their number by minimizing surface area.

8.13 Water: A Unique Liquid

Ours is a world based on water. Water covers nearly 71% of the earth's surface, it accounts for 66% of the mass of an adult human body, and it is needed by all living things. The water in our blood forms the transport system that circulates substances throughout our body, and water is the medium in which all biochemical reactions are carried out. Largely because of its strong hydrogen bonding, water has many properties that are quite different from those of other compounds.

Water has the highest specific heat of any liquid (Section 2.10), giving it the capacity to absorb a large quantity of heat while changing only slightly in temperature. (⊂⊃, p. 38) As a result, large lakes and other bodies of water tend to moderate the air temperature and climate of surrounding areas. Another consequence of the high specific heat of water is that the human body is better able to maintain a steady internal temperature under changing outside conditions.

▲ The moderate year-round temperatures in San Francisco are due to the large heat capacity of the surrounding waters.

In addition to a high specific heat, water has an unusually high *heat of vaporization* (540 cal/g), meaning that it carries away a large amount of heat when it evaporates. You can feel the effect of water evaporation on your wet skin when the wind blows. Even when comfortable, your body is still relying for cooling on the heat carried away from the skin and lungs by evaporating water. The heat generated by the chemical reactions of metabolism is carried by blood to the skin, where water moves through cell walls to the surface and evaporates. When metabolism, and therefore heat generation, speeds up, blood flow increases and capillaries dilate so that heat is brought to the surface faster.

Water is also unique in what happens as it changes from a liquid to a solid. Most substances are more dense as solids than as liquids because molecules are more closely packed in the solid than in the liquid. Water, however, is different. Liquid water has a maximum density of 1.000 g/mL at 3.98 °C but then becomes *less* dense as it cools. When it freezes, its density decreases still further to 0.917 g/mL.

◀ **FIGURE 8.22 Ice.** Ice consists of individual H_2O molecules held rigidly together in an ordered manner by hydrogen bonds. The open cage-like crystal structure shows why ice is less dense than liquid water.

As water freezes, each molecule is locked into position by hydrogen bonding to four other water molecules (Figure 8.22). The resulting structure has more open space than does liquid water, accounting for its lower density. As a result, ice floats on liquid water, and lakes and rivers freeze from the top down. If the reverse were true, fish would be killed in winter as they became trapped in ice at the bottom.

8.14 Solids

A brief look around us reveals that most substances are solids rather than liquids or gases. It is also obvious that there are many different kinds of solids. Some, such as iron and aluminum, are hard and metallic; others, such as sugar and table salt, are crystalline and easily broken; and still others, such as rubber and many plastics, are soft and amorphous.

The most fundamental distinction between solids is that some are crystalline and some are amorphous. A **crystalline solid** is one whose particles—whether atoms, ions, or molecules—have an ordered arrangement extending over a long range. This order on the atomic level is also seen on the visible level, because crystalline solids usually have flat faces and distinct angles.

Crystalline solid A solid whose atoms, molecules, or ions are rigidly held in an ordered arrangement.

◀ Crystalline solids, such as the gypsum (left) and fluorite (right) shown here, have flat faces and distinct angles. These regular macroscopic features reflect a similarly ordered arrangement of particles at the atomic level.

▲ The sand on this beach is silica, SiO_2, a covalent network solid. Each grain of sand is essentially one large molecule.

Crystalline solids can be further categorized as ionic, molecular, covalent network, or metallic. *Ionic solids* are those like sodium chloride, whose constituent particles are ions. A crystal of sodium chloride is composed of alternating Na^+ and Cl^- ions ordered in a regular three-dimensional arrangement and held together by ionic bonds, as discussed in Section 4.3. (, p. 83) *Molecular solids* are those like sucrose or ice, whose constituent particles are molecules held together by the intermolecular forces discussed in Sections 8.11 and 8.12. A crystal of ice, for example, is composed of H_2O molecules held together in a regular way by hydrogen bonding (Figure 8.22). *Covalent network solids* are those like diamond (Figure 8.23) or quartz (SiO_2), whose atoms are linked together by covalent bonds into a giant three-dimensional array. In effect, a covalent network solid is one *very* large molecule.

▲ **FIGURE 8.23** **Diamond.** Diamond is a covalent network solid—one very large molecule of carbon atoms linked by covalent bonds.

Metallic solids, such as silver or iron, can be viewed as vast three-dimensional arrays of metal cations immersed in a sea of electrons that are free to move about. This continuous electron sea acts both as a glue to hold the cations together and as a mobile carrier of charge to conduct electricity. Furthermore, the fact that bonding attractions extend uniformly in all directions explains why metals are malleable rather than brittle. When a metal crystal receives a sharp blow, no spatially oriented bonds are broken; instead, the electron sea simply adjusts to the new distribution of cations.

Amorphous solid A solid whose particles do not have an orderly arrangement.

An **amorphous solid**, by contrast with a crystalline solid, is one whose constituent particles are randomly arranged and have no ordered long-range structure. Amorphous solids often result when liquids cool before they can achieve internal order, or when their molecules are large and tangled together, as happens in many polymers. Glass is an amorphous solid, as are tar, the gemstone opal, and some hard candies. Amorphous solids differ from crystalline solids by softening over a wide temperature range rather than having sharp melting points, and by shattering to give pieces with curved rather than planar faces.

A summary of the different types of solids and their characteristics is given in Table 8.4.

8.15 Changes of State

What happens when a solid is heated? As more and more energy is added, molecules begin to stretch, bend, and vibrate more vigorously, and atoms or ions wiggle about with more energy. Finally, if enough energy is added and the motions become vigorous enough, particles start to break free from one another and the substance starts to melt. Addition of more heat continues the melting process until all particles have broken free and are in the liquid phase. The quantity of heat required to completely melt a substance once it reaches its melting point is called

TABLE 8.4   Types of Solids

SUBSTANCE	SMALLEST UNIT	INTERPARTICLE FORCES	PROPERTIES	EXAMPLES
Ionic solid	Ions	Attraction between positive and negative ions	Brittle and hard; high mp; crystalline	$NaCl$, KI, $Ca_3(PO_4)_2$
Molecular solid	Molecules	Intermolecular forces	Soft; low to moderate mp; crystalline	Ice, wax, frozen CO_2, all solid organic compounds
Covalent network	Atoms	Covalent bonds	Very hard; very high mp; crystalline	Diamond, quartz (SiO_2), tungsten carbide (WC)
Metal or alloy	Metal atoms	Metallic bonding (attraction between metal ions and surrounding mobile electrons)	Lustrous; soft (Na) to hard (Ti); high melting; crystalline	Elements (Fe, Cu, Sn, …), bronze (CuSn alloy), amalgams (Hg + other metals)
Amorphous solid	Atoms, ions, or molecules (including polymer molecules)	Any of the above	Noncrystalline; no sharp mp; able to flow (may be very slow); curved edges when shattered	Glasses, tar, some plastics

its **heat of fusion**. After melting is complete, further addition of heat causes the temperature of the liquid to rise.

The change of a liquid into a vapor proceeds in the same way as the change of a solid into a liquid. When you first put a pan of water on the stove, all the added heat goes into raising the temperature of the water. Once the boiling point is reached, further absorbed heat goes into freeing molecules from their neighbors as they escape into the gas state. The quantity of heat needed to completely vaporize a liquid once it reaches its boiling point is called its **heat of vaporization**. A liquid with a low heat of vaporization, like rubbing alcohol (isopropyl alcohol), evaporates rapidly and is said to be *volatile*. If you spill a volatile liquid on your skin, you will feel a cooling effect as it evaporates because it is absorbing heat from your body.

It is important to know the difference between heat that is added or removed to change the *temperature* of a substance and heat that is added or removed to change the *phase* of a substance. Remember that temperature is a measure of the kinetic energy in a substance (◁◼◻▷ Section 7.1, p. 183). When a substance is above or below its phase change temperature (i.e., melting point or boiling point) adding or removing heat will simply change the kinetic energy and, hence, the temperature of the substance. The amount of heat needed to produce a given temperature change was presented previously (◁◼◻▷ Section 2.10), but is worth presenting again here:

$$\text{Heat (cal)} = \text{Mass (g)} \times \text{Temperature change (}^{\circ}\text{C)} \times \text{Specific heat} \left(\frac{\text{cal}}{\text{g} \times {}^{\circ}\text{C}} \right)$$

In contrast, when a substance is at its phase change temperature, heat that is added is being used to overcome the intermolecular forces holding particles in that phase. The temperature remains constant until *all* particles have been converted to the next phase. The energy needed to complete the phase change depends only on the amount of the substance, and the heat of fusion (for melting) or the heat of vaporization (for boiling).

$$\text{Heat (cal)} = \text{Mass (g)} \times \text{Heat of fusion} \left(\frac{\text{cal}}{\text{g}} \right)$$

$$\text{Heat (cal)} = \text{Mass (g)} \times \text{Heat of vaporization} \left(\frac{\text{cal}}{\text{g}} \right)$$

If the intermolecular forces are strong then large amounts of heat must be added to overcome these forces, and the heats of fusion and vaporization will be large. A list of heats of fusion and heats of vaporization for some common substances is given in Table 8.5. Butane, for example, has a small heat of vaporization since the

Heat of fusion The quantity of heat required to completely melt one gram of a substance once it has reached its melting point.

Heat of vaporization The quantity of heat needed to completely vaporize one gram of a liquid once it has reached its boiling point.

TABLE 8.5 Melting Points, Boiling Points, Heats of Fusion, and Heats of Vaporization of Some Common Substances

SUBSTANCE	MELTING POINT (°C)	BOILING POINT (°C)	HEAT OF FUSION (cal/g)	HEAT OF VAPORIZATION (cal/g)
Ammonia	−77.7	−33.4	84.0	327
Butane	−138.4	−0.5	19.2	92.5
Ether	−116	34.6	23.5	85.6
Ethyl alcohol	−117.3	78.5	26.1	200
Isopropyl alcohol	−89.5	82.4	21.4	159
Sodium	97.8	883	14.3	492
Water	0.0	100.0	79.7	540

APPLICATION ▶ Biomaterials for Joint Replacement

Freely movable joints in the body, such as those in the shoulder, knee, or hip, are formed by the meeting of two bones. The bony surfaces are not in direct contact, of course; rather, they are covered by cartilage for nearly frictionless motion and are surrounded by a fluid-containing capsule for lubrication. The hip, for instance, is a ball-and-socket joint, formed where the rounded upper end of the femur meets a cup-shaped part of the pelvic bone called the acetabulum.

Unfortunately, joints can wear out or fail, particularly when the cartilage is damaged by injury or diseased by degenerative arthritis. At some point, it may even be necessary to replace the failing joint—an estimated 500,000 joint-replacement surgeries are performed each year in the United States (170,000 hips, 325,000 knees). Although total joint replacement is not without problems, the lifetime of an artificial joint is nearly 20 years in 80% of the cases.

The first joint-replacement material, used in 1962, was stainless steel, but slow corrosion in the body led to its abandonment in favor of more resistant titanium or cobalt–chromium alloys. A typical modern hip-replacement joint consists of three parts: a polished metal ball to replace the head of the femur, a titanium alloy stem that is cemented into the shaft of the femur for stability, and a polyethylene cup to replace the hip socket.

Even with these materials, though, abrasion at the ball/cup contact can lead to joint wear. Over time, the constant repetitive movement of the polyethylene socket over the metal ball results in billions of microscopic polyethylene particles being sloughed off into the surrounding fluid. In addition, the cement holding the metal stem to the femur can slowly degrade, releasing other particles. The foreign particles are attacked by the body's immune system, resulting in the release of enzymes that cause the death of adjacent bone cells, loosening of the metal stem, and ultimate failure of the joint.

A potential solution to the problem involves the use of biomaterials—new materials that are created specifically for use in biological systems and do not provoke an immune response. It has been found, for instance, that the titanium

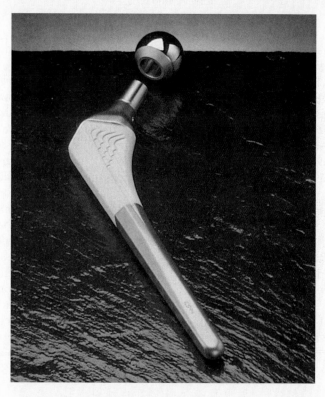

▲ This artificial hip joint is bonded to a thin layer of calcium phosphate to stimulate attachment of natural bone.

stem of the artificial joint can be bonded to an extremely thin layer of calcium phosphate, $Ca_3(PO_4)_2$, a close relative of hydroxyapatite $Ca_{10}(PO_4)_6(OH)_2$, the primary mineral constituent of bone (see the Chapter 4 Application, *Osteoporosis*). Natural bone then grows into the calcium phosphate, forming a strong natural bond to the stem, and making cement unnecessary. Other biomaterials are being designed to replace the polyethylene socket.

See Additional Problem 8.103 at the end of the chapter.

predominant intermolecular forces in butane (dispersion) are relatively weak. Water, on the other hand, has a particularly high heat of vaporization because of its unusually strong hydrogen bonding interactions. Thus, water evaporates more slowly than many other liquids, takes a long time to boil away, and absorbs more heat in the process. A so-called *heating curve*, which indicates the temperature and state changes as heat is added, is shown in Figure 8.24.

◀ **FIGURE 8.24 A heating curve for water, showing the temperature and state changes that occur when heat is added.** The horizontal lines at 0 °C and 100 °C represent the heat of fusion and heat of vaporization, respectively.

WORKED EXAMPLE **8.13** Heat of Fusion: Calculating Total Heat of Melting

Naphthalene, an organic substance often used in mothballs, has a heat of fusion of 35.7 cal/g and a molar mass of 128.0 g/mol. How much heat in kilocalories is required to melt 0.300 mol of naphthalene?

ANALYSIS The heat of fusion tells how much heat is required to melt 1 g. To find the amount of heat needed to melt 0.300 mol, we need a mole to mass conversion.

BALLPARK ESTIMATE Naphthalene has a molar mass of 128.0 g/mol, so 0.300 mol has a mass of about one-third this amount, or about 40 g. Approximately 35 cal is required to melt 1 g, so we need about 40 times this amount of heat, or ($35 \times 40 = 1400$ cal = 1.4 kcal).

SOLUTION

STEP 1: **Identify known information.** We know heat of fusion (cal/g), and the number of moles of naphthalene.

Heat of fusion = 35.7 cal/g

Moles of naphthalene = 0.300 mol

STEP 2: **Identify answer and units.**

Heat = ?? cal

STEP 3: **Identify conversion factors.** First convert moles of naphthalene to grams using the molar mass (128 g/mol) as a conversion factor. Then use the heat of fusion as a conversion factor to calculate the total heat necessary to melt the mass of naphthalene.

$$(0.300 \text{ mol naphthalene})\left(\frac{128.0 \text{ g}}{1 \text{ mol}}\right) = 38.4 \text{ g naphthalene}$$

Heat of fusion = 35.7 cal/g

STEP 4: **Solve.** Multiplying the mass of naphthalene by the heat of fusion then gives the answer.

$$(38.4 \text{ g naphthalene})\left(\frac{35.7 \text{ cal}}{1 \text{ g naphthalene}}\right) = 1370 \text{ cal} = 1.37 \text{ kcal}$$

BALLPARK CHECK The calculated result agrees with our estimate (1.4 kcal).

PROBLEM 8.21

How much heat in kilocalories is required to melt and boil 1.50 mol of iso-propyl alcohol (rubbing alcohol; molar mass = 60.0 g/mol)? The heat of fusion and heat of vaporization of isopropyl alcohol are given in Table 8.5.

APPLICATION ▶ CO_2 as an Environmentally Friendly Solvent

How can CO_2 be a solvent? After all, carbon dioxide is a gas, not a liquid, at room temperature. Furthermore, CO_2 at atmospheric pressure does not become liquid even when cooled. When the temperature drops to −78 °C at 1 atm pressure, CO_2 goes directly from gas to solid (dry ice) without first becoming liquid. Only when the pressure is raised does liquid CO_2 exist. At a room temperature of 22.4 °C, a pressure of 60 atm is needed to force gaseous CO_2 molecules close enough together so they condense to a liquid. Even as a liquid, though, CO_2 is not a particularly good solvent. Only when it enters an unusual and rarely seen state of matter called the *supercritical state* does CO_2 become a remarkable solvent.

To understand the supercritical state of matter, think about the liquid and gas states at the molecular level. In the liquid state, molecules are packed closely together, and most of the available volume is taken up by the molecules themselves. In the gas state, molecules are far apart, and most of the available volume is empty space. In the supercritical state, however, the situation is intermediate between liquid and gas. There is *some* space between molecules, but not much. The molecules are too far apart to be truly a liquid, yet they are too close together to be truly a gas. Supercritical CO_2 exists when the pressure is above 72.8 atm and the temperature is above 31.2 °C. This pressure is high enough to force molecules close together and prevent them from expanding into the gas state. Above this temperature, however, the molecules have too much kinetic energy to condense into the liquid state.

Because open spaces already exist between CO_2 molecules, it is energetically easy for dissolved molecules to slip in, and supercritical CO_2 is therefore an extraordinarily good solvent. Among its many applications, supercritical CO_2 is used in the beverage and food processing industries to decaffeinate

▲ The caffeine in these coffee beans can be removed by extraction with supercritical CO_2.

coffee beans and to obtain spice extracts from vanilla, pepper, cloves, nutmeg, and other seeds. In the cosmetics and perfume industry, fragrant oils are extracted from flowers using supercritical CO_2. Perhaps the most important future application is the use of carbon dioxide for dry-cleaning clothes, thereby replacing environmentally harmful chlorinated solvents.

The use of supercritical CO_2 as a solvent has many benefits, including the fact that it is nontoxic and nonflammable. Most important, though, is that the technology is environmentally friendly. Industrial processes using CO_2 are designed as closed systems so that CO_2 is recaptured after use and continually recycled. No organic solvent vapors are released into the atmosphere and no toxic liquids seep into groundwater supplies, as can occur with current procedures using chlorinated organic solvents. The future looks bright for this new technology.

See Additional Problems 8.104 and 8.105 at the end of the chapter.

KEY WORDS

Amorphous solid, *p. 244*

Avogadro's law, *p. 229*

Boiling point (bp), *p. 217*

Boyle's law, *p. 222*

Change of state, *p. 216*

Charles's law, *p. 225*

SUMMARY: REVISITING THE CHAPTER GOALS

1. **How do scientists explain the behavior of gases?** According to the *kinetic–molecular theory of gases,* the physical behavior of gases can be explained by assuming that they consist of particles moving rapidly at random, separated from other particles by great distances, and colliding without loss of energy. Gas *pressure* is the result of molecular collisions with a surface.

2. **How do gases respond to changes in temperature, pressure, and volume?** *Boyle's law* says that the volume of a fixed amount of gas at constant temperature is inversely proportional to its pressure ($P_1V_1 = P_2V_2$). *Charles's law* says that the volume of a fixed amount of gas at constant pressure is directly proportional to its Kelvin temperature ($V_1/T_1 = V_2/T_2$). *Gay-Lussac's law* says that the pressure of a fixed amount of gas at

constant volume is directly proportional to its Kelvin temperature ($P_1/T_1 = P_2/T_2$). Boyle's law, Charles's law, and Gay-Lussac's law together give the *combined gas law* ($P_1V_1/T_1 = P_2V_2/T_2$), which applies to changing conditions for a fixed quantity of gas. *Avogadro's law* says that equal volumes of gases at the same temperature and pressure contain the same number of moles ($V_1/n_1 = V_2/n_2$).

3. **What is the ideal gas law?** The four gas laws together give the *ideal gas law*, $PV = nRT$, which relates the effects of temperature, pressure, volume, and molar amount. At 0 °C and 1 atm pressure, called *standard temperature and pressure (STP)*, 1 mol of any gas (6.02×10^{23} molecules) occupies a volume of 22.4 L.

4. **What is partial pressure?** The amount of pressure exerted by an individual gas in a mixture is called the *partial pressure* of the gas. According to *Dalton's law*, the total pressure exerted by the mixture is equal to the sum of the partial pressures of the individual gases.

5. **What are the major intermolecular forces, and how do they affect the states of matter?** There are three major types of *intermolecular forces*, which act to hold molecules near one another in solids and liquids. *Dipole–dipole forces* are the electrical attractions that occur between polar molecules. *London dispersion forces* occur between all molecules as a result of temporary molecular polarities due to unsymmetrical electron distribution. These forces increase in strength with molecular weight and with the surface area of molecules. *Hydrogen bonding*, the strongest of the three intermolecular forces, occurs between a hydrogen atom bonded to O, N, or F and a nearby O, N, or F atom.

6. **What are the various kinds of solids, and how do they differ?** Solids are either crystalline or amorphous. *Crystalline solids* are those whose constituent particles have an ordered arrangement; *amorphous solids* lack internal order and do not have sharp melting points. There are several kinds of crystalline solids: *Ionic solids* are those like sodium chloride, whose constituent particles are ions. *Molecular solids* are those like ice, whose constituent particles are molecules held together by intermolecular forces. *Covalent network solids* are those like diamond, whose atoms are linked together by covalent bonds into a giant three-dimensional array. *Metallic solids*, such as silver or iron, also consist of large arrays of atoms, but their crystals have metallic properties such as electrical conductivity.

7. **What factors affect a change of state?** When a solid is heated, particles begin to move around freely at the *melting point*, and the substance becomes liquid. The amount of heat necessary to melt a given amount of solid at its melting point is its *heat of fusion*. As a liquid is heated, molecules escape from the surface of a liquid until an equilibrium is reached between liquid and gas, resulting in a *vapor pressure* of the liquid. At a liquid's *boiling point*, its vapor pressure equals atmospheric pressure, and the entire liquid is converted into gas. The amount of heat necessary to vaporize a given amount of liquid at its boiling point is called its *heat of vaporization*.

Combined gas law, *p. 228*
Crystalline solid, *p. 243*
Dalton's law, *p. 233*
Dipole–dipole force, *p. 235*
Gas constant (R), *p. 231*
Gas laws, *p. 222*
Gay-Lussac's law, *p. 227*
Heat of fusion, *p. 245*
Heat of vaporization, *p. 245*
Hydrogen bond, *p. 237*
Ideal gas, *p. 218*
Ideal gas law, *p. 231*
Intermolecular force, *p. 235*
Kinetic–molecular theory of gases, *p. 218*
London dispersion force, *p. 236*
Melting point (mp), *p. 217*
Normal boiling point, *p. 241*
Partial pressure, *p. 233*
Pressure (P), *p. 218*
Standard temperature and pressure (STP), *p. 230*
Standard molar volume, *p. 230*
Vapor, *p. 240*
Vapor pressure, *p. 241*

UNDERSTANDING KEY CONCEPTS

8.22 Assume that you have a sample of gas in a cylinder with a movable piston, as shown in the following drawing:

Redraw the apparatus to show what the sample will look like after the following changes:

(a) The temperature is increased from 300 K to 450 K at constant pressure.

(b) The pressure is increased from 1 atm to 2 atm at constant temperature.

(c) The temperature is decreased from 300 K to 200 K and the pressure is decreased from 3 atm to 2 atm.

8.23 Assume that you have a sample of gas at 350 K in a sealed container, as represented in part (a). Which of the drawings (b)–(d) represents the gas after the temperature is lowered from 350 K to 150 K?

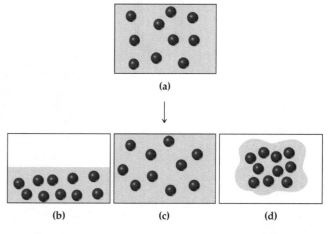

8.24 Assume that drawing (a) represents a sample of H_2O at 200 K. Which of the drawings (b)–(d) represents what the sample will look like when the temperature is raised to 300 K?

(a)

(b)

(c)

(d)

8.25 Three bulbs, two of which contain different gases and one of which is empty, are connected as shown in the following drawing:

Redraw the apparatus to represent the gases after the stopcocks are opened and the system is allowed to come to equilibrium.

8.26 Redraw the following open-end manometer to show what it would look like when stopcock A is opened.

8.27 The following graph represents the heating curve of a hypothetical substance:

(a) What is the melting point of the substance?
(b) What is the boiling point of the substance?
(c) Approximately what is the heat of fusion for the substance in kcal/mol?
(d) Approximately what is the heat of vaporization for the substance in kcal/mol?

8.28 Show the approximate level of the movable piston in drawings (a)–(c) after the indicated changes have been made to the gas.

(initial)
$T = 25\ °C$
$n = 0.075\ mol$
$P = 0.92\ atm$

(a)
$T = 50\ °C$
$n = 0.075\ mol$
$P = 0.92\ atm$

(b)
$T = 175\ °C$
$n = 0.075\ mol$
$P = 2.7\ atm$

(c)
$T = 25\ °C$
$n = 0.22\ mol$
$P = 2.7\ atm$

8.29 What is the partial pressure of each gas—red, yellow, and green—if the total pressure inside the following container is 600 mmHg?

ADDITIONAL PROBLEMS

GASES AND PRESSURE

8.30 How is 1 atm of pressure defined?

8.31 List four common units for measuring pressure.

8.32 What are the four assumptions of the kinetic–molecular theory of gases?

8.33 How does the kinetic–molecular theory of gases explain gas pressure?

8.34 Convert the following values into mmHg:

   (a) Standard pressure   (b) 25.3 psi
   (c) 7.5 atm   (d) 28.0 in. Hg
   (e) 41.8 Pa

8.35 Atmospheric pressure at the top of Mt. Whitney in California is 440 mmHg.

   (a) How many atmospheres is this?
   (b) How many pascals is this?

8.36 What is the pressure (in mmHg) inside a container of gas connected to a mercury-filled, open-end manometer of the sort shown in Figure 8.5 when the level in the arm connected to the container is 17.6 cm lower than the level in the arm open to the atmosphere, and the atmospheric pressure reading outside the apparatus is 754.3 mmHg?

8.37 What is the pressure (in atmospheres) inside a container of gas connected to a mercury-filled, open-end manometer of the sort shown in Figure 8.5 when the level in the arm connected to the container is 28.3 cm higher than the level in the arm open to the atmosphere, and the atmospheric pressure reading outside the apparatus is 1.021 atm?

BOYLE'S LAW

8.38 What is Boyle's law, and what variables must be kept constant for the law to hold?

8.39 Which assumption(s) of the kinetic–molecular theory explain the behavior of gases described by Boyle's Law? Explain your answer.

8.40 The pressure of gas in a 600.0 mL cylinder is 65.0 mmHg. To what volume must it be compressed to increase the pressure to 385 mmHg?

8.41 The volume of a balloon is 2.85 L at 1.00 atm. What pressure is required to compress the balloon to a volume of 1.70 L?

8.42 The use of chlorofluorocarbons (CFCs) as refrigerants and propellants in aerosol cans has been discontinued as a result of concerns about the ozone layer. If an aerosol can contained 350 mL of CFC gas at a pressure of 5.0 atm, what volume would this gas occupy at 1.0 atm?

8.43 A sample of neon gas used in a neon sign occupies a volume of 1.50 L at a pressure of 630 torr. Calculate the volume of the gas if the pressure in the glass tube of the sign is 793 torr.

CHARLES'S LAW

8.44 What is Charles's law, and what variables must be kept constant for the law to hold?

8.45 Which assumption(s) of the kinetic–molecular theory explain the behavior of gases described by Charles's Law? Explain your answer.

8.46 A hot-air balloon has a volume of 960 L at 18 °C. To what temperature must it be heated to raise its volume to 1200 L, assuming the pressure remains constant?

8.47 A hot-air balloon has a volume of 875 L. What is the original temperature of the balloon if its volume changes to 955 L when heated to 56 °C?

8.48 A gas sample has a volume of 185 mL at 38 °C. What is its volume at 97 °C?

8.49 A balloon has a volume of 43.0 L at 25 °C. What is its volume at −8 °C?

GAY-LUSSAC'S LAW

8.50 What is Gay-Lussac's law, and what variables must be kept constant for the law to hold?

8.51 Which assumption(s) of the kinetic–molecular theory explain the behavior of gases described by Gay-Lussac's Law? Explain your answer.

8.52 A glass laboratory flask is filled with gas at 25 °C and 0.95 atm pressure, sealed, and then heated to 117 °C. What is the pressure inside the flask?

8.53 An aerosol can has an internal pressure of 3.85 atm at 25 °C. What temperature is required to raise the pressure to 18.0 atm?

COMBINED GAS LAW

8.54 A gas has a volume of 2.84 L at 1.00 atm and 0 °C. At what temperature does it have a volume of 7.50 L at 520 mmHg?

8.55 A helium balloon has a volume of 3.50 L at 22.0 °C and 1.14 atm. What is its volume if the temperature is increased to 30.0 °C and the pressure is increased to 1.20 atm?

8.56 When H_2 gas was released by the reaction of HCl with Zn, the volume of H_2 collected was 75.4 mL at 23 °C and 748 mmHg. What is the volume of the H_2 at 0 °C and 1.00 atm pressure (STP)?

8.57 A compressed-air tank carried by scuba divers has a volume of 6.80 L and a pressure of 120 atm at 20 °C. What is the volume of air in the tank at 0 °C and 1.00 atm pressure (STP)?

8.58 What is the effect on the pressure of a gas if you simultaneously:

(a) Halve its volume and double its Kelvin temperature?
(b) Double its volume and halve its Kelvin temperature?

8.59 What is the effect on the volume of a gas if you simultaneously:

(a) Halve its pressure and double its Kelvin temperature?
(b) Double its pressure and double its Kelvin temperature?

8.60 A sample of oxygen produced in a laboratory experiment had a volume of 590 mL at a pressure of 775 mmHg and a temperature of 352 K. What is the volume of this sample at 25 °C and 800.0 mmHg pressure?

8.61 A small cylinder of helium gas used for filling balloons has a volume of 2.30 L and a pressure of 1850 atm at 25 °C. How many balloons can you fill if each one has a volume of 1.5 L and a pressure of 1.25 atm at 25 °C?

AVOGADRO'S LAW AND STANDARD MOLAR VOLUME

8.62 Explain Avogadro's law using the kinetic–molecular theory of gases.

8.63 What conditions are defined as standard temperature and pressure (STP)?

8.64 How many liters does 1 mol of gas occupy at STP?

8.65 How many moles of gas are in a volume of 48.6 L at STP?

8.66 Which sample contains more molecules: 1.0 L of O_2 at STP or 1.0 L of H_2 at STP? Which sample has the larger mass?

8.67 How many milliliters of Cl_2 gas must you have to obtain 0.20 g at STP?

8.68 What is the mass of CH_4 in a sample that occupies a volume of 16.5 L at STP?

8.69 Assume that you have 1.75 g of the deadly gas hydrogen cyanide, HCN. What is the volume of the gas at STP?

8.70 A typical room is 4.0 m long, 5.0 m wide, and 2.5 m high. What is the total mass of the oxygen in the room assuming that the gas in the room is at STP and that air contains 21% oxygen and 79% nitrogen?

8.71 What is the total mass of nitrogen in the room described in Problem 8.70?

IDEAL GAS LAW

8.72 What is the ideal gas law?

8.73 How does the ideal gas law differ from the combined gas law?

8.74 Which sample contains more molecules: 2.0 L of Cl_2 at STP, or 3.0 L of CH_4 at 300 K and 1.5 atm? Which sample weighs more?

8.75 Which sample contains more molecules: 2.0 L of CO_2 at 300 K and 500 mmHg, or 1.5 L of N_2 at 57 °C and 760 mmHg? Which sample weighs more?

8.76 If 2.3 mol of He has a volume of 0.15 L at 294 K, what is the pressure in atm?

8.77 If 3.5 mol of O_2 has a volume of 27.0 L at a pressure of 1.6 atm, what is its temperature in kelvins?

8.78 If 15.0 g of CO_2 gas has a volume of 0.30 L at 310 K, what is its pressure in mmHg?

8.79 If 20.0 g of N_2 gas has a volume of 4.00 L and a pressure of 6.0 atm, what is its temperature in degrees Celsius?

8.80 If 18.0 g of O_2 gas has a temperature of 350 K and a pressure of 550 mmHg, what is its volume?

8.81 How many moles of a gas will occupy a volume of 0.55 L at a temperature of 347 K and a pressure of 2.5 atm?

DALTON'S LAW AND PARTIAL PRESSURE

8.82 What is meant by *partial pressure*?

8.83 What is Dalton's law?

8.84 If the partial pressure of oxygen in air at 1.0 atm is 160 mmHg, what is the partial pressure on the summit of Mt. Whitney, where atmospheric pressure is 440 mmHg? Assume that the percent oxygen is the same.

8.85 Patients suffering from respiratory disorders are often treated in oxygen tents in which the atmosphere is enriched in oxygen. What is the partial pressure of O_2 in an oxygen tent consisting of 45% O_2 for an atmospheric pressure of 753 mmHg?

LIQUIDS AND INTERMOLECULAR FORCES

8.86 What is the vapor pressure of a liquid?

8.87 What is the value of a liquid's vapor pressure at its normal boiling point?

8.88 What is the effect of pressure on a liquid's boiling point?

8.89 What is a liquid's heat of vaporization?

8.90 What characteristic must a compound have to experience the following intermolecular forces?

(a) London dispersion forces
(b) Dipole–dipole forces
(c) Hydrogen bonding

8.91 In which of the following compounds are dipole–dipole attractions the most important intermolecular force?

(a) N_2 (b) HCN   (c) CCl_4
(d) $MgBr_2$ (e) CH_3Cl (f) CH_3CO_2H

8.92 Dimethyl ether (CH_3OCH_3) and ethanol (C_2H_5OH) have the same formula (C_2H_6O), but the boiling point of dimethyl ether is −25 °C while that of ethanol is 78 °C. Explain.

8.93 Iodine is a solid at room temperature (mp = 113.5 °C) while bromine is a liquid (mp = −7 °C). Explain in terms of intermolecular forces.

8.94 The heat of vaporization of water is 9.72 kcal/mol.

(a) How much heat (in kilocalories) is required to vaporize 3.00 mol of H_2O?
(b) How much heat (in kilocalories) is released when 320 g of steam condenses?

8.95 Patients with a high body temperature are often given "alcohol baths." The heat of vaporization of isopropyl alcohol (rubbing alcohol) is 159 cal/g. How much heat is removed from the skin by the evaporation of 190 g (about ½ cup) of isopropyl alcohol?

SOLIDS

8.96 What is the difference between an amorphous and a crystalline solid?

8.97 List three kinds of crystalline solids, and give an example of each.

8.98 The heat of fusion of acetic acid, the principal organic component of vinegar, is 45.9 cal/g. How much heat (in kilocalories) is required to melt 1.75 mol of solid acetic acid?

8.99 The heat of fusion of sodium metal is 630 cal/mol. How much heat (in kilocalories) is required to melt 262 g of sodium?

Applications

8.100 What is the difference between a systolic and a diastolic pressure reading? Is a blood pressure of 180/110 within the normal range? [*Blood Pressure, p. 223*]

8.101 What are the three most important greenhouse gases? [*Greenhouse Gases and Global Warming, p. 236*]

8.102 What evidence is there that global warming is occurring? [*Greenhouse Gases and Global Warming, p. 236*]

8.103 What is the mass ratio of calcium to phosphate in calcium phosphate, $Ca_3(PO_4)_2$? In hydroxyapatite, $Ca_{10}(PO_4)_6(OH)_2$? [*Biomaterials for Joint Replacement, p. 246*]

8.104 What is a supercritical fluid? [CO_2 *as an Environmentally Friendly Solvent, p. 248*]

8.105 What are the environmental advantages of using supercritical CO_2 in place of chlorinated organic solvents? [CO_2 *as an Environmentally Friendly Solvent, p. 248*]

General Questions and Problems

8.106 Use the kinetic–molecular theory to explain why gas pressure increases if the temperature is raised and the volume is kept constant.

8.107 Hydrogen and oxygen react according to the equation $2 H_2 + O_2 \longrightarrow 2 H_2O$. According to Avogadro's law, how many liters of hydrogen are required to react with 2.5 L of oxygen at STP?

8.108 If 3.0 L of hydrogen and 1.5 L of oxygen at STP react to yield water, how many moles of water are formed? What gas volume does the water have at a temperature of 100 °C and 1 atm pressure?

8.109 Approximately 240 mL/min of CO_2 is exhaled by an average adult at rest. Assuming a temperature of 37 °C and 1 atm pressure, how many moles of CO_2 is this?

8.110 How many grams of CO_2 are exhaled by an average resting adult in 24 hours? (See Problem 8.109.)

8.111 Imagine that you have two identical containers, one containing hydrogen at STP and the other containing oxygen at STP. How can you tell which is which without opening them?

8.112 When fully inflated, a hot-air balloon has a volume of 1.6×10^5 L at an average temperature of 375 K and 0.975 atm. Assuming that air has an average molar mass of 29 g/mol, what is the density of the air in the hot-air balloon? How does this compare with the density of air at STP?

8.113 A 10.0 g sample of an unknown gas occupies 14.7 L at a temperature of 25 °C and a pressure of 745 mmHg. What is the molar mass of the gas?

8.114 One mole of any gas has a volume of 22.4 L at STP. What are the molecular weights of the following gases, and what are their densities in grams per liter at STP?

(a) CH_4 (b) CO_2 (c) O_2

8.115 Gas pressure outside the space shuttle is approximately 1×10^{-14} mm Hg at a temperature of approximately 1 K. If the gas is almost entirely hydrogen atoms (H, not H_2), what volume of space is occupied by 1 mol of atoms? What is the density of H gas in atoms per liter?

8.116 Ethylene glycol, $C_2H_6O_2$, has one OH bonded to each carbon.

(a) Draw the Lewis dot structure of ethylene glycol.

(b) Draw the Lewis dot structure of chloroethane, C_2H_5Cl.

(c) Chloroethane has a slightly higher molar mass than ethylene glycol, but a much lower boiling point (3 °C versus 198 °C). Explain.

8.117 A rule of thumb for scuba diving is that the external pressure increases by 1 atm for every 10 m of depth. A diver using a compressed air tank is planning to descend to a depth of 25 m.

(a) What is the external pressure at this depth? (Remember that the pressure at sea level is 1 atm.)

(b) Assuming that the tank contains 20% oxygen and 80% nitrogen, what is the partial pressure of each gas in the diver's lungs at this depth?

8.118 The *Rankine* temperature scale used in engineering is to the Fahrenheit scale as the Kelvin scale is to the Celsius scale. That is, 1 Rankine degree is the same size as 1 Fahrenheit degree, and 0 °R = absolute zero .

(a) What temperature corresponds to the freezing point of water on the Rankine scale?

(b) What is the value of the gas constant R on the Rankine scale in $(L \cdot atm)/(°R \cdot mol)$?

8.119 Isooctane, C_8H_{18}, is the component of gasoline from which the term *octane rating* derives.

(a) Write a balanced equation for the combustion of isooctane to yield CO_2 and H_2O.

(b) Assuming that gasoline is 100% isooctane and that the density of isooctane is 0.792 g/mL, what mass of CO_2 (in kilograms) is produced each year by the annual U.S. gasoline consumption of 4.6×10^{10} L?

(c) What is the volume (in liters) of this CO_2 at STP?

CHAPTER 9

Solutions

CONCEPTS TO REVIEW

Enthalpy Changes
(Section 7.2)

Chemical Equilibrium
(Section 7.7)

Le Châtelier's Principle
(Section 7.9)

Partial Pressure of Gases
(Section 8.10)

**Intermolecular Forces
and Hydrogen Bonds**
(Section 8.11)

Vapor Pressure
(Section 8.12)

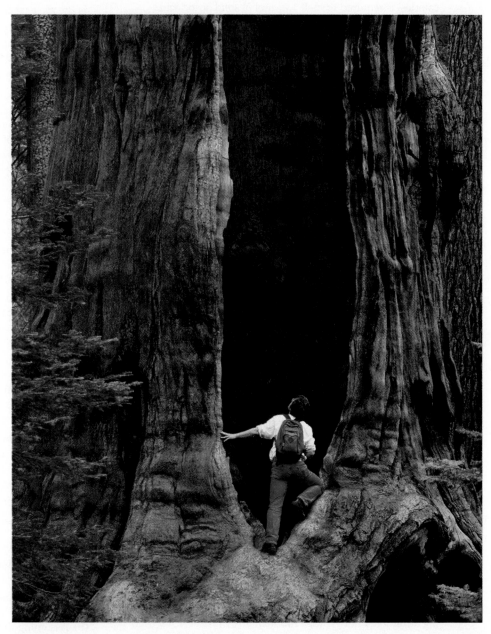

▲ The giant sequoia relies on osmotic pressure—a colligative property of solutions—to transport water and nutrients from the roots to the treetops 300 ft up.

CONTENTS

CHAPTER GOALS

Among the questions we will answer are the following:

1. **What are solutions, and what factors affect solubility?**

   THE GOAL: Be able to define the different kinds of mixtures and explain the influence on solubility of solvent and solute structure, temperature, and pressure.

2. **How is the concentration of a solution expressed?**

   THE GOAL: Be able to define, use, and convert between the most common ways of expressing solution concentrations.

3. **How are dilutions carried out?**

   THE GOAL: Be able to calculate the concentration of a solution prepared by dilution and explain how to make a desired dilution.

4. **What is an electrolyte?**

   THE GOAL: Be able to recognize strong and weak electrolytes and nonelectrolytes, and express electrolyte concentrations.

5. **How do solutions differ from pure solvents in their behavior?**

   THE GOAL: Be able to explain vapor pressure lowering, boiling point elevation, and freezing point depression for solutions.

6. **What is osmosis?**

   THE GOAL: Be able to describe osmosis and some of its applications.

U p to this point, we have been concerned primarily with pure substances, both elements and compounds. In day-to-day life, however, most of the materials we come in contact with are mixtures. Air, for example, is a gaseous mixture of primarily oxygen and nitrogen; blood is a liquid mixture of many different components; and many rocks are solid mixtures of different minerals. In this chapter, we look closely at the characteristics and properties of mixtures, with particular attention to the uniform mixtures we call *solutions*.

9.1 Mixtures and Solutions

As we saw in Section 1.3, a *mixture* is an intimate combination of two or more substances, both of which retain their chemical identities. (⊂⊃, p. 6) Mixtures can be classified as either *heterogeneous* or *homogeneous* as indicated in Figure 9.1, depending on their appearance. **Heterogeneous mixtures** are those in which the mixing is

Heterogeneous mixture A nonuniform mixture that has regions of different composition.

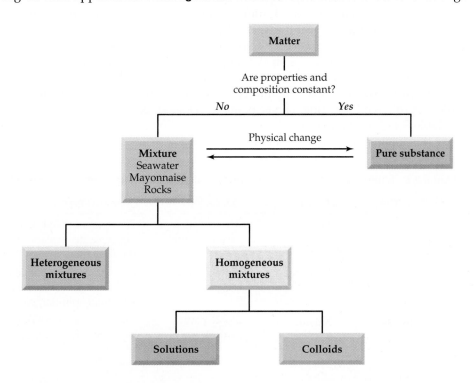

◄ **FIGURE 9.1 Classification of mixtures.** The components in heterogeneous mixtures are not uniformly mixed, and the composition varies with location. In homogeneous mixtures, the components are uniformly mixed at the molecular level.

not uniform and which therefore have regions of different composition. Rocky Road ice cream, for example, is a heterogeneous mixture, with something different in every spoonful. Granite and many other rocks are also heterogeneous, having a grainy character due to the heterogeneous mixing of different minerals. **Homogeneous mixtures** are those in which the mixing *is* uniform and that therefore have the same composition throughout. Seawater, a homogeneous mixture of soluble ionic compounds in water, is an example.

Homogeneous mixtures can be further classified as either *solutions* or *colloids* according to the size of their particles. **Solutions**, the most important class of homogeneous mixtures, contain particles the size of a typical ion or small molecule—roughly 0.1–2 nm in diameter. **Colloids**, such as milk and fog, are also homogeneous in appearance but contain larger particles than solutions—in the range 2–500 nm diameter.

Homogeneous mixture A uniform mixture that has the same composition throughout.

Solution A homogeneous mixture that contains particles the size of a typical ion or small molecule.

Colloid A homogeneous mixture that contains particles that range in diameter from 2 to 500 nm.

(a)

(b)

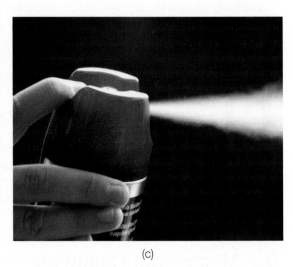

(c)

▲ (a) Wine is a solution of dissolved molecules, and (b) milk is a colloid with fine particles that do not separate out on standing. (c) An aerosol spray, by contrast, is a heterogeneous mixture of small particles visible to the naked eye.

Liquid solutions, colloids, and heterogeneous mixtures can be distinguished in several ways. For example, liquid solutions are transparent (although they may be colored). Colloids may appear transparent if the particle size is small, but they have a murky or opaque appearance if the particle size is larger. Neither solutions nor small-particle colloids separate on standing, and the particles in both are too small to be removed by filtration. Heterogeneous mixtures and large-particle colloids, also known as "suspensions," are murky and opaque and their particles will slowly settle on prolonged standing. House paint is an example.

Table 9.1 gives some examples of solutions, colloids, and heterogeneous mixtures. It is interesting to note that blood has characteristics of all three. About 45%

TABLE 9.1 Some Characteristics of Solutions, Colloids, and Heterogeneous Mixtures

TYPE OF MIXTURE	PARTICLE SIZE	EXAMPLES	CHARACTERISTICS
Solution	<2.0 nm	Air, seawater, gasoline, wine	Transparent to light; does not separate on standing; nonfilterable
Colloid	2.0–500 nm	Butter, milk, fog, pearl	Often murky or opaque to light; does not separate on standing; nonfilterable
Heterogeneous	>500 nm	Blood, paint, aerosol sprays	Murky or opaque to light; separates on standing; filterable

by volume of blood consists of suspended red and white cells, which settle slowly on standing; the remaining 55% is *plasma*, which contains ions in solution and colloidal protein molecules.

Although we usually think of solids dissolved in liquids when we talk about solutions, solutions actually occur in all three phases of matter (Table 9.2). Metal alloys like 14-karat gold (58% gold with silver and copper) and brass (10–40% zinc with copper), for instance, are solutions of one solid with another. For solutions in which a gas or solid is dissolved in a liquid, the dissolved substance is called the **solute** and the liquid is called the **solvent**. When one liquid is dissolved in another, the minor component is usually considered the solute and the major component is the solvent.

Solute   A substance dissolved in a liquid.

Solvent   The liquid in which another substance is dissolved.

TABLE 9.2   Some Different Types of Solutions

TYPE OF SOLUTION	EXAMPLE
Gas in gas	Air (O_2, N_2, Ar, and other gases)
Gas in liquid	Seltzer water (CO_2 in water)
Gas in solid	H_2 in palladium metal
Liquid in liquid	Gasoline (mixture of hydrocarbons)
Liquid in solid	Dental amalgam (mercury in silver)
Solid in liquid	Seawater (NaCl and other salts in water)
Solid in solid	Metal alloys such as 14-karat gold (Au, Ag, and Cu)

PROBLEM 9.1

Classify the following liquid mixtures as heterogeneous or homogeneous. Further classify each homogeneous mixture as a solution or colloid.

(a) Orange juice   **(b)** Apple juice

(c) Hand lotion   **(d)** Tea

9.2 The Solution Process

What determines whether a substance is soluble in a given liquid? Solubility depends primarily on the strength of the attractions between solute and solvent particles relative to the strengths of the attractions within the pure substances. Ethyl alcohol is soluble in water, for example, because hydrogen bonding (Section 8.11) is nearly as strong between water and ethyl alcohol molecules as it is between water molecules alone or ethyl alcohol molecules alone. (⊂◻⊃, p. 238)

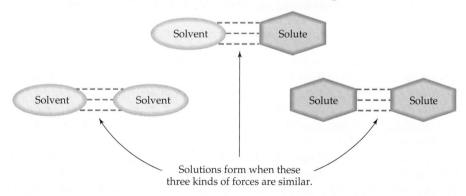

Solutions form when these three kinds of forces are similar.

A good rule of thumb for predicting solubility is that "like dissolves like," meaning that substances with similar intermolecular forces form solutions with one another, whereas substances with different intermolecular forces do not (Section 8.11). (⊂◻⊃, p. 235)

▲ Oil and water do not mix because they have different intermolecular forces, resulting in the formation of oil slicks.

Solvation The clustering of solvent molecules around a dissolved solute molecule or ion.

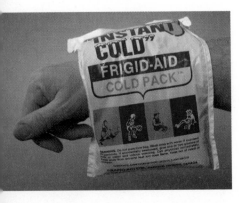

▲ Instant cold packs used to treat muscle strains and sprains often take advantage of the endothermic enthalpy of a solution of salts such as ammonium nitrate.

Polar solvents dissolve polar and ionic solutes; nonpolar solvents dissolve nonpolar solutes. Thus, a polar, hydrogen-bonding compound like water dissolves ethyl alcohol and sodium chloride, whereas a nonpolar organic compound like hexane (C_6H_{14}) dissolves other nonpolar organic compounds like fats and oils. Water and oil, however, do not dissolve one another, as summed up by the old saying, "Oil and water don't mix." The intermolecular forces between water molecules are so strong that after an oil–water mixture is shaken, the water layer re-forms, squeezing out the oil molecules.

Water solubility is not limited to ionic compounds and ethyl alcohol. Many polar organic substances, such as sugars, amino acids, and even some proteins, dissolve in water. In addition, small, moderately polar organic molecules such as chloroform ($CHCl_3$) are soluble in water to a limited extent. When mixed with water, a small amount of the organic compound dissolves, but the remainder forms a separate liquid layer. As the number of carbon atoms in organic molecules increases, though, water solubility decreases.

The process of dissolving an ionic solid in a polar liquid can be visualized as shown in Figure 9.2 for sodium chloride. When NaCl crystals are put in water, ions at the crystal surface come into contact with polar water molecules. Positively charged Na^+ ions are attracted to the negatively polarized oxygen of water, and negatively charged Cl^- ions are attracted to the positively polarized hydrogens. The combined forces of attraction between an ion and several water molecules pull the ion away from the crystal, exposing a fresh surface, until ultimately the crystal dissolves. Once in solution, Na^+ and Cl^- ions are completely surrounded by solvent molecules, a phenomenon called **solvation** (or, specifically for water, *hydration*). The water molecules form a loose shell around the ions, stabilizing them by electrical attraction.

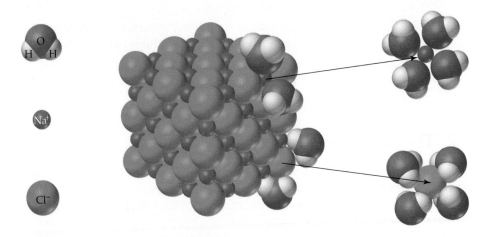

▲ **FIGURE 9.2 Dissolution of an NaCl crystal in water.** Polar water molecules surround the individual Na^+ and Cl^- ions at an exposed edge or corner, pulling them from the crystal surface into solution and surrounding them. Note how the negatively polarized oxygens of water molecules cluster around Na^+ ions and the positively polarized hydrogens cluster around Cl^- ions.

The dissolution of a solute in a solvent is a physical change since the solution components retain their chemical identities. Like all chemical and physical changes, the dissolution of a substance in a solvent has associated with it a heat change, or *enthalpy* change (Section 7.2). (⊂⊃, p. 184) Some substances dissolve exothermically, releasing heat and warming the resultant solution, whereas other substances dissolve endothermically, absorbing heat and cooling the resultant solution. Calcium chloride, for example, *releases* 19.4 kcal/mol of heat energy when it dissolves in water, but ammonium nitrate (NH_4NO_3) *absorbs* 6.1 kcal/mol of heat energy. Athletes and others take advantage of both situations when they use instant hot packs or cold packs to treat injuries. Both hot and cold packs consist of a pouch of water and a dry chemical, such as $CaCl_2$ or $MgSO_4$ for hot packs and NH_4NO_3 for cold packs. Squeezing the pack breaks the pouch and the solid dissolves, either raising or lowering the temperature.

WORKED EXAMPLE **9.1** Formation of Solutions

Which of the following pairs of substances would you expect to form solutions?

(a) Carbon tetrachloride (CCl_4) and hexane (C_6H_{14}).

(b) Octane (C_8H_{18}) and methyl alcohol (CH_3OH).

ANALYSIS Identify the kinds of intermolecular forces in each substance (Section 8.11). Substances with similar intermolecular forces tend to form solutions.

SOLUTION

(a) Hexane contains only C—H and C—C bonds, which are nonpolar. Carbon tetrachloride contains polar C—Cl bonds, but they are distributed symmetrically in the tetrahedral molecule so that it too is nonpolar. The major intermolecular force for both compounds is London dispersion forces, so they will form a solution.

(b) Octane contains only C—H and C—C bonds and so is nonpolar; the major intermolecular force is dispersion. Methyl alcohol contains polar C—O and O—H bonds; it is polar and forms hydrogen bonds. The intermolecular forces for the two substances are so dissimilar that they do not form a solution.

PROBLEM 9.2

Which of the following pairs of substances would you expect to form solutions?

(a) CCl_4 and water

(b) Benzene (C_6H_6) and $MgSO_4$

(c) Hexane (C_6H_{14}) and heptane (C_7H_{16})

(d) Ethyl alcohol (C_2H_5OH) and heptanol ($C_7H_{15}OH$)

Hygroscopic Having the ability to pull water molecules from the surrounding atmosphere.

9.3 Solid Hydrates

Some ionic compounds attract water strongly enough to hold onto water molecules even when crystalline, forming what are called *solid hydrates*. For example, the plaster of Paris used to make decorative objects and casts for broken limbs is calcium sulfate hemihydrate, $CaSO_4 \cdot \frac{1}{2}H_2O$. The dot between $CaSO_4$ and $\frac{1}{2}H_2O$ in the formula indicates that for every two $CaSO_4$ formula units in the crystal there is also one water molecule present.

$$CaSO_4 \cdot \tfrac{1}{2}H_2O \quad \text{A solid hydrate}$$

After being ground up and mixed with water to make plaster, $CaSO_4 \cdot \frac{1}{2}H_2O$ gradually changes into the crystalline dihydrate $CaSO_4 \cdot 2\,H_2O$, known as *gypsum*. During the change, the plaster hardens and expands in volume, causing it to fill a mold or shape itself closely around a broken limb. Table 9.3 lists some other ionic compounds that are handled primarily as hydrates.

Still other ionic compounds attract water so strongly that they pull water vapor from humid air to become hydrated. Compounds that show this behavior, such as calcium chloride ($CaCl_2$), are called **hygroscopic** and are often used as drying agents. You might have noticed a small bag of a hygroscopic compound (probably silica gel, SiO_2) included in the packing material of a new MP3 player, camera, or other electronic device to keep humidity low during shipping.

▲ Plaster of Paris ($CaSO_4 \cdot \frac{1}{2}H_2O$) slowly turns into gypsum ($CaSO_4 \cdot 2\,H_2O$) when added to water. In so doing, the plaster hardens and expands, causing it to fill a mold.

TABLE 9.3   Some Common Solid Hydrates

FORMULA	NAME	USES
$AlCl_3 \cdot 6\ H_2O$	Aluminum chloride hexahydrate	Antiperspirant
$CaSO_4 \cdot 2\ H_2O$	Calcium sulfate dihydrate (gypsum)	Cements, wallboard molds
$CaSO_4 \cdot \frac{1}{2}H_2O$	Calcium sulfate hemihydrate (plaster of Paris)	Casts, molds
$CuSO_4 \cdot 5\ H_2O$	Copper(II) sulfate pentahydrate (blue vitriol)	Pesticide, germicide, topical fungicide
$MgSO_4 \cdot 7\ H_2O$	Magnesium sulfate heptahydrate (epsom salts)	Laxative, anticonvulsant
$Na_2B_4O_7 \cdot 10\ H_2O$	Sodium tetraborate decahydrate (borax)	Cleaning compounds, fireproofing agent
$Na_2S_2O_3 \cdot 5\ H_2O$	Sodium thiosulfate pentahydrate (hypo)	Photographic fixer

PROBLEM 9.3

Write the formula of sodium sulfate decahydrate, known as Glauber's salt and used as a laxative.

PROBLEM 9.4

What masses of Glauber's salt must be used to provide 1.00 mol of sodium sulfate?

9.4 Solubility

We saw in Section 9.2 that ethyl alcohol is soluble in water because hydrogen bonding is nearly as strong between water and ethyl alcohol molecules as it is between water molecules alone or ethyl alcohol molecules alone. So similar are the forces in this particular case, in fact, that the two liquids are **miscible**, or mutually soluble in all proportions. Ethyl alcohol will continue to dissolve in water no matter how much is added.

Miscible Mutually soluble in all proportions.

Most substances, however, reach a solubility limit beyond which no more will dissolve in solution. Imagine, for instance that you are asked to prepare a saline solution (aqueous NaCl). You might measure out some water, add solid NaCl, and stir the mixture. Dissolution occurs rapidly at first but then slows down as more and more NaCl is added. Eventually the dissolution stops because an equilibrium is reached when the numbers of Na^+ and Cl^- ions leaving a crystal and going into solution are equal to the numbers of ions returning from solution to the crystal. At this point, the solution is said to be **saturated**. A maximum of 35.8 g of NaCl will dissolve in 100 mL of water at 20 °C. Any amount above this limit simply sinks to the bottom of the container and sits there.

Saturated solution A solution that contains the maximum amount of dissolved solute at equilibrium.

The equilibrium reached by a saturated solution is like the equilibrium reached by a reversible reaction (Section 7.7). (, p. 198) Both are dynamic situations in which no *apparent* change occurs because the rates of forward and backward processes are equal. Solute particles leave the solid surface and reenter the solid from solution at the same rate.

$$\text{Solid solute} \underset{\text{Crystallize}}{\overset{\text{Dissolve}}{\rightleftharpoons}} \text{Solution}$$

Solubility The maximum amount of a substance that will dissolve in a given amount of solvent at a specified temperature.

The maximum amount of a substance that will dissolve in a given amount of a solvent at a given temperature, usually expressed in grams per 100 mL (g/100 mL), is called the substance's **solubility**. Solubility is a characteristic property of a specific solute–solvent combination, and different substances have greatly differing solubilities. Only 9.6 g of sodium hydrogen carbonate will dissolve in 100 mL of water at 20 °C, for instance, but 204 g of sucrose will dissolve under the same conditions.

9.5 The Effect of Temperature on Solubility

As anyone who has ever made tea or coffee knows, temperature often has a dramatic effect on solubility. The compounds in tea leaves or coffee beans, for instance, dissolve easily in hot water but not in cold water. The effect of temperature is different for every substance, however, and is usually unpredictable. As shown in Figure 9.3(a), the solubilities of most molecular and ionic solids increase with increasing temperature, but the solubilities of others (NaCl) are almost unchanged, and the solubilities of still others [$Ce_2(SO_4)_3$] decrease with increasing temperature.

Solids that are more soluble at high temperature than at low temperature can sometimes form what are called **supersaturated solutions**, which contain even more solute than a saturated solution. Suppose, for instance, that a large amount of a substance is dissolved at a high temperature. As the solution cools, the solubility decreases and the excess solute should precipitate to maintain equilibrium. But if

Supersaturated solution A solution that contains more than the maximum amount of dissolved solute; a nonequilibrium situation.

(a)

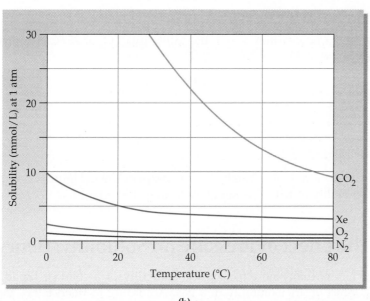

(b)

◀ **FIGURE 9.3 Solubilities of some (a) solids and (b) gases, in water as a function of temperature.** Most solid substances become more soluble as temperature rises (although the exact relationship is usually complex), while the solubility of gases decreases.

▲ **FIGURE 9.4 A supersaturated solution of sodium acetate in water.** When a tiny seed crystal is added, larger crystals rapidly grow and precipitate from the solution until equilibrium is reached.

the cooling is done very slowly, and if the container stands quietly, crystallization might not occur immediately and a supersaturated solution might result. Such a solution is unstable, however, and precipitation can occur dramatically when a tiny seed crystal is added to initiate crystallization (Figure 9.4).

Unlike solids, the influence of temperature on the solubility of gases *is* predictable: Addition of heat decreases the solubility of most gases, as seen in Figure 9.3(b) (helium is the only common exception). One result of this temperature-dependent decrease in gas solubility can sometimes be noted in a stream or lake near the outflow of warm water from an industrial operation. As water temperature increases, the concentration of dissolved oxygen in the water decreases, killing fish that cannot tolerate the lower oxygen levels.

WORKED EXAMPLE **9.2** Solubility of Gases: Effect of Temperature

From the following graph of solubility versus temperature for O_2, estimate the concentration of dissolved oxygen in water at 25 °C and at 35 °C. By what percentage does the concentration of O_2 change?

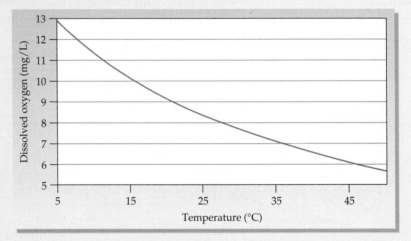

ANALYSIS The solubility of O_2 (on the *y*-axis) can be determined by finding the appropriate temperature (on the *x*-axis) and extrapolating. The percent change is calculated as

$$\frac{(\text{Solubility at 25 °C}) - (\text{Solubility at 35 °C})}{(\text{Solubility at 25 °C})} \times 100$$

SOLUTION

From the graph we estimate that the solubility of O_2 at 25 °C is approximately 8.3 mg/L and at 35 °C is 7.0 mg/L. The percent change in solubility is

$$\frac{8.3 - 7.0}{8.3} \times 100 = 16\%$$

PROBLEM 9.5

Look at the graph of solubility versus temperature in Figure 9.3, and estimate the solubility of KBr in water at 50 °C in g/100 mL.

9.6 The Effect of Pressure on Solubility: Henry's Law

Pressure has virtually no effect on the solubility of a solid or liquid, but it has a strong effect on the solubility of a gas. According to **Henry's law**, the solubility (or concentration) of a gas in a liquid is directly proportional to the partial pressure

(a) Equilibrium   **(b)** Pressure increase   **(c)** Equilibrium restored

◀ **FIGURE 9.5 Henry's law.** The solubility of a gas is directly proportional to its partial pressure. An increase in pressure causes more gas molecules to enter solution until equilibrium is restored between the dissolved and undissolved gas.

of the gas over the liquid. (Recall from Section 8.10 that each gas in a mixture exerts a partial pressure independent of other gases present (⊂⊃, p. 233). If the partial pressure of the gas doubles, solubility doubles; if the gas pressure is halved, solubility is halved (Figure 9.5).

> **Henry's law**   The solubility (or concentration) of a gas is directly proportional to the partial pressure of the gas if the temperature is constant. That is, concentration (C) divided by pressure (P) is constant when T is constant,
>
> or $\dfrac{C}{P_{gas}} = k$ (At a constant temperature)

Henry's law can be explained using Le Châtelier's principle (Section 7.9), which states that when a system at equilibrium is placed under stress, the equilibrium shifts to relieve that stress. (⊂⊃, p. 203) In the case of a saturated solution of a gas in a liquid, an equilibrium exists whereby gas molecules enter and leave the solution at the same rate. When the system is stressed by increasing the pressure of the gas, more gas molecules go into solution to relieve that increase. Conversely, when the pressure of the gas is decreased, more gas molecules come out of solution to relieve the decrease.

$$[\text{Pressure} \longrightarrow]$$
$$\text{Gas} + \text{Solvent} \rightleftharpoons \text{Solution}$$

As an example of Henry's law in action, think about the fizzing that occurs when you open a bottle of soft drink or champagne. The bottle is sealed under greater than 1 atm of CO_2 pressure, causing some of the CO_2 to dissolve. When the bottle is opened, however, CO_2 pressure drops and gas comes fizzing out of solution.

Writing Henry's law in the form $P_{gas} = C/k$ shows that partial pressure can be used to express the concentration of a gas in a solution, a practice especially common in health-related sciences. Table 9.4 gives some typical values and illustrates the convenience of having the same unit for concentration of a gas in both air and blood.

▲ The CO_2 gas dissolved under pressure comes out of solution when the bottle is opened and the pressure drops.

TABLE 9.4   Partial Pressures and Normal Gas Concentrations in Body Fluids

| | PARTIAL PRESSURE (mmHg) | | | |
SAMPLE	P_{N_2}	P_{O_2}	P_{CO_2}	P_{H_2O}
Inspired air (dry)	597	159	0.3	3.7
Alveolar air (saturated)	573	100	40	47
Expired air (saturated)	569	116	28	47
Arterial blood	573	95	40	
Venous blood	573	40	45	
Peripheral tissues	573	40	45	

Compare the oxygen partial pressures in saturated alveolar air (air in the lungs) and in arterial blood, for instance. The values are almost the same because the gases dissolved in blood come to equilibrium with the same gases in the lungs.

If the partial pressure of a gas over a solution changes while the temperature is constant, the new solubility of the gas can be found easily. Because C/P is a constant value at constant temperature, Henry's law can be restated to show how one variable changes if the other changes:

$$\frac{C_1}{P_1} = \frac{C_2}{P_2} = k \quad \text{(Where } k \text{ is constant at a fixed temperature)}$$

Worked Example 9.3 gives an illustration of how to use this equation.

WORKED EXAMPLE **9.3** Solubility of Gases: Henry's Law

At a partial pressure of oxygen in the atmosphere of 159 mmHg, the solubility of oxygen in blood is 0.44 g/100 mL. What is the solubility of oxygen in blood at 11,000 ft, where the partial pressure of O_2 is 56 mmHg?

ANALYSIS According to Henry's law, the solubility of the gas divided by its pressure is constant:

$$\frac{C_1}{P_1} = \frac{C_2}{P_2}$$

Of the four variables in this equation, we know P_1, C_1, and P_2, and we need to find C_2.

BALLPARK ESTIMATE The pressure drops by a factor of about 3 (from 159 mmHg to 56 mmHg). Since the ratio of solubility to pressure is constant, the solubility must also drop by a factor of 3 (from 0.44 g/100 mL to about 0.15 g/100 mL).

SOLUTION

STEP 1: Identify known information. We have values for P_1, C_1, and P_2.

$P_1 = 159 \text{ mmHg}$

$C_1 = 0.44 \text{ g/100 mL}$

$P_2 = 56 \text{ mmHg}$

STEP 2: Identify answer and units. We are looking for the solubility of O_2 (C_2) at a partial pressure P_2.

Solubility of O_2, $C_2 = \text{ ?? g/100 mL}$

STEP 3: Identify conversion factors or equations. In this case, we restate Henry's law to solve for C_2.

$$\frac{C_1}{P_1} = \frac{C_2}{P_2} \implies C_2 = \frac{C_1 P_2}{P_1}$$

STEP 4: Solve. Substitute the known values into the equation and calculate C_2.

$$C_2 = \frac{C_1 P_2}{P_1} = \frac{(0.44 \text{ g/100 mL})(56 \text{ mmHg})}{159 \text{ mmHg}} = 0.15 \text{ g/100 mL}$$

BALLPARK CHECK: The calculated answer matches our estimate.

PROBLEM 9.6

At 20 °C and a partial pressure of 760 mmHg, the solubility of CO_2 in water is 0.169 g/100 mL. What is the solubility of CO_2 at 2.5×10^4 mmHg?

PROBLEM 9.7

At a total atmospheric pressure of 1.00 atm, the partial pressure of CO_2 in air is approximately 4.0×10^{-4} atm. Using the data in Problem 9.6, what is the solubility of CO_2 in an open bottle of seltzer water at 20 °C?

9.7 Units of Concentration

Although we speak casually of a solution of, say, orange juice as either "dilute" or "concentrated," laboratory work usually requires an exact knowledge of a solution's concentration. As indicated in Table 9.5, there are several common methods for expressing concentration. The units differ, but all the methods describe how much solute is present in a given quantity of solution.

TABLE 9.5 Some Units for Expressing Concentration

CONCENTRATION MEASURE	SOLUTE MEASURE	SOLUTION MEASURE
Molarity, M	Moles	Volume (L)
Weight/volume percent, (w/v)%	Weight (g)	Volume (mL)
Volume/volume percent, (v/v)%	Volume*	Volume*
Parts per million, ppm	Parts*	10^6 parts*

Any units can be used as long as they are the same for both solute and solution.

Let us look at each of the four concentration measures listed in Table 9.5 individually, beginning with *molarity*.

Mole/Volume Concentration: Molarity

We saw in Chapter 6 that the various relationships between amounts of reactants and products in chemical reactions are calculated in *moles* (Sections 6.4–6.6). Thus, the most generally useful means of expressing concentration in the laboratory is **molarity (M)**, the number of moles of solute dissolved per liter of solution. For example, a solution made by dissolving 1.00 mol (58.5 g) of NaCl in enough water to give 1.00 L of solution has a concentration of 1.00 mol/L, or 1.00 M. The molarity of any solution is found by dividing the number of moles of solute by the number of liters of solution (solute + solvent):

$$\text{Molarity (M)} = \frac{\text{Moles of solute}}{\text{Liters of solution}}$$

Note that a solution of a given molarity is prepared by dissolving the solute in enough solvent to give a *final* solution volume of 1.00 L, not by dissolving it in an *initial* volume of 1.00 L. If an initial volume of 1.00 L were used, the final solution volume might be a bit larger than 1.00 L because of the additional volume of the solute. In practice, the appropriate amount of solute is weighed and placed in a *volumetric flask*, as shown in Figure 9.6. Enough solvent is then added to dissolve the solute, and further solvent is added until an accurately calibrated final volume is reached. The solution is then shaken until it is uniformly mixed.

(a)   (b)   (c)

◀ **FIGURE 9.6 Preparing a solution of known molarity.** (a) A measured number of moles of solute is placed in a volumetric flask. (b) Enough solvent is added to dissolve the solute by swirling. (c) Further solvent is carefully added until the calibration mark on the neck of the flask is reached, and the solution is shaken until uniform.

APPLICATION ▶ Breathing and Oxygen Transport

Like all other animals, humans need oxygen. When we breathe, the freshly inspired air travels through the bronchial passages and into the lungs. The oxygen then diffuses through the delicate walls of the approximately 150 million alveolar sacs of the lungs and into arterial blood, which transports it to all body tissues.

Only about 3% of the oxygen in blood is dissolved; the rest is chemically bound to *hemoglobin* molecules, large proteins with *heme* groups embedded in them. Each hemoglobin molecule contains four heme groups, and each heme group contains an iron atom that is able to bind one O_2 molecule. Thus, a single hemoglobin molecule can bind up to four molecules of oxygen. The entire system of oxygen transport and delivery in the body depends on the pickup and release of O_2 by hemoglobin (Hb) according to the following series of equilibria:

$$O_2(\text{lungs}) \rightleftharpoons O_2(\text{blood}) \quad (\text{Henry's law})$$

$$Hb + 4\,O_2(\text{blood}) \rightleftharpoons Hb(O_2)_4$$

$$Hb(O_2)_4 \rightleftharpoons Hb + 4\,O_2 \quad (\text{cell})$$

The delivery of oxygen depends on the concentration of O_2 in the various tissues, as measured by partial pressure (P_{O_2}, Table 9.4). The amount of oxygen carried by hemoglobin at any given value of P_{O_2} is usually expressed as a percent saturation and can be found from the curve shown in the accompanying figure. When $P_{O_2} = 100$ mmHg, the saturation in the lungs is 97.5%, meaning that each hemoglobin is carrying close to its maximum of four O_2 molecules. When $P_{O_2} = 26$ mmHg, however, the saturation drops to 50%.

So, how does the body ensure that enough oxygen is available to the various tissues? When large amounts of oxygen are needed—during a strenuous workout, for example—oxygen is released from hemoglobin to the hardworking, oxygen-starved muscle cells, where P_{O_2} is low. Increasing the

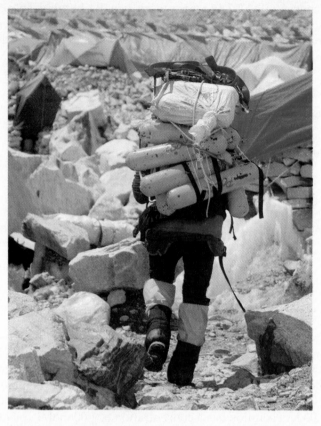

▲ At high altitudes, the partial pressure of oxygen in the air is too low to saturate hemoglobin sufficiently. Additional oxygen is therefore needed.

supply of oxygen to the blood (by breathing harder and faster) shifts all the equilibria toward the right, according to Le Châtelier's principle (Section 7.9), to supply the additional O_2 needed by the muscles.

What about people living at high altitudes? In Leadville, CO, for example, where the altitude is 10,156 ft, the P_{O_2} in the lungs is only about 68 mmHg. Hemoglobin is only 90% saturated with O_2 at this pressure, meaning that less oxygen is available for delivery to the tissues. The body responds by producing erythropoietin (EPO), a hormone (Chapter 20) that stimulates the bone marrow to produce more red blood cells and hemoglobin molecules. The increase in Hb provides more capacity for O_2 transport and drives the Hb + O_2 equilibria to the right.

World-class athletes use the mechanisms of increased oxygen transport associated with higher levels of hemoglobin to enhance their performance. High-altitude training centers have sprung up, with living and training regimens designed to increase blood EPO levels. Unfortunately, some athletes have also tried to "cheat" by using injections of EPO and synthetic analogs, and "blood doping" to boost performance. This has led the governing bodies of many sports federations, including the Olympic Committee, to start testing for such abuse.

See Additional Problem 9.92 at the end of the chapter.

▲ An oxygen-carrying curve for hemoglobin. The percent saturation of the oxygen binding sites on hemoglobin depends on the partial pressure of oxygen (P_{O_2}).

Molarity can be used as a conversion factor to relate the volume of a solution to the number of moles of solute it contains. If we know the molarity and volume of a solution, we can calculate the number of moles of solute. If we know the number of moles of solute and the molarity of the solution, we can find the solution's volume.

$$\text{Molarity} = \frac{\text{Moles of solute}}{\text{Volume of solution (L)}}$$

$$\text{Moles of solute} = \text{Molarity} \times \text{Volume of solution}$$

$$\text{Volume of solution} = \frac{\text{Moles of solute}}{\text{Molarity}}$$

The flow diagram in Figure 9.7 shows how molarity is used in calculating the quantities of reactants or products in a chemical reaction, and Worked Examples 9.5 and 9.6 show how the calculations are done. Note that Problem 9.10 employs *millimolar* (mM) concentrations, which are useful in healthcare fields for expressing low concentrations such as are often found in body fluids (1 mM = 0.001 M).

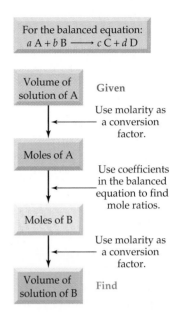

▶ **FIGURE 9.7 Molarity and conversions.** A flow diagram summarizing the use of molarity for conversions between solution volume and moles to find quantities of reactants and products for chemical reactions in solution.

WORKED EXAMPLE **9.4** Solution Concentration: Molarity

What is the molarity of a solution made by dissolving 2.355 g of sulfuric acid (H_2SO_4) in water and diluting to a final volume of 50.0 mL? The molar mass of H_2SO_4 is 98.1 g/mol.

ANALYSIS Molarity is defined as moles of solute per liter of solution: M = mol/L. Thus, we must first find the number of moles of sulfuric acid by doing a mass to mole conversion, and then divide the number of moles by the volume of the solution.

BALLPARK ESTIMATE The molar mass of sulfuric acid is about 100 g/mol, so 2.355 g is roughly 0.025 mol. The volume of the solution is 50.0 mL, or 0.05 L, so we have about 0.025 mol of acid in 0.05 L of solution, which is a concentration of about 0.5 M.

SOLUTION

STEP 1: Identify known information. We know the mass of sulfuric acid and the final volume of solution.

Mass of H_2SO_4 = 2.355 g

Volume of solution = 50.0 mL

STEP 2: Identify answer including units. We need to find the molarity (M) in units of moles per liter.

$$\text{Molarity} = \frac{\text{Moles } H_2SO_4}{\text{Liters of solution}}$$

STEP 3: Identify conversion factors and equations. We know both the amount of solute and the volume of solution, but first we must make two conversions: convert mass of H_2SO_4 to moles of H_2SO_4, using molar mass as a conversion factor, and convert volume from milliliters to liters:

$$(2.355 \text{ g } H_2SO_4)\left(\frac{1 \text{ mol } H_2SO_4}{98.1 \text{ g } H_2SO_4}\right) = 0.0240 \text{ mol } H_2SO_4$$

$$(50.0 \text{ mL})\left(\frac{1 \text{ L}}{1000 \text{ mL}}\right) = 0.0500 \text{ L}$$

STEP 4: Solve. Substitute the moles of solute and volume of solution into the molarity expression.

$$\text{Molarity} = \frac{0.0240 \text{ mol } H_2SO_4}{0.0500 \text{ L}} = 0.480 \text{ M}$$

BALLPARK CHECK: The calculated answer is close to our estimate, which was 0.5 M.

WORKED EXAMPLE **9.5** Molarity as Conversion Factor: Molarity to Mass

A blood concentration of 0.065 M ethyl alcohol (EtOH) is sufficient to induce a coma. At this concentration, what is the total mass of alcohol (in grams) in an adult male whose total blood volume is 5.6 L? The molar mass of ethyl alcohol is 46.0 g/mol. (Refer to the flow diagram in Figure 9.7 to identify which conversions are needed.)

ANALYSIS We are given a molarity (0.065 M) and a volume (5.6 L), which allows us to calculate the number of moles of alcohol in the blood. A mole to mass conversion then gives the mass of alcohol.

SOLUTION

$$(5.6 \text{ L blood})\left(\frac{0.065 \text{ mol EtOH}}{1 \text{ L blood}}\right) = 0.36 \text{ mol EtOH}$$

$$(0.36 \text{ mol EtOH})\left(\frac{46.0 \text{ g EtOH}}{1 \text{ mol EtOH}}\right) = 17 \text{ g EtOH}$$

WORKED EXAMPLE **9.6** Molarity as Conversion Factor: Molarity to Volume

In our stomachs, gastric juice that is about 0.1 M in HCl aids in digestion. How many milliliters of gastric juice will react completely with an antacid tablet that contains 500 mg of magnesium hydroxide? The molar mass of $Mg(OH)_2$ is 58.3 g/mol, and the balanced equation is

$$2\,HCl(aq) + Mg(OH)_2(aq) \longrightarrow MgCl_2(aq) + 2\,H_2O(l)$$

ANALYSIS We are given the molarity of HCl and need to find the volume. We first convert the mass of $Mg(OH)_2$ to moles and then use the coefficients in the balanced equation to find the moles of HCl that will react. Once we have the moles of HCl and the molarity in moles per liter, we can find the volume. These conversions are summarized in the following flow diagram.

SOLUTION

$$[500 \text{ mg Mg(OH)}_2]\left(\frac{1 \text{ g}}{1000 \text{ mg}}\right)\left[\frac{1 \text{ mol Mg(OH)}_2}{58.3 \text{ g Mg(OH)}_2}\right] = 0.008\,58 \text{ mol Mg(OH)}_2$$

$$[0.008\,58 \text{ mol Mg(OH)}_2]\left[\frac{2 \text{ mol HCl}}{1 \text{ mol Mg(OH)}_2}\right]\left(\frac{1 \text{ L HCl}}{0.1 \text{ mol HCl}}\right) = 0.2 \text{ L (200 mL)}$$

PROBLEM 9.8

What is the molarity of a solution that contains 50.0 g of vitamin B_1 hydrochloride (molar mass = 337 g/mol) in 160 mL of solution?

PROBLEM 9.9

How many moles of solute are present in the following solutions?

(a) 175 mL of 0.35 M $NaNO_3$ **(b)** 480 mL of 1.4 M HNO_3

PROBLEM 9.10

The concentration of cholesterol ($C_{27}H_{46}O$) in blood is approximately 5.0 mM. How many grams of cholesterol are in 250 mL of blood?

PROBLEM 9.11

What mass (in grams) of calcium carbonate is needed to react completely with 65 mL of 0.12 M HCl according to the following equation?

$$2\,HCl(aq) + CaCO_3(aq) \longrightarrow CaCl_2(aq) + H_2O(l) + CO_2(g)$$

Weight/Volume Percent Concentration, (w/v)%

One of the most common methods for expressing percent concentration is to give the number of grams (weight) as a percentage of the number of milliliters (volume) of the final solution—called the **weight/volume percent concentration, (w/v)%**. Mathematically, (w/v)% concentration is found by taking the number of grams of solute per milliliter of solution and multiplying by 100%:

$$(\text{w/v})\% \text{ concentration} = \frac{\text{Mass of solute (g)}}{\text{Volume of solution (mL)}} \times 100\%$$

For example, if 15 g of glucose is dissolved in enough water to give 100 mL of solution, the glucose concentration is 15 g/100 mL or 15% (w/v):

$$\frac{15 \text{ g glucose}}{100 \text{ mL solution}} \times 100\% = 15\% \text{ (w/v)}$$

To prepare 100 mL of a specific weight/volume solution, the weighed solute is dissolved in just enough solvent to give a final volume of 100 mL, not in an initial volume of 100 mL solvent. (If the solute is dissolved in 100 mL of *solvent*, the final volume of the *solution* will likely be a bit larger than 100 mL, since the volume of the solute is included.) In practice, solutions are prepared using a volumetric flask, as shown previously in Figure 9.5. Worked Example 9.7 illustrates how weight/volume percent concentration is found from a known mass and volume of solution.

WORKED EXAMPLE   **9.7** Solution Concentration: Weight/Volume Percent

A solution of heparin sodium, an anticoagulant for blood, contains 1.8 g of heparin sodium dissolved to make a final volume of 15 mL of solution. What is the weight/volume percent concentration of this solution?

ANALYSIS Weight/volume percent concentration is defined as the mass of the solute in grams divided by the volume of solution in milliliters and multiplied by 100%.

BALLPARK ESTIMATE The mass of solute (1.8 g) is smaller than the volume of solvent (15 mL) by a little less than a factor of 10. The weight/volume percent should thus be a little greater than 10%.

SOLUTION

$$(\text{w/v})\% \text{ concentration} = \frac{1.8 \text{ g heparin sodium}}{15 \text{ mL}} \times 100\% = 12\% \text{ (w/v)}$$

BALLPARK CHECK: The calculated (w/v)% is reasonably close to our original estimate of 10%.

WORKED EXAMPLE **9.8** Weight/Volume Percent as Conversion Factor: Volume to Mass

How many grams of NaCl are needed to prepare 250 mL of a 1.5% (w/v) saline solution?

ANALYSIS We are given a concentration and a volume, and we need to find the mass of solute by rearranging the equation for (w/v)% concentration.

BALLPARK ESTIMATE The desired (w/v)% value, 1.5%, is between 1 and 2%. For a volume of 250 mL, we would need 2.5 g of solute for a 1% (w/v) solution and 5.0 g of solute for a 2% solution. Thus, for our 1.5% solution, we need a mass midway between 2.5 and 5.0 g, or about 3.8 g.

SOLUTION

$$\text{Since} \quad (\text{w/v})\% = \frac{\text{Mass of solute in g}}{\text{Volume of solution in mL}} \times 100\%$$

$$\text{then} \quad \text{Mass of solute in g} = \frac{(\text{Volume of solution in mL})[(\text{w/v})]\%}{100\%}$$

$$= \frac{(250)(1.5\%)}{100\%} = 3.75 \text{ g} = 3.8 \text{ g NaCl}$$

$$(2 \text{ significant figures})$$

BALLPARK CHECK: The calculated answer matches our estimate.

WORKED EXAMPLE **9.9** Weight/Volume Percent as Conversion Factor: Mass to Volume

How many milliliters of a 0.75% (w/v) solution of the food preservative sodium benzoate are needed to obtain 45 mg?

ANALYSIS We are given a concentration and a mass, and we need to find the volume of solution by rearranging the equation for (w/v)% concentration. Remember that 45 mg = 0.045 g.

BALLPARK ESTIMATE A 0.75% (w/v) solution contains 0.75 g (750 mg) for every 100 mL of solution, so 10 mL contains 75 mg. To obtain 45 mg, we need a little more than half this volume, or a little more than 5 mL.

SOLUTION

$$\text{Since} \ (\text{w/v})\% = \frac{\text{Mass of solute in g}}{\text{Volume of solution in mL}} \times 100\%$$

$$\text{then} \quad \text{Volume of solution in mL} = \frac{(\text{Mass of solute in g})(100\%)}{(\text{w/v})\%}$$

$$= \frac{(0.045 \text{ g})(100\%)}{0.75\%} = 6.0 \text{ mL}$$

BALLPARK CHECK: The calculated answer is consistent with our estimate of a little more than 5 mL.

PROBLEM 9.12

In clinical lab reports, some concentrations are given in mg/dL. Convert a Ca^{2+} concentration of 8.6 mg/dL to weight/volume percent.

PROBLEM 9.13

What is the weight/volume percent concentration of a solution that contains 23 g of potassium iodide in 350 mL of aqueous solution?

PROBLEM 9.14

How many grams of solute are needed to prepare the following solutions?

(a) 125.0 mL of 16% (w/v) glucose ($C_6H_{12}O_6$)

(b) 65 mL of 1.8% (w/v) KCl

Volume/Volume Percent Concentration, (v/v)%

The concentration of a solution made by dissolving one liquid in another is often given by expressing the volume of solute as a percentage of the volume of final solution—the **volume/volume percent concentration, (v/v)%**. Mathematically, the volume of the solute (usually in milliliters) per milliliter of solution is multiplied by 100%:

$$(v/v)\% \text{ concentration} = \frac{\text{Volume of solute (mL)}}{\text{Volume of solution (mL)}} \times 100\%$$

For example, if 10.0 mL of ethyl alcohol is dissolved in enough water to give 100.0 mL of solution, the ethyl alcohol concentration is (10.0 mL/100.0 mL) × 100% = 10.0% (v/v).

WORKED EXAMPLE **9.10** Volume Percent: Volume of Solution to Volume of Solute

How many milliliters of methyl alcohol are needed to prepare 75 mL of a 5.0% (v/v) solution?

ANALYSIS We are given a solution volume (75 mL) and a concentration [5.0% (v/v), meaning 5.0 mL solute/100 mL solution]. The concentration acts as a conversion factor for finding the amount of methyl alcohol needed.

BALLPARK ESTIMATE A 5% (v/v) solution contains 5 mL of solute in 100 mL of solution, so the amount of solute in 75 mL of solution must be about three-fourths of 5 mL, which means between 3 and 4 mL.

SOLUTION

$$(75 \text{ mL solution})\left(\frac{5.0 \text{ mL methyl alcohol}}{100 \text{ mL solution}}\right) = 3.8 \text{ mL methyl alcohol}$$

BALLPARK CHECK: The calculated answer is consistent with our estimate of between 3 and 4 mL.

PROBLEM 9.15

How would you use a 500.0 mL volumetric flask to prepare a 7.5% (v/v) solution of acetic acid in water?

PROBLEM 9.16

What volume of solute (in milliliters) is needed to prepare the following solutions?

(a) 100 mL of 22% (v/v) ethyl alcohol   (b) 150 mL of 12% (v/v) acetic acid

Parts per Million (ppm)

The concentration units weight/volume percent, (w/v)%, and volume/volume percent, (v/v)%, can also be defined as *parts per hundred*(pph) since 1% means one item per 100 items. When concentrations are very small, as often occurs in dealing with trace amounts of pollutants or contaminants, it is more convenient to use **parts per million (ppm)** or **parts per billion (ppb)**. The "parts" can be in any unit of either mass or volume as long as the units of both solute and solvent are the same:

$$\text{ppm} = \frac{\text{Mass of solute (g)}}{\text{Mass of solution (g)}} \times 10^6 \quad \text{or} \quad \frac{\text{Volume of solute (mL)}}{\text{Volume of solution (mL)}} \times 10^6$$

$$\text{ppb} = \frac{\text{Mass of solute (g)}}{\text{Mass of solution (g)}} \times 10^9 \quad \text{or} \quad \frac{\text{Volume of solute (mL)}}{\text{Volume of solution (mL)}} \times 10^9$$

To take an example, the maximum allowable concentration in air of the organic solvent benzene (C_6H_6) is currently set by government regulation at 1 ppm. A concentration of 1 ppm means that if you take a million "parts" of air in any unit—say, mL—then 1 of those parts is benzene vapor and the other 999,999 parts are other gases:

$$1\ \text{ppm} = \frac{1\ \text{mL}}{1,000,000\ \text{mL}} \times 10^6$$

Because the density of water is approximately 1.0 g/mL at room temperature, 1.0 L (or 1000 mL) of an aqueous solution weighs 1000 g. Therefore, when dealing with very dilute concentrations of solutes dissolved in water, ppm is equivalent to mg solute/L solution, and ppb is equivalent to μg solute/L solution. To demonstrate that these units are equivalent, the conversion from ppm to mg/L is as follows:

$$1\ \text{ppm} = \left(\frac{1\ \text{g solute}}{10^6\ \text{g solution}}\right)\left(\frac{1\ \text{mg solute}}{10^{-3}\ \text{g solute}}\right)\left(\frac{10^3\ \text{g solution}}{1\ \text{L solution}}\right) = \frac{1\ \text{mg solute}}{1\ \text{L solution}}$$

WORKED EXAMPLE **9.11** ppm as Conversion Factor: Mass of Solution to Mass of Solute

The maximum allowable concentration of chloroform, $CHCl_3$, in drinking water is 100 ppb. What is the maximum amount (in grams) of chloroform allowed in a glass containing 400 g (400 mL) of water?

ANALYSIS We are given a solution amount (400 g) and a concentration (100 ppb). This concentration of 100 ppb means

$$100\ \text{ppb} = \frac{\text{Mass of solute (g)}}{\text{Mass of solution (g)}} \times 10^9$$

This equation can be rearranged to find the mass of solute.

BALLPARK ESTIMATE A concentration of 100 ppb means there are 100×10^{-9} g (1×10^{-7} g) of solute in 1 g of solution. In 400 g of solution, we should have 400 times this amount, or $400 \times 10^{-7} = 4 \times 10^{-5}$ g.

SOLUTION

$$\text{Mass of solute (g)} = \frac{\text{Mass of solution (g)}}{10^9} \times 100\ \text{ppb}$$

$$= \frac{400\ \text{g}}{10^9} \times 100\ \text{ppb} = 4 \times 10^{-5}\ \text{g (or 0.04 mg)}$$

BALLPARK CHECK: The calculated answer matches our estimate.

PROBLEM 9.17

What is the concentration in ppm of sodium fluoride in tap water that has been fluoridated by the addition of 32 mg of NaF for every 20 kg of solution?

PROBLEM 9.18

The maximum amounts of lead and copper allowed in drinking water are 0.015 mg/kg for lead and 1.3 mg/kg for copper. Express these values in parts per million, and tell the maximum amount of each (in grams) allowed in 100 g of water.

9.8 Dilution

Many solutions, from orange juice to chemical reagents, are stored in high concentrations and then prepared for use by *dilution*—that is, by adding additional solvent to lower the concentration. For example, you might make up 1/2 gal of orange juice by adding water to a canned concentrate. In the same way, you might buy a medicine or chemical reagent in concentrated solution and dilute it before use.

The key fact to remember about dilution is that the amount of *solute* remains constant; only the *volume* is changed by adding more solvent. If, for example, the initial and final concentrations are given in molarity, then we know that the number of moles of solute is the same both before and after dilution, and can be determined by multiplying molarity times volume:

$$\text{Number of moles} = \text{Molarity (mol/L)} \times \text{Volume (L)}$$

Because the number of moles remains constant, we can set up the following equation, where M_1 and V_1 refer to the solution before dilution, and M_2 and V_2 refer to the solution after dilution:

$$\text{Moles of solute} = M_1V_1 = M_2V_2$$

This equation can be rewritten to solve for M_2, the concentration of the solution after dilution:

$$M_2 = M_1 \times \frac{V_1}{V_2} \quad \text{where} \quad \frac{V_1}{V_2} \quad \text{is a } dilution\ factor$$

The equation shows that the concentration after dilution (M_2) can be found by multiplying the initial concentration (M_1) by a **dilution factor**, which is simply the ratio of the initial and final solution volumes (V_1/V_2). If, for example, the solution volume *increases* by a factor of 5, from 10 mL to 50 mL, then the concentration must *decrease* to 1/5 its initial value because the dilution factor is 10 mL/50 mL, or 1/5. Worked Example 9.12 shows how to use this relationship for calculating dilutions.

The relationship between concentration and volume can also be used to find what volume of initial solution to start with to achieve a given dilution:

$$\text{Since} \quad M_1V_1 = M_2V_2$$
$$\text{then} \quad V_1 = V_2 \times \frac{M_2}{M_1}$$

In this case, V_1 is the initial volume that must be diluted to prepare a less concentrated solution with volume V_2. The initial volume is found by multiplying the final volume (V_2) by the ratio of the final and initial concentrations (M_2/M_1). For example, to decrease the concentration of a solution to 1/5 its initial value, the initial volume must be 1/5 the desired final volume. Worked Example 9.13 gives a sample calculation.

▲ Orange juice concentrate is diluted with water before drinking.

Dilution factor The ratio of the initial and final solution volumes (V_1/V_2).

Although the preceding equations and following examples deal with concentration units of molarity, it is worth noting that the dilution equation can be generalized to the other concentration units presented in this section, or

$$C_1V_1 = C_2V_2$$

WORKED EXAMPLE 9.12 Dilution of Solutions: Concentration

What is the final concentration if 75 mL of a 3.5 M glucose solution is diluted to a volume of 450 mL?

ANALYSIS The number of moles of solute is constant, so

$$M_1V_1 = M_2V_2$$

Of the four variables in this equation, we know the initial concentration M_1 (3.5 M), the initial volume V_1 (75 mL), and the final volume V_2 (450 mL), and we need to find the final concentration M_2.

BALLPARK ESTIMATE The volume increases by a factor of 6, from 75 mL to 450 mL, so the concentration must decrease by a factor of 6, from 3.5 M to about 0.6 M.

SOLUTION

Solving the above equation for M_2 and substituting in the known values gives

$$M_2 = \frac{M_1V_1}{V_2} = \frac{(3.5 \text{ M glucose})(75 \text{ mL})}{450 \text{ mL}} = 0.58 \text{ M glucose}$$

BALLPARK CHECK: The calculated answer is close to our estimate of 0.6 M.

WORKED EXAMPLE 9.13 Dilution of Solutions: Volume

Aqueous NaOH can be purchased at a concentration of 1.0 M. How would you use this concentrated solution to prepare 750 mL of 0.32 M NaOH?

ANALYSIS The number of moles of solute is constant, so

$$M_1V_1 = M_2V_2$$

Of the four variables in this equation, we know the initial concentration M_1 (1.0 M), the final volume V_2 (750 mL), and the final concentration M_2 (0.32 M), and we need to find the initial volume V_1.

BALLPARK ESTIMATE We want the solution concentration to decrease by a factor of about 3, from 1.0 M to 0.32 M, which means we need to dilute the 1.0 M solution by a factor of 3. This means the final volume must be about 3 times greater than the initial volume. Because our final volume is to be 750 mL, we must start with an initial volume of about 250 mL.

SOLUTION

Solving the above equation for V_1 and substituting in the known values gives

$$V_1 = \frac{V_2M_2}{M_1} = \frac{(750 \text{ mL})(0.32 \text{ M})}{1.0 \text{ M}} = 240 \text{ mL}$$

To prepare the desired solution, dilute 240 mL of 1.0 M NaOH with water to make a final volume of 750 mL.

BALLPARK CHECK: The calculated answer (240 mL) is reasonably close to our estimate of 250 mL.

PROBLEM 9.19

Hydrochloric acid is normally purchased at a concentration of 12.0 M. What is the final concentration if 100.0 mL of 12.0 M HCl is diluted to 500.0 mL?

PROBLEM 9.20

Aqueous ammonia is commercially available at a concentration of 16.0 M. How much of the concentrated solution would you use to prepare 500.0 mL of a 1.25 M solution?

PROBLEM 9.21

The Environmental Protection Agency has set the limit for arsenic in drinking water at 0.010 ppm. To what volume would you need to dilute 1.5 L of water containing 5.0 ppm arsenic to reach the acceptable limit?

9.9 Ions in Solution: Electrolytes

Look at Figure 9.8, which shows a light bulb connected to a power source through a circuit that is interrupted by two metal strips dipped into a beaker of liquid. When the strips are dipped into pure water, the bulb remains dark, but when they are dipped into an aqueous NaCl solution, the circuit is closed and the bulb lights. As mentioned previously in Section 4.1, this simple demonstration shows that ionic compounds in aqueous solution can conduct electricity. (⊂⊃, p. 79)

(a)

(b)

▲ **FIGURE 9.8** **A simple demonstration shows that electricity can flow through a solution of ions.** (a) With pure water in the beaker, the circuit is incomplete, no electricity flows, and the bulb does not light. (b) With a concentrated NaCl solution in the beaker, the circuit is complete, electricity flows, and the light bulb glows.

Substances like NaCl that conduct an electric current when dissolved in water are called **electrolytes**. Conduction occurs because negatively charged Cl^- anions migrate through the solution toward the metal strip connected to the positive terminal of the power source, whereas positively charged Na^+ cations migrate toward the strip connected to the negative terminal. As you might expect, the ability of a solution to conduct electricity depends on the concentration of ions in solution. Distilled water contains virtually no ions and is nonconducting; ordinary tap water contains low concentrations of dissolved ions (mostly Na^+, K^+, Mg^{2+}, Ca^{2+}, and Cl^-) and is weakly conducting; and a concentrated solution of NaCl is strongly conducting.

Electrolyte A substance that produces ions and therefore conducts electricity when dissolved in water.

Strong electrolyte A substance that ionizes completely when dissolved in water.

Weak electrolyte A substance that is only partly ionized in water.

Nonelectrolyte A substance that does not produce ions when dissolved in water.

Ionic substances like NaCl that ionize completely when dissolved in water are called **strong electrolytes**, and molecular substances like acetic acid (CH_3CO_2H) that are only partially ionized are **weak electrolytes**. Molecular substances like glucose that do not produce ions when dissolved in water are **nonelectrolytes**.

Strong electrolyte; completely ionized

$$NaCl(s) \xrightarrow[\text{in water}]{\text{Dissolve}} Na^+(aq) + Cl^-(aq)$$

Weak electrolyte; partly ionized

$$CH_3CO_2H(l) \underset{\text{in water}}{\overset{\text{Dissolve}}{\rightleftharpoons}} CH_3CO_2^- (aq) + H^+ (aq)$$

Nonelectrolyte; not ionized

$$Glucose(s) \underset{\text{in water}}{\overset{\text{Dissolve}}{\rightleftharpoons}} Glucose(aq)$$

9.10 Electrolytes in Body Fluids: Equivalents and Milliequivalents

What happens if NaCl and KBr are dissolved in the same solution? Because the cations (K^+ and Na^+) and anions (Cl^- and Br^-) are all mixed together and no reactions occur between them, an identical solution could just as well be made from KCl and NaBr. Thus, we can no longer speak of having an NaCl + KBr solution; we can only speak of having a solution with four different ions in it.

A similar situation exists for blood and other body fluids, which contain many different anions and cations. Since they are all mixed together, it is difficult to "assign" specific cations to specific anions or to talk about specific ionic compounds. Instead, we are interested only in individual ions and in the total numbers of positive and negative charges. To discuss such mixtures, we use a new term—*equivalents* of ions.

Equivalent For ions, the amount equal to 1 mol of charge.

Gram-equivalent For ions, the molar mass of the ion divided by the ionic charge.

For ions, one **equivalent (Eq)** is equal to the number of ions that carry 1 mol of charge. Of more practical use is the unit **gram-equivalent**, which is the mass of the ion that contains one mole of charge. It can be calculated simply as the molar mass of the ion divided by the absolute value of its charge.

$$\text{One gram-equivalent of ion} = \frac{\text{Molar mass of ion (g)}}{\text{Charge on ion}}$$

If the ion has a charge of +1 or −1, 1 gram-equivalent of the ion is simply the molar mass of the ion in grams. Thus, 1 gram-equivalent of Na^+ is 23 g, and 1 gram-equivalent of Cl^- is 35.5 g. If the ion has a charge of +2 or −2, however, 1 gram-equivalent is equal to the ion's formula weight in grams divided by 2. Thus, 1 gram-equivalent of Mg^{2+} is (24.3 g)/2 = 12.2 g, and 1 gram-equivalent of CO_3^{2-} is [12.0 g + (3 × 16.0 g)]/2 = 30.0 g. The gram-equivalent is a useful conversion factor when converting from volume of solution to mass of ions, as seen in Worked Example 9.14.

The number of equivalents of a given ion per liter of solution can be found by multiplying the molarity of the ion (moles per liter) by the charge on the ion. Because ion concentrations in body fluids are often low, clinical chemists find it more convenient to talk about *milliequivalents* of ions rather than equivalents. One milliequivalent (mEq) of an ion is 1/1000 of an equivalent. For example, the normal concentration of Na^+ in blood is 0.14 Eq/L, or 140 mEq/L.

$$1 \text{ mEq} = 0.001 \text{ Eq} \qquad 1 \text{ Eq} = 1000 \text{ mEq}$$

Note that the gram-equivalent for an ion can now be expressed as grams per equivalent or as mg per mEq.

Average concentrations of the major electrolytes in blood plasma are given in Table 9.6. As you might expect, the total milliequivalents of positively and negatively charged electrolytes must be equal to maintain electrical neutrality. Adding

TABLE 9.6   Concentrations of Major Electrolytes in Blood Plasma

CATION	CONCENTRATION (mEq/L)
Na^+	136–145
Ca^{2+}	4.5–6.0
K^+	3.6–5.0
Mg^{2+}	3

ANION	CONCENTRATION (mEq/L)
Cl^-	98–106
HCO_3^-	25–29
SO_4^{2-} and HPO_4^{2-}	2

the milliequivalents of positive and negative ions in Table 9.6, however, shows a higher concentration of positive ions than negative ions. The difference, called the *anion gap*, is made up by the presence of negatively charged proteins and the anions of organic acids.

WORKED EXAMPLE   **9.14** Equivalents as Conversion Factors: Volume to Mass

The normal concentration of Ca^{2+} in blood is 5.0 mEq/L. How many milligrams of Ca^{2+} are in 1.00 L of blood?

ANALYSIS We are given a volume and a concentration in milliequivalents per liter, and we need to find an amount in milligrams. Thus, we need to calculate the gram-equivalent for Ca^{2+} and then use concentration as a conversion factor between volume and mass, as indicated in the following flow diagram:

BALLPARK ESTIMATE The molar mass of calcium is 40.08 g/mol, and the calcium ion carries a charge of 2+. Thus, 1 g-Eq of Ca^{2+} equals about 20 g/Eq or 20 mg/mEq. This means that the 5.0 mEq of Ca^{2+} ions in 1.00 L of blood corresponds to a mass of 5.0 mEq Ca^{2+} × 20 mg/mEq = 100 mg Ca^{2+}.

SOLUTION

$$(1.00 \text{ L blood})\left(\frac{5.0 \text{ mEq } Ca^{2+}}{1.0 \text{ L blood}}\right)\left(\frac{20.04 \text{ mg } Ca^{2+}}{1 \text{ mEq } Ca^{2+}}\right) = 100 \text{ mg } Ca^{2+}$$

BALLPARK CHECK: The calculated answer (100 mg of Ca^{2+} in 1.00 L of blood) matches our estimate.

PROBLEM 9.22

How many grams are in 1 Eq of the following ions? How many grams in 1 mEq?

(a) K^+ **(b)** Br^- **(c)** Mg^{2+} **(d)** SO_4^{2-} **(e)** Al^{3+} **(f)** PO_4^{3-}

9.11 Properties of Solutions

The properties of solutions are similar in many respects to those of pure solvents, but there are also some interesting and important differences. One such difference is that solutions have higher boiling points than the pure solvents; another is that solutions have lower freezing points. Pure water boils at 100.0 °C and freezes at 0.0 °C, for example, but a 1.0 M solution of NaCl in water boils at 101.0 °C and freezes at −3.7 °C.

Colligative property A property of a solution that depends only on the number of dissolved particles, not on their chemical identity.

The elevation of boiling point and the lowering of freezing point for a solution as compared with a pure solvent are examples of **colligative properties**—properties that depend on the *concentration* of a dissolved solute but not on its chemical identity. Other colligative properties are a lower vapor pressure for a solution compared with the pure solvent and *osmosis*, the migration of solvent molecules through a semipermeable membrane.

Colligative properties
- Vapor pressure is lower for a solution than for a pure solvent.
- Boiling point is higher for a solution than for a pure solvent.
- Freezing point is lower for a solution than for a pure solvent.
- Osmosis occurs when a solution is separated from a pure solvent by a semipermeable membrane.

Vapor Pressure Lowering in Solutions

We said in Section 8.12 that the vapor pressure of a liquid depends on the equilibrium between molecules entering and leaving the liquid surface. (, p. 241) Only those molecules at the surface of the liquid that are sufficiently energetic will evaporate. If, however, some of the liquid (solvent) molecules at the surface are replaced by other (solute) particles that do not evaporate, then the rate of evaporation of solvent molecules decreases and the vapor pressure of a solution is lower than that of the pure solvent (Figure 9.9). Note that the *identity* of the solute particles is irrelevant; only their concentration matters.

(a)   (b)

▲ **FIGURE 9.9 Vapor pressure lowering of solution.** (a) The vapor pressure of a solution is lower than (b) the vapor pressure of the pure solvent because fewer solvent molecules are able to escape from the surface of the solution.

APPLICATION ▶ Electrolytes, Fluid Replacement, and Sports Drinks

Athletes sweat. And the hotter the day, the more intense and longer lasting the activity, the more they sweat. Sweat loss during strenuous exercise on a hot day can amount to as much as 2 L/h, and the total sweat loss during a 24 h endurance run can exceed 16 L, or approximately 35 lb.

The composition of sweat is highly variable, not only with the individual but also with the time during the exercise and the athlete's overall conditioning. Typically, however, the Na^+ ion concentration in sweat is about 30–40 mEq/L, and that of K^+ ion is about 5–10 mEq/L. In addition, there are small amounts of other metal ions, such as Mg^{2+}, and there are sufficient Cl^- ions (35–50 mEq/L) to balance the positive charge of all these cations.

Obviously, all the water and dissolved electrolytes lost by an athlete through sweating must be replaced. Otherwise, dehydration, hyperthermia and heat stroke, dizziness, nausea, muscle cramps, impaired kidney function, and other difficulties ensue. As a rule of thumb, a sweat loss equal to 5% of body weight—about 3.5 L for a 150 lb person—is the maximum amount that can be safely allowed for a well-conditioned athlete.

Plain water works perfectly well to replace sweat lost during short bouts of activity up to a few hours in length, but

▲ Endurance athletes avoid serious medical problems by drinking sports drinks to replace water and electrolytes.

a carbohydrate–electrolyte beverage, or "sports drink," is much superior for rehydrating during and after longer activity in which substantial amounts of electrolytes have been lost. Some of the better known sports drinks are little more than overpriced sugar–water solutions, but others are carefully formulated and highly effective for fluid replacement. Nutritional research has shown that a serious sports drink should meet the following criteria. There are several dry-powder mixes on the market to choose from.

- The drink should contain 6–8% of soluble complex carbohydrates (about 15 g per 8 oz serving) and only a small amount of simple sugar for taste. The complex carbohydrates, which usually go by the name "maltodextrin," provide a slow release of glucose into the bloodstream. Not only does the glucose provide a steady source of energy, it also enhances the absorption of water from the stomach.

- The drink should contain electrolytes to replenish those lost in sweat. Concentrations of approximately 20 mEq/L for Na^+ ions, 10 mEq/L for K^+ ion, and 4 mEq/L for Mg^{2+} ions are recommended. These amounts correspond to about 100 mg sodium, 100 mg potassium, and 25 mg magnesium per 8 oz serving.

- The drink should be noncarbonated because carbonation can cause gastrointestinal upset during exercise, and it should not contain caffeine, which acts as a diuretic.

- The drink should taste good so the athlete will want to drink it. Thirst is a poor indicator of fluid requirements, and most people will drink less than needed unless a beverage is flavored.

In addition to complex carbohydrates, electrolytes, and flavorings, some sports drinks also contain vitamin A (as beta-carotene), vitamin C (ascorbic acid), and selenium, which act as antioxidants to protect cells from damage. Some drinks also contain the amino acid glutamine, which appears to lessen lactic acid buildup in muscles and thus helps muscles bounce back more quickly after an intense workout.

See Additional Problems 9.93 and 9.94 at the end of the chapter.

Boiling Point Elevation of Solutions

One consequence of the vapor pressure lowering for a solution is that the boiling point of the solution is higher than that of the pure solvent. Recall from Section 8.12 that boiling occurs when the vapor pressure of a liquid reaches atmospheric pressure. (◯◯◯, p. 241) But because the vapor pressure of a solution is lower than that of the pure solvent at a given temperature, the solution must be heated to a higher temperature for its vapor pressure to reach atmospheric pressure. Figure 9.10 shows a close-up plot of vapor pressure versus temperature for pure water and for

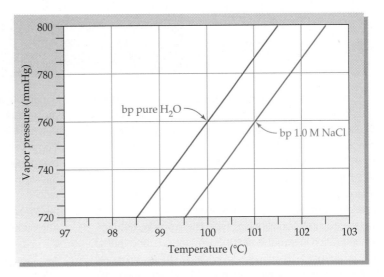

▲ **FIGURE 9.10 Vapor pressure and temperature.** A close-up plot of vapor pressure versus temperature for pure water (red curve) and for a 1.0 M NaCl solution (green curve). Pure water boils at 100.0 °C, but the solution does not boil until 101.0 °C.

a 1.0 M NaCl solution. The vapor pressure of pure water reaches atmospheric pressure (760 mmHg) at 100.0 °C, but the vapor pressure of the NaCl solution does not reach the same point until 101.0 °C.

For each mole of solute particles added, regardless of chemical identity, the boiling point of 1 kg of water is raised by 0.51 °C, or

$$\Delta T_{\text{boiling}} = \left(0.51\ ^\circ\text{C} \frac{\text{kg water}}{\text{mol particles}} \right) \left(\frac{\text{mol particles}}{\text{kg water}} \right)$$

The addition of 1 mol of a molecular substance like glucose to 1 kg of water therefore raises the boiling point from 100.0 °C to 100.51 °C. The addition of 1 mol of NaCl per kilogram of water, however, raises the boiling point by $2 \times 0.51\ ^\circ\text{C} = 1.02\ ^\circ\text{C}$ because the solution contains 2 mol of solute particles—Na^+ and Cl^- ions.

WORKED EXAMPLE **9.15** Properties of Solutions: Boiling Point Elevation

What is the boiling point of a solution of 0.75 mol of KBr in 1.0 kg of water?

ANALYSIS The boiling point increases 0.51 °C for each mole of solute per kilogram of water. Since KBr is a strong electrolyte, there are 2 mol of ions (K^+ and Br^-) for every 1 mol of KBr that dissolves.

BALLPARK ESTIMATE The boiling point will increase about 0.5 °C for every 1 mol of ions in 1 kg of water. Since 0.75 mol of KBr produce 1.5 mol of ions, the boiling point should increase by (1.5 mol ions) × 0.5 °C/mol ions) = 0.75 °C

SOLUTION

$$\Delta T_{\text{boiling}} = \left(0.51\ ^\circ\text{C} \frac{\text{kg water}}{\text{mol ions}} \right) \left(\frac{2\ \text{mol ions}}{1\ \text{mol KBr}} \right) \left(\frac{0.75\ \text{mol KBr}}{1.0\ \text{kg water}} \right) = 0.77\ ^\circ\text{C}$$

The normal boiling point of pure water is 100 °C, so the boiling point of the solution increases to 100.77 °C.

BALLPARK CHECK: The 0.77 °C increase is consistent with our estimate of 0.75 °C.

PROBLEM 9.24

What is the boiling point of a solution of 0.67 mol of $MgCl_2$ in 0.50 kg of water?

PROBLEM 9.25

When 1.0 mol of HF is dissolved in 1.0 kg of water, the boiling point of the resulting solution is 100.5 °C. Is HF a strong or weak electrolyte? Explain.

KEY CONCEPT PROBLEM 9.26

The following diagram shows plots of vapor pressure versus temperature for a solvent and a solution.

(a) Which curve represents the pure solvent, and which the solution?

(b) What are the approximate boiling points of the pure solvent and the solution?

(c) What is the approximate concentration of the solution in mol/kg, if 1 mol of solute particles raises the boiling point of 1 kg of solvent by 3.63 °C?

Freezing Point Depression of Solutions

Just as solutions have lower vapor pressure and consequently higher boiling points than pure solvents, they also have lower freezing points. Motorists in cold climates take advantage of this effect when they add "antifreeze" to the water in automobile cooling systems. Antifreeze is a nonvolatile solute, usually ethylene glycol ($HOCH_2CH_2OH$), that is added in sufficient concentration to lower the freezing point below the lowest expected outdoor temperature. In the same way, salt sprinkled on icy roads lowers the freezing point of ice below the road temperature and thus causes ice to melt.

Freezing point depression has much the same cause as vapor pressure lowering. Solute molecules are dispersed between solvent molecules throughout the solution, thereby making it more difficult for solvent molecules to come together and organize into ordered crystals.

For each mole of nonvolatile solute particles, the freezing point of 1 kg of water is lowered by 1.86 °C, or

$$\Delta T_{freezing} = \left(-1.86 \ °C\frac{kg \ water}{mol \ particles}\right)\left(\frac{mol \ particles}{kg \ water}\right)$$

Thus, addition of 1 mol of antifreeze to 1 kg of water lowers the freezing point from 0.00 °C to −1.86 °C, and addition of 1 mol of NaCl (2 mol of particles) to 1 kg of water lowers the freezing point from 0.00 °C to −3.72 °C.

▲ A mixture of salt and ice is used to provide the low temperatures needed to make old-fashioned hand-cranked ice cream.

WORKED EXAMPLE **9.16** Properties of Solutions: Freezing Point Depression

The cells of a tomato contain mostly an aqueous solution of sugar and other substances. If a typical tomato freezes at −2.5 °C, what is the concentration of dissolved particles in the tomato cells (in moles of particles per kg of water)?

ANALYSIS The freezing point decreases by 1.86 °C for each mole of solute dissolved in 1 kg of water. We can use the decrease in freezing point (2.5 °C) to find the amount of solute per kg of water.

BALLPARK ESTIMATE The freezing point will decrease by about 1.9 °C for every 1 mol of solute particles in 1 kg of water. To lower the freezing point by 2.5 °C therefore requires about 1.5 mol of particles per kg of water.

SOLUTION

$$\Delta T_{\text{freezing}} = -2.5 \ °C$$

$$= \left(-1.86 \ °C \ \frac{\text{kg water}}{\text{mol solute particles}}\right)\left(\frac{?? \ \text{mol solute particles}}{1.0 \ \text{kg water}}\right)$$

We can rearrange this expression to

$$(-2.5 \ °C)\left(\frac{1}{-1.86 \ °C} \ \frac{\text{mol solute particles}}{\text{kg water}}\right) = 1.3 \ \frac{\text{mol solute particles}}{\text{kg water}}$$

BALLPARK CHECK: The calculated answer is relatively close to our estimate (1.5 mol/kg).

PROBLEM 9.27

What is the freezing point of a solution of 1.0 mol of glucose in 1.0 kg of water?

PROBLEM 9.28

When 0.5 mol of a certain ionic substance is dissolved in 1.0 kg of water, the freezing point of the resulting solution is −2.8 °C. How many ions does the substance give when it dissolves?

9.12 Osmosis and Osmotic Pressure

Certain materials, including those that make up the membranes around living cells, are *semipermeable*. They allow water and other small molecules to pass through, but they block the passage of large solute molecules or ions. When a solution and a pure solvent, or two solutions of different concentration, are separated by a semipermeable membrane, solvent molecules pass through the membrane in a process called **osmosis**. Although the passage of solvent through the membrane takes place in both directions, passage from the pure solvent side to the solution side is favored and occurs more often. As a result, the amount of liquid on the pure solvent side decreases, the amount of liquid on the solution side increases, and the concentration of the solution decreases.

For the simplest explanation of osmosis, let us look at what happens on the molecular level. As shown in Figure 9.11, a solution inside a bulb is separated by a semipermeable membrane from pure solvent in the outer container. Solvent molecules in the outer container, because of their somewhat higher concentration, approach the membrane more frequently than do molecules in the bulb, thereby passing through more often and causing the liquid level in the attached tube to rise.

Osmosis The passage of solvent through a semipermeable membrane separating two solutions of different concentration.

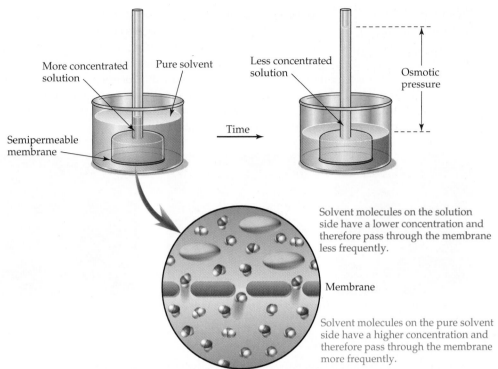

More concentrated solution

Pure solvent

Less concentrated solution

Osmotic pressure

Semipermeable membrane

Time

Solvent molecules on the solution side have a lower concentration and therefore pass through the membrane less frequently.

Membrane

Solvent molecules on the pure solvent side have a higher concentration and therefore pass through the membrane more frequently.

◀ **FIGURE 9.11 The phenomenon of osmosis.** A solution inside the bulb is separated from pure solvent in the outer container by a semipermeable membrane. Solvent molecules in the container have a slightly higher concentration than molecules in the bulb and therefore pass through the membrane more frequently. The liquid in the tube therefore rises until an equilibrium is reached. At equilibrium, the osmotic pressure exerted by the column of liquid in the tube is sufficient to prevent further net passage of solvent.

As the liquid in the tube rises, its increased weight creates an increased pressure that pushes solvent back through the membrane until the rates of forward and reverse passage become equal and the liquid level stops rising. The amount of pressure necessary to achieve this equilibrium is called the **osmotic pressure** (π) of the solution and can be determined from the expression

$$\pi = \left(\frac{n}{V}\right)RT$$

where n is the number of moles of particles in the solution, V is the solution volume, R is the gas constant (⬤, p. 231), and T is the absolute temperature of the solution. Note the similarity between this equation for the osmotic pressure of a solution and the equation for the pressure of an ideal gas, $P = (n/V)RT$. In both cases, the pressure has units of atmospheres.

Osmotic pressures can be extremely high, even for relatively dilute solutions. The osmotic pressure of a 0.15 M NaCl solution at 25 °C, for example, is 7.3 atm, a value that supports a difference in water level of approximately 250 ft!

As with other colligative properties, the amount of osmotic pressure depends only on the concentration of solute particles, not on their identity. Thus, it is convenient to use a new unit, *osmolarity* (osmol), to describe the concentration of particles in solution. The **osmolarity** of a solution is equal to the number of moles of dissolved particles (ions or molecules) per liter of solution. A 0.2 M glucose solution, for instance, has an osmolarity of 0.2 osmol, but a 0.2 M solution of NaCl has an osmolarity of 0.4 osmol because it contains 0.2 mol of Na^+ ions and 0.2 mol of Cl^- ions.

Osmosis is particularly important in living organisms because the membranes around cells are semipermeable. The fluids both inside and outside cells must therefore have the same osmolarity to prevent buildup of osmotic pressure and consequent rupture of the cell membrane.

In blood, the plasma surrounding red blood cells has an osmolarity of approximately 0.30 osmol and is said to be **isotonic** with (that is, has the same osmolarity as) the cell contents. If the cells are removed from plasma and placed in 0.15 M NaCl (called *physiological saline solution*), they are unharmed because the osmolarity of the saline solution (0.30 osmol) is the same as that of plasma. If, however, red blood cells are placed in pure water or in any solution with an osmolarity much

Osmotic pressure The amount of external pressure applied to the more concentrated solution to halt the passage of solvent molecules across a semipermeable membrane.

Osmolarity (osmol) The sum of the molarities of all dissolved particles in a solution.

Isotonic Having the same osmolarity.

Hypotonic Having an osmolarity *less than* the surrounding blood plasma or cells.

Hypertonic Having an osmolarity *greater than* the surrounding blood plasma or cells.

lower than 0.30 osmol (a **hypotonic** solution), water passes through the membrane into the cell, causing the cell to swell up and burst, a process called *hemolysis*.

Finally, if red blood cells are placed in a solution having an osmolarity greater than the cell contents (a **hypertonic** solution), water passes out of the cells into the surrounding solution, causing the cells to shrivel, a process called *crenation*. Figure 9.12 shows red blood cells under all three conditions: isotonic, hypotonic, and hypertonic. Therefore, it is critical that any solution used intravenously be isotonic to prevent red blood cells from being destroyed.

(a)　　　　　　　　　　(b)　　　　　　　　　　(c)

▶ **FIGURE 9.12　Red blood cells.** In (a) an isotonic solution the blood cells are normal in appearance, but the cells in (b) a hypotonic solution are swollen because of water gain, and those in (c) a hypertonic solution are shriveled because of water loss.

WORKED EXAMPLE　**9.17**　Properties of Solutions: Osmolarity

The solution of glucose commonly used intravenously has a concentration of 5.0% (w/v) glucose. What is the osmolarity of this solution? The molecular weight of glucose is 180 amu.

ANALYSIS Since glucose is a molecular substance that does not give ions in solution, the osmolarity of the solution is the same as the molarity. Recall from Section 9.7 that a solution of 5.0% (w/v) glucose has a concentration of 5.0 g glucose per 100 mL of solution, which is equivalent to 50 g per liter of solution. Thus, finding the molar concentration of glucose requires a mass to mole conversion.

BALLPARK ESTIMATE One liter of solution contains 50 g of glucose (MW= 180 g/mol). Thus, 50 g of glucose is equal to a little more than 0.25 mol, so a solution concentration of 50 g/L is equal to about 0.25 osmol, or 0.25 M.

SOLUTION

STEP 1: Identify known information. We know the (w/v)% concentration of the glucose solution.

$$5.0\% \ (w/v) = \frac{5.0 \text{ g glucose}}{100 \text{ mL solution}} \times 100\%$$

STEP 2: Identify answer and units. We are looking for osmolarity, which in this case is equal to the molarity of the solution because glucose is a molecular substance and does not dissociate into ions.

$$\text{Osmolarity} = \text{Molarity} = ?? \text{ mol/liter}$$

STEP 3: Identify conversion factors. The (w/v)% concentration is defined as grams of solute per 100 mL of solution, and molarity is defined as moles of solute per liter of solution. We will need to convert from milliliters to liters and then use molar mass to convert grams of glucose to moles of glucose.

$$\frac{\text{g glucose}}{100 \text{ mL}} \times \frac{1000 \text{ mL}}{L} = \frac{\text{g glucose}}{L}$$

$$\frac{\text{g glucose}}{L} \times \frac{1 \text{ mol glucose}}{180 \text{ g glucose}} = \frac{\text{moles glucose}}{L}$$

STEP 4: Solve. Starting with the (w/v)% glucose concentration, we first find the number of grams of glucose in 1 L of solution and then convert to moles of glucose per liter.

$$\left(\frac{5.0 \text{ g glucose}}{100 \text{ mL solution}}\right)\left(\frac{1000 \text{ mL}}{1 \text{ L}}\right) = 50 \frac{\text{g glucose}}{\text{L solution}}$$

$$\left(\frac{50 \text{ g glucose}}{1 \text{ L}}\right)\left(\frac{1 \text{ mol}}{180 \text{ g}}\right) = 0.28 \text{ M glucose} = 0.28 \text{ osmol}$$

BALLPARK CHECK: The calculated osmolarity is reasonably close to our estimate of 0.25 osmol

WORKED EXAMPLE **9.18** Properties of Solutions: Osmolarity

What mass of NaCl is needed to make 1.50 L of a 0.300 osmol solution? The molar mass of NaCl is 58.44 g/mol.

ANALYSIS Since NaCl is an ionic substance that produces 2 mol of ions (Na^+, Cl^-) when it dissociates, the osmolarity of the solution is twice the molarity. From the volume and the osmolarity we can determine the moles of NaCl needed and then perform a mole to mass converstion.

SOLUTION

STEP 1: Identify known information. We know the volume and the osmolarity of the final NaCl solution.

$$V = 1.50 \text{ L}$$
$$0.300 \text{ osmol} = \left(\frac{0.300 \text{ mol ions}}{L} \right)$$

STEP 2: Identify answer and units. We are looking for the mass of NaCl.

$$\text{Mass of NaCl} = \text{?? g}$$

STEP 3: Identify conversion factors. Starting with osmolarity in the form (moles NaCl/L), we can use volume to determine the number of moles of solute. We can then use molar mass for the mole to mass conversion.

$$\left(\frac{\text{moles NaCl}}{\cancel{L}} \right) \times (\cancel{L}) = \text{moles NaCl}$$

$$(\cancel{\text{moles NaCl}}) \times \left(\frac{\text{g NaCl}}{\cancel{\text{mole NaCl}}} \right) = \text{g NaCl}$$

STEP 4: Solve. Use the appropriate conversions, remembering that NaCl produces two ions per formula unit, to find the mass of NaCl.

$$\left(\frac{0.300 \cancel{\text{ mol ions}}}{\cancel{L}} \right)\left(\frac{1 \text{ mol NaCl}}{2 \cancel{\text{ mol ions}}} \right)(1.50 \cancel{L}) = 0.225 \text{ mol NaCl}$$

$$(0.225 \cancel{\text{ mol NaCl}})\left(\frac{58.44 \text{ g NaCl}}{\cancel{\text{mol NaCl}}} \right) = 13.1 \text{ g NaCl}$$

PROBLEM 9.29

What is the osmolarity of the following solutions?

(a) 0.35 M KBr   **(b)** 0.15 M glucose + 0.05 M K_2SO_4

PROBLEM 9.30

What is the osmolarity of a typical oral rehydration solution (ORS) for infants that contains 90 mEq/L Na^+, 20 mEq/L K^+, 110 mEq/L Cl^-, and 2.0% glucose? The molecular weight of glucose is 180 amu.

9.13 Dialysis

Dialysis is similar to osmosis, except that the pores in a dialysis membrane are larger than those in an osmotic membrane so that both solvent molecules and small solute particles can pass through, but large colloidal particles such as proteins cannot pass. (The exact dividing line between a "small" molecule and a "large" one is imprecise, and dialysis membranes with a variety of pore sizes are available.) Dialysis membranes include animal bladders, parchment, and cellophane.

Perhaps the most important medical use of dialysis is in artificial kidney machines, where *hemodialysis* is used to cleanse the blood of patients whose kidneys malfunction (Figure 9.13). Blood is diverted from the body and pumped through a long cellophane dialysis tube suspended in an isotonic solution formulated to contain many of the same components as blood plasma. These substances—glucose, NaCl, $NaHCO_3$, and KCl—have the same concentrations in the dialysis solution as they do in blood so that they have no net passage through the membrane.

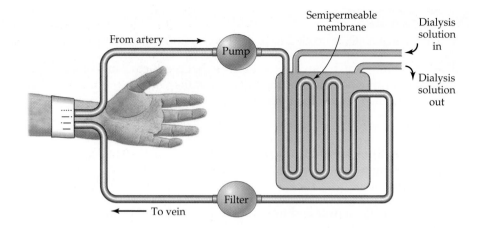

▶ **FIGURE 9.13 Operation of a hemodialysis unit used for purifying blood.** Blood is pumped from an artery through a coiled semipermeable membrane of cellophane. Small waste products pass through the membrane and are washed away by an isotonic dialysis solution.

APPLICATION ▶ Timed-Release Medications

There is much more in most medications than medicine. Even something as simple as a generic aspirin tablet contains a binder to keep it from crumbling, a filler to bring it to the right size and help it disintegrate in the stomach, and a lubricant to keep it from sticking to the manufacturing equipment. Timed-release medications are more complex still.

The widespread use of timed-release medication dates from the introduction of Contac decongestant in 1961. The original idea was simple: Tiny beads of medicine were encapsulated by coating them with varying thicknesses of a slow-dissolving polymer. Those beads with a thinner coat dissolve and release their medicine more rapidly; those with a thicker coat dissolve more slowly. Combining the right number of beads with the right thicknesses into a single capsule makes possible the gradual release of medication over a predictable time.

The technology of timed-release medications has become much more sophisticated in recent years, and the kinds of medications that can be delivered have become more numerous. Some medicines, for instance, either damage the stomach lining or are destroyed by the highly acidic environment in the stomach but can be delivered safely if given an *enteric coating*. The enteric coating is a polymeric material formulated so that it is stable in acid but reacts and is destroyed when it passes into the more basic environment of the intestines.

More recently, dermal patches have been developed to deliver drugs directly by diffusion through the skin. Patches are available to treat conditions from angina to motion sickness, as well as nicotine patches to help reduce cigarette cravings. One clever new device for timed release of medication through the skin uses the osmotic effect to force a drug from its reservoir. Useful only for drugs that do not dissolve in water, the device is divided into two compartments, one containing medication covered by a perforated membrane and the other containing a hygroscopic material (Section 9.3) covered by a semipermeable membrane. As moisture from the air diffuses through the membrane into the compartment with the hygroscopic material, the buildup of osmotic pressure squeezes the medication out of the other compartment through tiny holes.

▲ The small beads of medicine are coated with different thicknesses of a slow-dissolving polymer so that they dissolve and release medicine at different times.

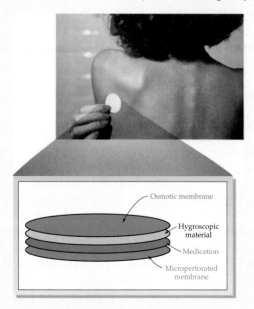

See Additional Problem 9.95 at the end of the chapter.

Small waste materials such as urea pass through the dialysis membrane from the blood to the solution side where they are washed away, but cells, proteins, and other important blood components are prevented by their size from passing through the membrane. In addition, the dialysis fluid concentration can be controlled so that imbalances in electrolytes are corrected. The wash solution is changed every 2 h, and a typical hemodialysis procedure lasts for 4–7 h.

As noted above, colloidal particles are too large to pass through a semipermeable membrane. Protein molecules, in particular, do not cross semipermeable membranes and thus play an essential role in determining the osmolarity of body fluids. The distribution of water and solutes across the capillary walls that separate blood plasma from the fluid surrounding cells is controlled by the balance between blood pressure and osmotic pressure. The pressure of blood inside the capillary tends to push water out of the plasma (filtration), but the osmotic pressure of colloidal protein molecules tends to draw water into the plasma (reabsorption). The balance between the two processes varies with location in the body. At the arterial end of a capillary, where blood pumped from the heart has a higher pressure, filtration is favored. At the venous end, where blood pressure is lower, reabsorption is favored, causing waste products from metabolism to enter the bloodstream.

Capillary

Red blood cells, proteins

Fluid (water)

O_2, nutrients, raw materials

CO_2, wastes

Arterial end

Venous end

◄ The delivery of oxygen and nutrients to the cells and the removal of waste products are regulated by osmosis.

SUMMARY: REVISITING THE CHAPTER GOALS

1. What are solutions, and what factors affect solubility? Mixtures are classified as either *heterogeneous*, if the mixing is nonuniform, or *homogeneous*, if the mixing is uniform. *Solutions* are homogeneous mixtures that contain particles the size of ions and molecules (<2.0 nm diameter), whereas larger particles (2.0–500 nm diameter) are present in *colloids*.

KEY WORDS

Colligative property, *p. 278*
Colloid, *p. 256*
Dilution factor, *p. 273*

The maximum amount of one substance (the *solute*) that can be dissolved in another (the *solvent*) is called the substance's *solubility*. Substances tend to be mutually soluble when their intermolecular forces are similar. The solubility in water of a solid often increases with temperature, but the solubility of a gas decreases with temperature. Pressure significantly affects gas solubilities, which are directly proportional to their partial pressure over the solution (*Henry's law*).

2. **How is the concentration of a solution expressed?** The concentration of a solution can be expressed in several ways, including molarity, weight/weight percent composition, weight/volume percent composition, and parts per million. *Molarity*, which expresses concentration as the number of moles of solute per liter of solution, is the most useful method when calculating quantities of reactants or products for reactions in aqueous solution.

3. **How are dilutions carried out?** A dilution is carried out by adding more solvent to an existing solution. Only the amount of solvent changes; the amount of solute remains the same. Thus, the molarity times the volume of the dilute solution is equal to the molarity times the volume of the concentrated solution: $M_1V_1 = M_2V_2$.

4. **What is an electrolyte?** Substances that form ions when dissolved in water and whose water solutions therefore conduct an electric current are called *electrolytes*. Substances that ionize completely in water are *strong electrolytes*, those that ionize partially are *weak electrolytes*, and those that do not ionize are *nonelectrolytes*. Body fluids contain small amounts of many different electrolytes, whose concentrations are expressed as moles of ionic charge, or equivalents, per liter.

5. **How do solutions differ from pure solvents in their behavior?** In comparing a solution to a pure solvent, the solution has a lower vapor pressure at a given temperature, a higher boiling point, and a lower melting point. Called *colligative properties*, these effects depend only on the number of dissolved particles, not on their chemical identity.

6. **What is osmosis?** *Osmosis* occurs when solutions of different concentration are separated by a semipermeable membrane that allows solvent molecules to pass but blocks the passage of solute ions and molecules. Solvent flows from the more dilute side to the more concentrated side until sufficient *osmotic pressure* builds up and stops the flow. An effect similar to osmosis occurs when membranes of larger pore size are used. In *dialysis*, the membrane allows the passage of solvent and small dissolved molecules but prevents passage of proteins and larger particles.

UNDERSTANDING KEY CONCEPTS

9.31 Assume that two liquids are separated by a semipermeable membrane. Make a drawing that shows the situation after equilibrium is reached.

Before equilibrium

9.32 When 1 mol of HCl is added to 1 kg of water, the boiling point increases by 1.0 °C, but when 1 mol of acetic acid, CH_3CO_2H, is added to 1 kg of water, the boiling point increases by only 0.5 °C. Explain.

9.33 When 1 mol of HF is added to 1 kg of water, the freezing point decreases by 1.9 °C, but when 1 mol of HBr is added, the freezing point decreases by 3.7 °C. Which is more highly separated into ions, HF or HBr? Explain.

9.34 The graph at the top of page 289 shows the solubilities of two substances as a function of temperature. Which of the substances is a gas, and which is a liquid? Explain.

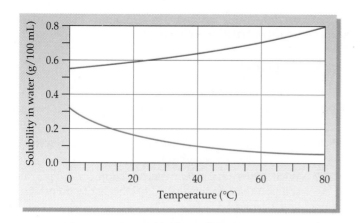

9.35 Assume that you have two full beakers, one containing pure water (blue) and the other containing an equal volume of a 10% (w/v) solution of glucose (green). Which of the drawings (a)–(c) best represents the two beakers after they have stood uncovered for several days and partial evaporation has occurred? Explain.

(a)   (b)   (c)

9.36 A beaker containing 150.0 mL of 0.1 M glucose is represented by (a). Which of the drawings (b)–(d) represents the solution that results when 50.0 mL is withdrawn from (a) and then diluted by a factor of 4?

(a)   (b)   (c)   (d)

9.37 The following diagram shows parts of the vapor pressure curves for a solvent and a solution. Which curve is which?

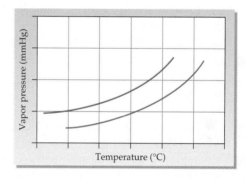

ADDITIONAL PROBLEMS

SOLUTIONS AND SOLUBILITY

9.38 What is the difference between a homogeneous mixture and a heterogeneous one?

9.39 How can you tell a solution from a colloid?

9.40 What characteristic of water allows it to dissolve ionic solids?

9.41 Why does water not dissolve motor oil?

9.42 Which of the following are solutions?

(a) Italian salad dressing
(b) Rubbing alcohol
(c) Algae in pond water
(d) Black coffee

9.43 Which of the following pairs of liquids are likely to be miscible?

(a) H_2SO_4 and H_2O
(b) C_8H_{18} and C_6H_6
(c) Na_3PO_4, and H_2O
(d) CS_2 and CCl_4

9.44 The solubility of NH_3 in water at an NH_3 pressure of 760.0 mmHg is 51.8 g/100 mL. What is the solubility of NH_3 if the partial pressure is reduced to 225.0 mmHg?

9.45 The solubility of CO_2 gas in water is 0.15 g/100 mL at a CO_2 pressure of 760 mmHg. What is the solubility of CO_2 in a soft drink (which is mainly water) that was bottled under a CO_2 pressure of 4.5 atm?

CONCENTRATION AND DILUTION OF SOLUTIONS

9.46 Is a solution highly concentrated if it is saturated? Is a solution saturated if it is highly concentrated?

9.47 How is weight/volume percent concentration defined?

9.48 How is molarity defined?

9.49 How is volume/volume percent concentration defined?

9.50 How would you prepare 750.0 mL of a 6.0% (v/v) ethyl alcohol solution?

9.51 A dilute solution of boric acid, H_3BO_3 is often used as an eyewash. How would you prepare 500.0 mL of a 0.50% (w/v) boric acid solution?

9.52 Describe how you would prepare 250 mL of a 0.10 M NaCl solution.

9.53 Describe how you would prepare 1.50 L of a 7.50% (w/v) $Mg(NO_3)_2$ solution.

9.54 What is the weight/volume percent concentration of the following solutions?

(a) 5.8 g KCl in 75 mL of solution
(b) 15 g sucrose in 380 mL of solution

9.55 The concentration of glucose in blood is approximately 90 mg/100 mL. What is the weight/volume percent concentration of glucose? What is the molarity of glucose?

9.56 How many grams of each substance are needed to prepare the following solutions?

(a) 50.0 mL of 8.0% (w/v) KCl
(b) 200.0 mL of 7.5% (w/v) acetic acid

9.57 Which of the following solutions is more concentrated?

(a) 0.50 M KCl or 5.0% (w/v) KCl
(b) 2.5% (w/v) $NaHSO_4$ or 0.025 M $NaHSO_4$

9.58 If you had only 23 g of KOH remaining in a bottle, how many milliliters of 10.0% (w/v) solution could you prepare? How many milliliters of 0.25 M solution?

9.59 Over-the-counter hydrogen peroxide solutions are 3% (w/v). What is this concentration in moles per liter?

9.60 The lethal dosage of potassium cyanide in rats is 10 mg KCN per kilogram of body weight. What is this concentration in parts per million?

9.61 The maximum concentration set by the U.S. Environmental Protection Agency for lead in drinking water is 15 ppb. What is this concentration in milligrams per liter? How many liters of water contaminated at this maximum level must you drink to consume 1.0 μg of lead?

9.62 What is the molarity of the following solutions?
(a) 12.5 g $NaHCO_3$ in 350.0 mL solution
(b) 45.0 g H_2SO_4 in 300.0 mL solution
(c) 30.0 g NaCl dissolved to make 500.0 mL solution

9.63 How many moles of solute are in the following solutions?
(a) 200 mL of 0.30 M acetic acid, CH_3CO_2H
(b) 1.50 L of 0.25 M NaOH
(c) 750 mL of 2.5 M nitric acid, HNO_3

9.64 How many milliliters of a 0.75 M HCl solution do you need to obtain 0.0040 mol of HCl?

9.65 Nalorphine, a relative of morphine, is used to combat withdrawal symptoms in heroin users. How many milliliters of a 0.40% (w/v) solution of nalorphine must be injected to obtain a dose of 1.5 mg?

9.66 A flask containing 450 mL of 0.50 M H_2SO_4 was accidentally knocked to the floor. How many grams of $NaHCO_3$ do you need to put on the spill to neutralize the acid according to the following equation?

$$H_2SO_4(aq) + 2\,NaHCO_3(aq) \longrightarrow$$
$$Na_2SO_4(aq) + 2\,H_2O(l) + 2\,CO_2(g)$$

9.67 How many milliliters of 0.0200 M $Na_2S_2O_3$ solution are needed to dissolve 0.450 g of AgBr?

$$AgBr(s) + 2\,Na_2S_2O_3(aq) \longrightarrow$$
$$Na_3Ag(S_2O_3)_2(aq) + NaBr(aq)$$

9.68 How much water must you add to 100.0 mL of orange juice concentrate if you want the final juice to be 20.0% of the strength of the original?

9.69 How much water would you add to 100.0 mL of 0.500 M NaOH if you wanted the final concentration to be 0.150 M?

9.70 An aqueous solution that contains 285 ppm of potassium nitrate (KNO_3) is being used to feed plants in a garden. What volume of this solution is needed to prepare 2.0 L of a solution that is 75 ppm in KNO_3?

9.71 What is the concentration of a NaCl solution, in (w/v)%, prepared by diluting 65 mL of a saturated solution, which has a concentration of 37 (w/v)%, to 480 mL?

9.72 Concentrated (12.0 M) hydrochloric acid is sold for household and industrial purposes under the name "muriatic acid." How many milliliters of 0.500 M HCl solution can be made from 25.0 mL of 12.0 M HCl solution?

9.73 Dilute solutions of $NaHCO_3$ are sometimes used in treating acid burns. How many milliliters of 0.100 M $NaHCO_3$ solution are needed to prepare 750.0 mL of 0.0500 M $NaHCO_3$ solution?

ELECTROLYTES

9.74 What is an electrolyte?

9.75 Give an example of a strong electrolyte and a nonelectrolyte.

9.76 What does it mean when we say that the concentration of Ca^{2+} in blood is 3.0 mEq/L?

9.77 What is the total anion concentration (in mEq/L) of a solution that contains 5.0 mEq/L Na^+, 12.0 mEq/L Ca^{2+}, and 2.0 mEq/L Li^+?

9.78 Kaochlor, a 10% (w/v) KCl solution, is an oral electrolyte supplement administered for potassium deficiency. How many milliequivalents of K^+ are in a 30 mL dose?

9.79 Calculate the gram-equivalent for each of the following ions:
(a) Ca^{2+} (b) K^+
(c) SO_4^{2-} (d) PO_4^{3-}

9.80 Look up the concentration of Cl^- ion in blood in Table 9.6. How many milliliters of blood would be needed to obtain 1.0 g of Cl^- ions?

9.81 Normal blood contains 3 mEq/L of Mg^{2+}. How many milligrams of Mg^{2+} are present in 150.0 mL of blood?

PROPERTIES OF SOLUTIONS

9.82 Which lowers the freezing point of 2.0 kg of water more, 0.20 mol NaOH or 0.20 mol $Ba(OH)_2$? Both compounds are strong electrolytes. Explain.

9.83 Which solution has the higher boiling point, 0.500 M glucose or 0.300 M KCl? Explain.

9.84 Methanol, CH_3OH, is sometimes used as an antifreeze for the water in automobile windshield washer fluids. How many grams of methanol must be added to 5.00 kg of water to lower its freezing point to −10.0 °C? For each mole of solute, the freezing point of 1 kg of water is lowered 1.86 °C.

9.85 Hard candy is prepared by dissolving pure sugar and flavoring in water and heating the solution to boiling. What is the boiling point of a solution produced by adding 650 g of cane sugar (molar mass 342.3 g/mol) to 1.5 kg of water? For each mole of nonvolatile solute, the boiling point of 1 kg of water is raised 0.51 °C.

OSMOSIS

9.86 Why do red blood cells swell up and burst when placed in pure water?

9.87 What does it mean when we say that a 0.15 M NaCl solution is isotonic with blood, whereas distilled water is hypotonic?

9.88 Which of the following solutions has the higher osmolarity?
(a) 0.25 M KBr or 0.20 M Na_2SO_4
(b) 0.30 M NaOH or 3.0% (w/v) NaOH

9.89 Which of the following solutions will give rise to a greater osmotic pressure at equilibrium: 5.00 g of NaCl in 350.0 mL water or 35.0 g of glucose in 400.0 mL water? For NaCl, MW = 58.5 amu; for glucose, MW = 180 amu.

9.90 A pickling solution is prepared by dissolving 270 g of NaCl in 3.8 L of water. Calculate the osmolarity of the solution.

9.91 An isotonic solution must be approximately 0.30 osmol. How much KCl is needed to prepare 175 mL of an isotonic solution?

Applications

9.92 How does the body increase oxygen availability at high altitude? [*Breathing and Oxygen Transport, p. 266*]

9.93 What are the major electrolytes in sweat, and what are their approximate concentrations in mEq/L? [*Electrolytes, Fluid Replacement, and Sports Drinks, p. 279*]

9.94 Why is a sports drink more effective than plain water for rehydration after extended exercise? [*Electrolytes, Fluid Replacement, and Sports Drinks, p. 279*]

9.95 How does an enteric coating on a medication work? [*Timed-Release Medications, p. 286*]

General Questions and Problems

9.96 Hyperbaric chambers, which provide high pressures (up to 6 atm) of either air or pure oxygen, are used to treat a variety of conditions, ranging from decompression sickness in deep-sea divers to carbon monoxide poisoning.

(a) What is the partial pressure of O_2 (in millimeters of Hg) in a hyperbaric chamber pressurized to 5 atm with air that is 18% in O_2?

(b) What is the solubility of O_2 (in grams per 100 mL) in the blood at this partial pressure? The solubility of O_2 is 2.1 g/100 mL for $P_{O_2} = 1$ atm.

9.97 Express the solubility of O_2 in Problem 9.96(b) in units of molarity.

9.98 Uric acid, the principal constituent of some kidney stones, has the formula $C_5H_4N_4O_3$. In aqueous solution, the solubility of uric acid is only 0.067 g/L. Express this concentration in (w/v)%, in parts per million, and in molarity.

9.99 Emergency treatment of cardiac arrest victims sometimes involves injection of a calcium chloride solution directly into the heart muscle. How many grams of $CaCl_2$ are administered in an injection of 5.0 mL of a 5.0% (w/v) solution? How many milliequivalents of Ca^{2+}?

9.100 Nitric acid, HNO_3, is available commercially at a concentration of 16 M. What volume would you use to prepare 750 mL of a 0.20 M solution?

9.101 One test for vitamin C (ascorbic acid, $C_6H_8O_6$) is based on the reaction of the vitamin with iodine:

$$C_6H_8O_6(aq) + I_2(aq) \longrightarrow C_6H_6O_6(aq) + 2\,HI(aq)$$

(a) If 25.0 mL of a fruit juice requires 13.0 mL of 0.0100 M I_2 solution for reaction, what is the molarity of the ascorbic acid in the fruit juice?

(b) The Food and Drug Administration recommends that 60 mg of ascorbic acid be consumed per day. How many milliliters of the fruit juice in part (a) must a person drink to obtain the recommended dosage?

9.102 *Ringer's solution*, used in the treatment of burns and wounds, is prepared by dissolving 8.6 g of NaCl, 0.30 g of KCl, and 0.33 g of $CaCl_2$ in water and diluting to a volume of 1.00 L. What is the molarity of each component?

9.103 What is the osmolarity of Ringer's solution (see Problem 9.102)? Is it hypotonic, isotonic, or hypertonic with blood plasma (0.30 osmol)?

9.104 The typical dosage of statin drugs for the treatment of high cholesterol is 10 mg. Assuming a total blood volume of 5.0 L, calculate the concentration of drug in the blood in units of (w/v)%.

9.105 Assuming the density of blood in healthy individuals is approximately 1.05 g/mL, report the concentration of drug in Problem 9.104 in units of ppm.

9.106 In many states, a person with a blood alcohol concentration of 0.080% (v/v) is considered legally drunk. What volume of total alcohol does this concentration represent, assuming a blood volume of 5.0 L?

9.107 Ammonia is very soluble in water (51.8 g/L at 20 °C and 760 mmHg).

(a) Show how NH_3 can hydrogen bond to water.

(b) What is the solubility of ammonia in water in moles per liter?

9.108 Cobalt(II) chloride, a blue solid, can absorb water from the air to form cobalt(II) chloride hexahydrate, a pink solid. The equilibrium is so sensitive to moisture in the air that $CoCl_2$ is used as a humidity indicator.

(a) Write a balanced equation for the equilibrium. Be sure to include water as a reactant to produce the hexahydrate.

(b) How many grams of water are released by the decomposition of 2.50 g of cobalt(II) chloride hexahydrate?

9.109 How many milliliters of 0.150 M $BaCl_2$ are needed to react completely with 35.0 mL of 0.200 M Na_2SO_4? How many grams of $BaSO_4$ will be formed?

9.110 Many compounds are only partially dissociated into ions in aqueous solution. Trichloroacetic acid (CCl_3CO_2H), for instance, is partially dissociated in water according to the equation

$$CCl_3CO_2H(aq) \rightleftharpoons H^+(aq) + CCl_3CO_2^-(aq)$$

For a solution prepared by dissolving 1.00 mol of trichloroacetic acid in 1.00 kg of water, 36.0% of the trichloroacetic acid dissociates to form H^+ and $CCl_3CO_2^-$ ions.

(a) What is the total concentration of dissolved ions and molecules in 1 kg of water?

(b) What is the freezing point of this solution? (The freezing point of 1 kg of water is lowered 1.86 °C for each mole of solute particles.)

CHAPTER 10

Acids and Bases

CONCEPTS TO REVIEW

Acids, Bases, and Neutralization Reactions

(Sections 4.11 and 6.10)

Reversible Reactions and Chemical Equilibrium

(Section 7.7)

Equilibrium Equations and Equilibrium Constants

(Section 7.8)

Units of Concentration; Molarity

(Section 9.7)

Ion Equivalents

(Section 9.10)

▲ Acids are found in many of the foods we eat, including tomatoes, peppers, and these citrus fruits.

292

A cids! The word evokes images of dangerous, corrosive liquids that eat away everything they touch. Although a few well-known substances such as sulfuric acid (H_2SO_4) do indeed fit this description, most acids are relatively harmless. In fact, many acids, such as ascorbic acid (vitamin C), are necessary for life.

10.1 Acids and Bases in Aqueous Solution

Let us take a moment to review what we said about acids and bases in Sections 4.11 and 6.10 before going on to a more systematic study:

- An acid is a substance that produces hydrogen ions, H^+, when dissolved in water.

- A base is a substance that produces hydroxide ions, OH^-, when dissolved in water.

- The neutralization reaction of an acid with a base yields water plus a *salt*, an ionic compound composed of the cation from the base and the anion from the acid.

The above definitions of acids and bases were proposed in 1887 by the Swedish chemist Svante Arrhenius and are useful for many purposes. The definitions are limited, however, because they refer only to reactions that take place in aqueous solution. (We will see shortly how the definitions can be broadened.) Another issue is that the H^+ ion is so reactive it does not exist in water. Instead, H^+ reacts with H_2O to give the **hydronium ion**, H_3O^+, as mentioned in Section 4.11. When gaseous HCl dissolves in water, for instance, H_3O^+ and Cl^- are formed. As described in Section 5.8, electrostatic potential maps show that the hydrogen of HCl is positively polarized and electron-poor (blue), whereas the oxygen of water is negatively polarized and electron-rich (red):

Hydronium ion The H_3O^+ ion, formed when an acid reacts with water.

Thus, the Arrhenius definition is updated to acknowledge that an acid yields H_3O^+ in water rather than H^+. In practice, however, the notations H_3O^+ and $H^+(aq)$ are often used interchangeably.

The Arrhenius definition of a base is correct as far as it goes, but it is important to realize that the OH^- ions "produced" by the base can come from either of two sources. Metal hydroxides, such as NaOH, KOH, and $Ba(OH)_2$, are ionic compounds that already contain OH^- ions and merely release those ions when they dissolve in water. Ammonia, however, is not ionic and contains no OH^- ions in its structure. Nonetheless, ammonia is a base because it undergoes a reaction with water when it dissolves, producing NH_4^+ and OH^- ions:

This OH^- ion comes from NaOH.

$$NaOH(s) \xrightarrow[\text{in } H_2O]{\text{Dissolve}} Na^+(aq) + OH^-(aq)$$

This OH^- ion comes from H_2O.

$$H-\underset{\underset{H}{|}}{\overset{..}{N}}-H(g) + H_2O(l) \rightleftharpoons H-\underset{\underset{H}{|}}{\overset{\overset{H}{|}}{N}}{}^{\pm}H(aq) + OH^-(aq)$$

The reaction of ammonia with water is a reversible process (Section 7.7) whose equilibrium strongly favors unreacted ammonia. (⊂⊃ , p. 198) Nevertheless, *some* OH^- ions are produced, so NH_3 is a base.

10.2 Some Common Acids and Bases

Acids and bases are present in a variety of foods and consumer products. Acids generally have a sour taste, and nearly every sour food contains an acid: Lemons, oranges, and grapefruit contain citric acid, for instance, and sour milk contains lactic acid. Bases are not so obvious in foods, but most of us have them stored under the kitchen or bathroom sink. Bases are present in many household cleaning agents, from perfumed toilet soap, to ammonia-based window cleaners, to the substance you put down the drain to dissolve hair, grease, and other materials that clog it.

Some of the most common acids and bases are listed below. It is a good idea at this point to learn their names and formulas, because we will refer to them often.

- **Sulfuric acid, H_2SO_4,** is probably the most important raw material in the chemical and pharmaceutical industries, and is manufactured in greater quantity worldwide than any other industrial chemical. Over 45 million tons are prepared in the United States annually for use in many hundreds of industrial processes, including the preparation of phosphate fertilizers. Its most common consumer use is as the acid found in automobile batteries. As anyone who has splashed battery acid on their skin or clothing knows, sulfuric acid is highly corrosive and can cause painful burns.

- **Hydrochloric acid, HCl,** or *muriatic acid* as it was historically known, has many industrial applications, including its use in metal cleaning and in the manufacture of high-fructose corn syrup. Aqueous HCl is also present as "stomach acid" in the digestive systems of most mammals.

- **Phosphoric acid, H_3PO_4,** is used in vast quantities in the manufacture of phosphate fertilizers. In addition, it is also used as an additive in foods and toothpastes. The tart taste of many soft drinks is due to the presence of phosphoric acid.

- **Nitric acid, HNO_3,** is a strong oxidizing agent that is used for many purposes, including the manufacture of ammonium nitrate fertilizer and military explosives. When spilled on the skin, it leaves a characteristic yellow coloration because of its reaction with skin proteins.

- **Acetic acid, CH_3CO_2H,** is the primary organic constituent of vinegar. It also occurs in all living cells and is used in many industrial processes such as the preparation of solvents, lacquers, and coatings.

▲ Hydrochloric acid, also known as muriatic acid, has many industrial applications.

- **Sodium hydroxide, NaOH,** also called *caustic soda* or *lye*, is the most commonly used of all bases. Industrially, it is used in the production of aluminum from its ore, in the production of glass, and in the manufacture of soap from animal fat. Concentrated solutions of NaOH can cause severe burns if allowed to sit on the skin for long. Drain cleaners often contain NaOH because it reacts with the fats and proteins found in grease and hair.

- **Calcium hydroxide, Ca(OH)$_2$,** or *slaked lime*, is made industrially by treating lime (CaO) with water. It has many applications, including its use in mortars and cements. An aqueous solution of Ca(OH)$_2$ is often called *limewater*.

- **Magnesium hydroxide, Mg(OH)$_2$,** or *milk of magnesia*, is an additive in foods, toothpaste, and many over-the-counter medications. Antacids such as Rolaids, Mylanta, and Maalox, for instance, all contain magnesium hydroxide.

- **Ammonia, NH$_3$,** is used primarily as a fertilizer, but it also has many other industrial applications including the manufacture of pharmaceuticals and explosives. A dilute solution of ammonia is frequently used around the house as a glass cleaner.

10.3 The Brønsted–Lowry Definition of Acids and Bases

The Arrhenius definition of acids and bases discussed in Section 10.1 applies only to reactions that take place in aqueous solution. A far more general definition was proposed in 1923 by the Danish chemist Johannes Brønsted and the English chemist Thomas Lowry. A **Brønsted–Lowry acid** is any substance that is able to give a hydrogen ion, H$^+$, to another molecule or ion. A hydrogen *atom* consists of a proton and an electron, so a hydrogen *ion*, H$^+$, is simply a proton. Thus, we often refer to acids as *proton donors*. The reaction need not occur in water, and a Brønsted–Lowry acid need not give appreciable concentrations of H$_3$O$^+$ ions in water.

Different acids can supply different numbers of H$^+$ ions, as we saw in Section 4.11. (⊂⊃, p. 98) Acids with one proton to donate, such as HCl and HNO$_3$, are called *monoprotic acids*; H$_2$SO$_4$ is a *diprotic acid* because it has two protons to donate, and H$_3$PO$_4$ is a *triprotic acid* because it has three protons to donate. Notice that the acidic H atoms (that is, the H atoms that are donated as protons) are bonded to electronegative atoms, such as chlorine or oxygen.

▲ Soap is manufactured by the reaction of vegetable oils and animal fats with the bases NaOH and KOH.

Brønsted–Lowry acid A substance that can donate a hydrogen ion, H$^+$, to another molecule or ion.

H—Cl

Hydrochloric acid
(monoprotic)

Nitric acid
(monoprotic)

Sulfuric acid
(diprotic)

Phosphoric acid
(triprotic)

Acetic acid (CH$_3$CO$_2$H), an example of an organic acid, actually has a total of 4 hydrogens, but only the one bonded to the electronegative oxygen is positively polarized and therefore acidic. The 3 hydrogens bonded to carbon are not acidic. Most organic acids are similar in that they contain many hydrogen atoms, but only the one in the —CO$_2$H group (blue in the electrostatic potential map) is acidic:

This hydrogen is acidic.

These 3 hydrogens are not acidic.

Brønsted–Lowry base A substance that can accept H$^+$ from an acid.

Whereas a Brønsted–Lowry acid is a substance that *donates* H$^+$ ions, a **Brønsted–Lowry base** is a substance that *accepts* H$^+$ from an acid. The reaction need not occur in water, and the Brønsted–Lowry base need not give appreciable concentrations of OH$^-$ ions in water. Gaseous NH$_3$, for example, acts as a base to accept H$^+$ from gaseous HCl and yield the ionic solid NH$_4{}^+$Cl$^-$:

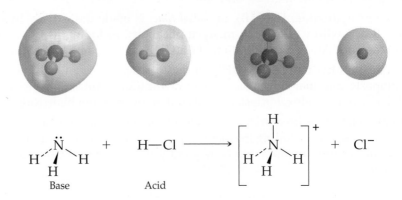

Putting the acid and base definitions together, *an acid–base reaction is one in which a proton is transferred*. The general reaction between proton-donor acids and proton-acceptor bases can be represented as

> Electrons on base form bond with H$^+$ from acid.

$$B: \; + \; H{-}A \rightleftarrows B\overset{+}{-}H \; + \; A^-$$

$$B:^- \; + \; H{-}A \rightleftarrows B{-}H \; + \; A^-$$

where the abbreviation HA represents a Brønsted–Lowry acid and B: or B:$^-$ represents a Brønsted–Lowry base. Notice in these acid–base reactions that both electrons in the product B—H bond come from the base, as indicated by the curved arrow flowing from the electron pair of the base to the hydrogen atom of the acid. Thus, the B—H bond that forms is a coordinate covalent bond (Section 5.4). (⟨⊂⊃, p. 115) In fact, a Brønsted–Lowry base *must* have such a lone pair of electrons; without them, it could not accept H$^+$ from an acid.

A base can be either neutral (B:) or negatively charged (B:$^-$). If the base is neutral, then the product has a positive charge (BH$^+$) after H$^+$ has added. Ammonia is an example:

> Adding an H$^+$ creates positive charge.

$$H{-}\underset{\overset{|}{H}}{\overset{\overset{\displaystyle H}{|}}{N}}: \;\; + \;\; H{-}A \;\rightleftarrows\; H{-}\underset{\overset{|}{H}}{\overset{\overset{\displaystyle H}{|}}{\overset{+}{N}}}{-}H \;\; + \;\; :A^-$$

Ammonia
(a neutral base, B:)

Ammonium ion

If the base is negatively charged, then the product is neutral (BH). Hydroxide ion is an example:

$$H{-}\ddot{\underset{..}{O}}:^- \;\; + \;\; H{-}A \;\rightleftarrows\; H{-}\ddot{\underset{..}{O}}{-}H \;\; + \;\; :A^-$$

Hydroxide ion
(a negatively charged
base, B:$^-$)

Water

An important consequence of the Brønsted–Lowry definitions is that the *products* of an acid–base reaction can also behave as acids and bases. Many acid–base reactions are reversible (Section 7.8), although in some cases the equilibrium constant for the reaction is quite large. (◖▭◗, p. 200) For example, suppose we have as a forward reaction an acid HA donating a proton to a base B to produce A⁻. This product A⁻ is a base because it can act as a proton acceptor in the reverse reaction. At the same time, the product BH⁺ acts as an acid because it donates a proton in the reverse reaction:

Double arrow indicates reversible reaction.

$$B{:} \ + \ H{-}A \ \rightleftarrows \ {:}A^- \ + \ \overset{+}{B}{-}H$$

Base   Acid   Base   Acid

Conjugate acid–base pair

Pairs of chemical species such as B, BH⁺ and HA, A⁻ are called **conjugate acid–base pairs**. They are species that are found on opposite sides of a chemical reaction whose formulas differ by only one H⁺. Thus, the product anion A⁻ is the **conjugate base** of the reactant acid HA, and HA is the **conjugate acid** of the base A⁻. Similarly, the reactant B is the conjugate base of the product acid BH⁺, and BH⁺ is the conjugate acid of the base B. The number of protons in a conjugate acid–base pair is always one greater than the number of protons in the base of the pair. To give some examples, acetic acid and acetate ion, the hydronium ion and water, and the ammonium ion and ammonia all make conjugate acid–base pairs:

Conjugate acid–base pair Two substances whose formulas differ by only a hydrogen ion, H⁺.

Conjugate base The substance formed by loss of H⁺ from an acid.

Conjugate acid The substance formed by addition of H⁺ to a base.

Conjugate acids
$$\left\{ \begin{array}{l} CH_3\overset{\displaystyle O}{\overset{\|}{C}}OH \ \rightleftarrows \ H^+ \ + \ CH_3\overset{\displaystyle O}{\overset{\|}{C}}O^- \\[2mm] H_3O^+ \ \rightleftarrows \ H^+ \ + \ H_2O \\[2mm] NH_4^+ \ \rightleftarrows \ H^+ \ + \ NH_3 \end{array} \right\}$$
Conjugate bases

WORKED EXAMPLE **10.1** Acids and Bases: Identifying Brønsted–Lowry Acids and Bases

Identify each of the following as a Brønsted–Lowry acid or base:

(a) PO_4^{3-}

(b) $HClO_4$

(c) CN^-

ANALYSIS A Brønsted–Lowry acid must have a hydrogen that it can donate as H⁺, and a Brønsted–Lowry base must have an atom with a lone pair of electrons that can bond to H⁺. Typically, a Brønsted–Lowry base is an anion derived by loss of H⁺ from an acid.

SOLUTION

(a) The phosphate anion (PO_4^{3-}) is a Brønsted–Lowry base derived by loss of 3 H⁺ ions from phosphoric acid, H_3PO_4.

(b) Perchloric acid ($HClO_4$) is a Brønsted–Lowry acid because it can donate an H⁺ ion.

(c) The cyanide ion (CN^-) is a Brønsted–Lowry base derived by removal of an H⁺ ion from hydrogen cyanide, HCN.

WORKED EXAMPLE   **10.2** Acids and Bases: Identifying Conjugate
Acid–Base Pairs

Write formulas for

    (a) The conjugate acid of the cyanide ion, CN^-

    (b) The conjugate base of perchloric acid, $HClO_4$

ANALYSIS A conjugate acid is formed by adding H^+ to a base; a conjugate base is formed by removing H^+ from an acid.

SOLUTION

    (a) HCN is the conjugate acid of CN^-.

    (b) ClO_4^- is the conjugate base of $HClO_4$.

PROBLEM 10.1

Which of the following would you expect to be Brønsted–Lowry acids?

(a) HCO_2H **(b)** H_2S **(c)** $SnCl_2$

PROBLEM 10.2

Which of the following would you expect to be Brønsted–Lowry bases?

(a) SO_3^{2-} **(b)** Ag^+ **(c)** F^-

PROBLEM 10.3

Write formulas for:

(a) The conjugate acid of HS^- **(b)** The conjugate acid of PO_4^{3-}

(c) The conjugate base of H_2CO_3 **(d)** The conjugate base of NH_4^+

⊷ KEY CONCEPT PROBLEM 10.4

For the reaction shown here, identify the Brønsted–Lowry acids, bases, and conjugate acid–base pairs.

10.4 Water as Both an Acid and a Base

Water is neither an acid nor a base in the Arrhenius sense because it does not contain appreciable concentrations of either H_3O^+ or OH^-. In the Brønsted–Lowry sense, however, water can act as *both* an acid and a base. When in contact with a base, water reacts as a Brønsted–Lowry acid and *donates* a proton to the base. In its reaction with ammonia, for example, water donates H^+ to ammonia to form the ammonium ion:

$$NH_3 + H_2O \longrightarrow NH_4^+ + OH^-$$

Ammonia	Water	Ammonium ion	Hydroxide ion
(base)	(acid)	(acid)	(base)

When in contact with an acid, water reacts as a Brønsted–Lowry base and *accepts* H^+ from the acid. This, of course, is exactly what happens when an acid such as HCl dissolves in water, as discussed in Section 10.1.

Water uses two electrons to form a bond to H^+.

$$H-\ddot{O}: + H-Cl \longrightarrow H-\overset{+}{\underset{..}{O}}-H + Cl^-$$

Water	(An acid)	Hydronium ion
(A base)		

Substances like water, which can react as either an acid or a base depending on the circumstances, are said to be **amphoteric** (am-pho-**tare**-ic). When water acts as an acid, it donates H^+ and becomes OH^-; when it acts as a base, it accepts H^+ and becomes H_3O^+.

Amphoteric Describing a substance that can react as either an acid or a base.

PROBLEM 10.5

Is water an acid or a base in the following reactions?

(a) $H_3PO_4(aq) + H_2O(l) \longrightarrow H_2PO_4^-(aq) + H_3O^+(aq)$

(b) $F^-(aq) + H_2O(l) \longrightarrow HF(aq) + OH^-(aq)$

(c) $NH_4^+(aq) + H_2O(aq) \longrightarrow NH_3(aq) + H_3O^+(aq)$

10.5 Acid and Base Strength

Some acids and bases, such as sulfuric acid (H_2SO_4), hydrochloric acid (HCl), or sodium hydroxide (NaOH), are highly corrosive. They react readily and, in contact with skin, can cause serious burns. Other acids and bases are not nearly as reactive. Acetic acid (CH_3COOH, the major component in vinegar) and phosphoric acid (H_3PO_4) are found in many food products. Why are some acids and bases relatively "safe," while others must be handled with extreme caution? The answer lies in how easily they produce the active ions for an acid (H^+) or a base (OH^-).

As indicated in Table 10.1, acids differ in their ability to give up a proton. The six acids at the top of the table are **strong acids**, meaning that they give up a proton easily and are essentially 100% **dissociated**, or split apart into ions, in water. Those remaining are **weak acids**, meaning that they give up a proton with difficulty and are substantially less than 100% dissociated in water. In a similar way, the bases at the top of the table are **weak bases** because they have little affinity for a proton, and the bases at the bottom of the table are **strong bases** because they grab and hold a proton tightly.

Note that diprotic acids, such as sulfuric acid, undergo two stepwise dissociations in water. The first dissociation yields HSO_4^- and occurs to the extent of nearly 100%, so H_2SO_4 is a strong acid. The second dissociation yields SO_4^{2-} and takes place to a much lesser extent because separation of a positively charged H^+ from the negatively charged HSO_4^- anion is difficult. Thus, HSO_4^- is a weak acid:

$$H_2SO_4(l) + H_2O(l) \longrightarrow H_3O^+(aq) + HSO_4^-(aq)$$

$$HSO_4^-(aq) + H_2O(l) \rightleftharpoons H_3O^+(aq) + SO_4^{2-}(aq)$$

Strong acid An acid that gives up H^+ easily and is essentially 100% dissociated in water.

Dissociation The splitting apart of an acid in water to give H^+ and an anion.

Weak acid An acid that gives up H^+ with difficulty and is less than 100% dissociated in water.

Weak base A base that has only a slight affinity for H^+ and holds it weakly.

Strong base A base that has a high affinity for H^+ and holds it tightly.

TABLE 10.1 Relative Strengths of Acids and Conjugate Bases

		ACID		CONJUGATE BASE		
Increasing acid strength ↑	**Strong acids: 100% dissociated**	Perchloric acid	$HClO_4$	ClO_4^-	Perchlorate ion	**Little or no reaction as bases** — **Increasing base strength**
		Sulfuric acid	H_2SO_4	HSO_4^-	Hydrogen sulfate ion	
		Hydriodic acid	HI	I^-	Iodide ion	
		Hydrobromic acid	HBr	Br^-	Bromide ion	
		Hydrochloric acid	HCl	Cl^-	Chloride ion	
		Nitric acid	HNO_3	NO_3^-	Nitrate ion	
		Hydronium ion	H_3O^+	H_2O	**Water**	
	Weak acids	Hydrogen sulfate ion	HSO_4^-	SO_4^{2-}	Sulfate ion	**Very weak bases**
		Phosphoric acid	H_3PO_4	$H_2PO_4^-$	Dihydrogen phosphate ion	
		Nitrous acid	HNO_2	NO_2^-	Nitrite ion	
		Hydrofluoric acid	HF	F^-	Fluoride ion	
		Acetic acid	CH_3COOH	CH_3COO^-	Acetate ion	
	Very weak acids	Carbonic acid	H_2CO_3	HCO_3^-	Bicarbonate ion	**Weak bases**
		Dihydrogen phosphate ion	$H_2PO_4^-$	HPO_4^{2-}	Hydrogen phosphate ion	
		Ammonium ion	NH_4^+	NH_3	Ammonia	
		Hydrocyanic acid	HCN	CN^-	Cyanide ion	
		Bicarbonate ion	HCO_3^-	CO_3^{2-}	Carbonate ion	
		Hydrogen phosphate ion	HPO_4^{2-}	PO_4^{3-}	Phosphate ion	
		Water	H_2O	OH^-	**Hydroxide ion**	**Strong base** ↓

Perhaps the most striking feature of Table 10.1 is the inverse relationship between acid strength and base strength. *The stronger the acid, the weaker its conjugate base; the weaker the acid, the stronger its conjugate base.* HCl, for example, is a strong acid, so Cl^- is a very weak base. H_2O, however, is a very weak acid, so OH^- is a strong base.

Why is there an inverse relationship between acid strength and base strength? To answer this question, think about what it means for an acid or base to be strong or weak. A strong acid $H-A$ is one that readily gives up a proton, meaning that its conjugate base A^- has little affinity for the proton. But this is exactly the definition of a weak base—a substance that has little affinity for a proton. As a result, the reverse reaction occurs to a lesser extent, as indicated by the size of the forward and reverse arrows in the reaction:

Larger arrow indicates forward reaction is stronger.

$$H-A + H_2O \rightleftharpoons H_3O^+ + A^-$$

If this is a strong acid because it gives up a proton readily . . .

. . . then this is a weak base because it has little affinity for a proton.

In the same way, a weak acid is one that gives up a proton with difficulty, meaning that its conjugate base has a high affinity for the proton. But this is just the definition of a strong base—a substance that has a high affinity for the proton. The reverse reaction now occurs more readily.

$$H\!-\!A \; + \; H_2O \; \underset{\longleftarrow}{\overset{\longrightarrow}{\rightleftharpoons}} \; H_3O^+ \; + \; A^-$$

If this is a weak acid because it gives up a proton with difficulty . . .

| Larger arrow indicates reverse reaction is stronger. |

. . . then this is a strong base because it has a high affinity for a proton.

Knowing the relative strengths of different acids as shown in Table 10.1 makes it possible to predict the direction of proton-transfer reactions. *An acid–base proton-transfer equilibrium always favors reaction of the stronger acid with the stronger base, and formation of the weaker acid and base.* That is, the proton always leaves the stronger acid (whose weaker conjugate base cannot hold the proton) and always ends up in the weaker acid (whose stronger conjugate base holds the proton tightly). Put another way, in a contest for the proton, the stronger base always wins.

$$\text{Stronger acid} \; + \; \text{Stronger base} \; \rightleftharpoons \; \text{Weaker base} \; + \; \text{Weaker acid}$$

To try out this rule, compare the reactions of acetic acid with water and with hydroxide ion. The idea is to write the equation, identify the acid on each side of the arrow, and then decide which acid is stronger and which is weaker. For example, the reaction of acetic acid with water to give acetate ion and hydronium ion is favored in the reverse direction, because acetic acid is a weaker acid than H_3O^+:

$$\underset{\text{Weaker acid}}{CH_3\overset{\displaystyle O}{\overset{\|}{C}}OH} \; + \; H_2O \; \rightleftharpoons \; CH_3\overset{\displaystyle O}{\overset{\|}{C}}O^- \; + \; \underset{\text{Stronger acid}}{H_3O^+}$$

Reverse reaction is favored.

This base holds the proton less tightly . . . . . . than this base does.

On the other hand, the reaction of acetic acid with hydroxide ion to give acetate ion and water is favored in the forward direction, because acetic acid is a stronger acid than H_2O:

$$\underset{\text{Stronger acid}}{CH_3\overset{\displaystyle O}{\overset{\|}{C}}OH} \; + \; OH^- \; \rightleftharpoons \; CH_3\overset{\displaystyle O}{\overset{\|}{C}}O^- \; + \; \underset{\text{Weaker acid}}{H_2O}$$

Forward reaction is favored.

This base holds the proton more tightly . . . . . . than this base does.

WORKED EXAMPLE | **10.3** Acid/Base Strength: Predicting Direction of H-transfer Reactions

Write a balanced equation for the proton-transfer reaction between phosphate ion (PO_4^{3-}) and water, and determine in which direction the equilibrium is favored.

ANALYSIS Look in Table 10.1 to see the relative acid and base strengths of the species involved in the reaction. The acid–base proton-transfer equilibrium will favor reaction of the stronger acid and formation of the weaker acid.

SOLUTION

Phosphate ion is the conjugate base of a weak acid (HPO_4^{2-}) and is therefore a relatively strong base. Table 10.1 shows that HPO_4^{2-} is a stronger acid than H_2O, and OH^- is a stronger base than PO_4^{3-}, so the reaction is favored in the reverse direction:

$$\underset{\text{Weaker base}}{PO_4^{3-}(aq)} \; + \; \underset{\text{Weaker acid}}{H_2O(l)} \; \rightleftharpoons \; \underset{\text{Stronger acid}}{HPO_4^{2-}(aq)} \; + \; \underset{\text{Stronger base}}{OH^-(aq)}$$

APPLICATION ▶ GERD—Too Much Acid or Not Enough?

Strong acids are very caustic substances that can dissolve even metals, and no one would think of ingesting them. However, the major component of the gastric juices secreted in the stomach is hydrochloric acid—a strong acid—and the acidic environment in the stomach is vital to good health and nutrition.

Stomach acid is essential for the digestion of proteins and for the absorption of certain micronutrients, such as calcium, magnesium, iron, and vitamin B_{12}. It also creates a sterile environment in the gut by killing yeast and bacteria that may be ingested. If these gastric juices leak up into the esophagus, the tube through which food and drink enter the stomach, they can cause the burning sensation in the chest or throat known as either heartburn or acid indigestion. Persistent irritation of the esophagus is known as gastroesophageal reflux disease (GERD) and, if untreated, can lead to more serious health problems.

Hydrogen ions and chloride ions are secreted separately from the cytoplasm of cells lining the stomach and then combine to form HCl that is usually close to 0.10 M. The HCl is then released into the stomach cavity, where the concentration is diluted to about 0.01–0.001 M. Unlike the esophagus, the stomach is coated by a thick mucus layer that protects the stomach wall from damage by this caustic solution.

Those who suffer from acid indigestion can obtain relief using over-the-counter antacids, such as Tums or Rolaids (see Section 10.14, p. 320). Chronic conditions such as GERD, however, are often treated with prescription medications. GERD can be treated by two classes of drugs. Proton-pump inhibitors (PPI), such as Prevacid and Prilosec, prevent the production the H^+ ions in the parietal cells, while H2-receptor blockers (Tagamet, Zantac, and Pepcid) prevent the release of stomach acid into the lumen. Both drugs effectively decrease the production of stomach acid to ease the symptoms of GERD.

Ironically, GERD can also be caused by not having enough stomach acid—a condition known as *hypochlorhydria*. The valve that controls the release of stomach contents to the small intestine is triggered by acidity. If this valve fails to open because the stomach is not acidic enough, the contents of the stomach can be churned up into the esophagus.

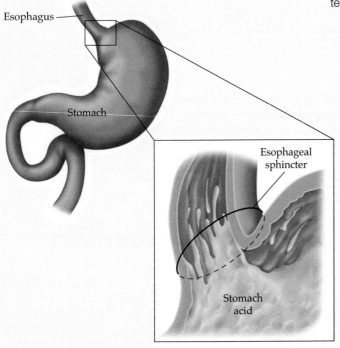

▲ The burning sensation and other symptoms associated with GERD are caused by the reflux of the acidic contents of the stomach into the esophagus.

▲ If not treated, GERD can cause ulcers and scarring of esophageal tissue.

See Additional Problem 10.96 at the end of the chapter.

PROBLEM 10.6

Use Table 10.1 to identify the stronger acid in the following pairs:

(a) H_2O or NH_4^+
(b) H_2SO_4 or CH_3CO_2H
(c) HCN or H_2CO_3

PROBLEM 10.7

Use Table 10.1 to identify the stronger base in the following pairs:

(a) F^- or Br^- **(b)** OH^- or HCO_3^-

PROBLEM 10.8

Write a balanced equation for the proton-transfer reaction between a hydrogen phosphate ion and a hydroxide ion. Identify each acid–base pair, and determine in which direction the equilibrium is favored.

◀○ KEY CONCEPT PROBLEM 10.9

From this electrostatic potential map of the amino acid alanine, identify the most acidic hydrogens in the molecule:

Alanine

10.6 Acid Dissociation Constants

The reaction of a weak acid with water, like any chemical equilibrium, can be described by an equilibrium equation (Section 7.8), where square brackets indicate the concentrations of the enclosed species in molarity (moles per liter). (⚇, p. 200)

For the reaction $HA(aq) + H_2O(l) \rightleftharpoons H_3O^+(aq) + A^-(aq)$

We have $K = \dfrac{[H_3O^+][A^-]}{[HA][H_2O]}$

Because water is a solvent as well as a participant for the reaction, its concentration is essentially constant and has no effect on the equilibrium. Therefore, we usually put the equilibrium constant K and the water concentration $[H_2O]$ together to make a new constant called the **acid dissociation constant, K_a**. The acid dissociation constant is simply the hydronium ion concentration $[H_3O^+]$ times the conjugate base concentration $[A^-]$ divided by the undissociated acid concentration [HA]:

Acid dissociation constant $K_a = K[H_2O] = \dfrac{[H_3O^+][A^-]}{[HA]}$

For a strong acid, the H_3O^+ and A^- concentrations are much larger than the HA concentration, so K_a is very large. In fact, the K_a values for strong acids such as HCl are so large that it is difficult and not very useful to measure them. For a weak acid, however, the H_3O^+ and A^- concentrations are smaller than the HA concentration, so K_a is small. Table 10.2 gives K_a values for some common acids and illustrates several important points:

- Strong acids have K_a values much greater than 1 because dissociation is favored.
- Weak acids have K_a values much less than 1 because dissociation is not favored.

TABLE 10.2   Some Acid Dissociation Constants, K_a, at 25 °C

ACID	K_a	ACID	K_a
Hydrofluoric acid (HF)	3.5×10^{-4}	*Polyprotic acids*	
Hydrocyanic acid (HCN)	4.9×10^{-10}	Sulfuric acid	
Ammonium ion (NH_4^+)	5.6×10^{-10}	H_2SO_4	Large
		HSO_4^-	1.2×10^{-2}
Organic acids		Phosphoric acid	
Formic acid (HCOOH)	1.8×10^{-4}	H_3PO_4	7.5×10^{-3}
Acetic acid (CH_3COOH)	1.8×10^{-5}	$H_2PO_4^-$	6.2×10^{-8}
Propanoic acid	1.3×10^{-5}	HPO_4^{2-}	2.2×10^{-13}
(CH_3CH_2COOH)		Carbonic acid	
Ascorbic acid (vitamin C)	7.9×10^{-5}	H_2CO_3	4.3×10^{-7}
		HCO_3^-	5.6×10^{-11}

- Donation of each successive H^+ from a polyprotic acid is more difficult than the one before it, so K_a values become successively lower.
- Most organic acids, which contain the $-CO_2H$ group, have K_a values near 10^{-5}.

PROBLEM 10.10

Benzoic acid has $K_a = 6.5 \times 10^{-5}$, and citric acid has $K_a = 7.2 \times 10^{-4}$. Which of the two is the stronger acid?

10.7 Dissociation of Water

We saw previously that water is amphoteric – it can act as an acid when a base is present and as a base when an acid is present. What about when no other acids or bases are present, however? In this case, one water molecule acts as an acid while another water molecule acts as a base, reacting to form the hydronium and hydroxide ions:

$$H_2O(l) + H_2O(l) \rightleftharpoons H_3O^+(aq) + OH^-(aq)$$

Because each dissociation reaction yields one H_3O^+ ion and one OH^- ion, the concentrations of the two ions are identical. At 25 °C, the concentration of each is 1.00×10^{-7} M. We can write the equilibrium constant expression for the dissociation of water as

$$K = \frac{[H_3O^+][OH^-]}{[H_2O][H_2O]}$$

and

$$K_a = K[H_2O] = \frac{[H_3O^+][OH^-]}{[H_2O]}$$

where $[H_3O^+] = [OH^-] = 1.00 \times 10^{-7}$ M   (at 25 °C)

As both a reactant and a solvent, the concentration of water is essentially constant. We can therefore put the acid dissociation constant K_a and the water concentration $[H_2O]$ together to make a new constant called the **ion-product constant for water (K_w)**, which is simply the H_3O^+ concentration times the OH^- concentration. At 25 °C, $K_w = 1.00 \times 10^{-14}$.

$$\textit{Ion-product constant for water} \quad K_w = K_a[H_2O] = [H_3O^+][OH^-]$$
$$= (1.00 \times 10^{-7})(1.00 \times 10^{-7})$$
$$= 1.00 \times 10^{-14} \quad (\text{at } 25\ °C)$$

The importance of the equation $K_w = [H_3O^+][OH^-]$ is that it applies to all aqueous solutions, not just to pure water. Since the product of $[H_3O^+]$ times $[OH^-]$ is always constant for any solution, we can determine the concentration of one species if we know the concentration of the other. If an acid is present in solution, for instance, so that $[H_3O^+]$ is large, then $[OH^-]$ must be small. If a base is present in solution so that $[OH^-]$ is large, then $[H_3O^+]$ must be small. For example, for a 0.10 M HCl solution, we know that $[H_3O^+] = 0.10$ M because HCl is 100% dissociated. Thus, we can calculate that $[OH^-] = 1.0 \times 10^{-13}$ M:

$$\text{Since} \quad K_w \times [H_3O^+][OH^-] = 1.00 \times 10^{-14}$$

$$\text{we have} \quad [OH^-] = \frac{K_w}{[H_3O^+]} = \frac{1.00 \times 10^{-14}}{0.10} = 1.0 \times 10^{-13}\ M$$

Similarly, for a 0.10 M NaOH solution, we know that $[OH^-] = 0.10$ M, so $[H_3O^+] = 1.0 \times 10^{-13}$ M:

$$[H_3O^+] = \frac{K_w}{[OH^-]} = \frac{1.00 \times 10^{-14}}{0.10} = 1.0 \times 10^{-13}\ M$$

Solutions are identified as acidic, neutral, or basic (*alkaline*) according to the value of their H_3O^+ and OH^- concentrations:

Acidic solution: $[H_3O^+] > 10^{-7}$ M and $[OH^-] < 10^{-7}$ M

Neutral solution: $[H_3O^+] = 10^{-7}$ M and $[OH^-] = 10^{-7}$ M

Basic solution: $[H_3O^+] < 10^{-7}$ M and $[OH^-] > 10^{-7}$ M

WORKED EXAMPLE   **10.4** Water Dissociation Constant: Using K_w to Calculate $[OH^-]$

Milk has an H_3O^+ concentration of 4.5×10^{-7} M. What is the value of $[OH^-]$? Is milk acidic, neutral, or basic?

ANALYSIS The OH^- concentration can be found by dividing K_w by $[H_3O^+]$. An acidic solution has $[H_3O^+] > 10^{-7}$ M, a neutral solution has $[H_3O^+] = 10^{-7}$ M, and a basic solution has $[H_3O^+] < 10^{-7}$ M.

BALLPARK ESTIMATE Since the H_3O^+ concentration is slightly *greater* than 10^{-7} M, the OH^- concentration must be slightly *less* than 10^{-7} M, on the order of 10^{-8}.

SOLUTION

$$[OH^-] = \frac{K_w}{[H_3O^+]} = \frac{1.00 \times 10^{-14}}{4.5 \times 10^{-7}} = 2.2 \times 10^{-8}\ M$$

Milk is slightly acidic because its H_3O^+ concentration is slightly larger than 1×10^{-7} M.

BALLPARK CHECK The OH^- concentration is of the same order of magnitude as our estimate.

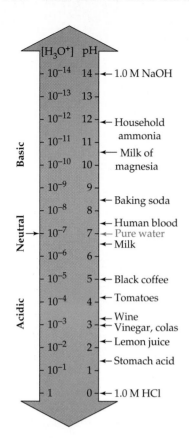

▲ **FIGURE 10.1 The pH scale and the pH values of some common substances.** A low pH corresponds to a strongly acidic solution, a high pH corresponds to a strongly basic solution, and a pH of 7 corresponds to a neutral solution.

p function The negative common logarithm of some variable, $pX = -\log(X)$.

pH A measure of the acid strength of a solution; the negative common logarithm of the H_3O^+ concentration.

▲ Adding only a teaspoonful of concentrated (6 M) hydrochloric acid lowers the pH of this pool from 7 to 6. Lowering the pH from 7 to 1 would take 400 gallons.

PROBLEM 10.11

Identify the following solutions as either acidic or basic. What is the value of $[OH^-]$ in each?

(a) Beer, $[H_3O^+] = 3.2 \times 10^{-5}$ M

(b) Household ammonia, $[H_3O^+] = 3.1 \times 10^{-12}$ M

10.8 Measuring Acidity in Aqueous Solution: pH

In many fields, from medicine to chemistry to winemaking, it is necessary to know the exact concentration of H_3O^+ or OH^- in a solution. If, for example, the H_3O^+ concentration in blood varies only slightly from a value of 4.0×10^{-8} M, death can result.

Although correct, it is nevertheless awkward to refer to low concentrations of H_3O^+ using molarity. If you were asked which concentration is higher, 9.0×10^{-8} M or 3.5×10^{-7} M, you would probably have to stop and think for a moment before answering. Fortunately, there is an easier way to express and compare H_3O^+ concentrations—the *pH scale*.

The pH of an aqueous solution is a number, usually between 0 and 14, that indicates the H_3O^+ concentration of the solution. A pH smaller than 7 corresponds to an acidic solution, a pH larger than 7 corresponds to a basic solution, and a pH of exactly 7 corresponds to a neutral solution. The pH scale and pH values of some common substances are shown in Figure 10.1

Mathematically, a **p function** is defined as the negative common logarithm of some variable. The **pH** of a solution, therefore, is the negative common logarithm of the H_3O^+ concentration:

$$\textbf{pH} = -\log[H^+] \quad (or[H_3O^+])$$

If you have studied logarithms, you may remember that the common logarithm of a number is the power to which 10 must be raised to equal the number. The pH definition can therefore be restated as

$$[H_3O^+] = 10^{-pH}$$

For example, in neutral water at 25 °C, where $[H_3O^+] = 1 \times 10^{-7}$ M, the pH is 7; in a strong acid solution where $[H_3O^+] = 1 \times 10^{-1}$ M, the pH is 1; and in a strong base solution where $[H_3O^+] = 1 \times 10^{-14}$ M, the pH is 14:

Acidic solution: pH < 7, $[H_3O^+] > 1 \times 10^{-7}$ M

Neutral solution: pH = 7, $[H_3O^+] = 1 \times 10^{-7}$ M

Basic solution: pH > 7, $[H_3O^+] < 1 \times 10^{-7}$ M

Keep in mind that the pH scale covers an enormous range of acidities because it is a *logarithmic* scale, which involves powers of 10 (Figure 10.2). A change of only 1 pH unit means a tenfold change in $[H_3O^+]$, a change of 2 pH units means a hundredfold change in $[H_3O^+]$, and a change of 12 pH units means a change of 10^{12} (a million) in $[H_3O^+]$.

To get a feel for the size of the quantities involved, think of a typical backyard swimming pool, which contains about 100,000 L of water. You would have to add only 0.10 mol of HCl (3.7 g) to lower the pH of the pool from 7.0 (neutral) to 6.0, but you would have to add 10,000 mol of HCl (370 kg!) to lower the pH of the pool from 7.0 to 1.0.

The logarithmic pH scale is a convenient way of reporting the relative acidity of solutions, but using logarithms can also be useful when calculating H_3O^+ and

OH⁻ concentrations. Remember that the equilibrium between H_3O^+ and OH^- in aqueous solutions is expressed by K_w, where

$$K_w = [H_3O^+][OH^-] = 1 \times 10^{-14} \quad \text{(at 25 °C)}$$

If we convert this equation to its negative logarithmic form, we obtain

$$-\log(K_w) = -\log(H_3O^+) - \log(OH^-)$$

$$-\log(1 \times 10^{-14}) = -\log(H_3O^+) - \log(OH^-)$$

or $14.00 = \text{pH} + \text{pOH}$

The logarithmic form of the K_w equation can simplify the calculation of solution pH from OH⁻ concentration, as demonstrated in Worked Example 10.7.

WORKED EXAMPLE   **10.5** Measuring Acidity: Calculating pH from $[H_3O^+]$

The H_3O^+ concentration in coffee is about 1×10^{-5} M. What pH is this?

ANALYSIS The pH is the negative common logarithm of the H_3O^+ concentration: pH = $-\log[H_3O^+]$.

SOLUTION
Since the common logarithm of 1×10^{-5} M is -5, the pH is 5.0.

WORKED EXAMPLE   **10.6** Measuring Acidity: Calculating $[H_3O^+]$ from pH

Lemon juice has a pH of about 2. What $[H_3O^+]$ is this?

ANALYSIS In this case, we are looking for the $[H_3O^+]$, where $[H_3O^+] = 10^{-\text{pH}}$.

SOLUTION
Since pH = 2.0, $[H_3O^+] = 10^{-2} = 1 \times 10^{-2}$ M.

WORKED EXAMPLE   **10.7** Measuring Acidity: Using K_w to Calculate $[H_3O^+]$ and pH

A cleaning solution is found to have $[OH^-] = 1 \times 10^{-3}$ M. What is the pH?

ANALYSIS To find pH, we must first find the value of $[H_3O^+]$ by using the equation $[H_3O^+] = K_w/[OH^-]$. Alternatively, we can calculate the pOH of the solution and then use the logarithmic form of the K_w equation: pH = 14.00 − pOH.

SOLUTION
Rearranging the K_w equation, we have

$$[H_3O^+] = \frac{K_w}{[OH^-]} = \frac{1.00 \times 10^{-14}}{1 \times 10^{-3}} = 1 \times 10^{-11} \text{ M}$$

$$\text{pH} = -\log(1 \times 10^{-11}) = 11.0$$

Using the logarithmic form of the K_w equation, we have

$$\text{pH} = 14.0 - \text{pOH} = 14.0 - (-\log(OH^-))$$

$$\text{pH} = 14.0 - (-\log(1 \times 10^{-3}))$$

$$\text{pH} = 14.0 - 3.0 = 11.0$$

Basicity increases

[H⁺]	pH	[OH⁻]
10^{-14}	14	10^{-0}
10^{-13}	13	10^{-1}
10^{-12}	12	10^{-2}
10^{-11}	11	10^{-3}
10^{-10}	10	10^{-4}
10^{-9}	9	10^{-5}
10^{-8}	8	10^{-6}
10^{-7}	7	10^{-7}
10^{-6}	6	10^{-8}
10^{-5}	5	10^{-9}
10^{-4}	4	10^{-10}
10^{-3}	3	10^{-11}
10^{-2}	2	10^{-12}
10^{-1}	1	10^{-13}

Acidity increases

▲ **FIGURE 10.2** The relationship of the pH scale to H⁺ and OH⁻ concentrations.

WORKED EXAMPLE **10.8** Measuring Acidity: Calculating pH of Strong Acid Solutions

What is the pH of a 0.01 M solution of HCl?

ANALYSIS To find pH, we must first find the value of $[H_3O^+]$.

SOLUTION
Since HCl is a strong acid (Table 10.1), it is 100% dissociated, and the H_3O^+ concentration is the same as the HCl concentration: $[H_3O^+] = 0.01$ M, or 1×10^{-2} M, and pH $= 2.0$.

PROBLEM 10.12

Which solution has the higher H_3O^+ concentration, one with pH $= 5$ or one with pH $= 9$? Which has the higher OH^- concentration?

PROBLEM 10.13

Give the pH of solutions with the following concentrations:

(a) $[H_3O^+] = 1 \times 10^{-5}$ M

(b) $[OH^-] = 1 \times 10^{-9}$ M

PROBLEM 10.14

Give the hydronium ion concentrations of solutions with the following values of pH. Which of the solutions is most acidic? Which is most basic?

(a) pH 13.0   (b) pH 3.0   (c) pH 8.0

PROBLEM 10.15

What is the pH of a 1×10^{-4} M solution of HNO_3?

10.9 Working with pH

Converting between pH and H_3O^+ concentration is easy when the pH is a whole number, but how do you find the H_3O^+ concentration of blood, which has a pH of 7.4, or the pH of a solution with $[H_3O^+] = 4.6 \times 10^{-3}$ M? Sometimes it is sufficient to make an estimate. The pH of blood (7.4) is between 7 and 8, so the H_3O^+ concentration of blood must be between 1×10^{-7} and 1×10^{-8} M. To be exact about finding pH values, though, requires a calculator.

Converting from pH to $[H_3O^+]$ requires finding the *antilogarithm* of the negative pH, which is done on many calculators with an "INV" key and a "log" key. Converting from $[H_3O^+]$ to pH requires finding the logarithm, which is commonly done with a "log" key and an "expo" or "EE" key for entering exponents of 10. Consult your calculator instructions if you are not sure how to use these keys. Remember that the sign of the number given by the calculator must be changed from minus to plus to get the pH.

The H_3O^+ concentration in blood with pH $= 7.4$ is

$$[H_3O^+] = \text{antilog}(-7.4) = 4 \times 10^{-8} \text{ M}$$

The pH of a solution with $[H_3O^+] = 4.6 \times 10^{-3}$ M is

$$pH = -\log(4.6 \times 10^{-3}) = -(-2.34) = 2.34$$

A note about significant figures: An antilogarithm contains the same number of digits that the original number has to the right of the decimal point. A logarithm contains the same number of digits to the right of the decimal point that the original number has

$$antilog(-7.4) = 4 \times 10^{-8} \qquad \log(4.6 \times 10^{-3}) = -2.34$$

1 digit after decimal point   1 digit   2 digits   2 digits after decimal point

WORKED EXAMPLE **10.9** Working with pH: Converting a pH to $[H_3O^+]$

Soft drinks usually have a pH of approximately 3.1. What is the $[H_3O^+]$ concentration in a soft drink?

ANALYSIS To convert from a pH value to an $[H_3O^+]$ concentration requires using the equation $[H_3O^+] = 10^{-pH}$, which requires finding an antilogarithm on a calculator.

BALLPARK ESTIMATE Because the pH is between 3.0 and 4.0, the $[H_3O^+]$ must be between 1×10^{-3} and 1×10^{-4}. A pH of 3.1 is very close to 3.0, so the $[H_3O^+]$ must be just slightly below 1×10^{-3} M.

SOLUTION
Entering the negative pH on a calculator (-3.1) and pressing the "INV" and "log" keys gives the answer 7.943×10^{-4}, which must be rounded off to 8×10^{-4} since the pH has only one digit to the right of the decimal point.

BALLPARK CHECK The calculated $[H_3O^+]$ of 8×10^{-4} M is between 1×10^{-3} M and 1×10^{-4} M and, as we estimated, just slightly below 1×10^{-3} M. (Remember, 8×10^{-4} is 0.8×10^{-3}.)

WORKED EXAMPLE **10.10** Working with pH: Calculating pH for Strong Acid Solutions

What is the pH of a 0.0045 M solution of $HClO_4$?

ANALYSIS Finding pH requires first finding $[H_3O^+]$ and then using the equation $pH = -\log[H_3O^+]$. Since $HClO_4$ is a strong acid (see Table 10.1), it is 100% dissociated, and so the H_3O^+ concentration is the same as the $HClO_4$ concentration.

BALLPARK ESTIMATE Because $[H^+] = 4.5 \times 10^{-3}$ M is close to midway between 1×10^{-2} M and 1×10^{-3} M, the pH must be close to the midway point between 2.0 and 3.0. (Unfortunately, because the logarithm scale is not linear, trying to estimate the midway point is not a simple process.)

SOLUTION
$[H_3O^+] = 0.0045$ M $= 4.5 \times 10^{-3}$ M. Taking the negative logarithm gives $pH = 2.35$.

BALLPARK CHECK The calculated pH is consistent with our estimate.

WORKED EXAMPLE **10.11** Working with pH: Calculating pH for Strong Base Solutions

What is the pH of a 0.0032 M solution of NaOH?

ANALYSIS Since NaOH is a strong base, the OH^- concentration is the same as the NaOH concentration. Starting with the OH^- concentration, finding pH requires either using the K_w equation to find $[H_3O^+]$ or calculating pOH and then using the logarithmic form of the K_w equation.

BALLPARK ESTIMATE Because $[OH^-] = 3.2 \times 10^{-3}$ M is close to midway between 1×10^{-2} M and 1×10^{-3} M, the pOH must be close to the midway point between 2.0 and 3.0. Subtracting the pOH from 14 would therefore yield a pH between 11 and 12.

SOLUTION

$$[OH^-] = 0.0032 \text{ M} = 3.2 \times 10^{-3} \text{ M}$$

$$[H_3O^+] = \frac{K_w}{(3.2 \times 10^{-3})} = 3.1 \times 10^{-12} \text{ M}$$

Taking the negative logarithm gives pH $= -\log(3.1 \times 10^{-12}) = 11.51$. Alternatively, we can calculate pOH and subtract from 14.00 using the logarithmic form of the K_w equation. For $[OH^-] = 0.0032$ M,

$$pOH = -\log(3.2 \times 10^{-3}) = 2.49$$

$$pH = 14.00 - 2.49 = 11.51$$

Since the given OH^- concentration included two significant figures, the final pH includes two significant figures beyond the decimal point.

BALLPARK CHECK The calculated pH is consistent with our estimate.

PROBLEM 10.16

Identify the following solutions as acidic or basic, estimate $[H_3O^+]$ values for each, and rank them in order of increasing acidity:

(a) Saliva, pH = 6.5   (b) Pancreatic juice, pH = 7.9
(c) Orange juice, pH = 3.7   (d) Wine, pH = 3.5

PROBLEM 10.17

Find the pH of the following solutions:

(a) Seawater with $[H_3O^+] = 5.3 \times 10^{-9}$ M
(b) A urine sample with $[H_3O^+] = 8.9 \times 10^{-6}$ M

PROBLEM 10.18

What is the pH of a 0.0025 M solution of HCl?

10.10 Laboratory Determination of Acidity

Acid–base indicator A dye that changes color depending on the pH of a solution.

The pH of water is an important indicator of water quality in applications ranging from swimming pool and spa maintenance to municipal water treatment. There are several ways to measure the pH of a solution. The simplest but least accurate method is to use an **acid–base indicator**, a dye that changes color depending on

(a)   (b)

▲ **FIGURE 10.3   Finding pH.**   (a) The color of universal indicator in solutions of known pH from 1 to 12. (b) Testing pH with a paper strip. Comparing the color of the strip with the code on the package gives the approximate pH.

the pH of the solution. For example, the well-known dye *litmus* is red below pH 4.8 but blue above pH 7.8 and the indicator *phenolphthalein* (fee-nol-**thay**-lean) is colorless below pH 8.2 but red above pH 10. To make pH determination particularly easy, test kits are available that contain a mixture of indicators known as *universal indicator* to give approximate pH measurements in the range 2–10 (Figure 10.3a). Also available are rolls of "pH paper," which make it possible to determine pH simply by putting a drop of solution on the paper and comparing the color that appears to the color on a calibration chart (Figure 10.3b).

A much more accurate way to determine pH uses an electronic pH meter like the one shown in Figure 10.4. Electrodes are dipped into the solution, and the pH is read from the meter.

▲ **FIGURE 10.4   Using a pH meter to obtain an accurate reading of pH.** Is milk of magnesia acidic or basic?

APPLICATION ▶   pH of Body Fluids

Each fluid in our bodies has a pH range suited to its function, as shown in the accompanying table. The stability of cell membranes, the shapes of huge protein molecules that must be folded in certain ways to function, and the activities of enzymes are all dependent on appropriate H_3O^+ concentrations.

pH of Body Fluids

FLUID	pH
Blood plasma	7.4
Interstitial fluid	7.4
Cytosol	7.0
Saliva	5.8–7.1
Gastric juice	1.6–1.8
Pancreatic juice	7.5–8.8
Intestinal juice	6.3–8.0
Urine	4.6–8.0
Sweat	4.0–6.8

Blood plasma and the interstitial fluid surrounding cells, which together comprise one-third of body water, have a

slightly basic pH of 7.4. In fact, one of the functions of blood is to neutralize the acid by-products of cellular metabolism. The fluid within cells, called the *cytosol*, is slightly more acidic than the fluid outside, so a pH differential exists.

The strongly acidic gastric juice in the stomach has three important functions. First, gastric juice aids in the digestion of proteins by causing them to denature, or unfold. Second, it kills most of the bacteria we consume along with our food. Third, it converts the enzyme that breaks down proteins from an inactive form to the active form.

When the acidic mixture of partially digested food (*chyme*) leaves the stomach and enters the small intestine, it triggers secretion by the pancreas of an alkaline fluid containing bicarbonate ions, HCO_3^-. A principal function of this pancreatic juice and other intestinal fluids is to dilute and neutralize the hydrochloric acid carried along from the stomach.

Urine has a wide normal pH range, depending on the diet and recent activities. It is generally acidic, though, because one important function of urine is to eliminate a quantity of hydrogen ion equal to that produced by the body each day. Without this elimination, the body would soon be overwhelmed by acid.

See Additional Problem 10.97 at the end of the chapter.

10.11 Buffer Solutions

Buffer A combination of substances that act together to prevent a drastic change in pH; usually a weak acid and its conjugate base.

Much of the body's chemistry depends on maintaining the pH of blood and other fluids within narrow limits. This is accomplished through the use of **buffers**—combinations of substances that act together to prevent a drastic change in pH.

Most buffers are mixtures of a weak acid and a roughly equal concentration of its conjugate base—for example, a solution that contains 0.10 M acetic acid and 0.10 M acetate ion. If a small amount of OH^- is added to a buffer solution, the pH increases, but not by much because the acid component of the buffer neutralizes the added OH^-. If a small amount of H_3O^+ is added to a buffer solution, the pH decreases, but again not by much because the base component of the buffer neutralizes the added H_3O^+.

To see why buffer solutions work, look at the equation for the acid dissociation constant of an acid HA.

For the reaction: $$HA(aq) + H_2O(l) \rightleftharpoons A^-(aq) + H_3O^+(aq)$$

we have $$K_a = \frac{[H_3O^+][A^-]}{[HA]}$$

Rearranging this equation shows that the value of $[H_3O^+]$, and thus the pH, depends on the ratio of the undissociated acid concentration to the conjugate base concentration, $[HA]/[A^-]$:

$$[H_3O^+] = K_a\frac{[HA]}{[A^-]}$$

In the case of the acetic acid–acetate ion buffer, for instance, we have

$$CH_3CO_2H(aq) + H_2O(l) \rightleftharpoons H_3O^+(aq) + CH_3CO_2^-(aq)$$
$$\text{(0.10 M)} \qquad\qquad\qquad\qquad \text{(0.10 M)}$$

and $$[H_3O^+] = K_a\frac{[CH_3CO_2H]}{[CH_3CO_2^-]}$$

Initially, the pH of the 0.10 M acetic acid–0.10 M acetate ion buffer solution is 4.74. When acid is added, most is removed by reaction with $CH_3CO_2^-$. The equilibrium reaction shifts to the left, and as a result the concentration of CH_3CO_2H increases and the concentration of $CH_3CO_2^-$ decreases. As long as the changes in $[CH_3CO_2H]$ and $[CH_3CO_2^-]$ are relatively small, however, the ratio of $[CH_3CO_2H]$ to $[CH_3CO_2^-]$ changes only slightly, and there is little change in the pH.

When base is added to the buffer, most is removed by reaction with CH_3CO_2H. The equilibrium shifts to the right, and so the concentration of CH_3CO_2H decreases and the concentration of $CH_3CO_2^-$ increases. Here too, though, as long as the concentration changes are relatively small, there is little change in the pH.

The ability of a buffer solution to resist changes in pH when acid or base is added is illustrated in Figure 10.5. Addition of 0.010 mol of H_3O^+ to 1.0 L of pure water changes the pH from 7 to 2, and addition of 0.010 mol of OH^- changes the pH from 7 to 12. A similar addition of acid to 1.0 L of a 0.10 M acetic acid–0.10 M acetate ion buffer, however, changes the pH only from 4.74 to 4.68, and addition of base changes the pH only from 4.74 to 4.85.

As we did with K_w, we can convert the rearranged K_a equation to its logarithmic form to obtain

$$pH = pK_a - \log\left(\frac{[HA]}{[A^-]}\right)$$

$$\text{or}\quad pH = pK_a + \log\left(\frac{[A^-]}{[HA]}\right)$$

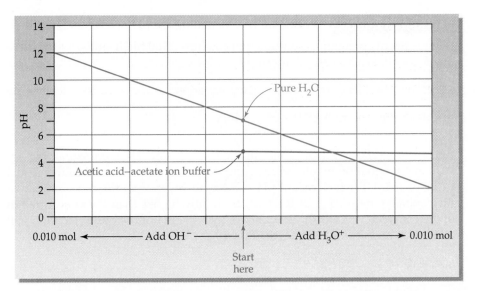

▲ **FIGURE 10.5 A comparison of the change in pH.** When 0.010 mol of acid and 0.010 mol of base are added to 1.0 L of pure water and to 1.0 L of a 0.10 M acetic acid–0.10 M acetate ion buffer, the pH of the water varies between 12 and 2, while the pH of the buffer varies only between 4.85 and 4.68.

This expression is known as the **Henderson–Hasselbalch equation** and is very useful in buffer applications, particularly in biology and biochemistry. Examination of the Henderson–Hasselbalch equation provides useful insights into how to prepare a buffer and into the factors that affect the pH of a buffer solution.

The effective pH range of a buffer will depend on the pK_a of the acid HA and on the relative concentrations of HA and conjugate base A^-. In general, the most effective buffers meet the following conditions:

- The pK_a for the weak acid should be close to the desired pH of the buffer solution.
- The ratio of [HA] to $[A^-]$ should be close to 1, so that neither additional acid nor additional base changes the pH of the solution dramatically.
- The molar amounts of HA and A^- in the buffer should be approximately 10 times greater than the molar amounts of either acid or base you expect to add so that the ratio $[A^-]/[HA]$ does not undergo a large change.

Henderson–Hasselbalch equation The logarithmic form of the K_a equation for a weak acid, used in applications involving buffer solutions.

WORKED EXAMPLE **10.12** Buffers: Selecting a Weak Acid for a Buffer Solution

Which of the organic acids in Table 10.2 would be the most appropriate for preparing a pH 4.15 buffer solution?

ANALYSIS The pH of the buffer solution depends on the pK_a of the weak acid. Remember that $pK_a = -\log(K_a)$.

SOLUTION
The K_a and pK_a values for the four organic acids in Table 10.2 are tabulated below. The ascorbic acid ($pK_a = 4.10$) will produce a buffer solution closest to the desired pH of 4.15.

ORGANIC ACID	K_a	pK_a
Formic acid (HCOOH)	1.8×10^{-4}	3.74
Acetic acid (CH₃COOH)	1.8×10^{-5}	4.74
Propanoic acid (CH₃CH₂COOH)	1.3×10^{-5}	4.89
Ascorbic acid (vitamin C)	7.9×10^{-5}	4.10

WORKED EXAMPLE 10.13 Buffers: Calculating the pH of a Buffer Solution

What is the pH of a buffer solution that contains 0.100 M HF and 0.120 M NaF? The K_a of HF is 3.5×10^{-4}, and so $pK_a = 3.46$.

ANALYSIS The Henderson–Hasselbalch equation can be used to calculate the pH of a buffer solution: $pH = pK_a + \log\left(\dfrac{[F^-]}{[HF]}\right)$.

BALLPARK ESTIMATE If the concentrations of F^- and HF were equal, the log term in our equation would be zero, and the pH of the solution would be equal to the pK_a for HF, which means pH = 3.46. However, since the concentration of the conjugate base ($[F^-] = 0.120$ M) is slightly higher than the concentration of the conjugate acid ($[HF] = 0.100$ M), then the pH of the buffer solution will be slightly higher (more basic) than the pK_a.

SOLUTION

$$pH = pK_a + \log\left(\frac{[F^-]}{[HF]}\right)$$

$$pH = 3.46 + \log\left(\frac{(0.120)}{(0.100)}\right) = 3.46 + 0.08 = 3.54$$

BALLPARK CHECK The calculated pH of 3.54 is consistent with the prediction that the final pH will be slightly higher than the pK_a of 3.46.

WORKED EXAMPLE 10.14 Buffers: Measuring the Effect of Added Base on pH

What is the pH of 1.00 L of the 0.100 M hydrofluoric acid–0.120 M fluoride ion buffer system described in Worked Example 10.13 after 0.020 mol of NaOH is added?

ANALYSIS Initially, the 0.100 M HF–0.120 M NaF buffer has pH = 3.54, as calculated in Worked Example 10.13. The added base will react with the acid as indicated in the neutralization reaction,

$$HF(aq) + OH^-(aq) \longrightarrow H_2O(l) + F^-(aq)$$

which means [HF] decreases and $[F^-]$ increases. With the pK_a and the concentrations of HF and F^- known, pH can be calculated using the Henderson–Hasselbalch equation.

BALLPARK ESTIMATE After the neutralization reaction, there is more conjugate base (F^-) and less conjugate acid (HF), and so we expect the pH to increase slightly from the initial value of 3.54.

SOLUTION
When 0.020 mol of NaOH is added to 1.00 L of the buffer, the HF concentration *decreases* from 0.100 M to 0.080 M as a result of an acid–base reaction. At the same time, the F^- concentration *increases* from 0.120 M to 0.140 M because additional F^- is produced by the neutralization. Using these new values gives

$$pH = 3.46 + \log\left(\frac{(0.140)}{(0.080)}\right) = 3.46 + 0.24 = 3.70$$

The addition of 0.020 mol of base causes the pH of the buffer to rise only from 3.54 to 3.70.

BALLPARK CHECK The final pH, 3.70, is slightly more basic than the initial pH of 3.54, consistent with our prediction.

PROBLEM 10.19

What is the pH of 1.00 L of the 0.100 M hydrofluoric acid–0.120 M fluoride ion buffer system described in Worked Example 10.13 after 0.020 mol of HNO_3 is added?

PROBLEM 10.20

The ammonia/ammonium buffer system is used to optimize polymerase chain reactions (PCR) used in DNA studies. The equilibrium for this buffer can be written as

$$NH_4^+(aq) \rightleftharpoons H^+(aq) + NH_3(aq)$$

Calculate the pH of a buffer that contains 0.050 M ammonium chloride and 0.080 M ammonia. The K_a of ammonium is 5.6×10^{-10}.

KEY CONCEPT PROBLEM 10.21

A buffer solution is prepared using CN^- (from NaCN salt) and HCN in the amounts indicated. The K_a for HCN is 4.9×10^{-10}. Calculate the pH of the buffer solution.

● ● = HCN   ● = CN^-

10.12 Buffers in the Body

The pH of body fluids is maintained by three major buffer systems. Two of these buffers, the carbonic acid–bicarbonate (H_2CO_3–HCO_3^-) system and the dihydrogen phosphate–hydrogen phosphate system, depend on weak acid–conjugate base interactions exactly like those of the acetate buffer system described in the preceding section:

$$H_2CO_3(aq) + H_2O(l) \rightleftharpoons HCO_3^-(aq) + H_3O^+(aq) \qquad pK_a = 6.37$$
$$H_2PO_4^-(aq) + H_2O(l) \rightleftharpoons HPO_4^{2-}(aq) + H_3O^+(aq) \qquad pK_a = 7.21$$

The third buffer system depends on the ability of proteins to act as either proton acceptors or proton donors at different pH values.

To illustrate the action of buffers in the body, take a look at the carbonic acid–bicarbonate system, the principal buffer in blood serum and other extracellular fluids. (The hydrogen phosphate system is the major buffer within cells.) Because carbonic acid is unstable and therefore in equilibrium with CO_2 and water, there is an extra step in the bicarbonate buffer mechanism:

$$CO_2(aq) + H_2O(l) \rightleftharpoons H_2CO_3(aq) \rightleftharpoons HCO_3^-(aq) + H_3O^+(aq)$$

As a result, the bicarbonate buffer system is intimately related to the elimination of CO_2, which is continuously produced in cells and transported to the lungs to be exhaled.

Because most CO_2 is present simply as the dissolved gas rather than as H_2CO_3, the acid dissociation constant for carbonic acid in blood can be written using $[CO_2]$:

$$K_a = \frac{[H_3O^+][HCO_3^-]}{[CO_2]}$$

which can be rearranged to

$$[H_3O^+] = K_a\frac{[CO_2]}{[HCO_3^-]}$$

An increase in $[CO_2]$ raises $[H_3O^+]$ and lowers pH.

A decrease in $[CO_2]$ lowers $[H_3O^+]$ and raises pH.

Converting this rearranged equation to the logarithmic form of the Henderson–Hasselbalch equation yields

$$pH = pK_a + \log\left(\frac{[HCO_3^-]}{[CO_2]}\right)$$

This rearranged equation shows that an increase in $[CO_2]$ makes the ratio of $[HCO_3^-]$ to $[CO_2]$ smaller, thereby decreasing the pH; that is, the blood becomes more acidic. Similarly, a decrease in $[CO_2]$ makes the ratio of $[HCO_3^-]$ to $[CO_2]$ larger, thereby increasing the pH; that is, the blood becomes more basic. At the normal blood pH of 7.4, the ratio $[HCO_3^-]/[CO_2]$ is about 20 to 1.

The relationships between the bicarbonate buffer system, the lungs, and the kidneys are shown in Figure 10.6. Under normal circumstances, the reactions shown in the figure are at equilibrium. Addition of excess acid (red arrows) causes formation of H_2CO_3 and results in lowering of H_3O^+ concentration. Removal of acid (blue arrows) causes formation of more H_3O^+ by dissociation of H_2CO_3. The maintenance of pH by this mechanism is supported by a reserve of bicarbonate ions in body fluids. Such a buffer can accommodate large additions of H_3O^+ before there is a significant change in the pH, a condition that meets the body's needs because excessive production of acid is a more common body condition than excessive loss of acid.

▶ **FIGURE 10.6 Relationships of the bicarbonate buffer system to the lungs and the kidneys.** The red and blue arrows show the responses to the stresses of increased or decreased respiratory rate and removal or addition of acid.

A change in the breathing rate provides a quick further adjustment in the bicarbonate buffer system. When the CO_2 concentration in the blood starts to rise, the breathing rate increases to remove CO_2, thereby decreasing the acid concentration (red arrows in Figure 10.6). When the CO_2 concentration in the blood starts to

APPLICATION ▶ Buffers in the Body: Acidosis and Alkalosis

A group of teenagers at a rock concert experience a collective fainting spell. A person taking high doses of aspirin for chronic pain appears disoriented and is having trouble breathing. An insulin-dependent diabetic patient complains of tiredness and stomach pains. An athlete who recently completed a highly strenuous workout suffers from muscle cramps and nausea. A patient on an HIV drug regimen experiences increasing weakness and numbness in the hands and feet. What do all these individuals have in common? They are all suffering from abnormal fluctuations in blood pH, resulting in conditions known as *acidosis* (pH < 7.35) or *alkalosis* (pH > 7.45).

The highly complex series of reactions and equilibria that take place throughout the body are very sensitive to pH—variations of even a few tenths of a pH unit can produce severe physiological symptoms. The carbonate–bicarbonate buffer system (Section 10.12) maintains the pH of blood serum at a fairly constant value of 7.4. The effective pH depends on the relative amounts of CO_2 and bicarbonate dissolved in the blood:

$$CO_2(aq) + H_2O(l)$$
$$\rightleftharpoons H_2CO_3(aq) \rightleftharpoons HCO_3^-(aq) + H_3O^+(aq)$$

Anything that significantly shifts the balance between dissolved CO_2 and HCO_3^- can raise or lower the pH. How does this happen, and how does the body compensate?

Respiratory acidosis can be caused by a decrease in respiration, which leads to a buildup of excess CO_2 in the blood and a corresponding decrease in pH. This could be caused by a blocked air passage due to inhaled food—removal of the blockage restores normal breathing and a return to the optimal pH. *Metabolic acidosis* results from an excess of other acids in the blood that reduce the bicarbonate concentration. High doses of aspirin (acetyl salicylic acid, Section 17.5), for example, increase the hydronium ion concentration and decrease the pH. Strenuous exercise generates excess lactate in the muscles, which is released into the bloodstream (Section 23.11). The liver converts lactate into glucose, which is the body's major source of energy; this process consumes bicarbonate ions, which decreases the pH. Some HIV drug therapies can damage cellular mitochondria (Section 21.3),

resulting in a buildup of lactic acid in the cells and blood stream. In the case of the diabetic patient, lack of insulin causes the body to start burning fat, which generates ketones and keto acids (Chapter 16), organic compounds that lower the blood pH.

The body attempts to correct acidosis by increasing the rate and depth of respiration—breathing faster "blows off" CO_2, shifting the CO_2–bicarbonate equilibrium to the left and lowering the pH. The net effect is rapid reversal of the acidosis. Although this may be sufficient for cases of respiratory acidosis, it provides only temporary relief for metabolic acidosis. A long-term solution depends on removal of excess acid by the kidneys, which can take several hours.

What about our teenage fans? In their excitement they have hyperventilated—their increased breathing rate has removed too much CO_2 from their blood and they are suffering from *respiratory alkalosis*. The body responds by "fainting" to decrease respiration and restore the CO_2 levels in the blood. When they regain consciousness, they will be ready to rock once again.

▲ Hyperventilation, the rapid breathing due to excitement or stress, removes CO_2 and increases blood pH resulting in respiratory alkalosis.

See Additional Problems 10.98 and 10.99 at the end of the chapter.

fall, the breathing rate decreases and acid concentration increases (blue arrows in Figure 10.6).

Additional backup to the bicarbonate buffer system is provided by the kidneys. Each day a quantity of acid equal to that produced in the body is excreted in the urine. In the process, the kidney returns HCO_3^- to the extracellular fluids, where it becomes part of the bicarbonate reserve.

⊂⊃ Looking Ahead

In Chapter 29, we will see how the regulation of blood pH by the bicarbonate buffer system is particularly important in preventing *acidosis* and *alkalosis*. ⊂⊃

10.13 Acid and Base Equivalents

We said in Section 9.10 that it is sometimes useful to think in terms of ion *equivalents* (Eq) and *gram-equivalents* (g-Eq) when we are primarily interested in an ion itself rather than the compound that produced the ion. (⊂⊃⊃, p. 276) For similar reasons, it can also be useful to consider acid or base equivalents and gram-equivalents.

When dealing with ions, the property of interest was the charge on the ion. Therefore, 1 Eq of an ion was defined as the number of ions that carry 1 mol of charge, and 1 g-Eq of any ion was defined as the molar mass of the ion divided by the ionic charge. For acids and bases, the property of interest is the number of H^+ ions (for an acid) or the number of OH^- ions (for a base) per formula unit. Thus, 1 **equivalent of acid** contains 1 mol of H^+ ions, and 1 g-Eq of an acid is the mass in grams that contains 1 mol of H^+ ions. Similarly, 1 **equivalent of base** contains 1 mol of OH^- ions, and 1 g-Eq of a base is the mass in grams that contains 1 mol of OH^- ions:

Equivalent of acid Amount of an acid that contains 1 mole of H^+ ions.

Equivalent of base Amount of base that contains 1 mole of OH^- ions.

$$\text{One gram-equivalent of acid} = \frac{\text{Molar mass of acid (g)}}{\text{Number of } H^+ \text{ ions per formula unit}}$$

$$\text{One gram-equivalent of base} = \frac{\text{Molar mass of base (g)}}{\text{Number of } OH^- \text{ ions per formula unit}}$$

Thus 1 g-Eq of the monoprotic acid HCl is

$$1 \text{ g-Eq HCl} = \frac{36.5 \text{ g}}{1 \text{ } H^+ \text{ per HCl}} = 36.5 \text{ g}$$

which is the molar mass of the acid, but one gram-equivalent of the diprotic acid H_2SO_4 is

$$1 \text{ g-Eq } H_2SO_4 = \frac{98.0 \text{ g}}{2 \text{ } H^+ \text{ per } H_2SO_4} = 49.0 \text{ g}$$

which is the molar mass divided by 2 because 1 mol of H_2SO_4 contains 2 mol of H^+.

$$\text{One equivalent of } H_2SO_4 = \frac{\text{Molar mass of } H_2SO_4}{2} = \frac{98.0 \text{ g}}{2} = 49.0 \text{ g}$$

Divide by 2 because H_2SO_4 is diprotic.

Using acid–base equivalents has two practical advantages: First, they are convenient when only the acidity or basicity of a solution is of interest rather than the identity of the acid or base. Second, they show quantities that are chemically equivalent in their properties; 36.5 g of HCl and 49.0 g of H_2SO_4 are chemically equivalent quantities because each reacts with 1 Eq of base. *One equivalent of any acid neutralizes one equivalent of any base.*

Because acid–base equivalents are so useful, clinical chemists sometimes express acid and base concentrations in *normality* rather than molarity. The **normality (N)** of an acid or base solution is defined as the number of equivalents (or milliequivalents) of acid or base per liter of solution. For example, a solution made by dissolving 1.0 g-Eq (49.0 g) of H_2SO_4 in water to give 1.0 L of solution has a concentration of 1.0 Eq/L, which is 1.0 N. Similarly, a solution that contains 0.010 Eq/L of acid is 0.010 N and has an acid concentration of 10 mEq/L:

$$\text{Normality (N)} = \frac{\text{Equivalents of acid or base}}{\text{Liters of solution}}$$

The values of molarity (M) and normality (N) are the same for monoprotic acids, such as HCl, but are not the same for diprotic or triprotic acids. A solution made by diluting 1.0 g-Eq (49.0 g = 0.50 mol) of the diprotic acid H_2SO_4 to a volume of 1.0 L has a *normality* of 1.0 N but a *molarity* of 0.50 M. For any acid or base, normality is always equal to molarity times the number of H^+ or OH^- ions produced per formula unit:

Normality of acid = (Molarity of acid) × (Number of H^+ ions produced per formula unit)

Normality of base = (Molarity of base) × (Number of OH^- ions produced per formula unit)

WORKED EXAMPLE **10.15** Equivalents: Mass to Equivalent Conversion for Diprotic Acid

How many equivalents are in 3.1 g of the diprotic acid H_2S? The molar mass of H_2S is 34.0 g.

ANALYSIS The number of acid or base equivalents is calculated by doing a gram to mole conversion using molar mass as the conversion factor and then multiplying by the number of H^+ ions produced.

BALLPARK ESTIMATE The 3.1 g is a little less than 0.10 mol of H_2S. Since it is a diprotic acid, (two H^+ per mole), this represents a little less than 0.2 Eq of H_2S.

SOLUTION

$$(3.1 \ \text{g } H_2S)\left(\frac{1 \ \text{mol } H_2S}{34.0 \ \text{g } H_2S}\right)\left(\frac{2 \ \text{Eq } H_2S}{1 \ \text{mol } H_2S}\right) = 0.18 \ \text{Eq } H_2S$$

BALLPARK CHECK The calculated value of 0.18 is consistent with our prediction of a little less than 0.2 Eq of H_2S.

WORKED EXAMPLE **10.16** Equivalents: Calculating Equivalent Concentrations

What is the normality of a solution made by diluting 6.5 g of H_2SO_4 to a volume of 200 mL? What is the concentration of this solution in milliequivalents per liter? The molar mass of H_2SO_4 is 98.0 g.

ANALYSIS Calculate how many equivalents of H_2SO_4 are in 6.5 g by using the molar mass of the acid as a conversion factor and then determine the normality of the acid.

SOLUTION

STEP 1: **Identify known information.** We know the molar mass of H_2SO_4, the mass of H_2SO_4 to be dissolved, and the final volume of solution.

MW of H_2SO_4 = 98.0 g/mol
Mass of H_2SO_4 = 6.5 g
Volume of solution = 200 mL

STEP 2: **Identify answer including units.** We need to calculate the normality of the final solution.

Normality = ?? (equiv./L)

STEP 3: **Identify conversion factors.** We will need to convert the mass of H_2SO_4 to moles, and then to equivalents of H_2SO_4. We will then need to convert volume from mL to L.

$$(6.5 \ \text{g } H_2SO_4)\left(\frac{1 \ \text{mol } H_2SO_4}{98.0 \ \text{g } H_2SO_4}\right)\left(\frac{2 \ \text{Eq } H_2SO_4}{1 \ \text{mol } H_2SO_4}\right)$$

$$= 0.132 \ \text{Eq } H_2SO_4 \ (\text{don't round yet!})$$

$$(200 \ \text{mL})\left(\frac{1 \ \text{L}}{1000 \ \text{mL}}\right) = 0.200 \ \text{L}$$

STEP 4: **Solve.** Dividing the number of equivalents by the volume yields the Normality.

$$\frac{0.132 \ \text{Eq } H_2SO_4}{0.200 \ \text{L}} = 0.66 \ \text{N}$$

The concentration of the sulfuric acid solution is 0.66 N, or 660 mEq/L.

PROBLEM 10.22

How many equivalents are in the following?

(a) 5.0 g HNO_3 (b) 12.5 g $Ca(OH)_2$ (c) 4.5 g H_3PO_4

PROBLEM 10.23

What are the normalities of the solutions if each sample in Problem 10.22 is dissolved in water and diluted to a volume of 300.0 mL?

10.14 Some Common Acid–Base Reactions

Among the most common of the many kinds of Brønsted–Lowry acid–base reactions are those of an acid with hydroxide ion, an acid with bicarbonate or carbonate ion, and an acid with ammonia or a related nitrogen-containing compound. Let us look briefly at each of the three types.

Reaction of Acids with Hydroxide Ion

One equivalent of an acid reacts with 1 Eq of a metal hydroxide to yield water and a salt in a neutralization reaction (Section 6.10): (⬤▭, p. 165)

$$HCl(aq) + KOH(aq) \longrightarrow H_2O(l) + KCl(aq)$$

(An acid)   (A base)   (Water)   (A salt)

Such reactions are usually written with a single arrow because their equilibria lie far to the right and they have very large equilibrium constants ($K = 5 \times 10^{15}$; Section 7.8). The net ionic equation (Section 6.13) for all such reactions makes clear why acid-base equivalents are useful and why the properties of the acid and base disappear in neutralization reactions: The equivalent ions for the acid (H^+) and the base (OH^-) are used up in the formation of water.

$$H^+(aq) + OH^-(aq) \longrightarrow H_2O(l)$$

PROBLEM 10.24

Maalox, an over-the-counter antacid, contains aluminum hydroxide, $Al(OH)_3$, and magnesium hydroxide, $Mg(OH)_2$. Write balanced equations for the reaction of both with stomach acid (HCl).

Reaction of Acids with Bicarbonate and Carbonate Ion

Bicarbonate ion reacts with acid by accepting H^+ to yield carbonic acid, H_2CO_3. Similarly, carbonate ion accepts two protons in its reaction with acid. As mentioned on p. 315, though, that H_2CO_3 is unstable, rapidly decomposing to carbon dioxide gas and water:

$$H^+(aq) + HCO_3^-(aq) \longrightarrow [H_2CO_3(aq)] \longrightarrow H_2O(l) + CO_2(g)$$
$$2\,H^+(aq) + CO_3^{2-}(aq) \longrightarrow [H_2CO_3(aq)] \longrightarrow H_2O(l) + CO_2(g)$$

Most metal carbonates are insoluble in water—marble, for example, is almost pure calcium carbonate, $CaCO_3$—but they nevertheless react easily with aqueous acid. In fact, geologists often test for carbonate-bearing rocks by putting a few drops of aqueous HCl on the rock and watching to see if bubbles of CO_2 form (Figure 10.7). This reaction is also responsible for the damage to marble and

▲ **FIGURE 10.7 Marble.** Marble, which is primarily $CaCO_3$, releases bubbles of CO_2 when treated with hydrochloric acid.

limestone artwork caused by acid rain (See Application, p. 324). The most common application involving carbonates and acid, however, is the use of antacids that contain carbonates, such as Tums or Rolaids, to neutralize excess stomach acid.

PROBLEM 10.25

Write a balanced equation for each of the following reactions:

(a) $KHCO_3(aq) + H_2SO_4(aq) \longrightarrow$?
(b) $MgCO_3(aq) + HNO_3(aq) \longrightarrow$?

Reaction of Acids with Ammonia

Acids react with ammonia to yield ammonium salts, such as ammonium chloride, NH_4Cl, most of which are water-soluble:

$$NH_3(aq) + HCl(aq) \longrightarrow NH_4Cl(aq)$$

Living organisms contain a group of compounds called *amines*, which contain nitrogen atoms bonded to carbon. Amines react with acids just as ammonia does, yielding water-soluble salts. Methylamine, for example, an organic compound found in rotting fish, reacts with HCl:

▲ This limestone statue adorning the Rheims Cathedral in France has been severely eroded by acid rain.

$$H-\overset{\displaystyle H}{\underset{\displaystyle H}{C}}-\overset{\displaystyle H}{N:} \; + \; H-Cl \longrightarrow H-\overset{\displaystyle H}{\underset{\displaystyle H}{C}}-\overset{\displaystyle H}{\underset{\displaystyle H}{N}}\overset{+}{}-H \quad Cl^-$$

Methylamine   Methylammonium chloride

◷◷ Looking Ahead

In Chapter 15, we will see that amines occur in all living organisms, both plant and animal, as well as in many pharmaceutical agents. Amines called amino acids form the building blocks from which proteins are made, as we will see in Chapter 18. ◷◷

PROBLEM 10.26

What products would you expect from the reaction of ammonia and sulfuric acid in aqueous solution?

$$NH_3(aq) + H_2SO_4(aq) \longrightarrow \; ?$$

PROBLEM 10.27

Show how ethylamine ($C_2H_5NH_2$) reacts with hydrochloric acid to form an ethylammonium salt.

10.15 Titration

Determining the pH of a solution gives the solution's H_3O^+ concentration but not necessarily its total acid concentration. That is because the two are not the same thing. The H_3O^+ concentration gives only the amount of acid that has dissociated into ions, whereas total acid concentration gives the sum of dissociated plus undissociated acid. In a 0.10 M solution of acetic acid, for instance, the total acid concentration is 0.10 M, yet the H_3O^+ concentration is only 0.0013 M (pH = 2.89) because acetic acid is a weak acid that is only about 1% dissociated.

Titration A procedure for determining the total acid or base concentration of a solution.

The total acid or base concentration of a solution can be found by carrying out a **titration** procedure, as shown in Figure 10.8. Let us assume, for instance, that we want to find the acid concentration of an HCl solution. (We could equally well need to find the base concentration of an NaOH solution.) We begin by measuring out a known volume of the HCl solution and adding an acid–base indicator. Next, we fill a calibrated glass tube called a *buret* with an NaOH solution of known concentration, and we slowly add the NaOH to the HCl until neutralization is complete (the *end point*), identified by a color change in the indicator.

(a)   (b)

▲ **FIGURE 10.8 Titration of an acid solution of unknown concentration with a base solution of known concentration.**   (a) A measured volume of the acid solution is placed in the flask along with an indicator. (b) The base of known concentration is then added from a buret until the color change of the indicator shows that neutralization is complete (the *end point*).

Reading from the buret gives the volume of the NaOH solution that has reacted with the known volume of HCl. Knowing both the concentration and volume of the NaOH solution then allows us to calculate the molar amount of NaOH, and the coefficients in the balanced equation allow us to find the molar amount of HCl that has been neutralized. Dividing the molar amount of HCl by the volume of the HCl solution gives the concentration. The calculation thus involves mole–volume conversions just like those done in Section 9.7. (⬭, p. 265) Figure 10.9 shows a flow diagram of the strategy, and Worked Example 10.17 shows how to calculate total acid concentration.

▲ **FIGURE 10.9 A flow diagram for an acid–base titration.**   This diagram summarizes the calculations needed to determine the concentration of an HCl solution by titration with an NaOH solution of known concentration. The steps are similar to those shown in Figure 9.7.

WORKED EXAMPLE **10.17** Titrations: Calculating Total Acid Concentration

When a 5.00 mL sample of household vinegar (dilute aqueous acetic acid) is titrated, 44.5 mL of 0.100 M NaOH solution is required to reach the end point. What is the acid concentration of the vinegar in moles per liter, equivalents per liter, and milliequivalents per liter? The neutralization reaction is

$$CH_3CO_2H(aq) + NaOH(aq) \longrightarrow CH_3CO_2^-Na^+(aq) + H_2O(l)$$

ANALYSIS To find the molarity of the vinegar, we need to know the number of moles of acetic acid dissolved in the 5.00 mL sample. Following a flow diagram similar to Figure 10.9, we use the volume and molarity of NaOH to find the number of moles. From the chemical equation, we use the mole ratio to find the number of moles of acid, and then divide by the volume of the acid solution. Because acetic acid is a monoprotic acid, the normality of the solution is numerically the same as its molarity.

BALLPARK ESTIMATE The 5.00 mL of vinegar required nearly nine times as much NaOH solution (44.5 mL) for complete reaction. Since the neutralization stoichiometry is 1:1, the molarity of the acetic acid in the vinegar must be nine times greater than the molarity of NaOH, or 0.90 M.

SOLUTION
Substitute the known information and appropriate conversion factors into the flow diagram, and solve for the molarity of the acetic acid:

$$(44.5 \text{ mL NaOH})\left(\frac{0.100 \text{ mol NaOH}}{1000 \text{ mL}}\right)\left(\frac{1 \text{ mol } CH_3CO_2H}{1 \text{ mol NaOH}}\right)$$

$$\times \left(\frac{1}{0.005\ 00 \text{ L}}\right) = 0.890 \text{ M } CH_3CO_2H$$

$$= 0.890 \text{ N } CH_3CO_2H$$

Expressed in milliequivalents, this concentration is

$$\frac{0.890 \text{ Eq}}{L} \times \frac{1000 \text{ mEq}}{1 \text{ Eq}} = 890 \text{ mEq/L}$$

BALLPARK CHECK The calculated result (0.890 M) is very close to our estimate of 0.90 M.

PROBLEM 10.28

A titration is carried out to determine the concentration of the acid in an old bottle of aqueous HCl whose label has become unreadable. What is the HCl concentration if 58.4 mL of 0.250 M NaOH is required to titrate a 20.0 mL sample of the acid?

APPLICATION ▶ Acid Rain

As the water that evaporates from oceans and lakes condenses into raindrops, it dissolves small quantities of gases from the atmosphere. Under normal conditions, rain is slightly acidic, with a pH close to 5.6, because of atmospheric CO_2 that dissolves to form carbonic acid:

$$CO_2(aq) + H_2O(l) \rightleftharpoons$$
$$H_2CO_3(aq) \rightleftharpoons HCO_3^-(aq) + H_3O^+(aq)$$

In recent decades, however, the acidity of rainwater in many industrialized areas of the world has increased by a factor of over 100, to a pH between 3 and 3.5.

The primary cause of this so-called *acid rain* is industrial and automotive pollution. Each year, large power plants and smelters pour millions of tons of sulfur dioxide (SO_2) gas into the atmosphere, where some is oxidized by air to produce sulfur trioxide (SO_3). Sulfur oxides then dissolve in rain to form dilute sulfurous acid (H_2SO_3) and sulfuric acid (H_2SO_4):

$$SO_2(g) + H_2O(l) \longrightarrow H_2SO_3(aq)$$
$$SO_3(g) + H_2O(l) \longrightarrow H_2SO_4(aq)$$

Nitrogen oxides produced by the high-temperature reaction of N_2 with O_2 in coal-burning plants and in automobile engines further contribute to the problem. Nitrogen dioxide (NO_2) dissolves in water to form dilute nitric acid (HNO_3) and nitric oxide (NO):

$$3\ NO_2(g) + H_2O(l) \longrightarrow 2\ HNO_3(aq) + NO(g)$$

Oxides of both sulfur and nitrogen have always been present in the atmosphere, produced by such natural sources as volcanoes and lightning bolts, but their amounts have increased dramatically over the last century because of industrialization. The result is a notable decrease in the pH of rainwater in more densely populated regions, including Europe and the eastern United States.

Many processes in nature require such a fine pH balance that they are dramatically upset by the shift that has occurred in the pH of rain. Some watersheds contain soils that have high "buffering capacity" and so are able to neutralize acidic compounds in acid rain (Section 10.11). Other areas, such as the northeastern United States and eastern Canada, where soil buffering capacity is poor, have experienced negative ecological effects. Acid rain releases aluminum salts from soil, and the ions then wash into streams. The low pH and increased aluminum levels are so toxic to fish and other organisms that many lakes and streams in these areas are devoid of aquatic life. Massive tree die-offs have occurred throughout central and eastern Europe as acid rain has lowered the pH of the soil and has leached nutrients from leaves.

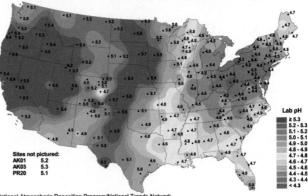

Hydrogen ion concentration as pH from measurements made at the Central Analytical Laboratory, 1996

Sites not pictured:
AK01   5.2
AK03   5.3
PR20   5.1

National Atmospheric Deposition Program/National Trends Network
http://nadp.sws.uiuc.edu

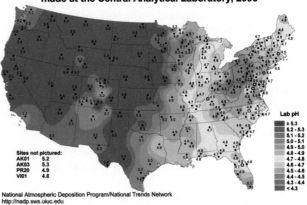

Hydrogen ion concentration as pH from measurements made at the Central Analytical Laboratory, 2006

Sites not pictured:
AK01   5.2
AK03   5.3
PR20   4.9
VI01   4.8

National Atmospheric Deposition Program/National Trends Network
http://nadp.sws.uiuc.edu

▲ These maps compare the average pH of precipitation in the United States in 1996 and in 2006. During this period, total acid deposition in much of the eastern United States decreased substantially.

Fortunately, acidic emissions in the United States have been greatly reduced in recent years as a result of the Clean Air Act Amendments of 1990. Industrial emissions of SO_2 and nitrogen oxides decreased by over 40% from 1990 to 2007, resulting in a decrease in acid rain depositions, particularly in the eastern United States and Canada (see accompanying figure). While significant reductions have been realized, most environmental scientists agree that additional reductions in these pollutant emissions are necessary to ensure the recovery of affected lakes and streams.

See Additional Problems 10.100 and 10.101 at the end of the chapter.

PROBLEM 10.29

How many milliliters of 0.150 M NaOH are required to neutralize 50.0 mL of 0.200 M H_2SO_4? The balanced neutralization reaction is:

$$H_2SO_4(aq) + 2\,NaOH(aq) \longrightarrow Na_2SO_4(aq) + 2\,H_2O(l).$$

PROBLEM 10.30

A 21.5 mL sample of a KOH solution of unknown concentration requires 16.1 mL of 0.150 M H_2SO_4 solution to reach the end point in a titration. What is the molarity of the KOH solution?

10.16 Acidity and Basicity of Salt Solutions

It is tempting to think of all salt solutions as neutral; after all, they come from the neutralization reaction between an acid and a base. In fact, salt solutions can be neutral, acidic, or basic, depending on the ions present, because some ions react with water to produce H_3O^+ and some ions react with water to produce OH^-. To predict the acidity of a salt solution, it is convenient to classify salts according to the acid and base from which they are formed in a neutralization reaction. The classification and some examples are given in Table 10.3.

TABLE 10.3 Acidity and Basicity of Salt Solutions

ANION DERIVED FROM ACID THAT IS:	CATION DERIVED FROM BASE THAT IS:	SOLUTION	EXAMPLE
Strong	Weak	Acidic	NH_4Cl, NH_4NO_3
Weak	Strong	Basic	$NaHCO_3$, KCH_3CO_2
Strong	Strong	Neutral	$NaCl$, KBr, $Ca(NO_3)_2$
Weak	Weak	More information needed	

The general rule for predicting the acidity or basicity of a salt solution is that the stronger partner from which the salt is formed dominates. That is, a salt formed from a strong acid and a weak base yields an acidic solution because the strong acid dominates; a salt formed from a weak acid and a strong base yields a basic solution because the base dominates; and a salt formed from a strong acid and a strong base yields a neutral solution because neither acid nor base dominates. Here are some examples.

Salt of Strong Acid + Weak Base $\longrightarrow$ Acidic Solution

A salt such as NH_4Cl, which can be formed by reaction of a strong acid (HCl) with a weak base (NH_3), yields an acidic solution. The Cl^- ion does not react with water, but the NH_4^+ ion is a weak acid that gives H_3O^+ ions:

$$NH_4^+(aq) + H_2O(l) \rightleftharpoons NH_3(aq) + H_3O^+(aq)$$

Salt of Weak Acid + Strong Base $\longrightarrow$ Basic Solution

A salt such as sodium bicarbonate, which can be formed by reaction of a weak acid (H_2CO_3) with a strong base (NaOH), yields a basic solution. The Na^+ ion does not react with water, but the HCO_3^- ion is a weak base that gives OH^- ions:

$$HCO_3^-(aq) + H_2O(l) \rightleftharpoons H_2CO_3(aq) + OH^-(aq)$$

Salt of Strong Acid + Strong Base $\longrightarrow$ Neutral Solution

A salt such as NaCl, which can be formed by reaction of a strong acid (HCl) with a strong base (NaOH), yields a neutral solution. Neither the Cl^- ion nor the Na^+ ion reacts with water.

Salt of Weak Acid + Weak Base

Both cation and anion in this type of salt react with water, so we cannot predict whether the resulting solution will be acidic or basic without quantitative information. The ion that reacts to the greater extent with water will govern the pH—it may be either the cation or the anion.

WORKED EXAMPLE **10.18** Acidity and Basicity of Salt Solutions

Predict whether the following salts produce an acidic, basic, or neutral solution:

(a) $BaCl_2$ (b) NaCN   (c) NH_4NO_3

ANALYSIS Look in Table 10.1 (p. 300) to see the classification of acids and bases as strong or weak.

SOLUTION

(a) $BaCl_2$ gives a neutral solution because it is formed from a strong acid (HCl) and a strong base $[Ba(OH)_2]$.

(b) NaCN gives a basic solution because it is formed from a weak acid (HCN) and a strong base (NaOH).

(c) NH_4NO_3 gives an acidic solution because it is formed from a strong acid (HNO_3) and a weak base (NH_3).

PROBLEM 10.31

Predict whether the following salts produce an acidic, basic, or neutral solution:

(a) K_2SO_4 (b) Na_2HPO_4 (c) MgF_2 (d) NH_4Br

KEY WORDS

Acid dissociation constant (K_a), p. 303

Acid–base indicator, p. 310

Amphoteric, p. 299

Brønsted–Lowry acid, p. 295

Brønsted–Lowry base, p. 296

Buffer, p. 312

Conjugate acid, p. 297

Conjugate acid–base pair, p. 297

Conjugate base, p. 297

SUMMARY: REVISITING THE CHAPTER GOALS

1. **What are acids and bases?** According to the *Brønsted–Lowry definition*, an acid is a substance that donates a hydrogen ion (a proton, H^+) and a base is a substance that accepts a hydrogen ion. Thus, the generalized reaction of an acid with a base involves the reversible transfer of a proton:

$$B: + H—A \rightleftarrows A:^- + H—B^+$$

In aqueous solution, water acts as a base and accepts a proton from an acid to yield a *hydronium ion*, H_3O^+. Reaction of an acid with a metal hydroxide, such as KOH, yields water and a salt; reaction with bicarbonate ion (HCO_3^-) or carbonate ion (CO_3^{2-}) yields water, a salt, and CO_2 gas; and reaction with ammonia yields an ammonium salt.

2. **What effect does the strength of acids and bases have on their reactions?** Different acids and bases differ in their ability to give up or accept a proton. A *strong acid* gives up a proton easily and is 100% *dissociated* in aqueous solution; a *weak acid* gives up a proton with difficulty, is only slightly dissociated in water, and establishes an equilibrium between dissociated and undissociated forms. Similarly, a *strong base* accepts and holds a proton

readily, whereas a *weak base* has a low affinity for a proton and establishes an equilibrium in aqueous solution. The two substances that are related by the gain or loss of a proton are called a *conjugate acid–base pair*. The exact strength of an acid is defined by an *acid dissociation constant, K_a*:

$$\text{For the reaction} \quad HA + H_2O \rightleftharpoons H_3O^+ + A^-$$

$$\text{we have} \quad K_a = \frac{[H_3O^+][A^-]}{[HA]}$$

A proton-transfer reaction always takes place in the direction that favors formation of the weaker acid.

3. **What is the ion-product constant for water?** Water is *amphoteric*; that is, it can act as either an acid or a base. Water also dissociates slightly into H_3O^+ ions and OH^- ions; the product of whose concentrations in any aqueous solution is the *ion-product constant for water*, $K_w = [H_3O^+][OH^-] = 1.00 \times 10^{-14}$ at 25 °C.

4. **What is the pH scale for measuring acidity?** The acidity or basicity of an aqueous solution is given by its *pH*, defined as the negative logarithm of the hydronium ion concentration, $[H_3O^+]$. A pH below 7 means an acidic solution; a pH equal to 7 means a neutral solution; and a pH above 7 means a basic solution.

5. **What is a buffer?** The pH of a solution can be controlled through the use of a *buffer* that acts to remove either added H^+ ions or added OH^- ions. Most buffer solutions consist of roughly equal amounts of a weak acid and its conjugate base. The bicarbonate buffer present in blood and the hydrogen phosphate buffer present in cells are particularly important examples.

6. **How is the acid or base concentration of a solution determined?** Acid (or base) concentrations are determined in the laboratory by *titration* of a solution of unknown concentration with a base (or acid) solution of known strength until an indicator signals that neutralization is complete.

UNDERSTANDING KEY CONCEPTS

10.32 Identify the Brønsted–Lowry acid and base in the following reactions:

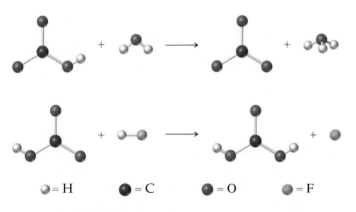

$$\bigcirc = H \qquad \bullet = C \qquad \bullet = O \qquad \bullet = F$$

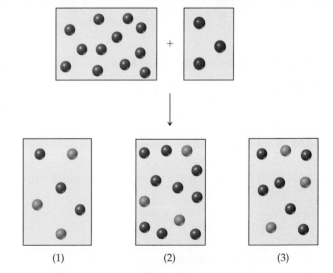

10.33 An aqueous solution of OH^-, represented as a blue sphere, is allowed to mix with a solution of an acid H_nA, represented as a red sphere. Three possible outcomes are depicted by boxes (1)–(3), where the green spheres represent A^{n-}, the anion of the acid:

Which outcome corresponds to the following reactions?

(a) $HF + OH^- \longrightarrow H_2O + F^-$

(b) $H_2SO_3 + 2\,OH^- \longrightarrow 2\,H_2O + SO_3^{2-}$

(c) $H_3PO_4 + 3\,OH^- \longrightarrow 3\,H_2O + PO_4^{3-}$

10.34 Electrostatic potential maps of acetic acid (CH_3CO_2H) and ethyl alcohol (CH_3CH_2OH) are shown. Identify the most acidic hydrogen in each, and tell which of the two is likely to be the stronger acid.

CH₃CO₂H   CH₃CH₂OH

10.35 The following pictures represent aqueous acid solutions. Water molecules are not shown.

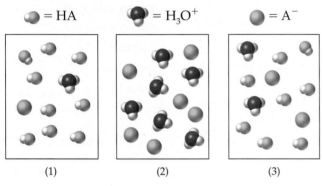

(1)   (2)   (3)

(a) Which picture represents the weakest acid?
(b) Which picture represents the strongest acid?
(c) Which picture represents the acid with the smallest value of K_a?

10.36 The following pictures represent aqueous solutions of a diprotic acid H_2A. Water molecules are not shown.

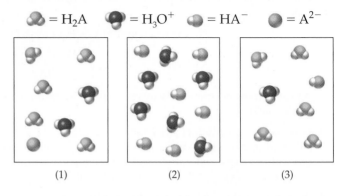

(1)   (2)   (3)

(a) Which picture represents a solution of a weak diprotic acid?
(b) Which picture represents an impossible situation?

10.37 Assume that the red spheres in the buret represent H^+ ions, the blue spheres in the flask represent OH^- ions, and you are carrying out a titration of the base with the acid. If the volumes in the buret and the flask are identical and the concentration of the acid in the buret is 1.00 M, what is the concentration of the base in the flask?

ADDITIONAL PROBLEMS

ACIDS AND BASES

10.38 What happens when a strong acid such as HBr is dissolved in water?

10.39 What happens when a weak acid such as CH_3CO_2H is dissolved in water?

10.40 What happens when a strong base such as KOH is dissolved in water?

10.41 What happens when a weak base such as NH_3 is dissolved in water?

10.42 What is the difference between a monoprotic acid and a diprotic acid? Give an example of each.

10.43 What is the difference between H^+ and H_3O^+?

10.44 Which of the following are strong acids? Look at Table 10.1 (*p. 300*) if necessary.

(a) $HClO_4$ (b) H_2CO_3
(c) H_3PO_4 (d) NH_4^+
(e) HI   (f) $H_2PO_4^-$

10.45 Which of the following are weak bases? Look at Table 10.1 (*p. 300*) if necessary.

(a) NH_3 (b) $Ca(OH)_2$
(c) HPO_4^{2-} (d) LiOH
(e) CN^- (f) NH_2^-

BRØNSTED–LOWRY ACIDS AND BASES

10.46 Identify the following substances as a Brønsted–Lowry base, a Brønsted–Lowry acid, or neither:

(a) HCN   (b) $CH_3CO_2^-$
(c) $AlCl_3$ (d) H_2CO_3
(e) Mg^{2+} (f) $CH_3NH_3^+$

10.47 Label the Brønsted–Lowry acids and bases in the following equations, and tell which substances are conjugate acid–base pairs.

(a) $CO_3^{2-}(aq) + HCl(aq) \longrightarrow HCO_3^-(aq) + Cl^-(aq)$
(b) $H_3PO_4(aq) + NH_3(aq) \longrightarrow H_2PO_4^-(aq) + NH_4^+(aq)$

(c) $NH_4^+(aq) + CN^-(aq) \rightleftharpoons NH_3(aq) + HCN(aq)$

(d) $HBr(aq) + OH^-(aq) \longrightarrow H_2O(l) + Br^-(aq)$

(e) $H_2PO_4^-(aq) + N_2H_4(aq)$
$$\rightleftharpoons HPO_4^{2-}(aq) + N_2H_5^+(aq)$$

10.48 Write the formulas of the conjugate acids of the following Brønsted–Lowry bases:

(a) $ClCH_2CO_2^-$

(b) C_5H_5N

(c) SeO_4^{2-}

(d) $(CH_3)_3N$

10.49 Write the formulas of the conjugate bases of the following Brønsted–Lowry acids:

(a) HCN

(b) $(CH_3)_2NH_2^+$

(c) H_3PO_4

(d) $HSeO_3^-$

10.50 The hydrogen-containing anions of many polyprotic acids are amphoteric. Write equations for HCO_3^- and $H_2PO_4^-$ acting as bases with the strong acid HCl and as acids with the strong base NaOH.

10.51 Write balanced equations for proton-transfer reactions between the listed pairs. Indicate the conjugate pairs, and determine the favored direction for each equilibrium.

(a) HCl and PO_4^{3-}

(b) HCN and SO_4^{2-}

(c) $HClO_4$ and NO_2^-

(d) CH_3O^- and HF

10.52 Tums, a drugstore remedy for acid indigestion, contains $CaCO_3$. Write an equation for the reaction of Tums with gastric juice (HCl).

10.53 Write balanced equations for the following acid–base reactions:

(a) $LiOH + HNO_3 \longrightarrow$

(b) $BaCO_3 + HI \longrightarrow$

(c) $H_3PO_4 + KOH \longrightarrow$

(d) $Ca(HCO_3)_2 + HCl \longrightarrow$

(e) $Ba(OH_2) + H_2SO_4 \longrightarrow$

ACID AND BASE STRENGTH: K_a AND pH

10.54 How is K_a defined? Write the equation for K_a for the generalized acid HA.

10.55 Rearrange the equation you wrote in Problem 10.54 to solve for $[H_3O^+]$ in terms of K_a.

10.56 How is K_w defined, and what is its numerical value at 25 °C?

10.57 How is pH defined?

10.58 A solution of 0.10 M HCl has a pH = 1.00, whereas a solution of 0.10 M CH_3COOH has a pH = 2.88. Explain.

10.59 Calculate $[H_3O^+]$ for the 0.10 M CH_3COOH solution in Problem 10.58. What percent of the weak acid is dissociated?

10.60 Write the expressions for the acid dissociation constants for the three successive dissociations of phosphoric acid, H_3PO_4, in water.

10.61 Find K_a values in Table 10.2, and decide which acid in the following pairs is stronger:

(a) HCO_3H or HF

(b) HSO_4^- or HCN

(c) $H_3PO_4^-$ or HPO_4^{2-}

(d) $CH_3CH_2CO_2H$ or CH_3CO_2H

10.62 Which substance in the following pairs is the stronger base? Look at Table 10.1 if necessary.

(a) OH^- or PO_4^{3-}

(b) Br^- or NO_2^-

(c) NH_3 or OH^-

(d) CN^- or H_2O

(e) I^- or HPO_4^{2-}

10.63 Based on the K_a values in Table 10.1, rank the following solutions in order of increasing pH: 0.10 M HCOOH, 0.10 M HF, 0.10 M H_2CO_3, 0.10 M HSO_4^-, 0.10 M NH_4^+.

10.64 The electrode of a pH meter is placed in a sample of urine, and a reading of 7.9 is obtained. Is the sample acidic, basic, or neutral? What is the concentration of H_3O^+ in the urine sample?

10.65 A 0.10 M solution of the deadly poison hydrogen cyanide, HCN, has a pH of 5.2. Is HCN acidic or basic? Is it strong or weak?

10.66 Normal gastric juice has a pH of about 2. Assuming that gastric juice is primarily aqueous HCl, what is the HCl concentration?

10.67 Human spinal fluid has a pH of 7.4. Approximately what is the H_3O^+ concentration of spinal fluid?

10.68 What is the approximate pH of a 0.10 M solution of a strong monoprotic acid? Of a 0.10 M solution of a strong base, such as KOH?

10.69 Calculate the pOH of each solution in Problems 10.64–10.67.

10.70 Approximately what pH do the following H_3O^+ concentrations correspond to?

(a) Fresh egg white: $[H_3O^+] = 2.5 \times 10^{-8}$ M

(b) Apple cider: $[H_3O^+] = 5.0 \times 10^{-4}$ M

(c) Household ammonia: $[H_3O^+] = 2.3 \times 10^{-12}$ M

10.71 What are the OH^- concentration and pOH for each solution in Problem 10.70? Rank the solutions according to increasing acidity.

10.72 What are the H_3O^+ and OH^- concentrations of solutions that have the following pH values?

(a) pH 4

(b) pH 11

(c) pH 0

(d) pH 1.38

(e) pH 7.96

10.73 About 12% of the acid in a 0.10 M solution of a weak acid dissociates to form ions. What are the H_3O^+ and OH^- concentrations? What is the pH of the solution?

BUFFERS

10.74 What are the two components of a buffer system? How does a buffer work to hold pH nearly constant?

10.75 Which system would you expect to be a better buffer: $HNO_3 + Na^+NO_3^-$, or $CH_3CO_2H + CH_3CO_2^-Na^+$? Explain.

10.76 The pH of a buffer solution containing 0.10 M acetic acid and 0.10 M sodium acetate is 4.74.

    (a) Write the Henderson–Hasselbalch equation for this buffer.

    (b) Write the equations for reaction of this buffer with a small amount of HNO_3 and with a small amount of NaOH.

10.77 Which of the following buffer systems would you use if you wanted to prepare a solution having a pH of approximately 9.5?

    (a) 0.08 M $H_2PO_4^-$/0.12 M HPO_4^{2-}

    (b) 0.08 M NH_4^+/0.12 M NH_3

10.78 What is the pH of a buffer system that contains 0.200 M hydrocyanic acid (HCN) and 0.150 M sodium cyanide (NaCN)? The pK_a of hydrocyanic acid is 9.31.

10.79 What is the pH of 1.00 L of the 0.200 M hydrocyanic acid–0.150 M cyanide ion buffer system described in Problem 10.78 after 0.020 mol of HCl is added? After 0.020 mol of NaOH is added?

10.80 What is the pH of a buffer system that contains 0.15 M NH_4^+ and 0.10 M NH_3? The pK_a of NH_4^+ is 9.25.

10.81 How many moles of NaOH must be added to 1.00 L of the solution described in Problem 10.80 to increase the pH to 9.25?

CONCENTRATIONS OF ACID AND BASE SOLUTIONS

10.82 What does it mean when we talk about acid *equivalents* and base *equivalents*?

10.83 How is normality defined as a means of expressing acid or base concentration?

10.84 Calculate the gram-equivalent for each of the following acids and bases.

    (a) HNO_3 **(b)** H_3PO_4

    (c) KOH   **(d)** $Mg(OH)_2$

10.85 What mass of each of the acids and bases in Problem 10.84 is needed to prepare 500 mL of 0.15 N solution?

10.86 How many milliliters of 0.0050 N KOH are required to neutralize 25 mL of 0.0050 N H_2SO_4? To neutralize 25 mL of 0.0050 N HCl?

10.87 What is the normality of a 0.12 M H_2SO_4 solution? Of a 0.12 M H_3PO_4 solution?

10.88 How many equivalents of an acid or base are in the following?

    (a) 0.25 mol $Mg(OH)_2$

    (b) 2.5 g $Mg(OH)_2$

    (c) 15 g CH_3CO_2H

10.89 What mass of citric acid (triprotic, $C_6H_5O_7H_3$) contains 152 mEq of citric acid?

10.90 What are the molarity and the normality of a solution made by dissolving 5.0 g of $Ca(OH)_2$ in enough water to make 500.0 mL of solution?

10.91 What are the molarity and the normality of a solution made by dissolving 25 g of citric acid (triprotic, $C_6H_5O_7H_3$) in enough water to make 800 mL of solution?

10.92 Titration of a 12.0 mL solution of HCl requires 22.4 mL of 0.12 M NaOH. What is the molarity of the HCl solution?

10.93 What volume of 0.085 M HNO_3 is required to titrate 15.0 mL of 0.12 M $Ba(OH)_2$ solution?

10.94 Titration of a 10.0 mL solution of KOH requires 15.0 mL of 0.0250 M H_2SO_4 solution. What is the molarity of the KOH solution?

10.95 If 35.0 mL of a 0.100 N acid solution is needed to reach the end point in titration of 21.5 mL of a base solution, what is the normality of the base solution?

Applications

10.96 The concentration of HCl when released to the stomach cavity is diluted to between 0.01 and 0.001 M [*GERD— Too Much Acid or Not Enough? p. 302*]

    (a) What is the pH range in the stomach cavity?

    (b) Write a balanced equation for the neutralization of stomach acid by $NaHCO_3$.

    (c) How many grams of $NaHCO_3$ are required to neutralize 15.0 mL of a solution having a pH of 1.8?

10.97 Which body fluid is most acidic? Which is most basic? [*pH of Body Fluids, p. 311*]

10.98 Metabolic acidosis is often treated by administering bicarbonate intravenously. Explain how this treatment can increase blood serum pH. [*Buffers in the Body: Acidosis and Alkalosis, p. 317*]

10.99 The normal $[HCO_3^-]/[CO_2]$ ratio in the blood is about 20 to 1 at a pH = 7.4. What is this ratio at pH = 7.3 (acidosis) and at pH = 7.5 (alkalosis)? [*Buffers in the Body: Acidosis and Alkalosis, p. 317*]

10.100 Rain typically has a pH of about 5.6. What is the H_3O^+ concentration in rain? [*Acid Rain, p. 324*]

10.101 Acid rain with a pH as low as 1.5 has been recorded in West Virginia. [*Acid Rain, p. 324*]

    (a) What is the H_3O^+ concentration in this acid rain?

    (b) How many grams of HNO_3 must be dissolved to make 25 L of solution that has a pH of 1.5?

General Questions and Problems

10.102 Alka-Seltzer, a drugstore antacid, contains a mixture of $NaHCO_3$, aspirin, and citric acid, $C_6H_5O_7H_3$. Why does Alka-Seltzer foam and bubble when dissolved in water? Which ingredient is the antacid?

10.103 How many milliliters of 0.50 M NaOH solution are required to titrate 40.0 mL of a 0.10 M H_2SO_4 solution to an end point?

10.104 Which solution contains more acid, 50 mL of a 0.20 N HCl solution or 50 mL of a 0.20 N acetic acid solution? Which has a higher hydronium ion concentration? Which has a lower pH?

10.105 One of the buffer systems used to control the pH of blood involves the equilibrium between $H_2PO_4^-$ and HPO_4^{2-}. The pK_a for $H_2PO_4^-$ is 7.21.

(a) Write the Henderson–Hasselbalch equation for this buffer system.

(b) What HPO_4^{2-} to $H_2PO_4^-$ ratio is needed to maintain the optimum blood pH of 7.40?

10.106 A 0.15 M solution of HCl is used to titrate 30.0 mL of a $Ca(OH)_2$ solution of unknown concentration. If 140 mL of HCl is required, what is the concentration (in molarity) of the $Ca(OH)_2$ solution?

10.107 Which of the following combinations produces an effective buffer solution? Assuming equal concentrations of each acid and its conjugate base, calculate the pH of each buffer solution.

(a) NaF and HF   (b) $HClO_4$ and $NaClO_4$

(c) NH_4Cl and NH_3 (d) KBr and HBr

10.108 One method of analyzing ammonium salts is to treat them with NaOH and then heat the solution to remove the NH_3 gas formed.

$$NH_4^+(aq) + OH^-(aq) \longrightarrow NH_3(g) + H_2O(l)$$

(a) Label the Brønsted–Lowry acid–base pairs.

(b) If 2.86 L of NH_3 at 60 °C and 755 mmHg is produced by the reaction of NH_4Cl, how many grams of NH_4Cl were in the original sample?

10.109 One method of reducing acid rain is *scrubbing* the combustion products before they are emitted from power plant smoke stacks. The process involves addition of an aqueous suspension of lime (CaO) to the combustion chamber and stack, where the lime reacts with SO_2 to give calcium sulfite ($CaSO_3$).

(a) Write the balanced chemical equation for this reaction.

(b) How much lime is needed to remove 1 kg of SO_2?

10.110 Sodium oxide, Na_2O, reacts with water to give NaOH.

(a) Write a balanced equation for the reaction.

(b) What is the pH of the solution prepared by allowing 1.55 g of Na_2O to react with 500.0 mL of water? Assume that there is no volume change.

(c) How many milliliters of 0.0100 M HCl are needed to neutralize the NaOH solution prepared in (b)?

Nuclear Chemistry

▲ The age of this skull, from a hominid discovered in 2004 in Indonesia, is estimated to be 18,000 years.

CONTENTS

CHAPTER GOALS

In this chapter we will answer the following questions about nuclear chemistry:

1. **What is a nuclear reaction, and how are equations for nuclear reactions balanced?**

THE GOAL: Be able to write and balance equations for nuclear reactions.

2. **What are the different kinds of radioactivity?**

THE GOAL: Be able to list the characteristics of three common kinds of radiation—α, β, and γ (alpha, beta, and gamma).

3. **How are the rates of nuclear reactions expressed?**

THE GOAL: Be able to explain half-life and calculate the quantity of a radioisotope remaining after a given number of half-lives.

4. **What is ionizing radiation?**

THE GOAL: Be able to describe the properties of the different types of ionizing radiation and their potential for harm to living tissue.

5. **How is radioactivity measured?**

THE GOAL: Be able to describe the common units for measuring radiation.

6. **What is transmutation?**

THE GOAL: Be able to explain nuclear bombardment and balance equations for nuclear bombardment reactions.

7. **What are nuclear fission and nuclear fusion?**

THE GOAL: Be able to explain nuclear fission and nuclear fusion.

I n all of the reactions we have discussed thus far, only the *bonds* between atoms have changed; the chemical identities of atoms themselves have remained unchanged. Anyone who reads the paper or watches television knows, however, that atoms *can* change, often resulting in the conversion of one element into another. Atomic weapons, nuclear energy, and radioactive radon gas in our homes are all topics of societal importance, and all involve *nuclear chemistry*—the study of the properties and reactions of atomic nuclei.

11.1 Nuclear Reactions

Recall from Section 3.2 that an atom is characterized by its *atomic number, Z,* and its *mass number, A.* (⬭, p. 53) The atomic number, written below and to the left of the element symbol, gives the number of protons in the nucleus and identifies the element. The mass number, written above and to the left of the element symbol, gives the total number of **nucleons**, a general term for both protons (p) and neutrons (n). The most common isotope of carbon, for example, has 12 nucleons: 6 protons and 6 neutrons: $^{12}_{6}C$.

Nucleon A general term for both protons and neutrons.

Atoms with identical atomic numbers but different mass numbers are called *isotopes* (Section 3.3), and the nucleus of a specific isotope is called a **nuclide**. (⬭, p. 54) Thirteen isotopes of carbon are known—two occur commonly (^{12}C and ^{13}C) and one (^{14}C) is produced in small amounts in the upper atmosphere by the action of neutrons from cosmic rays on ^{14}N. The remaining ten carbon isotopes have been produced artificially. Only the two commonly occurring isotopes are stable indefinitely. The others undergo spontaneous **nuclear reactions**, which change their nuclei. Carbon-14, for example, slowly decomposes to give nitrogen-14 plus an electron, a process we can write as

Nuclide The nucleus of a specific isotope of an element.

Nuclear reaction A reaction that changes an atomic nucleus, usually causing the change of one element into another.

$$^{14}_{6}C \longrightarrow {}^{14}_{7}N + {}^{0}_{-1}e$$

The electron is often written as $^{0}_{-1}e$, where the superscript 0 indicates that the mass of an electron is essentially zero when compared with that of a proton or neutron, and the subscript −1 indicates that the charge is −1. (The subscript in this instance is not a true atomic number.)

Nuclear reactions, such as the spontaneous decay of ^{14}C, are distinguished from chemical reactions in several ways:

- A *nuclear* reaction involves a change in an atom's nucleus, usually producing a different element. A *chemical* reaction, by contrast, involves only a change in distribution of the outer-shell electrons around the atom and never changes the nucleus itself or produces a different element.

- Different isotopes of an element have essentially the same behavior in chemical reactions but often have completely different behavior in nuclear reactions.

- The rate of a nuclear reaction is unaffected by a change in temperature or pressure or by the addition of a catalyst.

- The nuclear reaction of an atom is essentially the same whether it is in a chemical compound or in an uncombined, elemental form.

- The energy change accompanying a nuclear reaction can be up to several million times greater than that accompanying a chemical reaction. The nuclear transformation of 1.0 g of uranium-235 releases 3.4×10^8 kcal, for example, whereas the chemical combustion of 1.0 g of methane releases only 12 kcal.

11.2 The Discovery and Nature of Radioactivity

The discovery of *radioactivity* dates to the year 1896 when the French physicist Henri Becquerel made a remarkable observation. While investigating the nature of phosphorescence—the luminous glow of some minerals and other substances that remains when the light is suddenly turned off—Becquerel happened to place a sample of a uranium-containing mineral on top of a photographic plate that had been wrapped in black paper and put in a drawer to protect it from sunlight. On developing the plate, Becquerel was surprised to find a silhouette of the mineral. He concluded that the mineral was producing some kind of unknown radiation, which passed through the paper and exposed the photographic plate.

Radioactivity The spontaneous emission of radiation from a nucleus.

Marie Sklodowska Curie and her husband, Pierre, took up the challenge and began a series of investigations into this new phenomenon, which they termed **radioactivity**. They found that the source of the radioactivity was the element uranium (U) and that two previously unknown elements, which they named polonium (Po) and radium (Ra), were also radioactive. For these achievements, Becquerel and the Curies shared the 1903 Nobel Prize in physics.

Further work on radioactivity by the English scientist Ernest Rutherford established that there were at least two types of radiation, which he named *alpha* (α) and *beta* (β) after the first two letters of the Greek alphabet. Shortly thereafter, a third type of radiation was found and named for the third Greek letter, *gamma* (γ).

Subsequent studies showed that when the three kinds of radiation are passed between two plates with opposite electrical charges, each is affected differently. Alpha radiation bends toward the negative plate and must therefore have a positive charge. Beta radiation, by contrast, bends toward the positive plate and must have a negative charge, whereas gamma radiation does not bend toward either plate and has no charge (Figure 11.1).

▲ **FIGURE 11.1 The effect of an electric field on α, β, and γ, radiation.** The radioactive source in the shielded box emits radiation, which passes between the two electrically charged plates. Alpha radiation is deflected toward the negative plate, β radiation is deflected toward the positive plate, and γ radiation is not deflected.

Another difference among the three kinds of radiation soon became apparent when it was discovered that alpha and beta radiations are composed of small particles with a measurable mass, whereas **gamma (γ) radiation** consists of high-energy electromagnetic waves and has no mass (see the Application "Atoms and Light" in Chapter 3). (⊂⊃ , p. 72) Rutherford was able to show that a **beta (β) particle** is an electron (e$^-$) and that an **alpha (α) particle** is simply a helium nucleus, He^{2+}. (Recall that a helium *atom* consists of two protons, two neutrons, and two electrons. When the two electrons are removed, the remaining helium nucleus, or α particle, has only the two protons and two neutrons.)

Yet a third difference among the three kinds of radiation is their penetrating power. Because of their relatively large mass, α particles move slowly (up to about one-tenth the speed of light) and can be stopped by a few sheets of paper or by the top layer of skin. Beta particles, because they are much lighter, move at up to nine-tenths the speed of light and have about 100 times the penetrating power of α particles. A block of wood or heavy protective clothing is necessary to stop β radiation, which can otherwise penetrate the skin and cause burns and other damage. Gamma rays move at the speed of light (3.00×10^8 m/s) and have about 1000 times the penetrating power of α particles. A lead block several inches thick is needed to stop γ radiation, which can otherwise penetrate and damage the body's internal organs.

The characteristics of the three kinds of radiation are summarized in Table 11.1. Note that an α particle, even though it is an ion with a 2+ charge, is usually written using the symbol $_2^4$He without the charge. A β particle is usually written $_{-1}^0$e, as noted previously.

Gamma (γ) radiation Radioactivity consisting of high-energy light waves.

Beta (β) particle An electron (e$^-$), emitted as radiation.

Alpha (α) particle A helium nucleus (He^{2+}), emitted as α radiation.

TABLE 11.1 Characteristics of α, β, and γ Radiation

TYPE OF RADIATION	SYMBOL	CHARGE	COMPOSITION	MASS (AMU)	VELOCITY	RELATIVE PENETRATING POWER
Alpha	α, $_2^4$He	+2	Helium nucleus	4	Up to 10% speed of light	Low (1)
Beta	β, $_{-1}^0$e	−1	Electron	1/1823	Up to 90% speed of light	Medium (100)
Gamma	γ, $_0^0\gamma$	0	High-energy radiation	0	Speed of light (3.00×10^8 m/s)	High (1000)

11.3 Stable and Unstable Isotopes

Every element in the periodic table has at least one radioactive isotope, or **radioisotope**, and more than *3300* radioisotopes are known. Their radioactivity is the result of having unstable nuclei, although the exact causes of this instability are not fully understood. Radiation is emitted when an unstable radioactive nucleus, or **radionuclide**, spontaneously changes into a more stable one.

For elements in the first few rows of the periodic table, stability is associated with a roughly equal number of neutrons and protons (Figure 11.2). Hydrogen, for example, has stable $_1^1$H (protium) and $_1^2$H (deuterium) isotopes, but its $_1^3$H isotope (tritium) is radioactive. As elements get heavier, the number of neutrons relative to protons in stable nuclei increases. Lead-208 ($_{82}^{208}$Pb), for example, the most abundant stable isotope of lead, has 126 neutrons and 82 protons in its nuclei. Nevertheless, of the 35 known isotopes of lead, only 3 are stable whereas 32 are radioactive. In fact, there are only 264 stable isotopes among all the elements. All isotopes of elements with atomic numbers higher than that of bismuth (83) are radioactive.

Most of the more than 3300 known radioisotopes have been made in high-energy particle accelerators by reactions that will be described in Section 11.10. Such isotopes are called *artificial radioisotopes* because they are not found in nature. All isotopes of the transuranium elements (those heavier than uranium) are artificial. The much smaller number of radioactive isotopes found in the earth's crust, such as $_{92}^{238}$U, are called *natural radioisotopes*.

Aside from their radioactivity, different radioisotopes of the same element have the same chemical properties as stable isotopes, which accounts for their great

Radioisotope A radioactive isotope.

Radionuclide The nucleus of a radioactive isotope.

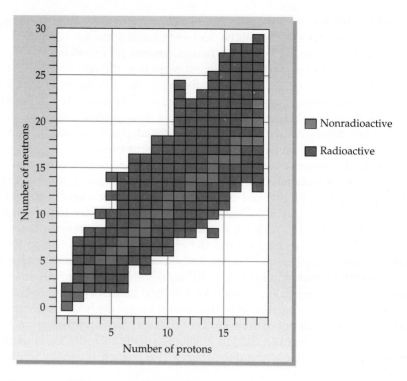

▲ **FIGURE 11.2 A plot of the numbers of neutrons and protons for known isotopes of the first 18 elements.** Stable (nonradioactive) isotopes of these elements have equal or nearly equal numbers of neutrons and protons.

usefulness as *tracers*. A chemical compound tagged with a radioactive atom undergoes exactly the same reactions as its nonradioactive counterpart. The difference is that the tagged compound can be located with a radiation detector and its whereabouts determined, as discussed in the Application "Body Imaging" on page 352.

11.4 Nuclear Decay

Think for a minute about the consequences of α and β radiation. If radioactivity involves the spontaneous emission of a small particle from an unstable atomic nucleus, then the nucleus itself must undergo a change. With that understanding of radioactivity came the startling discovery that atoms of one element can change into atoms of another element, something that had previously been thought impossible. The spontaneous emission of a particle from an unstable nucleus is called **nuclear decay**, or *radioactive decay*, and the resulting change of one element into another is called **transmutation**.

> **Nuclear decay:** Radioactive element $\longrightarrow$ New element + Emitted particle

We now look at what happens to a nucleus when nuclear decay occurs.

Alpha Emission

When an atom of uranium-238 ($^{238}_{92}U$) emits an α particle, the nucleus loses two protons and two neutrons. Because the number of protons in the nucleus has now changed from 92 to 90, the *identity* of the atom has changed from uranium to thorium. Furthermore, since the total number of nucleons has decreased by 4, uranium-238 has become thorium-234 ($^{234}_{90}Th$) (Figure 11.3).

Note that the equation for a nuclear reaction is not balanced in the usual chemical sense because the kinds of atoms are not the same on both sides of the arrow. Instead, we say that a nuclear equation is balanced when the number of nucleons is the same on both sides of the equation and when the sums of the charges on the nuclei plus any ejected subatomic particles (protons or electrons) are the same on

Nuclear decay The spontaneous emission of a particle from an unstable nucleus.

Transmutation The change of one element into another.

$$^{238}_{92}U \longrightarrow \; ^{234}_{90}Th + \; ^{4}_{2}He$$

$^{238}_{92}U$	$^{234}_{90}Th$	$^{4}_{2}He$
92 protons	90 protons	2 protons
146 neutrons	144 neutrons	2 neutrons
238 total	234 total	4 total

◀ **FIGURE 11.3 Alpha emission.** Emission of an α particle from an atom of uranium-238 produces an atom of thorium-234.

both sides. In the decay of $^{238}_{92}U$ to give $^{4}_{2}He$ and $^{234}_{90}Th$, for example, there are 238 nucleons and 92 nuclear charges on both sides of the nuclear equation.

$$\begin{array}{c} \text{92 protons} \\ \underline{\text{146 neutrons}} \\ \text{238 nucleons} \end{array} \longrightarrow \; ^{238}_{92}U \longrightarrow \; ^{4}_{2}He + \; ^{234}_{90}Th \begin{array}{c} \text{90 protons} \\ \underline{\text{144 neutrons}} \\ \text{234 nucleons} \end{array}$$

$$\begin{array}{c} \text{2 protons} \\ \underline{\text{2 neutrons}} \\ \text{4 nucleons} \end{array}$$

WORKED EXAMPLE **11.1** Balancing Nuclear Reactions: Alpha Emission

Polonium-208 is one of the α emitters studied by Marie Curie. Write the equation for the α decay of polonium-208, and identify the element formed.

ANALYSIS Look up the atomic number of polonium (84) in the periodic table, and write the known part of the nuclear equation, using the standard symbol for polonium-208:

$$^{208}_{84}Po \longrightarrow \; ^{4}_{2}He + \; ?$$

Then calculate the mass number and atomic number of the product element, and write the final equation.

SOLUTION
The mass number of the product is $208 - 4 = 204$, and the atomic number is $84 - 2 = 82$. A look at the periodic table identifies the element with atomic number 82 as lead (Pb).

$$^{208}_{84}Po \longrightarrow \; ^{4}_{2}He + \; ^{204}_{82}Pb$$

Check your answer by making sure that the mass numbers and atomic numbers on the two sides of the equation are balanced:

Mass numbers: $208 = 4 + 204$ Atomic numbers: $84 = 2 + 82$

PROBLEM 11.1

High levels of radioactive radon-222 ($^{222}_{86}Rn$) have been found in many homes built on radium-containing rock, leading to the possibility of health hazards. What product results from α emission by radon-222?

PROBLEM 11.2

What isotope of radium (Ra) is converted into radon-222 by α emission?

Beta Emission

Whereas α emission leads to the loss of two protons and two neutrons from the nucleus, β emission involves the *decomposition* of a neutron to yield an electron and a proton. This process can be represented as

$$\,^1_0n \longrightarrow \,^1_1p + \,^0_{-1}e$$

where the electron ($\,^0_{-1}e$) is ejected as a β particle, and the proton is retained by the nucleus. Note that the electrons emitted during β radiation come from the *nucleus* and not from the occupied orbitals surrounding the nucleus.

The net result of β emission is that the atomic number of the atom increases by 1 because there is a new proton. The mass number of the atom remains the same, however, because a neutron has changed into a proton leaving the total number of nucleons unchanged. For example, iodine-131 ($\,^{131}_{53}I$), a radioisotope used in detecting thyroid problems, undergoes nuclear decay by β emission to yield xenon-131 ($\,^{131}_{54}Xe$):

Note that the superscripts (mass numbers) are balanced in this equation because a β particle has a mass near zero, and the subscripts are balanced because a β particle has a charge of -1.

WORKED EXAMPLE **11.2** Balancing Nuclear Reactions: Beta Emission

Write a balanced nuclear equation for the β decay of chromium-55.

ANALYSIS Write the known part of the nuclear equation:

$$\,^{55}_{24}Cr \longrightarrow \,^0_{-1}e + ?$$

Then calculate the mass number and atomic number of the product element, and write the final equation.

SOLUTION
The mass number of the product stays at 55, and the atomic number increases by 1, $24 + 1 = 25$, so the product is manganese-55.

$$\,^{55}_{24}Cr \longrightarrow \,^0_{-1}e + \,^{55}_{25}Mn$$

Check your answer by making sure that the mass numbers and atomic numbers on the two sides of the equation are balanced:

Mass numbers: $55 = 0 + 55$ Atomic numbers: $24 = -1 + 25$

PROBLEM 11.3

Carbon-14, a β emitter, is a rare isotope used in dating archaeological artifacts. Write a nuclear equation for the decay of carbon-14.

PROBLEM 11.4

Write nuclear equations for β emission from the following radioisotopes:

(a) $^{3}_{1}\text{H}$ (b) $^{210}_{82}\text{Pb}$ (c) $^{20}_{9}\text{F}$

Gamma Emission

Emission of γ rays, unlike the emission of α and β particles, causes no change in mass or atomic number because γ rays are simply high-energy electromagnetic waves. Although γ emission can occur alone, it usually accompanies α or β emission as a mechanism for the new nucleus that results from a transmutation to get rid of some extra energy.

Since γ emission affects neither mass number nor atomic number, it is often omitted from nuclear equations. Nevertheless, γ rays are of great importance. Their penetrating power makes them by far the most dangerous kind of external radiation for humans and also makes them useful in numerous medical applications. Cobalt-60, for example, is used in cancer therapy as a source of penetrating γ rays that kill cancerous tissue.

$$^{60}_{27}\text{Co} \longrightarrow ^{60}_{28}\text{Ni} + ^{0}_{-1}\text{e} + ^{0}_{0}\gamma$$

Positron Emission

In addition to α, β, and γ radiation, there is another common type of radioactive decay process called *positron emission*, which involves the conversion of a proton in the nucleus into a neutron plus an ejected **positron**, $^{0}_{1}\text{e}$ or β^{+}. A positron, which can be thought of as a "positive electron," has the same mass as an electron but a positive charge. This process can be represented as

$$^{1}_{1}\text{p} \longrightarrow ^{1}_{0}\text{n} + ^{0}_{1}\text{e}$$

Positron A "positive electron," which has the same mass as an electron but a positive charge.

The result of positron emission is a decrease in the atomic number of the product nucleus because a proton has changed into a neutron, but no change in the mass number. Potassium-40, for example, undergoes positron emission to yield argon-40, a nuclear reaction important in geology for dating rocks. Note once again that the sum of the two subscripts on the right of the nuclear equation (18 + 1 = 19) is equal to the subscript in the $^{40}_{19}\text{K}$ nucleus on the left.

19 protons / 21 neutrons / 40 nucleons $\longrightarrow$ $^{40}_{19}\text{K}$ $\longrightarrow$ $^{40}_{18}\text{Ar}$ + $^{0}_{1}\text{e}$

0 nucleons but 1 charge

18 protons / 22 neutrons / 40 nucleons

Electron Capture

Electron capture, symbolized E.C., is a process in which the nucleus captures an inner-shell electron from the surrounding electron cloud, thereby converting a proton into a neutron. The mass number of the product nucleus is unchanged, but the atomic number decreases by 1, just as in positron emission. The conversion of mercury-197 into gold-197 is an example:

Electron capture (E.C.) A process in which the nucleus captures an inner-shell electron from the surrounding electron cloud, thereby converting a proton into a neutron.

80 protons / 117 neutrons / 197 nucleons   Inner-shell electron   79 protons / 118 neutrons / 197 nucleons

$$^{197}_{80}\text{Hg} + ^{0}_{-1}\text{e} \longrightarrow ^{197}_{79}\text{Au}$$

Do not plan on using this reaction to get rich, however. Mercury-197 is not one of the naturally occurring isotopes of Hg and is typically produced by transmutation reactions as discussed in Section 11.10.

Characteristics of the five kinds of radioactive decay processes are summarized in Table 11.2.

TABLE 11.2   A Summary of Radioactive Decay Processes

PROCESS	SYMBOL	CHANGE IN ATOMIC NUMBER	CHANGE IN MASS NUMBER	CHANGE IN NUMBER OF NEUTRONS
α emission	$^4_2$He or α	-2	-4	-2
β emission	$^0_{-1}$e or β^{-*}	$+1$	0	-1
γ emission	$^0_0\gamma$ or γ	0	0	0
Positron emission	$^0_1$e or β^{+*}	-1	0	$+1$
Electron capture	E.C.	-1	0	$+1$

Superscripts are used to indicate the charge associated with the two forms of beta decay; β^-, or a beta particle, carries a -1 charge, while β^+, or a positron, carries a $+1$ charge.

WORKED EXAMPLE   **11.3** Balancing Nuclear Reactions: Electron Capture, Positron Emission

Write balanced nuclear equations for the following processes:

(a) Electron capture by polonium-204: $^{204}_{84}$Po $+ \, ^0_{-1}$e $\longrightarrow$?

(b) Positron emission from xenon-118: $^{118}_{54}$Xe $\longrightarrow \, ^0_1$e $+$?

ANALYSIS The key to writing nuclear equations is to make sure that the number of nucleons is the same on both sides of the equation and that the number of charges is the same.

SOLUTION

(a) In electron capture, the mass number is unchanged and the atomic number decreases by 1, giving bismuth-204: $^{204}_{84}$Po $+ \, ^0_{-1}$e $\longrightarrow \, ^{204}_{83}$Bi

Check your answer by making sure that the number of nucleons and the number of charges are the same on both sides of the equation:

   Mass number: $204 + 0 = 204$ Atomic number: $84 + (-1) = 83$

(b) In positron emission, the mass number is unchanged and the atomic number decreases by 1, giving iodine-118: $^{118}_{54}$Xe $\longrightarrow \, ^0_1$e $+ \, ^{118}_{53}$I.

CHECK! Mass number: $118 = 0 + 118$ Atomic number: $54 = 1 + 53$

PROBLEM 11.5

Write nuclear equations for positron emission from the following radioisotopes:

(a) $^{38}_{20}$Ca   **(b)** $^{118}_{54}$Xe   **(c)** $^{79}_{37}$Rb

PROBLEM 11.6

Write nuclear equations for electron capture by the following radioisotopes:

(a) $^{62}_{30}$Zn   **(b)** $^{110}_{50}$Sn   **(c)** $^{81}_{36}$Kr

●━○ KEY CONCEPT PROBLEM 11.7

The red arrow in this graph indicates the changes that occur in the nucleus of an atom during a nuclear reaction. Identify the isotopes involved as product and reactant, and name the type of decay process.

11.5 Radioactive Half-Life

The rate of radioactive decay varies greatly from one radioisotope to another. Some radioisotopes, such as uranium-238, decay at a barely perceptible rate over billions of years, but others, such as carbon-17, decay within thousandths of a second.

Rates of nuclear decay are measured in units of **half-life ($t_{1/2}$)**, defined as the amount of time required for one-half of a radioactive sample to decay. For example, the half-life of iodine-131 is 8.021 days. If today you have 1.000 g of $^{131}_{53}I$, then 8.021 days from now you will have only 50% of that amount (0.500 g) because one-half of the sample will have decayed into $^{131}_{54}Xe$. After 8.021 more days (16.063 days total), you will have only 25% (0.250 g) of your original $^{131}_{53}I$ sample; after another 8.021 days (24.084 days total), you will have only 12.5% (0.125 g); and so on. Each passage of a half-life causes the decay of one-half of whatever sample remains. The half-life is the same no matter what the size of the sample, the temperature, or any other external conditions. There is no known way to slow down, speed up, or otherwise change the characteristics of radioactive decay.

Half-life ($t_{1/2}$) The amount of time required for one-half of a radioactive sample to decay.

$$1.000 \text{ g } ^{131}_{53}I \xrightarrow[\text{days}]{8} \begin{array}{c} 0.500 \text{ g } ^{131}_{53}I \\ 0.500 \text{ g } ^{131}_{54}Xe \end{array} \xrightarrow[\text{days}]{8} \begin{array}{c} 0.250 \text{ g } ^{131}_{53}I \\ 0.750 \text{ g } ^{131}_{54}Xe \end{array} \xrightarrow[\text{days}]{8} \begin{array}{c} 0.125 \text{ g } ^{131}_{53}I \\ 0.875 \text{ g } ^{131}_{54}Xe \end{array} \longrightarrow$$

One half-life   Two half-lives   Three half-lives
              (16 days total)   (24 days total)

The fraction of radioisotope remaining after the passage of each half-life is represented by the curve in Figure 11.4 and can be calculated as

$$\text{fraction remaining} = (0.5)^n$$

where n is the number of half-lives that have elapsed.

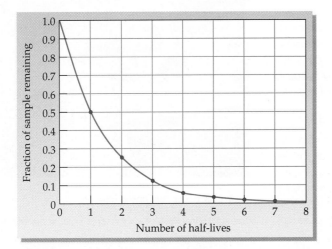

◀ **FIGURE 11.4 The decay of a radioactive nucleus over time.** All nuclear decays follow this curve, whether the half-lives are measured in years, days, minutes, or seconds. That is, the fraction of sample remaining after one half-life is 0.50, the fraction remaining after two half-lives is 0.25, the fraction remaining after three half-lives is 0.125, and so on.

APPLICATION ▶ Medical Uses of Radioactivity

The origins of nuclear medicine date from 1901 when the French physician Henri Danlos first used radium in the treatment of a tubercular skin lesion. Since that time, the use of radioactivity has become a crucial part of modern medical care, both diagnostic and therapeutic. Current nuclear techniques can be grouped into three classes: (1) in vivo procedures, (2) radiation therapy, and (3) imaging procedures. The first two are described here, and the third one is described on page 352 in the Application "Body Imaging."

In Vivo Procedures

In vivo studies—those that take place inside the body—are carried out to assess the functioning of a particular organ or body system. A *radiopharmaceutical* agent is administered, and its path in the body—whether absorbed, excreted, diluted, or concentrated—is determined by analysis of blood or urine samples.

Among the many in vivo procedures utilizing radioactive agents is a simple method for the determination of whole-blood volume by injecting a known quantity of red blood cells labeled with radioactive chromium-51. After a suitable interval to allow the labeled cells to be distributed evenly throughout the body, a blood sample is taken and blood volume is calculated by comparing the concentration of labeled cells in the blood with the quantity of labeled cells injected. This and similar procedures are known as *isotope dilution* and are described by

$$R_{sample} = R_{tracer}\left(\frac{W_{sample}}{W_{system} + W_{tracer}}\right)$$

where R_{sample} is the counting rate of the analyzed sample, R_{tracer} is the counting rate of the tracer added to the system, and W refers to either the mass or volume of the analyzed sample, added tracer, or total system as indicated.

Therapeutic Procedures

Therapeutic procedures—those in which radiation is purposely used as a weapon to kill diseased tissue—involve either external or internal sources of radiation. External radiation therapy for the treatment of cancer is often carried out with γ rays emanating from a cobalt-60 source. The highly radioactive source is shielded by a thick lead container and has a small opening directed toward the site of the tumor. By focusing the radiation beam on the tumor, the tumor receives the full exposure while exposure of surrounding parts of the body is minimized. Nevertheless, enough healthy tissue is affected so that most patients treated in this manner suffer the effects of radiation sickness.

Internal radiation therapy is a much more selective technique than external therapy. In the treatment of thyroid disease, for example, a radioactive substance such as iodine-131 is administered. This powerful β emitter is incorporated into the iodine-containing hormone thyroxine, which concentrates in the thyroid gland. Because β particles penetrate no farther than several millimeters, the localized ^{131}I produces

a high radiation dose that destroys only the surrounding diseased tissue. To treat some tumors, such as those in the female reproductive system, a radioactive source is placed physically close to the tumor for a specific amount of time.

Boron neutron-capture therapy (BNCT) is a relatively new technique in which boron-containing drugs are administered to a patient and concentrate in the tumor site. The tumor is then irradiated with a neutron beam from a nuclear reactor. The boron absorbs a neutron and undergoes transmutation to produce an alpha particle and a lithium nucleus. These highly energetic particles have very low penetrating power and can kill nearby tumor tissue while sparing the healthy surrounding tissue. Because one disadvantage of BNCT is the need for access to a nuclear reactor, this treatment is available only in limited locations.

▲ A person's blood volume can be found by injecting a small amount of radioactive chromium-51 and measuring the dilution factor.

▲ T/B/W when new photo chosen.

See Additional Problems 11.70 and 11.71 at the end of the chapter.

The half-lives of some useful radioisotopes are given in Table 11.3. As you might expect, radioisotopes that are used internally for medical applications have fairly short half-lives so that they decay rapidly and do not remain in the body for prolonged periods.

TABLE 11.3   Half-Lives of Some Useful Radioisotopes

RADIOISOTOPE	SYMBOL	RADIATION	HALF-LIFE	USE
Tritium	$^{3}_{1}H$	β	12.33 years	Biochemical tracer
Carbon-14	$^{14}_{6}C$	β	5730 years	Archaeological dating
Sodium-24	$^{24}_{11}Na$	β	14.959 hours	Examining circulation
Phosphorus-32	$^{32}_{15}P$	β	14.262 days	Leukemia therapy
Potassium-40	$^{40}_{19}K$	β, β^{+}	1.277×10^{9} years	Geological dating
Cobalt-60	$^{60}_{27}Co$	β, γ	5.271 years	Cancer therapy
Arsenic-74	$^{74}_{33}As$	β^{+}	17.77 days	Locating brain tumors
Technetium-99*m**	$^{99m}_{43}Tc$	γ	6.01 hours	Brain scans
Iodine-131	$^{131}_{53}I$	β	8.021 days	Thyroid therapy
Uranium-235	$^{235}_{92}U$	α, γ	7.038×10^{8} years	Nuclear reactors

The m in technetium-99m stands for metastable, *meaning that the nucleus undergoes γ emission but does not change its mass number or atomic number.*

WORKED EXAMPLE   **11.4** Nuclear Reactions: Half-Life

Phosphorus-32, a radioisotope used in leukemia therapy, has a half-life of about 14 days. Approximately what percent of a sample remains after 8 weeks?

ANALYSIS Determine how many half-lives have elapsed. For an integral number of half-lives, we can multiply the starting amount (100%) by 1/2 for each half-life that has elapsed.

SOLUTION
Since one half-life of $^{32}_{15}P$ is 14 days (2 weeks), 8 weeks represents four half-lives. The fraction that remains after 8 weeks is thus

Four half-lives

$$\text{Final Percentage} = 100\% \times (0.5)^4 = 100\% \times \left(\tfrac{1}{2} \times \tfrac{1}{2} \times \tfrac{1}{2} \times \tfrac{1}{2}\right)$$
$$= 100\% \times \tfrac{1}{16} = 6.25\%$$

WORKED EXAMPLE   **11.5** Nuclear Reactions: Half-Life

As noted on page 341 and in Table 11.3, iodine-131 has a half-life of about 8 days. Approximately what fraction of a sample remains after 20 days?

ANALYSIS Determine how many half-lives have elapsed. For a non-integral number (i.e., fraction) of half-lives, use the equation below to determine the fraction of radioisotope remaining.

$$\text{fraction remaining} = (0.5)^n$$

BALLPARK ESTIMATE Since the half-life of iodine-131 is 8 days, an elapsed time of 20 days is 2.5 half-lives. The fraction remaining should be between 0.25 (fraction remaining after two half-lives) and 0.125 (fraction remaining after three half-lives). Since the relationship between the number of half-lives and fraction remaining is not linear (see Figure 11.4), the fraction remaining will not be exactly halfway between these values but instead will be slightly closer to the lower fraction, say 0.17.

SOLUTION

$$\text{fraction remaining } = (0.5)^n = (0.5)^{2.5} = 0.177$$

BALLPARK CHECK: The fraction remaining is close to our estimate of 0.17.

PROBLEM 11.8

The half-life of carbon-14, an isotope used in archaeological dating, is 5730 years. What percentage of $^{14}_{6}C$ remains in a sample estimated to be 17,000 years old?

◆◎ KEY CONCEPT PROBLEM 11.9

What is the half-life of the radionuclide that shows the following decay curve?

Decay series A sequential series of nuclear disintegrations leading from a heavy radioisotope to a non-radioactive product.

▲ Radon gas can be detected and measured by this home detection kit.

11.6 Radioactive Decay Series

When a radioactive isotope decays, nuclear change occurs and a different element is formed. Often, this newly formed nucleus is stable, but sometimes the product nucleus is itself radioactive and undergoes further decay. In fact, some radioactive nuclei undergo a whole **decay series** of nuclear disintegrations before they ultimately reach a nonradioactive product. This is particularly true for the isotopes of heavier elements. Uranium-238, for example, undergoes a series of 14 sequential nuclear reactions, ultimately stopping at lead-206 (Figure 11.5).

One of the intermediate radionuclides in the uranium-238 decay series is radium-226. Radium-226 has a half-life of 1600 years and undergoes α decay to produce radon-222, a gas. Rocks, soil, and building materials that contain radium are sources of radon-222, which can seep through cracks in basements and get into the air inside homes and other buildings. Radon itself is a gas that passes in and out of the lungs without being incorporated into body tissue. If, however, a radon-222 atom should happen to decay while in the lungs, the solid decay product polonium-218 results. Further decay of the ^{218}Po emits α particles, which can damage lung tissue.

▲ **FIGURE 11.5** **The decay series from $^{238}_{92}$U to $^{206}_{82}$Pb.** Each isotope except for the last is radioactive and undergoes nuclear decay. The long slanted arrows represent α emissions, and the short horizontal arrows represent β emissions.

11.7 Ionizing Radiation

High-energy radiation of all kinds is often grouped together under the name **ionizing radiation**. This includes not only α particles, β particles, and γ rays, but also *X rays* and *cosmic rays*. **X rays** are like γ rays; they have no mass and consist of high-energy electromagnetic radiation. The only difference between them is that the energy of X rays is somewhat less than that of γ rays (see the Application "Atoms and Light" in Chapter 3). **Cosmic rays** are not rays at all but are a mixture of high-energy particles that shower the earth from outer space. They consist primarily of protons, along with some α and β particles.

The interaction of any kind of ionizing radiation with a molecule knocks out an electron, converting the atom or molecule into an extremely reactive ion:

$$\text{Molecule} \xrightarrow[\text{radiation}]{\text{ionizing}} \text{Ion} + e^-$$

The reactive ion can react with other molecules nearby, creating still other fragments that can in turn cause further reactions. In this manner, a large dose of ionizing radiation can destroy the delicate balance of chemical reactions in living cells, ultimately causing the death of an organism.

A small dose of ionizing radiation may not cause visible symptoms but can nevertheless be dangerous if it strikes a cell nucleus and damages the genetic machinery inside. The resultant changes might lead to a genetic mutation, to cancer, or to cell death. The nuclei of rapidly dividing cells, such as those in bone marrow, the lymph system, the lining of the intestinal tract, or an embryo, are the most readily damaged. Because cancer cells are also rapidly dividing they are highly susceptible to the effects of ionizing radiation, which is why radiation therapy is an effective treatment for many types of cancer (see Application on p. 342). Some properties of ionizing radiation are summarized in Table 11.4.

Ionizing radiation A general name for high-energy radiation of all kinds.

X rays Electromagnetic radiation with an energy somewhat less than that of γ rays.

Cosmic rays A mixture of high-energy particles—primarily of protons and various atomic nuclei—that shower the earth from outer space.

TABLE 11.4   Some Properties of Ionizing Radiation

TYPE OF RADIATION	ENERGY RANGE*	PENETRATING DISTANCE IN WATER**
α	3–9 MeV	0.02–0.04 mm
β	0–3 MeV	0–4 mm
X	100 eV–10 keV	0.01–1 cm
γ	10 keV–10 MeV	1–20 cm

*The energies of subatomic particles are often measured in electron volts (eV): $1\ eV = 6.703 \times 10^{-19}\ cal.$
**Distance at which one-half of the radiation is stopped.*

The effects of ionizing radiation on the human body vary with the energy of the radiation, its distance from the body, the length of exposure, and the location of the source outside or inside the body. When coming from outside the body, γ rays and X rays are potentially more harmful than α and β particles because they pass through clothing and skin and into the body's cells. Alpha particles are stopped by clothing and skin, and β particles are stopped by wood or several layers of clothing. These types of radiation are much more dangerous when emitted within the body, however, because all their radiation energy is given up to the immediately surrounding tissue. Alpha emitters are especially hazardous internally and are almost never used in medical applications.

Health professionals who work with X rays or other kinds of ionizing radiation protect themselves by surrounding the source with a thick layer of lead or other dense material. Protection from radiation is also afforded by controlling the distance between the worker and the radiation source because radiation intensity (I) decreases with the square of the distance from the source. The intensities of radiation at two different distances, 1 and 2, are given by the equation

$$\frac{I_1}{I_2} = \frac{d_2{}^2}{d_1{}^2}$$

For example, suppose a source delivers 16 units of radiation at a distance of 1.0 m. Doubling the distance to 2.0 m decreases the radiation intensity to one-fourth:

$$\frac{16\ \text{units}}{I_2} = \frac{(2\ \text{m})^2}{(1\ \text{m})^2}$$

$$I_2 = 16\ \text{units} \times \frac{1\ \text{m}^2}{4\ \text{m}^2} = 4\ \text{units}$$

WORKED EXAMPLE   **11.6** Ionizing Radiation: Intensity versus Distance from the Source

If a radiation source gives 75 units of radiation at a distance of 2.4 m, at what distance does the source give 25 units of radiation?

ANALYSIS Radiation intensity (I) decreases with the square of the distance (d) from the source according to the equation

$$\frac{I_1}{I_2} = \frac{d_2{}^2}{d_1{}^2}$$

We know three of the four variables in this equation (I_1, I_2, and d_1), and we need to find d_2.

BALLPARK ESTIMATE In order to decrease the radiation intensity from 75 units to 25 units (a factor of 3), the distance must *increase* by a factor of $\sqrt{3} = 1.7$. Thus, the distance should increase from 2.4 m to about 4 m.

SOLUTION

STEP 1: Identify known information. We know three of the four variables.	$I_1 = 75$ units $I_2 = 25$ units $d_1 = 2.4$ m
STEP 2: Identify answer and units.	$d_2 = ???$ m
STEP 3: Identify equation. Rearrange the equation relating intensity and distance to solve for d_2.	$$\frac{I_1}{I_2} = \frac{d_2{}^2}{d_1{}^2}$$ $$d_2{}^2 = \frac{I_1 d_1{}^2}{I_2} \implies d_2 = \sqrt{\frac{I_1 d_1{}^2}{I_2}}$$
STEP 4: Solve. Substitute in known values so that unwanted units cancel.	$$d_2 = \sqrt{\frac{(75 \ \text{units})(2.4 \ \text{m})^2}{(25 \ \text{units})}} = 4.2 \ \text{m}$$

BALLPARK CHECK The calculated result is consistent with our estimate of about 4 m.

PROBLEM 11.10

A β-emitting radiation source gives 250 units of radiation at a distance of 4.0 m. At what distance does the radiation drop to one-tenth its original value?

11.8 Detecting Radiation

Small amounts of naturally occurring radiation have always been present, but people have been aware of it only within the past 100 years. The problem is that radiation is invisible. We cannot see, hear, smell, touch, or taste radiation, no matter how high the dose. We can, however, detect radiation by taking advantage of its ionizing properties.

The simplest device for detecting exposure to radiation is the photographic film badge worn by people who routinely work with radioactive materials. The film is protected from exposure to light, but any other radiation striking the badge causes the film to fog (remember Becquerel's discovery). At regular intervals, the film is developed and compared with a standard to indicate the radiation exposure.

Perhaps the best-known method for detecting and measuring radiation is the *Geiger counter*, an argon-filled tube containing two electrodes (Figure 11.6). The inner walls of the tube are coated with an electrically conducting material and given a negative charge, and a wire in the center of the tube is given a positive charge. As radiation enters the tube through a thin window, it strikes and ionizes argon atoms, which briefly conduct a tiny electric current between the walls and the center electrode. The passage of the current is detected, amplified, and used to produce a clicking sound or to register on a meter. The more radiation that enters the tube, the more frequent the clicks. Geiger counters are useful for seeking out a radiation source in a large area and for gauging the intensity of emitted radiation.

The most versatile method for measuring radiation in the laboratory is the *scintillation counter*, a device in which a substance called a *phosphor* emits a flash of light when struck by radiation. The number of flashes are counted electronically and converted into an electrical signal.

▲ This photographic film badge is a common device for monitoring radiation exposure.

▲ Radiation is conveniently detected and measured using this scintillation counter, which electronically counts the flashes produced when radiation strikes a phosphor.

▶ **FIGURE 11.6** **A Geiger counter for measuring radiation.** As radiation enters the tube through a thin window, it ionizes argon atoms and produces electrons that conduct a tiny electric current between the walls and the center electrode. The current flow then registers on the meter.

11.9 Measuring Radiation

Radiation intensity is expressed in different ways, depending on what characteristic of the radiation is measured (Table 11.5). Some units measure the number of nuclear decay events, while others measure exposure to radiation or the biological consequences of radiation.

TABLE 11.5 Common Units for Measuring Radiation

UNIT	QUANTITY MEASURED	DESCRIPTION
Curie (Ci)	Decay events	Amount of radiation equal to 3.7×10^{10} disintegrations per second
Roentgen (R)	Ionizing intensity	Amount of radiation producing 2.1×10^9 charges per cubic centimeter of dry air
Rad	Energy absorbed per gram of tissue	1 rad = 1 R
Rem	Tissue damage	Amount of radiation producing the same damage as 1 R of X rays
Sievert (Sv)	Tissue damage	1 Sv = 100 rem

The *curie* (Ci), the *millicurie* (mCi), and the *microcurie* (μCi) measure the number of radioactive disintegrations occurring each second in a sample. One curie is the decay rate of 1 g of radium, equal to 3.7×10^{10} disintegrations per second; 1 mCi = 0.001 Ci = 3.7×10^7 disintegrations per second; and 1 μCi = 0.000 001 Ci = 3.7×10^4 disintegrations per second.

APPLICATION ▶ Irradiated Food

The idea of irradiating food to kill harmful bacteria is not new; it goes back almost as far as the earliest studies on radiation. Not until the 1940s did serious work get under way, however, when U.S. Army scientists found that irradiation increased the shelf-life of ground beef. Nevertheless, widespread civilian use of the technique has been a long time in coming, spurred on in recent years by outbreaks of food poisoning that resulted in several deaths.

The principle of food irradiation is simple: Exposure of contaminated food to ionizing radiation—usually γ rays produced by cobalt-60 or cesium-137—destroys the genetic material of any bacteria or other organisms present, thereby killing them. Irradiation will not, however, kill viruses or prions (⬭ , p. 584), the cause of mad-cow disease. The food itself undergoes little if any change when irradiated and does not itself become radioactive. The only real argument against food irradiation, in fact, is that it is *too* effective. Knowing that irradiation will kill nearly all harmful organisms, a food processor might be tempted to cut back on normal sanitary practices!

Food irradiation has been implemented to a much greater extent in Europe than in the United States. The largest marketers of irradiated food are Belgium, France, and the Netherlands, which irradiate between 10,000 and 20,000 tons of food per year. One of the major concerns in the United States is the possible generation of *radiolytic products*, compounds formed in food by exposure to ionizing radiation. The U.S. Food and Drug Administration, after studying the matter extensively, has declared that food irradiation is safe and that it does not appreciably alter the vitamin or other nutritional content of food. Spices, fruits, pork, and vegetables were

approved for irradiation in 1986, followed by poultry in 1990 and red meat, particularly ground beef, in 1997. In 2000, approval was extended to whole eggs and sprouting seeds. Should the food industry adopt irradiation of meat as its standard practice, such occurrences as the 1993 Seattle outbreak of *E. coli* poisoning caused by undercooked hamburgers will become a thing of the past.

▲ Irradiating food kills bacteria and extends shelf-life. The strawberries in these two containers were picked at the same time, but only the batch on the right was irradiated.

See Additional Problems 11.72 and 11.73 at the end of the chapter.

The dosage of a radioactive substance administered orally or intravenously is usually given in millicuries. To calculate the size of a dose, it is necessary to determine the decay rate of the isotope solution per milliliter. Because the emitter concentration is constantly decreasing as it decays, the activity must be measured immediately before administration. Suppose, for example, that a solution containing iodine-131 for a thyroid function study is found to have a decay rate of 0.020 mCi/mL and the dose administered is to be 0.050 mCi. The amount of the solution administered must be

$$\frac{0.05 \ \text{mCi}}{\text{Dose}} \times \frac{1 \ \text{mL} \ ^{131}\text{I solution}}{0.020 \ \text{mCi}} = 2.5 \ \text{mL} \ ^{131}\text{I solution/dose}$$

- **Roentgen** The *roentgen* (R) is a unit for measuring the ionizing intensity of γ or X radiation. In other words, the roentgen measures the capacity of the radiation for affecting matter. One roentgen is the amount of radiation that produces 2.1×10^9 units of charge in 1 cm^3 of dry air at atmospheric pressure. Each collision of ionizing radiation with an atom produces one ion, or one unit of charge.

- **Rad** The *rad* (radiation absorbed dose) is a unit for measuring the energy absorbed per gram of material exposed to a radiation source and is defined as the absorption of 1×10^{-5} J of energy per gram. The energy absorbed varies with the type of material irradiated and the type of radiation. For most purposes, though, the roentgen and the rad are so close that they can be considered identical when used for X rays and γ rays: 1 R = 1 rad.

- **Rem** The *rem* (roentgen equivalent for man) measures the amount of tissue damage caused by radiation, taking into account the differences in energy of different types of radiation. One rem is the amount of radiation that produces the same effect as 1 R of X rays.

  Rems are the preferred units for medical purposes because they measure equivalent doses of different kinds of radiation. For example, 1 rad of α radiation causes 20 times more tissue damage than 1 rad of γ rays, but 1 rem of α radiation and 1 rem of γ rays cause the same amount of damage. Thus, the rem takes both ionizing intensity and biological effect into account, whereas the rad deals only with intensity.

- **SI Units** In the SI system, the *becquerel* (Bq) is defined as one disintegration per second. The SI unit for energy absorbed is the *gray* (Gy; 1 Gy = 100 rad). For radiation dose, the SI unit is the *sievert* (Sv), which is equal to 100 rem.

The biological consequences of different radiation doses are given in Table 11.6. Although the effects seem fearful, the average radiation dose received annually by most people is only about 0.27 rem. About 80% of this *background radiation* comes from natural sources (rocks and cosmic rays); the remaining 20% comes from medical procedures such as X rays and from consumer products. The amount due to emissions from nuclear power plants and to fallout from testing of nuclear weapons in the 1950s is barely detectable.

TABLE 11.6 Biological Effects of Short-Term Radiation on Humans

DOSE (REM)	BIOLOGICAL EFFECTS
0–25	No detectable effects
25–100	Temporary decrease in white blood cell count
100–200	Nausea, vomiting, longer-term decrease in white blood cells
200–300	Vomiting, diarrhea, loss of appetite, listlessness
300–600	Vomiting, diarrhea, hemorrhaging, eventual death in some cases
Above 600	Eventual death in nearly all cases

▲ After the 1986 nuclear-reactor disaster at Chernobyl, security police in Ukraine limited access to the area within 30 km of the site. *(©Shirley Clive/Greenpeace International)*

PROBLEM 11.11

Radiation released during the 1986 Chernobyl nuclear power plant disaster is expected to increase the background radiation level worldwide by about 5 mrem. By how much will this increase the annual dose of the average person. Express your answer as a percentage.

PROBLEM 11.12

A solution of selenium-75, a radioisotope used in the diagnosis of pancreatic disease, is found just prior to administration to have an activity of 44 μCi/mL. How many milliliters should be administered intravenously for a dose of 175 μCi?

Artificial transmutation The change of one atom into another brought about by a nuclear bombardment reaction.

11.10 Artificial Transmutation

Very few of the approximately 3300 known radioisotopes occur naturally. Most are made from stable isotopes by **artificial transmutation**, the change of one atom into another brought about by nuclear bombardment reactions.

When an atom is bombarded with a high-energy particle, such as a proton, neutron, α particle, or even the nucleus of another element, an unstable nucleus is created in the collision. A nuclear change then occurs, and a different element is produced. For example, transmutation of ^{14}N to ^{14}C occurs in the upper atmosphere when neutrons produced by cosmic rays collide with atmospheric nitrogen. In the collision, a neutron dislodges a proton (^1H) from the nitrogen nucleus as the neutron and nucleus fuse together:

$$^{14}_{7}N + {}^{1}_{0}n \longrightarrow {}^{14}_{6}C + {}^{1}_{1}H$$

Artificial transmutation can lead to the synthesis of entirely new elements never before seen on earth. In fact, all the *transuranium elements*—those elements with atomic numbers greater than 92—have been produced by bombardment reactions. For example, plutonium-241 (^{241}Pu) can be made by bombardment of uranium-238 with α particles:

$$^{238}_{92}U + {}^{4}_{2}He \longrightarrow {}^{241}_{94}Pu + {}^{1}_{0}n$$

Plutonium-241 is itself radioactive, with a half-life of 14.35 years, decaying by β emission to yield americium-241, which in turn decays by α emission with a half-life of 432.2 years. (If the name *americium* sounds vaguely familiar, it is because this radioisotope is used in smoke detectors.)

$$^{241}_{94}Pu \longrightarrow {}^{241}_{95}Am + {}^{0}_{-1}e$$

Note that all the equations just given for artificial transmutations are balanced. The sum of the mass numbers and the sum of the charges are the same on both sides of each equation.

▲ Smoke detectors contain a small amount of americium-241. The α particles emitted by this radioisotope ionize the air within the detector, causing it to conduct a tiny electric current. When smoke enters the chamber, conductivity drops and an alarm is triggered.

WORKED EXAMPLE   **11.7** Balancing Nuclear Reactions: Transmutation

Californium-246 is formed by bombardment of uranium-238 atoms. If four neutrons are also formed, what particle is used for the bombardment?

ANALYSIS First write an incomplete nuclear equation incorporating the known information:

$$^{238}_{92}U + ? \longrightarrow {}^{246}_{98}Cf + 4\,{}^{1}_{0}n$$

Then find the numbers of nucleons and charges necessary to balance the equation. In this instance, there are 238 nucleons on the left and $246 + 4 = 250$ nucleons on the right, so the bombarding particle must have $250 - 238 = 12$ nucleons. Furthermore, there are 92 nuclear charges on the left and 98 on the right, so the bombarding particle must have $98 - 92 = 6$ protons.

SOLUTION
The missing particle is $^{12}_{6}C$.

$$^{238}_{92}U + {}^{12}_{6}C \longrightarrow {}^{246}_{98}Cf + 4\,{}^{1}_{0}n$$

PROBLEM 11.13

What isotope results from α decay of the americium-241 in smoke detectors?

PROBLEM 11.14

The element berkelium, first prepared at the University of California at Berkeley in 1949, is made by α bombardment of $^{241}_{95}Am$. Two neutrons are also produced during the reaction. What isotope of berkelium results from this transmutation? Write a balanced nuclear equation.

APPLICATION ▶ Body Imaging

We are all familiar with the appearance of a standard X-ray image, produced when X rays pass through the body and the intensity of the radiation that exits is recorded on film. X-ray imaging is, however, only one of a host of noninvasive imaging techniques that are now in common use.

Among the most widely used imaging techniques are those that give diagnostic information about the health of various parts of the body by analyzing the distribution pattern of a radioactively tagged substance in the body. A radiopharmaceutical agent that is known to concentrate in a specific organ or other body part is injected into the body, and its distribution pattern is monitored by an external radiation detector such as a γ-ray camera. Depending on the medical condition, a diseased part might concentrate more of the radiopharmaceutical than normal and thus show up on the film as a radioactive hot spot against a cold background. Alternatively, the diseased part might concentrate less of the radiopharmaceutical than normal and thus show up as a cold spot on a hot background.

Among the radioisotopes most widely used for diagnostic imaging is technetium-99m, whose short half-life of only six hours minimizes the patient's exposure to radioactivity. Bone scans using this nuclide, such as that shown in the accompanying photograph, are an important tool in the diagnosis of cancer and other conditions.

Several other techniques now used in medical diagnosis are made possible by *tomography*, a technique in which computer processing allows production of images through "slices" of the body. In X-ray tomography, commonly known as *CAT* or *CT* scanning (computerized tomography), the X-ray source and an array of detectors move rapidly in a circle around a patient's body, collecting up to 90,000 readings. CT scans can detect structural abnormalities such as tumors without the use of radioactive materials.

Combining tomography with radioisotope imaging gives cross-sectional views of regions that concentrate a radioactive substance. One such technique, *positron emission tomography* (PET), utilizes radioisotopes that emit positrons and ultimately yield γ rays. Oxygen-15, nitrogen-13, carbon-11, and

▲ A bone scan carried out with radioactive technetium-99m. Color has been added to help the visualization.

fluorine-18 are commonly used for PET because they can be readily incorporated into many physiologically active compounds. An ^{18}F-labeled glucose derivative, for instance, is useful for imaging brain regions that respond to various stimuli. The disadvantage of PET scans is that the necessary radioisotopes are so short-lived that they must be produced on-site immediately before use. The cost of PET is therefore high, because a hospital must install and maintain the necessary nuclear facility.

Magnetic resonance imaging (MRI) is a medical imaging technique that uses powerful magnetic and radio-frequency fields to interact with specific nuclei in the body (usually the nuclei of hydrogen atoms) to generate images in which the contrast between soft tissues is much better than that seen with CT. The original name for this technique was *nuclear magnetic resonance imaging*, but the *nuclear* was eliminated because in the public mind this word conjured up negative images of ionizing radiation. Ironically, MRI does not involve any nuclear radiation at all.

See Additional Problems 11.74 and 11.75 at the end of the chapter.

PROBLEM 11.15

Write a balanced nuclear equation for the reaction of argon-40 with a proton:

$$^{40}_{18}\text{Ar} + ^{1}_{1}\text{H} \longrightarrow \text{?} + ^{1}_{0}\text{n}$$

11.11 Nuclear Fission and Nuclear Fusion

In the preceding section, we saw that particle bombardment of various elements causes artificial transmutation and results in the formation of new, usually heavier elements. Under very special conditions with a very few isotopes, however, different kinds of nuclear events occur. Certain very heavy nuclei can split apart, and certain very light nuclei can fuse together. The two resultant processes—**nuclear fission** for the fragmenting of heavy nuclei and **nuclear fusion** for the joining together of light nuclei—have changed the world since their discovery in the late 1930s and early 1940s.

Nuclear fission The fragmenting of heavy nuclei.

Nuclear fusion The joining together of light nuclei.

The huge amounts of energy that accompany these nuclear processes are the result of mass-to-energy conversions and are predicted by Einstein's equation

$$E = mc^2$$

where E = energy, m = mass change associated with the nuclear reaction, and c = the speed of light (3.0×10^8 m/s). Based on this relationship, a mass change as small as 1 µg results in a release of 2.15×10^4 kcal of energy!

Nuclear Fission

Uranium-235 is the only naturally occurring isotope that undergoes nuclear fission. When this isotope is bombarded by a stream of relatively slow-moving neutrons, its nucleus splits to give isotopes of other elements. The split can take place in more than 400 ways, and more than 800 different fission products have been identified. One of the more frequently occurring pathways generates barium-142 and krypton-91, along with two additional neutrons plus the one neutron that initiated the fission:

$$\frac{1}{0}n + \frac{235}{92}U \longrightarrow \frac{142}{56}Ba + \frac{91}{36}Kr + 3\,\frac{1}{0}n$$

As indicated by the balanced nuclear equation above, *one* neutron is used to initiate fission of a ^{235}U nucleus, but *three* neutrons are released. Thus, a nuclear **chain reaction** can be started: 1 neutron initiates one fission that releases 3 neutrons. The 3 neutrons initiate three new fissions that release 9 neutrons. The 9 neutrons initiate nine fissions that release 27 neutrons, and so on at an ever faster pace (Figure 11.7). It is worth noting that the neutrons produced by fission reactions are highly energetic. They possess penetrating power greater than α and β particles, but less than γ rays. In a nuclear fission reactor, the neutrons must first be slowed down to allow them to react. If the sample size is small, many of the neutrons escape before initiating additional fission events, and the chain reaction stops. If a sufficient amount of ^{235}U is present, however—an amount called the **critical mass**—then the chain reaction becomes self-sustaining. Under high-pressure conditions that confine the ^{235}U to a small volume, the chain reaction occurs so rapidly that a nuclear explosion results. For ^{235}U, the critical mass is about 56 kg, although the amount can be reduced to approximately 15 kg by placing a coating of ^{238}U around the ^{235}U to reflect back some of the escaping neutrons.

Chain reaction A reaction that, once started, is self-sustaining.

Critical mass The minimum amount of radioactive material needed to sustain a nuclear chain reaction.

An enormous quantity of heat is released during nuclear fission—the fission of just 1.0 g of uranium-235 produces 3.4×10^8 kcal, for instance. This heat can be used to convert water to steam, which can be harnessed to turn huge generators and produce electric power. The use of nuclear power is much more advanced in some countries than in others, with Lithuania and France leading the way by generating about 86% and 77%, respectively, of their electricity in nuclear plants. In the United States, only about 22% of the electricity is nuclear-generated.

Two major objections that have caused much public debate about nuclear power plants are safety and waste disposal. Although a nuclear explosion is not possible under the conditions that exist in a power plant, there is a serious potential radiation hazard should an accident rupture the containment vessel holding the nuclear fuel and release radioactive substances to the environment. Perhaps even more important is the problem posed by disposal of radioactive wastes from nuclear plants. Many of these wastes have such long half-lives that hundreds or even thousands of years must elapse before they will be safe for humans to approach. How to dispose of such hazardous materials safely is an unsolved problem.

▲ Energy from the fission of uranium-235 is used to produce steam and generate electricity in this nuclear power plant.

▲ **FIGURE 11.7** **A chain reaction.** Each fission event produces additional neutrons that induce more fissions. The rate of the process increases at each stage. Such chain reactions usually lead to the formation of many different fission products in addition to the two indicated.

PROBLEM 11.16

What other isotope besides tellurium-137 is produced by nuclear fission of uranium-235?

$$^{235}_{92}\text{U} + ^{1}_{0}\text{n} \longrightarrow ^{137}_{52}\text{Te} + 2\,^{1}_{0}\text{n} + ?$$

Nuclear Fusion

Just as heavy nuclei such as ^{235}U release energy when they undergo *fission*, very light nuclei such as the isotopes of hydrogen release enormous amounts of energy when they undergo *fusion*. In fact, it is just such a fusion reaction of hydrogen nuclei to produce helium that powers our sun and other stars. Among the processes thought to occur in the sun are those in the following sequence leading to helium-4:

$$^{1}_{1}\text{H} + ^{2}_{1}\text{H} \longrightarrow ^{3}_{2}\text{He}$$
$$^{3}_{2}\text{He} + ^{3}_{2}\text{He} \longrightarrow ^{4}_{2}\text{He} + 2\,^{1}_{1}\text{H}$$
$$^{3}_{2}\text{He} + ^{1}_{1}\text{H} \longrightarrow ^{4}_{2}\text{He} + ^{0}_{1}\text{e}$$

APPLICATION ▶ Archaeological Radiocarbon Dating

Biblical scrolls are found in a cave near the Dead Sea. Are they authentic? A mummy is discovered in an Egyptian tomb. How old is it? The burned bones of a man are dug up near Lubbock, Texas. How long ago did humans live on the North American continent? Using a technique called *radiocarbon dating*, archaeologists can answer these and many other questions. (The Dead Sea Scrolls are 1900 years old and authentic, the mummy is 3100 years old, and the human remains found in Texas are 9900 years old.)

Radiocarbon dating depends on the slow and constant production of radioactive carbon-14 atoms in the upper atmosphere by bombardment of nitrogen atoms with neutrons from cosmic rays. Carbon-14 atoms combine with oxygen to yield $^{14}CO_2$, which slowly mixes with ordinary $^{12}CO_2$ and is then taken up by plants during photosynthesis. When these plants are eaten by animals, carbon-14 enters the food chain and is distributed evenly throughout all living organisms.

As long as a plant or animal is living, a dynamic equilibrium is established in which the organism excretes or exhales the same amount of ^{14}C that it takes in. As a result, the ratio of ^{14}C to ^{12}C in the living organism is the same as that in the atmosphere—about 1 part in 10^{12}. When the plant or animal dies, however, it no longer takes in more ^{14}C. Thus, the $^{14}C/^{12}C$ ratio in the organism slowly decreases as ^{14}C undergoes radioactive decay. At 5730 years (one ^{14}C half-life) after the death of the organism, the $^{14}C/^{12}C$ ratio has decreased by a factor of 2; at 11,460 years after death, the $^{14}C/^{12}C$ ratio has decreased by a factor of 4; and so on.

By measuring the amount of ^{14}C remaining in the traces of any once-living organism, archaeologists can determine how long ago the organism died. Human hair from well-preserved remains, charcoal or wood fragments from once-living trees, and cotton or linen from once-living plants are all useful sources for radiocarbon dating. The accuracy of the technique lessens as a sample gets older and the amount of ^{14}C it contains diminishes, but artifacts with an age of 1000–20,000 years can be dated with reasonable accuracy.

▲ Radiocarbon dating has determined that these charcoal paintings in the Lascaux cave in France are approximately 15,000 years old.

See Additional Problems 11.76 and 11.77 at the end of the chapter.

Under the conditions found in stars, where the temperature is on the order of 2×10^7 K and pressures approach 10^5 atmospheres, nuclei are stripped of all their electrons and have enough kinetic energy that nuclear fusion readily occurs. The energy of our sun, and all the stars, comes from thermonuclear fusion reactions in their core that fuse hydrogen and other light elements transmuting them into heavier elements. On earth, however, the necessary conditions for nuclear fusion are not easily created. For more than 50 years scientists have been trying to create the necessary conditions for fusion in laboratory reactors, including the Tokamak Fusion Test Reactor (TFTR) at Princeton, New Jersey, and the Joint European Torus (JET) at Culham, England. Recent advances in reactor design have raised hopes that a commercial fusion reactor will be realized within the next 20 years.

If the dream becomes reality, controlled nuclear fusion can provide the ultimate cheap, clean power source. The fuel is deuterium (^2H), available in the oceans in limitless amounts, and there are few radioactive by-products.

▲ A researcher stands inside the D3D Tokamak nuclear fusion reactor at the General Atomics facility in San Diego, California.

SUMMARY: REVISITING THE CHAPTER GOALS

1. **What is a nuclear reaction, and how are equations for nuclear reactions balanced?** A *nuclear reaction* is one that changes an atomic nucleus, causing the change of one element into another. Loss of an α particle leads to a new atom whose atomic number is 2 less than

KEY WORDS

Alpha (α) particle, *p. 335*
Artificial transmutation, *p. 350*

that of the starting atom. Loss of a β particle leads to an atom whose atomic number is 1 greater than that of the starting atom:

$$\alpha \text{ emission: } {}^{238}_{92}\text{U} \longrightarrow {}^{234}_{90}\text{Th} + {}^{4}_{2}\text{He}$$

$$\beta \text{ emission: } {}^{131}_{53}\text{I} \longrightarrow {}^{131}_{54}\text{Xe} + {}^{0}_{-1}\text{e}$$

A nuclear reaction is balanced when the sum of the *nucleons* (protons and neutrons) is the same on both sides of the reaction arrow and when the sum of the charges on the nuclei plus any ejected subatomic particles is the same.

2. **What are the different kinds of radioactivity?** *Radioactivity* is the spontaneous emission of radiation from the nucleus of an unstable atom. The three major kinds of radiation are called *alpha* (α), *beta* (β), and *gamma* (γ). Alpha radiation consists of helium nuclei, small particles containing two protons and two neutrons (${}^{4}_{2}\text{He}$); β radiation consists of electrons (${}^{0}_{-1}\text{e}$); and γ radiation consists of high-energy light waves. Every element in the periodic table has at least one radioactive isotope, or *radioisotope*.

3. **How are the rates of nuclear reactions expressed?** The rate of a nuclear reaction is expressed in units of *half-life* ($t_{1/2}$), where one half-life is the amount of time necessary for one half of the radioactive sample to decay.

4. **What is ionizing radiation?** High-energy radiation of all types—α particles, β particles, γ rays, and X rays—is called *ionizing radiation*. When any of these kinds of radiation strikes an atom, it dislodges an electron and gives a reactive ion that can be lethal to living cells. Gamma rays and X rays are the most penetrating and most harmful types of external radiation; α and β particles are the most dangerous types of internal radiation because of their high energy and the resulting damage to surrounding tissue.

5. **How is radioactivity measured?** Radiation intensity is expressed in different ways according to the property being measured. The *curie* (*Ci*) measures the number of radioactive disintegrations per second in a sample; the *roentgen* (*R*) measures the ionizing ability of radiation; the *rad* measures the amount of radiation energy absorbed per gram of tissue; and the *rem* measures the amount of tissue damage caused by radiation. Radiation effects become noticeable with a human exposure of 25 rem and become lethal at an exposure above 600 rem.

6. **What is transmutation?** *Transmutation* is the change of one element into another brought about by a nuclear reaction. Most known radioisotopes do not occur naturally but are made by bombardment of an atom with a high-energy particle. In the ensuing collision between particle and atom, a nuclear change occurs and a new element is produced by *artificial transmutation*.

7. **What are nuclear fission and nuclear fusion?** With a very few isotopes, including ${}^{235}_{92}\text{U}$, the nucleus is split apart by neutron bombardment to give smaller fragments. A large amount of energy is released during this *nuclear fission*, leading to use of the reaction for generating electric power. *Nuclear fusion* results when small nuclei such as those of tritium (${}^{3}_{1}\text{H}$) and deuterium (${}^{2}_{1}\text{H}$) combine to give a heavier nucleus.

UNDERSTANDING KEY CONCEPTS

11.17 Magnesium-28 decays by β emission to give aluminum-28. If yellow spheres represent ${}^{28}_{12}\text{Mg}$ atoms and blue spheres represent ${}^{28}_{13}\text{Al}$ atoms, how many half-lives have passed in the following sample?

11.18 Write a balanced nuclear equation to represent the decay reaction described in Problem 11.17.

11.19 Refer to Figure 11.4 and then make a drawing similar to those in Problem 11.17 representing the decay of a sample of ${}^{28}_{12}\text{Mg}$ after approximately four half-lives have passed.

11.20 Write the symbol of the isotope represented by the following drawing. Blue spheres represent neutrons and red spheres represent protons.

11.21 Shown below is a portion of the decay series for plutonium-241 (${}^{241}_{94}\text{Pu}$). The series has two kinds of arrows: shorter arrows pointing right and longer arrows pointing left. Which arrow corresponds to an α emission, and which to a β emission? Explain.

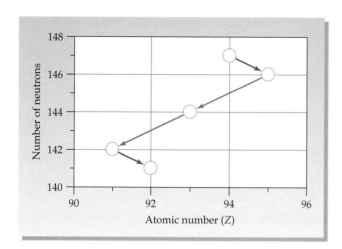

11.22 Identify and write the symbol for each nuclide in the decay series shown in Problem 11.21.

11.23 Identify the isotopes involved, and tell the type of decay process occurring in the following nuclear reaction:

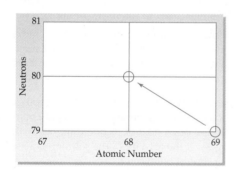

11.24 What is the half-life of the radionuclide that shows the following decay curve?

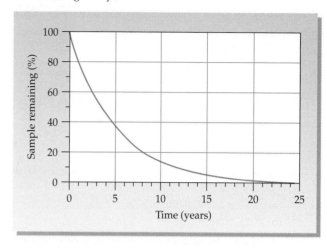

11.25 What is wrong with the following decay curve? Explain.

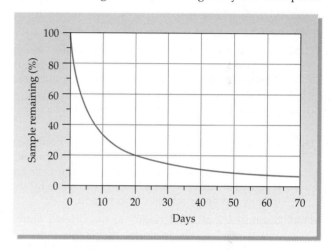

ADDITIONAL PROBLEMS

RADIOACTIVITY

11.26 What does it mean to say that a substance is radioactive?

11.27 Describe how α radiation, β radiation, γ radiation, positron emission, and electron capture differ.

11.28 List several ways in which a nuclear reaction differs from a chemical reaction.

11.29 What word is used to describe the change of one element into another?

11.30 What symbol is used for an α particle in a nuclear equation?

11.31 What symbol is used for a β particle in a nuclear equation? For a positron?

11.32 Which kind of radiation, α, β, or γ, has the highest penetrating power, and which has the lowest?

11.33 What happens when ionizing radiation strikes an atom in a chemical compound?

11.34 How does ionizing radiation lead to cell damage?

11.35 What are the main sources of background radiation?

11.36 How can a nucleus emit an electron during β decay when there are no electrons present in the nucleus to begin with?

11.37 What is the difference between an α particle and a helium atom?

NUCLEAR DECAY AND TRANSMUTATION

11.38 What does it mean to say that a nuclear equation is balanced?

11.39 What are transuranium elements, and how are they made?

11.40 What happens to the mass number and atomic number of an atom that emits an α particle? A β particle?

11.41 What happens to the mass number and atomic number of an atom that emits a γ ray? A positron?

11.42 How does nuclear fission differ from normal radioactive decay?

11.43 What characteristic of uranium-235 fission causes a chain reaction?

11.44 What products result from radioactive decay of the following β emitters?

(a) $^{35}_{16}S$ (b) $^{24}_{10}Ne$ (c) $^{90}_{38}Sr$

11.45 What products result from radioactive decay of the following α emitters?

(a) $^{190}_{78}$Pt   (b) $^{208}_{87}$Fr   (c) $^{245}_{96}$Cm

11.46 Identify the starting radioisotopes needed to balance each of these nuclear reactions:

(a) $? + ^4_2$He $\rightarrow ^{113}_{49}$In

(b) $? + ^4_2$He $\rightarrow ^{13}_7$N + $^1_0$n

11.47 Identify the product radioisotope needed to balance each of these nuclear reactions:

(a) $^{140}_{55}$Cs $\rightarrow ? + ^{\ 0}_{-1}$e

(b) $^{248}_{96}$Cm $\rightarrow ? + ^4_2$He

11.48 Balance the following equations for the nuclear fission of $^{235}_{92}$U:

(a) $^{235}_{92}$U + $^1_0$n $\rightarrow ^{160}_{62}$Sm + $^{72}_{30}$Zn + ? $^1_0$n

(b) $^{235}_{92}$U + $^1_0$n $\rightarrow ^{87}_{35}$Br + ? + 3 $^1_0$n

11.49 Complete and balance the following nuclear equations:

(a) $^{126}_{50}$Sn $\rightarrow ^{\ 0}_{-1}$e + ?

(b) $^{210}_{88}$Ra $\rightarrow ^4_2$He + ?

(c) $^{76}_{36}$Kr + $^{\ 0}_{-1}$e $\rightarrow ?$

11.50 For centuries, alchemists dreamed of turning base metals into gold. The dream finally became reality when it was shown that mercury-198 can be converted into gold-198 on bombardment by neutrons. What small particle is produced in addition to gold-198? Write a balanced nuclear equation for the reaction.

11.51 Cobalt-60 (half-life = 5.3 years) is used to irradiate food, to treat cancer, and to disinfect surgical equipment. It is produced by irradiation of cobalt-59 in a nuclear reactor. It decays to nickel-60. Write nuclear equations for the formation and decay reactions of cobalt-60.

11.52 Bismuth-212 attaches readily to monoclonal antibodies and is used in the treatment of various cancers. It is formed after the parent isotope undergoes a decay series consisting of four α decays and one β decay. What is the parent isotope for this decay series?

11.53 Meitnerium-266 ($^{266}_{109}$Mt) was prepared in 1982 by bombardment of bismuth-209 atoms with iron-58. What other product must also have been formed? Write a balanced nuclear equation for the transformation.

HALF-LIFE

11.54 What does it mean when we say that strontium-90, a waste product of nuclear power plants, has a half-life of 28.8 years?

11.55 What percentage of the original mass remains in a radioactive sample after two half-lives have passed? After three half-lives? After 3.5 half-lives?

11.56 Selenium-75, a β emitter with a half-life of 120 days, is used medically for pancreas scans. Approximately how much selenium-75 would remain from a 0.050 g sample that has been stored for one year?

11.57 Approximately how long would it take a sample of selenium-75 to lose 99% of its radioactivity? (See Problem 11.56.)

11.58 The half-life of mercury-197 is 64.1 hours. If a patient undergoing a kidney scan is given 5.0 ng of mercury-197, how much will remain after 7 days? After 30 days?

11.59 Gold-198, a β emitter used to treat leukemia, has a half-life of 2.695 days. The standard dosage is about 1.0 mCi/kg body weight.

(a) What is the product of the β emission of gold-198?

(b) How long does it take a 30.0 mCi sample of gold-198 to decay so that only 3.75 mCi remains?

(c) How many millicuries are required in a single dosage administered to a 70.0 kg adult?

MEASURING RADIOACTIVITY

11.60 Describe how a Geiger counter works.

11.61 Describe how a film badge works.

11.62 Describe how a scintillation counter works.

11.63 Why are rems the preferred units for measuring the health effects of radiation?

11.64 Approximately what amount (in rems) of short-term exposure to radiation produces noticeable effects in humans?

11.65 Match each unit in the left column with the property being measured in the right column:

1. curie   (a) Ionizing intensity of radiation
2. rem   (b) Amount of tissue damage
3. rad   (c) Number of disintegrations per second
4. roentgen   (d) Amount of radiation per gram of tissue

11.66 Technetium-99m is used for radioisotope-guided surgical biopsies of certain bone cancers. A patient must receive an injection of 28 mCi of technetium-99m 6–12 hours before surgery. If the activity of the solution is 15 mCi, what volume should be injected?

11.67 Sodium-24 is used to study the circulatory system and to treat chronic leukemia. It is administered in the form of saline (NaCl) solution, with a therapeutic dosage of 180 μCi/kg body weight. How many milliliters of a 6.5 mCi/mL solution are needed to treat a 68 kg adult?

11.68 A selenium-75 source is producing 300 rem at a distance of 2.0 m. What is its intensity at 25 m?

11.69 If a radiation source has an intensity of 650 rem at 1.0 m, what distance is needed to decrease the intensity of exposure to below 25 rem, the level at which no effects are detectable?

Applications

11.70 What are the three main classes of techniques used in nuclear medicine? Give an example of each. [*Medical Uses of Radioactivity, p. 342*]

11.71 A 2 mL solution containing 1.25 μCi/mL is injected into the blood stream of a patient. After dilution, a 1.00 mL sample is withdrawn and found to have an activity of 2.6×10^{-4} μCi. Calculate total blood volume. [*Medical Uses of Radioactivity, p. 342*]

11.72 What is the purpose of food irradiation, and how does it work? [*Irradiated Food, p. 349*]

11.73 What kind of radiation is used to treat food? [*Irradiated Food, p. 349*]

11.74 What are the advantages of CT and PET relative to conventional X rays? [*Body Imaging, p. 352*]

11.75 What advantages does MRI have over CT and PET imaging? [*Body Imaging, p. 352*]

11.76 Why is ^{14}C dating useful only for samples that contain material from objects that were once alive? [*Archaeological Radiocarbon Dating, p. 355*]

11.77 Some dried beans with a $^{14}C/^{12}C$ ratio one-eighth of the current value are found in an old cave. How old are the beans? [*Archaeological Radiocarbon Dating, p. 355*]

General Questions and Problems

11.78 Harmful chemical spills can often be cleaned up by treatment with another chemical. For example, a spill of H_2SO_4 might be neutralized by addition of $NaHCO_3$. Why is it that the harmful radioactive wastes from nuclear power plants cannot be cleaned up just as easily?

11.79 Why is a scintillation counter or Geiger counter more useful for determining the existence and source of a new radiation leak than a film badge?

11.80 Technetium-99m, used for brain scans and to monitor heart function, is formed by decay of molybdenum-99.

(a) By what type of decay does ^{99}Mo produce ^{99m}Tc?

(b) Molybdenum-99 is formed by neutron bombardment of a natural isotope. If one neutron is absorbed and there are no other by-products of this process, from what isotope is ^{99}Mo formed?

11.81 The half-life of technetium-99m (Problem 11.80) is 6.01 hours. If a sample with an initial activity of 15 μCi is injected into a patient, what is the activity in 24 hours, assuming that none of the sample is excreted?

11.82 Plutonium-238 is an α emitter used to power batteries for heart pacemakers.

(a) Write the balanced nuclear equation for this emission.

(b) Why is a pacemaker battery enclosed in a metal case before being inserted into the chest cavity?

11.83 Sodium-24, a beta-emitter used in diagnosing circulation problems, has a half-life of 15 hours.

(a) Write the balanced nuclear equation for this emission.

(b) What fraction of sodium-24 remains after 50 hours?

11.84 High levels of radioactive fallout after the 1986 accident at the Chernobyl nuclear power plant in what is now Ukraine resulted in numerous miscarriages and many instances of farm animals born with severe defects. Why are embryos and fetuses particularly susceptible to the effects of radiation?

11.85 One way to demonstrate the dose factor of ionizing radiation (penetrating distance $\times$ ionizing energy) is to think of radiation as cookies. Imagine that you have four cookies—an α cookie, a β cookie, a γ cookie, and a neutron cookie. Which one would you eat, which would you hold in your hand, which would you put in your pocket, and which would you throw away?

11.86 What are the main advantages of fusion relative to fission as an energy source? What are the drawbacks?

11.87 Write a balanced nuclear equation for

(a) α emission of ^{162}Re and

(b) β emission of ^{188}W.

11.88 Balance the following transmutation reactions:

(a) $^{253}_{99}Es + ? \rightarrow ^{256}_{101}Md + ^{1}_{0}n$

(b) $^{250}_{98}Cf + ^{11}_{5}B \rightarrow ? + 4\,^{1}_{0}n$

11.89 The most abundant isotope of uranium, ^{238}U, does not undergo fission. In a *breeder reactor*, however, a ^{238}U atom captures a neutron and emits two beta particles to make a fissionable isotope of plutonium, which can then be used as fuel in a nuclear reactor. Write the balanced nuclear equation.

11.90 Boron is used in *control rods* for nuclear reactors because it can absorb neutrons and emit α particles. Balance the equation

$$^{10}_{5}B + ^{1}_{0}n \longrightarrow ? + ^{4}_{2}He$$

11.91 Thorium-232 decays by a ten-step series, ultimately yielding lead-208. How many α particles and how many β particles are emitted?

11.92 Californium-246 is formed by bombardment of uranium-238 atoms. If four neutrons are formed as by-products, what particle is used for the bombardment?

Introduction to Organic Chemistry: Alkanes

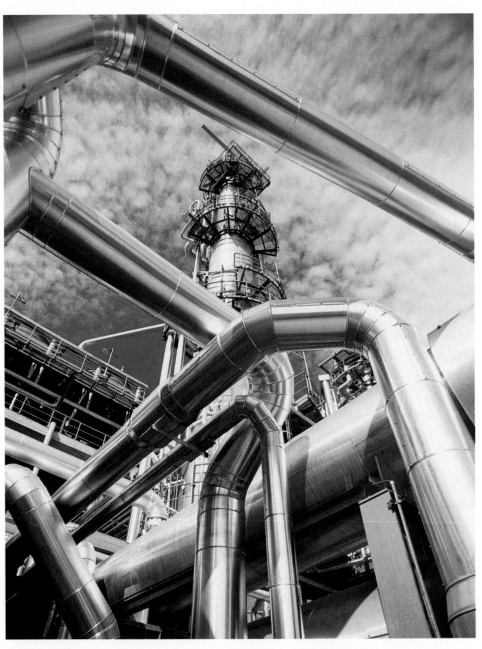

▲ The gasoline, kerosene, and other products of this petroleum refinery are primarily mixtures of simple organic compounds called alkanes.

CONTENTS

CHAPTER GOALS

In this and the next five chapters, we will look at the chemistry of organic compounds, beginning with answers to the following questions:

1. **What are the basic properties of organic compounds?**

   THE GOAL: Be able to identify organic compounds and the types of bonds contained in them.

2. **What are functional groups, and how are they used to classify organic molecules?**

   THE GOAL: Be able to classify organic molecules into families by functional group.

3. **What are isomers?**

   THE GOAL: Be able to recognize and draw constitutional isomers.

4. **How are organic molecules drawn?**

   THE GOAL: Be able to convert between structural formulas and condensed or line structures.

5. **What are alkanes and cycloalkanes, and how are they named?**

   THE GOAL: Be able to name an alkane or cycloalkane from its structure, or write the structure, given the name.

6. **What are the general properties and chemical reactions of alkanes?**

   THE GOAL: Be able to describe the physical properties of alkanes and the products formed in the combustion and halogenation reactions of alkanes.

A s knowledge of chemistry slowly grew in the 1700s, mysterious differences were noted between compounds obtained from living sources and those obtained from minerals. It was found, for instance, that chemicals from living sources were often liquids or low-melting solids, whereas chemicals from mineral sources were usually high-melting solids. Furthermore, chemicals from living sources were generally more difficult to purify and work with than those from minerals. To express these differences, the term *organic chemistry* was introduced to mean the study of compounds from living organisms, and *inorganic chemistry* was used to refer to the study of compounds from minerals.

Today we know that there are no fundamental differences between organic and inorganic compounds: The same scientific principles are applicable to both. The only common characteristic of compounds from living sources is that they contain the element carbon as their primary component. Thus, organic chemistry is now defined as the study of carbon-based compounds.

Why is carbon special? The answer derives from its position in the periodic table. As a group 4A nonmetal, carbon atoms have the unique ability to form four strong covalent bonds. Also, unlike atoms of other elements, carbon atoms can readily form strong bonds with other carbon atoms to produce long chains and rings. As a result, only carbon is able to form such an immense array of compounds, from methane with one carbon atom to DNA with billions of carbons.

12.1 The Nature of Organic Molecules

Let us begin a study of **organic chemistry**—the chemistry of carbon compounds—by reviewing what we have seen in earlier chapters about the structures of organic molecules:

Organic chemistry The study of carbon compounds.

- **Carbon is tetravalent; it always forms four bonds** (Section 5.2). In methane, for example, carbon is connected to four hydrogen atoms:

Methane, CH_4

- **Organic molecules have covalent bonds** (Section 5.2). In ethane, for example, the bonds result from the sharing of two electrons, either between two C atoms or a C and a H atom:

Ethane, C_2H_6

- **Organic molecules contain polar covalent bonds when carbon bonds to an electronegative element on the right side of the periodic table** (Section 5.8). In chloromethane, for example, the electronegative chlorine atom attracts electrons more strongly than carbon, resulting in polarization of the C—Cl bond so that carbon has a partial positive charge, $\delta+$, and chlorine has a partial negative charge, $\delta-$. In electrostatic potential maps (Section 5.8), the chlorine atom is therefore in the red region of the map and the carbon atom in the blue region:

Chloromethane, CH_3Cl

- **Carbon forms multiple covalent bonds by sharing more than two electrons with a neighboring atom** (Section 5.3). In ethylene, for example, the two carbon atoms share four electrons in a double bond; in acetylene (also called ethyne), the two carbons share six electrons in a triple bond:

Ethylene

H—C≡C—H
Acetylene, C_2H_2

- **Organic molecules have specific three-dimensional shapes** (Section 5.7). When carbon is bonded to four atoms, as in methane, CH_4, the bonds are oriented toward the four corners of a regular tetrahedron with carbon in the center. Such three-dimensionality is commonly shown using normal lines for bonds in the plane of the page, dashed lines for bonds receding behind the page, and wedged lines for bonds coming out of the page:

- **Organic molecules often contain hydrogen, nitrogen, and oxygen, in addition to carbon** (Section 5.6). Nitrogen can form single, double, and triple bonds to carbon; oxygen can form single and double bonds:

$$C—N \quad C—O \quad C—H$$
$$C=N \quad C=O$$
$$C≡N$$

Covalent bonding makes organic compounds quite different from the inorganic compounds we have been concentrating on up to this point. For example, inorganic compounds such as NaCl have high melting points and high boiling points because they consist of large numbers of oppositely charged ions held together by strong electrical attractions (Section 4.4). (, p. 84) Organic compounds, by contrast, consist of atoms joined by covalent bonds into individual molecules. Because the molecules are attracted to one another only by weak non-ionic intermolecular forces (Section 8.11), organic compounds generally have lower melting and boiling points than inorganic salts. (⊂◯⊃, p. 235) Because of their relatively low melting and boiling points, simple organic compounds are usually liquids at room temperature, and a few are gases.

Other important differences between organic and inorganic compounds include solubility and electrical conductivity. Whereas many inorganic compounds dissolve in water to yield solutions of ions that conduct electricity (Section 9.9), most organic compounds are insoluble in water, and almost all of those that are soluble do not conduct electricity. (⊂◯⊃, p. 275) Only small polar organic molecules, such as glucose and ethyl alcohol, or large molecules with many polar groups, such as some proteins, dissolve in water. This lack of water solubility for organic compounds has important practical consequences, varying from the difficulty in removing greasy dirt and cleaning up environmental oil spills to drug delivery.

◀ Oil spills can be a serious environmental problem because oil is insoluble in water.

⊂◯⊃ **Looking Ahead**

The interior of a living cell is largely a water solution that contains many hundreds of different compounds. In later chapters, we will see how cells use membranes composed of water-insoluble organic molecules to enclose their watery interiors and to regulate the flow of substances across the cell boundary. ⊂◯⊃

12.2 Families of Organic Molecules: Functional Groups

More than 18 *million* organic compounds are described in the scientific literature. Each of these 18 million compounds has unique physical properties, such as a melting point and a boiling point, each has unique chemical properties, and many of them have unique biological properties (both desired and undesired). How can we ever understand them all?

Chemists have learned through experience that organic compounds can be classified into families according to their structural features and that the chemical behavior of the members of a family is often predictable based on these specific grouping of atoms. Instead of 18 million compounds with seemingly random chemical reactivity, there are just a few general families of organic compounds whose chemistry falls into simple patterns.

The structural features that allow us to classify organic compounds into distinct chemical families are called **functional groups**. A functional group is an atom or group of atoms that has a characteristic physical and chemical behavior. Each functional group is always part of a larger molecule, and a molecule may have more than one class of functional group present, as we shall soon see. An important property of functional groups is that a given functional group *tends to undergo the same reactions in every molecule of which it is a part*. For example, the carbon–carbon double bond is a common functional group. Ethylene (C_2H_4), the simplest compound with a double bond, undergoes many chemical reactions similar to those of oleic acid ($C_{18}H_{34}O_2$), a much larger and more complex compound that also contains a double bond. Both, for example, react with hydrogen gas in the same manner, as shown in Figure 12.1. These identical reactions with hydrogen are typical: *The chemistry of an organic molecule is primarily determined by the functional groups it contains, not by its size and complexity.*

Functional group An atom or group of atoms within a molecule that has a characteristic physical and chemical behavior.

(a) Ethylene

(b) Oleic acid

► **FIGURE 12.1 The reactions of (a) ethylene and (b) oleic acid with hydrogen.** The carbon–carbon double-bond functional group adds 2 hydrogen atoms in both cases, regardless of the complexity of the rest of the molecule.

Table 12.1 lists some of the most important families of organic molecules and their distinctive functional groups. Compounds that contain a $C=C$ double bond, for instance, are in the *alkene* family; compounds that have an —OH group bound to a tetravalent carbon are in the *alcohol* family; and so on.

Much of the chemistry discussed in this and the next five chapters is the chemistry of the families listed in Table 12.1, so it is best to memorize the names and become familiar with their structures now. Note that they fall into three groups:

Hydrocarbon An organic compound that contains only carbon and hydrogen.

- The first four families in Table 12.1 are **hydrocarbons**, organic compounds that contain only carbon and hydrogen. *Alkanes* have only single bonds and contain no functional groups. As we will see, the absence of functional groups makes alkanes relatively unreactive. *Alkenes* contain a carbon–carbon double-bond functional group; *alkynes* contain a carbon–carbon triple-bond functional group; and *aromatic* compounds contain a six-membered ring of carbon atoms with three alternating double bonds.

- The next four families in Table 12.1 have functional groups that contain only single bonds and have a carbon atom bonded to an electronegative atom.

TABLE 12.1 Some Important Families of Organic Molecules

FAMILY NAME	FUNCTIONAL GROUP STRUCTURE*	SIMPLE EXAMPLE	NAME ENDING
Alkane	Contains only C—H and C—C single bonds	CH_3CH_3 Ethane	*-ane*
Alkene	C=C	$H_2C=CH_2$ Ethylene	*-ene*
Alkyne	—C≡C—	H—C≡C—H Acetylene (Ethyne)	*-yne*
Aromatic	(ring structure with alternating double bonds)	Benzene	None
Alkyl halide	—C—X (X=F, Cl, Br, I)	CH_3—Cl Methyl chloride	None
Alcohol	—C—O—H	CH_3—OH Methyl alcohol (Methanol)	*-ol*
Ether	—C—O—C—	CH_3—O—CH_3 Dimethyl ether	None
Amine	—C—N	CH_3—NH_2 Methylamine	*-amine*
Aldehyde	—C—C—H with =O	CH_3—C—H (with =O) Acetaldehyde (Ethanal)	*-al*
Ketone	—C—C—C— with =O	CH_3—C—CH_3 (with =O) Acetone	*-one*
Carboxylic acid	—C—C—OH with =O	CH_3—C—OH (with =O) Acetic acid	*-ic acid*
Anhydride	—C—C—O—C—C— with =O =O	CH_3—C—O—C—CH_3 (with =O =O) Acetic anhydride	None
Ester	—C—C—O—C— with =O	CH_3—C—O—CH_3 (with =O) Methyl acetate	*-ate*
Amide	—C—C—NH_2, —C—C—N—H, with =O =O; —C—C—N— with =O	CH_3—C—NH_2 (with =O) Acetamide	*-amide*

*The bonds whose connections are not specified are assumed to be attached to carbon or hydrogen atoms in the rest of the molecule.

Alkyl halides have a carbon–halogen bond; *alcohols* have a carbon–oxygen bond; *ethers* have two carbons bonded to the same oxygen; and *amines* have a carbon–nitrogen bond.

- The remaining families in Table 12.1 have functional groups that contain a carbon–oxygen double bond: *aldehydes, ketones, carboxylic acids, anhydrides, esters,* and *amides.*

WORKED EXAMPLE **12.1** Molecular Structures: Identifying Functional Groups

To which family of organic compounds do the following compounds belong? Explain.

ANALYSIS Identify each functional group from the list in Table 12.1, and name the corresponding family to which the compound belongs.

SOLUTION

- **(a)** This compound contains only carbon and hydrogen atoms, so it is a *hydrocarbon*. There is a carbon–carbon double bond, so it is an *alkene*.
- **(b)** The O—H group bonded to tetravalent carbon identifies this compound as an *alcohol*.
- **(c)** This compound also contains only carbon and hydrogen atoms, which identifies it as a *hydrocarbon*. The six-membered carbon ring with alternating double bonds also identifies this compound as an *aromatic* hydrocarbon compound.
- **(d)** The carbon–oxygen double bond in the middle of the carbon chain (as opposed to at either end of the chain) identifies this compound as a *ketone*.

WORKED EXAMPLE **12.2** Molecular Structures: Drawing Functional Groups

Given the family of organic compounds to which the compound belongs, propose structures for compounds having the following chemical formulas.

- **(a)** An amine having the formula C_2H_7N
- **(b)** An alkyne having the formula C_3H_4
- **(c)** An ether having the formula $C_4H_{10}O$

ANALYSIS Identify the functional group for each compound from Table 12.1. Once the atoms in this functional group are eliminated from the chemical formula, the remaining structure can be determined. (Remember that each carbon atom forms four bonds, nitrogen forms three bonds, oxygen forms two bonds, and hydrogen forms only one bond.)

SOLUTION

(a) Amines have a $C—NH_2$ group. Eliminating these atoms from the formula leaves 1 C atom and 5 H atoms. Since only the carbons are capable of forming more than one bond, the 2 C atoms must be bonded together. The remaining H atoms are then bonded to the carbons until each C has 4 bonds.

$$H-\underset{\underset{H}{|}}{\overset{\overset{H}{|}}{C}}-\underset{\underset{H}{|}}{\overset{\overset{H}{|}}{C}}-N\overset{H}{\underset{H}{\diagdown}}$$

(b) The alkynes contain a $C\equiv C$ bond. This leaves 1 C atom and 4 H atoms. Attach this C to one of the carbons in the triple bond, and then distribute the H atoms until each carbon has a full complement of four bonds.

$$H-\underset{\underset{H}{|}}{\overset{\overset{H}{|}}{C}}-C\equiv C-H$$

(c) The ethers contain a $C—O—C$ group. Eliminating these atoms leaves 2 C atoms and 10 H atoms. The C atoms can be distributed on either end of the ether group, and the H atoms are then distributed until each carbon atom has a full complement of four bonds.

$$H-\underset{\underset{H}{|}}{\overset{\overset{H}{|}}{C}}-\underset{\underset{H}{|}}{\overset{\overset{H}{|}}{C}}-O-\underset{\underset{H}{|}}{\overset{\overset{H}{|}}{C}}-\underset{\underset{H}{|}}{\overset{\overset{H}{|}}{C}}-H \quad \text{or} \quad H-\underset{\underset{H}{|}}{\overset{\overset{H}{|}}{C}}-\underset{\underset{H}{|}}{\overset{\overset{H}{|}}{C}}-\underset{\underset{H}{|}}{\overset{\overset{H}{|}}{C}}-O-\underset{\underset{H}{|}}{\overset{\overset{H}{|}}{C}}-H$$

PROBLEM 12.1

Many organic compounds contain more than one functional group. Locate and identify the functional groups in (a) lactic acid, from sour milk; (b) methyl methacrylate, used in making Lucite and Plexiglas; and (c) phenylalanine, an amino acid found in proteins.

(a) $CH_3-\underset{\underset{OH}{|}}{\overset{\overset{H}{|}}{C}}-\overset{\overset{O}{\|}}{C}-OH$

(b) $CH_2=\underset{\underset{CH_3}{|}}{C}-\overset{\overset{O}{\|}}{C}-O-CH_3$

(c) $H-C\underset{\underset{H}{\overset{|}{C}}}{\overset{\overset{H}{\overset{|}{C}}}{=}}C\underset{C-C}{C}-CH_2-\underset{\underset{NH_2}{|}}{\overset{\overset{H}{|}}{C}}-\overset{\overset{O}{\|}}{C}-OH$

PROBLEM 12.2

Propose structures for molecules that fit the following descriptions:

(a) C_2H_4O containing an aldehyde functional group

(b) $C_3H_6O_2$ containing a carboxylic acid functional group

12.3 The Structure of Organic Molecules: Alkanes and Their Isomers

Alkane A hydrocarbon that has only single bonds.

Hydrocarbons that contain only single bonds belong to the family of organic molecules called **alkanes**. Imagine how one carbon and four hydrogens can combine, and you will realize there is only one possibility: methane, CH_4. Now imagine how two carbons and six hydrogens can combine—only ethane, CH_3CH_3, is possible. Likewise with the combination of three carbons with eight hydrogens—only propane, $CH_3CH_2CH_3$, is possible. The general rule for *all* hydrocarbons except methane is that each carbon *must* be bonded to at least one other carbon. The carbon atoms bond together to form the "backbone" of the compound, with the hydrogens on the periphery. The general formula for alkanes is C_nH_{2n+2}, where n is the number of carbons in the compound.

Methane

Ethane

Propane

Isomers Compounds with the same molecular formula but different structures.

As larger numbers of carbons and hydrogens combine, the ability to form *isomers* arises. Compounds that have the same molecular formula but different structural formulas are called **isomers** of one another. For example, there are two ways in which molecules that have the formula C_4H_{10} can be formed: The four carbons can either be joined in a contiguous row or have a branched arrangement:

Straight chain

Branched chain

Branch point

The same is seen with the molecules that have the formula C_5H_{12}, for which three isomers are possible:

Straight chain

$$5 \ \ -\overset{|}{\underset{|}{C}}- \ + \ 12 \ H- \ \ gives$$

Branched chain

Compounds with all their carbons connected in a continuous chain are called **straight-chain alkanes**; those with a branching connection of carbons are called **branched-chain alkanes**. Note that in a straight-chain alkane, you can draw a line through all the carbon atoms without lifting your pencil from the paper. In a branched-chain alkane, however, you must either lift your pencil from the paper or retrace your steps to draw a line through all the carbons.

The two isomers of C_4H_{10} and the three isomers of C_5H_{12} shown above are **constitutional isomers**—compounds with the same molecular formula but with different connections among their constituent atoms. Needless to say, the number of possible alkane isomers grows rapidly as the number of carbon atoms increases.

Constitutional isomers of a given molecular formula are chemically completely different from one another. They have different structures, different physical properties such as melting and boiling points, and potentially different physiological properties. For example, ethyl alcohol and dimethyl ether both have the formula C_2H_6O, but ethyl alcohol is a liquid with a boiling point of 78.5 °C and dimethyl ether is a gas with a boiling point of −23 °C (Table 12.2). Clearly, molecular formulas by

Straight-chain alkane An alkane that has all its carbons connected in a row.

Branched-chain alkane An alkane that has a branching connection of carbons.

Constitutional isomers Compounds with the same molecular formula but different connections among their atoms.

TABLE 12.2 Some Properties of Ethyl Alcohol and Dimethyl Ether

NAME AND MOLECULAR FORMULA	STRUCTURE		BOILING POINT	MELTING POINT	PHYSIOLOGICAL ACTIVITY
Ethyl alcohol C_2H_6O			78.5 °C	− 117.3 °C	Central-nervous-system depressant
Dimethyl ether C_2H_6O			− 23 °C	− 138.5 °C	Nontoxic; anesthetic at high concentration

themselves are not very useful in organic chemistry; a knowledge of structure is also necessary.

WORKED EXAMPLE 12.3 Molecular Structures: Drawing Isomers

Draw all isomers that have the formula C_6H_{14}.

ANALYSIS Knowing that all the carbons must be bonded together to form the molecule, find all possible arrangements of the 6 carbon atoms. Begin with the isomer that has all 6 carbons in a straight chain, then draw the isomer that has 5 carbons in a straight chain, using the remaining carbon to form a branch, then repeat for the isomer having 4 carbons in a straight chain and 2 carbons in branches. Once each carbon backbone is drawn, arrange the hydrogens around the carbons to complete the structure. (Remember that each carbon can only have *four* bonds.)

SOLUTION
The straight-chain isomer contains all 6 carbons bonded to form a chain with no branches. The branched isomers are drawn by starting with either a 5-carbon chain or a 4-carbon chain, and adding the extra carbons as branches in the middle of the chain. Hydrogens are added until each carbon has a full complement of 4 bonds.

PROBLEM 12.3

Draw the straight-chain isomer with the formula C_7H_{16}.

PROBLEM 12.4

Draw any two of the seven branched-chain isomers with the formula C_7H_{16}.

12.4 Drawing Organic Structures

Condensed structure A short-hand way of drawing structures in which C—C and C—H bonds are understood rather than shown.

Drawing structural formulas that show every atom and every bond in a molecule is both time-consuming and awkward, even for relatively small molecules. Much easier is the use of **condensed structures** (Section 5.6), which are simpler but still show the essential information about which functional groups are present and how atoms are connected. (⬤ , p. 118) In condensed structures, C—C and C—H single bonds are not shown; rather, they are "understood." If a carbon atom has 3 hydrogens bonded to it, we write CH_3; if the carbon has 2 hydrogens bonded to it, we write CH_2; and so on. For example, the 4-carbon, straight-chain alkane (butane) and its branched-chain isomer (2-methylpropane) can be written as the following condensed structures:

Butane — Structural formula — Condensed formula — 2-Methylpropane — Structural formula — Condensed formula

$CH_3CH_2CH_2CH_3$; CH_3CHCH_3

Note in these condensed structures for butane and 2-methylpropane that the horizontal bonds between carbons are not usually shown—the CH_3 and CH_2 units are simply placed next to one another—but that the vertical bond in 2-methyl-propane *is* shown for clarity.

Occasionally, as a further simplification, not all the CH_2 groups (called **methylenes**) are shown. Instead, CH_2 is shown once in parentheses, with a subscript to the right of the) indicating the number of methylene units strung together. For example, the 6-carbon straight-chain alkane (hexane) can be written as

Methylene Another name for a CH_2 unit.

$$CH_3CH_2CH_2CH_2CH_2CH_3 = CH_3(CH_2)_4CH_3$$

WORKED EXAMPLE **12.4** Molecular Structures: Writing Condensed Structures

Write condensed structures for the isomers from Worked Example 12.3.

ANALYSIS Eliminate all horizontal bonds, substituting reduced formula components (CH_3, CH_2, and so on) for each carbon in the compound. Show vertical bonds to branching carbons for clarity.

SOLUTION

$CH_3CH_2CH_2CH_2CH_2CH_3$ or $CH_3(CH_2)_4CH_3$

$CH_3CH_2CH_2CHCH_3$

$CH_3CH_2CHCH_2CH_3$

PROBLEM 12.5

Draw the following three isomers of C_5H_{12} as condensed structures:

(a) Pentane

(b) 2-Methylbutane

(c) 2,2-Dimethylpropane

Line structure A shorthand way of drawing structures in which carbon and hydrogen atoms are not shown. Instead, a carbon atom is understood to be wherever a line begins or ends and at every intersection of two lines, and hydrogens are understood to be wherever they are needed to have each carbon form four bonds.

Another way of representing organic molecules is to use **line structures**, which are structures in which the symbols C and H do not appear. Instead, a chain of carbon atoms and their associated hydrogens are represented by a zigzag arrangement of short lines, with any branches off the main chain represented by additional lines. The line structure for 2-methylbutane, for instance, is

same as

$$CH_3CHCH_2CH_3$$

with CH_3 above the second carbon.

Line structures are a simple and quick way to represent organic molecules without the clutter arising from showing all carbons and hydrogens present. Chemists, biologists, pharmacists, doctors, and nurses all use line structures to conveniently convey to one another very complex organic structures. Another advantage is that a line structure gives a more realistic depiction of the angles seen in a carbon chain.

Drawing a molecule in this way is simple, provided one follows these guidelines:

1. Each carbon-carbon bond is represented by a line.

2. Anywhere a line ends or begins, as well as any vertex where two lines meet, represents a carbon atom.

3. Any atom other than another carbon or a hydrogen attached to a carbon must be shown.

4. Since a neutral carbon atom forms four bonds, all bonds not shown for any carbon are understood to be the number of carbon-hydrogen bonds needed to have the carbon form four bonds.

Converting line structures to structural formulas or to condensed structures is simply a matter of correctly interpreting each line ending and each intersection in a line structure. For example, the common pain reliever ibuprofen has the condensed and line structures

Finally, it is important to note that chemists and biochemists often use a mixture of structural formulas, condensed structures, and line structures to represent the molecules they study. As you progress through this textbook, you will see many complicated molecules represented in this way, so it is a good idea to get used to thinking interchangably in all three formats.

WORKED EXAMPLE | 12.5 Molecular Structures: Converting Condensed Structures to Line Structures

Convert the following condensed structures to line structures:

$$
\text{(a) } CH_3CH_2\overset{\overset{\displaystyle CH_3}{|}}{C}H\overset{}{C}H\overset{\overset{}{|}}{C}H_2CH_3
$$
$$
\underset{\displaystyle CH_3}{}
$$

$$
\text{(b) } CH_3\overset{\overset{\displaystyle OH}{|}}{C}H\overset{}{C}H\overset{\overset{\displaystyle Cl}{}}{{-}}\overset{}{C}\,CH_2CH_3
$$
$$
\underset{\displaystyle CH_3 \quad CH_3}{}
$$

ANALYSIS Find the longest continuous chain of carbon atoms in the condensed structure. Begin the line structure by drawing a zigzag line in which the number of vertices plus line ends equals the number of carbon atoms in the chain. Show branches coming off the main chain by drawing vertical lines at the vertices as needed. Show all atoms that are not carbons or are not hydrogens attached to carbons.

SOLUTION

(a) Begin by drawing a zigzag line in which the total number of ends + vertices equals the number of carbons in the longest chain (here 6, with the carbons numbered for clarity):

Looking at the condensed structure, you see CH_3 groups on carbons 3 and 4; these two methyl groups are represented by lines coming off those carbons in the line structure:

This is the complete line structure. Notice that the hydrogens are not shown, but understood. For example, carbon 4 has three bonds shown: one to carbon 3, one to carbon 5, and one to the branch methyl group; the fourth bond this carbon must have is understood to be to a hydrogen.

(b) Proceed as in (a), drawing a zigzag line for the longest chain of carbon atoms, which again contains 6 carbons. Next draw a line coming off each carbon bonded to a CH_3 group (carbons 3 and 4). Both the OH and the Cl groups must be shown to give the final structure:

Note from this line structure than it does not matter in such a two-dimensional drawing what direction you show for a group that branches off the main chain, as long as it is attached to the correct carbon. This is true for condensed structures as well. Quite often the direction that a group is shown coming off a main chain of carbon atoms is chosen simply for aesthetic reasons.

WORKED EXAMPLE **12.6** Molecular Structures: Converting Line Structures to Condensed Structures

Convert the following line structures to condensed structures:

(a)

(b)

ANALYSIS Convert all vertices and line ends to carbons. Write in any noncarbon atoms and any hydrogens bonded to a noncarbon atom. Add hydrogens as needed so that each carbon has four groups attached. Remove lines connecting carbons except for branches.

SOLUTION

(a) Anywhere a line ends and anywhere two lines meet, write a C:

Because there are no atoms other than carbons and hydrogens in this molecule, the next step is to add hydrogens as needed to have four bonds for each carbon:

Finally, eliminate all lines except for branches to get the condensed structure:

$$CH_3CH_2 \overset{\overset{\textstyle CH_3}{|}}{\underset{\underset{\textstyle CH_2CH_3}{|}}{C}} CH_2CH_3$$

(b) Begin the condensed structure with a drawing showing a carbon at each line end and at each intersection of two lines:

Next write in all the noncarbon atoms and the hydrogen bonded to the oxygen. Then add hydrogens so that each carbon forms four bonds:

Eliminate all lines except for branches for the completed condensed structure:

$$HOCH_2 \overset{\overset{\textstyle CH_3}{|}}{\underset{\underset{\textstyle NH_2}{|}}{C}} CH_2Br$$

PROBLEM 12.6

Convert the following condensed structures to line structures:

(a)
$$CH_3CH_2C-CH_2CH_2CH_3$$
with CH_2CH_3 above and CH_2OH below the central carbon

(b)
$$CH_3CH\ CH\ CH_2CHCH_3$$
with CH_2CH_3 and CH_3 above, and $CH_3CHCH_2CH_3$ below

(c)
$$CH_3C-CHCH_2CH_2CHCH_2CH_3$$
with Br and Cl above, CH_3 and $CHCH_2CH_3$ below

PROBLEM 12.7

Convert the following line structures to condensed structures:

(a)

(b)

12.5 The Shapes of Organic Molecules

Every carbon atom in an alkane has its four bonds pointing toward the four corners of a tetrahedron, but chemists do not usually worry about three-dimensional shapes when writing condensed structures. Condensed structures do not imply any particular three-dimensional shape; they only indicate the connections between atoms without specifying geometry. Line structures do try to give some feeling for the shape of a molecule, but even here the ability to show three-dimensional shape is limited unless dashed and wedged lines are used for the bonds (page 125).

Butane, for example, has no one single shape because *rotation* takes place around carbon–carbon single bonds. The two parts of a molecule joined by a carbon–carbon single bond in a noncyclic structure are free to spin around the bond, giving rise to an infinite number of possible three-dimensional geometries, or **conformations**. The various conformations of a molecule such as butane are called **conformers** of one another. Conformers differ from one another as a result of rotation around carbon–carbon single bonds. Although the conformers of a given molecule have different three-dimensional shapes and different energies, the conformers cannot be separated from one another. A given butane molecule might be in its fully extended conformation at one instant but in a twisted conformation an instant later (Figure 12.2). An actual sample of butane contains a great many molecules that are constantly changing conformation. At any given instant, however, most of the molecules have the least crowded, lowest-energy extended conformation shown in Figure 12.2a. The same is true for all other alkanes: At any given instant, most molecules are in the least crowded conformation.

Conformation The specific three-dimensional arrangement of atoms in a molecule.

Conformer Molecular structures having identical connections between atoms; that is, they represent identical compounds.

▶ **FIGURE 12.2 Some conformations of butane (there are many others as well).** The least crowded, extended conformation in (a) is the lowest-energy one.

(a)   (b)   (c)

As long as any two structures have identical connections between atoms, they are conformers of each other and represent the same compound, no matter how the structures are drawn. Sometimes you have to mentally rotate structures to see whether they are conformers or different molecules. To see that the following two structures represent conformers of the same compound rather than two isomers, picture one of them flipped right to left so that the red CH_3 groups are on the same side:

$$CH_3CHCH_2CH_2CH_3 \qquad CH_3CH_2CH_2CHCH_3$$
$$| \qquad\qquad\qquad\qquad\quad |$$
$$CH_2 \qquad\qquad\qquad\qquad\quad CH_2$$
$$| \qquad\qquad\qquad\qquad\qquad |$$
$$OH \qquad\qquad\qquad\qquad\quad OH$$

Another way to determine whether two structures are conformers is to name each one using the IUPAC nomenclature rules (Section 12.6). If two structures have the same name, they are conformers of the same compound.

WORKED EXAMPLE   **12.7** Molecular Structures: Identifying Conformers

The following structures all have the formula C_7H_{16}. Which of them represent the same molecule?

        CH_3 CH_3
        $|$ $|$

(a) $CH_3CHCH_2CH_2CH_2CH_3$ **(b)** $CH_3CH_2CH_2CH_2CHCH_3$

                          CH_3
                          $|$

(c) $CH_3CH_2CH_2CHCH_2CH_3$

ANALYSIS Pay attention to the *connections* between atoms. Do not get confused by the apparent differences caused by writing a structure right to left versus left to right. Begin by identifying the longest chain of carbon atoms in the molecule.

SOLUTION
Molecule (a) has a straight chain of 6 carbons with a $—CH_3$ branch on the second carbon from the end. Molecule (b) also has a straight chain of 6 carbons with a $—CH_3$ branch on the second carbon from the end and is therefore identical to (a). That is, (a) and (b) are conformers of the same molecule. The only difference between (a) and (b) is that one is written "forward" and one is written "backward." Molecule (c), by contrast, has a straight chain of 6 carbons with a $—CH_3$ branch on the *third* carbon from the end and is therefore an isomer of (a) and (b).

WORKED EXAMPLE   **12.8** Molecular Structures: Identifying Conformers
                                   and Isomers

Are the following pairs of compounds the same (conformers), isomers, or unrelated?

            CH_3 CH_3
            $|$ $|$

(a) $CH_3CHCH_2CH_2$ $CH_3CHCH_2CH_2CH_3$
            $|$
           CH_3

                                 CH_2CH_3
                                 $|$

(b) $CH_3CH_2CHCH_3$ CH_3CHCH_2
              $|$ $|$
            CH_2CH_3 CH_3

                                 O
                                 $\|$

(c) $CH_3CH_2OCH_3$ CH_3CH_2CH

ANALYSIS First compare molecular formulas to see if the compounds are related, and then look at the structures to see if they are the same compound or isomers. Find the longest continuous carbon chain in each, and then compare the locations of the substituents connected to the longest chain.

SOLUTION

(a) Both compounds have the same molecular formula (C_6H_{14}) so they are related. Since the —CH_3 group is on the second carbon from the end of a 5-carbon chain in both cases, these structures represent the same compound and are conformers of each other.

$$\underset{\underset{CH_3}{|}}{\overset{\overset{CH_3}{|}}{CH_3CHCH_2CH_2}} \qquad \overset{\overset{CH_3}{|}}{CH_3CHCH_2CH_2CH_3}$$

(b) Both compounds have the same molecular formula (C_6H_{14}) and the longest chain in each is 5 carbon atoms. A comparison shows, however, that the —CH_3 group is on the middle carbon atom in one structure and on the second carbon atom in the other. These compounds are isomers of each other.

$$\underset{\underset{CH_2CH_3}{|}}{CH_3CH_2CHCH_3} \qquad \underset{\underset{CH_3}{|}}{\overset{\overset{CH_2CH_3}{|}}{CH_3CHCH_2}}$$

(c) These compounds have different formulas (C_3H_8O and C_3H_6O), so they are unrelated; they are neither conformers nor isomers of each other.

PROBLEM 12.8

Which of the following structures are conformers?

(a) $\underset{}{\overset{\overset{CH_3}{|}\quad\overset{CH_3}{|}}{CH_2CH_2CHCH_2CH_3}}$ (b) $\underset{\underset{CH_3}{|}}{\overset{\overset{CH_3}{|}}{CH_3CH_2CH_2CCH_3}}$

(c) $\overset{\overset{CH_3}{|}}{CH_3CH_2CHCH_2CH_2CH_3}$

PROBLEM 12.9

There are 18 isomers with the formula C_8H_{18}. Draw condensed structures for as many as you can and then convert those condensed structures to line structures.

12.6 Naming Alkanes

When relatively few pure organic chemicals were known, new compounds were named at the whim of their discoverer. Thus, urea is a crystalline substance first isolated from urine, and the barbiturates were named by their discoverer in honor of his friend Barbara. As more and more compounds became known, however, the need for a systematic method of naming compounds became apparent.

The system of naming (*nomenclature*) now used is one devised by the International Union of Pure and Applied Chemistry, IUPAC (pronounced **eye**-you-pack). In the IUPAC system for organic compounds, a chemical name has three

APPLICATION ▶ Displaying Molecular Shapes

Molecular shapes are critical to the proper functioning of biological molecules. The tiniest difference in shape can cause two compounds to behave differently or to have different physiological effects in the body. It is therefore critical that chemists be able both to determine molecular shapes with great precision and to visualize these shapes in useful ways.

Three-dimensional shapes of molecules can be determined by *X-ray crystallography*, a technique that allows us to "see" molecules in a crystal using X-ray waves rather than light waves. The molecular "picture" obtained by X-ray crystallography looks at first like a series of regularly spaced dark spots against a lighter background. After computerized manipulation of the data, however, recognizable molecules can be drawn. Relatively small molecules like morphine are usually displayed in either a ball-and-stick format (a), which emphasizes the connections among atoms, or in a space-filling format (b), which emphasizes the overall shape. Chemists find this useful in designing new organic molecules that have specific biological properties that make the molecules useful as therapeutic agents.

(a)   (b)

▲ This computer-generated model of morphine is displayed in both (a) ball-and-stick format and (b) space-filling format.

Enormous biological molecules like enzymes and other proteins are best displayed on computer terminals where their structures can be enlarged, rotated, and otherwise manipulated for the best view. An immunoglobulin molecule, for instance, is so large that little detail can be seen in ball-and-stick or space-filling views. Nevertheless, a cleft inside the molecule is visible if the model is rotated in just the right way.

See Additional Problem 12.64 at the end of the chapter.

▲ Computer-generated models of an immunoglobulin, one of the antibodies in blood that protect us from harmful invaders such as bacteria and viruses.

Substituent An atom or group of atoms attached to a parent compound.

parts: *prefix, parent,* and *suffix.* The prefix specifies the location of functional groups and other **substituents** in the molecule; the parent tells how many carbon atoms are present in the longest continuous chain; and the suffix identifies what family the molecule belongs to:

$$\text{Prefix} - \text{Parent} - \text{Suffix}$$

Where are substituents located? — How many carbons? — What family does the molecule belong to?

Straight-chain alkanes are named by counting the number of carbon atoms and adding the family suffix *-ane.* With the exception of the first four compounds— *meth*ane, *eth*ane, *prop*ane, and *but*ane—whose parent names have historical origins, the alkanes are named from Greek numbers according to the number of carbons present (Table 12.3). Thus, *pent*ane is the 5-carbon alkane, *hex*ane is the 6-carbon alkane, and so on. The first ten alkane names are so common that they should be memorized.

TABLE 12.3   Names of Straight-Chain Alkanes

NUMBER OF CARBONS	STRUCTURE	NAME
1	CH_4	*Meth*ane
2	CH_3CH_3	*Eth*ane
3	$CH_3CH_2CH_3$	*Prop*ane
4	$CH_3CH_2CH_2CH_3$	*But*ane
5	$CH_3CH_2CH_2CH_2CH_3$	*Pent*ane
6	$CH_3CH_2CH_2CH_2CH_2CH_3$	*Hex*ane
7	$CH_3CH_2CH_2CH_2CH_2CH_2CH_3$	*Hept*ane
8	$CH_3CH_2CH_2CH_2CH_2CH_2CH_2CH_3$	*Oct*ane
9	$CH_3CH_2CH_2CH_2CH_2CH_2CH_2CH_2CH_3$	*Non*ane
10	$CH_3CH_2CH_2CH_2CH_2CH_2CH_2CH_2CH_2CH_3$	*Dec*ane

Alkyl group The part of an alkane that remains when a hydrogen atom is removed.

Methyl group The $-CH_3$ alkyl group.

Ethyl group The $-CH_2CH_3$ alkyl group.

Substituents such as $-CH_3$ and $-CH_2CH_3$ that branch off the main chain are called **alkyl groups**. An alkyl group can be thought of as the part of an alkane that remains when 1 hydrogen atom is removed to create an available bonding site. For example, removal of a hydrogen from methane gives the **methyl group,** $-CH_3$, and removal of a hydrogen from ethane gives the **ethyl group,** $-CH_2CH_3$. Notice that these alkyl groups are named simply by replacing the *-ane* ending of the parent alkane with an *-yl* ending:

Alkyl groups are derived from a parent alkane.

Both methane and ethane have only one "kind" of hydrogen. It does not matter which of the 4 methane hydrogens is removed, so there is only one possible methyl group. Similarly, it does not matter which of the 6 equivalent ethane hydrogens is removed, so only one ethyl group is possible.

The situation is more complex for larger alkanes, which contain more than one kind of hydrogen. Propane, for example, has two different kinds of hydrogens. Removal of any one of the 6 hydrogens attached to an end carbon yields a straight-chain alkyl group called **propyl**, whereas removal of either one of the 2 hydrogens attached to the central carbon yields a branched-chain alkyl group called **isopropyl**:

Propyl group The straight-chain alkyl group —$CH_2CH_2CH_3$.

Isopropyl group The branched-chain alkyl group —$CH(CH_3)_2$.

$$-\overset{\overset{\displaystyle H}{|}}{\underset{\underset{\displaystyle H}{|}}{C}} - \overset{\overset{\displaystyle H}{|}}{\underset{\underset{\displaystyle H}{|}}{C}} - \overset{\overset{\displaystyle H}{|}}{\underset{\underset{\displaystyle H}{|}}{C}} - H \ = \ -CH_2CH_2CH_3$$

Propyl group (straight chain)

Remove H from end carbon

$$H - \overset{\overset{\displaystyle H}{|}}{\underset{\underset{\displaystyle H}{|}}{C}} - \overset{\overset{\displaystyle H}{|}}{\underset{\underset{\displaystyle H}{|}}{C}} - \overset{\overset{\displaystyle H}{|}}{\underset{\underset{\displaystyle H}{|}}{C}} - H$$

Propane Remove H from inside carbon

$$H - \overset{\overset{\displaystyle H}{|}}{\underset{\underset{\displaystyle H}{|}}{C}} - \overset{\overset{\displaystyle H}{|}}{\underset{\underset{\displaystyle H}{|}}{C}} - \overset{\overset{\displaystyle H}{|}}{\underset{\underset{\displaystyle H}{|}}{C}} - H \ = \ CH_3CHCH_3 \ \ \text{or} \ \ (CH_3)_2CH-$$

Isopropyl group (branched chain)

It is important to realize that alkyl groups are not compounds but rather are simply partial structures that help us name compounds. The names of some common alkyl groups are listed in Table 12.4; you will want to memorize them.

TABLE 12.4 Some Common Alkyl Groups*

CH_3- Methyl	CH_3CH_2- Ethyl	$CH_3CH_2CH_2-$ n-Propyl	$\overset{\overset{\displaystyle CH_3}{\|}}{CH_3CH-}$ Isopropyl
$CH_3CH_2CH_2CH_2-$ n-Butyl	$\overset{\overset{\displaystyle \|}{CH_3CHCH_2CH_3}}{}$ sec-Butyl	$\overset{\overset{\displaystyle CH_3}{\|}}{CH_3CHCH_2-}$ Isobutyl	$\underset{\underset{\displaystyle CH_3}{\|}}{\overset{\overset{\displaystyle \|}{CH_3CCH_3}}{}}$ tert-Butyl

The red bond shows the connection to the rest of the molecule.

Notice that four butyl (four-carbon) groups are listed in Table 12.4: butyl, sec-butyl, isobutyl, and tert-butyl. The prefix sec- stands for secondary, and the prefix tert- stands for tertiary, referring to the number of other carbon atoms attached to the branch point. There are four possible substitution patterns, called primary, secondary, tertiary, and quaternary. A **primary (1°) carbon atom** has 1 other carbon attached to it (typically indicated as an —R group in the molecular structure), a **secondary (2°) carbon atom** has 2 other carbons attached, a **tertiary (3°) carbon atom** has 3 other carbons attached, and a **quaternary (4°) carbon atom** has 4 other carbons attached:

Primary (1°) carbon atom A carbon atom with 1 other carbon attached to it.

Secondary (2°) carbon atom A carbon atom with 2 other carbons attached to it.

Tertiary (3°) carbon atom A carbon atom with 3 other carbons attached to it.

Quaternary (4°) carbon atom A carbon atom with 4 other carbons attached to it.

$$R - \overset{\overset{\displaystyle H}{|}}{\underset{\underset{\displaystyle H}{|}}{C}} - H \qquad R - \overset{\overset{\displaystyle R}{|}}{\underset{\underset{\displaystyle H}{|}}{C}} - H \qquad R - \overset{\overset{\displaystyle R}{|}}{\underset{\underset{\displaystyle R}{|}}{C}} - H \qquad R - \overset{\overset{\displaystyle R}{|}}{\underset{\underset{\displaystyle R}{|}}{C}} - R$$

Primary carbon (1°) has one other carbon attached.

Secondary carbon (2°) has two other carbons attached.

Tertiary carbon (3°) has three other carbons attached.

Quaternary carbon (4°) has four other carbons attached.

*The symbol **R** is used here and in later chapters as a general abbreviation for any organic substituent*. You should think of it as representing the **R**est of the molecule, which we are not bothering to specify. The R is used to allow you to focus on a particular structural feature of a molecule without the "clutter" of the other atoms in the molecule detracting from it. The R might represent a methyl, ethyl, or propyl group, or any of a vast number of other possibilities. For example, the generalized formula R—OH for an alcohol might refer to an alcohol as simple as CH_3OH or CH_3CH_2OH or one as complicated as cholesterol.

Branched-chain alkanes can be named by following four steps:

STEP 1: Name the main chain. Find the longest continuous chain of carbons, and name the chain according to the number of carbon atoms it contains. The longest chain may not be immediately obvious because it is not always written on one line; you may have to "turn corners" to find it.

Name as a substituted pentane, not as a substituted butane, because the *longest* chain has five carbons.

STEP 2: Number the carbon atoms in the main chain, beginning at the end nearer the first branch point:

The first (and only) branch occurs at C2 if we start numbering from the left, but would occur at C4 if we started from the right by mistake.

STEP 3: Identify the branching substituents, and number each according to its point of attachment to the main chain:

The main chain is a pentane. There is one —CH_3 substituent group connected to C2 of the chain.

If there are two substituents on the same carbon, assign the same number to both. There must always be as many numbers in the name as there are substituents.

The main chain is a hexane. There are two substituents, a —CH_3 and a —CH_2CH_3, both connected to C3 of the chain.

STEP 4: Write the name as a single word, using hyphens to separate the numbers from the different prefixes and commas to separate numbers if necessary. If two or more different substituent groups are present, cite them in alphabetical order. If two or more identical substituents are present, use one of the prefixes *di-, tri-, tetra-,* and so forth, but do not use these prefixes for alphabetizing purposes.

$$CH_3-\underset{\underset{2}{|}}{\overset{\overset{CH_3}{|}}{CH}}-\underset{3}{CH_2}-\underset{4}{CH_2}-\underset{5}{CH_3}$$

2-Methylpentane (a five-carbon main chain with a 2-methyl substituent)

$$\underset{1}{CH_3}-\underset{2}{CH_2}-\underset{\underset{3}{|}}{\overset{\overset{CH_2-CH_3}{|}}{C}}-\underset{4}{CH_2}-\underset{5}{CH_2}-\underset{6}{CH_3}$$
$$CH_3$$

3-Ethyl-3-methylhexane (a six-carbon main chain with 3-ethyl and 3-methyl substituents cited alphabetically)

$$\underset{}{CH_3}-\underset{\underset{3}{|}}{\overset{\overset{\overset{2}{CH_2}-\overset{1}{CH_3}}{|}}{C}}-\underset{4}{CH_2}-\underset{5}{CH_2}-\underset{6}{CH_3}$$
$$CH_3$$

3,3-Dimethylhexane (a six-carbon main chain with two 3-methyl substitutents)

WORKED EXAMPLE **12.9** Naming Organic Compounds: Alkanes

What is the IUPAC name of the following alkane?

$$CH_3-\overset{\overset{CH_3}{|}}{CH}-CH_2-CH_2-\overset{\overset{CH_3}{|}}{CH}-CH_2-CH_3$$

ANALYSIS Follow the four steps outlined in the text.

SOLUTION

STEP 1: The longest continuous chain of carbon atoms is seven, so the main chain is a *hept*ane.

STEP 2: Number the main chain beginning at the end nearer the first branch:

$$\underset{1}{CH_3}-\underset{2}{\overset{\overset{CH_3}{|}}{CH}}-\underset{3}{CH_2}-\underset{4}{CH_2}-\underset{5}{\overset{\overset{CH_3}{|}}{CH}}-\underset{6}{CH_2}-\underset{7}{CH_3}$$

STEP 3: Identify and number the substituents (a 2-methyl and a 5-methyl in this case):

$$\underset{1}{CH_3}-\underset{2}{\overset{\overset{CH_3}{|}}{CH}}-\underset{3}{CH_2}-\underset{4}{CH_2}-\underset{5}{\overset{\overset{CH_3}{|}}{CH}}-\underset{6}{CH_2}-\underset{7}{CH_3}$$

Substituents: 2-methyl, 5-methyl

STEP 4: Write the name as one word, using the prefix *di-* because there are two methyl groups. Separate the two numbers by a comma, and use a hyphen between the numbers and the word.

Name: 2, 5-Dimethylheptane

WORKED EXAMPLE **12.10** Molecular Structure: Identifying 1°, 2°, 3°, and 4° Carbons

Identify each carbon atom in the following molecule as primary, secondary, tertiary, or quaternary.

$$CH_3\overset{\overset{CH_3}{|}}{CH}CH_2CH_2\underset{\underset{CH_3}{|}}{\overset{\overset{CH_3}{|}}{C}}CH_3$$

ANALYSIS Look at each carbon atom in the molecule, count the number of other carbon atoms attached, and make the assignment accordingly: primary (1 carbon attached); secondary (2 carbons attached); tertiary (3 carbons attached); quaternary (4 carbons attached).

SOLUTION

$$\text{Primary} \quad \underset{\substack{| \\ CH_3CHCH_2CH_2CCH_3 \\ }}{CH_3} \quad \underset{\substack{| \\ CH_3}}{CH_3} \quad \text{Primary}$$

Tertiary

Secondary

Quaternary

WORKED EXAMPLE **12.11** Molecular Structures: Drawing Condensed Structures from Names

Draw condensed structures corresponding to the following IUPAC names:

(a) 2,3-Dimethylpentane

(b) 3-Ethylheptane

ANALYSIS Starting with the parent chain, add the named alkyl substituent groups to the appropriately numbered carbon atom(s).

SOLUTION

(a) The parent chain has 5 carbons (*pent*ane), with two methyl groups (—CH_3) attached to the second and third carbon in the chain:

$$\underset{1 \quad 2 \quad 3 \quad 4 \quad 5}{CH_3CH \ CH \ CH_2CH_3}$$
$$\overset{CH_3CH_3}{\underset{| \ |}{}}$$

(b) The parent chain has 7 carbons (*hept*ane), with one ethyl group (—CH_2CH_3) attached to the third carbon in the chain:

$$\underset{1 \quad 2 \quad 3 \quad 4 \quad 5 \quad 6 \quad 7}{CH_3CH_2CH \ CH_2CH_2CH_2CH_3}$$
$$\overset{CH_2CH_3}{\underset{|}{}}$$

PROBLEM 12.10

What are the IUPAC names of the following alkanes?

(a) $$CH_3-\underset{\underset{CH_2-CH_3}{|}}{CH}-CH_2-CH_2-CH_2-\underset{\overset{|}{CH_3}}{CH}-CH_3$$

(b) $$CH_3-CH_2-CH_2-CH_2-\underset{\underset{CH_2-CH_3}{|}}{\overset{\overset{CH_2-CH_3}{|}}{C}}-CH_2-CH_3$$

PROBLEM 12.11

Draw both condensed and line structures corresponding to the following IUPAC names and label each carbon as primary, secondary, tertiary, or quaternary:

(a) 3-Methylhexane   (b) 3,4-Dimethyloctane

(c) 2,2,4-Trimethylpentane

PROBLEM 12.12

Draw and name alkanes that meet the following descriptions:

(a) An alkane with a tertiary carbon atom

(b) An alkane that has both a tertiary and a quaternary carbon atom

KEY CONCEPT PROBLEM 12.13

What are the IUPAC names of the following alkanes?

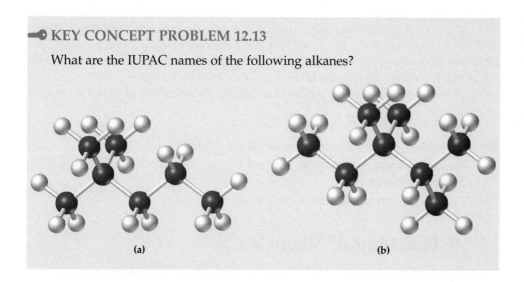

(a)   (b)

12.7 Properties of Alkanes

Alkanes contain only nonpolar C—C and C—H bonds, so the only intermolecular forces influencing them are weak London dispersion forces (Section 8.11). (⊂⊃, p. 235) The effect of these forces is shown in the regularity with which the melting and boiling points of straight-chain alkanes increase with molecular size (Figure 12.3). The first four alkanes—methane, ethane, propane, and butane—are gases at room temperature and pressure. Alkanes with 5–15 carbon atoms are liquids; those with 16 or more carbon atoms are generally low-melting, waxy solids.

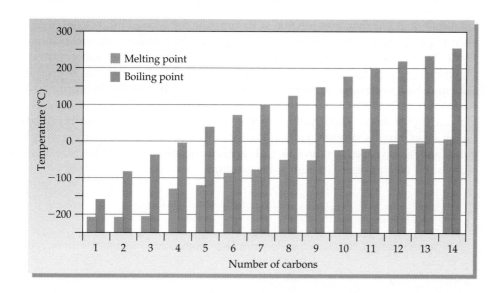

◄ **FIGURE 12.3** The boiling and melting points for the C_1–C_{14} straight-chain alkanes increase with molecular size.

In keeping with their low polarity, alkanes are insoluble in water but soluble in nonpolar organic solvents, including other alkanes (Section 9.2). (⊂⊃, p. 257) Because alkanes are generally less dense than water, they float on its surface.

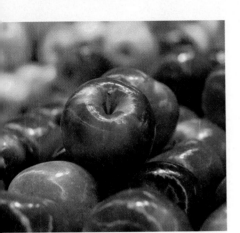

▲ The waxy coating that makes these apples so shiny is a mixture of higher-molecular-weight alkanes.

Low-molecular-weight alkanes are volatile and must be handled with care because their vapors are flammable. Mixtures of alkane vapors and air can explode when ignited by a single spark.

The physiological effects of alkanes are limited. Methane, ethane, and propane gases are nontoxic, and the danger of inhaling them lies in potential suffocation due to lack of oxygen. Breathing the vapor of higher alkanes in large concentrations can induce loss of consciousness. There is also a danger in breathing droplets of liquid alkanes because they dissolve nonpolar substances in lung tissue and cause pneumonia-like symptoms.

Mineral oil, petroleum jelly, and paraffin wax are mixtures of higher alkanes. All are harmless to body tissue and are used in numerous food and medical applications. Mineral oil passes through the body unchanged and is sometimes used as a laxative. Petroleum jelly (sold as Vaseline) softens, lubricates, and protects the skin. Paraffin wax is used in candle making, on surfboards, and in home canning.

Properties of Alkanes

- Odorless or mild odor; colorless; tasteless; nontoxic
- Nonpolar; insoluble in water but soluble in nonpolar organic solvents; less dense than water
- Flammable; otherwise not very reactive

12.8 Reactions of Alkanes

Alkanes do not react with acids, bases, or most other common laboratory *reagents* (a substance that causes a reaction to occur). Their only major reactions are with oxygen (combustion) and with halogens (halogenation).

Combustion

Combustion A chemical reaction that produces a flame, usually because of burning with oxygen.

The reaction of an alkane with oxygen occurs during **combustion**, an oxidation reaction that commonly takes place in a controlled manner in an engine or furnace (Section 7.3). (▭▭▭, p. 184) Carbon dioxide and water are the products of complete combustion of any hydrocarbon, and a large amount of heat is released (ΔH is a negative number). Some examples were given in Table 7.1.

$$CH_4(g) + 2\ O_2(g) \longrightarrow CO_2(g) + 2\ H_2O(l) \qquad \Delta H = -213\ \text{kcal/mol}$$

When hydrocarbon combustion is incomplete because of faulty engine or furnace performance, carbon monoxide and carbon-containing soot are among the products. Carbon monoxide is a highly toxic and dangerous substance, especially so because it has no odor and can easily go undetected (See the Application "CO and NO: Pollutants or Miracle Molecules?" in Chapter 5). Breathing air that contains as little as 2% CO for only one hour can cause respiratory and nervous system damage or death. The supply of oxygen to the brain is cut off by carbon monoxide because it binds strongly to blood hemoglobin at the site where oxygen is normally bound. By contrast with CO, CO_2 is nontoxic and causes no harm, except by suffocation when present in high concentration.

> **PROBLEM 12.14**
>
> Write a balanced equation for the complete combustion of ethane with oxygen.

Halogenation

The second notable reaction of alkanes is *halogenation*, the replacement of an alkane hydrogen by a chlorine or bromine in a process initiated by heat or light. Only one

H at a time is replaced; however, if allowed to react for a long enough time, all H's will be replaced with halogens. Complete chlorination of methane, for example, yields carbon tetrachloride:

$$CH_4 + 4\,Cl_2 \xrightarrow{\text{Heat or light}} CCl_4 + 4\,HCl$$

Although the above equation for the reaction of methane with chlorine is balanced, it does not fully represent what actually happens. In fact, this reaction, like many organic reactions, yields a mixture of products:

$$CH_4 + Cl_2 \longrightarrow CH_3Cl + HCl$$
$$\xrightarrow{Cl_2} CH_2Cl_2 + HCl$$
$$\xrightarrow{Cl_2} CHCl_3 + HCl$$
$$\xrightarrow{Cl_2} CCl_4 + HCl$$

CH_3Cl, chloromethane
CH_2Cl_2, dichloromethane
$CHCl_3$, chloroform
CCl_4, carbon tetrachloride

When we write the equation for an organic reaction, our attention is usually focused on converting a particular reactant into a desired product; any minor by-products and inorganic compounds (such as the HCl formed in the chlorination of methane) are often of little interest and are ignored. Thus, it is not always necessary to balance the equation for an organic reaction as long as the reactant, the major product, and any necessary reagents and conditions are shown. A chemist who plans to convert methane into bromomethane might therefore write the equation as

$$CH_4 \xrightarrow[\text{Light, heat}]{Br_2} CH_3Br$$

Like many equations for organic reactions, this equation is not balanced.

In using this convention, it is customary to put reactants and reagents above the arrow and conditions, solvents, and catalysts below the arrow.

PROBLEM 12.15

Write the structures of all possible products with 1 and 2 chlorine atoms that form in the reaction of propane with Cl_2.

12.9 Cycloalkanes

The organic compounds described thus far have all been open-chain, or *acyclic*, alkanes. **Cycloalkanes**, which contain rings of carbon atoms, are also well known and are widespread throughout nature. To form a closed ring requires an additional C—C bond and the loss of 2 H atoms; the general formula for cycloalkanes, therefore, is C_nH_{2n}, which, as we will find in the next chapter, is the same as that for alkenes. Compounds of all ring sizes from 3 through 30 and beyond have been prepared in the laboratory. The two simplest cycloalkanes—cyclopropane and cyclobutane—contain 3 and 4 carbon atoms, respectively:

Cycloalkane An alkane that contains a ring of carbon atoms.

CH₂
/ \
H₂C — CH₂
Cyclopropane
(mp −128 °C, bp −33 °C)

H₂C — CH₂
| |
H₂C — CH₂
Cyclobutane
(mp −50 °C, bp −12 °C)

APPLICATION ▶ Petroleum

Many alkanes occur naturally throughout plants and animals, but natural gas and petroleum deposits provide the world's most abundant supply. *Natural gas* consists chiefly of methane, along with smaller amounts of ethane, propane, and butane. *Petroleum* is a complex liquid mixture of hydrocarbons that must be separated, or *refined*, into different *fractions* before it can be used. The vast majority of petroleum products are used as fuels and lubricating oils in the transportation industry, but petroleum-based products are also found in plastics, medicines, food items, and a host of other products.

▲ The crude petroleum from this off-shore well is an enormously complex mixture of alkanes and other organic molecules.

Petroleum has been used throughout history in such diverse applications as a component in mortar and for coating walls and boat hulls. Native Americans used it in magic and paints, and often sold it to pioneers for medicinal uses (as Seneca oil or Genesee oil). The modern petroleum industry began in 1859 in Oil Creek, Pennsylvania, when American oil pioneer E. L. Drake drilled the first oil-producing well.

Petroleum refining begins with distillation to separate the crude oil into three main fractions according to boiling points: straight-run gasoline (bp 30–200 °C), kerosene (bp 175–300 °C), and gas oil (bp 275–400 °C). The residue is then further distilled under reduced pressure to recover lubricating oils, waxes, and asphalt. But distillation of petroleum is just the beginning of the process for making gasoline. It has long been known that straight-chain alkanes burn less smoothly in engines than do branched-chain alkanes, as measured by a compound's *octane number*. Heptane, a straight-chain alkane and particularly poor fuel, is assigned an octane rating of 0, whereas 2,2,4-trimethylpentane, a branched-chain alkane commonly known as isooctane, is given a rating of 100. Straight-run gasoline, with its high percentage of unbranched alkanes, is thus a poor fuel. Petroleum chemists, however, have devised methods to remedy the problem. One of these methods, called *catalytic cracking*, involves taking the kerosene fraction (C_{11}–C_{14}) and "cracking" it into smaller C_3–C_5 molecules at high temperature. These small hydrocarbons are then catalytically recombined to yield C_7–C_{10} branched-chain molecules that are perfectly suited for use as automobile fuel.

In addition to the obvious fuel-based applications, petroleum is the source of paraffin wax (used in candy, candles, and polishes) and petroleum jelly (used in medical products and toiletries). Petroleum "feedstocks" are often converted into the basic chemical building blocks used to produce plastics, rubber, synthetic fibers, drugs, and detergents.

See Additional Problems 12.65 and 12.66 at the end of the chapter.

Note that if we flatten the rings in cyclopropane and cyclobutane, the C—C—C bond angles are 60° and 90°, respectively—values that are considerably compressed from the normal 109.5° tetrahedral value. As a result, these compounds are less stable and more reactive than other cycloalkanes. The five-membered (cyclopentane) ring has nearly ideal bond angles. So does the six-membered (cyclohexane) ring, which accomplishes this nearly ideal state by adopting a puckered, nonplanar shape called a *chair conformation*, further discussion of which, while important, is beyond the scope of this textbook. Both cyclopentane and cyclohexane rings are therefore stable, and many naturally occurring and biochemically active molecules contain such rings.

Cyclopentane—all bond angles are near 109°.

Cyclohexane—all bond angles are near 109.5°.

Cyclic and acyclic alkanes are similar in many of their properties. Cyclopropane and cyclobutane are gases, whereas larger cycloalkanes are liquids or solids. Like alkanes, cycloalkanes are nonpolar, insoluble in water, and flammable. Because of their cyclic structures, however, cycloalkane molecules are more rigid and less flexible than their open-chain counterparts. Rotation is not possible around the carbon–carbon bonds in cycloalkanes without breaking open the ring.

12.10 Drawing and Naming Cycloalkanes

Even condensed structures become awkward when we work with large molecules that contain rings. Thus, line structures are used almost exclusively in drawing cycloalkanes, with *polygons* used for the cyclic parts of the molecules. A triangle represents cyclopropane, a square represents cyclobutane, a pentagon represents cyclopentane, and so on.

Cyclopropane   Cyclobutane   Cyclopentane   Cyclohexane   Cycloheptane

Methylcyclohexane, for example, looks like this in a line structure:

is the same as

This three-way intersection is a CH group.

These intersections represent CH₂ groups.

Cycloalkanes are named by a straightforward extension of the rules for naming open-chain alkanes. In most cases, only two steps are needed:

STEP 1: Use the cycloalkane name as the parent. That is, compounds are named as alkyl-substituted cycloalkanes rather than as cycloalkyl-substituted alkanes. If there is only one substituent on the ring, it is not even necessary to assign a number because all ring positions are identical.

Parent compound: Cyclohexane
Name: Methylcyclohexane
(not cyclohexylmethane)

STEP 2: Identify and number the substituents. Start numbering at the group that has alphabetical priority, and proceed around the ring in the direction that gives the second substituent the lower possible number.

1-ethyl-3-methylcyclohexane
(not 1-ethyl-5-methylcyclohexane or
1-methyl-3-ethylcyclohexane or
1-methyl-5-ethylcyclohexane)

WORKED EXAMPLE | **12.12** Naming Organic Compounds: Cycloalkanes

What is the IUPAC name of the following cycloalkane?

ANALYSIS First identify the parent cycloalkane, then add the positions and identity of any substituents.

SOLUTION

STEP 1: The parent cycloalkane contains 6 carbons (*hex*ane); hence, *cyclohexane*.

STEP 2: There are two substituents; a *methyl* (—CH₃) and an *isopropyl* (CH₃CHCH₃). Alphabetically, the isopropyl group is given priority (number 1); the methyl group is then found on the third carbon in the ring.

1-isopropyl-3-methylcyclohexane

WORKED EXAMPLE | **12.13** Molecular Structures: Drawing Line Structures for Cycloalkanes

Draw a line structure for 1,4-dimethylcyclohexane.

ANALYSIS This structure consists of a 6-carbon ring with two methyl groups attached at positions 1 and 4. Draw a hexagon to represent a cyclohexane ring, and attach a —CH₃ group at an arbitrary position that becomes the first carbon in the chain, designated as C1. Then count around the ring to the fourth carbon (C4), and attach another —CH₃ group.

SOLUTION

Note that the second methyl group is written here as H₃C— because it is attached on the left side of the ring.

1,4-dimethylcyclohexane

PROBLEM 12.16

What are the IUPAC names of the following cycloalkanes?

PROBLEM 12.17

Draw line structures that represent the following IUPAC names:

(a) 1,1-Diethylcyclohexane **(b)** 1,3,5-Trimethylcycloheptane

KEY CONCEPT PROBLEM 12.18

What is the IUPAC name of the following cycloalkane?

SUMMARY: REVISITING THE CHAPTER GOALS

1. **What are the basic properties of organic compounds?** Compounds made up primarily of carbon atoms are classified as organic. Many organic compounds contain carbon atoms that are joined in long chains by a combination of single (C—C), double (C=C), or triple (C≡C) bonds.

2. **What are functional groups, and how are they used to classify organic molecules?** Organic compounds can be classified into various families according to the functional groups they contain. A *functional group* is a part of a larger molecule and is composed of a group of atoms that has characteristic structure and chemical reactivity. A given functional group undergoes nearly the same chemical reactions in every molecule where it occurs. In this chapter we focused primarily on *alkanes*, hydrocarbon compounds that contain only single bonds between all C atoms.

3. **What are isomers?** *Isomers* are compounds that have the same formula but different structures. Isomers that differ in their connections among atoms are called *constitutional isomers*.

4. **How are organic molecules drawn?** Organic compounds can be represented by *structural formulas* in which all atoms and bonds are shown, by *condensed structures* in which not all bonds are drawn, or by *line structures* in which the carbon skeleton is represented by lines and the locations of C and H atoms are understood.

5. **What are alkanes and cycloalkanes, and how are they named?** Compounds that contain only carbon and hydrogen are called *hydrocarbons*, and hydrocarbons that have only single bonds are called *alkanes*. A *straight-chain alkane* has all its carbons connected in a row, a *branched-chain alkane* has a branching connection of atoms somewhere along its chain, and a *cycloalkane* has a ring of carbon atoms. Alkanes have the general formula C_nH_{2n+2}, whereas cycloalkanes have the formula C_nH_{2n}. Straight-chain alkanes are named by adding the family ending *-ane* to a parent; this tells how many carbon atoms are present. Branched-chain alkanes are named by using the longest continuous chain of carbon atoms for the parent and then identifying the *alkyl groups* present as branches off the main chain. The position of the substituent groups on the main chain are identified by numbering the carbons in the chain so that the substituents have the lowest number. Cycloalkanes are named by adding *cyclo-* as a prefix to the name of the alkane.

KEY WORDS

Alkane, *p. 368*

Alkyl group, *p. 380*

Branched-chain alkane, *p. 369*

Combustion, *p. 386*

Condensed structure, *p. 370*

Conformation, *p. 376*

Conformer, *p. 376*

Constitutional isomers, *p. 369*

Cycloalkane, *p. 387*

Ethyl group, *p. 380*

Functional group, *p. 364*

Hydrocarbon, *p. 364*

Isomers, *p. 368*

Isopropyl group, *p. 381*

Line structure, *p. 372*

Methyl group, *p. 380*

Methylene group, *p. 371*

Organic chemistry, *p. 361*

Primary (1°) carbon atom, *p. 381*

Propyl group, *p. 381*

Quaternary (4°) carbon atom, *p. 381*

Secondary (2°) carbon atom, *p. 381*

Straight-chain alkane, *p. 369*

Substituent, *p. 380*

Tertiary (3°) carbon atom, *p. 381*

6. What are the general properties and chemical reactions of alkanes? Alkanes are generally soluble only in nonpolar organic solvents, have weak intermolecular forces, and are nontoxic. Their principal chemical reactions are *combustion*, a reaction with oxygen that gives carbon dioxide and water, and *halogenation*, a reaction in which hydrogen atoms are replaced by chlorine or bromine.

SUMMARY OF REACTIONS

1. Combustion of an alkane with oxygen (Section 12.8):

$$CH_4 + 2\,O_2 \longrightarrow CO_2 + 2\,H_2O$$

2. Halogenation of an alkane to yield an alkyl halide (Section 12.8):

$$CH_4 + Cl_2 \longrightarrow CH_3Cl + HCl$$

UNDERSTANDING KEY CONCEPTS

12.19 How many hydrogen atoms are needed to complete the hydrocarbon formulas for the following carbon backbones?

(a)   (b)   (c)

12.20 Convert the following models into condensed structures (gray = C; ivory = H; red = O):

(a)   (b)

12.21 Convert the following models into line drawings (gray = C; ivory = H; red = O; blue = N):

(a)   (b)

12.22 Identify the functional groups in the following compounds:

(a)   (b)

12.23 Give systematic names for the following alkanes:

(a)   (b)

12.24 Give systematic names for the following cycloalkanes:

(a)   (b)

12.25 The following two compounds are isomers, even though both can be named 1,3-dimethylcyclopentane. What is the difference between them?

(a)   (b)

ADDITIONAL PROBLEMS

ORGANIC MOLECULES AND FUNCTIONAL GROUPS

12.26 What characteristics of carbon make possible the existence of so many different organic compounds?

12.27 What are functional groups, and why are they important?

12.28 Why are most organic compounds nonconducting and insoluble in water?

12.29 If you were given two unlabeled bottles, one containing hexane and one containing water, how could you tell them apart?

12.30 What is meant by the term *polar covalent bond*? Give an example of such a bond.

12.31 Give examples of compounds that are members of the following families:

(a) Alcohol   (b) Amine
(c) Carboxylic acid   (d) Ether

12.32 Locate and identify the functional groups in the following molecules (—SO$_2$N— is a sulfanilamide):

(a)

Viagra

(b)

Aspirin

12.33 Identify the functional groups in the following molecules:

(a)

Vitamin A

(b)

Ambien

12.34 Propose structures for molecules that fit the following descriptions:

(a) A ketone with the formula C$_5$H$_{10}$O
(b) An ester with the formula C$_6$H$_{12}$O$_2$
(c) A compound with the formula C$_2$H$_5$NO$_2$ that is both an amine and a carboxylic acid

12.35 Propose structures for molecules that fit the following descriptions:

(a) An amide with the formula C$_4$H$_9$NO
(b) An aldehyde that has a ring of carbons, C$_6$H$_{10}$O
(c) An aromatic compound that is also an ether, C$_8$H$_{10}$O

ALKANES AND ISOMERS

12.36 What requirement must be met for two compounds to be isomers?

12.37 If one compound has the formula C$_5$H$_{10}$ and another has the formula C$_4$H$_{10}$, are the two compounds isomers? Explain.

12.38 What is the difference between a secondary carbon and a tertiary carbon? Between a primary carbon and a quaternary carbon?

12.39 Why is it not possible for a compound to have a *quintary* carbon (five R groups attached to C)?

12.40 Give examples of compounds that meet the following descriptions:

(a) An alkane with two tertiary carbons
(b) A cycloalkane with only secondary carbons

12.41 Give examples of compounds that meet the following descriptions:

(a) A branched-chain alkane with only primary and quaternary carbons
(b) A cycloalkane with three substituents

12.42 There are three isomers with the formula C$_3$H$_8$O. Draw the condensed structure and the line structure for each isomer.

12.43 Write condensed structures for the following molecular formulas. (You may have to use rings and/or multiple bonds in some instances.)

(a) C$_2$H$_7$N
(b) C$_4$H$_8$ (Write the line structure as well.)
(c) C$_2$H$_4$O
(d) CH$_2$O$_2$ (Write the line structure as well.)

12.44 How many isomers can you write that fit the following descriptions?

(a) Alcohols with formula C$_4$H$_{10}$O
(b) Amines with formula C$_3$H$_9$N
(c) Ketones with formula C$_5$H$_{10}$O

12.45 How many isomers can you write that fit the following descriptions?

(a) Aldehydes with formula C$_5$H$_{10}$O
(b) Esters with formula C$_4$H$_8$O$_2$
(c) Carboxylic acids with formula C$_4$H$_8$O$_2$

12.46 Which of the following pairs of structures are identical, which are isomers, and which are unrelated?

(a) CH$_3$CH$_2$CH$_3$ and CH$_3$
                                    |
                                 CH$_2$CH$_3$

(b) CH$_3$—N—CH$_3$ and CH$_3$CH$_2$—N—H
          | |
          H   H

(c) $CH_3CH_2CH_2$—O—CH_3 and

$$CH_3CH_2CH_2-\overset{\overset{\displaystyle O}{\|}}{C}-CH_3$$

(d) $CH_3-\overset{\overset{\displaystyle O}{\|}}{C}-CH_2CH_2CH(CH_3)_2$ and

$$CH_3CH_2-\overset{\overset{\displaystyle O}{\|}}{C}-CH_2CH_2CH_2CH_3$$

(e) $CH_3CH{=}CHCH_2CH_2$—O—H and

$$CH_3CH_2\underset{\underset{\displaystyle CH_3}{|}}{CH}-\overset{\overset{\displaystyle O}{\|}}{C}-H$$

12.47 Which structure(s) in each group represent the same compound, and which represent isomers?

(a)
$$H-\overset{\overset{\displaystyle H}{|}}{\underset{\underset{\displaystyle H}{|}}{C}}-\overset{\overset{\displaystyle H}{|}}{\underset{\underset{\displaystyle H}{|}}{C}}-\overset{\overset{\displaystyle H}{|}}{\underset{\underset{\displaystyle H}{|}}{C}}-\overset{\overset{\displaystyle H}{|}}{\underset{\underset{\displaystyle H}{|}}{C}}-H$$

(b)
$$CH_3\underset{\underset{\displaystyle Br}{|}}{\overset{\overset{\displaystyle CH_3}{|}}{CH}}CHCH_3 \qquad CH_3\underset{\underset{\displaystyle Br}{|}}{\overset{\overset{\displaystyle CH_3}{|}}{CH}}CHCH_3$$

$$\underset{\underset{\displaystyle Br}{|}}{\overset{\overset{\displaystyle CH_3}{|}}{CH_2}}CHCH_2CH_3$$

12.48 What is wrong with the following structures?

(a) $CH_3{=}CHCH_2CH_2OH$

(b) $CH_3CH_2CH{=}\overset{\overset{\displaystyle O}{\|}}{C}-CH_3$

(c) $CH_2CH_2CH_2C{\equiv}\underset{\underset{\displaystyle CH_3}{|}}{C}CH_3$

12.49 There are two things wrong with the following structure. What are they?

ALKANE NOMENCLATURE

12.50 What are the IUPAC names of the following alkanes?

(a) $CH_3CH_2CH_2CH_2\underset{\underset{\displaystyle CH_3}{|}}{\overset{\overset{\displaystyle CH_2CH_3}{|}}{CH}}CHCH_2CH_3$

(b) $CH_3CH_2CH_2\underset{\underset{\displaystyle CH_2CH_3}{|}}{\overset{\overset{\displaystyle CH_3CHCH_3}{|}}{CH}}CH_2CHCH_3$

(c) $CH_3\underset{\underset{\displaystyle CH_3}{|}}{\overset{\overset{\displaystyle CH_3}{|}}{C}}CH_2CH_2CH_2\overset{\overset{\displaystyle CH_3}{|}}{CH}CH_3$

(d) $CH_3CH_2CH_2\underset{\underset{\displaystyle CH_3CHCH_3}{|}}{\overset{\overset{\displaystyle CH_2CH_2CH_2CH_3}{|}}{C}}CH_3$

(e) $CH_3\underset{\underset{\displaystyle CH_3}{|}}{\overset{\overset{\displaystyle CH_3}{|}}{C}}CH_2\underset{\underset{\displaystyle CH_3}{|}}{\overset{\overset{\displaystyle CH_3}{|}}{C}}CH_3$

(f) $CH_3CH_2\underset{\underset{\displaystyle CH_3CH_2}{|}}{\overset{\overset{\displaystyle CH_3CH_2}{|}}{C}}CH_2\underset{\underset{\displaystyle CH_3}{|}}{CH}$

(g) $CH_3(CH_2)_7\underset{\underset{\displaystyle CH_3}{|}}{\overset{\overset{\displaystyle CH_3}{|}}{C}}-CH_3$

12.51 Give IUPAC names for the five isomers with the formula C_6H_{14}.

12.52 Write condensed structures for the following compounds:
(a) 4-*tert*-Butyl-3,3,5-trimethylheptane
(b) 2,4-Dimethylpentane
(c) 4,4-Diethyl-3-methyloctane
(d) 3-Isopropyl-2,3,6,7-tetramethylnonane
(e) 3-Isobutyl-1-isopropyl-5-methylcycloheptane
(f) 1,1,3-Trimethylcyclopentane

12.53 Draw structures that correspond to the following IUPAC names:
(a) 1,1-Dimethylcyclopropane
(b) 1,2,3,4-Tetramethylcyclopentane
(c) 4-*tert*-Butyl-1,1-dimethylcyclohexane
(d) Cycloheptane
(e) 1,3,5-Triisopropylcyclohexane
(f) 1,3,5,7-Tetramethylcyclooctane

12.54 Name the following cycloalkanes:

(a)

(b)

(c)

$$CH_2CH_2CH_3$$

$$CH_2CH_3$$

(d)

$$CH_3$$
$$CH_3$$
$$CH_3 \quad -CH_2CH_2CH_2CH_3$$
$$CH_3$$
$$CH_3$$

12.55 Name the following cycloalkanes:

(a)

(b)

$$CH_3$$
$$CH_3CH_2 \qquad CH_2CH_3$$

(c)

$$CH_3$$
$$CH_3CH_2CH_2 \qquad CH_2CH_3$$

12.56 The following names are incorrect. Tell what is wrong with each, and provide the correct names.

(a)

$$CH_3$$
$$CH_3CCH_2CH_2CH_3$$
$$CH_3$$

2,2-Methylpentane

(b)

$$CH_3 \qquad CH_3$$
$$CH-CH_2-CH$$
$$CH_3 \qquad CH_3$$

1,1-Diisopropylmethane

(c)

$$CH_3$$
$$CH_3CHCH_2-$$

1-Cyclobutyl-2-methylpropane

12.57 The following names are incorrect. Write the structural formula that agrees with the apparent name, and then write the correct name of the compound.

(a) 2-Ethylbutane
(b) 2-Isopropyl-2-methylpentane
(c) 5-Ethyl-1,1-methylcyclopentane
(d) 3-Ethyl-3,5,5-trimethylhexane
(e) 1,2-Dimethyl-4-ethylcyclohexane
(f) 2,4-Diethylpentane
(g) 5,5,6,6-Methyl-7,7-ethyldecane

12.58 Draw structures and give IUPAC names for the nine isomers of C_7H_{16}.

12.59 Draw the structural formulas and name all cyclic isomers with the formula C_6H_{12}.

REACTIONS OF ALKANES

12.60 Propane, commonly known as LP gas, burns in air to yield CO_2 and H_2O. Write a balanced equation for the reaction.

12.61 Write a balanced equation for the combustion of isooctane, C_8H_{16}, a component of gasoline.

12.62 Write the formulas of the three singly chlorinated isomers formed when 2,2-dimethylbutane reacts with Cl_2 in the presence of light.

12.63 Write the formulas of the seven doubly brominated isomers formed when 2,2-dimethylbutane reacts with Br_2 in the presence of light.

Applications

12.64 Why is it important to know the shape of a molecule? [*Displaying Molecular Shapes, p. 379*]

12.65 How does petroleum differ from natural gas? [*Petroleum, p. 388*]

12.66 What types of hydrocarbons burn most efficiently in an automobile engine? [*Petroleum, p. 388*]

General Questions and Problems

12.67 Identify the functional groups in the following molecules:

(a) Testosterone, a male sex hormone

(b) Aspartame, an artificial sweetener

$$HOCCH_2CHCNHCHCOCH_3$$
$$NH_2 \qquad CH_2$$

12.68 Label each carbon in Problem 12.67 as primary, secondary, tertiary, or quaternary.

12.69 If someone reported the preparation of a compound with the formula C_3H_9 most chemists would be skeptical. Why?

12.70 Most lipsticks are about 70% castor oil and wax. Why is lipstick more easily removed with petroleum jelly than with water?

12.71 When cyclopentane is exposed to Br_2 in the presence of light, reaction occurs. Write the formulas of:

(a) All possible monobromination products
(b) All possible dibromination products

12.72 Which do you think has a higher boiling point, pentane or neopentane (2,2-dimethylpropane)? Why?

12.73 Propose structures for the following:

(a) An aldehyde, C_4H_8O
(b) An iodo-substituted alkene, C_5H_9I
(c) A cycloalkane, C_7H_{14}
(d) A diene (dialkene), C_5H_8

Glossary

1,4 Link A glycosidic link between the hemiacetal hydroxyl group at C1 of one sugar and the hydroxyl group at C4 of another sugar.

Acetal A compound that has two ether-like —OR groups bonded to the same carbon atom.

Acetyl coenzyme A (acetyl-SCoA) Acetyl-substituted coenzyme A—the common intermediate that carries acetyl groups into the citric acid cycle.

Acetyl group A $CH_3C=O$ group.

Achiral The opposite of chiral; having no right- or left-handedness and no nonsuperimposable mirror images.

Acid A substance that provides H^+ ions in water.

Acid dissociation constant (K_a) The equilibrium constant for the dissociation of an acid (HA), equal to $[H^+][A^-]/[HA]$

Acidosis The abnormal condition associated with a blood plasma pH below 7.35; may be respiratory or metabolic.

Acid–base indicator A dye that changes color depending on the pH of a solution.

Activation (of an enzyme) Any process that initiates or increases the action of an enzyme.

Activation energy (E_{act}) The amount of energy necessary for reactants to surmount the energy barrier to reaction; affects reaction rate.

Active site A pocket in an enzyme with the specific shape and chemical makeup necessary to bind a substrate.

Active transport Movement of substances across a cell membrane with the assistance of energy (for example, from ATP).

Actual Yield The amount of product actually formed in a reaction.

Acyl group An $RC=O$ group.

Addition reaction A general reaction type in which a substance X—Y adds to the multiple bond of an unsaturated reactant to yield a saturated product that has only single bonds.

Addition reaction, aldehydes and ketones Addition of an alcohol or other compound to the carbon–oxygen double bond to give a carbon–oxygen single bond.

Adenosine triphosphate (ATP) The principal energy-carrying molecule; removal of a phosphoryl group to give ADP releases free energy.

Aerobic In the presence of oxygen.

Agonist A substance that interacts with a receptor to cause or prolong the receptor's normal biochemical response.

Alcohol A compound that has an —OH group bonded to a saturated, alkane-like carbon atom, R—OH.

Alcoholic fermentation The anaerobic breakdown of glucose to ethanol plus carbon dioxide by the action of yeast enzymes.

Aldehyde A compound that has a carbonyl group bonded to one carbon and one hydrogen, RCHO.

Aldose A monosaccharide that contains an aldehyde carbonyl group.

Alkali metal An element in group 1A of the periodic table.

Alkaline earth metal An element in group 2A of the periodic table.

Alkaloid A naturally occurring nitrogen-containing compound isolated from a plant; usually basic, bitter, and poisonous.

Alkalosis The abnormal condition associated with a blood plasma pH above 7.45; may be respiratory or metabolic.

Alkane A hydrocarbon that has only single bonds.

Alkene A hydrocarbon that contains a carbon–carbon double bond.

Alkoxide ion The anion resulting from deprotonation of an alcohol, RO^-.

Alkoxy group An —OR group.

Alkyl group The part of an alkane that remains when a hydrogen atom is removed.

Alkyl halide A compound that has an alkyl group bonded to a halogen atom, R—X.

Alkyne A hydrocarbon that contains a carbon–carbon triple bond.

Allosteric control An interaction in which the binding of a regulator at one site on a protein affects the protein's ability to bind another molecule at a different site.

Allosteric enzyme An enzyme whose activity is controlled by the binding of an activator or inhibitor at a location other than the active site.

Alpha (α) particle A helium nucleus (He^{2+}), emitted as α-radiation.

Alpha- (α-) amino acid An amino acid in which the amino group is bonded to the carbon atom next to the —COOH group.

Alpha- (α-) helix Secondary protein structure in which a protein chain forms a right-handed coil stabilized by hydrogen bonds between peptide groups along its backbone.

Amide A compound that has a carbonyl group bonded to a carbon atom and a nitrogen atom group, $RCONR_2'$, where the R' groups may be alkyl groups or hydrogen atoms.

Amine A compound that has one or more organic groups bonded to nitrogen; primary, RNH_2; secondary, R_2NH; or tertiary, R_3N.

Amino acid A molecule that contains both an amino group and a carboxylic acid functional group.

Amino acid pool The entire collection of free amino acids in the body.

Amino group The —NH_2 functional group.

Amino-terminal (N-terminal) amino acid The amino acid with the free —NH_3^+ group at the end of a protein.

Ammonium ion A positive ion formed by addition of hydrogen to ammonia or an amine (may be primary, secondary, or tertiary).

Ammonium salt An ionic compound composed of an ammonium cation and an anion; an amine salt.

Amorphous solid A solid whose particles do not have an orderly arrangement.

Amphoteric Describing a substance that can react as either an acid or a base.

Anabolism Metabolic reactions that build larger biological molecules from smaller pieces.

Anaerobic In the absence of oxygen.

Anion A negatively charged ion.

Anomeric carbon atom The hemiacetal C atom in a cyclic sugar; the C atom bonded to an —OH group and an O in the ring.

Anomers Cyclic sugars that differ only in positions of substituents at the hemiacetal carbon (the anomeric carbon); the α form has the —OH on the opposite side from the —CH_2OH; the β form has the —OH on the same side as the —CH_2OH.

Antagonist A substance that blocks or inhibits the normal biochemical response of a receptor.

Antibody (immunoglobulin) Glycoprotein molecule that identifies antigens.

Anticodon A sequence of three ribonucleotides on tRNA that recognizes the complementary sequence (the codon) on mRNA.

Antigen A substance foreign to the body that triggers the immune response.

Antioxidant A substance that prevents oxidation by reacting with an oxidizing agent.

Aqueous solution A solution in which water is the solvent.

Aromatic The class of compounds containing benzene-like rings.

Artificial transmutation The change of one atom into another brought about by a nuclear bombardment reaction.

Atom The smallest and simplest particle of an element.

Atomic mass unit (amu) A convenient unit for describing the mass of an atom; 1 amu = 1/12 the mass of a carbon-12 atom.

Atomic number (Z) The number of protons in an atom.

Atomic theory A set of assumptions proposed by English scientist John Dalton to explain the chemical behavior of matter.

Atomic weight The weighted average mass of an element's atoms.

ATP synthase The enzyme complex in the inner mitochondrial membrane at which hydrogen ions cross the membrane and ATP is synthesized from ADP.

Autoimmune disease Disorder in which the immune system identifies normal body components as antigens and produces antibodies to them.

Avogadro's law Equal volumes of gases at the same temperature and pressure contain equal numbers of molecules (V/n = constant, or $V_1/n_1 = V_2/n_2$).

Avogadro's number (N_A) The number of units in 1 mole of anything; 6.02×10^{23}.

Balanced equation Describing a chemical equation in which the numbers and kinds of atoms are the same on both sides of the reaction arrow.

Base A substance that provides OH^- ions in water.

Base pairing The pairing of bases connected by hydrogen bonding (G-C and A-T), as in the DNA double helix.

Beta- (β-) Oxidation pathway A repetitive series of biochemical reactions that degrades fatty acids to acetyl-SCoA by removing carbon atoms two at a time.

Beta (β) particle An electron (e^-), emitted as β radiation.

Beta- (β-) Sheet Secondary protein structure in which adjacent protein chains either in the same molecule or in different molecules are held in place by hydrogen bonds along the backbones.

Bile acids Steroid acids derived from cholesterol that are secreted in bile.

Bile Fluid secreted by the liver and released into the small intestine from the gallbladder during digestion; contains bile acids, bicarbonate ion, and other electrolytes.

Binary compound A compound formed by combination of two different elements.

Blood clot A network of fibrin fibers and trapped blood cells that forms at the site of blood loss.

Blood plasma Liquid portion of the blood: an extracellular fluid.

Blood serum Fluid portion of blood remaining after clotting has occurred.

Boiling point (bp) The temperature at which liquid and gas are in equilibrium.

Bond angle The angle formed by three adjacent atoms in a molecule.

Bond dissociation energy The amount of energy that must be supplied to break a bond and separate the atoms in an isolated gaseous molecule.

Bond length The optimum distance between nuclei in a covalent bond.

Boyle's law The pressure of a gas at constant temperature is inversely proportional to its volume ($PV = $ constant, or $P_1V_1 = P_2V_2$).

Branched-chain alkane An alkane that has a branching connection of carbons.

Brønsted–Lowry acid A substance that can donate a hydrogen ion, H^+, to another molecule or ion.

Brønsted–Lowry base A substance that can accept H^+ from an acid.

Buffer A combination of substances that act together to prevent a drastic change in pH; usually a weak acid and its conjugate base.

Carbohydrate A member of a large class of naturally occurring polyhydroxy ketones and aldehydes.

Carbonyl compound Any compound that contains a carbonyl group $C=O$.

Carbonyl group A functional group that has a carbon atom joined to an oxygen atom by a double bond, $C=O$.

Carbonyl-group substitution reaction A reaction in which a new group replaces (substitutes for) a group attached to a carbonyl-group carbon in an acyl group.

Carboxyl group The —COOH functional group.

Carboxyl-terminal (C-terminal) amino acid The amino acid with the free —COO$^-$ group at the end of a protein.

Carboxylate anion The anion that results from ionization of a carboxylic acid, RCOO$^-$.

Carboxylic acid A compound that has a carbonyl group bonded to a carbon atom and an —OH group, RCOOH.

Carboxylic acid salt An ionic compound containing a carboxylic anion and a cation.

Catabolism Metabolic reaction pathways that break down food molecules and release biochemical energy.

Catalyst A substance that speeds up the rate of a chemical reaction but is itself unchanged.

Cation A positively charged ion.

Centromeres The central regions of chromosomes.

Chain reaction A reaction that, once started, is self-sustaining.

Change of state The conversion of a substance from one state to another—for example, from a liquid to a gas.

Charles's law The volume of a gas at constant pressure is directly proportional to its Kelvin temperature ($V/T = $ constant, or $V_1/T_1 = V_2/T_2$).

Chemical change A change in the chemical makeup of a substance.

Chemical compound A pure substance that can be broken down into simpler substances by chemical reactions.

Chemical equation An expression in which symbols and formulas are used to represent a chemical reaction.

Chemical equilibrium A state in which the rates of forward and reverse reactions are the same.

Chemical formula A notation for a chemical compound using element symbols and subscripts to show how many atoms of each element are present.

Chemical reaction A process in which the identity and composition of one or more substances are changed.

Chemistry The study of the nature, properties, and transformations of matter.

Chiral carbon atom (chirality center) A carbon atom bonded to four different groups.

Chiral Having right- or left-handedness; able to have two different mirror-image forms.

Chromosome A complex of proteins and DNA; visible during cell division.

Cis-trans isomers Alkenes that have the same connections between atoms but differ in their three-dimensional structures because of the way that groups are attached to different sides of the double bond. The cis isomer has hydrogen atoms on the same side of the double bond; the trans isomer has them on opposite sides.

Citric acid cycle The series of biochemical reactions that breaks down acetyl groups to produce energy carried by reduced coenzymes and carbon dioxide.

Clones Identical copies of organisms, cells, or DNA segments from a single ancestor.

Codon A sequence of three ribonucleotides in the messenger RNA chain that codes for a specific amino acid; also the three nucleotide sequence (a stop codon) that stops translation.

Coefficient A number placed in front of a formula to balance a chemical equation.

Coenzyme An organic molecule that acts as an enzyme cofactor.

Cofactor A nonprotein part of an enzyme that is essential to the enzyme's catalytic activity; a metal ion or a coenzyme.

Colligative property A property of a solution that depends only on the number of dissolved particles, not on their chemical identity.

Colloid A homogeneous mixture that contains particles that range in diameter from 2 to 500 nm.

Combined gas law The product of the pressure and volume of a gas is proportional to its temperature ($PV/T = $ constant, or $P_1V_1/T_1 = P_2V_2/T_2$).

Combustion A chemical reaction that produces a flame, usually because of burning with oxygen.

Competititve (enzyme) inhibition Enzyme regulation in which an inhibitor competes with a substrate for binding to the enzyme active site.

Concentration A measure of the amount of a given substance in a mixture.

Concentration gradient A difference in concentration within the same system.

Condensed structure A shorthand way of drawing structures in which C—C and C—H bonds are understood rather than shown.

Conformation The specific three-dimensional arrangement of atoms in a molecule at a given instant.

Conformers Molecular structures having identical connections between atoms.

Conjugate acid The substance formed by addition of H^+ to a base.

Conjugate acid–base pair Two substances whose formulas differ by only a hydrogen ion, H^+.

Conjugate base The substance formed by loss of H^+ from an acid.

Conjugated protein A protein that incorporates one or more non-amino acid units in its structure.

Constitutional isomers Compounds with the same molecular formula but different connections among their atoms.

Conversion factor An expression of the relationship between two units.

Coordinate covalent bond The covalent bond that forms when both electrons are donated by the same atom.

Cosmic rays A mixture of high-energy particles—primarily of protons and various atomic nuclei—that shower the earth from outer space.

Covalent bond A bond formed by sharing electrons between atoms.

Critical mass The minimum amount of radioactive material needed to sustain a nuclear chain reaction.

Crystalline solid A solid whose atoms, molecules, or ions are rigidly held in an ordered arrangement.

Cycloalkane An alkane that contains a ring of carbon atoms.

Cycloalkene A cyclic hydrocarbon that contains a double bond.

Cytoplasm The region between the cell membrane and the nuclear membrane in a eukaryotic cell.

Cytosol The fluid part of the cytoplasm surrounding the organelles within a cell.

d-Block element A transition metal element that results from the filling of d orbitals.

D-Sugar Monosaccharide with the —OH group on the chiral carbon atom farthest

from the carbonyl group pointing to the right in a Fischer projection.

Dalton's law The total pressure exerted by a mixture of gases is equal to the sum of the partial pressures exerted by each individual gas.

Decay series A sequential series of nuclear disintegrations leading from a heavy radioisotope to a nonradioactive product.

Degree of unsaturation The number of carbon–carbon double bonds in a molecule.

Dehydration The loss of water from an alcohol to yield an alkene.

Denaturation The loss of secondary, tertiary, or quaternary protein structure due to disruption of noncovalent interactions and/or disulfide bonds that leaves peptide bond and primary structure intact.

Density The physical property that relates the mass of an object to its volume; mass per unit volume.

Deoxyribonucleotide A nucleotide containing 2-deoxy-D-ribose.

Diabetes mellitus A chronic condition due to either insufficient insulin or failure of insulin to activate crossing of cell membranes by glucose.

Diastereomers Stereoisomers that are not mirror images of each other.

Digestion A general term for the breakdown of food into small molecules.

Dilution factor The ratio of the initial and final solution volumes (V_1/V_2).

Dipole–dipole force The attractive force between positive and negative ends of polar molecules.

Disaccharide A carbohydrate composed of two monosaccharides.

Dissociation The splitting apart of an acid in water to give H^+ and an anion.

Disulfide A compound that contains a sulfur–sulfur bond, RS–SR.

Disulfide bond (in protein) An S–S bond formed between two cysteine side chains; can join two peptide chains together or cause a loop in a peptide chain.

DNA (deoxyribonucleic acid) The nucleic acid that stores genetic information; a polymer of deoxyribonucleotides.

Double bond A covalent bond formed by sharing two electron pairs.

Double helix Two strands coiled around each other in a screwlike fashion; in most organisms the two polynucleotides of DNA form a double helix.

Drug Any substance that alters body function when it is introduced from an external source.

Eicosanoid A lipid derived from a 20-carbon unsaturated carboxylic acid.

Electrolyte A substance that produces ions and therefore conducts electricity when dissolved in water.

Electron A negatively charged subatomic particle.

Electron affinity The energy released on adding an electron to a single atom in the gaseous state.

Electron capture A process in which the nucleus captures an inner-shell electron from the surrounding electron cloud, thereby converting a proton into a neutron.

Electron configuration The specific arrangement of electrons in an atom's shells and subshells.

Electron shell A grouping of electrons in an atom according to energy.

Electron subshell A grouping of electrons in a shell according to the shape of the region of space they occupy.

Electron-dot symbol An atomic symbol with dots placed around it to indicate the number of valence electrons.

Electron-transport chain The series of biochemical reactions that passes electrons from reduced coenzymes to oxygen and is coupled to ATP formation.

Electronegativity The ability of an atom to attract electrons in a covalent bond.

Element A fundamental substance that can't be broken down chemically into any simpler substance.

Elimination reaction A general reaction type in which a saturated reactant yields an unsaturated product by losing groups from two adjacent carbon atoms.

Enantiomers, optical isomers The two mirror-image forms of a chiral molecule.

Endergonic A nonspontaneous reaction or process that absorbs free energy and has a positive ΔG.

Endocrine system A system of specialized cells, tissues, and ductless glands that excretes hormones and shares with the nervous system the responsibility for maintaining constant internal body conditions and responding to changes in the environment.

Endothermic A process or reaction that absorbs heat and has a positive ΔH.

Energy The capacity to do work or supply heat.

Enthalpy A measure of the amount of energy associated with substances involved in a reaction.

Enthalpy change (ΔH) An alternative name for heat of reaction.

Entropy (S) The amount of disorder in a system.

Enzyme A protein or other molecule that acts as a catalyst for a biological reaction.

Equilibrium constant (K) Value of the equilibrium constant expression for a given reaction.

Equivalent For ions, the amount equal to 1 mol of charge.

Equivalent of acid Amount of an acid that contains 1 mole of H^+ ions.

Equivalent of base Amount of base that contains 1 mole of OH^- ions.

Erythrocytes Red blood cells; transporters of blood gases.

Essential amino acid An amino acid that cannot be synthesized by the body and thus must be obtained in the diet.

Ester A compound that has a carbonyl group bonded to a carbon atom and an —OR' group, RCOOR'.

Esterification The reaction between an alcohol and a carboxylic acid to yield an ester plus water.

Ether A compound that has an oxygen atom bonded to two organic groups, R—O—R.

Ethyl group The —CH_2CH_3 alkyl group.

Exergonic A spontaneous reaction or process that releases free energy and has a negative ΔG.

Exon A nucleotide sequence in DNA that is part of a gene and codes for part of a protein.

Exothermic A process or reaction that releases heat and has a negative ΔH.

Extracellular fluid Fluid outside cells.

ƒ-Block element An inner transition metal element that results from the filling of ƒ orbitals.

Facilitated diffusion Passive transport across a cell membrane with the assistance of a protein that changes shape.

Factor–label method A problem-solving procedure in which equations are set up so that unwanted units cancel and only the desired units remain.

Fat A mixture of triacylglycerols that is solid because it contains a high proportion of saturated fatty acids.

Fatty acid A long-chain carboxylic acid; those in animal fats and vegetable oils often have 12–22 carbon atoms.

Feedback control Regulation of an enzyme's activity by the product of a reaction later in a pathway.

Fermentation The production of energy under anaerobic conditions.

Fibrin Insoluble protein that forms the fiber framework of a blood clot.

Fibrous protein A tough, insoluble protein whose protein chains form fibers or sheets.

Filtration (kidney) Filtration of blood plasma through a glomerulus and into a kidney nephron.

Fischer projection Structure that represents chiral carbon atoms as the intersections of two lines, with the horizontal lines representing bonds pointing out of the page and the vertical lines representing bonds pointing behind the page. For sugars, the aldehyde or ketone is at the top.

Formula unit The formula that identifies the smallest neutral unit of a compound.

Formula weight The sum of the atomic weights of the atoms in one formula unit of any compound.

Free radical An atom or molecule with an unpaired electron.

Free-energy change (ΔG) The criterion for spontaneous change (negative ΔG; $\Delta G = \Delta H - T\,\Delta S$).

Functional group An atom or group of atoms within a molecule that has a characteristic structure and chemical behavior.

Gamma (γ) radiation Radioactivity consisting of high-energy light waves.

Gas A substance that has neither a definite volume nor a definite shape.

Gas constant (R) The constant R in the ideal gas law, $PV = nRT$.

Gas laws A series of laws that predict the influence of pressure (P), volume (V), and temperature (T) on any gas or mixture of gases.

Gay-Lussac's law For a fixed amount of gas at a constant voume, pressure is directly proportional to the Kelvin temperature (P/T = constant, or $P_1/T_1 = P_2/T_2$).

Gene Segment of DNA that directs the synthesis of a single polypeptide.

Genetic (enzyme) control Regulation of enzyme activity by control of the synthesis of enzymes.

Genetic code The sequence of nucleotides, coded in triplets (codons) in mRNA, that determines the sequence of amino acids in protein synthesis.

Genome All of the genetic material in the chromosomes of an organism; its size is given as the number of base pairs.

Genomics The study of whole sets of genes and their functions.

Globular protein A water–soluble protein whose chain is folded in a compact shape with hydrophilic groups on the outside.

Glomerular filtrate Fluid that enters the nephron from the glomerulus; filtered blood plasma.

Gluconeogenesis The biochemical pathway for the synthesis of glucose from noncarbohydrates, such as lactate, amino acids, or glycerol.

Glycerophospholipid (phosphoglyceride) A lipid in which glycerol is linked by ester bonds to two fatty acids and one phosphate, which is in turn linked by another ester bond to an amino alcohol (or other alcohol).

Glycogenesis The biochemical pathway for synthesis of glycogen.

Glycogenolysis The biochemical pathway for breakdown of glycogen to free glucose.

Glycol A dialcohol, or diol having the two –OH groups on adjacent carbons.

Glycolipid A lipid with a fatty acid bonded to the C2—NH$_2$ and a sugar bonded to the C1—OH group of sphingosine.

Glycolysis The biochemical pathway that breaks down a molecule of glucose into two molecules of pyruvate plus energy.

Glycoprotein A protein that contains a short carbohydrate chain.

Glycoside A cyclic acetal formed by reaction of a monosaccharide with an alcohol, accompanied by loss of H$_2$O.

Glycosidic bond Bond between the anomeric carbon atom of a monosaccharide and an —OR group.

Gram-equivalent For ions, the molar mass of the ion divided by the ionic charge.

Group One of the 18 vertical columns of elements in the periodic table.

Guanosine diphosphate (GDP) An energy-carrying molecule that can gain or lose a phosphoryl group to transfer energy.

Guanosine triphosphate (GTP) An energy-carrying molecule similar to ATP; removal of a phosphoryl group to give GDP releases free energy.

Half-life ($t_{1/2}$) The amount of time required for one-half of a radioactive sample to decay.

Halogen An element in group 7A of the periodic table.

Halogenation (alkene) The addition of Cl$_2$ or Br$_2$ to a multiple bond to give a 1,2-dihalide product.

Halogenation (aromatic) The substitution of a halogen group (—X) for a hydrogen on an aromatic ring.

Heat The kinetic energy transferred from a hotter object to a colder object when the two are in contact.

Heat of fusion The quantity of heat required to completely melt a substance once it has reached its melting point.

Heat of reaction (ΔH) The amount of heat absorbed or released in a reaction.

Heat of vaporization The quantity of heat needed to completely vaporize a liquid once it has reached its boiling point.

Hemiacetal A compound with both an alcohol-like —OH group and an ether-like —OR group bonded to the same carbon atom.

Hemostasis The stopping of bleeding.

Henderson-Hasselbalch equation The logarithmic form of the K_a equation for a weak acid, used in applications involving buffer solutions.

Henry's law The solubility of a gas in a liquid is directly proportional to its partial pressure over the liquid at constant temperature.

Heterocycle A ring that contains nitrogen or some other atom in addition to carbon.

Heterogeneous mixture A nonuniform mixture that has regions of different composition.

Heterogeneous nuclear RNA The initially synthesized mRNA strand containing both introns and exons.

Homogeneous mixture A uniform mixture that has the same composition throughout.

Hormone A chemical messenger secreted by cells of the endocrine system and transported through the bloodstream to target cells with appropriate receptors where it elicits a response.

Hydration The addition of water to a multiple bond to give an alcohol product.

Hydrocarbon An organic compound that contains only carbon and hydrogen.

Hydrogen bond The attraction between a hydrogen atom bonded to an electronegative O, N, or F atom and another nearby electronegative O, N, or F atom.

Hydrogenation The addition of H$_2$ to a multiple bond to give a saturated product.

Hydrohalogenation The addition of HCl or HBr to a multiple bond to give an alkyl halide product.

Hydrolysis A reaction in which a bond or bonds are broken and the H— and —OH of water add to the atoms of the broken bond or bonds.

Hydronium ion The H$_3$O$^+$ ion, formed when an acid reacts with water.

Hydrophilic Water-loving; a hydrophilic substance dissolves in water.

Hydrophobic Water-fearing; a hydrophobic substance does not dissolve in water.

Hygroscopic Having the ability to pull water molecules from the surrounding atmosphere.

Hyperglycemia Higher-than-normal blood glucose concentration.

Hypertonic Having an osmolarity greater than the surrounding blood plasma or cells.

Hypoglycemia Lower-than-normal blood glucose concentration.

Hypotonic Having an osmolarity less than the surrounding blood plasma or cells.

Ideal gas A gas that obeys all the assumptions of the kinetic–molecular theory.

Ideal gas law A general expression relating pressure, volume, temperature, and amount for an ideal gas: $PV = nRT$.

Immune response Defense mechanism of the immune system dependent on the recognition of specific antigens, including viruses, bacteria, toxic substances, and infected cells; either cell-mediated or antibody-mediated.

Induced-fit model A model of enzyme action in which the enzyme has a flexible active site that changes shape to best fit the substrate and catalyze the reaction.

Inflammation Result of the inflammatory response: includes swelling, redness, warmth, and pain.

Inflammatory response A nonspecific defense mechanism triggered by antigens or tissue damage.

Inhibition (of an enzyme) Any process that slows or stops the action of an enzyme.

Inner transition metal element An element in one of the 14 groups shown separately at the bottom of the periodic table.

Intermolecular force A force that acts between molecules and holds molecules close to one another in liquids and solids.

Interstitial fluid Fluid surrounding cells: an extracellular fluid.

Intracellular fluid Fluid inside cells.

Intron A portion of DNA between coding regions of a gene (exons); is transcribed and then removed from final messenger RNA.

Ion An electrically charged atom or group of atoms.

Ion-product constant for water (K_w) The product of the H$_3$O$^+$ and OH$^-$ molar concentrations in water or any aqueous solution ($K_w = $ [H$_3$O$^+$][OH$^-$] $= 1.00 \times 10^{-14}$).

Ionic bond The electrical attractions between ions of opposite charge in a crystal.

Ionic compound A compound that contains ionic bonds.

Ionic equation An equation in which ions are explicitly shown.

Ionic solid A crystalline solid held together by ionic bonds.

Ionization energy The energy required to remove one electron from a single atom in the gaseous state.

Ionizing radiation A general name for high-energy radiation of all kinds.

Irreversible (enzyme) inhibition Enzyme deactivation in which an inhibitor forms covalent bonds to the active site, permanently blocking it.

Isoelectric point (pI) The pH at which a sample of an amino acid has equal number of + and − charges.

Isomers Compounds with the same molecular formula but different structures.

Isopropyl group The branched-chain alkyl group —CH(CH$_3$)$_2$.

Isotonic Having the same osmolarity.

Isotopes Atoms with identical atomic numbers but different mass numbers.

Ketoacidosis Lowered blood pH due to accumulation of ketone bodies.

Ketogenesis The synthesis of ketone bodies from acetyl-SCoA.

Ketone A compound that has a carbonyl group bonded to two carbons in organic groups that can be the same or different, R$_2$C=O, RCOR'.

Ketone bodies Compounds produced in the liver that can be used as fuel by muscle and brain tissue; 3-hydroxybutyrate, acetoacetate, and acetone.

Ketose A monosaccharide that contains a ketone carbonyl group.

Kinetic energy The energy of an object in motion.

Kinetic–molecular theory (KMT) of gases A group of assumptions that explain the behavior of gases.

L-Sugar Monosaccharide with the —OH group on the chiral carbon atom farthest from the carbonyl group pointing to the left in a Fischer projection.

Law of conservation of energy Energy can be neither created nor destroyed in any physical or chemical change.

Law of conservation of mass Matter can be neither created nor destroyed in any physical or chemical change.

Le Châtelier's principle When a stress is applied to a system in equilibrium, the equilibrium shifts to relieve the stress.

Lewis base A compound containing an unshared pair of electrons.

Lewis structure A molecular representation that shows both the connections among atoms and the locations of lone-pair valence electrons.

Limiting reagent The reactant that runs out first in a chemical reaction.

Line structure A shorthand way of drawing structures in which atoms aren't shown; instead, a carbon atom is understood to be at every intersection of lines, and hydrogens are filled in mentally.

Lipid A naturally occurring molecule from a plant or animal that is soluble in nonpolar organic solvents.

Lipid bilayer The basic structural unit of cell membranes; composed of two parallel sheets of membrane lipid molecules arranged tail to tail.

Lipogenesis The biochemical pathway for synthesis of fatty acids from acetyl-SCoA.

Lipoprotein A lipid–protein complex that transports lipids.

Liposome A spherical structure in which a lipid bilayer surrounds a water droplet.

Liquid A substance that has a definite volume but that changes shape to fit its container.

London dispersion force The short-lived attractive force due to the constant motion of electrons within molecules.

Lone pair A pair of electrons that is not used for bonding.

Main group element An element in one of the two groups on the left or the six groups on the right of the periodic table.

Markovnikov's rule In the addition of HX to an alkene, the H becomes attached to the carbon that already has the most H's, and the X becomes attached to the carbon that has fewer H's.

Mass A measure of the amount of matter in an object.

Mass number (A) The total number of protons and neutrons in an atom.

Matter The physical material that makes up the universe; anything that has mass and occupies space.

Melting point (mp) The temperature at which solid and liquid are in equilibrium.

Messenger RNA (mRNA) The RNA that carries the code transcribed from DNA and directs protein synthesis.

Metal A malleable element with a lustrous appearance that is a good conductor of heat and electricity.

Metalloid An element whose properties are intermediate between those of a metal and a nonmetal.

Methyl group The $-CH_3$ alkyl group.

Methylene Another name for a CH_2 unit.

Micelle A spherical cluster formed by the aggregation of soap or detergent molecules so that their hydrophobic ends are in the center and their hydrophilic ends are on the surface.

Miscible Mutually soluble in all proportions.

Mitochondrial matrix The space surrounded by the inner membrane of a mitochondrion.

Mitochondrion (plural, mitochondria) An egg-shaped organelle where small molecules are broken down to provide the energy for an organism.

Mixture A blend of two or more substances, each of which retains its chemical identity.

Mobilization (of triacylglycerols) Hydrolysis of triacylglycerols in adipose tissue and release of fatty acids into the bloodstream.

Molar mass The mass in grams of one mole of a substance, numerically equal to the molecular weight.

Molarity (M) Concentration expressed as the number of moles of solute per liter of solution.

Mole The amount of a substance corresponding to 6.02×10^{23} units.

Molecular compound A compound that consists of molecules rather than ions.

Molecular formula A formula that shows the numbers and kinds of atoms in one molecule of a compound.

Molecular weight The sum of the atomic weights of the atoms in a molecule.

Molecule A group of atoms held together by covalent bonds.

Monomer A small molecule that is used to prepare a polymer.

Monosaccharide (simple sugar) A carbohydrate with 3–7 carbon atoms.

Mutagen A substance that causes mutations.

Mutarotation Change in rotation of plane-polarized light resulting from the equilibrium between cyclic anomers and the open-chain form of a sugar.

Mutation An error in base sequence that is carried along in DNA replication.

***n*-propyl group** The straight-chain alkyl group $-CH_2CH_2CH_3$.

Native protein A protein with the shape (secondary, tertiary, and quaternary structure) in which it exists naturally in living organisms.

Net ionic equation An equation that does not include spectator ions.

Neurotransmitter A chemical messenger that travels between a neuron and a neighboring neuron or other target cell to transmit a nerve impulse.

Neutralization reaction The reaction of an acid with a base.

Neutron An electrically neutral subatomic particle.

Nitration The substitution of a nitro group $(-NO_2)$ for a hydrogen on an aromatic ring.

Noble gas An element in group 8A of the periodic table.

Noncompetitive (enzyme) inhibition Enzyme regulation in which an inhibitor binds to an enzyme elsewhere than at the active site, thereby changing the shape of the enzyme's active site and reducing its efficiency.

Noncovalent forces Forces of attraction other than covalent bonds that can act between molecules or within molecules.

Nonelectrolyte A substance that does not produce ions when dissolved in water.

Nonessential amino acid One of eleven amino acids that are synthesized in the body and are therefore not necessary in the diet.

Nonmetal An element that is a poor conductor of heat and electricity.

Normal boiling point The boiling point at a pressure of exactly 1 atmosphere.

Normality (N) A measure of acid (or base) concentration expressed as the number of acid (or base) equivalents per liter of solution.

Nuclear decay The spontaneous emission of a particle from an unstable nucleus.

Nuclear fission The fragmenting of heavy nuclei.

Nuclear fusion The joining together of light nuclei.

Nuclear reaction A reaction that changes an atomic nucleus, usually causing the change of one element into another.

Nucleic acid A polymer of nucleotides.

Nucleon A general term for both protons and neutrons.

Nucleoside A five-carbon sugar bonded to a cyclic amine base; like a nucleotide but missing the phosphate group.

Nucleotide A five-carbon sugar bonded to a cyclic amine base and one phosphate group (a nucleoside monophosphate); monomer for nucleic acids.

Nucleus The dense, central core of an atom that contains protons and neutrons.

Nuclide The nucleus of a specific isotope of an element.

Octet rule Main-group elements tend to undergo reactions that leave them with 8 valence electrons.

Oil A mixture of triacylglycerols that is liquid because it contains a high proportion of unsaturated fatty acids.

Orbital A region of space within an atom where an electron in a given subshell can be found.

Organic chemistry The study of carbon compounds.

Osmolarity (osmol) The sum of the molarities of all dissolved particles in a solution.

Osmosis The passage of solvent through a semipermeable membrane separating two solutions of different concentration.

Osmotic pressure The amount of external pressure applied to the more concentrated solution to halt the passage of solvent molecules across a semipermeable membrane.

Oxidation The loss of one or more electrons by an atom.

Oxidation number A number that indicates whether an atom is neutral, electron-rich, or electron-poor.

Oxidation–Reduction, or Redox, reaction A reaction in which electrons are transferred from one atom to another.

Oxidative deamination Conversion of an amino acid $-NH_2$ group to an α-keto group, with removal of NH_4^+.

Oxidative phosphorylation The synthesis of ATP from ADP using energy released in the electron-transport chain.

Oxidizing agent A reactant that causes an oxidation by taking electrons from or increasing the oxidation number of another reactant.

***p*-Block element** A main group element that results from the filling of p orbitals.

Partial pressure The pressure exerted by a gas in a mixture.

Parts per billion (ppb) Number of parts per one billion (10^9) parts.

Parts per million (ppm) Number of parts per one million (10^6) parts.

Passive transport Movement of a substance across a cell membrane without the use of energy, from a region of higher concentration to a region of lower concentration.

Pentose phosphate pathway The biochemical pathway that produces ribose (a pentose), NADPH, and other sugar phosphates from glucose; an alternative to glycolysis.

Peptide bond An amide bond that links two amino acids together.

Percent yield The percent of the theoretical yield actually obtained from a chemical reaction.

Period One of the 7 horizontal rows of elements in the periodic table.

Periodic table A table of the elements in order of increasing atomic number and grouped according to their chemical similarities.

pH A measure of the acid strength of a solution; the negative common logarithm of the H_3O^+ concentration.

Phenol A compound that has an —OH group bonded directly to an aromatic, benzene-like ring, Ar—OH.

Phenyl The C_6H_5— group.

Phosphate ester A compound formed by reaction of an alcohol with phosphoric acid; may be a monoester, $ROPO_3H_2$; a diester, $(RO)_2PO_3H$; or a triester, $(RO)_3PO$; also may be a di- or triphosphate.

Phospholipid A lipid that has an ester link between phosphoric acid and an alcohol (glycerol or sphingosine).

Phosphoryl group The $—PO_3^{2-}$ group in organic phosphates.

Phosphorylation Transfer of a phosphoryl group, $—PO_3^{2-}$, between organic molecules.

Physical change A change that does not affect the chemical makeup of a substance or object.

Physical quantity A physical property that can be measured.

Polar covalent bond A bond in which the electrons are attracted more strongly by one atom than by the other.

Polyatomic ion An ion that is composed of more than one atom.

Polymer A large molecule formed by the repetitive bonding together of many smaller molecules.

Polymorphism A variation in DNA sequence within a population.

Polysaccharide (complex carbohydrate) A carbohydrate that is a polymer of monosaccharides.

Polyunsaturated fatty acid A long-chain fatty acid that has two or more carbon–carbon double bonds.

Positron A "positive electron," which has the same mass as an electron but a positive charge.

Potential energy Energy that is stored because of position, composition, or shape.

Precipitate An insoluble solid that forms in solution during a chemical reaction.

Pressure The force per unit area pushing against a surface.

Primary carbon atom A carbon atom with one other carbon attached to it.

Primary protein structure The sequence in which amino acids are linked by peptide bonds in a protein.

Product A substance that is formed in a chemical reaction and is written on the right side of the reaction arrow in a chemical equation.

Property A characteristic useful for identifying a substance or object.

Protein A large biological molecule made of many amino acids linked together through amide (peptide) bonds.

Proton A positively charged subatomic particle.

Pure substance A substance that has uniform chemical composition throughout.

Quaternary ammonium ion A positive ion with four organic groups bonded to the nitrogen atom.

Quaternary ammonium salt An ionic compound composed of a quaternary ammonium ion and an anion.

Quaternary carbon atom A carbon atom with four other carbons attached to it.

Quaternary protein structure The way in which two or more protein chains aggregate to form large, ordered structures.

Radioactivity The spontaneous emission of radiation from a nucleus.

Radioisotope A radioactive isotope.

Radionuclide The nucleus of a radioactive isotope.

Reabsorption (kidney) Movement of solutes out of filtrate in a kidney tubule.

Reactant A substance that undergoes change in a chemical reaction and is written on the left side of the reaction arrow in a chemical equation.

Reaction mechanism A description of the individual steps by which old bonds are broken and new bonds are formed in a reaction.

Reaction rate A measure of how rapidly a reaction occurs.

Rearrangement reaction A general reaction type in which a molecule undergoes bond reorganization to yield an isomer.

Receptor A molecule or portion of a molecule with which a hormone, neurotransmitter, or other biochemically active molecule interacts to initiate a response in a target cell.

Recombinant DNA DNA that contains segments from two different species.

Reducing agent A reactant that causes a reduction by giving up electrons or increasing the oxidation number of another reactant.

Reducing sugar A carbohydrate that reacts in basic solution with a mild oxidizing agent.

Reduction The gain of one or more electrons by an atom.

Reductive deamination Conversion of an α-keto acid to an amino acid by reaction with NH_4^+.

Regular tetrahedron A geometric figure with four identical triangular faces.

Replication The process by which copies of DNA are made when a cell divides.

Residue (amino acid) An amino acid unit in a polypeptide.

Resonance The phenomenon where the true structure of a molecule is an average among two or more conventional structures.

Reversible reaction A reaction that can go in either the forward direction or the reverse direction, from products to reactants or reactants to products.

Ribonucleotide A nucleotide containing D-ribose.

Ribosomal RNA (rRNA) The RNA that is complexed with proteins in ribosomes.

Ribosome The structure in the cell where protein synthesis occurs; composed of protein and rRNA.

RNA (ribonucleic acids) The nucleic acids (messenger, transfer, and ribosomal) responsible for putting the genetic information to use in protein synthesis; polymers of ribonucleotides.

Rounding off A procedure used for deleting nonsignificant figures.

s-Block element A main group element that results from the filling of an s orbital.

Salt An ionic compound formed from reaction of an acid with a base.

Saponification The reaction of an ester with aqueous hydroxide ion to yield an alcohol and the metal salt of a carboxylic acid.

Saturated A molecule whose carbon atoms bond to the maximum number of hydrogen atoms.

Saturated fatty acid A long-chain carboxylic acid containing only carbon–carbon single bonds.

Saturated solution A solution that contains the maximum amount of dissolved solute at equilibrium.

Scientific Method Systematic process of observation, hypothesis, and experimentation to expand and refine a body of knowledge.

Scientific notation A number expressed as the product of a number between 1 and 10, times the number 10 raised to a power.

Second messenger Chemical messenger released inside a cell when a hydrophilic hormone or neurotransmitter interacts with a receptor on the cell surface.

Secondary carbon atom A carbon atom with two other carbons attached to it.

Secondary protein structure Regular and repeating structural patterns (for example, α-helix, β-sheet) created by hydrogen bonding between backbone atoms in neighboring segments of protein chains.

Secretion (kidney) Movement of solutes into filtrate in a kidney tubule.

SI units Units of measurement defined by the International System of Units.

Side chain (amino acid) The group bonded to the carbon next to the carboxyl group in an amino acid; different in different amino acids.

Significant figures The number of meaningful digits used to express a value.

Simple diffusion Passive transport by the random motion of diffusion through the cell membrane.

Simple protein A protein composed of only amino acid residues.

Single bond A covalent bond formed by sharing one electron pair.

Single nucleotide polymorphism Common single-base-pair variation in DNA.

Soap The mixture of salts of fatty acids formed on saponification of animal fat.

Solid A substance that has a definite shape and volume.

Solubility The maximum amount of a substance that will dissolve in a given amount of solvent at a specified temperature.

Solute A substance dissolved in a liquid.

Solution A homogeneous mixture that contains particles the size of a typical ion or small molecule.

Solvation The clustering of solvent molecules around a dissolved solute molecule or ion.

Solvent The liquid in which another substance is dissolved.

Specific gravity The density of a substance divided by the density of water at the same temperature.

Specific heat The amount of heat that will raise the temperature of 1 g of a substance by 1 °C.

Specificity (enzyme) The limitation of the activity of an enzyme to a specific

substrate, specific reaction, or specific type of reaction.

Spectator ion An ion that appears unchanged on both sides of a reaction arrow.

Sphingolipid A lipid derived from the amino alcohol sphingosine.

Spontaneous process A process or reaction that, once started, proceeds on its own without any external influence.

Standard molar volume The volume of one mole of a gas at standard temperature and pressure (22.4 L).

Standard temperature and pressure (STP) Standard conditions for a gas, defined as 0 °C (273 K) and 1 atm (760 mmHg) pressure.

State of matter The physical state of a substance as a solid, a liquid, or a gas.

Stereoisomers Isomers that have the same molecular and structural formulas, but different spatial arrangements of their atoms.

Steroid A lipid whose structure is based on the following tetracyclic (four-ring) carbon skeleton:

Straight-chain alkane An alkane that has all its carbons connected in a row.

Strong acid An acid that gives up H^+ easily and is essentially 100% dissociated in water.

Strong base A base that has a high affinity for H^+ and holds it tightly.

Strong electrolyte A substance that ionizes completely when dissolved in water.

Structural formula A molecular representation that shows the connections among atoms by using lines to represent covalent bonds.

Subatomic particles Three kinds of fundamental particles from which atoms are made: protons, neutrons, and electrons.

Substituent An atom or group of atoms attached to a parent compound.

Substitution reaction A general reaction type in which an atom or group of atoms in a molecule is replaced by another atom or group of atoms.

Substrate A reactant in an enzyme catalyzed reaction.

Sulfonation The substitution of a sulfonic acid group ($-SO_3H$) for a hydrogen on an aromatic ring.

Supersaturated solution A solution that contains more than the maximum amount of dissolved solute; a nonequilibrium situation.

Synapse The place where the tip of a neuron and its target cell lie adjacent to each other.

Telomeres The ends of chromosomes; in humans, contain long series of repeating groups of nucleotides.

Temperature The measure of how hot or cold an object is.

Tertiary carbon atom A carbon atom with three other carbons attached to it.

Tertiary protein structure The way in which an entire protein chain is coiled and folded into its specific three-dimensional shape.

Theoretical yield The amount of product formed assuming complete reaction of the limiting reagent.

Thiol A compound that contains an $-SH$ group, $R-SH$.

Titration A procedure for determining the total acid or base concentration of a solution.

Transamination The interchange of the amino group of an amino acid and the keto group of an α-keto acid.

Transcription The process by which the information in DNA is read and used to synthesize RNA.

Transfer RNA (tRNA) The RNA that transports amino acids into position for protein synthesis.

Transition metal element An element in one of the 10 smaller groups near the middle of the periodic table.

Translation The process by which RNA directs protein synthesis.

Transmutation The change of one element into another.

Triacylglycerol (triglyceride) A triester of glycerol with three fatty acids.

Triple bond A covalent bond formed by sharing three electron pairs.

Turnover number The maximum number of substrate molecules acted upon by one molecule of enzyme per unit time.

Unit A defined quantity used as a standard of measurement.

Unsaturated A molecule that contains a carbon–carbon multiple bond, to which more hydrogen atoms can be added.

Unsaturated fatty acid A long-chain carboxylic acid containing one or more carbon–carbon double bonds.

Urea cycle The cyclic biochemical pathway that produces urea for excretion.

Valence electron An electron in the outermost, or valence, shell of an atom.

Valence shell The outermost electron shell of an atom.

Valence-shell electron-pair repulsion (VSEPR) model A method for predicting molecular shape by noting how many electron charge clouds surround atoms and assuming that the clouds orient as far away from one another as possible.

Vapor The gas molecules in equilibrium with a liquid.

Vapor pressure The partial pressure of gas molecules in equilibrium with a liquid.

Vitamin An organic molecule, essential in trace amounts that must be obtained in the diet because it is not synthesized in the body.

Volume/volume percent concentration [(v/v)%] Concentration expressed as the number of milliliters of solute dissolved in 100 mL of solution.

Wax A mixture of esters of long-chain carboxylic acids with long-chain alcohols.

Weak acid An acid that gives up H^+ with difficulty and is less than 100% dissociated in water.

Weak base A base that has only a slight affinity for H^+ and holds it weakly.

Weak electrolyte A substance that is only partly ionized in water.

Weight A measure of the gravitational force that the earth or other large body exerts on an object.

Weight/volume percent concentration [(w/v)%] Concentration expressed as the number of grams of solute per 100 mL of solution.

Whole blood Blood plasma plus blood cells.

X rays Electromagnetic radiation with an energy somewhat less than that of γ rays.

Zwitterion A neutral dipolar ion that has one + charge and one − charge.

Zymogen A compound that becomes an active enzyme after undergoing a chemical change.

Study Guide and
Full Solutions Manual

Chapter 1 – Matter and Life

Chapter Outline

I. Matter and its properties (Sections 1.1–1.2).
  A. Matter is anything that is physically real (Section 1.1).
  B. Properties are the characteristics of matter.
    1. Physical properties are those properties that can be measured without altering the identity of a substance. Examples include mass, melting point, boiling point, and color.
    2. Chemical properties must be determined by changing the identity of the substance. Examples include rusting, combustion, and chemical reactivity.
    3. A physical change does not alter the identity of a substance.
    4. A chemical change is a process in which one or more substances undergoes a change in identity.
  C. States of matter (Section 1.2).
    1. The states of matter are solid, liquid, and gas.
      a. Solids have definite volume and definite shape.
      b. Liquids have definite volume and indefinite shape.
      c. Gases have indefinite volume and indefinite shape.
    2. Changes of state are melting, boiling, condensing, and freezing.
II. Classification of matter (Sections 1.3–1.6).
  A. Mixtures (Section 1.3).
    1. Mixtures vary in composition and properties.
    2. Mixtures can be separated by physical methods.
  B. Pure substances.
    1. Pure substances include chemical compounds and chemical elements.
    2. Pure substances don't vary in composition and properties.
    3. Chemical compounds can be broken down to elements by chemical change.
      a. A chemical reaction represents a chemical change between pure substances (Section 1.4).
      b. In a chemical reaction, the reactants are written on the left, the products are written on the right, and an arrow connects them (Section 1.5).
    4. Chemical elements can't be broken down.
  C. Elements (Sections 1.5–1.6).
    1. There are 117 elements; 90 of them occur naturally.
    2. Elements are represented by one- or two-letter symbols.
    3. The symbols for elements can be combined to produce chemical formulas.
    4. Elements are presented in a table—the periodic table.
    5. Elements can be classified as metals, nonmetals, or metalloids.
      a. Metals are solids that are lustrous, brittle, malleable, and good conductors of heat and electricity.
      b. Nonmetals may be solid, liquid, or gas and are poor conductors.
      c. Metalloids have characteristics intermediate between metals and nonmetals.

Taken from *Study Guide and Full Solutions Manual* for *Fundamentals of General, Organic, and Biological Chemistry,* Sixth Edition by Susan E. McMurry

Solutions to Chapter 1 Problems

1.1   All of the listed items are made of chemicals. (a) Apple juice, and (d) coffee beans consist of "natural" chemicals; (b) laundry bleach, and (c) glass consist of "synthetic" chemicals.

1.2   *Change in physical properties*:   (a) grinding a metal surface;   (d) a puddle evaporating
         Change in chemical properties: (b) fruit ripening;   (c) wood burning

1.3   At 10°C, acetic acid is a solid.

1.4   *Mixtures*: (a) concrete; (d) wood
         Pure substances: (b) helium; (c) a lead weight

1.5   *Physical changes*: (a) dissolving sugar in water; (c) frying an egg
         Chemical change: (b) production of carbon dioxide by heating limestone

1.6   The process is a chemical change.

1.7   (a) Na = sodium   (b) Ti = titanium   (c) Sr = strontium   (d) Y = yttrium
         (e) F = fluorine   (f) H = hydrogen

1.8   (a) U = uranium   (b) Ca = calcium   (c) Nd = neodymium   (d) K = potassium
         (e) W = tungsten   (f) Sn = tin

1.9   (a) Ammonia (NH_3) contains one nitrogen atom and three hydrogen atoms.
         (b) Sodium bicarbonate ($NaHCO_3$) contains one sodium atom, one hydrogen atom, one carbon atom, and three oxygen atoms.
         (c) Octane (C_8H_{18}) contains eight carbon atoms and eighteen hydrogen atoms.
         (d) Vitamin C ($C_6H_8O_6$) contains six carbon atoms, eight hydrogen atoms, and six oxygen atoms.

1.10

Element	Name	Number in Periodic Table	Metal or Nonmetal?
(a) Cr	chromium	24	metal
(b) K	potassium	19	metal
(c) S	sulfur	16	nonmetal
(d) Rn	radon	86	nonmetal

1.11

(a) B	boron	5
(b) Si	silicon	14
(c) Ge	germanium	32
(d) As	arsenic	33
(e) Sb	antimony	51
(f) Te	tellurium	52
(g) At	astatine	85

The metalloids occur at the boundary between metals and nonmetals.

Understanding Key Concepts

1.12   From top to bottom: helium (He), neon (Ne), argon (Ar), krypton (Kr), xenon (Xe), radon (Rn)

1.13   From top to bottom: copper (Cu), silver (Ag), gold (Au).

1.14   Green: boron (B) – metalloid
Blue: bromine (Br) – nonmetal
Red: vanadium (V) – metal

1.15   The element, americium (Am), is a metal.

Chemistry and the Properties of Matter

1.16   Chemistry is the study of matter—its nature, properties, and transformations.

1.17   Nylon is synthetic; rose fragrance and yeast are natural.

1.18   *Physical changes:* (a) boiling water; (c) dissolving sugar in water; (e) breaking of glass
Chemical changes: (b) decomposing water by passing a current through it; (d) exploding of potassium when placed in water

1.19   *Physical changes:* (a) steam condensing; (d) breaking of a dinner plate; (e) nickel sticking to a magnet
Chemical changes: (b) milk souring; (c) ignition of matches; (f) exploding of nitroglycerin

States and Classification of Matter

1.20   A *gas* is a substance that has no definite shape or volume.
A *liquid* has no definite shape but has a definite volume.
A *solid* has a definite volume and a definite shape.

1.21   Melting, boiling, condensation, and freezing are all changes of state. *Melting* occurs when a solid is heated and becomes a liquid. *Boiling* occurs when a liquid is heated and becomes a gas. *Condensation* occurs when a gas is cooled and becomes a liquid. *Freezing* occurs when a liquid is cooled and becomes a solid. All changes of state are physical changes.

1.22   Sulfur dioxide is a gas at 25°C.

1.23   Menthol is a solid at 25°C, a liquid at 60°C, and a gas at 260°C.

1.24   *Mixtures:* (a) pea soup; (b) seawater; (d) urine; (f) multivitamin tablet
Pure substances: (c) propane (C_3H_8); (e) lead

1.25   *Mixtures:* (a) blood; (c) dishwashing liquid; (d) toothpaste
Pure substances: (b) silicon; (e) gold; (f) NH_3
Silicon and gold are elements, and NH_3 is a compound.

1.26   *Element:*   (a) aluminum foil
        Compounds: (b) table salt; (c) water
        Mixtures: (d) air; (e) banana; (f) notebook paper

1.27   (a) gasoline — (i) mixture; (iii) liquid
        (b) iodine — (ii) solid; (v) chemical element
        (c) water — (iii) liquid; (vi) chemical compound
        (d) air — (i) mixture; (iv) gas
        (e) sodium bicarbonate — (ii) solid; (vi) chemical compound

1.28   *Reactant*   *Products*

        Hydrogen peroxide   ⟶   water   +   oxygen
        chemical compound   *chemical compound*   *element*

1.29   *Reactants*   *Products*

        Sodium   +   water   ⟶   hydrogen + sodium hydroxide
        element   *chemical compound*   *element*   *chemical compound*

Elements and Their Symbols

1.30   There are 117 elements presently known; 90 elements occur naturally.

1.31   Metallic elements are found on the left side of the periodic table.
        Nonmetallic elements are found on the right side of the periodic table.
        Metalloids are found in a zigzag band between the metallic elements and the nonmetallic elements.

1.32   *Metals* are elements that are solids at room temperature (except for Hg), are lustrous and malleable, and are good conductors of heat and electricity.

        Nonmetals are elements that are gases or brittle solids (except for Br) and are poor conductors.

        Metalloids are elements that have properties intermediate between those of metals and nonmetals.

1.33   Oxygen (O) is the most abundant element in both the earth's crust and in the human body.

1.34   (a) Gadolinium (Gd); (b) Germanium (Ge); (c) Technetium (Tc);   (d) Arsenic (As); (e) Cadmium (Cd)

1.35   (a) W; (b) Hg; (c) B; (d) Au; (e) Si; (f) Ar; (g) Ag; (h) Mg

1.36   (a) nitrogen; (b) potassium; (c) chlorine; (d) calcium; (e) phosphorus; (f) manganese

1.37   (a) tellurium (b) rhenium (c) beryllium (d) chromium (e) plutonium (f) manganese

1.38   The first letter of a chemical symbol is always capitalized; the second letter, if any, is never capitalized. Thus, Co stands for cobalt, and CO stands for carbon monoxide, a compound composed of carbon (C) and oxygen (O).

1.39   S is the first letter of the name of the element sulfur. The N in Na, the symbol for sodium, is the first letter of its Latin name *natrium*.

1.40   (a) The symbol for bromine is Br (the second letter in a symbol is never capitalized).
(b) The symbol for manganese is Mn (Mg is the symbol for magnesium).
(c) The symbol for carbon is C (Ca is the symbol for calcium).
(d) The symbol for potassium is K; the first letter of a symbol is always capitalized.

1.41   (a) Carbon dioxide has the formula CO_2 (the number 2 is a subscript).
(b) The O in carbon dioxide must be capitalized to show that it is composed of carbon and oxygen.
(c) Table salt is composed of sodium (Na) and chlorine (Cl).

1.42   (a) "Fool's gold" is a compound with the formula FeS_2; the symbol for iron is Fe.
(b) The formula for "laughing gas" is N_2O; the symbol for nitrogen is N.

1.43   (a) Soldering compound is a mixture containing tin (Sn) and lead (Pb).
(b) White gold is a mixture containing gold (Au) and nickel (Ni).

1.44   (a) $MgSO_4$: magnesium, sulfur, oxygen
(b) $FeBr_2$: iron, bromine
(c) CoP: cobalt, phosphorus
(d) AsH_3: arsenic, hydrogen
(e) $CaCr_2O_7$: calcium, chromium, oxygen

1.45   (a) C_3H_8 (b) H_2SO_4 (c) $C_9H_8O_4$ (d) C_3H_8O
   3 carbons   2 hydrogens   9 carbons   3 carbons
   8 hydrogens   1 sulfur   8 hydrogens   8 hydrogens
                       4 oxygens   4 oxygens   1 oxygen

1.46   Carbon, hydrogen, nitrogen, and oxygen are present in glycine. The formula $C_2H_5NO_2$ represents 10 atoms.

1.47   The formula of benzyl salicylate ($C_{14}H_{12}O_3$) represents 29 atoms, 14 of which are carbon.

1.48   Ibuprofen: $C_{13}H_{18}O_2$

1.49   Penicillin V: $C_{16}H_{18}N_2O_5S$

1.50   (a) Osmium (Os) is a metal.
(b) Xenon (Xe) is a nonmetal.

1.51   (a) Tantalum (Ta) is a metal.
(b) Germanium (Ge) is a metalloid.

Applications

1.52 ASA contains nine carbons, eight hydrogens, and four oxygens, totaling 21 atoms. It is a solid at room temperature.

1.53 Only soluble forms of mercury are toxic. Hg_2Cl_2 passes through the body before it can be chemically converted to a soluble form, but elemental mercury vapor remains in the lungs long enough to be converted to a soluble compound.

General Questions and Problems

1.54 (a) A *physical change* is a change in the property of a substance that doesn't alter its chemical makeup. A *chemical change* alters a substance's chemical makeup.
(b) *Melting point* is the temperature at which a change of state from solid to liquid occurs. *Boiling point* is the temperature at which a change of state from liquid to gas occurs.
(c) An *element* is a pure substance that can't be broken down chemically into simpler substances. A *compound* is a pure substance that has a definite composition and that can be broken down chemically to yield elements. A *mixture* can vary in both composition and properties, and its components can be separated by physical methods.
(d) A *chemical symbol* is composed of one or two letters and represents an element. A *chemical formula* is a grouping of chemical symbols that gives the number of atoms for each element in a chemical compound.
(e) A *reactant* is a substance that undergoes change in a chemical reaction.
A *product* is a substance formed as a result of a chemical reaction.
(f) A *metal* is a lustrous malleable element that is a good conductor of heat and electricity; a *nonmetal* is an element that is a poor conductor.

1.55 (a) True. (b) False. Melting is a physical change. (c) False. The correct formula is PbO.
(d) False. The resulting product is a mixture, not a compound. (e) True.

1.56 Chemical compounds: (a) H_2O_2; (c) CO; (e) $NaHCO_3$
Elements: (b) Al; (d) N_2

1.57 The white solid is a chemical compound, and the brown gas and molten metal are elements.

1.58 The liquid is a mixture.

1.59 Remove the iron filings with a magnet. Add water to the remaining mixture, and filter out the sand. Evaporate the water to recover the salt.

1.60 (a) Fe; (b) Cu; (c) Co; (d) Mo; (e) Cr; (f) F; (g) S

1.61 (no answer)

1.62 If the undiscovered elements follow the pattern of the periodic table, element 115 would be placed below bismuth and would be a metal. Element 117 would be placed below astatine and might be either a metal or a metalloid. Element 119 would be placed below francium and would be a metal.

1.63 If element 119 (see previous problem) is placed below francium, then the element placed below uranium would be element 124.

Self-Test for Chapter 1

Multiple Choice

1. Which of the following is a chemical property?
   (a) melting point (b) reaction with acid (c) hardness (d) transparency

2. The change of state that occurs when a gas is cooled to a liquid is called:
   (a) boiling (b) melting (c) evaporation (d) condensation

3. Which of the following is not an element?
   (a) Fluorine (b) Freon (c) Neon (d) Radon

4. The chemical formula for fructose is $C_6H_{12}O_6$. How many different elements does fructose contain?
   (a) 24 (b) 18 (c) 6 (d) 3

5. How many atoms does the formula for fructose represent?
   (a) 24 (b) 18 (c) 6 (d) 3

6. A solution of fructose in water is a:
   (a) mixture (b) pure substance (c) chemical compound (d) element

7. Which of the following is not a characteristic of a metal?
   (a) electrical conductivity (b) malleability (c) brittleness (d) luster

8. All of the following have uniform composition except: (a) element (b) solution (c) pure substance (d) chemical compound

Sentence Completion

1. Sulfur is a _____element.

2. Color is a _____ property.

3. _____ is the symbol for the element bismuth.

4. When a substance _____, it changes from gas to liquid.

5. Matter is anything that has _____ and _____.

6. A _____ has definite volume but indefinite shape.

7. A _____ _____ doesn't vary in its properties or composition.

8. Symbols of elements are combined to produce _____ _____.

9. A _____ substance can be beaten or rolled into different shapes.

10. ____, ____, ____, and ____ are four elements present in all living organisms.

True or False

1. Cobalt is an element essential for human life.

2. Rust formation is a chemical change.

3. A chemical compound is a pure substance.

4. The components of a solution are separable by chemical methods.

5. The formula C_2H_4O represents three atoms.

6. A metalloid has properties intermediate between metals and nonmetals.

7. The chemical symbol for silver is Si.

8. In the chemical reaction carbon + oxygen —> carbon dioxide, the reactants are elements.

9. Methyl bromide, a compound formerly used for fumigation, has a melting point of –93.7 °C and a boiling point of 3.6 °C and is a liquid at room temperature.

10. Nonmetals may be solids, liquids, or gases.

Chapter 2 Measurements in Chemistry

Chapter Outline

I. Measurements (Sections 2.1–2.3).
   A. Physical quantities (Section 2.1).
      1. All physical quantities consist of a number plus a unit.
         a. SI units, the standard units for scientists, are the kilogram, the meter, and the kelvin.
         b. Metric units are the gram, the meter, the liter, and the degree Celsius.
         c. Other units, such as those for speed and concentration, can be derived from SI and metric units.
      2. Prefixes are used with units to indicate multiples of 10.
   B. Measuring mass (Section 2.2).
      1. Mass is the amount of matter in a substance.
      2. Mass differs from weight (a measure of the gravitational pull exerted on an object).
      3. The SI unit of mass is the kilogram, but in chemistry the gram and milligram are more often used.
   C. Measuring length (Section 2.3).
      The meter is the standard unit for length.
   D. Measuring volume.
      1. Volume is the amount of space that a substance occupies.
      2. Units for volume are the liter (L) and the cubic meter (m^3)—the SI unit.
II. Numbers in measurement (Sections 2.4–2.6).
   A. Significant figures (Section 2.4).
      1. All measurements have a degree of uncertainty.
      2. For any measurement, the number of digits known with certainty, plus one digit considered uncertain, is known as the number of significant figures.
      3. Rules for significant figures:
         a. Zeroes in the middle of a number are always significant.
         b. Zeroes at the beginning of a number are never significant.
         c. Zeroes at the end of a number but after a decimal point are significant.
         d. Zeroes at the end of a number but before an implied decimal point may or may not be significant.
      4. Some numbers are exact and have an unlimited number of significant figures.
   B. Scientific notation (Section 2.5).
      1. In scientific notation, a number is written as the product of a number between 1 and 10 times 10 raised to a power.
         a. For numbers greater than 10, the power of 10 is positive.
         b. For numbers less than 1, the power of 10 is negative.
      2. Scientific notation is helpful in indicating the number of significant figures in a number.
   C. Rounding off numbers (Section 2.6).
      1. Numbers must be rounded off if they contain more digits than are significant.
      2. Rounding in calculations.
         a. In multiplication or division, the result can't have more significant figures than any of the original numbers.
         b. In addition or subtraction, the result can't have more digits to the right of the decimal point than any of the original numbers.

3. Rules of rounding:
    a. If the digit to be removed is 4 or less, drop it and remove all following digits.
    b. If the digit to be removed is 5 or greater, add 1 to the digit to the left of the digit you drop.

III. Calculations (Sections 2.7–2.8).
   A. Converting a quantity from one unit to another (Section 2.7).
      1. In the *factor-label* method:
         (quantity in old units) x (conversion factor) = (quantity in new units).
         a. The conversion factor is a fraction that converts one unit to another.
         b. All conversion factors are equal to 1.
      2. In the factor-label method, units are treated as numbers.
      3. In the factor-label method, all unwanted units cancel.
   B. Problem solving (Section 2.8).
      1. Identify the information known.
      2. Identify the information needed in the answer.
      3. Use conversion factors to convert the given information to the answer.
      4. Make a "ballpark" estimate of the answer and compare it to the calculated answer.

IV. Heat (Sections 2.9–2.10).
   A. Measuring temperature (Section 2.9).
      1. Units of temperature are the degree Fahrenheit, the degree Celsius, and the kelvin.
      2. Temperature in °C = Temperature in K – 273.15°.
      3. $°F = \left(\dfrac{9\,°F}{5\,°C} \times °C\right) + 32\,°F.$
      4. $°C = \dfrac{5\,°C}{9\,°F} \times (°F - 32\,°F).$
   B. Energy and heat (Section 2.10).
      1. All chemical reactions are accompanied by a change in energy.
         a. Potential energy is stored energy.
         b. Kinetic energy is the energy of motion.
      2. Heat is the energy transferred from a hotter object to a cooler object when the two are in contact.
      3. Units of energy are the joule (SI) and the calorie.
      4. $\text{Specific heat} = \dfrac{\text{calories}}{\text{grams} \times °C}.$

V. Density and specific gravity (Sections 2.11–2.12).
   A. Density (Section 2.11).
      1. Density = mass (g) / volume (mL or cm^3).
      2. Density is temperature dependent.
   B. Specific gravity (Section 2.12).
      1. $\text{Specific gravity} = \dfrac{\text{density of substance (g/mL)}}{\text{density of water (1 g/mL)}}.$
      2. Specific gravity has no units.

Solutions to Chapter 2 Problems

2.1   (a) dL = deciliter   (b) mg = milligram   (c) ns = nanosecond
          (d) km = kilometer   (e) μg = microgram

2.2   (a) liter = L   (b) kilogram = kg   (c) nanometer = nm
          (d) megameter = Mm

2.3   (a) 1 nm = 0.000 000 001 m   (b) 1 dg = 0.1 g   (c) 1 km = 1000 m
          (d) 1 μs = 0.000 001 s   (e) 1 ng = 0.000 000 001 g

2.4

Number	Significant Figures	Reason
(a) 3.45 m	3	
(b) 0.1400 kg	4	Rule 3
(c) 10.003 L	5	Rule 1
(d) 35 cents	Exact	

2.5   32.3 °C. The answer has three significant figures.

2.6   In scientific notation, a number is written as the product of a number between 1 and 10 times 10 raised to a power. In (a), 58 g = 5.8 x 10^1 g.

Value	Scientific Notation
(a) 0.058 g	5.8 x 10^{-2} g
(b) 46,792 m	4.6792 x 10^4 m
(c) 0.006 072 cm	6.072 x 10^{-3} cm
(d) 345.3 kg	3.453 x 10^2 kg

2.7

Value in Scientific Notation	Value in Standard Notation
(a) 4.885 x 10^4 mg	48,850 mg
(b) 8.3 x 10^{-6} m	0.000 0083 m
(c) 4.00 x 10^{-2} m	0.0400 m

2.8   (a) 6.3000 x 10^5 (b) 1.30 x 10^3 (c) 7.942 x 10^{11}

2.9   0.000 000 000 278 m = 2.78 x 10^{-10} m. (The decimal point must be moved 10 places to the right.)

$$2.78 \times 10^{-10} \text{ m} \times \frac{1 \text{ pm}}{10^{-12} \text{ m}} = 2.78 \times 10^2 \text{ pm}$$

2.10   (a) 2.30 g   (b) 188.38 mL   (c) 0.009 L   (d) 1.000 kg

2.11 Remember:
(1) The sum or difference of two numbers can't have more digits to the right of the decimal point than either of the two numbers.
(2) The product or quotient of two numbers can't have more significant figures than either of the two numbers.

Calculation	*Rounded to:*
(a) 4.87 mL + 46.0 mL = 50.87 mL	50.9 mL
(b) 3.4 x 0.023 g = 0.0782 g	0.078 g
(c) 19.333 m − 7.4 m = 11.933 m	11.9 m
(d) 55 mg − 4.671 mg + 0.894 mg = 51.223 mg	51 mg
(e) 62,911 ÷ 611 = 102.96399	103

2.12

(a) $\dfrac{1 \text{ L}}{1000 \text{ mL}}$, $\dfrac{1000 \text{ mL}}{1 \text{ L}}$; $\dfrac{1 \text{ mL}}{0.001 \text{ L}}$, $\dfrac{0.001 \text{ L}}{1 \text{ mL}}$

(b) $\dfrac{1 \text{ g}}{0.03527 \text{ oz}}$, $\dfrac{0.03527 \text{ oz}}{1 \text{ g}}$; $\dfrac{1 \text{ oz}}{28.35 \text{ g}}$, $\dfrac{28.35 \text{ g}}{1 \text{ oz}}$

(c) $\dfrac{1 \text{ L}}{1.057 \text{ qt}}$, $\dfrac{1.057 \text{ qt}}{1 \text{ L}}$; $\dfrac{1 \text{ qt}}{0.9464 \text{ L}}$, $\dfrac{0.9464 \text{ L}}{1 \text{ qt}}$

2.13

(a) $16.0 \text{ oz} \times \dfrac{28.35 \text{ g}}{1 \text{ oz}} = 454 \text{ g}$ (b) $2500 \text{ mL} \times \dfrac{1 \text{ L}}{1000 \text{ mL}} = 2.5 \text{ L}$

(c) $99.0 \text{ L} \times \dfrac{1 \text{ qt}}{0.9464 \text{ L}} = 105 \text{ qt}$

2.14

$0.840 \text{ quart} \times \dfrac{1 \text{ L}}{1.057 \text{ quart}} \times \dfrac{1000 \text{ mL}}{1 \text{ L}} = 795 \text{ mL}$

2.15 This is a *long* unit conversion! Remember that all units must cancel at the end, except for the units needed in the final answer (meters and seconds). Nautical miles must be converted to meters, and hours must be converted to seconds. Also remember the definition of a knot—1 nautical mile per hour.

$\dfrac{14.3 \text{ naut. mi}}{1 \text{ hr}} \times \dfrac{6076.1155 \text{ ft}}{1 \text{ naut. mi}} \times \dfrac{0.3048 \text{ m}}{1 \text{ ft}} \times \dfrac{1 \text{ hr}}{60 \text{ min}} \times \dfrac{1 \text{ min}}{60 \text{ s}} = 7.36 \text{ m/s}$

2.16

(a) $7.5 \text{ lb} \times \dfrac{1 \text{ kg}}{2.205 \text{ lb}} = 3.4 \text{ kg}$

Ballpark check: Since a kilogram is approximately 2 pounds, the infant is expected to weigh about 3.5 lb. The ballpark check is close to the exact solution.

(b) $4.0 \text{ oz} \times \dfrac{29.57 \text{ mL}}{1 \text{ oz}} = 120 \text{ mL}$

Ballpark check: There are approximately 30 mL in an ounce, and the ballpark check thus gives an answer of 120 mL, which agrees with the exact solution.
Remember that the answers must have the correct number of significant figures.

2.17

$$2 \times 0.324 \text{ g} \times \dfrac{1000 \text{ mg}}{1 \text{ g}} \times \dfrac{1}{135 \text{ lb}} \times \dfrac{2.205 \text{ lb}}{1 \text{ kg}} = 10.6 \dfrac{\text{mg}}{\text{kg}}$$

$$2 \times 0.324 \text{ g} \times \dfrac{1000 \text{ mg}}{1 \text{ g}} \times \dfrac{1}{40 \text{ lb}} \times \dfrac{2.205 \text{ lb}}{1 \text{ kg}} = 36 \dfrac{\text{mg}}{\text{kg}}$$

2.18   From Section 2.9, we find the formula:

$$(°F - 32 \, °F) \times \dfrac{5 \, °C}{9 \, °F} = °C$$

Substituting 136°F into the preceding formula:

$$(136 \, °F - 32 \, °F) \times \dfrac{5 \, °C}{9 \, °F} = 57.8 \, °C$$

Ballpark check: The numerator in the preceding expression is approximately 500 °C. Dividing by 9°F gives the answer 55.5 °C, which approximates the exact solution.

2.19

$$°F = \left(\dfrac{9 \, °F}{5 \, °C} \times °C\right) + 32 \, °F; \text{ in this problem, } °C = -38.9 \, °$$

$$= (1.8 \, °F \times -38.9 \, °) + 32 \, °F = -38.0 \, °F$$

$$= (273.15 - 38.9) \text{K} = 234.3 \text{ K}$$

2.20

$$\text{Heat (cal)} = \text{mass (g)} \times \text{temperature change (°C)} \times \text{specific heat} \left(\dfrac{\text{cal}}{\text{g} \cdot °C}\right)$$

$$= 350 \text{ g} \times (25 \, °C - 3 \, °C) \times \dfrac{1.0 \text{ cal}}{\text{g} \cdot °C}$$

$$= 7700 \text{ cal} = 7.7 \times 10^3 \text{ cal}$$

Ballpark check: The temperature change is approximately 20 °C. The mass of Coca-Cola times the temperature change equals 7000, a number close to the exact solution.

2.21

$$\text{Specific heat} = \dfrac{\text{calories}}{\text{grams} \times °C}$$

$$\text{Specific heat} = \dfrac{161 \text{ cal}}{75 \text{ g} \times 10 \, °C} = 0.21 \dfrac{\text{cal}}{\text{g} \cdot °C}$$

2.22 Solids with densities greater than water will sink; solids with densities less than water will float.
Solids that float: ice, human fat, cork, balsa wood
Solids that sink: gold, table sugar, earth

2.23

$$12.37 \text{ g } \times \frac{1 \text{ mL}}{1.474 \text{ g}} = 8.392 \text{ mL}$$

Ballpark check: Since the density of chloroform is approximately 1.5, the volume needed is about two-thirds of the mass needed.

2.24

$$\text{Density} = \frac{\text{Mass}}{\text{Volume}} = \frac{16.8 \text{ g}}{7.60 \text{ cm}^3} = 2.21 \frac{\text{g}}{\text{cm}^3}$$

2.25 Battery acid is more dense than water.

Understanding Key Concepts

2.26 The graduated cylinder contains 34 mL; the paper clip is 2.7 cm long. Both answers have two significant figures.

2.27 (no answer)

2.28 The specific gravity is found by reading the liquid level on the scale of the hydrometer.
(a) The specific gravity of this solution is 0.978.
(b) The answer has three significant figures.
(c) The solution is less dense than water.

2.29

The smaller graduated cylinder is more precise for two reasons. (1) The distance between two gradations represents a smaller volume, making it easier to measure volumes more accurately. (2) The percent error is greater when a small volume is measured in a large graduated cylinder.

2.30 The length of the pencil is either 8.0 cm or 3 1/8 in.

2.31   The liquid level is 0.11 mL before dispensing the sample and 0.25 mL after dispensing, indicating a sample size of 0.14 mL.

2.32   (a) They are equally precise.
(b) The volume is approximately 360 mL; the exact value is 355 mL.

2.33   If two identical hydrometers are placed in ethanol and in chloroform, the hydrometer in chloroform will float higher. Since a hydrometer bulb sinks until it displaces a volume of liquid equal to its mass, it displaces a smaller volume of chloroform, the denser liquid, and the bulb floats higher.

Definitions and Units

2.34   A *physical quantity* is a physical property that can be measured; it consists of a number plus a unit.

2.35   *Mass* is the measure of the amount of matter in an object. *Weight* is the measure of the gravitational force exerted on an object by the Earth, moon, or other large body.

2.36–2.37

Quantity	SI Unit	Metric Unit
Mass	kilogram (kg)	gram (g)
Volume	cubic meter (m^3)	liter (L)
Length	meter (m)	meter (m)
Temperature	kelvin (K)	degree Celsius (°C)

2.38   A cubic decimeter and a liter represent the same volume expressed in two different systems of units.

2.39   A kelvin is the same size as a Celsius degree. The lowest temperature in the SI system, 0 K, is the coldest temperature possible. In the Celsius system, 0°C is the temperature at which water freezes and is equivalent to 273.15 K.

2.40   (a) centiliter   (b) decimeter   (c) millimeter   (d) nanoliter
(e) milligram   (f) cubic meter   (g) cubic centimeter

2.41   (a) ng   (b) cm   (c) μL   (d) μm   (e) mg

2.42

$$1 \text{ mg} \times \frac{10^{-3} \text{ g}}{1 \text{ mg}} \times \frac{10^{12} \text{ pg}}{1 \text{ g}} = 10^9 \text{ pg}$$

$$35 \text{ ng} \times \frac{10^{-9} \text{ g}}{1 \text{ ng}} \times \frac{10^{12} \text{ pg}}{1 \text{ g}} = 3.5 \times 10^4 \text{ pg}$$

2.43

$$1 \text{ L} \times \frac{10^6 \ \mu\text{L}}{1 \text{ L}} = 10^6 \ \mu\text{L} \ ; \quad 20 \text{ mL} \times \frac{10^3 \ \mu\text{L}}{1 \text{ mL}} = 2 \times 10^4 \ \mu\text{L}$$

Scientific Notation and Significant Figures

2.44 (a) 9.457×10^3 (b) 7×10^{-5} (c) 2.000×10^{10}
       (d) 1.2345×10^{-2} (e) 6.5238×10^2

2.45 (a) 5280   (b) 0.082 05
       (c) 0.000 018 4   (d) 63,700

2.46 (a) six   (b) three   (c) three   (d) four
       (e) 1–5   (f) 2–3

2.47 (a) five   (b) three   (c) four   (d) one   (e) three

2.48 (a) 7926 mi; 7900 mi; 7926.38 mi (b) $7.926\,381 \times 10^3$ mi

2.49 (a) 2.4×10^5 (b) 3.0×10^{-1} (c) 3.0
       (d) 2.4×10^2 (e) 5.0×10^4 (f) 6.6×10^2

2.50 (a) 12.1 g   (b) 96.19 cm   (c) 263 mL   (d) 20.9 mg

2.51 (a) 3.3×10^4 ft   (b) 15 m^2 (c) 0.30 cm^3 (d) 81 cm^3

Unit Conversions and Problem Solving

2.52 (a) 0.3614 cg   (b) 0.0120 ML   (c) 0.0144 mm   (d) 60.3 ng   (e) 1.745 dL
       (f) 1.5×10^5 cm

2.53

(a) $56.4 \text{ mi} \times \dfrac{1.609 \text{ km}}{1 \text{ mi}} = 90.7 \text{ km}$

$56.4 \text{ mi} \times \dfrac{1.609 \text{ km}}{1 \text{ mi}} \times \dfrac{1 \text{ Mm}}{10^3 \text{ km}} = 9.07 \times 10^{-2} \text{ Mm}$

(b) $2.0 \text{ L} \times \dfrac{1.057 \text{ qt}}{1 \text{ L}} = 2.1 \text{ qt}$

$2.0 \text{ L} \times \dfrac{10^3 \text{ mL}}{1 \text{ L}} \times \dfrac{1 \text{ fl oz}}{29.57 \text{ mL}} = 68 \text{ fl oz}$

(c) $7.0 \text{ ft} \times \dfrac{12 \text{ in.}}{1 \text{ ft}} = 84.0 \text{ in.};\ \ 84.0 \text{ in.} + 2.0 \text{ in} = 86.0 \text{ in.}$

$86.0 \text{ in.} \times \dfrac{1 \text{ cm}}{0.3937 \text{ in.}} = 218 \text{ cm};\ \ 218 \text{ cm} \times \dfrac{1 \text{ m}}{100 \text{ cm}} = 2.18 \text{ m}$

(d) $1.35 \text{ lb} \times \dfrac{1 \text{ kg}}{2.205 \text{ lb}} = 0.612 \text{ kg};\ \ 0.612 \text{ kg} \times \dfrac{10^4 \text{ dg}}{1 \text{ kg}} = 6.12 \times 10^3 \text{ dg}$

2.54 (a) 97.8 kg (b) 0.133 mL (c) 0.46 ng (d) 2.99 Mm

2.55 (a) kilo (k) (b) milli (m) (c) mega (M) (d) micro (μ)

2.56

$$\frac{100 \text{ km}}{1 \text{ hr}} \text{ x } \frac{0.6214 \text{ mi}}{1 \text{ km}} = 62.1 \frac{\text{mi}}{\text{hr}}$$

$$\frac{62.1 \text{ mi}}{1 \text{ hr}} \text{ x } \frac{5280 \text{ ft}}{1 \text{ mi}} \text{ x } \frac{1 \text{ hr}}{60 \text{ min}} \text{ x } \frac{1 \text{ min}}{60 \text{ s}} = 91.1 \frac{\text{ft}}{\text{s}}$$

2.57

$$\frac{1200 \text{ ft}}{1 \text{ s}} \text{ x } \frac{1 \text{ mi}}{5280 \text{ ft}} \text{ x } \frac{60 \text{ s}}{1 \text{ min}} \text{ x } \frac{60 \text{ min}}{1 \text{ hr}} = 820 \frac{\text{mi}}{\text{hr}}$$

$$\frac{1200 \text{ ft}}{1 \text{ s}} \text{ x } \frac{0.3048 \text{ m}}{1 \text{ ft}} = 370 \frac{\text{m}}{\text{s}}$$

2.58

$$\frac{1 \text{ cell}}{6 \text{ x } 10^{-6} \text{ m}} \text{ x } \frac{1 \text{ m}}{39.37 \text{ in}} = 4 \text{ x } 10^3 \frac{\text{cells}}{\text{in}}$$

2.59 $1 \text{ ft}^2 = (0.3048 \text{ m})^2 = 0.09290 \text{ m}^2$

$$418,000 \text{ m}^2 \text{ x } \frac{1 \text{ ft}^2}{0.0929 \text{ m}^2} = 4.50 \text{ x } 10^6 \text{ ft}^2$$

2.60

$$\frac{200 \text{ mg}}{1 \text{ dL}} \text{ x } \frac{10 \text{ dL}}{1 \text{ L}} \text{ x } 5 \text{ L} = 10^4 \text{ mg}; \quad 10^4 \text{ mg x } \frac{1 \text{ g}}{10^3 \text{ mg}} = 10 \text{ g cholesterol}$$

2.61

$$\frac{50 \text{ tab}}{1 \text{ bottle}} \text{ x } \frac{250 \text{ mg}}{1 \text{ tab}} \text{ x } \frac{1 \text{ bottle}}{\$1.95} = \frac{6.41 \text{ x } 10^3 \text{ mg}}{\$1}$$

$$\frac{100 \text{ tab}}{1 \text{ bottle}} \text{ x } \frac{200 \text{ mg}}{1 \text{ tab}} \text{ x } \frac{1 \text{ bottle}}{\$3.75} = \frac{5.33 \text{ x } 10^3 \text{ mg}}{\$1}$$

The bottle selling for \$1.95 is the better bargain.

2.62

$$\frac{1.2 \text{ x } 10^4 \text{ cells}}{1 \text{ mm}^3} \text{ x } \frac{10^6 \text{ mm}^3}{1 \text{ L}} \text{ x } 5 \text{ L} = 6 \text{ x } 10^{10} \text{ cells}$$

2.63

$$1200 \text{ mg x } \frac{1.0 \text{ cup}}{290 \text{ mg}} = 4.1 \text{ cups}$$

Energy, Heat, and Temperature

2.64

$$°C = \frac{5\,°C}{9\,°F} \times (°F - 32\,°F) = \frac{5\,°C}{9\,°F} \times (98.6\,°F - 32\,°F) = \frac{66.6\,°C}{1.8} = 37.0\,°C, \text{ or } 310.2\,K$$

2.65 $273.15\,K - 195.8 = 77.4\,K$

$$°F = \left(\frac{9°F}{5°C} \times °C\right) + 32°F = \left(\frac{9°F}{5°C} \times (-195.8°C)\right) + 32°F = -352.4°F + 32°F = -320.4\,°F$$

2.66

$$\text{Heat (cal)} = \text{mass (g)} \times \text{temperature change (°C)} \times \text{specific heat}\left(\frac{cal}{g \cdot °C}\right)$$

$$= 30.0\,g \times (30.0\,°C - 10.0\,°C) \times \frac{0.895\,cal}{g \cdot °C} = 537\,cal$$

$$= 0.537\,kcal$$

2.67

$$\text{Mass (g)} = \frac{\text{heat (cal)}}{\text{temperature change(°C)} \times \text{specific heat}\left(\frac{cal}{g \cdot °C}\right)}$$

$$\text{Mass (g)} = \frac{52.7\,cal}{16.2\,°C \times 0.092\left(\frac{cal}{g \cdot °C}\right)} = 35\,g$$

2.68

$$\text{Specific heat} = \frac{cal}{g \cdot °C} = \frac{23\,cal}{5.0\,g \times 50\,°C} = 0.092\,\frac{cal}{g \cdot °C}$$

2.69

$$\text{Heat (cal)} = \text{mass (g)} \times \text{temperature change (°C)} \times \text{specific heat}\left(\frac{cal}{g \cdot °C}\right)$$

$$\text{Mass of fat} = \frac{0.94\,g}{1\,cm^3} \times 10\,cm^3 = 9.4\,g$$

$$\text{Heat (cal)} = 9.4\,g \times 10\,°C \times 0.45\left(\frac{cal}{g \cdot °C}\right) = 42\,cal$$

2.70

$$\text{For mercury: Temperature change (°C)} = \frac{250\,cal}{150\,g \times 0.033\,\frac{cal}{g \cdot °C}} = 51\,°C$$

$$\text{Final temp} = 25\,°C + 51\,°C = 76\,°C$$

For iron: Temperature change (°C) = $\dfrac{250 \text{ cal}}{150 \text{ g} \times 0.106 \dfrac{\text{cal}}{\text{g} \cdot °C}}$ = 15.7 °C

· Final temp = 25.0 °C + 15.7 °C = 40.7 °C

2.71

Specific heat = $\dfrac{\text{cal}}{\text{g} \cdot °C}$ = $\dfrac{100 \text{ cal}}{125 \text{ g} \times 28 °C}$ = 0.029 $\dfrac{\text{cal}}{\text{g} \cdot °C}$

The calculated value for specific heat, 0.029 cal/g ·°C, is closest in value to the specific heat of gold, 0.031 cal/g ·°C.

Density and Specific Gravity

2.72

250 mg $\times$ $\dfrac{1 \text{ g}}{10^3 \text{ mg}}$ $\times$ $\dfrac{1 \text{ cm}^3}{1.40 \text{ g}}$ = 0.179 cm³

2.73 From the expression for density, we know that 1 L of hydrogen has a mass of 0.0899 g. We need to find the number of liters that have a mass of 1.0078 g.

1.0078 g $\times$ $\dfrac{1 \text{ L}}{0.0899 \text{ g}}$ = 11.2 L

2.74 To find the density of lead, divide the mass of lead by the volume of the bar in cm³. 0.500 cm $\times$ 1.55 cm $\times$ 25.00 cm = 19.38 cm³.

$\dfrac{220.9 \text{ g}}{19.38 \text{ cm}^3}$ = 11.4 $\dfrac{\text{g}}{\text{cm}^3}$

2.75 The volume of lithium is 0.82 cm $\times$ 1.45 cm $\times$ 1.25 cm = 1.5 cm³.

$\dfrac{0.794 \text{ g}}{1.5 \text{ cm}^3}$ = 0.53 $\dfrac{\text{g}}{\text{cm}^3}$

2.76

$\dfrac{3.928 \text{ g}}{5.000 \text{ mL}}$ = 0.7856 $\dfrac{\text{g}}{\text{mL}}$; specific gravity = 0.7856

2.77 Specific gravity = 1.1088; density = 1.1088 g/mL

1.00 kg $\times$ $\dfrac{1000 \text{ g}}{1 \text{ kg}}$ $\times$ $\dfrac{1 \text{ mL}}{1.1088 \text{ g}}$ = 902 mL; 2.00 lb $\times$ $\dfrac{454 \text{ g}}{1 \text{ lb}}$ $\times$ $\dfrac{1 \text{ mL}}{1.1088 \text{ g}}$ = 819 mL

Applications

2.78

(a) $2.0 \times 10^{-8} \text{m} \times \dfrac{1 \text{ cm}}{0.01 \text{ m}} = 2.0 \times 10^{-6} \text{ cm}$

(b) $\dfrac{1 \text{ cell.}}{2.0 \times 10^{-6} \text{cm}} \times \dfrac{1 \text{ cm}}{0.3937 \text{ in}} = 1.3 \times 10^{6} \dfrac{\text{cells}}{\text{in}}$

2.79 Recall from Section 2.3 that $1 \text{ cc} = 1 \text{ mL} = 1 \times 10^{-3} \text{ L}$.

(a) $9.0 \times 10^{-14} \text{ L} \times \dfrac{1 \text{ cc}}{1 \times 10^{-3} \text{ L}} = 9.0 \times 10^{-11} \text{ cc}$

(b) $V = 4/3 \pi r^3$; $r^3 = \dfrac{3}{4\pi} V = \dfrac{3}{4\pi} 90 \times 10^{-12} \text{cm}^3 = 21.5 \times 10^{-12} \text{cm}^3$

$r = 3 \times 10^{-4} \text{ cm}$; $d = 6 \times 10^{-4} \text{ cm}$

2.80

$(28 \, ^\circ\text{F} - 32 \, ^\circ\text{F}) \times \dfrac{5 \, ^\circ\text{C}}{9 \, ^\circ\text{F}} = -2.2 \, ^\circ\text{C} = 271 \text{ K}$

2.81

$^\circ\text{F} = \left(\dfrac{9 ^\circ\text{F}}{5 ^\circ\text{C}} \times \, ^\circ\text{C} \right) + 32 ^\circ\text{F}$

For $^\circ\text{C} = 37 \, ^\circ\text{C}$, $^\circ\text{F} = 99 \, ^\circ\text{F}$.   For $^\circ\text{C} = 47 \, ^\circ\text{C}$, $^\circ\text{F} = 117 \, ^\circ\text{F}$

2.82 (a) BMI = 29   (b) BMI = 23.7   (c) BMI = 24.4
Individual (a), with a body mass index that borders on obese, is most likely to have increased health risks.

2.83

$5.0 \text{ lb} \times \dfrac{454 \text{ g}}{1 \text{ lb}} \times \dfrac{1 \text{ mL}}{0.94 \text{ g}} \times \dfrac{1 \text{ L}}{10^3 \text{ mL}} = 2.4 \text{ L}$

General Questions and Problems

2.84

$3.125 \text{ in.} \times \dfrac{2.54 \text{ cm}}{1 \text{ in.}} = 7.95 \text{ cm}$

The difference in the calculated length (7.95 cm) and the measured length (8.0 cm) is due to the lack of precision of the ruler and to rounding.

2.85 One carat $= 200 \text{ mg} = 0.200 \text{ g}$

$\dfrac{0.200 \text{ g}}{1 \text{ carat}} \times 44.4 \text{ carat} = 8.88 \text{ g}$

2.86

$$°C = \frac{5\,°C}{9\,°F}\,(°F - 32\,°F) = \frac{5\,°C}{9\,°F}\,(350\,°F - 32\,°F) = \frac{5\,°C}{9\,°F}\,(318\,°F) = 177\,°C$$

2.87

$$2 \times 250\text{ mg} \times \frac{1\text{ g}}{1000\text{ mg}} \times \frac{1}{130\text{ lb}} \times \frac{2.21\text{lb}}{1\text{ kg}} = 8.5 \times 10^{-3}\,\frac{g}{kg}\text{ for the woman}$$

$$\frac{8.5 \times 10^{-3}\text{g}}{1\text{kg}} \times 40\text{ lb} \times \frac{0.454\text{ kg}}{1\text{ lb}} = 0.15\text{ g}$$

A 40-lb child would need 0.15 g, or 150 mg, of penicillin to receive the same dose as a 130-lb woman. The child would thus need about 1.2 of the 125 mg penicillin tablets.

2.88 3.9×10^{-2} g/dL iron, 8.3×10^{-3} g/dL calcium, 2.24×10^{-1} g/dL cholesterol

2.89

$$1.3\,\frac{g}{L} \times 4.0\text{ m} \times 3.0\text{ m} \times 2.5\text{ m} \times 1000\,\frac{L}{m^3} = 3.9 \times 10^4\text{ g}$$

$$3.9 \times 10^4\text{ g} \times \frac{1\text{ lb}}{454\text{ g}} = 86\text{ lb}$$

2.90

$$75\,\frac{mL}{beat} \times 72\,\frac{beats}{min} \times 60\,\frac{min}{hr} \times 24\,\frac{hr}{day} = 7.8 \times 10^6\,\frac{mL}{day}$$

2.91

$$15\text{ g} \times \frac{1000.0\text{ mL}}{50.00\text{ g}} = 300\text{ mL}$$

2.92

$$0.14\text{ mL} \times \frac{0.963\text{ g}}{1\text{ mL}} = 0.13\text{ g}$$

2.93 (a) The effective range of an alcohol thermometer in °C is 115 °C + 78.5 °C = 193.5 °C. Since a Fahrenheit degree is 9/5 of a Celsius degree, the range in °F is 9/5 x 193.5 = 348°F

(b) The thermometer can contain either 0.79 g alcohol or 13.6 g mercury.

2.94

$$\frac{85\text{ mg}}{100\text{ mL}} \times \frac{1\text{ g}}{10^3\text{mg}} \times \frac{10^3\text{ mL}}{1\text{ L}} \times \frac{0.9464\text{ L}}{1\text{ qt}} \times \frac{1\text{ qt}}{2\text{ pt}} \times 11\text{ pt} = 4.4\text{ g}$$

$$4.4\text{ g} \times \frac{1\text{ lb}}{454\text{ g}} = 0.0097\text{ lb}$$

2.95

$$\frac{3000\text{ mL}}{1\text{ day}} \times \frac{5\text{ g}}{100\text{ mL}} \times \frac{4\text{ kcal}}{1\text{ g}} = 600\text{ kcal/day}$$

2.96

$$\left(\frac{100 \text{ mL}}{1 \text{ kg}} \times 10 \text{ kg}\right) + \left(\frac{50 \text{ mL}}{1 \text{ kg}} \times 10 \text{ kg}\right) + \left(\frac{20 \text{ mL}}{1 \text{ kg}} \times 35 \text{ kg}\right) = 2200 \text{ mL}$$

2.97

$$7.5 \text{ grains} \times \frac{1 \text{ fluidram}}{10 \text{ grains}} \times \frac{3.72 \text{ mL}}{1 \text{ fluidram}} = 2.8 \text{ mL}$$

2.98

Heat (cal) = mass (g) x temperature change (°C) x specific heat $\left(\dfrac{\text{cal}}{\text{g} \cdot \text{°C}}\right)$

For water: specific heat = 1.00 cal /(g·°C);

$$\text{mass} = 3.00 \text{ L} \times \frac{10^3 \text{ mL}}{1 \text{ L}} \times \frac{1.00 \text{ g}}{1 \text{ mL}} = 3.00 \times 10^3 \text{ g};$$
$$\text{temperature change} = 90.0 \text{ °C} - 18.0 \text{ °C} = 72.0 \text{ °C}$$

Calories needed = $3.00 \times 10^3 \text{ g} \times 72.0\text{°C} \times \dfrac{1.00 \text{ cal}}{\text{g} \cdot \text{°C}} = 2.16 \times 10^5 \text{ cal} = 216 \text{ kcal}$

$$216 \text{ kcal} \times \frac{1.0 \text{ tbsp}}{100 \text{ kcal}} = 2.2 \text{ tbsp butter}$$

2.99

$$\text{Specific heat} = \frac{\text{cal}}{\text{g} \cdot \text{°C}} = \frac{1350 \text{ cal}}{1620 \text{ g} \times 7.8 \text{ °C}} = 0.107 \frac{\text{cal}}{\text{g} \cdot \text{°C}}$$

The calculated specific heat, 0.107 cal/g · °C, is closer to the value for iron than for gold.

2.100

$$\frac{1620 \text{ g}}{205 \text{ mL}} = 7.90 \frac{\text{g}}{\text{mL}}$$

The value calculated for density very nearly agrees with the density of iron (7.86 g/mL).

2.101

$$98.0 \text{ g} \times \frac{1 \text{ mL}}{1.83 \text{ g}} = 53.6 \text{ mL H}_2\text{SO}_4$$

2.102

$$2.01 \times 10^{11} \text{ lb} \times \frac{454 \text{ g}}{1 \text{ lb}} \times \frac{1 \text{ mL}}{1.83 \text{ g}} \times \frac{1 \text{ L}}{1000 \text{ mL}} = 4.99 \times 10^{10} \text{ L}$$

2.103

$$0.22 \text{ in.} \times \frac{25.4 \text{ mm}}{1 \text{ in.}} = 5.6 \text{ mm}$$

2.104 (a)

$$\frac{200 \text{ mg}}{100 \text{ mL}} \times \frac{1000 \text{ mL}}{1 \text{ L}} = 2 \times 10^3 \frac{\text{mg}}{\text{L}}$$

(b)

$$\frac{200 \text{ mg}}{100 \text{ mL}} \times \frac{10^3 \text{ μg}}{1 \text{ mg}} \times \frac{1000 \text{ mL}}{1 \text{ L}} = 2 \times 10^6 \frac{\text{μg}}{\text{L}}$$

(c)

$$\frac{200 \text{ mg}}{100 \text{ mL}} \times \frac{1 \text{ g}}{1000 \text{ mg}} \times \frac{1000 \text{ mL}}{1 \text{ L}} = 2 \frac{\text{g}}{\text{L}}$$

(d)

$$\frac{200 \text{ mg}}{100 \text{ mL}} \times \frac{10^6 \text{ ng}}{1 \text{ mg}} \times \frac{1 \text{ mL}}{10^3 \mu\text{L}} = 2 \times 10^3 \frac{\text{ng}}{\mu\text{L}}$$

2.105 (a) Gallium is a metal.
(b) To find the density of gallium in g/cm^3, divide the mass in grams by the volume in cm^3.

Mass of Ga: 0.2133 lb x (454 g/ lb) = 96.84 g
Volume of Ga: (1.00 in. x 2.54 cm/in.)^3 = 16.39 cm^3

$$\frac{96.84 \text{ g}}{16.39 \text{ cm}^3} = 5.91 \frac{\text{g}}{\text{cm}^3}$$

2.106 The initial temperature: 293.2 K – 273.2 K = 20.0 K = 20.0 °C
The temperature change: 3.0°F/min x 8.42 min = 25.3°F = 14.1 °C (since a Celsius degree is 1.8 times larger than a Fahrenheit degree)
The final temperature: 20.0 °C + 14.1 °C = 34.1 °C

2.107 At the crossover point, °F = °C.

$$°F = \left(\frac{9 \, °F}{5 \, °C} \times °C\right) + 32 \, °F \quad \text{If } °C = °F, °F = \frac{9}{5} °F + 32°; 5 \, °F = 9 \, °F + 160°$$

The crossover temperature is °F = °C = –40°.

2.108 Use the dimensions of the cork and of the lead to find their respective volumes. Multiply the volume of each substance by its density to arrive at the mass of each.
Volume of cork: 1.30 cm x 5.50 cm x 3.00 cm = 21.5 cm^3
Volume of lead: (1.15 cm)^3 = 1.52 cm^3

Mass of cork: Mass of lead:

$$21.5 \text{ cm}^3 \times \frac{0.235 \text{ g}}{1 \text{ cm}^3} = 5.05 \text{ g cork} \quad 1.52 \text{ cm}^3 \times \frac{11.35 \text{ g}}{1 \text{ cm}^3} = 17.3 \text{ g lead}$$

Add the two masses, and divide by the sum of the two volumes to find the density of the combination.

$$\text{Density} = \frac{5.05 \text{ g} + 17.3 \text{ g}}{21.5 \text{ cm}^3 + 1.52 \text{ cm}^3} = \frac{22.40 \text{ g}}{23.0 \text{ cm}^3} = 0.974 \text{ g/cm}^3$$

The combination will float because its density is less than the density of water.

Self-Test for Chapter 2

1. Write the full name of these units:
    (a) μm   (b) dL   (c) Mg   (d) L   (e) ng

2. Write the abbreviation for each of the following units:
    (a) kiloliter   (b) picogram   (c) centimeter   (d) hectoliter

3.   *Quantity*   *Significant Figures?*

    (a) 1.0037 g
    (b) 0.0080 L
    (c) 0.008 L
    (d) 2 aspirin
    (e) 273,000 mi

4. Express the following in scientific notation:
    (a) 0.000 070 3 g   (b) 137,100 m   (c) 0.011 L   (d) 18,371,008 mm
    How many significant figures do each of these quantities have?

5. Round the following to three significant figures:
    (a) 807.3 L   (b) 4,773,112 people   (c) 0.00127 g   (d) 10370 μm
    Express each of these quantities in scientific notation.

6. Convert the following quantities:
    (a) 256 g = _____ lb   (b) 417 mm = _____ m
    (c) 2.0 gallons = _____ L   (d) 2.17 m = _____ inches
    (e) 35°C = _____ °F   (f) 298 K = _____ °C
    (g) 175 mL = _____ fl oz   (h) 175 mg = _____ oz

7. If the specific heat of gold is 0.031 cal/g °C, how many calories does it take to heat 10 g of gold from 0 °C to 100 °C?

8. If the density of ethanol is 0.7893 g/mL, how many grams does 275 mL of ethanol weigh?

Multiple Choice

1. Which of the following is not an SI unit?
    (a) kg   (b) L   (c) m   (d) K

2. How many significant figures does the number 4500 have?
    (a) 2   (b) 3   (c) 4   (d) any of the above

3. Which of the following quantities is larger than a gram?
    (a) 1 nanogram   (b) 1 dekagram   (c) 1 centigram   (d) 1 microgram

4. Which of the following conversion factors do you need for converting 3.2 lb/qt to kg/L?
    (a) $\dfrac{1 \text{ kg}}{2.2 \text{ lb}}$ x $\dfrac{1 \text{ qt}}{0.95 \text{ L}}$ (b) $\dfrac{2.2 \text{ lb}}{1 \text{ kg}}$ x $\dfrac{1 \text{ qt}}{0.95 \text{ L}}$ (c) $\dfrac{2.2 \text{ lb}}{1 \text{ kg}}$ x $\dfrac{0.95 \text{ L}}{1 \text{ qt}}$ (d) $\dfrac{1 \text{ kg}}{2.2 \text{ lb}}$ x $\dfrac{0.95 \text{ L}}{1 \text{ qt}}$

5. When written in scientific notation, the exponent in the number 0.000 007 316 is:
    (a) 10^{-6} (b) 6   (c) -6 (d) 10^{6}

6. Which of the following is more dense than water?
    (a) ice   (b) human fat   (c) ethyl alcohol   (d) urine

7. How many zeros are significant in the number 0.007 006?
    (a) 1   (b) 2   (c) 3   (d) 4

8. Which of the following temperatures doesn't equal the other two?
    (a) 100 °F   (b) 37.8 °C   (c) 297.8 K

9. To measure the amount of heat needed to raise the temperature of a given substance, you need to know all of the following except:
    (a) the mass of the substance   (b) the specific heat of the substance   (c) the density of the substance   (d) the initial and final temperature

10. For which of the following is specific gravity a useful measure?
    (a) to describe the amount of solids in urine   (b) to indicate the amount of heat necessary to raise the temperature of one gram of a substance by 1°C   (c) to determine if an object will float on water

Sentence Completion

1. The fundamental SI units are _____, _____, _____, and _____.

2. Physical quantities are described by a _____ and a _____.

3. The amount of heat necessary to raise the temperature of one gram of a substance by one degree is the substance's _____ _____.

4. The prefix _____ indicates 10^{-9}.

5. The number 0.003 06 has _____ significant figures.

6. To convert from grams to pounds, use the conversion factor _____.

7. Two units for measuring energy are _____ and _____.

8. The method used for converting units is called the _____ _____ method.

9. _____ _____ is the density of a substance divided by the density of water at the same temperature.

10. The size of a degree is the same in both _____ and _____ units.

True or False

1.   The units of specific gravity are g/mL.

2.   The number 0.07350 has four significant figures.

3.   The sum of 57.35 and 1.3 has four significant figures.

4.   The conversion factor 1.057 quarts/liter is used to convert quarts into liters.

5.   Some SI units are the same as metric units.

6.   The temperature in °C is always a larger number than the temperature in K.

7.   Raising the temperature of 10 g of water by 10 °C takes less heat than raising the temperature of 10 g of gold by 10 °C.

8.   Mass measures the amount of matter in an object.

9.   Ice is more dense than water.

10.   A nanogram is larger than a picogram.

Match each entry on the left with its partner on the right.

1.	50037	(a) Converts pounds to kilograms
2.	1 centimeter	(b) 0.1 grams
3.	$\dfrac{2.205 \text{ lb}}{1 \text{ kg}}$	(c) Larger than one inch
4.	263 K	(d) −17.8 °C
5.	1 dekagram	(e) Five significant figures
6.	0.048	(f) SI unit of volume measure
7.	1 m^3	(g) Converts kilograms to pounds
8.	1 liter	(h) 10 grams
9.	1 decimeter	(i) −10 °C
10.	$\dfrac{1 \text{ kg}}{2.205 \text{ lb}}$	(j) Smaller than one inch
11.	0°F	(k) Metric unit of volume measure
12.	1 decigram	(l) Two significant figures

Chapter 3   Atoms and the Periodic Table

Chapter Outline

I.   Atomic Theory (Sections 3.1–3.3).
   A. Fundamental assumptions about atoms (Section 3.1).
      1. All matter is composed of atoms.
      2. The atoms of each element are different from the atoms of all other elements.
      3. Chemical compounds consist of elements combined in definite proportions.
      4. Chemical reactions only change the way that atoms are combined in compounds; the atoms themselves are unchanged.
   B. Nature of the atom (Sections 3.1).
      1. Atoms are very small ($\sim 10^{-11}$ m in diameter).
      2. Atoms consist of subatomic particles.
         a. A proton is positively charged and has a mass of 1.6726×10^{-24} g.
         b. A neutron has no charge and has a mass of 1.6749×10^{-24} g.
         c. An electron is negatively charged and has a mass of 9.1093×10^{-28} g.
      3. The masses of atoms are expressed in relative terms.
         a. Under this system, a carbon atom with six protons and six neutrons is given a mass of exactly 12 atomic mass units (amu).
         b. Consequently, a proton and a neutron each have a mass of approximately 1 amu.
      4. Atoms are held together by the interplay of attractive and repulsive forces of positively charged protons and negatively charged electrons.
      5. Protons and neutrons are located in the nucleus of an atom, and electrons move about the nucleus.
      6. The size of the nucleus is small compared to the size of the atom.
   C. Composition of atoms (Section 3.2).
      1. Atoms of different elements differ from each other according to how many protons they contain.
      2. Z stands for the number of protons an atom has and is known as the atomic number.
      3. The number of electrons in an atom is the same as the number of protons.
      4. The mass number A stands for the number of protons plus the number of neutrons.
   D. Isotopes and atomic weight (Section 3.3).
      1. Isotopes are atoms of the same element that differ only in the number of neutrons.
      2. Isotopes are represented by showing the mass number as a superscript on the left side of the symbol for the chemical element; the atomic number is shown as a subscript on the left side.
      3. Most elements occur in nature as a mixture of isotopes.
      4. The atomic weight of an element can be calculated if the percent of contributing isotopes is known.
II. The Periodic Table (Sections 3.4–3.5).
   A. The periodic table is a classification of elements according to their properties (Section 3.4).
      1. Elements are arranged by increasing atomic number in seven rows called periods.
      2. Elements are also arranged in 18 vertical columns called groups.
         a. Main group elements occur on the left and right of the periodic table.
         b. Transition metal groups occur in the middle of the periodic table.
         c. Inner transition metal groups are shown separately at the bottom.
      3. The elements in each group have similar chemical properties.

B. Chemical characteristics of groups of elements (Section 3.5).
   1. Group 1A—Alkali metals (Li, Na, K, Rb, Cs, Fr).
      a. Shiny, soft, low-melting.
      b. React violently with water.
   2. Group 2A—Alkaline earth metals (Be, Mg, Ca, Sr, Ba, Ra).
      a. Lustrous, shiny metals.
      b. Less reactive than metals in group 1A.
   3. Group 7A—Halogens (F, Cl, Br, I, At).
      a. Corrosive, nonmetals (except At).
      b. Found in nature only in combination with other elements.
   4. Group 8A—Noble gases (He, Ne, Ar, Kr, Xe, Rn). Extremely unreactive.
C. Neighboring groups have similar behaviors.
   1. Metals.
      a. Found on the left side of the periodic table.
      b. Silvery, ductile, good conductors.
   2. Nonmetals.
      a. Found on the right side of the periodic table.
      b. Eleven of the 17 nonmetals are gases.
      c. Solid nonmetals are brittle and are poor conductors of electricity.
   3. Metalloids.
      a. Occur on the boundary between metals and nonmetals.
      b. Have intermediate chemical behavior.
III. Electrons (Sections 3.6–3.9).
  A. The properties of the elements are due to the distribution of electrons in their atoms (Section 3.6).
  B. Location of electrons.
   1. Electrons are located in specific regions about the nucleus.
   2. The energies of electrons are quantized.
   3. The locations of electrons are described by shells, subshells and orbitals.
      a. Shells.
         i. Shells describe the energy level of an electron.
         ii. Shells are related to an electron's distance from the nucleus.
      b. Subshells.
         i. Subshells describe the energy levels of electrons within each shell.
         ii. The four types of subshell are *s, p, d,* and *f.*
      c. Orbitals.
         i. Orbitals are the regions of subshells in which electrons of a specific energy can be found.
         ii. An *s* subshell contains one orbital, a *p* subshell contains three orbitals, a *d* subshell contains five orbitals, and an *f* subshell contains seven orbitals.
         iii. Each orbital can hold two electrons, and they must be of opposite spin.
         iv. An *s* orbital is spherical, and a *p* orbital is dumbbell-shaped.
   4. Since the exact position of electrons can't be specified, orbitals are often referred to as electron clouds.
  C. Electron configurations (Section 3.7).
   1. The specific arrangement of electrons in an atom's shells and subshells is known as its electron configuration.
   2. This arrangement can be predicted by using three rules.
      a. Electrons occupy the lowest orbitals available within each subshell.
         Within each shell, the subshell energy levels increase in the order *s, p, d, f.*
      b. If two or more orbitals have the same energy, each orbital is half filled before any orbital is completely filled.
      c. Each orbital can hold only two electrons, and they must be of opposite spin.
   3. The number of electrons in each subshell is given by a superscript.

D. Electron configuration and the periodic table (Sections 3.8–3.9).
 1. Properties of elements are determined by their location in the periodic table.
 2. The periodic table is divided into four regions.
     a. Elements in groups 1A and 2A are *s*-block elements because they result from filling *s* orbitals.
     b. Groups 3A–8A are *p*-block elements.
     c. Transition metals are *d*-block elements.
     d. Inner transition metals are *f*-block elements.
 3. The periodic table can be used as a reminder of the order of orbital filling.
 4. Elements within a group of the periodic table have similar electronic configurations of their valence electronic shells and thus similar chemical behavior.
 5. The valence electrons in a compound can be represented by electron dots (Section 3.9).

Solutions to Chapter 3 Problems

3.1   Use the conversion factor that relates mass and amu.

$$2.33 \times 10^{-23} \text{ g} \times \frac{1 \text{ amu}}{1.660\ 539 \times 10^{-24} \text{ g}} = 14.0 \text{ amu}$$

3.2

$$150 \times 10^{12} \text{ atoms} \times \frac{56 \text{ amu}}{1 \text{ atom}} \times \frac{1.660\ 539 \times 10^{-24} \text{ g}}{1 \text{ amu}} = 1.39 \times 10^{-8} \text{ g}$$

3.3

(a) $1.0 \text{ g} \times \dfrac{1 \text{ amu}}{1.660\ 539 \times 10^{-24} \text{ g}} \times \dfrac{1 \text{ atom}}{1.0 \text{ amu}} = 6.0 \times 10^{23} \text{ atoms}$

(b) $12.0 \text{ g} \times \dfrac{1 \text{ amu}}{1.660\ 539 \times 10^{-24} \text{ g}} \times \dfrac{1 \text{ atom}}{12.0 \text{ amu}} = 6.02 \times 10^{23} \text{ atoms}$

(c) $23.0 \text{ g} \times \dfrac{1 \text{ amu}}{1.660\ 539 \times 10^{-24} \text{ g}} \times \dfrac{1 \text{ atom}}{23.0 \text{ amu}} = 6.02 \times 10^{23} \text{ atoms}$

3.4   In each of the preceding examples, the mass in grams equals the mass in amu, and the number of atoms in all three samples is identical.

3.5   (a) Re   (b) Ca   (c) Te

3.6   Recall that the *atomic number* (Z) shows how many protons an atom contains. Cobalt, with an atomic number of 27, thus contains 27 protons.
Cobalt also contains 27 electrons, since the number of protons equals the number of electrons.
The *mass number* (A) shows the number of protons plus the number of neutrons. To find the number of neutrons in an atom, subtract the atomic number from the mass number.
For cobalt: Mass number – atomic number = 60 – 27 = 33.
The cobalt atom has 33 neutrons.

3.7   From Problem 3.6, we know that $A - Z$ = number of neutrons.
In this problem, $A = 98$, and the number of neutrons = 55. Thus $Z = 43$. The table of elements in the front of the book shows that technetium is the element with $Z = 43$.

3.8   Contribution from ^{39}K: 93.12% of 38.96 amu = 36.27 amu
Contribution from ^{41}K: 6.88% of 40.96 amu =   2.82 amu
— —
Atomic weight = 39.10 amu

The calculated value agrees exactly with the reported value.

3.9   Both bromine isotopes have 35 protons. The isotope with mass number 79 has 44 neutrons, and the isotope with mass number 81 has 46 neutrons.
The atomic number is written at the lower left of the element symbol, and the mass number is written at the upper left.

$$^{79}_{35}\text{Br} \quad \text{and} \quad ^{81}_{35}\text{Br}$$

3.10

(a) $^{11}_{5}\text{B}$ (b) $^{56}_{26}\text{Fe}$ (c) $^{37}_{17}\text{Cl}$

3.11   Aluminum is in group 3A (or 13) and period 3.

3.12   The group 1B element in period 5 is silver (Ag).
The group 2A element in period 4 is calcium (Ca).

3.13   *Group 5A Element   Period*
— — — — — — — — — — — — — —
Nitrogen (N)   2
Phosphorus (P)   3
Arsenic (As)   4
Antimony (Sb)   5
Bismuth (Bi)   6

3.14   Metals: titanium (Ti), scandium (Sc)
Nonmetals: selenium (Se), argon (Ar)
Metalloids: tellurium (Te), astatine (At)

3.15   (a) Krypton: (ii) nonmetal; (iv) main group element; (v) noble gas
(b) Strontium: (i) metal; (iv) main group element
(c) Nitrogen: (ii) nonmetal; (iv) main group element
(d) Cobalt: (i) metal; (iii) transition element

3.16   The red element, zinc (Zn), is a metal found in period 4, group 2B (or 12).
The blue element, oxygen, is a nonmetal found in period 2, group 6A (or 16).

3.17   (a) A maximum of six electrons can occupy a $3p$ subshell.
(b) A maximum of two electrons can occupy a $2s$ subshell.
(c) A maximum of six electrons can occupy a $2p$ subshell.

3.18   Ten electrons are present in this atom, which is neon.

3.19   Twelve electrons are present in this atom, which is magnesium.

3.20 To find the electron configuration of an atom, first find its atomic number. For C (carbon), the atomic number is 6; thus, carbon has 6 protons and 6 electrons. Then assign electrons to the proper orbitals. For carbon, the electron configuration is $1s^2\,2s^2\,2p^2$.

Element	Atomic Number	Electron Configuration
(a) C (carbon)	6	$1s^2\,2s^2\,2p^2$
(b) P (phosphorus)	15	$1s^2\,2s^2\,2p^6\,3s^2\,3p^3$
(c) Cl (chlorine)	17	$1s^2\,2s^2\,2p^6\,3s^2\,3p^5$
(d) K (potassium)	19	$1s^2\,2s^2\,2p^6\,3s^2\,3p^6\,4s^1$

3.21 Element 14 (Si): $1s^2\,2s^2\,2p^6\,3s^2\,3p^2$
Element 36 (Kr): $1s^2\,2s^2\,2p^6\,3s^2\,3p^6\,4s^2\,3d^{10}\,4p^6$

3.22 Element 33 (As): $1s^2\,2s^2\,2p^6\,3s^2\,3p^6\,4s^2\,3d^{10}\,4p^3$. The $4p$ subshell is incompletely filled. Notice that only one electron occupies each orbital of the $4p$ subshell.
$\uparrow\ \uparrow\ \uparrow$ $4p^3$

3.23 The atom has 31 electrons (and 31 protons) and can be identified as gallium.

3.24 (a) F: $1s^2\,2s^2\,2p^5$; [He] $\mathbf{2s^2\,2p^5}$ (b) Al: $1s^2\,2s^2\,2p^6\,3s^2\,3p^1$; [Ne] $\mathbf{3s^2\,3p^1}$

(c) As: $1s^2\,2s^2\,2p^6\,3s^2\,3p^6\,4s^2\,3d^{10}\,4p^3$; [Ar] $\mathbf{4s^2\,3d^{10}\,4p^3}$
(Valence electrons are bold.)

3.25 In group 2A, all elements have the outer-shell configuration ns^2.

3.26 Chlorine, in group 7A (17), has seventeen electrons. Its electron configuration is $1s^2\,2s^2\,2p^6\,3s^2\,3p^5$. Two electrons are in shell 1, eight electrons are in shell 2, and seven electrons are in shell 3. The outer shell configuration is $3s^2\,3p^5$.

3.27 The elements form group 6A (16) and have the general valence-shell configuration ns^2np^4.

3.28

$\cdot\overset{\displaystyle\cdot}{\underset{}{X}}\cdot$

3.29

$:\overset{\displaystyle\cdot\cdot}{\underset{\displaystyle\cdot\cdot}{Rn}}:$ $\cdot\overset{\displaystyle\cdot}{Pb}\cdot$ $:\overset{\displaystyle\cdot\cdot}{\underset{\displaystyle\cdot\cdot}{Xe}}:$ $\cdot Ra\cdot$

Understanding Key Concepts

3.30 Drawing (a) represents a p orbital (dumbbell-shaped), and drawing (b) represents an s orbital (spherical).

3.31

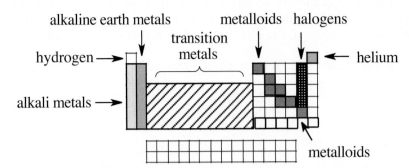

3.32   The element marked in red is a gas (fluorine—group 7A).
The element marked in blue has atomic number 79 (gold).
All elements in group 2A have chemical behavior similar to the element marked in green (calcium). These include beryllium, magnesium, strontium, barium, and radium.

3.33

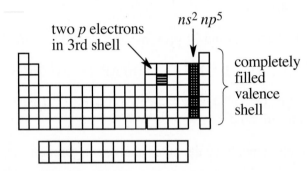

3.34   Selenium (Z = 34) is the element whose orbital-filling diagram is shown. Notice that it is possible to identify the element by counting its electrons, which equal the number of protons and give the value of Z.

3.35   As: $1s^2\, 2s^2\, 2p^6\, 3s^2\, 3p^6$ ↑↓   ↑↓ ↑↓ ↑↓ ↑↓ ↑↓   ↑ ↑ ↑
                                          4s   3d   4p

Atomic Theory and the Composition of Atoms

3.36   (1) All matter is composed of atoms.
(2) The atoms of a given element differ from the atoms of all other elements.
(3) Chemical compounds consist of atoms combined in specific proportions.
(4) Chemical reactions change only the way that atoms are combined in compounds; the atoms themselves are unchanged.

3.37   Atoms of different elements differ in the number of protons and electrons they have.

3.38

(a) Bi: 208.9804 amu x $\dfrac{1.660\,539 \times 10^{-24}\ \text{g}}{1\ \text{amu}}$ = 3.470201 x 10^{-22} g

(b) Xe: 131.29 amu x $\dfrac{1.660\,539 \times 10^{-24}\ \text{g}}{1\ \text{amu}}$ = 2.1801 x 10^{-22} g

(c) He: 4.0026 amu x $\dfrac{1.660\,539 \times 10^{-24}\ \text{g}}{1\ \text{amu}}$ = 6.6465 x 10^{-24} g

3.39

(a) $\dfrac{2.66 \times 10^{-23}\ g}{1\ \text{atom O}} \times \dfrac{1\ \text{amu}}{1.660\ 539 \times 10^{-24}\ g} = 16.0\ \text{amu}$

(b) $\dfrac{1.31 \times 10^{-22}\ g}{1\ \text{atom Br}} \times \dfrac{1\ \text{amu}}{1.660\ 539 \times 10^{-24}\ g} = 78.9\ \text{amu}$

3.40

$6.022 \times 10^{23}\ \text{atoms} \times \dfrac{1.660\ 539 \times 10^{-24}\ g}{1\ \text{amu}} \times \dfrac{14.01\ \text{amu}}{1\ \text{atom}} = 14.01\ g$

3.41

$6.022 \times 10^{23}\ \text{atoms} \times \dfrac{1.660\ 539 \times 10^{-24}\ g}{1\ \text{amu}} \times \dfrac{16.00\ \text{amu}}{1\ \text{atom}} = 16.00\ g$

3.42

$15.99\ g \times \dfrac{1\ \text{amu}}{1.660\ 539 \times 10^{-24}\ g} \times \dfrac{1\ \text{atom}}{15.99\ \text{amu}} = 6.022 \times 10^{23}\ \text{atoms}$

3.43

$12.00\ g \times \dfrac{1\ \text{amu}}{1.660\ 539 \times 10^{-24}\ g} \times \dfrac{1\ \text{atom}}{12.00\ \text{amu}} = 6.022 \times 10^{23}\ \text{atoms}$

3.44

Particle	Mass in amu	Charge
Proton	1.007 276	+1
Neutron	1.008 665	0
Electron	$5.485\ 799 \times 10^{-4}$	−1

3.45 Protons and neutrons are found in a dense central region called the nucleus. Electrons move about the nucleus in large, specifically defined regions called orbitals.

3.46 (a) Potassium (K) (b) Tin (Sn) (c) Zinc (Zn)

3.47 (a) Phosphorus (P) (b) Niobium (Nb) (c) Cobalt (Co)

3.48

Isotope	Argon-36	Argon-38	Argon-40
Number of neutrons	18	20	22

3.49

Isotope	(a) $^{27}_{13}\text{Al}$	(b) $^{28}_{14}\text{Si}$	(c) $^{11}_{5}\text{B}$	(d) $^{115}_{47}\text{Ag}$
Number of protons	13	14	5	47
Number of neutrons	14	14	6	68
Number of electrons	13	14	5	47

3.50 Symbols (a) and (c) represent isotopes because they have the same atomic number but different mass numbers.

3.51

(a) $^{206}_{84}$Po   (b) $^{224}_{88}$Ra   (c) $^{197}_{79}$Au   (d) $^{84}_{36}$Kr

3.52 (a) fluorine-19   (b) neon-19   (c) fluorine-21   (d) magnesium-21

3.53 (a) 122   (b) 136   (c) 118   (d) 48

3.54

(a) $^{14}_{6}$C   (b) $^{39}_{19}$K   (c) $^{20}_{10}$Ne

3.55

(a) $^{19}_{9}$F   (b) $^{79}_{35}$Br   (c) $^{51}_{23}$V

3.56

$^{12}_{6}$C – six neutrons $^{13}_{6}$C – seven neutrons $^{14}_{6}$C – eight neutrons

3.57

$^{131}_{53}$I

3.58 Contribution from ^{63}Cu: 69.17% of 62.93 amu = 43.53 amu
Contribution from ^{65}Cu: 30.83% of 64.93 amu = 20.02 amu
_____

Average atomic weight = 63.55 amu

3.59 Contribution from ^{7}Li: 92.58% of 7.016 amu = 6.495 amu
Contribution from ^{6}Li: 7.42% of 6.015 amu = 0.446 amu
_____

Average atomic weight = 6.941 amu

The Periodic Table

3.60 The third period in the periodic table contains 8 elements because 8 electrons are needed to fill the *s* subshell (2 electrons) and *p* subshell (6 electrons) of the third shell.

3.61 The fourth period contains 18 elements because 18 electrons are needed to fill the *s* subshell (2 electrons) and *p* subshell (6 electrons) of the fourth shell, plus the *d* subshell (10 electrons) of the third shell.

3.62 Americium (Am; atomic number 95) is a metal.

3.63 Antimony (Sb; atomic number 51) is a metalloid.

3.64 (a) They are metals.
(b) They are transition metals.
(c) The 3*d* subshell is being filled.

3.65 (a) They are metals.
(b) They are lanthanides, which are a subgroup of the inner transition elements.
(c) The 4*f* subshell is being filled.

3.66 (a) Rubidium: (i) metal; (v) main group element; (vii) alkali metal
(b) Tungsten: (i) metal; (iv) transition element
(c) Germanium: (iii) metalloid; (v) main group element
(d) Krypton: (ii) nonmetal; (v) main group element; (vi) noble gas

3.67 (a) Calcium: (i) metal; (v) main group element; (viii) alkaline earth metal
(b) Palladium: (i) metal; (iv) transition element
(c) Carbon: (ii) nonmetal; (v) main group element
(d) Radon: (ii) nonmetal; (v) main group element; (v) noble gas

3.68 Selenium is chemically similar to sulfur.

3.69 Calcium is chemically similar to magnesium.

3.70 The alkali metal family is composed of lithium, sodium, potassium, rubidium, cesium, and francium.

3.71 Fluorine, chlorine, bromine, iodine, and astatine make up the halogen family.

Electron Configuration

3.72 A maximum of two electrons can go into an orbital.

3.73 An *s* orbital is spherical and centered on the nucleus. A *p* orbital is dumbbell-shaped, and the three *p* orbitals extend out from the nucleus at 90° angles to each other.

3.74 First shell—2 electrons
Second shell—8 electrons
Third shell—18 electrons

3.75 The third shell contains nine orbitals: one *s* orbital, three *p* orbitals, and five *d* orbitals. The fourth shell contains sixteen orbitals: one *s* orbital, three *p* orbitals, five *d* orbitals, and seven *f* orbitals.

3.76 The third shell contains three subshells: 3*s*, 3*p*, 3*d*. The fourth shell contains four subshells: 4*s*, 4*p*, 4*d*, 4*f*. The fifth shell contains five subshells: 5*s*, 5*p*, 5*d*, 5*f*, and an additional subshell.

3.77 It would contain nine orbitals and would be filled by 18 electrons.

3.78 Ten electrons are present; the element is neon.

3.79 Fourteen electrons are present; the element is silicon.

3.80 (a) Sulfur   (b) Bromine   (c) Silicon

$3p^4$ $4p^5$ $3p^2$

3.81 (a) Strontium   (b) Technetium   (c) Palladium

$5s$ $5s$ $4d$ $5s$ $4d$

3.82
Element	Sulfur	Bromine	Silicon	Strontium	Technetium	Palladium
Number of unpaired electrons	2	1	2	0	5	2

3.83
Element	Electron configuration
(a) Ca	$1s^2\,2s^2\,2p^6\,3s^2\,3p^6\,4s^2$
(b) S	$1s^2\,2s^2\,2p^6\,3s^2\,3p^4$
(c) F	$1s^2\,2s^2\,2p^5$
(d) Cd	$1s^2\,2s^2\,2p^6\,3s^2\,3p^6\,4s^2\,3d^{10}\,4p^6\,5s^2\,4d^{10}$

3.84 The element with atomic number 12 (Mg) has two electrons in its outer shell.

$$\cdot Mg \cdot$$

3.85 The number of valence electrons for elements in a main group is the same as the group number. Thus, group 4A elements have four valence electrons.

$$\cdot \overset{\displaystyle\cdot}{\underset{\displaystyle\cdot}{X}} \cdot$$

3.86 Beryllium: $2s$;   Arsenic: $4p$

3.87 Group 5A(15) has the configuration $ns^2\,np^3$.

3.88
Element:	(a) Kr	(b) C	(c) Ca	(d) K	(e) B	(f) Cl
Number of valence-shell electrons:	8	4	2	1	3	7

:Kr: ·C·   ·Ca·   ·K   ·B·   :Cl·

3.89 Group 7A: $ns^2\,np^5$;   Group 1A: ns^1

Applications

3.90 A normal light microscope can't reach the degree of precision of a scanning tunneling microscope.

3.91 A "plum pudding" model of atoms would not account for the periodic properties of elements.

3.92 Hydrogen and helium are the first two elements made in stars.

3.93 A gravitational collapse of stars results in the synthesis of elements heavier than iron and produces an explosion known as a supernova.

3.94

	Higher Energy	*Lower Energy*
(a)	ultraviolet	infrared
(b)	gamma waves	microwaves
(c)	X rays	visible light

3.95 Ultraviolet rays are more damaging to the skin because they are of higher energy than visible light.

General Questions and Problems

3.96 Helium, neon, argon, krypton, xenon, and radon make up the noble gas family.

3.97 Hydrogen can be placed in group 1A because it has one electron in its outermost (only) electron shell. Hydrogen can be placed in group 7A because only one electron is needed to fill its outermost (only) electron shell.

3.98 Tellurium has a greater atomic weight because its nuclei contain, on the average, more neutrons than an iodine nucleus.

3.99 The new element beneath francium has the atomic number 119.

3.100 Pb: $1s^2 2s^2 2p^6 3s^2 3p^6 4s^2 3d^{10} 4p^6 5s^2 4d^{10} 5p^6 6s^2 4f^{14} 5d^{10} 6p^2$
Shell 1: 2 electrons   Shell 2:   8 electrons   Shell 3: 18 electrons
Shell 4: 32 electrons   Shell 5: 18 electrons   Shell 6:   4 electrons

3.101 Highest-energy occupied subshell: (a) $Ar - 3p$; (b) $Mg - 3s$; (c) $Tc - 4d$; (d) $Fe - 3d$

3.102 Contribution from ^{79}Br: 50.69% of 78.92 amu = 40.00 amu
Contribution from ^{81}Br: 49.31% of 80.91 amu = 39.90 amu
$$\overline{}$$
Average atomic weight = 79.90 amu

3.103 Contribution from ^{24}Mg: 78.99% of 23.99 amu = 18.95 amu
Contribution from ^{25}Mg: 10.00% of 24.99 amu =   2.50 amu
Contribution from ^{26}Mg: 11.01% of 25.98 amu =   2.86 amu
$$\overline{}$$
Average atomic weight = 24.31 amu

3.104 One atom of carbon weighs more than one atom of hydrogen because the mass of carbon (12 amu) is greater than the mass of hydrogen (1 amu).

3.105 10^{23} atoms of carbon weigh 12×10^{23} amu, and 10^{23} atoms of hydrogen weigh 1×10^{23} amu. Thus the weight of carbon is 12 times greater than that of hydrogen.

3.106 If 10^{23} hydrogen atoms weigh about 1 g, then 10^{23} carbon atoms will weigh about 12 g.

3.107 Using the reasoning from Problem 3.106, we predict that 10^{23} sodium atoms will weigh about 23 grams.

3.108 The unidentified element is strontium, which occurs directly below calcium in group 2A and thus has similar chemical behavior. Strontium is a metal, has 38 protons, and is in the fifth period.

$$\cdot Sr \cdot$$

3.109 The outer-shell electrons of germanium are in the $4s$ and $4p$ orbitals.

3.110 Tin, a metal, has an electron configuration by shell of 2 8 18 18 4.

3.111

$$8.6 \text{ mg } \times \frac{1 \text{ g}}{10^3 \text{ mg}} \times \frac{1 \text{ amu}}{1.660\ 539 \times 10^{-24} \text{ g}} \times \frac{1 \text{ atom}}{40.08 \text{ amu}} = 1.3 \times 10^{20} \text{ atoms}$$

3.112 (a) Electrons must fill the $4s$ subshell before entering the $3d$ subshell. The correct configuration:

$$1s^2\ 2s^2\ 2p^6\ 3s^2\ 3p^6\ 4s^2\ 3d^8$$

(b) Electrons must fill the $2s$ subshell before entering the $2p$ subshell. The correct configuration:

$$1s^2\ 2s^2\ 2p^3$$

(c) Silicon has 14 electrons. The p orbitals must be half-filled before any one orbital is completely filled. The correct configuration:

$$1s^2\ 2s^2\ 2p^6\ 3s^2\ \underset{3p}{\uparrow\ \uparrow\ \_}$$

(d) The $3s$ electrons must have opposite spins. The correct configuration:

$$1s^2\ 2s^2\ 2p^6\ \underset{3s}{\uparrow\downarrow}$$

3.113 Count the electrons in each example to arrive at the atomic number. Then look up the answer in the periodic table.
(a) Cr   (b) Cu   (c) Mo   (d) Ag

3.114 An electron will fill or half-fill a d subshell instead of filling an s subshell of a higher shell.

3.115 The last orbital filled in element 117 is $7p$.

Self-Test for Chapter 3

Multiple Choice

1. Which of the following is a metalloid?
   (a) carbon   (b) aluminum   (c) silicon   (d) phosphorus

2. Which of the following has a partially filled d subshell?
   (a) calcium   (b) vanadium   (c) zinc   (d) arsenic

3. Which of the following is not a part of atomic theory?
   (a) All metal is composed of atoms.   (b) The atoms of each element are different from the atoms of other elements.   (c) In chemical compounds, atoms are combined in specific proportions.   (d) Chemical reactions only change the way that atoms are combined.

4. How many isotopes of hydrogen are there?
   (a) one   (b) two   (c) three   (d) can't be determined

5. What holds protons and neutrons together in the nucleus?
   (a) attraction   (b) repulsion   (c) electrons   (d) internuclear forces

6. Which of the following has a mass number of 33?
   (a) $^{74}_{33}\text{As}$ (b) $^{35}_{17}\text{Cl}$ (c) $^{32}_{16}\text{S}$ (d) $^{33}_{16}\text{S}$

7. In which order are subshells usually filled?
   (a) s, p, d, f (b) d, f, p, s (c) s, p, f, d (d) s, d, p, f

8. The element with atomic number 38 is:
   (a) an alkali metal   (b) an alkaline earth metal   (c) a transition metal   (d) a metalloid

9. The element that has atomic weight = 91 and has 40 electrons is:
   (a) protactinium   (b) niobium   (c) antimony   (d) zirconium

10. The element that has electron configuration $1s^2\, 2s^2\, 2p^6\, 3s^2\, 3p^6\, 4s^2\, 3d^7$ is:
    (a) copper   (b) rhodium   (c) arsenic   (d) cobalt

11. An element that has electrons in its f subshell is:
    (a) europium   (b) technetium   (c) antimony   (d) xenon

12. $^{195}_{78}\text{X}$ is the symbol for:
    (a) gold   (b) platinum   (c) iridium   (d) iron

Sentence Completion

1. A _____ orbital is dumbbell-shaped.

2. An atomic mass unit is also known as a _____.

3. The nucleus of an atom is made up of _____ and _____.

4.   The _____ _____ indicates the number of protons in an atom.

5.   The electrons in an atom are grouped by energy into _____.

6.   Elements belonging to the same _____ have similar chemical properties.

7.   The atomic number of aluminum is _____.

8.   Protons, neutrons, and electrons are known as _____ _____.

9.   Atoms having the same number of protons but different numbers of neutrons are called _____.

10.   The third shell contains _____ electrons.

11.   The word _____ means that electrons can have certain energy values and no others.

True or False

1.   Bismuth is a metal.

2.   The mass of an electron is approximately 1 amu.

3.   A $4s$ electron is higher in energy than a $3d$ electron.

4.   Isotopes have the same number of protons but different numbers of neutrons.

5.   An atom's atomic number indicates the number of protons and neutrons the atom has.

6.   Elements in group 2A are more reactive than elements in group 1A.

7.   Elements in the same period have similar chemical properties.

8.   More elements are metals than are nonmetals.

9.   All compounds consist of atoms combined in specific proportions.

10.   A subshell contains only two electrons.

11.   An element can have the same number of protons, neutrons, and electrons.

12.   Atomic weight always increases with atomic number.

Match each entry on the left with its partner on the right.

1. $1s^2\ 2s^2$

(a) Mendeleev

2.   Group

(b) Number of protons in an element

3.   Atomic mass unit

(c) Reactive metals

4.   Formulated the periodic table

(d) Average mass of a large number of an element's atoms

5.   Neutron

(e) Column in the periodic table

6. $^{28}_{14}\text{Si}$

(f) Row in the periodic table

7.   Group 1A

(g) Element with atomic mass of 14 amu

8.   Atomic number

(h) Electron configuration of beryllium

9. $^{29}_{14}\text{Si}$

(i) Element having 15 neutrons

10.   Atomic weight

(j) Subatomic particle with zero charge

11. $^{14}_{7}\text{N}$

(k) Dalton

12.   Period

(l) Element with atomic number 14

Chapter Outline

I. Ions (Sections 4.1–4.2).
   A. Ions are formed when a neutral atom either gains an electron (to form an anion) or loses an electron (to form a cation).
      1. Ionization energy measures the ease with which an atom gives up an electron.
         a. Energy must be supplied in order to remove an electron.
         b. Elements on the far left of the periodic table have smaller ionization energies and lose electrons more easily.
         c. Elements on the far right of the periodic table have larger ionization energies and lose electrons with difficulty.
      2. Electron affinity measures the ease with which an atom gains an electron.
         a. Energy is released when an atom gains an electron.
         b. Elements on the far right of the periodic table have larger electron affinities and gain electrons easily.
         c. Elements on the far left of the periodic table have smaller electron affinities and gain electrons less easily.
   B. Main group elements in the middle of the periodic table neither lose or gain electrons easily.
II. Formation of ionic compounds (Sections 4.3–4.6).
   A. Compounds formed between an element on the far left side of the periodic table and an element on the far right of the periodic table are electronically neutral (Section 4.3).
      1. These compounds consist of a large number of cations and anions packed together in a regular arrangement in a crystal.
      2. The bonds between ions in the crystal are known as ionic bonds.
      3. The crystal is known as an ionic solid.
   B. Properties of ionic compounds (Section 4.4).
      1. Ionic compounds are crystalline.
      2. Solutions of ionic compounds conduct electricity.
      3. Ionic compounds are high-melting.
      4. Many, but not all, ionic compounds are water-soluble.
   C. The octet rule (Section 4.5).
      1. Main group elements undergo reactions that leave them with eight valence electrons – an octet.
III. Ions of some common elements (Sections 4.6–4.8).
   A. Cations (Section 4.6)

      1. Group 1A $M\cdot \longrightarrow M^+ + e^-$

      2. Group 2A $\cdot M\cdot \longrightarrow M^{2+} + 2e^-$
      3. Group 3A Al^{3+} is the only common cation.
      4. Transition metals often form more than one cation.

B. Anions.

1. Group 6A $:\overset{\cdot}{\underset{\cdot}{X}}: + 2e^- \longrightarrow :\overset{\cdot\cdot}{\underset{\cdot\cdot}{X}}:^{2-}$

2. Group 7A $:\overset{\cdot}{\underset{\cdot\cdot}{X}}: + e^- \longrightarrow :\overset{\cdot\cdot}{\underset{\cdot\cdot}{X}}:^-$

C. Group 4A, group 5A and group 8A elements don't usually form cations or anions.
D. Naming ions (Section 4.7).
   1. Main group cations are named by identifying the metal and then adding the word "ion."
   2. Transition metal cations are named by identifying the metal, specifying the charge, and adding the word "ion."
   3. Anions are named by replacing the end of the name of the element with -ide and adding the word "ion."
   4. Polyatomic ions (Section 4.8).
      a. Polyatomic ions are composed of more than one atom.
      b. Subscripts in polyatomic ions indicate how many of each ion are present in the formula unit (no subscripts are necessary if only one ion is present).
      c. The names of polyatomic ions should be memorized.
IV. Ionic compounds (Sections 4.9–4.11).
   A. Formulas of ionic compounds (Section 4.9).
      1. Formulas are written so that the number of positive charges equals the number of negative charges.
         a. Cations are listed first, anions second.
         b. It is not necessary to write the charges of the ions.
         c. Use parentheses around a polyatomic ion if it has a subscript.
      2. A formula unit shows the simplest neutral unit of an ionic compound.
   B. Naming ionic compounds (Section 4.10).
      Ionic compounds are named by citing the cation and then the anion, with a space between the two words.
   C. Acids and bases (Section 4.11).
      1. Acids are compounds that provide H^+ ions in solution.
      2. Bases are compounds that provide OH^- ions in solution.
      3. Some acids and bases can each provide more than one H^+ or OH^- ion in solution.

Solutions to Chapter 4 Problems

4.1   The Mg^{2+} ion is a cation.

4.2   The O^{2-} ion is an anion.

4.3   The ion shown, O^{-2}, is an anion because it has two more negative charges than positive charges.

4.4   Figure 4.1 shows approximate ionization energies for helium, neon, argon and krypton. In line with this trend, it is predicted that the ionization energy of xenon should be somewhat less than that of krypton but greater than the ionization energy of most other elements.

4.5   (a) According to Figure 4.1, B ($Z = 5$) loses an electron more easily than Be ($Z = 4$).
(b) Ca ($Z = 20$) loses an electron more easily than Co ($Z = 27$).
(c) Sc ($Z = 21$) loses an electron more easily than Se ($Z = 34$).

4.6   (a) According to Figure 4.1, H gains an electron more easily than He. Because the electron affinity for He is zero, it does not accept an electron.
(b) S gains an electron more easily than Si.
(c) Cr gains an electron more easily than Mn.

4.7   Potassium (atomic number 19): $1s^2\, 2s^2\, 2p^6\, 3s^2\, 3p^6\, 4s^1$
Argon (atomic number 18): $1s^2\, 2s^2\, 2p^6\, 3s^2\, 3p^6$
Potassium can attain the noble-gas configuration of argon by losing an electron from its $4s$ subshell, forming the K^+ cation.

4.8   Aluminum (atomic number 13): $1s^2\, 2s^2\, 2p^6\, 3s^2\, 3p^1$
Neon (atomic number 10): $1s^2\, 2s^2\, 2p^6$
Aluminum can attain the noble-gas configuration of neon by losing three electrons, two from its $3s$ subshell, and one from its $3p$ subshell, resulting in the formation of the Al^{3+} ion.

4.9

$$X: \ + \ :\dot{Y}: \ \longrightarrow \ X^{2+} \ + \ :\ddot{Y}:^{2-}$$

Y gains electrons, and X loses electrons.

4.10   Molybdenum, a transition metal, is more likely to form a cation than an anion.

4.11   Strontium loses two electrons to form the Sr^{2+} cation, and bromine gains an electron to form the Br^- anion. Only chromium, a transition metal, can form more than one cation.

4.12

(a) $:\dot{Se}\cdot \ + \ 2e^- \ \longrightarrow \ :\ddot{Se}:^{2-}; \quad Se \ + \ 2e^- \ \longrightarrow \ Se^{2-}$

(b) $\cdot Ba \cdot \ \longrightarrow \ Ba^{2+} \ + \ 2e^-; \quad Ba \ \longrightarrow \ Ba^{2+} \ + \ 2e^-$

(c) $:\ddot{Br}\cdot \ + \ e^- \ \longrightarrow \ :\ddot{Br}:^-; \quad Br \ + \ e^- \ \longrightarrow \ Br^-$

4.13   (a) Cu^{2+} copper(II) ion (cupric ion)   (b) F^- fluoride ion
(c) Mg^{2+} magnesium ion   (d) S^{2-} sulfide ion

4.14   (a) Ag^+ (b) Fe^{2+} (c) Cu^+ (d) Te^{2-}

4.15 Na^+ sodium ion; K^+ potassium ion;
Ca^{2+} calcium ion; Cl^- chloride ion

4.16   (a) NO_3^- nitrate ion;   (b) CN^- cyanide ion;
(c) OH^- hydroxide ion;   (d) HPO_4^{2-} hydrogen phosphate ion

4.17 (a) HCO_3^- bicarbonate ion;　　(b) NH_4^+ ammonium ion;
(c) PO_4^{3-} phosphate ion;　　(d) MnO_4^- permanganate ion

4.18 (a) The two ions are Ag^+ and I^-. Since they have the same charge, only one of each ion is needed. The formula is AgI.
(b) Ions: Ag^+, O^{2-}. Two Ag^+ ions will balance the O^{2-} ion. The formula is Ag_2O.
(c) The ions are Ag^+ and PO_4^{3-}. Three Ag^+ ions are needed to balance the charge of the PO_4^{3-} anion. The formula is Ag_3PO_4.

4.19 (a) Na_2SO_4　　(b) $FeSO_4$　　　(c) $Cr_2(SO_4)_3$

4.20 $(NH_4)_2CO_3$

4.21 $Al_2(SO_4)_3$;　　　$Al(CH_3CO_2)_3$

4.22 Use the periodic table to identify the elements present and use the rules described in Section 4.10 to write the formulas. The formulas are K_2S (blue), $BaBr_2$ (red), and Al_2O_3 (green).

4.23 Since there are three calcium ions for every two nitride ions, the formula is Ca_3N_2. Calcium ion has a +2 charge, and nitride ion has a –3 charge.

4.24 $BaSO_4$. One barium ion is present for each sulfate ion.

4.25 Ag_2S—silver(I) sulfide. The charge on silver is +1.

4.26 (a) SnO_2　　tin(IV) oxide　　　(b) $Ca(CN)_2$　calcium cyanide
(c) Na_2CO_3　sodium carbonate　　(d) Cu_2SO_4　　copper(I) sulfate
(e) $Ba(OH)_2$　barium hydroxide　　(f) $Fe(NO_3)_2$　iron(II) nitrate

4.27 (a) Li_3PO_4　(b) $CuCO_3$　(c) $Al_2(SO_3)_3$　　(d) CuF　(e) $Fe_2(SO_4)_3$　　(f) NH_4Cl

4.28 Cr_2O_3 chromium(III) oxide

4.29 Acids provide H^+ ions when dissolved in water.
Bases provide OH^- ions when dissolved in water.

$$\text{Acids:}\quad HF \xrightarrow{\text{dissolve in water}} H^+ + F^-$$

$$HCN \xrightarrow{\text{dissolve in water}} H^+ + CN^-$$

$$\text{Bases:}\quad Ca(OH)_2 \xrightarrow{\text{dissolve in water}} Ca^{2+} + 2\,OH^-$$

$$LiOH \xrightarrow{\text{dissolve in water}} Li^+ + OH^-$$

4.30 Solution (a) represents HCl; the drawing shows that there are equal numbers of cations and anions in solution. Solution (b) represents H_2SO_4; two cations are present for each anion.

Understanding Key Concepts

4.31

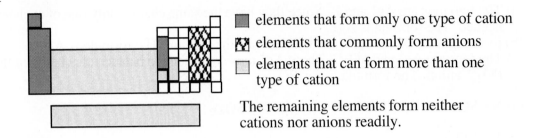

elements that form only one type of cation

elements that commonly form anions

elements that can form more than one type of cation

The remaining elements form neither cations nor anions readily.

4.32

elements that commonly form +2 ions

elements that commonly form −2 ions

an element that forms a +3 ion

4.33 Drawing (a) shows an ion that has two more electrons than protons and thus represents an O^{2-} ion.
Drawing (b) represents Na^+, an ion with one more proton than electron.
Drawing (c) represents calcium, a neutral atom.

4.34 Drawing (a) represents a sodium atom, and drawing (b) represents an Na^+ ion. The Na atom is larger because its $3s$ electron lies in an orbital that is farther from the nucleus.

4.35 Drawing (a) represents a chlorine atom, and drawing (b) represents a Cl^- anion. The anion is larger because its extra electron is not as tightly held by the positively charged nucleus as are the electrons of the atom.

4.36 red—MgO (magnesium oxide);   blue—LiCl (lithium chloride);
green—$AlBr_3$ (aluminum bromide)

4.37 Use the ratios of atoms to assign answers. Picture (a) represents ZnS, because one cation is present for each anion. Picture (b) represents $PbBr_2$, (c) represents CrF_3, and (d) represents Al_2O_3.

Ions and Ionic Bonding

4.38

(a) · Be ·   (b) :Ne: (c) · Sr ·   (d) · Al ·

4.39

(a) $:\overset{\bullet}{\underset{\bullet}{N}}\cdot$ (b) $:\overset{\bullet}{\underset{\bullet\bullet}{Se}}\cdot$ (c) $:\overset{\bullet\bullet}{\underset{\bullet\bullet}{I}}\cdot$ (d) $\cdot Sr\overset{\bullet}{\cdot}$

4.40   (a) $Ca \rightarrow Ca^{2+} + 2\,e^-$ (b) $Au \rightarrow Au^+ + e^-$
       (c) $F + e^- \rightarrow F^-$ (d) $Cr \rightarrow Cr^{3+} + 3\,e^-$

4.41   (a) $P + 3\,e^- \rightarrow P^{3-}$ (b) $Li \rightarrow Li^+ + e^-$
       (c) $Co \rightarrow Co^{2+} + 2\,e^-$ (d) $Tl \rightarrow Tl^{3+} + 3\,e^-$

4.42   (a) False. A cation is formed by *loss* of one or more electrons from an atom. (b), (c) False. Group 4A elements rarely form ions. (d) True.

4.43   (a) False. Ions have a regular arrangement in ionic solids.   (b) False. Ions vary in size. (c) True.   (d) False. Ionic solids have high melting points and boiling points.

Ions and the Octet Rule

4.44   The *octet rule* states that main group atoms undergo reactions in order to achieve a noble gas electron configuration with eight outer-shell electrons.

4.45   Electrons belonging to hydrogen and helium occupy the first shell, which can hold only two electrons. Thus, even though H^- has the configuration of a noble gas (He), it can't have an electron octet.

4.46   An ion with 34 protons and 36 electrons has a –2 charge.

4.47   An ion with 20 protons and 18 electrons has a +2 charge.

4.48   (a) $X^{2+} = Sr^{2+}$; $X = Sr$ The strontium ion has the same electron configuration as the noble gas krypton.
       (b) $X^- = Br^-$; $X = Br$ The bromide ion also has the same electron configuration as the noble gas krypton.

4.49 $Z^{3+} = Ga^{3+}$; $Z = Ga$. The Z^{3+} cation has 31 protons and 28 electrons.

4.50   (a) Rb^+ $1s^2\,2s^2\,2p^6\,3s^2\,3p^6\,4s^2\,3d^{10}\,4p^6$
       (b) Br^- $1s^2\,2s^2\,2p^6\,3s^2\,3p^6\,4s^2\,3d^{10}\,4p^6$
       (c) S^{2-} $1s^2\,2s^2\,2p^6\,3s^2\,3p^6$
       (d) Ba^{2+} $1s^2\,2s^2\,2p^6\,3s^2\,3p^6\,4s^2\,3d^{10}\,4p^6\,5s^2\,4d^{10}\,5p^6$
       (e) Al^{3+} $1s^2\,2s^2\,2p^6$

4.51   (a) Ar   (b) He   (c) Ne   (d) Ne   (e) Ne

Periodic Properties and Ion Formation

4.52   (a) O   (b) Li   (c) Zn   (d) N

4.53   (a) S   (b) I   (c) Br

4.54   None of the ions are stable because all lack eight outer-shell electrons.

4.55   (a) Magnesium forms only the Mg^{2+} cation.
(b) Silicon does not form cations.
(c) Manganese, a transition metal, can form several different cations.

4.56 Cr^{2+}: $1s^2\, 2s^2\, 2p^6\, 3s^2\, 3p^6\, 3d^4$
Cr^{3+}: $1s^2\, 2s^2\, 2p^6\, 3s^2\, 3p^6\, 3d^3$

4.57 Co : $1s^2\, 2s^2\, 2p^6\, 3s^2\, 3p^6\, 3d^7\, 4s^2$
Co^{2+}: $1s^2\, 2s^2\, 2p^6\, 3s^2\, 3p^6\, 3d^7$
Co^{3+}: $1s^2\, 2s^2\, 2p^6\, 3s^2\, 3p^6\, 3d^6$

4.58   The ionization energy of Li^+ is much greater than that of Li. Li readily loses an electron to form an ion with eight outer-shell electrons, but Li^+ would need to lose one electron from a stable octet in order to form the Li^{2+} cation.

4.59   (a) $K \rightarrow K^+ + e^-$ loss of an electron by K
$K^+ + e^- \rightarrow K$ gain of an electron by K^+
(b) The second equation is the reverse of the first equation.
(c) Ionization energy of K $=$ $-$ (electron affinity of K^+)

Symbols, Formulas, and Names for Ions

4.60   (a) S^{2-} sulfide ion   (b) Sn^{2+} tin(II) ion   (c) Sr^{2+} strontium ion
(d) Mg^{2+} magnesium ion   (e) Au^+ gold(I) ion

4.61   (a) Cu^{2+} cupric ion   copper(II) ion
(b) Fe^{2+} ferrous ion   iron(II) ion
(c) Hg_2^{2+} mercurous ion   mercury(I) ion

4.62   (a) Se^{2-} (b) O^{2-} (c) Ag^+

4.63   (a) Fe^{3+} (b) Co^{2+} (c) Pb^{4+}

4.64   (a) OH^- (b) HSO_4^- (c) $CH_3CO_2^-$ (d) MnO_4^- (e) OCl^- (f) NO_3^-
(g) CO_3^{2-} (h) $Cr_2O_7^{2-}$

4.65   (a) SO_3^{2-} sulfite ion   (b) CN^- cyanide ion
(c) H_3O^+ hydronium ion   (d) PO_4^{3-} phosphate ion

Names and Formulas for Ionic Compounds

4.66   (a) $Al_2(SO_4)_3$ (b) Ag_2SO_4 (c) $ZnSO_4$ (d) $BaSO_4$

4.67   (a) $SrCO_3$ (b) $Fe_2(CO_3)_3$ (c) $(NH_4)_2CO_3$ (d) $Sn(CO_3)_2$

4.68   (a) $NaHCO_3$ (b) KNO_3 (c) $CaCO_3$ (d) NH_4NO_3

4.69   (a) $Ca(OCl)_2$ (b) $CuSO_4$ (c) Na_3PO_4

4.70

	S^{2-}	Cl^-	PO_4^{3-}	CO_3^{2-}
Copper(II)	CuS	$CuCl_2$	$Cu_3(PO_4)_2$	$CuCO_3$
Ca^{2+}	CaS	$CaCl_2$	$Ca_3(PO_4)_2$	$CaCO_3$
NH_4^+	$(NH_4)_2S$	NH_4Cl	$(NH_4)_3PO_4$	$(NH_4)_2CO_3$
Ferric ion	Fe_2S_3	$FeCl_3$	$FePO_4$	$Fe_2(CO_3)_3$

4.71

	O^{2-}	HSO_4^-	HPO_4^{2-}	$C_2O_4^{2-}$
Na^+	Na_2O	$NaHSO_4$	Na_2HPO_4	$Na_2C_2O_4$
Zn^{2+}	ZnO	$Zn(HSO_4)_2$	$ZnHPO_4$	ZnC_2O_4
NH_4^+	$(NH_4)_2O$	NH_4HSO_4	$(NH_4)_2HPO_4$	$(NH_4)_2C_2O_4$
Ferrous ion	FeO	$Fe(HSO_4)_2$	$FeHPO_4$	FeC_2O_4

4.72

copper(II) sulfide	copper(II) chloride	copper(II) phosphate	copper(II) carbonate
calcium sulfide	calcium chloride	calcium phosphate	calcium carbonate
ammonium sulfide	ammonium chloride	ammonium phosphate	ammonium carbonate
ferric sulfide	ferric chloride	ferric phosphate	ferric carbonate

4.73

sodium oxide	sodium bisulfate	sodium hydrogen phosphate	sodium oxalate
zinc oxide	zinc bisulfate	zinc hydrogen phosphate	zinc oxalate
ammonium oxide	ammonium bisulfate	ammonium hydrogen phosphate	ammonium oxalate
ferrous oxide	ferrous bisulfate	ferrous hydrogen phosphate	ferrous oxalate

4.74 (a) $MgCO_3$ magnesium carbonate   (b) $Ca(CH_3CO_2)_2$ calcium acetate
(c) $AgCN$ silver(I) cyanide   (d) $Na_2Cr_2O_7$ sodium dichromate

4.75 (a) $Fe(OH)_2$ iron(II) hydroxide   (b) $KMnO_4$ potassium permanganate
(c) Na_2CrO_4 sodium chromate   (d) $Ba_3(PO_4)_2$ barium phosphate

4.76 $Ca_3(PO_4)_2$ (d) is the correct formula because the six positive charges from the three Ca^{2+} ions are balanced by the six negative charges of the two PO_4^{3-} ions.

4.77 (a) Na_2SO_4 (b) $Ba_3(PO_4)_2$ (c) $Ga_2(SO_4)_3$

Acids and Bases

4.78 An acid provides H^+ ions when dissolved in water. A base provides OH^- ions when dissolved in water.

4.79 Acids: H_2CO_3, HCN
Bases: $Mg(OH)_2$, KOH

4.80

(a) H_2CO_3 $\xrightarrow{\text{dissolve in water}}$ $2H^+$ + CO_3^-

(b) HCN $\xrightarrow{\text{dissolve in water}}$ H^+ + CN^-

(c) $Mg(OH)_2$ $\xrightarrow{\text{dissolve in water}}$ Mg^{2+} + $2OH^-$

(d)   KOH $\xrightarrow{\text{dissolve in water}}$ K^+ + OH^-

4.81 (a) carbonate anion   (b) cyanide anion

Applications

4.82 To a geologist, a mineral is a naturally occurring crystalline compound. To a nutritionist, a mineral is a metal ion essential for human health.

4.83 Salt is usually obtained by mining salt beds. It can also be obtained by evaporating seawater.

4.84 For most people, the effect of salt consumption on blood pressure elevation is slight, but a small proportion of people may suffer high blood pressure as a result of excessive salt consumption.

4.85 Most of the calcium present in the body is found in bones and teeth.

4.86 Sodium protects against fluid loss and is necessary for muscle contraction and transmission of nerve impulses.

4.87 Too little iron in the blood leads to anemia, which becomes more severe if blood is removed.

4.88

Ion	Name	Charge	Total Charge
Ca^{2+}	calcium ion	2+	$10 \times (2+) = 20+$
PO_4^{3-}	phosphate ion	3–	$6 \times (3-) = 18-$
OH^-	hydroxide ion	1–	$2 \times (1-) = 2-$

The formula correctly represents a neutral compound because the number of positive charges equals the number of negative charges.

4.89 $Ca_{10}(PO_4)_6(OH)_2 + 2\,F^- \rightarrow Ca_{10}(PO_4)_6F_2 + 2\,OH^-$

General Questions and Problems

4.90 The hydride ion has the same electron configuration ($1s^2$) as the noble gas helium.

4.91 The H^- ion has a stable noble gas configuration, but the Li^- ion doesn't and is thus likely to be unstable. (Notice in Figure 4.1 that the electron affinity of Li is very small, indicating that Li is unlikely to gain an electron to form Li^-.)

4.92 (a) CrO_3 (b) VCl_5 (c) MnO_2 (d) MoS_2

4.93 $Pb_3(AsO_4)_2$

4.94 (a) A gluconate ion has one negative charge.
(b) Three gluconate ions are in one formula unit of iron(III) gluconate, and the formula is Fe(gluconate)$_3$.

4.95 (a) Cu_3PO_4 copper(I) phosphate   (b) Na_2SO_4 sodium sulfate
(c) MnO_2 manganese(IV) oxide   (d) $AuCl_3$ gold(III) chloride
(e) $Pb(CO_3)_2$ lead(IV) carbonate   (f) Ni_2S_3 nickel(III) sulfide

4.96 (a) $Co(CN)_2$ (b) UO_3 (c) $SnSO_4$ (d) MnO_2 (e) K_3PO_4 (f) Ca_3P_2
(g) $LiHSO_4$ (h) $Al(OH)_3$

4.97

Ion	Protons	Electrons	Neutrons
(a) $^{16}O^{2-}$	8	10	8
(b) $^{89}Y^{3+}$	39	36	50
(c) $^{133}Cs^{+}$	55	54	78
(d) $^{81}Br^{-}$	35	36	46

4.98 (a) X is likely to be a metal, because metals are more likely to form cations.
(b) Y is likely to be a nonmetal.
(c) The formula for the product is X_2Y_3.
(d) X is likely to be in Group 3A or Group 3B (or to be a transition metal) and Y is likely to be in Group 6A.

4.99 (a) Fe^{+3} (b) Ni^{+2} (c) Cr^{+6}

Self-Test for Chapter 4

Multiple Choice

1. How many atoms does a formula unit of Li_2CO_3 contain?
   (a) 3   (b) 4   (c) 5   (d) 6

2. How many ions are produced when a formula unit of Li_2CO_3 is dissolved in water?
   (a) 3   (b) 4   (c) 5   (d) 6

3. Which of the following is not a property of ionic compounds?
   (a) crystalline   (b) conductor of electricity   (c) high melting   (d) 1:1 ratio of cations to anions

4. Which of the following is the correct name for $Fe(NO_3)_3$?
   (a) ferrous nitrate   (b) iron nitrate   (c) iron(III) nitrate   (d) iron(II) nitrate

5. Bromine has a:
   (a) large ionization energy and large electron affinity   (b) large ionization energy and small electron affinity   (c) small ionization energy and large electron affinity   (d) small ionization energy and small electron affinity

6. H_2CrO_4 is an acid that:
    (a) can provide one H^+ ion when dissolved   (b) can provide two H^+ ions when dissolved
    (c) can provide one OH^- when dissolved   (d) H_2CrO_4 is not an acid.

7. An element that loses three electrons to attain the electron configuration of argon is:
    (a) titanium   (b) scandium   (c) calcium   (d) potassium

8. The formula for gold(III) chloride is:
    (a) Au_3Cl (b) $AuCl$ (c) $AuCl_2$ (d) $AuCl_3$

9. Which of the following anions is not biologically important?
    (a) Cl^- (b) Br^- (c) HCO_3^- (d) HPO_4^-

10. The redness of rubies is due to which ion?
    (a) iron   (b) titanium   (c) aluminum   (d) chromium

Sentence Completion

1. _____ _____ measures the ease with which an atom gives up an electron.

2. The name of K_3PO_4 is _____ _____.

3. Radium (atomic number 88) loses _____ electrons to achieve a noble gas configuration.

4. NO_3^- is an example of a _____ ion.

5. The formulas of ionic compounds are _____ formulas.

6. Atoms of main group elements tend to combine in chemical compounds so that they attain _____ outer-shell electrons.

7. A _____ provides OH^- ions in water.

8. _____ is the principal mineral component of bone.

9. Ionic compounds are usually _____ solids.

10. The first three elements in group ____A form neither cations nor anions.

True or False

1. Zinc can form ions with different charges.

2. Na^+ and F^- have the same electron configuration.

3. Ionization energy measures the amount of energy released when an ion is formed from a neutral atom.

4. $Co(CO_3)_2$ is a possible compound.

5. A solution of H_3PO_4 contains only H^+ and $H_2PO_4^-$ ions.

6. Ionic crystals conduct electricity.

7. Cuprous ion is the same as copper(II) ion.

8. Many ionic compounds are not water-soluble.

9. Group 5A consists of metals and nonmetals.

10. Elements in group 7A have the largest ionization energies.

11. The octet rule is limited to main group elements.

12. Both men and women suffer the same percent bone loss over their lifetimes.

Match each entry on the left with its partner on the right.

1.	$FeBr_2$	(a)	Sulfite anion
2.	S^{2-}	(b)	Electron-dot symbol
3.	NH_4^+	(c)	Alkali metal
4.	SO_3^{2-}	(d)	Has the same electron configuration as Na^+
5.	Ca	(e)	Iron(II) bromide
6.	$FeBr_3$	(f)	Transition metal
7.	Ar	(g)	Sulfate anion
8.	$\cdot Be \cdot$	(h)	Alkaline earth metal
9.	Co	(i)	Has the same electron configuration as Cl^-
10.	SO_4^{2-}	(j)	Iron(III) bromide
11.	Ne	(k)	Polyatomic cation
12.	K	(l)	Sulfide anion

Chapter 5   Molecular Compounds

Chapter Outline

I. Covalent bonds (Sections 5.1–5.4).
    A Formation of covalent bonds (Section 5.1).
        1. Covalent bonds occur when two atoms share electrons.
        2. Electron sharing results from the overlap of orbitals of two atoms.
        3. The optimum distance between nuclei of two atoms is the bond length.
        4. Seven elements exist as diatomic molecules: H_2, N_2, O_2, F_2, Cl_2, Br_2, I_2.
    B. Covalent bonds and the periodic table (Section 5.2).
        1. Molecular compounds result when atoms form covalent bonds to another atom or to more than one atom.
        2 The octet rule states that each atom in a molecular compound shares the number of electrons necessary to achieve a noble-gas configuration.
        3 Most main group elements form from one to four covalent bonds and obey the octet rule.
           a. Boron forms only three bonds because it has only three valence electrons.
           b. Sulfur and phosphorus may form five or six bonds if they use *d* orbitals.
    C. Multiple covalent bonds (Section 5.3).
        1. Some atoms can share more than one electron pair to form multiple bonds.
           a. A double bond is formed when two pairs are shared.
           b. A triple bond is formed when three pairs are shared.
        2. Even when multiple bonds occur, the atoms still obey the octet rule.
    D. Coordinate bonds occur when one atom donates both of the shared electrons (Section 5.4).
II. Formulas, structures, and shapes (Sections 5.5–5.7).
    A. Formulas (Section 5.5).
        1. Molecular formulas show the numbers and kinds of atoms in one molecule of a compound.
        2. Structural formulas show how atoms are connected.
        3. Lewis structures are structural formulas that show electron lone pairs (Section 5.6).
           a. One approach to drawing Lewis structures involves knowing common bonding patterns.
           b. The other approach is a general method.
              i. Find the number of valence electrons for all atoms.
             ii. Draw a line between each pair of connected atoms to represent an electron pair.
             iii. Place lone pairs around all peripheral atoms to give them octets.
             iv. Place remaining electrons around the central atom.
             v. If the central atom doesn't have an octet, use an electron pair from a neighboring atom to form a multiple bond to the central atom.
        4. Some larger organic molecules are written as condensed structures.
    B. Molecular shapes can be predicted by using the VSEPR model (Section 5.7).
        1. Draw a Lewis structure of the molecule, and identify the atom whose geometry you want to know.
        2. Count the number of charge clouds around the atom.
        3. Predict shape by assuming that the charge clouds orient in space so that they are as far apart as possible.
           a. If there are two charge clouds, the geometry is linear.
           b. If there are three charge clouds, the geometry is linear or bent.
           c. If there are four charge clouds, the geometry is tetrahedral, trigonal pyramidal, or bent.

III. Polar covalent bonds (Sections 5.8–5.9).
    A. Polar covalent bonds occur when the electrons in a covalent bond are attracted more to one atom than another (Section 5.8).
        1. The ability of an atom to attract electrons is called electronegativity.
        2. Atoms with electronegativity differences < 1.9 form polar covalent bonds.
        3. Atoms with electronegativity differences > 1.9 form ionic bonds.
    B. Molecules containing polar covalent bonds can be polar (Section 5.9).
        1. Molecular polarity depends on both the presence of polar covalent bonds and on molecular shape.
        2. Polarity has a dramatic effect on molecular properties.
IV. Molecular compounds (Sections 5.10–5.11).
    A. Naming binary molecular compounds (Section 5.10).
        1. Name the first element in the compound, using a prefix if necessary.
        2. Name the second element, using an *-ide* ending and using a prefix if necessary.
    B. Properties of molecular compounds (Section 5.11).
        1. Molecular compounds are electrically neutral and have no charged particles.
        2. Molecular compounds have low melting and boiling points.
        3. Molecular compounds may be solids, liquids, or gases.

Solutions to Chapter 5 Problems

5.1

    shared electron pair

Each iodine atom achieves the noble gas configuration of xenon.

5.2 (a) PH_3 hydrogen—one covalent bond;   phosphorus—three covalent bonds
    (b) H_2Se hydrogen—one covalent bond;   selenium—two covalent bonds
    (c) HCl hydrogen—one covalent bond;   chlorine—one covalent bond
    (d) SiF_4 fluorine—one covalent bond;   silicon—four covalent bonds

5.3 Lead is a member of group 4A and should form four covalent bonds, as do carbon and silicon. $PbCl_4$ is thus a more likely formula for a compound containing lead and chlorine than is $PbCl_5$.

5.4 (a) CH_2Cl_2. Carbon forms four covalent bonds. Two bonds form between carbon and hydrogen, and the other two form between carbon and chlorine.
    (b) BH_3. Boron forms three covalent bonds.
    (c) NI_3. Nitrogen forms three covalent bonds.
    (d) $SiCl_4$. Silicon, like carbon, forms four covalent bonds.

5.5   In acetic acid, all hydrogen atoms have two outer-shell electrons and all carbon and oxygen atoms have eight outer-shell electrons.

Acetic acid

5.6

Methyl ethyl ketone

Neither of the two circled atoms in the structure on the left has a complete octet, even when electrons not involved in bonding are considered. A double bond between carbon and oxygen allows all atoms to have electron octets.

5.7   C and N must be bonded to each other. After drawing the C—N bond and all bonds to hydrogens, two electrons remain; they are a lone pair on nitrogen. All atoms now have a noble gas configuration.

CH_5N: 14 valence electrons

5.8

(a)

(b)

(c)

5.9   (a) For phosgene, $COCl_2$:

Step 1:   Total valence electrons
4 e⁻ (from C) + 6 e⁻ (from O) + 2 x 7 e⁻ (from Cl) = 24 e⁻

Step 2:   Six electrons are involved in the covalent bonds.

$$\begin{array}{c} O \\ | \\ Cl-C-Cl \end{array}$$

Step 3:   The other 18 electrons are placed in nine lone pairs.

$$\begin{array}{c} :\ddot{O}: \\ | \\ :\ddot{Cl}-C-\ddot{Cl}: \end{array}$$

Step 4:   All electrons are used up in the preceding structure, but carbon doesn't have an electron octet, so one electron pair must be moved from oxygen to form a carbon–oxygen double bond.

Step 5:   The 24 electrons have been used up, and all atoms have a complete octet.

$$\begin{array}{c} :\ddot{O}: \\ \| \\ :\ddot{Cl}-C-\ddot{Cl}: \end{array}$$

(b) For OCl^-:

Step 1:   Total valence electrons
6 e⁻ (from O) + 7 e⁻ (from Cl) + 1 e⁻ (negative charge) = 14 e⁻

Step 2:   Two electrons used.   O—Cl

Step 3:   Twelve additional electrons used. $:\ddot{O}-\ddot{Cl}:^-$

Step 4:   The above structure uses 14 valence electrons, and all atoms have complete octets.

(c) For H_2O_2:

Step 1:   2 e⁻ (from 2 H) + 2 x 6 e⁻ (from O) = 14 electrons

Step 2:   Six electrons are involved in covalent bonds.   H—O—O—H

Step 3:   The other eight electrons are placed in four lone pairs. $H-\ddot{O}-\ddot{O}-H$

Step 4:   The 14 electrons have been used up, and all atoms have complete octets.

(d) For SCl_2: 20 electrons

$$:\ddot{Cl}-\ddot{S}-\ddot{Cl}:$$

5.10

HNO$_3$:   24 electrons

5.11   (a) The molecular formula for methyl methacrylate is C$_6$H$_{10}$O$_2$.
(b) Methyl methacrylate has two double bonds and four electron lone pairs.

Methyl methacrylate

5.12

tetrahedral

5.13   Carbon, the central atom, is surrounded by four bonds. Referring to Table 5.1, we see that chloroform has tetrahedral geometry.

Chloroform

Each carbon of dichloroethylene is surrounded by three charge clouds. Dichloroethylene is planar, with 120° bond angles.

Dichloroethylene

5.14   Both ammonium ion and sulfate ion are tetrahedral.

Ammonium ion

Sulfate ion

5.15   Both molecules are bent and have bond angles of approximately 95°.

5.16

Methionine

a. bent
b. tetrahedral
c. tetrahedral
d. planar triangular
e. pyramidal

5.17   Use Figure 5.7 to predict electronegativity:

Least electronegative — — — — — — — —> *Most electronegative*

H (2.1), P (2.1) < S (2.5) < N (3.0) < O (3.5)

5.18

Electronegativity		Difference	Type of Bond
(a) I (2.5),	Cl (3.0)	0.5	polar covalent
(b) Li (1.0),	O (3.5)	2.5	ionic
(c) Br (2.8),	Br (2.8)	0	covalent
(d) P (2.1),	Br (2.8)	0.7	polar covalent

5.19

Electronegativity	Bond polarity

(a)   F (4.0), S (2.5)

$$\overset{\delta-\quad\delta+}{F-S}$$

(b)   P (2.1), O (3.5)

$$\overset{\delta+\quad\delta-}{P-O}$$

(c)   As (2.0), Cl (3.0)

$$\overset{\delta+\quad\delta-}{As-Cl}$$

5.20

Formaldehyde is polar because of the polarity of the carbon–oxygen bond and because of the two electron lone pairs.

5.21 The —CH₃ portions of diethyl ether are tetrahedral. The C–O–C portion is bent and has a bond angle of 112°. The molecule has the indicated polarity because of the polar C–O bonds and because of the two lone pairs of electrons.

5.22

The difference in electronegativity between Li (1.0) and C (2.5) indicates that the bond between them is polar covalent, with carbon the more electronegative atom. The electrostatic potential map shows that carbon is electron-rich (red) and lithium is electron-poor (blue).

5.23 (a) S₂Cl₂ Disulfur dichloride   (b) ICl Iodine chloride
(c) ICl₃ Iodine trichloride

5.24 (a) SeF₄ Selenium tetrafluoride   (b) P₂O₅ Diphosphorus pentoxide
(c) BrF₃ Bromine trifluoride

5.25 The compound is a molecular solid because it has a low melting point and doesn't conduct electricity.

5.26 AlCl₃ is a covalent compound, and Al₂O₃ is ionic.

Understanding Key Concepts

5.27 Drawing (a) represents an ionic compound because ions are held together by strong attractive forces in all directions. Drawing (b) represents a covalent compound because the covalent bonds that hold atoms together in a molecule are much stronger than the forces between molecules.

5.28 Drawing (a), which shows molecules composed of one sulfur atom and two oxygen atoms, depicts SO₂.

5.29 (a) tetrahedral geometry   (b) pyramidal geometry   (c) planar triangular geometry

5.30 All models except (c) represent a molecule with a tetrahedral central atom. In models (b) and (d), some atoms are hidden.

5.31

(a) (b)

Acetaminophen   C₈H₉NO₂

(c) All carbons except for the starred carbon have planar triangular geometry.
The starred carbon has tetrahedral geometry. Nitrogen has pyramidal geometry.

5.32

Vitamin C

5.33

(a) (b)

Thalidomide $C_{13}H_{10}N_2O_4$

(c) All carbons except for the starred carbons have planar triangular geometry.
   The starred carbons have tetrahedral geometry.
   The nitrogens have pyramidal geometry.

5.34

:O: ← electron-rich

Acetamide

The electrostatic potential maps show that oxygen is the most electron-rich atom (red) in acetamide. The hydrogens are most electron-poor (blue).

Covalent Bonds

5.35 A covalent bond is a chemical bond in which two electrons are shared between two atoms. An ionic bond is formed by the attraction of a positively charged ion to a negatively charged ion. In an ionic bond, both electrons of the electron pair "belong" to the negatively charged ion.

5.36 In a covalent bond, each atom donates an electron to the bond. Both electrons in a coordinate covalent bond come from the same atom.

5.37 (a) oxygen (i) (iv)   (b) potassium (iii)   (c) phosphorus (ii)
       (d) iodine (i) (iv)   (e) hydrogen (i) (ii)   (f) cesium (iii)

5.38 Form covalent bonds: (a) aluminum and bromine; (b) carbon and fluorine
       Form ionic bonds: (c) cesium and iodine; (d) zinc and fluorine; (e) lithium and chlorine

5.39

5.40 Tellurium, a group 6A element, forms two covalent bonds, as do oxygen, sulfur, and other members of group 6A.

5.41 Germanium, a group 4A element, forms four covalent bonds.

5.42 Coordinate covalent bonds: (b) $Cu(NH_3)_4^{2+}$ (c) NH_4^+

5.43 Coordinate covalent bonds: (b) BF_4^- (c) H_3O^+

5.44 Since tin is a member of group 4A, it forms four covalent bonds. $SnCl_4$ is the most likely formula for a molecular compound of tin and chlorine.

5.45 A low-boiling, low-melting compound of gallium and chlorine is most likely covalent (ionic compounds are high-boiling and high-melting). Since gallium is a group 3A element, a likely formula is $GaCl_3$.

5.46 The indicated bond is coordinate covalent because both electrons in the bond come from nitrogen.

$$:N{\equiv}N{-}\overset{..}{\underset{..}{O}}:\quad\text{coordinate covalent}$$

5.47 The indicated bond is coordinate covalent because both electrons in the bond come from sulfur.

$$\begin{array}{c}:\overset{..}{O}:\\ |\ \leftarrow\text{coordinate covalent}\\ S\\ :\overset{..}{\underset{..}{C}l}\diagup\ \diagdown\overset{..}{\underset{..}{C}l}:\end{array}$$

Structural Formulas

5.48 (a) A *molecular formula* shows the numbers and kinds of atoms in a molecule; a *structural formula* shows how the atoms in a molecule are bonded to one another.
(b) A *structural formula* shows the bonds between atoms; a *condensed structure* shows central atoms and the atoms connected to them written as groups but does not show bonds.
(c) A *lone pair* of valence electrons is a pair that is not shared; a *shared pair* of electrons is shared between two atoms as a covalent bond.

5.49 Two possible methods to distinguish between the compounds:
(a) Take the melting point of the two compounds. The covalent solid melts at a lower temperature.
(b) Try to dissolve the two solids in water. The ionic solid is more likely to be water-soluble than the covalent solid.

5.50 (a) N_2 10 valence electrons (b) CO 10 valence electrons
(c) CH_3CH_2CHO 24 valence electrons (d) OF_2 20 valence electrons

5.51

(a) :C≡O: (b) $CH_3\overset{..}{\underset{..}{S}}H$ (c) $H-\overset{..}{\overset{+}{O}}-H$ with H below (d) $H_3C-\overset{..}{N}-CH_3$ with H below

5.52 A compound with the formula C_2H_8 can't exist because any structure drawn would violate the rules of valence.

5.53 Structure (a) is correct. Structure (b) has two carbons with incomplete octets. Structure (c) has one carbon with an incomplete octet and an oxygen bonded to three groups.

5.54

(a) $H-\overset{..}{\underset{..}{O}}-N=\overset{..}{\underset{..}{O}}$

(b) H–C–C≡N: with H above and below the first C

(c) $H-\overset{..}{\underset{..}{F}}:$

5.55

$$\left[\overset{:O:}{\underset{}{:\overset{..}{\underset{..}{O}}-N-\overset{..}{\underset{..}{O}}:}} \right]^{-}$$

Three oxygen atoms and one nitrogen atom yield a total of 23 valence electrons. An additional electron is added so that the octet rule is satisfied for all atoms.

5.56 (a) $CH_3CH_2CH_3$ (b) $H_2C=CHCH_3$ (c) CH_3CH_2Cl

5.57

(a)

H–C–C–C–C–H (with H, O, H, H above and H, H, H below)

(b)

H–C–C–C–OH (with H, H, O above and H, H below)

(c)

H–C–C–O–C–H (with H, H, H above and H, H, H below)

5.58 CH_3COOH

Drawing Lewis Structures

5.59

(a)

(b)

(c)

(d)

(e)

(f)

5.60

(a)

(b)

(c)

5.61

Ethanol

5.62

Dimethyl ether

5.63

Hydrazine

5.64

Tetrachloroethylene contains a double bond.

5.65

Carbon disulfide contains two carbon–sulfur double bonds.

5.66

H—N—O—H   Hydroxylamine

(with lone pairs on N and O, and an H below N)

5.67 Each atom of nitrate ion has 4 inner-shell electrons, plus the 24 electrons pictured, for a total of 32 electrons. Together, carbon and the three oxygens have 31 protons. Since there is one more electron than proton, nitrate ion has a charge of –1.

$$\left[\begin{array}{c} :O: \\ \| \\ :O—N—O: \end{array}\right]^{-}$$

5.68

(a) $\left[\begin{array}{c} :O: \\ \| \\ H—C—O: \end{array}\right]^{-}$ (b) $\left[\begin{array}{c} :O: \\ \| \\ :O—C—O: \end{array}\right]^{2-}$ (c) $\left[\begin{array}{c} :O: \\ | \\ :O—S—O: \end{array}\right]^{2-}$ (d) $\left[:S—C≡N:\right]^{-}$

(e) $\left[\begin{array}{c} :O: \\ | \\ :O—P—O: \\ | \\ :O: \end{array}\right]^{3-}$ (f) $\left[:O—Cl=O\right]^{-}$

Molecular Geometry

5.69 Use Table 5.1 to predict molecular geometry. B equals the number of bonds, and E equals the number of electron lone pairs:

Molecule	Number of bonds	Number of Lone Pairs	Shape	Bond Angle
(a) AB_3	3	0	planar triangular	120°
(b) AB_2E	2	1	bent	120°

5.70 As in the previous problem, use Table 5.1.

Molecule	Number of bonds	Number of Lone Pairs	Shape	Bond Angle
(a) AB_4	4	0	tetrahedral	109°
(b) AB_3E	3	1	pyramidal	109°
(c) AB_2E_2	2	2	bent	109°

5.71

(a)

bond angle = 109°

(b)

bond angle = 105°

(c)

bond angle = 120°

(d)

bond angle = 109°

(e)

bond angle = 109°

5.72

Molecule	Number of Bonding Pairs Around Central Atom	Number of Lone Pairs	Shape	Bond Angle
(a) SiF_4	4	0	tetrahedral	109°
(b) CF_2Cl_2	4	0	tetrahedral	109°
(c) SO_3	3*	0	planar triangular	120°
(d) BBr_3	3	0	planar triangular	120°
(e) NF_3	3	1	pyramidal	109°

* For determining shape, the double bond counts as one bond pair, and the number of bonds is three.

5.73

tetrahedral →

planar triangular

Alanine

5.74

Vinyl acetate

All carbons are planar triangular, except for the starred carbon, which is tetrahedral.

Polarity of Bonds and Molecules

5.75 The most electronegative elements are found on the upper right side of the periodic table. The least electronegative elements are found on the left side of the periodic table.

5.76 Using the periodic table, count up from element 114. Element 119 should occur under francium and accordingly should be one of the least electronegative elements, with an electronegativity of 0.8.

5.77 *Less electronegative* $---->$ *More electronegative*

$$K < Li < C < Br < Cl$$

5.78 *More electronegative* $---->$ *Less electronegative*

$$Cl > C > Cu > Ca > Cs$$

5.79

$$\overset{\delta+\ \ \delta-}{\text{(a) I—Br}} \quad \overset{\delta-\ \ \delta+}{\text{(b) O—H}} \quad \overset{\delta+\ \ \delta-}{\text{(c) C—F}} \quad \overset{\delta-\ \ \delta+}{\text{(d) N—C}} \quad \text{(e) nonpolar}$$

5.80

$$\overset{\delta-\ \ \delta+}{\text{(a) O—Br}} \quad \overset{\delta-\ \ \delta+}{\text{(b) N—H}} \quad \overset{\delta+\ \ \delta-}{\text{(c) P—O}} \quad \text{(d) nonpolar} \quad \overset{\delta-\ \ \delta+}{\text{(e) C—Li}}$$

5.81

Electronegativity		Difference	Type of Bond
(a) Be (1.5),	F (4.0)	2.5	ionic
(b) Ca (1.0),	Cl (3.0)	2.0	ionic
(c) O (3.5),	H (2.1)	1.4	polar covalent
(d) Be (1.5),	Br (2.8)	1.3	polar covalent

5.82 Use Figure 5.7 to determine bond polarities.

Least polar bonds $---->$ *Most polar bonds*

$$PH_3 < HCl < H_2O < CF_4$$

5.83 Both compounds have dipole moments due to the lone pair electrons of the central atom. The dipole moment of NH_3 is greater because of the bond polarities of the three N–H bonds; the P–H bonds are nonpolar.

5.84

(a)

H—Cl

polar

(b)

H—P—H with H below

polar

(c)

H—O with H below

polar

(d) nonpolar

5.85

$$:\!\overset{..}{O}\!=\!C\!=\!\overset{..}{O}\!:$$

$$^+S\!=\!\overset{..}{\underset{..}{O}}$$
$$^-:\!\overset{..}{\underset{..}{O}}\!:$$

The bond polarities of the individual bonds cancel in CO_2, but the bent geometry in SO_2 makes it polar.

5.86 Both molecules are polar because of the lone pair electrons. Water is more polar because the bonds between oxygen and hydrogen are polar covalent, but the bonds between sulfur and hydrogen are nonpolar.

Names and Formulas of Molecular Compounds

5.87 (a) NO_2 nitrogen dioxide   (b) SF_6 sulfur hexafluoride
         (c) BrI_5 bromine pentaiodide   (d) N_2O_3 dinitrogen trioxide
         (e) NI_3 nitrogen triiodide   (f) IF_7 iodine heptafluoride

5.88 (a) $SiCl_4$ silicon tetrachloride   (b) NaH sodium hydride
         (c) SbF_5 antimony pentafluoride   (d) OsO_4 osmium tetroxide

5.89 (a) PI_3 (b) $AsCl_3$ (c) P_4S_3 (d) Al_2F_6 (c) N_2O_4 (f) $AsCl_5$

5.90 (a) SeO_2 (b) XeO_4 (c) N_2S_5 (d) P_3Se_4

Applications

5.91 Carbon monoxide is reactive because its lone electron pairs can form coordinate covalent bonds with other molecules. Nitric oxide is reactive because it has an unpaired electron.

:C:::O: :N::O:

5.92 A vasodilator is a chemical that relaxes arterial walls, causing a drop in blood pressure.

5.93 A polymer is formed of many repeating units contained in a long chain.

5.94 Carbohydrates, proteins, and DNA are all examples of polymers that occur in nature.

5.95 Chemical names are complicated because the name of each of the 20 million known chemicals must be unique and must contain enough information for chemists to identify the composition and structure of each chemical.

5.96 The name of a chemical gives no clue as to whether the chemical is natural or synthetic, although certain chemicals are unlikely to occur in nature.

General Questions and Problems

5.97 (a) It was thought that noble gases couldn't form bonds because they already had a full electron octet.

(b)

Xenon tetrafluoride

5.98

(a)

(b) The C=O carbon atoms have planar triangular geometry, and the other carbons have tetrahedral geometry.
(c) The C=O bonds are polar.

5.99

Both molecules are expected to be polar because of their C—O bonds.

5.100 Consult Figure 5.4 for help.

(a) Carbon forms four bonds. The correct formula is CCl_4.
(b) Nitrogen forms three bonds. The correct formula is N_2H_4.
(c) Sulfur forms two bonds. The correct formula is H_2S.
(d) C_2OS *could* actually be correct (S=C=C=O), but compounds with such adjacent double bonds are rare. More likely is the formula COS, a structural relative of carbon dioxide (S=C=O).

5.101 (a) $BaCl_2$ (i)   (b) $Ca(NO_3)_2$ (i), (ii)   (c) BCl_4^- (ii), (iii)   (d) $TiBr_4$ (ii)

5.102

(a)

(b) Phosphonium ion is tetrahedral.

(c) Phosphorus donates its lone pair of electrons to H^+ to form a coordinate covalent bond.
(d) Number of electrons: 15 (from P) + 3 (from 3 H) = 18
     Number of protons: 15 (from P) + 4 (from 4 H) = 19
PH_4^+ is positive because the number of protons exceeds the number of electrons by one.

5.103 Both figures show that the halogens and the group 6A elements are the most electronegative. It is surprising to see in Figure 4.1 that group 5A elements have virtually zero electron affinity, whereas their electronegativities given in Figure 5.7 are significant.

5.104 *Compound*   *Name*

(a) $CaCl_2$ calcium chloride
(b) $TeCl_2$ tellurium dichloride
(c) BF_3 boron trifluoride
(d) $MgSO_4$ magnesium sulfate
(e) K_2O potassium oxide
(f) FeF_3 iron(III) fluoride
(g) PF_3 phosphorus trifluoride

5.105 $TiBr_4$ is a molecular compound, and TiO_2 is an ionic compound. The electronegativity difference between Ti and Br (approx. 1.4) indicates polar covalent bonds, whereas the electronegativity difference between Ti and O (approx. 2.1) indicates ionic bonds.

5.106

Chloral hydrate

5.107

Dichromate ion

5.108

Oxalic acid

5.109

(a)

(b)

5.110

(a)

(b)

Self-Test for Chapter 5

Multiple Choice

1. Which of these diatomic molecules contains a double bond?
    (a) H_2 (b) I_2 (c) O_2 (d) N_2

2. Which of these molecules is pyramidal?
    (a) CBr_4 (b) $AlCl_3$ (c) SF_6 (d) PH_3

3. Choose the element that forms three covalent bonds and has one lone pair of electrons.
    (a) C (b) N (c) O (d) F

4. How many charge clouds does the molecule H_2S have?
    (a) 2 (b) 3 (c) 4 (d) can't tell

5. Which of the following double bonds is not likely to be found in organic molecules?
    (a) O=O (b) C=C (c) C=O (d) C=N

6. All of the following are true about the polyatomic ion BF_4^- except:
    (a) All atoms don't have electron octets. (b) It has polar covalent bonds. (c) It contains a coordinate covalent bond. (d) It has a tetrahedral shape.

7. One of these molecules doesn't contain a polar covalent bond. Which is it?
    (a) $BeBr_2$ (b) PCl_3 (c) CO_2 (d) CS_2

8. Which of the following compounds is polar?
    (a) $BeBr_2$ (b) PCl_3 (c) CO_2 (d) CS_2

9. A name for S_2F_2 is:
    (a) sulfur fluoride (b) sulfur difluoride (c) disulfur fluoride (d) disulfur difluoride

10. Which of the following is not true for molecular compounds?
    (a) They are water-soluble. (b) They can be solids, liquids, or gases. (c) They are composed of nonmetals. (d) They have low melting points.

Sentence Completion

1. An _____ element strongly attracts electrons.

2. A molecular compound that occurs in living organisms is called a _____ .

3. In Lewis structures, a line represents a _____ bond.

4. _____ and _____ are the most common triple bonds in chemical compounds.

5. The formula X_2 represents a _____ molecule.

6. A molecule whose central atom forms three bonds and has no lone pairs has a _____ _____ shape.

7. _____ orbitals in sulfur and phosphorus can be used for covalent bonds.

8. N_2 contains a _____ bond.

9.   _____ molecular compounds are formed from only two elements.

10.   Many molecular compounds are soluble in _____ liquids.

11.   Large organic molecules are often written as _____ structures.

True or False

1. Br_2 is a molecular compound.

2.   Six electrons are used to form a triple bond.

3.   Coordinate covalent bonds occur only in cations or anions, not in neutral compounds.

4.   The first step in drawing a Lewis structure is to find the total number of electrons in the combined atoms.

5. $AlCl_3$ is a pyramidal molecule.

6.   The shape of ionic compounds can be predicted by the VSEPR model.

7.   Electronegativity decreases in going down the periodic table.

8. CI_4 contains polar covalent bonds.

9.   Both planar and bent molecules have bond angles of 120°.

10.   Group 7A elements can form more than one covalent bond.

11.   Bent compounds may have either one or two lone pairs.

Match each entry on the left with its partner on the right.

1. BCl_3

2. Planar molecule

3. Bent molecule

4. Cl_2

5. BCl_4^-

6. NaI

7. C≡O

8. SF_6

9. Linear molecule

10. O=C=O

11. Pyramidal molecule

12. CH_3Cl

(a) Contains a pure covalent bond

(b) $BeCl_2$

(c) Central atom has more than an electron octet

(d) NH_3

(e) Contains a triple bond

(f) H_2O

(g) Contains a double bond

(h) Central atom doesn't have an electron octet

(i) Contains an ionic bond

(j) $AlCl_3$

(k) Contains a coordinate covalent bond

(l) Contains a polar covalent bond

Chapter Outline

I. Chemical equations (Sections 6.1–6.2).
    A. Writing chemical equations (Section 6.1).
        1. A chemical equation describes a chemical reaction.
            a. The reactants are written on the left.
            b. The products are written on the right.
            c. An arrow goes between them to indicate the chemical change.
        2. The number and kinds of atoms must be the same on both sides of the equation. This is known as the law of conservation of mass.
        3. Numbers that are placed in front of formulas are called coefficients.
        4. States of matter (s), (g), (l) are often placed after chemical formulas.
    B. Balancing chemical equations (Section 6.2).
        1. Write an unbalanced equation using the correct formulas for all substances.
        2. Add appropriate coefficients to balance the atoms of each type, one at a time.
        3. Check to make sure that the numbers and kinds of atoms are balanced.
        4. Make sure all coefficients are reduced to their lowest whole-number values.
II. Molar relationships (Sections 6.3–6.7).
    A. The mole (Section 6.3).
        1. Molecular weight is the sum of the atomic weights of atoms in a molecule.
        2. Formula weight is the sum of the atomic weights of atoms in a formula unit.
        3. One mole of any pure substance has a mass equal to its molecular or formula weight in grams.
            a. Avogadro's number (6.022×10^{23}), known as the mole, represents the number of formula units that has a mass in grams equal to its weight in amu.
    B. Mole–mass relationships (Section 6.4–6.6).
        1. Gram–mole conversions (Section 6.4).
            a. Molar mass is the mass in grams of one mole of any substance.
            b. Molar mass is a conversion factor that allows calculation of moles from grams and of grams from moles.
        2. Molar relationships from chemical equations (Section 6.5).
            a. The coefficients in an equation tell how many moles of reactant or product are involved in the reaction.
            b. The coefficients can be put in a mole ratio, which can be used as a conversion factor.
        3. Mass relationships (Section 6.6).
            a. Mole–mole conversions are made by using mole ratios.
            b. Mole–mass conversions are made by using molar mass as a conversion factor.
            c. Mass–mass conversions can be made by a mass–mole conversion of one substance, using mole ratios, and making a mole–mass conversion of the other substance.
        4. A summary of calculations using mole–mass relationships:
            a. Write the balanced equation.
            b. Choose mole–mass relationships and mole ratios to calculate the desired quantity.
            c. Set up the factor-label method to calculate the answer.
            d. Check the answer with a ballpark solution.
    C. Percent yield (Section 6.7).
        1. Percent yield = actual yield/theoretical yield x 100%.
        2. Theoretical yield is found by using a mass–mass calculation.

III. Chemical reactions (Sections 6.8–6.13).
  A. Classes of chemical reactions (Section 6.8).
    1. Precipitation reactions occur when an insoluble solid is formed.
    2. Acid–base reactions occur when an acid and a base react to yield water and a salt.
    3. Redox reactions occur when electrons are transferred between reaction partners.
  B. Precipitation reactions (Section 6.9).
    1. To predict whether a precipitation reaction occurs, you must know the solubilities of the products.
    2. Table 6.1 gives general solubility rules to predict if a precipitation reaction will occur.
  C. Acid–base reactions (Section 6.10).
    1. Acid–base reactions are known as neutralization reactions because when the reaction is complete the solution is neither acidic nor basic.
    2. An example: HA(*aq*) + MOH(*aq*) —> H$_2$O(*l*) + MA(*aq*)
    3. When a carbonate or bicarbonate is one of the reactants, CO$_2$ is also produced.
  D. Redox reactions (Sections 6.11–6.12).
    1. Definition of redox reactions (Section 6.11).
      a. A redox reaction occurs when electrons are transferred from one atom to another.
      b. The substance that loses electrons is oxidized and is known as the reducing agent.
      c. The substance that gains electrons is reduced and is known as the oxidizing agent.
      d. Redox reactions occur during corrosion, combustion, respiration, and photography.
    2. Recognizing redox reactions (Section 6.12).
      a. With some substances, it isn't obvious if a redox reaction has occurred.
      b. In a neutral compound, oxidation numbers are assigned to each element to indicate electron ownership.
      c. To assign oxidation numbers:
        i. An atom in its elemental state has an oxidation number of zero.
        ii. A monatomic ion has an oxidation number equal to its charge.
        iii. In a molecular compound, an atom usually has the same oxidation number that it would have if it were a monatomic ion.
        iv. The sum of the oxidation numbers in a neutral compound is zero.
        v. The oxidation number of oxygen is usually –2; the oxidation number of hydrogen is usually +1.
  E. Net ionic equations (Section 6.13).
    1. A molecular equation shows reactants and products as molecules and doesn't indicate if they are ions.
    2. An ionic equation is written if ions are involved and shows all ionic reactants and products.
    3. A net ionic equation includes only the ions that undergo change and deletes spectator ions.

Solutions to Chapter 6 Problems

6.1 (a) Solid cobalt(II) chloride plus gaseous hydrogen fluoride yield solid cobalt(II) fluoride plus gaseous hydrogen chloride.

(b) Aqueous lead(II) nitrate plus aqueous potassium iodide yield solid lead(II) iodide plus aqueous potassium nitrate.

6.2 An equation is balanced if the number and types of atoms on the left side equals the number and types of atoms on the right side.

(a) On the left: 2 H + Cl + K + O
     On the right: 2 H + Cl + K + O The equation is balanced.

(b) On the left: 1 C + 4 H + 2 Cl
    On the right: 1 C + 3 H + 3 Cl   The equation is not balanced.
(c) Balanced
(d) Not balanced in H, O.

6.3   *Step 1*: Write the unbalanced equation.

$$O_2 \longrightarrow O_3$$

Step 2: Balance the atoms of each type, one by one.

$$3\,O_2 \longrightarrow 2\,O_3 \quad \text{The equation is balanced.}$$

6.4   (a) $Ca(OH)_2 + 2\,HCl \longrightarrow CaCl_2 + 2\,H_2O$

    (b) $4\,Al + 3\,O_2 \longrightarrow 2\,Al_2O_3$

    (c) $2\,CH_3CH_3 + 7\,O_2 \longrightarrow 4\,CO_2 + 6\,H_2O$

    (d) $2\,AgNO_3 + MgCl_2 \longrightarrow 2\,AgCl + Mg(NO_3)_2$

6.5   *Step 1:* $A + B_2 \longrightarrow A_2B_2$

    Step 2: $2\,A + B_2 \longrightarrow A_2B_2$ The equation is balanced.

6.6   (a) For ibuprofen, $C_{13}H_{18}O_2$:

At. wt of 13 C = 13 x 12.0 amu = 156.0 amu
At. wt of 18 H = 18 x 1.0 amu = 18.0 amu
At. wt of 2 O = 2 x 16.0 amu = 32.0 amu
MW of $C_{13}H_{18}O_2$ = 206.0 amu

    (b) For phenobarbital, $C_{12}H_{12}N_2O_3$:

At. wt of 12 C = 12 x 12.0 amu = 144.0 amu
At. wt of 12 H = 12 x 1.0 amu = 12.0 amu
At. wt of 2 N = 2 x 14.0 amu = 28.0 amu
At. wt of 3 O = 3 x 16.0 amu = 48.0 amu
MW of $C_{12}H_{12}N_2O_3$ = 232.0 amu

6.7   At. wt of 6 C = 6 x 12.0 amu =   72.0 amu
At. wt of 8 H = 8 x 1.0 amu =   8.0 amu
At. wt of 6 O = 6 x 16.0 amu =   96.0 amu
MW of $C_6H_8O_6$ = 176.0 amu

Since the molecular weight of ascorbic acid is 176.0 amu, 6.022×10^{23} molecules have a mass of 176 g.

$$500 \text{ mg ascorbic acid} \times \frac{1 \text{ g}}{10^3 \text{ mg}} \times \frac{6.022 \times 10^{23} \text{ molecules}}{176 \text{ g}} = 1.71 \times 10^{21} \text{ molecules}$$

A 500 mg tablet contains 1.71×10^{21} molecules of ascorbic acid.

6.8   At. wt of 9 C = 9 x 12.0 amu =   108.0 amu
      At. wt of 8 H = 8 x 1.0 amu =   8.0 amu
      <u>At. wt of 4 O = 4 x 16.0 amu =   64.0 amu</u>
      MW of $C_9H_8O_4$ = 180.0 amu

$$5.0 \times 10^{20} \text{ molecules} \times \frac{180.0 \text{ g}}{1 \text{ mol}} \times \frac{1 \text{ mol}}{6.022 \times 10^{23} \text{ molecules}} = 0.15 \text{ g}$$

5.0×10^{20} molecules of aspirin weigh 0.15 g.

6.9

Cytosine $C_4H_5N_3O$

At. wt of 4 C = 4 x 12.0 amu = 48.0 amu
At. wt of 5 H = 5 x 1.0 amu =   5.0 amu
At. wt of 3 N = 3 x 14.0 amu = 42.0 amu
<u>At. wt of 1 O = 1 x 16.0 amu = 16.0 amu</u>
MW of $C_4H_5N_3O$ = 111.0 amu

6.10   Molar mass of C_2H_6O = 46.0 g/mol

$$10.0 \text{ g} \times \frac{1 \text{ mol}}{46.0 \text{ g}} = 0.217 \text{ mol in a } 10.0 \text{ g sample}$$

Ballpark check: The sample size, 10.0 g, is about 1/5 mol, or about 0.2 mol.

$$0.10 \text{ mol} \times \frac{46.0 \text{ g}}{1 \text{ mol}} = 4.6 \text{ g in a } 0.10 \text{ mol sample}$$

6.11   Molar mass of acetaminophen = 151 g

$$0.0225 \text{ mol} \times \frac{151 \text{ g}}{1 \text{ mol}} = 3.40 \text{ g}$$

5.00 g acetaminophen weighs more than 0.0225 mol.

6.12   (a) $Ni(s) + 2\,HCl(aq) \longrightarrow NiCl_2(aq) + H_2(g)$

$$9.81 \text{ mol HCl} \times \frac{1 \text{ mol Ni}}{2 \text{ mol HCl}} = 4.90 \text{ mol Ni}$$

(b) $6.00 \text{ mol Ni} \times \dfrac{1 \text{ mol NiCl}_2}{1 \text{ mol Ni}} = 6.00 \text{ mol NiCl}_2 \text{ from } 6.00 \text{ mol Ni}$

$12.00 \text{ mol HCl} \times \dfrac{1 \text{ mol NiCl}_2}{2 \text{ mol HCl}} = 6.00 \text{ mol NiCl}_2 \text{ from } 12.00 \text{ mol HCl}$

6.00 mol $NiCl_2$ can be formed from 6.00 mol Ni and 12.00 mol HCl.

6.13 $6\,CO_2 + 6\,H_2O \longrightarrow C_6H_{12}O_6 + 6\,O_2$

$$15.0 \text{ mol glucose} \times \frac{6 \text{ mol CO}_2}{1 \text{ mol glucose}} = 90.0 \text{ mol CO}_2$$

6.14   (a) This is a mole-to-mole problem.

$$9.90 \text{ mol SiO}_2 \times \frac{4 \text{ mol HF}}{1 \text{ mol SiO}_2} = 39.6 \text{ mol HF}$$

(b) This is a mass-to-mass problem.

$$23.0 \text{ g SiO}_2 \times \frac{1 \text{ mol SiO}_2}{60.1 \text{ g SiO}_2} \times \frac{2 \text{ mol H}_2\text{O}}{1 \text{ mol SiO}_2} \times \frac{18.0 \text{ g H}_2\text{O}}{1 \text{ mol H}_2\text{O}} = 13.8 \text{ g H}_2\text{O}$$

Ballpark check: About 1/3 mol SiO_2 is used to produce 2/3 mol H_2O. Since the molar mass of H_2O is 18 g, we expect about 12 g H_2O, which is reasonably close to the calculated answer.

6.15   For WO_3:

$$5.00 \text{ g W} \times \frac{1 \text{ mol W}}{183.8 \text{ g W}} \times \frac{1 \text{ mol WO}_3}{1 \text{ mol W}} \times \frac{231.8 \text{ g WO}_3}{1 \text{ mol WO}_3} = 6.31 \text{ g WO}_3$$

For H_2:

$$5.00 \text{ g W} \times \frac{1 \text{ mol W}}{183.8 \text{ g W}} \times \frac{3 \text{ mol H}_2}{1 \text{ mol W}} \times \frac{2.02 \text{ g H}_2}{1 \text{ mol H}_2} = 0.165 \text{ g H}_2$$

6.31 g WO_3 and 0.165 g H_2 are needed to produce 5.00 g W.

Ballpark check: About 3/4 of the mass of WO_3 is composed of W. Thus, 5.00 g W comes from about 4/3 x 5.00 g W = 6.33 g WO_3, a result almost identical to the calculated result.

6.16 First, find the limiting reagent.

$$19.4 \text{ g } C_2H_4 \text{ x } \frac{1 \text{ mol } C_2H_4}{28.0 \text{ g } C_2H_4} = 0.693 \text{ mol } C_2H_4; \; 50 \text{ g HCl x } \frac{1 \text{ mol HCl}}{36.5 \text{ g HCl}} = 1.4 \text{ mol HCl}$$

Ethylene is the limiting reagent.

$$19.4 \text{ g ethylene } \text{ x } \frac{1 \text{ mol ethylene}}{28.0 \text{ g ethylene}} \text{ x } \frac{1 \text{ mol ethyl chloride}}{1 \text{ mol ethylene}} \text{ x } \frac{64.5 \text{ g ethyl chloride}}{1 \text{ mol ethyl chloride}}$$

$$= 44.7 \text{ g ethyl chloride}$$

$$\frac{25.5 \text{ g ethyl chloride actually formed}}{44.7 \text{ g theoretical yield of ethyl chloride}} \text{ x } 100\% = 57.0\%$$

Ballpark check: The amount of ethylene reactant corresponds to about 2/3 mol. The theoretical yield of product is about 2/3 mol ethyl chloride (somewhat more than 40 g). Since the actual yield is 25.5 g, the percent yield should be around 60%.

6.17 Note: to save space, ethylene oxide will be represented as EO, and ethylene glycol as EG.

$$35.0 \text{ g EO x } \frac{1 \text{ mol EO}}{44.0 \text{ g EO}} \text{ x } \frac{1 \text{ mol EG}}{1 \text{ mol EO}} \text{ x } \frac{62.0 \text{ g EG}}{1 \text{ mol EG}} = 49.3 \text{ g ethylene glycol}$$

This quantity represents the maximum possible amount of ethylene glycol that can be produced. If the reaction occurs in 96.0% yield, then 49.3 g EG x 0.960 = 47.3 g EG is actually formed.

Ballpark check: A bit more than 3/4 mol EO is used to produce the same number of mol of EG, corresponding to about 47 g EG, close to the calculated result. The percent yield is also in close agreement.

6.18 According to the equation $A_2 + 2 B_2 \longrightarrow 2 AB_2$, two B_2 are needed for each A_2. In the illustration, there are seven A_2 and 17 B_2. Since the seven A_2 can consume only 14 B_2, A_2 is the limiting reagent.

6.19 (a) $AgNO_3(aq) + KCl(aq) \longrightarrow AgCl(s) + KNO_3(aq)$
Precipitation: Solid AgCl is formed.

(b) $2 Al(s) + 3 Br_2(l) \longrightarrow 2 AlBr_3(s)$
Redox reaction: Al^{+3} is formed from Al, and Br^- is formed from Br_2.

(c) $Ca(OH)_2(aq) + 2 HNO_3(aq) \longrightarrow 2 H_2O(l) + Ca(NO_3)_2(aq)$
Acid–base neutralization

6.20 Use Table 6.1 for solubility guidelines.

Insoluble
(a) $CdCO_3$ (most carbonates are insoluble)
(c) $PbSO_4$ (exception to the rule that sulfates are soluble)
(e) Hg_2Cl_2 (exception to the rule that chlorides are soluble)

Soluble
(b) Na_2S
(d) $(NH_4)_3PO_4$

6.21   As in Worked Example 6.16, identify the products, and use Table 6.1 to predict their solubility. If the products are insoluble, a precipitation reaction will occur.

(a) $NiCl_2(aq) + (NH_4)_2S(aq) \longrightarrow 2\ NH_4Cl(aq) + NiS(s)$
A precipitation reaction will occur.

(b) $2\ AgNO_3(aq) + CaBr_2(aq) \longrightarrow Ca(NO_3)_2(aq) + 2\ AgBr(s)$
A precipitation reaction will occur.

6.22   (a) $2\ CsOH(aq) + H_2SO_4(aq) \longrightarrow Cs_2SO_4(aq) + 2\ H_2O(l)$

(b) $Ca(OH)_2(aq) + 2\ CH_3CO_2H(aq) \longrightarrow Ca(CH_3CO_2)_2(aq) + 2\ H_2O(l)$

(c) $NaHCO_3(aq) + HBr(aq) \longrightarrow NaBr(aq) + CO_2(g) + H_2O(l)$

6.23

	Oxidized Reactant/ *Reducing Agent*	*Reduced Reactant/* *Oxidizing Agent*
(a)	Fe	Cu^{2+}
(b)	Mg	Cl_2
(c)	Al	Cr_2O_3

The oxidizing agent is the reduced reactant, and the reducing agent is the oxidized reactant.

6.24 $2\ K(s) + Br_2(l) \longrightarrow 2\ KBr(s)$
Reducing agent   Oxidizing agent

6.25

	Compound	*Oxidation Number of Metal*	*Name*
(a)	VCl_3	+3	vanadium(III) chloride
(b)	$SnCl_4$	+4	tin(IV) chloride
(c)	CrO_3	+6	chromium(VI) oxide
(d)	$Cu(NO_3)_2$	+2	copper(II) nitrate
(e)	$NiSO_4$	+2	nickel(II) sulfate

6.26 Oxidation numbers are written above the atoms.

(a) $\overset{+1-2}{Na_2S}(aq) + \overset{+2-1}{NiCl_2}(aq) \longrightarrow 2\,\overset{+1-1}{NaCl}(aq) + \overset{+2-2}{NiS}(s)$

This reaction is not a redox reaction because no atoms change oxidation numbers.

(b) $2\,\overset{0}{Na}(s) + 2\,\overset{+1-2}{H_2O}(l) \longrightarrow 2\,\overset{+1-2+1}{NaOH}(aq) + \overset{0}{H_2}(g)$

Sodium is oxidized and hydrogen is reduced in this reaction.

(c) $\overset{0}{C}(s) + \overset{0}{O_2}(g) \longrightarrow \overset{+4-2}{CO_2}(g)$

Carbon is oxidized and oxygen is reduced in this redox reaction.

(d) $\overset{+2-2}{CuO}(s) + 2\,\overset{+1-1}{HCl}(aq) \longrightarrow \overset{+2-1}{CuCl_2}(aq) + \overset{+1-2}{H_2O}(l)$

This is not a redox reaction because no atoms change oxidation number.

(e) $2\,\overset{+7-2}{MnO_4^-}(aq) + 5\,\overset{+4-2}{SO_2}(g) + 2\,\overset{+1-2}{H_2O}(l) \longrightarrow 2\,\overset{+2}{Mn^{2+}}(aq) + 5\,\overset{+6-2}{SO_4^{2-}}(aq) + 4\,\overset{+1}{H^+}(aq)$

In this redox reaction, the oxidation number of Mn changes from +7 to +2 and the oxidation number of S changes from +4 to +6.

6.27 (a) Write the equation, including all ions.

$$Zn(s) + Pb^{2+} + 2\,NO_3^- \longrightarrow Zn^{2+} + 2\,NO_3^- + Pb(s)$$

The nitrate ions on each side cancel.

$$Zn(s) + Pb^{2+}(aq) \longrightarrow Zn^{2+}(aq) + Pb(s)$$

(b) $OH^-(aq) + H^+(aq) \longrightarrow H_2O(l)$

K^+ and SO_4^{2-} cancel, and coefficients are reduced.

(c) $2\,Fe^{3+}(aq) + Sn^{2+}(aq) \longrightarrow 2\,Fe^{2+}(aq) + Sn^{4+}(aq)$

The chloride ions cancel.

Understanding Key Concepts

6.28 Product mixture (d) is the only mixture that contains the same number of atoms as (a).

6.29 (c) $2\,A + B_2 \longrightarrow A_2B_2$

6.30 (d) $\longrightarrow$ (c)
reactants   products

6.31 Methionine: $C_5H_{11}NO_2S$

At. wt of   5 C =   5 x 12.0 amu =   60.0 amu
At. wt of 11 H = 11 x 1.0   amu =   11.0 amu
At. wt of   N =   =   14.0 amu
At. wt of   2 O =   2 x 16.0 amu =   32.0 amu
At. wt of   S =   =   32.1 amu

MW of $C_5H_{11}NO_2S$ = 149.1 amu

6.32 (a) $A_2 + 3B_2 \longrightarrow 2AB_3$

(b) $1.0 \text{ mol } A_2 \times \dfrac{2 \text{ mol } AB_3}{1 \text{ mol } A_2} = 2.0 \text{ mol } AB_3$

$1.0 \text{ mol } B_2 \times \dfrac{2 \text{ mol } AB_3}{3 \text{ mol } B_2} = 0.67 \text{ mol } AB_3$

6.33 (a) Mixing of sodium and carbonate ions produces outcome (1). No insoluble product is formed, and sodium and carbonate ions remain in solution.
(b) Mixing barium and chromate ions produces outcome (2). $BaCrO_4$ precipitate forms (one barium ion for each chromate ion), and the excess barium ions remain in solution.
(c) Mixing silver and sulfite ions yields outcome (3). Ag_2SO_3 precipitate forms (two silver ions for each sulfite ion), and no Ag^+ or SO_3^{2-} ions remain in solution.

6.34 The observed product is a precipitate that contains two cations per anion. From the list of cations, Ag^+ is the only one that forms precipitates and has a 2:1 cation/anion ratio with the anions listed. The anion can be either CO_3^{2-} or CrO_4^{2-}, since both form precipitates with Ag^+. Thus, the possible products are Ag_2CO_3 and Ag_2CrO_4.

6.35 *Note:* To save space, ethylene oxide will be represented as EO, and ethylene glycol as EG.

$9.0 \text{ g } H_2O \times \dfrac{1 \text{ mol } H_2O}{18.0 \text{ g } H_2O} \times \dfrac{1 \text{ mol } EO}{1 \text{ mol } H_2O} \times \dfrac{44.0 \text{ g } EO}{1 \text{ mol } EO} = 22 \text{ g ethylene oxide}$

$9.0 \text{ g } H_2O \times \dfrac{1 \text{ mol } H_2O}{18.0 \text{ g } H_2O} \times \dfrac{1 \text{ mol } EG}{1 \text{ mol } H_2O} \times \dfrac{62.0 \text{ g } EG}{1 \text{ mol } EG} = 31 \text{ g ethylene glycol}$

Balancing Chemical Equations

6.36 A balanced equation is an equation in which the number of atoms of each kind is the same on both sides of the reaction arrow.

6.37 Changing the subscripts on a substance to balance an equation changes the identity of the substance and makes the equation meaningless.

6.38 (a) $SO_2(g) + H_2O(g) \longrightarrow H_2SO_3(aq)$

(b) $2K(s) + Br_2(l) \longrightarrow 2KBr(s)$

(c) $C_3H_8(g) + 5O_2(g) \longrightarrow 3CO_2(g) + 4H_2O(g)$

6.39 $4NH_3(g) + Cl_2(g) \longrightarrow N_2H_4(l) + 2NH_4Cl(s)$

6.40 (a) $2C_2H_6(g) + 7O_2(g) \longrightarrow 4CO_2(g) + 6H_2O(l)$

(b) balanced

(c) $2Mg(s) + O_2(g) \longrightarrow 2MgO(s)$

(d) $2K(s) + 2H_2O(l) \longrightarrow 2KOH(aq) + H_2(g)$

6.41 (a) balanced

(b) $C_2H_8N_2 + 2 N_2O_4 \longrightarrow 3 N_2 + 2 CO_2 + 4 H_2O$

(c) balanced

(d) $2 N_2O \longrightarrow 2 N_2 + O_2$

6.42 (a) $Hg(NO_3)_2(aq) + 2 LiI(aq) \longrightarrow 2 LiNO_3(aq) + HgI_2(s)$

(b) $I_2(s) + 5 Cl_2(g) \longrightarrow 2 ICl_5(s)$

(c) $4 Al(s) + 3 O_2(g) \longrightarrow 2 Al_2O_3(s)$

(d) $CuSO_4(aq) + 2 AgNO_3(aq) \longrightarrow Ag_2SO_4(s) + Cu(NO_3)_2(aq)$

(e) $2 Mn(NO_3)_3(aq) + 3 Na_2S(aq) \longrightarrow Mn_2S_3(s) + 6 NaNO_3(aq)$

(f) $4 NO_2(g) + O_2(g) \longrightarrow 2 N_2O_5(g)$

(g) $P_4O_{10}(s) + 6 H_2O(l) \longrightarrow 4 H_3PO_4(aq)$

6.43 $Na_2CO_3(aq) + 2 HNO_3(aq) \longrightarrow CO_2(g) + 2 NaNO_3(aq) + H_2O(l)$

6.44 (a) $2 C_4H_{10}(g) + 13 O_2(g) \longrightarrow 8 CO_2(g) + 10 H_2O(l)$

(b) $C_2H_6O(g) + 3 O_2(g) \longrightarrow 2 CO_2(g) + 3 H_2O(l)$

(c) $2 C_8H_{18}(g) + 25 O_2(g) \longrightarrow 16 CO_2(g) + 18 H_2O(l)$

Molar Masses and Moles

6.45 One mole of a substance is an amount equal to its formula weight in grams. One mole of a molecular compound contains 6.022×10^{23} molecules.

6.46 Molecular weight is the sum of the atomic weights of the individual atoms in a molecule. Formula weight is the sum of the atomic weights of the individual atoms in a formula unit of any compound, whether molecular or ionic.
Molar mass is the mass in grams of 6.022×10^{23} molecules or formula units of any substance.

6.47

$$\frac{6.022 \times 10^{23} \text{ units } Na_2SO_4}{1 \text{ mol } Na_2SO_4} \times \frac{2 \text{ Na}^+ \text{ ions}}{1 \text{ unit } Na_2SO_4} = \frac{1.204 \times 10^{24} \text{ Na}^+ \text{ ions}}{1 \text{ mol } Na_2SO_4}$$

$$\frac{6.022 \times 10^{23} \text{ units } Na_2SO_4}{1 \text{ mol } Na_2SO_4} \times \frac{1 \text{ SO}_4^{2-} \text{ ion}}{1 \text{ unit } Na_2SO_4} = \frac{6.022 \times 10^{23} \text{ SO}_4^{2-} \text{ ions}}{1 \text{ mol } Na_2SO_4}$$

6.48 Each formula unit of K_2SO_4 contains three ions—two K^+ ions and one SO_4^{2-} ion. Thus, one mole of K_2SO_4 contains three moles of ions, and

$$1.75 \text{ mol } K_2SO_4 \times \frac{3 \text{ mol ions}}{1 \text{ mol } K_2SO_4} = 5.25 \text{ mol ions}$$

6.49

$$16.2 \text{ g Ca} \times \frac{1 \text{ mol}}{40.1 \text{ g Ca}} \times \frac{6.022 \times 10^{23} \text{ atoms}}{1 \text{ mol}} = 2.43 \times 10^{23} \text{ atoms}$$

6.50

$$2.68 \times 10^{22} \text{ atoms} \times \frac{1 \text{ mol}}{6.022 \times 10^{23} \text{ atoms}} \times \frac{238.0 \text{ g}}{1 \text{ mol}} = 10.6 \text{ g uranium}$$

6.51–6.53

Compound	Molar Mass	Moles C	Atoms C	Grams C
(a) $CaCO_3$	100.1 g	1	6.022×10^{23}	12.00
(b) $CO(NH_2)_2$	60.05	1	6.022×10^{23}	12.00
(c) $C_2H_6O_2$	62.0	2	1.204×10^{24}	24.0

6.54   Molar mass of caffeine = 194 g

$$125 \text{ mg caffeine} \times \frac{1 \text{ g}}{10^3 \text{ mg}} \times \frac{1 \text{ mol caffeine}}{194 \text{ g caffeine}} = 6.44 \times 10^{-4} \text{ mol caffeine}$$

6.55   Molar mass of aspirin = 180 g

$$500 \text{ mg aspirin} \times \frac{1 \text{ g}}{10^3 \text{ mg}} \times \frac{1 \text{ mol aspirin}}{180 \text{ g aspirin}} = 2.78 \times 10^{-3} \text{ mol aspirin}$$

6.56   Molar mass of $C_{16}H_{13}ClN_2O$:
(16 x 12.0 g) + (13 x 1.0 g) + (35.5 g) + (2 x 14.0 g) + 16.0 g = 284.5 g/ mol Valium

6.57, 6.58, 6.61

Compound	Molar Mass	Number of Moles in 4.50 g	Number of Grams in 0.075 mol
(a) $Al_2(SO_4)_3$	342.1 g	0.0132 mol	25.7 g
(b) $NaHCO_3$	84.0 g	0.0536 mol	6.30 g
(c) $C_4H_{10}O$	74.0 g	0.0608 mol	5.55 g
(d) $C_{16}H_{18}N_2O_5S$	350.1 g	0.0129 mol	26.3 g

Note: Slightly different values for molar mass result when exact atomic weights are used.

6.59   Note: For simplicity, calcium citrate is indicated by "C cit", and 1000 mg = 1.00 g

$$1.00 \text{ g Ca} \times \frac{1 \text{ mol Ca}}{40.1 \text{ g Ca}} \times \frac{1 \text{ mol C cit}}{3 \text{ mol Ca}} \times \frac{498.5 \text{ g C cit}}{1 \text{ mol C cit}} = 4.14 \text{ g calcium citrate}$$

6.60   Molar mass of aspirin = 180 g

$$0.0015 \text{ mol aspirin} \times \frac{180 \text{ g aspirin}}{1 \text{ mol aspirin}} = 0.27 \text{ g aspirin}$$

$$0.0015 \text{ mol} \times \frac{6.022 \times 10^{23} \text{ molecules}}{1 \text{ mol}} = 9.0 \times 10^{20} \text{ molecules aspirin}$$

6.62

$$8.5 \times 10^{20} \text{ formula units } \times \frac{1 \text{ mol}}{6.022 \times 10^{23} \text{ formula units}} = 1.4 \times 10^{-3} \text{ mol}$$

$$0.0014 \text{ mol } CaC_2O_4 \times \frac{128 \text{ g } CaC_2O_4}{1 \text{ mol } CaC_2O_4} = 0.18 \text{ g } CaC_2O_4$$

Mole and Mass Relationships from Chemical Equations

6.63   (a) $N_2(g) + O_2(g) \longrightarrow 2 NO(g)$

(b) 7.50 mol of N_2 are needed to react with 7.50 mol of O_2.

(c) $3.81 \text{ mol } N_2 \times \dfrac{2 \text{ mol NO}}{1 \text{ mol } N_2} = 7.62 \text{ mol NO}$

(d) $0.250 \text{ mol NO} \times \dfrac{1 \text{ mol } O_2}{2 \text{ mol NO}} = 0.125 \text{ mol } O_2$

6.64   (a) $C_4H_8O_2(l) + 2 H_2(g) \longrightarrow 2 C_2H_6O(l)$

(b) 3.0 mol of ethyl alcohol are produced from 1.5 mol of ethyl acetate.

(c) $1.5 \text{ mol } C_4H_8O_2 \times \dfrac{2 \text{ mol } C_2H_6O}{1 \text{ mol } C_4H_8O_2} \times \dfrac{46.0 \text{ g } C_2H_6O}{1 \text{ mol } C_2H_6O} = 138 \text{ g } C_2H_6O$

(d) $12.0 \text{ g } C_4H_8O_2 \times \dfrac{1 \text{ mol } C_4H_8O_2}{88.0 \text{ g } C_4H_8O_2} \times \dfrac{2 \text{ mol } C_2H_6O}{1 \text{ mol } C_4H_8O_2} \times \dfrac{46.0 \text{ g } C_2H_6O}{1 \text{ mol } C_2H_6O}$
$$= 12.5 \text{ g } C_2H_6O$$

(e) $12.0 \text{ g } C_4H_8O_2 \times \dfrac{1 \text{ mol } C_4H_8O_2}{88.0 \text{ g } C_4H_8O_2} \times \dfrac{2 \text{ mol } H_2}{1 \text{ mol } C_4H_8O_2} \times \dfrac{2.0 \text{ g } H_2}{1 \text{ mol } H_2} = 0.55 \text{ g } H_2$

6.65   (a) Molar mass of $Mg(OH)_2 = 24.3 \text{ g} + (2 \times 16.0 \text{ g}) + (2 \times 1.0 \text{ g}) = 58.3 \text{ g}$

(b) $1.2 \text{ g } Mg(OH)_2 \times \dfrac{1 \text{ mol } Mg(OH)_2}{58.3 \text{ g } Mg(OH)_2} = 0.021 \text{ mol } Mg(OH)_2$

Since there are 3 teaspoons in a tablespoon, the dose per teaspoon is 0.007 mol.

6.66   (a) $N_2(g) + 3 H_2(g) \longrightarrow 2 NH_3(g)$

(b) $16.0 \text{ g } NH_3 \times \dfrac{1 \text{ mol } NH_3}{17.0 \text{ g } NH_3} \times \dfrac{1 \text{ mol } N_2}{2 \text{ mol } NH_3} = 0.471 \text{ mol } N_2$

(c) $75.0 \text{ g } N_2 \times \dfrac{1 \text{ mol } N_2}{28.0 \text{ g } N_2} \times \dfrac{3 \text{ mol } H_2}{1 \text{ mol } N_2} \times \dfrac{2.0 \text{ g } H_2}{1 \text{ mol } H_2} = 16.1 \text{ g } H_2$

6.67 (a) $N_2H_4(l) + 3 O_2(g) \longrightarrow 2 NO_2(g) + 2 H_2O(g)$

(b) $165 \text{ g } N_2H_4 \times \dfrac{1 \text{ mol } N_2H_4}{32.0 \text{ g } N_2H_4} \times \dfrac{3 \text{ mol } O_2}{1 \text{ mol } N_2H_4} = 15.5 \text{ mol } O_2$

(c) $15.5 \text{ mol } O_2 \times \dfrac{32.0 \text{ g } O_2}{1 \text{ mol } O_2} = 496 \text{ g } O_2$

6.68 (a) $Fe_2O_3(s) + 3 CO(g) \longrightarrow 2 Fe(s) + 3 CO_2(g)$

(b) $3.02 \text{ g } Fe_2O_3 \times \dfrac{1 \text{ mol } Fe_2O_3}{159.6 \text{ g } Fe_2O_3} \times \dfrac{3 \text{ mol } CO}{1 \text{ mol } Fe_2O_3} \times \dfrac{28.0 \text{ g } CO}{1 \text{ mol } CO} = 1.59 \text{ g } CO$

(c) $1.68 \text{ mol } Fe_2O_3 \times \dfrac{3 \text{ mol } CO}{1 \text{ mol } Fe_2O_3} \times \dfrac{28.0 \text{ g } CO}{1 \text{ mol } CO} = 141 \text{ g } CO$

6.69 (a) $2 Mg(s) + O_2(g) \longrightarrow 2 MgO(s)$

(b) $25.0 \text{ g } Mg \times \dfrac{1 \text{ mol } Mg}{24.3 \text{ g } Mg} \times \dfrac{1 \text{ mol } O_2}{2 \text{ mol } Mg} \times \dfrac{32.0 \text{ g } O_2}{1 \text{ mol } O_2} = 16.5 \text{ g } O_2$

41.5 g MgO will result from reaction of 25.0 g Mg and 16.5 g O_2.

(c) $25.0 \text{ g } O_2 \times \dfrac{1 \text{ mol } O_2}{32.0 \text{ g } O_2} \times \dfrac{2 \text{ mol } Mg}{1 \text{ mol } O_2} \times \dfrac{24.3 \text{ g } Mg}{1 \text{ mol } Mg} = 38.0 \text{ g } Mg$

63.0 g MgO will result from reaction of 25.0 g O_2 and 38.0 g Mg.

6.70 $TiO_2(s) \longrightarrow Ti(s) + O_2(g)$

$95 \text{ kg Ti} \times \dfrac{1 \text{ mol Ti}}{47.9 \text{ g Ti}} \times \dfrac{1 \text{ mol } TiO_2}{1 \text{ mol Ti}} \times \dfrac{79.9 \text{ g } TiO_2}{1 \text{ mol } TiO_2} = 158 \text{ kg } TiO_2$

6.71

$105 \text{ kg } Fe_2O_3 \times \dfrac{10^3 \text{ g}}{1 \text{ kg}} \times \dfrac{1 \text{ mol } Fe_2O_3}{159.6 \text{ g } Fe_2O_3} \times \dfrac{3 \text{ mol } CO}{1 \text{ mol } Fe_2O_3} = 1.97 \times 10^3 \text{ mol } CO$

Percent Yield

6.72

(a) $25.0 \text{ g } CO \times \dfrac{1 \text{ mol } CO}{28.0 \text{ g } CO} = 0.893 \text{ mol } CO$; $6.00 \text{ g } H_2 \times \dfrac{1 \text{ mol } H_2}{2.02 \text{ g } H_2} = 2.97 \text{ mol } H_2$
Carbon monoxide is the limiting reagent.

(b) $10.0 \text{ g } CO \times \dfrac{1 \text{ mol } CO}{28.0 \text{ g } CO} \times \dfrac{1 \text{ mol } CH_3OH}{1 \text{ mol } CO} \times \dfrac{32.0 \text{ g } CH_3OH}{1 \text{ mol } CH_3OH} = 11.4 \text{ g } CH_3OH$

(c) $\dfrac{9.55 \text{ g}}{11.4 \text{ g}} \times 100\% = 83.8\% \text{ yield}$

6.73

(a) $75.0 \text{ kg N}_2\text{H}_4 \times \dfrac{1 \text{ kmol N}_2\text{H}_4}{32.0 \text{ kg N}_2\text{H}_4} = 2.34 \text{ kmol N}_2\text{H}_4$

$75.0 \text{ kg O}_2 \times \dfrac{1 \text{ kmol O}_2}{32.0 \text{ kg O}_2} = 2.34 \text{ kmol O}_2$

Although the same number of moles of each are present, O_2 is the limiting reagent because three moles of O_2 are needed to react with each mole of hydrazine, according to the balanced equation.

(b) $75.0 \text{ kg O}_2 \times \dfrac{1 \text{ kmol O}_2}{32.0 \text{ kg O}_2} \times \dfrac{2 \text{ kmol NO}_2}{3 \text{ kmol O}_2} \times \dfrac{46.0 \text{ kg NO}_2}{1 \text{ kmol NO}_2} = 71.8 \text{ kg NO}_2$

(c) $\dfrac{59.3 \text{ g actually formed}}{71.8 \text{ g theoretical yield}} \times 100\% = 82.6\%$

6.74 (a) $CH_4(g) + 2\,Cl_2(g) \longrightarrow CH_2Cl_2(l) + 2\,HCl(g)$

(b) $50.0 \text{ g CH}_4 \times \dfrac{1 \text{ mol CH}_4}{16.0 \text{ g CH}_4} \times \dfrac{2 \text{ mol Cl}_2}{1 \text{ mol CH}_4} \times \dfrac{71.0 \text{ g Cl}_2}{1 \text{ mol Cl}_2} = 444 \text{ g Cl}_2$

(c) If the reaction occurred in 100% yield:

$50.0 \text{ g CH}_4 \times \dfrac{1 \text{ mol CH}_4}{16.0 \text{ g CH}_4} \times \dfrac{1 \text{ mol CH}_2\text{Cl}_2}{1 \text{ mol CH}_4} \times \dfrac{85.0 \text{ g CH}_2\text{Cl}_2}{1 \text{ mol CH}_2\text{Cl}_2} = 266 \text{ g CH}_2\text{Cl}_2$

Since the reaction occurs in 76% yield:

$266 \text{ g} \times 0.76 = 202 \text{ g CH}_2\text{Cl}_2$ are actually formed.

6.75

(a) $55.8 \text{ g K}_2\text{PtCl}_4 \times \dfrac{1 \text{ mol K}_2\text{PtCl}_4}{415.3 \text{ g K}_2\text{PtCl}_4} \times \dfrac{2 \text{ mol NH}_3}{1 \text{ mol K}_2\text{PtCl}_4} \times \dfrac{17.0 \text{ g NH}_3}{1 \text{ mol NH}_3} = 4.57 \text{ g NH}_3$

(b) If the reaction occurred in 100% yield:

$55.8 \text{ g K}_2\text{PtCl}_4 \times \dfrac{1 \text{ mol K}_2\text{PtCl}_4}{415.3 \text{ g K}_2\text{PtCl}_4} \times \dfrac{1 \text{ mol cisplatin}}{1 \text{ mol K}_2\text{PtCl}_4} \times \dfrac{300.1 \text{ g cisplatin}}{1 \text{ mol cisplatin}}$

$= 40.3 \text{ g cisplatin}$

Since the reaction occurs in 95% yield, $40.3 \text{ g} \times 0.95 = 38 \text{ g}$ cisplatin are actually formed.

Types of Chemical Reactions

6.76 (a) $Mg(s) + 2\,HCl(aq) \longrightarrow MgCl_2(aq) + H_2(g)$ redox reaction

(b) $KOH(aq) + HNO_3(aq) \longrightarrow KNO_3(aq) + H_2O(l)$ neutralization reaction

(c) $Pb(NO_3)_2(aq) + 2\,HBr(aq) \longrightarrow PbBr_2(s) + 2\,HNO_3(aq)$ precipitation reaction

(d) $Ca(OH)_2(aq) + 2\,H_2SO_4(aq) \longrightarrow 2\,H_2O(l) + CaSO_4(aq)$ neutralization reaction

6.77

(a) $2 H^+(aq) + SO_4^{2-}(aq) + 2 K^+(aq) + 2 OH^-(aq) \rightarrow 2 K^+(aq) + SO_4^{2-}(aq) + 2 H_2O(l)$

$H^+(aq) + OH^-(aq) \rightarrow H_2O(l)$

(b) $Mg^{2+}(aq) + 2 OH^-(aq) + 2 H^+(aq) + 2 Cl^-(aq) \rightarrow Mg^{2+}(aq) + 2 Cl^-(aq) + 2 H_2O(l)$

$H^+(aq) + OH^-(aq) \rightarrow H_2O(l)$

6.78

(a) $Ba^{2+}(aq) + 2 NO_3^-(aq) + 2 K^+(aq) + SO_4^{2-}(aq) \rightarrow BaSO_4(s) + 2 K^+(aq) + 2 NO_3^-(aq)$

$Ba^{2+}(aq) + SO_4^{2-}(aq) \rightarrow BaSO_4(s)$

(b) $Zn(s) + 2 H^+(aq) + SO_4^{2-}(aq) \rightarrow Zn^{2+}(aq) + H_2(g) + SO_4^{2-}(aq)$

$Zn(s) + 2 H^+(aq) \rightarrow Zn^{2+}(aq) + H_2(g)$

6.79   Use Section 6.9 as a guide.
Only $ZnSO_4$ is soluble in water.

6.80   Use Section 6.9 as a guide.
Only $Ba(NO_3)_2$ is soluble in water.

6.81   A precipitation reaction occurs only in (b). A neutralization occurs with the reagents in (a).

(b) $FeCl_2(aq) + 2 KOH(aq) \longrightarrow Fe(OH)_2(s) + 2 KCl(aq)$

6.82   If the products consist of soluble ions, no reaction will occur. No reaction occurs in (b) and (c).

(a) $2 NaBr(aq) + Hg_2(NO_3)_2(aq) \longrightarrow Hg_2Br_2(s) + 2 NaNO_3(aq)$

(d) $(NH_4)_2CO_3(aq) + CaCl_2(aq) \longrightarrow CaCO_3(s) + 2 NH_4Cl(aq)$

(e) $2 KOH(aq) + MnBr_2(aq) \longrightarrow Mn(OH)_2(s) + 2 KBr(aq)$

(f) $3 Na_2S(aq) + 2 Al(NO_3)_3(aq) \longrightarrow Al_2S_3(s) + 6 NaNO_3(aq)$

6.83   In net ionic reactions, no spectator ions appear. Otherwise, the equations are balanced for number of atoms and charge, and coefficients are reduced to their lowest common denominators.

(a) $Mg(s) + Cu^{2+}(aq) \longrightarrow Mg^{2+}(aq) + Cu(s)$

(b) $2 Cl^-(aq) + Pb^{2+}(aq) \longrightarrow PbCl_2(s)$

(c) $2 Cr^{3+}(aq) + 3 S^{2-}(aq) \longrightarrow Cr_2S_3(s)$

6.84   (a) $2 Au^{3+}(aq) + 3 Sn(s) \longrightarrow 3 Sn^{2+}(aq) + 2 Au(s)$

(b) $2 I^-(aq) + Br_2(l) \longrightarrow 2 Br^-(aq) + I_2(s)$

(c) $2 Ag^+(aq) + Fe(s) \longrightarrow Fe^{2+}(aq) + 2 Ag(s)$

Redox Reactions and Oxidation Numbers

6.85   In general, the best reducing agents are metals. The most reactive reducing agents are in groups 1A and 2A. The most reactive oxidizing agents are in groups 6A and 7A.

6.86   The most easily reduced elements are found in groups 6A and 7A. The most easily oxidized elements are in groups 1A and 2A.

6.87   *Gains electrons:* (a) oxidizing agent, (d) substance undergoing reduction
Loses electrons: (b) reducing agent, (c) substance undergoing oxidation

6.88   Oxidation number increases: (b) reducing agent, (c) substance undergoing oxidation
Oxidation number decreases: (a) oxidizing agent, (d) substance undergoing reduction

6.89
(a) $\overset{+5\ -2}{N_2O_5}$ (b) $\overset{+4\ -2}{SO_3^{2-}}$ (c) $\overset{0\ +1\ -2}{CH_2O}$ (d) $\overset{+1\ +5\ -2}{HClO_3}$

6.90   (a) Co: +3   (b) Fe: +2   (c) U: +6   (d) Cu: +2   (e) Ti: +4   (f) Sn: +2

6.91   The reduced element gains electrons, and the oxidized element loses electrons.

	(a)	(b)	(c)
Oxidized	Si	Br	Sb
Reduced	Cl	Cl	Cl

6.92

	(a)	(b)	(c)	(d)
Oxidized	S	Na	Zn	Cl
Reduced	O	Cl	Cu	F

Applications

6.93   The most serious error in calculating Avogadro's number by spreading oil on water is the estimate of the size of the area the oil covered. Some approximations that Franklin made, but that can be determined with reasonable precision, are the volume of oil, the mass of the oil, its density and its molar mass. Other assumptions, involving the thickness of the oil layer and the arrangement of oil molecules on the surface of the water, are also sources of error.

6.94   The formula for ferrous sulfate is $FeSO_4$. Its molar mass is 151.9 g/mol.

$$250 \text{ mg FeSO}_4 \ \times \ \frac{55.8 \text{ g Fe}}{151.9 \text{ g FeSO}_4} \ = \ 91.8 \text{ mg Fe}$$

6.95

$$\frac{0.067 \text{ g}}{1 \text{ L}} \ \times \ \frac{1 \text{ mol}}{190 \text{ g}} \ = \ \frac{3.5 \times 10^{-4} \text{ mol}}{1 \text{ L}}$$

3.5×10^{-4} mol of sodium urate dissolve in 1.00 L of water.

6.96   Elemental zinc is the reducing agent and Mn^{+4} is the oxidizing agent.

General Questions and Problems

6.97

(a) $15.0 \text{ g Zn } \times \dfrac{1 \text{ mol Zn}}{65.4 \text{ g Zn}} \times \dfrac{1 \text{ mol H}_2}{1 \text{ mol Zn}} \times \dfrac{2.02 \text{ g H}_2}{1 \text{ mol H}_2} = 0.463 \text{ g H}_2$

(b) In this redox reaction, H^+ is reduced (oxidizing agent) and Zn is oxidized (reducing agent).

6.98

$80.0 \text{ kg H}_2\text{O } \times \dfrac{1 \text{ mol H}_2\text{O}}{18.0 \text{ g H}_2\text{O}} \times \dfrac{1 \text{ mol Li}_2\text{O}}{1 \text{ mol H}_2\text{O}} \times \dfrac{29.8 \text{ g Li}_2\text{O}}{1 \text{ mol Li}_2\text{O}} = 132 \text{ kg Li}_2\text{O}$

This is not a redox reaction because the oxidation numbers of reactant and product atoms remain the same.

6.99 (a) $2 \text{ Al}(s) + \text{Fe}_2\text{O}_3(s) \longrightarrow \text{Al}_2\text{O}_3(l) + 2 \text{ Fe}(l)$

(b) $2 \text{ NH}_4\text{NO}_3(s) \longrightarrow 2 \text{ N}_2(g) + \text{O}_2(g) + 4 \text{ H}_2\text{O}(g)$

6.100 Molar mass of batrachotoxin $(\text{C}_{31}\text{H}_{42}\text{N}_2\text{O}_6) = 538 \text{ g/mol}$

$0.05 \text{ μg } \times \dfrac{1 \text{ g}}{10^6 \text{ μg}} \times \dfrac{1 \text{ mol}}{538 \text{ g}} \times \dfrac{6.022 \times 10^{23} \text{ molecules}}{1 \text{ mol}} = 6 \times 10^{13} \text{ molecules}$

6.101 $\text{CuCl}_2(aq) + \text{Na}_2\text{CO}_3(aq) \longrightarrow \text{CuCO}_3(s) + 2 \text{ NaCl}(aq)$
A precipitate of CuCO_3 forms

$\text{Cu}^{2+}(aq) + \text{CO}_3{}^{2-}(aq) \longrightarrow \text{CuCO}_3(s)$

6.102 (a) $\text{C}_{12}\text{H}_{22}\text{O}_{11}(s) \longrightarrow 12 \text{ C}(s) + 11 \text{ H}_2\text{O}(l)$

(b) $60.0 \text{ g sucrose } \times \dfrac{1 \text{ mol sucrose}}{342 \text{ g sucrose}} \times \dfrac{12 \text{ mol C}}{1 \text{ mol sucrose}} \times \dfrac{12.0 \text{ g C}}{1 \text{ mol C}} = 25.3 \text{ g carbon}$

(c) $6.50 \text{ g C } \times \dfrac{1 \text{ mol C}}{12.0 \text{ g C}} \times \dfrac{11 \text{ mol H}_2\text{O}}{12 \text{ mol C}} \times \dfrac{18.0 \text{ g H}_2\text{O}}{1 \text{ mol H}_2\text{O}} = 8.94 \text{ g H}_2\text{O}$

6.103 (a) $\text{Cu}(s) + 4 \text{ H}^+(aq) + 2 \text{ NO}_3{}^-(aq) \longrightarrow \text{Cu}^{2+}(aq) + 2 \text{ NO}_2(g) + 2 \text{ H}_2\text{O}(l)$

(b) $35.0 \text{ g HNO}_3 \times \dfrac{1 \text{ mol HNO}_3}{63.0 \text{ g HNO}_3} \times \dfrac{1 \text{ mol Cu}}{4 \text{ mol HNO}_3} \times \dfrac{63.5 \text{ g Cu}}{1 \text{ mol Cu}} = 8.82 \text{ g Cu}$

35.0 g HNO_3 is more than enough to dissolve 5.00 g Cu.

6.104

(a) $1.50 \text{ g C}_2\text{H}_6\text{O} \times \dfrac{1 \text{ mol C}_2\text{H}_6\text{O}}{46.0 \text{ g C}_2\text{H}_6\text{O}} \times \dfrac{2 \text{ mol K}_2\text{Cr}_2\text{O}_7}{3 \text{ mol C}_2\text{H}_6\text{O}} \times \dfrac{294.2 \text{ g K}_2\text{Cr}_2\text{O}_7}{1 \text{ mol K}_2\text{Cr}_2\text{O}_7}$

   $= 6.40 \text{ g K}_2\text{Cr}_2\text{O}_7$

(b) $80.0 \text{ g C}_2\text{H}_6\text{O} \times \dfrac{1 \text{ mol C}_2\text{H}_6\text{O}}{46.0 \text{ g C}_2\text{H}_6\text{O}} \times \dfrac{3 \text{ mol C}_2\text{H}_4\text{O}_2}{3 \text{ mol C}_2\text{H}_6\text{O}} \times \dfrac{60.0 \text{ g C}_2\text{H}_4\text{O}_2}{1 \text{ mol C}_2\text{H}_4\text{O}_2}$

   $= 104 \text{ g C}_2\text{H}_4\text{O}_2$

6.105

$100.0 \text{ lb C}_6\text{H}_{12}\text{O}_6 \times \dfrac{454 \text{ g}}{1 \text{ lb}} \times \dfrac{1 \text{ mol C}_6\text{H}_{12}\text{O}_6}{180.0 \text{ g C}_6\text{H}_{12}\text{O}_6} \times \dfrac{2 \text{ mol C}_2\text{H}_6\text{O}}{1 \text{ mol C}_6\text{H}_{12}\text{O}_6} \times \dfrac{46.0 \text{ g C}_2\text{H}_6\text{O}}{1 \text{ mol C}_2\text{H}_6\text{O}}$

   $= 2.32 \times 10^4 \text{ g C}_2\text{H}_6\text{O}$

$2.32 \times 10^4 \text{ g ethanol} \times \dfrac{1 \text{ mL ethanol}}{0.789 \text{ g ethanol}} \times \dfrac{1 \text{ qt}}{946.4 \text{ mL}} = 31.1 \text{ qt ethanol}$

6.106 (a) $\text{Al(OH)}_3(aq) + 3 \text{ HNO}_3(aq) \longrightarrow \text{Al(NO}_3)_3(aq) + 3 \text{ H}_2\text{O}(l)$

(b) $3 \text{ AgNO}_3(aq) + \text{FeCl}_3(aq) \longrightarrow 3 \text{ AgCl}(s) + \text{Fe(NO}_3)_3(aq)$

(c) $(\text{NH}_4)_2\text{Cr}_2\text{O}_7(s) \longrightarrow \text{Cr}_2\text{O}_3(s) + 4 \text{ H}_2\text{O}(g) + \text{N}_2(g)$

(d) $\text{Mn}_2(\text{CO}_3)_3(s) \longrightarrow \text{Mn}_2\text{O}_3(s) + 3 \text{ CO}_2(g)$

6.107 (a) $\text{P}_4 + 5 \text{ O}_2 \longrightarrow 2 \text{ P}_2\text{O}_5$

(b) The reactants both have an oxidation number of zero. In the product, the oxidation number of oxygen is –2, and the oxidation number of phosphorus is +5. P_4 is the reducing agent, and O_2 is the oxidizing agent.

6.108 (a) $2 \text{ SO}_2(g) + \text{O}_2(g) \longrightarrow 2 \text{ SO}_3(g)$

(b) $\text{SO}_3(g) + \text{H}_2\text{O}(g) \longrightarrow \text{H}_2\text{SO}_4(l)$

(c) The oxidation number of sulfur is +4 in SO_2 and is +6 in both SO_3 and H_2SO_4.

Self-Test for Chapter 6

Multiple Choice

1. Which of the following salts is soluble in water?
    (a) FeSO_4 (b) BaSO_4 (c) SrSO_4 (d) PbSO_4

2. Which of the following compounds has sulfur in a +1 oxidation state?
    (a) S_2F_2 (b) H_2SO_4 (c) SO_2 (d) Na_2S

3. What mass of CaCO_3 has the same number of molecules as 21 g of NaF?
    (a) 10 g (b) 20 g (c) 50 g (d) 100 g

4.   In the equation $P_2O_5 + 3\,H_2O \longrightarrow 2\,H_3PO_4$ the mole ratio of product to H_2O is:
(a) 2:1   (b) 2:3   (c) 3:2   (d) 1:2

5.   When the equation $SiCl_4 + H_2O \longrightarrow SiO_2 + HCl$ is balanced, the coefficients are:
(a) 1,1,1,1   (b) 1,1,1,2   (c) 1,2,1,2   (d) 1,2,1,4

6.   Which of the following is not a redox process?
(a) respiration   (b) corrosion   (c) neutralization   (d) combustion

7.   If you wanted to remove Ba^{2+} from solution, which reagent would you add?
(a) CH_3CO_2H (b) NaOH   (c) H_2SO_4 (d) HCl

8.   In the reaction $2\,Ca + O_2 \longrightarrow 2\,CaO$, how many grams of CaO can be produced from 20 g
of Ca? (a) 20 g   (b) 28 g   (c) 40 g   (d) 56 g

9.   When HCl is added to a solution, bubbles of gas appear. Which compound is probably
present in the solution?
(a) $SrCO_3$ (b) $Ca(OH)_2$ (c) AgBr   (d) K_2SO_4

10. $3\,NO_2 + H_2O \longrightarrow 2\,HNO_3 + NO$

All the following statements about this reaction are true except:
(a) The starting material is both oxidized and reduced.
(b) NO_2 in the atmosphere might contribute to acid rain.
(c) At least 6 g of H_2O are needed to react completely with 46 g of NO_2.
(d) 92 g of NO_2 produces 28 g of NO.

Sentence Completion

1.   The numbers placed in front of formulas to balance equations are called _____.

2.   A _____ is a solid that forms during a reaction.

3.   Ions that appear on both sides of the reaction arrow are _____ ions.

4.   The substances in a reaction can be solids, liquids, or gases, or they can be in _____

solution.

5.   Grams and moles can be converted by using _____ _____ as a conversion factor.

6.   The amount of a substance produced in a reaction, divided by the amount that could

theoretically be produced, is the _____ _____.

7.   In a chemical equation, _____ are shown on the left of the reaction arrow.

8.   The oxidation state of gold in $AuCl_3$ is _____.

9.   In the reaction $2\,Mg + O_2 \longrightarrow 2\,MgO$, Mg is the _____ agent.

10.   A reaction between an acid and a base is a _____ reaction.

True or False

1. A mole of oxygen atoms has the same mass as a mole of nitrogen atoms.

2. The coefficients in chemical reactions show the relative numbers of moles of reactants and products.

3. Limestone ($CaCO_3$) can be dissolved by treatment with HNO_3.

4. In a redox equation, the oxidizing agent is oxidized and the reducing agent is reduced.

5. If all coefficients in a chemical equation are even numbers, the equation is not properly balanced.

6. Mole ratios are used to convert between moles and grams of a compound.

7. In the reaction between K and Cl_2, K is the oxidizing agent.

8. In the reaction $4 Al + 3 O_2 \longrightarrow 2 Al_2O_3$, the mole ratio of product to Al is 2.

9. Most sodium salts are soluble in water.

10. The same compound can be both oxidized and reduced in a reaction.

Match each entry on the left with its partner on the right.

1. Zn   (a) Converts moles Na to grams Na

2. $C_3H_8O + O_2 \longrightarrow C_3H_6O + H_2O$ (b) Molar mass of NaF

3. 42.0 amu   (c) Redox reaction

4. 23.0 g sodium / 1 mol   (d) Precipitation reaction

5. $CoCO_3$ (e) Salt soluble in water

6. $S + O_2 \longrightarrow SO_2$ (f) Unbalanced equation

7. $HCl + NaOH \longrightarrow NaCl + H_2O$ (g) Converts grams Na to moles Na

8. 42.0 g   (h) Oxidized in a battery

9. 1 mol / 23.0 g sodium   (i) Salt insoluble in water

10. MnO_2 (j) Neutralization reaction

11. $AgNO_3 + NaCl \longrightarrow AgCl + NaNO_3$ (k) Formula weight of NaF

12. $CoCl_2$ (l) Reduced in a battery

Chapter Outline

I. Energy (Sections 7.1–7.4).
   A. Energy and chemical bonds (Section 7.1).
      1. There are two kinds of energy.
         a. Potential energy is stored energy.
         b. Kinetic energy is the energy of motion.
      2. Chemical bonds are a form of potential energy.
      3. Whether a reaction occurs, and how much heat is associated, depends on the potential energy of reactants and products.
   B. Heat changes during chemical reactions (Section 7.2).
      1. Bond dissociation energies measure the strength of covalent bonds.
         a. Bond breaking requires heat and is endothermic.
         b. Bond formation releases heat and is exothermic.
      2. The reverse of an endothermic process is exothermic, and the reverse of an exothermic process is endothermic.
      3. The law of conservation of energy states that energy can neither be created nor destroyed during any physical or chemical change.
      4. The difference between the energy needed for breaking bonds and the energy released in forming bonds is the heat of reaction, also known as enthalpy (ΔH).
   C. Exothermic and endothermic reactions: ΔH (Section 7.3).
      1. In exothermic reactions, the bond dissociation energies of the products are greater than the bond dissociation energies of the reactants, and ΔH is negative.
      2. In endothermic reactions, the bond dissociation energies of the products are smaller than the bond dissociation energies of the reactants, and ΔH is positive.
      3. The amount of heat released in the reverse of a reaction is equal to that absorbed in the forward reaction, but ΔH has the opposite sign.
   D. Free energy: ΔG (Section 7.4).
      1. Spontaneous processes.
         a. A spontaneous process proceeds without any external influence.
         b. A nonspontaneous process needs a constant external source of energy.
      2. Entropy (ΔS) measures the amount of disorder in a system.
         a. If disorder increases, ΔS is positive.
         b. If disorder decreases, ΔS is negative.
      3. The absorption of heat and the increase or decrease in disorder determine if a reaction will be spontaneous.
         a. $\Delta G = \Delta H - T\Delta S$.
         b. If ΔG is negative, the process is spontaneous, and the reaction is exergonic.
         c. If ΔG is positive, the process isn't spontaneous, and the reaction is endergonic.
      4. ΔG for the reverse of a reaction is equal in value to ΔG for the forward reaction, but the sign is changed.
      5. Some nonspontaneous processes become spontaneous when temperature increases.
II. Reaction rates (Sections 7.5–7.6).
   A. How reactions occur (Section 7.5).
      1. In addition to the value of ΔG, other factors determine if a reaction will occur.
         a. Reactants must collide in the correct orientation.
         b. The energy of collision must be great enough to cause bond breaking.

      c. Many reactions with a favorable free energy don't occur at room temperature, and heat must be added to get them started.

   2. The energy changes during a reaction can be graphed on a reaction energy diagram.

   3. The amount of energy needed to produce favorable collisions is the activation energy E_{act}.

      a. E_{act} determines the reaction rate.

      b. The size of E_{act} is unrelated to the size of ΔH.

  B. Factors that affect reaction rate (Section 7.6).

   1. Increasing temperature increases reaction rate.

   2. Increasing the concentration of reactants increases reaction rate.

   3. Catalysts increase the reaction rate by lowering E_{act}.

III. Chemical equilibrium (Sections 7.7–7.9).

  A. Reversible reactions (Section 7.7).

   1. Some reactions proceed to virtual completion.

   2. Other reactions go to partial completion, at which point products begin to reform starting material.

      a. These reactions are reversible.

      b. The reaction from left to right is the forward reaction.

      c. The reaction from right to left is the reverse reaction.

   3. At some point the rate of the forward reaction equals the rate of the reverse reaction, and equilibrium is established.

   4. It is not necessary for the concentrations of products and reactants to be equal at equilibrium.

  B. Equilibrium (Section 7.8).

   1. Equilibrium equations.

      a. For the reaction a A + b B $\longrightarrow$ c C + d D,

$$K = \frac{[C]^c[D]^d}{[A]^a[B]^b}$$

      b. K = equilibrium constant.

      c. Expression on the right = equilibrium constant expression.

   2. The value of K determines the position of equilibrium.

      a. When $K \gg 1$, reaction goes to completion.

      b. When $K > 1$, the forward reaction is favored.

      c. When K is of intermediate value, significant amounts of reactants and products are present at equilibrium.

      d. When $K < 1$, the reverse reaction is favored.

      e. When $K \ll 1$, there is essentially no reaction.

  C. Effect of changing reaction conditions (Section 7.9).

   1. Le Châtelier's principle: When a stress is applied to a system, the equilibrium shifts to remove the stress.

   2. Effect of changing concentration.

      a. Increasing the concentration of reactants favors the forward reaction.

      b. Increasing the concentration of products favors the reverse reaction.

   3. Effect of changing temperature.

      a. Decreasing temperature favors an exothermic reaction.

      b. Increasing temperature favors an endothermic reaction.

   4. Effect of changing pressure.

      a. No effect unless one of the reactants or products is a gas.

      b. Increasing pressure shifts the equilibrium in the direction that produces fewer gas molecules.

Solutions to Chapter 7 Problems

7.1   (a) The reaction is endothermic because heat appears on the left side of the equation and is absorbed in the reaction.
(b) $\Delta H = +678$ kcal
(c) $C_6H_{12}O_6(aq) + 6\ O_2(g) \longrightarrow 6\ CO_2(g) + 6\ H_2O(l) + 678$ kcal

7.2   (a) The reaction is endothermic because ΔH is positive.

(b) $\dfrac{801\ \text{kcal}}{4\ \text{mol Al}} \times 1.00\ \text{mol Al} = 200$ kcal required

(c) $10.0\ \text{g Al} \times \dfrac{1\ \text{mol Al}}{27.0\ \text{g Al}} \times \dfrac{801\ \text{kcal}}{4\ \text{mol Al}} = 74.2$ kcal required

7.3

$127\ \text{g NO} \times \dfrac{1\ \text{mol}}{30.0\ \text{g NO}} \times \dfrac{43\ \text{kcal}}{2\ \text{mol NO}} = 91$ kcal absorbed

7.4   (a) Entropy increases.
(b) Entropy increases because disorder increases when liquids vaporize.
(c) Entropy decreases because one mole of product is formed for each two moles of reactant and because a gaseous reactant is converted into a solid product.

7.5   (a) Formation of lime from limestone doesn't occur at 25 °C because ΔG is positive.
(b) Entropy increases because a gas is formed from a solid.
(c) The reaction is spontaneous at higher temperatures. In the expression $\Delta G = \Delta H - T\Delta S$, the term $T\Delta S$ becomes larger at high temperature and causes ΔG to become negative.

7.6 $\Delta G = \Delta H - T\Delta S$: $\Delta H = +1.44$ kcal/mol $\Delta S = +5.26$ cal/(mol · K)
(a) If $T = 263$ K,
$T\Delta S = 263\ \text{K} \times \dfrac{5.26\ \text{cal}}{\text{mol K}} \times \dfrac{1\ \text{kcal}}{10^3\ \text{cal}} = \dfrac{1.38\ \text{kcal}}{\text{mol}}$

$\Delta G = 1.44$ kcal/mol $- 1.38$ kcal/mol $= +0.06$ kcal/mol
At 263 K, melting is not spontaneous because ΔG is positive.

(b) If $T = 273$ K,
$T\Delta S = 273\ \text{K} \times \dfrac{5.26\ \text{cal}}{\text{mol K}} \times \dfrac{1\ \text{kcal}}{10^3\ \text{cal}} = \dfrac{1.44\ \text{kcal}}{\text{mol}}$

$\Delta G = 1.44$ kcal/mol $- 1.44$ kcal/mol $= +0.00$ kcal/mol
At 273 K, $\Delta G = 0$, and melting and freezing are in equilibrium.

(c) If $T = 283$ K,
$T\Delta S = 283\ \text{K} \times \dfrac{5.26\ \text{cal}}{\text{mol K}} \times \dfrac{1\ \text{kcal}}{10^3\ \text{cal}} = \dfrac{1.49\ \text{kcal}}{\text{mol}}$

$\Delta G = 1.44$ kcal/mol $- 1.49$ kcal/mol $= -0.05$ kcal/mol
At 283 K, melting is spontaneous because ΔG is negative.

7.7 (a) The sign of ΔS is positive because disorder increases from reactant to products. (b) In the expression $\Delta G = \Delta H - T\Delta S$, ΔH is a negative number. Because ΔS is positive, $(-T\Delta S)$ is negative at all temperatures. Thus, ΔG is negative at all temperatures, and the reaction is spontaneous at all temperatures.

7.8

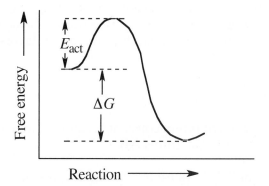

In this reaction, E_{act} is large, the reaction is slow, and the free-energy change is large and negative.

7.9

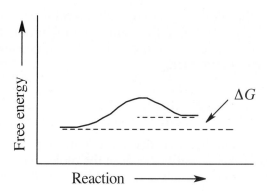

In this reaction, ΔG is small and positive. E_{act} can be small or large, but it is always larger than ΔG.

7.10 (a) If the temperature is increased, the reaction rate increases. (b) Removal of the catalyst decreases the reaction rate. (c) Halving the concentration of H_2 decreases the rate.

7.11

$$K = \frac{[\text{products}]}{[\text{reactants}]}$$

(a) $K = \dfrac{[NO_2]^2}{[N_2O_4]}$ (b) $K = \dfrac{[CH_3Cl][HCl]}{[CH_4][Cl_2]}$ (c) $K = \dfrac{[Br_2][F_2]^5}{[BrF_5]^2}$

Don't forget that the coefficients of the reactants and products appear as exponents in the equilibrium expression.

7.12   If K is greater than 1, the reaction favors products. If K is less than 1, the reaction favors reactants.
(a) Products are strongly favored.
(b) Reactants are strongly favored.
(c) Products are somewhat favored.

7.13   In the expression for the equilibrium constant, the concentration of the product HI is squared in the numerator. The concentrations of the reactants appear in the denominator. Substitute the given concentrations into the expression. The equilibrium favors products.

$$K = \frac{[HI]^2}{[H_2][I_2]} = \frac{[0.507]^2}{[0.0510][0.174]} = 29.0$$

7.14   The reaction that forms CD has a larger equilibrium constant because it has a greater ratio of product to reactant than does the reaction that forms AB.

7.15   High pressure favors the production of SO_3 because increasing the pressure shifts the equilibrium in the direction that decreases the number of molecules in the gas phase. Low temperature favors the production of SO_3 because exothermic reactions are favored by lower temperatures.

7.16   (a) Increasing the temperature shifts the equilibrium to the left, favoring reactants.
(b) Increasing the pressure shifts the equilibrium to the right, favoring product.
(b) Removing CH_4 from the reaction vessel causes more CH_4 to be formed and shifts the equilibrium toward the right, favoring product.

Understanding Key Concepts

7.17 ΔH is positive because energy must be supplied in order to break the attractive forces between molecules of the crystal. ΔS is also positive because the molecules of gas are more disordered than the molecules of solid. ΔG is negative because it is stated in the problem that the reaction is spontaneous.

7.18 ΔH is negative because energy is released when a liquid condenses. ΔS is negative because disorder decreases when a gas condenses. ΔG is negative because it is stated in the problem that the reaction is spontaneous.

7.19   (a) $2 A_2 + B_2 \longrightarrow 2 A_2B$

(b) ΔG is negative because the reaction is spontaneous. ΔS is negative because the product mixture has fewer gas molecules and less disorder than the reactant mixture. ΔH must be negative in order for ΔG to be negative since $(-T \Delta S)$ is positive.

7.20   (a) The blue curve represents the faster reaction, since less energy is needed to surmount the energy barrier leading to formation of products.
(b) The red curve represents a spontaneous reaction since the energy of its products is less than the energy of its reactants: ΔG is negative.

7.21   The red curve represents the catalyzed reaction, since a catalyst lowers the energy barrier of a reaction.

7.22

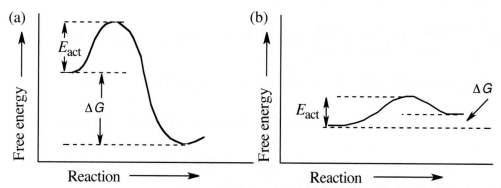

7.23 (a) ΔS is positive because the product has more disorder than the reactants.
(b) At low temperatures, the reaction is nonspontaneous because ΔH is positive and $T\Delta S$ is small. As the temperature rises, a certain temperature is reached at which $\Delta H = T\Delta S$. At this temperature, $\Delta G = 0$. Above this temperature, ΔG is negative and the reaction is spontaneous.

Enthalpy and Heat of Reaction

7.24 In an endothermic reaction, the total enthalpy of the products is greater than the total enthalpy of the reactants. In other words, the reactants have stronger bonds and are more stable, while the products have weaker bonds and are less stable. Energy must therefore be supplied for the reaction to take place.

7.25 In a chemical reaction, the difference in bond energies between products and reactants is known as the *heat of reaction*, or enthalpy change.

7.26 (a) ΔH is positive.

(b) $5.8 \text{ mol Br}_2 \times \dfrac{7.4 \text{ kcal}}{1 \text{ mol Br}_2} = 43 \text{ kcal needed}$

(c) $82 \text{ g Br}_2 \times \dfrac{1 \text{ mol Br}_2}{159.8 \text{ g Br}_2} \times \dfrac{7.4 \text{ kcal}}{1 \text{ mol Br}_2} = 3.8 \text{ kcal needed}$

7.27 (a) ΔH is negative.

(b) $2.5 \text{ mol H}_2\text{O} \times \dfrac{-1.44 \text{ kcal}}{1 \text{ mol H}_2\text{O}} = -3.6 \text{ kcal}$

(c) $32 \text{ g H}_2\text{O} \times \dfrac{1 \text{ mol H}_2\text{O}}{18 \text{ g H}_2\text{O}} \times \dfrac{-1.44 \text{ kcal}}{1 \text{ mol H}_2\text{O}} = -2.6 \text{ kcal}$

(d) $+1.44 \text{ kcal/mol}$

7.28   (a) $C_6H_{12}O_6 + 6 O_2 \longrightarrow 6 CO_2 + 6 H_2O$

(b) $\dfrac{-3.8 \text{ kcal}}{1 \text{ g glucose}} \times \dfrac{180 \text{ g glucose}}{1 \text{ mol glucose}} \times 1.50 \text{ mol glucose} = -1.0 \times 10^3 \text{ kcal}$

(c) The production of glucose from CO_2 and H_2O is an endothermic process.

$\dfrac{3.8 \text{ kcal}}{1 \text{ g glucose}} \times 15.0 \text{ g glucose} = 57 \text{ kcal needed to produce 15 g glucose}$

7.29   (a) $2 C_8H_{18} + 25 O_2 \longrightarrow 16 CO_2 + 18 H_2O + \text{heat}$
(b) ΔH is negative, because energy is released.

(c) $\dfrac{239.5 \text{ kcal}}{5.00 \text{ g } C_8H_{18}} \times \dfrac{114 \text{ g } C_8H_{18}}{1 \text{ mol } C_8H_{18}} = \dfrac{5460 \text{ kcal}}{1 \text{ mol } C_8H_{18}} \text{ released}$

(d) $450.0 \text{ kcal} \times \dfrac{1 \text{ mol } C_8H_{18}}{5460 \text{ kcal}} = 0.0824 \text{ mol } C_8H_{18}$

$0.0824 \text{ mol} \times \dfrac{114 \text{ g}}{1 \text{ mol}} = 9.39 \text{ g } C_8H_{18}$

(e) $17.0 \text{ g } C_8H_{18} \times \dfrac{239.5 \text{ kcal}}{5.00 \text{ g } C_8H_{18}} = 814 \text{ kcal released}$

Entropy and Free Energy

7.30   Increase in entropy: (a)
Decrease in entropy: (b), (c)

7.31   (a) Entropy decreases because there is an increase in order.
(b) Entropy decreases because there are fewer moles of gaseous product than reactant.
(c), (f) Entropy decreases because formation of a precipitate decreases entropy.
(d), (e) Entropy increases because there are more moles of gaseous products than gaseous reactants.

7.32   A spontaneous process is one that, once started, proceeds without any external influence.

7.33   A reaction with a negative free-energy change is spontaneous, and a reaction with a positive free-energy change is nonspontaneous.

7.34   The two factors that influence the spontaneity of a reaction are (1) the release or absorption of heat, and (2) the increase or decrease in entropy.

7.35   An exothermic reaction releases heat (negative ΔH), whereas an exergonic reaction is spontaneous (negative ΔG).

7.36   The free-energy change (ΔG) of a chemical reaction shows whether or not a reaction is spontaneous. If the sign of ΔG is negative, the reaction is spontaneous. Of the two factors that contribute to ΔG (ΔH and ΔS), ΔH is usually larger at low temperatures. Thus if a reaction is spontaneous (negative ΔG) it is usually exothermic (negative ΔH).

7.37   If an exothermic reaction is accompanied by a large decrease in entropy, the $(-T\Delta S)$ term in the expression for ΔG becomes large and positive and outweighs the negative enthalpy term, resulting in a positive value for ΔG and indicating a nonspontaneous reaction.

7.38   (a) Dissolution of NaCl is endothermic since ΔH is positive.
(b Entropy increases because disorder increases.
(c) Since the dissolution of NaCl is spontaneous, ΔG for the reaction must be negative. Because we already know that ΔH is positive, it must be true that $T\Delta S$ is the major contributor to ΔG.

7.39   (a) Entropy decreases because two atoms of liquid and one molecule of gas react to yield two molecules of solid.
(b) Because ΔS is negative, $-T\Delta S$ is positive. The reaction is spontaneous up to the temperature at which $\Delta H = T\Delta S$; above this temperature, the reaction no longer is spontaneous.

7.40   (a) $H_2(g) + Br_2(l) \longrightarrow 2\,HBr(g)$
(b) Entropy increases because the number of gaseous product molecules is greater than the number of gaseous reactant molecules and the sign of ΔS is positive.
(c) The process is spontaneous at all temperatures because ΔH is negative and ΔS is positive.
(d) $\Delta G = \Delta H - T\Delta S$; $\Delta H = -17.4$ kcal/mol; $\Delta S = 27.2$ cal/(mol·K); $T = 300$ K

$$T\Delta S = 300\text{ K} \times \frac{27.2\text{ cal}}{\text{mol K}} \times \frac{1\text{ kcal}}{10^3\text{ cal}} = \frac{8.16\text{ kcal}}{\text{mol}}$$

$$\Delta G = -17.4\text{ kcal/mol} - 8.16\text{ kcal/mol} = -25.6\text{ kcal/mol}$$

7.41   (a) ΔS is negative because two molecules of a gas combine to form one molecule of liquid.
(b) This reaction is spontaneous only up to a certain temperature, above which $T\Delta S$ is greater than ΔH and the reaction becomes nonspontaneous.

Rates of Chemical Reactions

7.42   The *activation energy* of a reaction is the amount of energy needed for reactants to surmount the energy barrier to reaction.

7.43   A reaction with $E_{act} = +5$ kcal is faster than one with $E_{act} = +10$ kcal because less energy is needed to surmount the energy barrier.

7.44

7.45

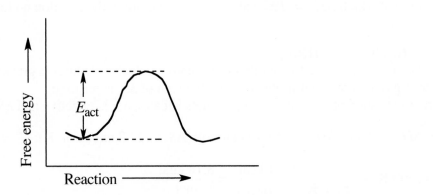

The free-energy change is zero.

7.46   Increasing temperature increases reaction rate for two reasons:
1. Particles move faster and collide more often.
2. Collisions occur with more energy.

7.47   Increasing concentration increases the reaction rate because the increased crowding of reactants causes more collisions.

7.48   A catalyst is a substance that increases reaction rate by lowering the activation energy barrier, yet remains unchanged when the reaction is completed.

7.49   A catalyst that reduces the energy of activation of a forward reaction by 5.0 kcal/mol (from 28.0 kcal/mol to 23.0 kcal/mol) also reduces the energy of activation of the reverse reaction by 5.0 kcal/mol. Lowering the energy of activation of the reverse reaction, however, will not cause it to take place if it is not spontaneous.

7.50   (a) The negative value of ΔG indicates that diamonds spontaneously turn into graphite at 25°C.
(b) Because this behavior is not observed, the activation energy of the reaction must be extremely high and the reaction rate must be extremely slow.

7.51   (a) The reaction of hydrogen with carbon is not spontaneous at 25°C because ΔG is positive.
(b) It is not possible to find a catalyst for the reaction because it is not spontaneous.

Chemical Equilibria

7.52 In a reversible reaction, chemical equilibrium is a state in which the rates of the forward reaction and the reverse reaction are equal. The amounts of reactants and products need not be equal at equilibrium.

7.53 Catalysts lower the height of the activation energy barrier for both forward and reverse reactions by the same amount but don't change the equilibrium constant.

7.54

(a) $K = \dfrac{[CO_2]^2}{[CO]^2[O_2]}$ (b) $K = \dfrac{[C_2H_4Cl_2][HCl]^2}{[C_2H_6][Cl_2]^2}$

(c) $K = \dfrac{[H_3O^+][F^-]}{[HF][H_2O]}$ (d) $K = \dfrac{[O_3]^2}{[O_2]^3}$

7.55

(a) $K = \dfrac{[H_2S]^2}{[S_2][H_2]^2} = 2.8 \times 10^{-21}$ (b) $K = \dfrac{[CH_3OH]}{[CO][H_2]^2} = 10.5$

(c) $K = \dfrac{[BrCl]^2}{[Br_2][Cl_2]} = 58.0$ (d) $K = \dfrac{[I]^2}{[I_2]} = 6.8 \times 10^{-3}$

A reaction with K greater than 1 favors products.
A reaction with K less than 1 favors reactants.
　　Favors reactants: (a), (d)
　　Favors products: (b), (c)

7.56

$$K = \frac{[NO_2]^2}{[N_2O_4]} = \frac{(0.0325\ \text{mol/L})^2}{(0.147\ \text{mol/L})} = 7.19 \times 10^{-3}$$

7.57

$$K = \frac{[CO_2]^2}{[CO]^2[O_2]} = \frac{(0.11\ \text{mol/L})^2}{(0.025\ \text{mol/L})^2\ (0.015\ \text{mol/L})} = 1.3 \times 10^3$$

7.58

(a) $K = 7.19 \times 10^{-3} = \dfrac{(0.0250\ \text{mol/L})^2}{[N_2O_4]}$; $[N_2O_4] = 0.0869\ \text{mol/L}$

(b) $K = 7.19 \times 10^{-3} = \dfrac{[NO_2]^2}{(0.0750\ \text{mol/L})}$; $[NO_2] = 0.0232\ \text{mol/L}$

7.59

$$\text{(a)}\quad 1.3 \times 10^3 = \frac{(0.18\ \text{mol/L})^2}{(0.0200\ \text{mol/L})^2\,[O_2]}$$

$$[O_2] = \frac{(0.18\ \text{mol/L})^2}{(0.0200\ \text{mol/L})^2 \times 1.3 \times 10^3} = 0.062\ \text{mol/L}$$

(b) $[CO_2]^2 = K \times [CO]^2 \times [O_2] = 1.3 \times 10^3 \times (0.080\ \text{mol/L})^2 \times 0.520\ \text{mol/L} = 4.3\ \text{mol/L}$

7.60 If the pressure is raised, relatively more reactants than products are found at equilibrium, because high pressure favors the reaction that produces fewer gas molecules.

7.61 If the pressure is lowered, a relatively greater concentration of reactants than products is found at equilibrium, because lower pressure favors the reaction that produces more gas molecules.

Le Châtelier's Principle

7.62 (a) The reaction is endothermic.
(b) Reactants are favored at equilibrium.
(c) (1) Increasing pressure favors formation of ozone, since increased pressure shifts the equilibrium in the direction of the reaction that produces fewer gas molecules.
(2) Increasing the O_2 concentration increases the amount of O_3 formed.
(3) Increasing the concentration of O_3 shifts the equilibrium to the left.
(4) A catalyst has no effect on the equilibrium.
(5) Increasing the temperature shifts the equilibrium to the right because the reaction is endothermic.

7.63 (a) This reaction is exothermic.
(b) Products are favored at equilibrium.
(c) (1) Increasing pressure has no effect on the equilibrium.
(2) Increasing the HCl concentration shifts the equilibrium to the left.
(3) Decreasing the Cl_2 concentration decreases the amount of HCl formed.
(4) Increasing the H_2 concentration increases the amount of HCl formed.
(5) A catalyst has no effect on the equilibrium.

7.64 According to Le Châtelier's principle, an increase in pressure shifts the equilibrium in the direction that decreases the number of molecules in the gas phase.
(a) The concentration of products decreases.
(b) The concentration of products remains the same.
(c) The concentration of products increases.

7.65 A decrease in volume increases the system pressure.
(a) The equilibrium shifts to favor reactants.
(b) The equilibrium shifts to favor products.
(c) The position of equilibrium remains the same.

7.66 $$CO(g) + H_2O(g) \rightleftharpoons CO_2(g) + H_2(g) \quad \Delta H = -9.8\ \text{kcal/mol}$$
Because it has a negative value of ΔH, the reaction is exothermic, and the equilibrium favors products. Decreasing the temperature increases the amount of H_2.

7.67 $$3\,O_2(g) \rightleftharpoons 2\,O_3(g) \quad \Delta H = +68\ \text{kcal/mol}$$
Increasing the temperature of the reaction increases the equilibrium constant.

7.68 $H_2(g) + I_2(g) \rightleftharpoons 2\, HI(g)$ $\Delta H = -2.2\ kcal/mol$
(a) Adding I_2 to the reaction mix increases the equilibrium concentration of HI.
(b) Removing H_2 causes the equilibrium concentration of HI to decrease.
(c) Addition of a catalyst does not change the equilibrium concentration of HI.
(d) Increasing the temperature decreases the concentration of HI.

7.69 $Fe^{3+}(aq) + Cl^-(aq) \rightleftharpoons FeCl^{2+}(aq)$
(a) Addition of $Fe(NO_3)_3$ increases the equilibrium concentration of $FeCl^{2+}$.
(b) Removal of Cl^- by precipitation decreases the concentration of $FeCl^{2+}$.
(c) Increasing the temperature of the endothermic reaction increases the equilibrium concentration of $FeCl^{2+}$.
(d) Addition of a catalyst does not change the equilibrium concentration of $FeCl^{2+}$.

Applications

7.70   A gram of fat contains more energy (9 kcal/g) than a gram of carbohydrate (4 kcal/g).

7.71   The chips contain 22.5 g carbohydrate and 22.5 g fat. A small bag of potato chips contains 290 Cal (kcal).

22.5 g carbohydrate x $\dfrac{4.0\ kcal}{1\ g\ carbohydrate}$ = 90 kcal; 22.5 g fat x $\dfrac{9.0\ kcal}{1\ g\ fat}$ = 200 kcal

7.72   Body temperature is regulated by the thyroid gland and by the hypothalamus region of the brain.

7.73   Dilation of the blood vessels cools the body by allowing more blood to flow close to the surface of the body.

7.74   Nitrogen fixation is the conversion of N_2 into chemically usable nitrogen compounds. In nature this is accomplished by microorganisms that live in the roots of legumes and by lightning.

7.75   (1) The energy of activation is very large. (2) Very little H_2 is present in the atmosphere.

General Questions and Problems

7.76   (a) $C_2H_5OH + 3\,O_2 \longrightarrow 2\,CO_2 + 3\,H_2O + 327\ kcal$
(b) ΔH is negative because energy is released.

(c) 5.00 g C_2H_5OH x $\dfrac{1\ mol\ C_2H_5OH}{46.0\ g\ C_2H_5OH}$ x $\dfrac{327\ cal}{1\ mol}$ = 35.5 kcal

(d) Calories needed = specific heat of H_2O x mass (g) x temperature change (°C)
Specific heat of water = 1.00 cal /(g · °C); mass of 500 mL H_2O = 500 g;
Temperature change = 80.0 °C
Calories = $\dfrac{1.00\ cal}{g \cdot °C}$ x 500.0 g x 80.0 °C = 4.00 x 10^4 cal = 40.0 kcal

40.0 kcal x $\dfrac{5.00\ g\ C_2H_5OH}{35.5\ kcal}$ = 5.63 g C_2H_5OH

(e) $\dfrac{35.5\ kcal}{5.00\ g\ C_2H_5OH}$ x $\dfrac{0.789\ g\ C_2H_5OH}{1\ mL\ C_2H_5OH}$ = 5.60 kcal/mL

7.77 $$N_2(g) + 3 H_2(g) \longrightarrow 2 NH_3(g) \quad \Delta H = -22 \text{ kcal/mol}$$

(a) The production of ammonia from its elements is an exothermic process.

(b) $\dfrac{-22 \text{ kcal}}{2 \text{ mol NH}_3} \times 0.700 \text{ mol NH}_3 = -7.7 \text{ kcal}$

7.78 (a) $Fe_3O_4(s) + 4 H_2(g) \longrightarrow 3 Fe(s) + 4 H_2O(g) \quad \Delta H = +36 \text{ kcal/mol}$

(b) $55 \text{ g Fe} \times \dfrac{1 \text{ mol Fe}}{55.8 \text{ g Fe}} \times \dfrac{36 \text{ kcal}}{1 \text{ mol Fe}_3O_4} \times \dfrac{1 \text{ mol Fe}_3O_4}{3 \text{ mol Fe}} = 12 \text{ kcal required}$

(c) $75 \text{ g Fe} \times \dfrac{1 \text{ mol Fe}}{55.8 \text{ g Fe}} \times \dfrac{4 \text{ mol H}_2}{3 \text{ mol Fe}} \times \dfrac{2.0 \text{ g H}_2}{1 \text{ mol H}_2} = 3.6 \text{ g H}_2$

(d) Reactants are favored in this reaction.

7.79 (a) CO removes Hb from the bloodstream because the reaction of CO with Hb is more favored than the reaction of O_2 with Hb. Less Hb is available to react with O_2, and less HbO_2 is available to the tissues.

(b) Administering high doses of O_2 to a victim of CO poisoning shifts the equilibrium in the following reaction to the right.
$$Hb(CO)(aq) + O_2(aq) \rightleftharpoons HbO_2(aq) + CO(aq)$$

This shift results in displacement of CO from Hb(CO) and in formation of HbO_2 to replenish body tissues with O_2.

7.80

$1700 \text{ kcal} \times \dfrac{1 \text{ g}}{3.8 \text{ kcal}} = 450 \text{ g glucose}$

7.81

(a) $10.0 \text{ g H}_2O \times \dfrac{1 \text{ mol H}_2O}{18.0 \text{ g H}_2O} \times \dfrac{9.72 \text{ kcal}}{1 \text{ mol H}_2O} = 5.40 \text{ kcal needed}$

(b) 5.40 kcal are released.

7.82 (a) $4 NH_3(g) + 5 O_2(g) \rightleftharpoons 4 NO(g) + 6 H_2O(g) + \text{heat}$

(b) $K = \dfrac{[NO]^4 [H_2O]^6}{[NH_3]^4 [O_2]^5}$

(c) (1) Raising the pressure shifts the equilibrium to the left and favors reactants.
(2) Adding $NO(g)$ shifts the equilibrium to the left and favors reactants.
(3) Decreasing NH_3 shifts the equilibrium to the left and favors reactants.
(4) Lowering the temperature shifts the equilibrium to the right and favors products.

7.83 (a) $2 CH_3OH(l) + 3 O_2(g) \longrightarrow 2 CO_2(g) + 4 H_2O(g)$

(b) $50.0 \text{ g } CH_3OH \times \dfrac{1 \text{ mol } CH_3OH}{32.0 \text{ g } CH_3OH} \times \dfrac{-174 \text{ kcal}}{1 \text{ mol } CH_3OH} = -272 \text{ kcal}$

7.84

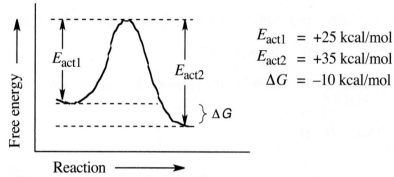

$E_{act1} = +25 \text{ kcal/mol}$
$E_{act2} = +35 \text{ kcal/mol}$
$\Delta G = -10 \text{ kcal/mol}$

(a) The forward process is exergonic.
(b) $\Delta G = -10 \text{ kcal/mol}$

7.85

$5.00 \text{ g } \times \dfrac{1 \text{ mol Al}}{27.0 \text{ g Al}} \times \dfrac{-202.9 \text{ kcal}}{2 \text{ mol Al}} = -18.8 \text{ kcal}$

18.8 kcal of heat is released.

7.86

$1.00 \text{ g } \times \dfrac{1 \text{ mol Na}}{23.0 \text{ g}} \times \dfrac{-88.0 \text{ kcal}}{2 \text{ mol Na}} = -1.91 \text{ kcal}$

1.91 kcal of heat is evolved. The reaction is exothermic.

Self-Test for Chapter 7

Multiple Choice

1. In which of the following processes does entropy decrease?
   (a) $C_6H_{12}O_6(s) + 6 O_2(g) \longrightarrow 6 CO_2(g) + 6 H_2O(l)$

   (b) $2 Na(s) + 2 H_2O(l) \longrightarrow 2 NaOH(aq) + H_2(g)$

   (c) $2 Mg(s) + O_2(g) \longrightarrow 2 MgO(s)$

   (d) $Zn(s) + CuSO_4(aq) \longrightarrow Cu(s) + ZnSO_4(aq)$

2. The reaction that will proceed at any temperature has:
   (a) negative ΔH, negative ΔS (b) negative ΔH, positive ΔS (c) positive ΔH, positive ΔS
   (d) positive ΔH, negative ΔS

3. Which of the conditions in Problem 2 indicates the reaction with the largest positive value of ΔG?

4. In the reaction $CH_3CO_2H + CH_3OH \rightleftharpoons CH_3CO_2CH_3 + H_2O$, the yield of $CH_3CO_2CH_3$ can be improved by:
   (a) distilling off the $CH_3CO_2CH_3$ (b) removing the water   (c) using more CH_3CO_2H and CH_3OH (d) all of the above

5. The equilibrium expression for the reaction $C_6H_6 + 3\,H_2 \longrightarrow C_6H_{12}$ is:

(a) $\dfrac{[C_6H_{12}]}{[C_6H_6]\,[H_2]}$ (b) $\dfrac{[C_6H_{12}]}{[C_6H_6]\,[H_2]^3}$ (c) $\dfrac{[C_6H_{12}]}{[C_6H_6]\,[3\,H_2]}$ (d) $\dfrac{[C_6H_6]\,[H_2]^3}{[C_6H_{12}]}$

6. A reaction with which of the following K values is most likely to go to completion at room temperature?
    (a) $K = 10^5$ (b) $K = 10^2$ (c) $K = 10^{-1}$ (d) $K = 10^{-4}$

7. In which of the following reactions will increasing the pressure decrease the yield of product?
    (a) $2\,Mg(s) + O_2(g) \longrightarrow 2\,MgO(s)$
    (b) $H_2C{=}CH_2(g) + H_2(g) \longrightarrow CH_3CH_3(g)$
    (c) $C(s) + H_2O(g) \longrightarrow CO(g) + H_2(g)$
    (d) $3\,O_2(g) \longrightarrow 2\,O_3(g)$

8. According to Le Châtelier's principle, which of the following changes also changes the value of K?
    (a) changing temperature   (b) changing concentration   (c) changing pressure   (d) all of the above

9. All of the following statements are true about the reaction $3\,O_2(g) \longrightarrow 2\,O_3(g)$ (heat of formation = +34 kcal/mol at 25°C) except :
    (a) The reaction is endothermic.   (b) ΔS is negative.   (c) ΔG is positive.   (d) The rate of the reverse reaction increases with temperature.

10. In the reaction $Si + O_2 \longrightarrow SiO_2$ ($\Delta H = -218$ kcal/mol at 25°C), what is ΔH in kcal when 80 g of O_2 reacts with 70 g of Si?
    (a) 218 kcal   (b) –218 kcal   (c) –436 kcal   (d) –545 kcal

Sentence Completion

1. A reaction that has equal amounts of reactants and products at equilibrium has $K =$ ___.

2. The law of _____ ___ _____ states that energy can be neither created nor destroyed.

3. Addition of a _____ increases the rate of a reaction.

4. A reaction that easily proceeds in either direction is _____.

5. A reaction that absorbs heat from the surroundings is an _____ reaction.

6. An _____ _____ ____ gives the relationship between the concentrations of products and reactants at equilibrium.

7. The rate of a reaction can be increased by increasing _____ or ____ or by adding a _____.

8. The reactions that continually take place in the body are known as _____.

9. ____ ___ is unrelated to reaction spontaneity.

10. For a chemical reaction to occur, reactant molecules must _____.

True or False

1. The caloric value of food tells how much energy is absorbed when food is burned in oxygen.

2. In a chemical equilibrium, both product and reactant concentrations remain constant.

3. According to Le Châtelier's principle, changing pressure only affects equilibrium if gaseous reactants or products are involved.

4. In an exothermic reaction, the bond dissociation energies of the products are greater than the bond dissociation energies of the reactants.

5. A reaction with a large E_{act} will probably have a large heat of reaction.

6. Raising the temperature of a reaction always increases the rate of reaction.

7. A very unfavorable reaction may take place if the temperature is high enough.

8. Catalysts increase the rate of a reaction by increasing the number of collisions between reactants.

9. At chemical equilibrium, all chemical reaction stops.

10. At low temperatures, the spontaneity of a reaction is determined by ΔH.

Match each entry on the left with its partner on the right.

1. Enzyme

2. Exergonic reaction

3. K

4. Enthalpy

5. Reaction energy diagram

6. Free energy

7. Exothermic reaction

8. Endergonic reaction

9. E_{act}

10. Entropy

11. Reversible reaction

12. Endothermic reaction

(a) Shows energy relationships in a reaction

(b) A reaction that gives off heat

(c) Reduces the size of E_{act}

(d) Energy needed for a reaction to occur

(e) Measure of the amount of disorder in a reaction.

(f) Reaction that is not spontaneous

(g) Reaction that can go in either direction

(h) Reaction that absorbs heat

(i) Difference in energy of products and reactants

(j) Reaction that is spontaneous

(k) Determines if a reaction is spontaneous

(l) Measures the ratio of products to reactants

Chapter Outline

I. Introduction to gases, liquids, and solids (Section 8.1).
   A. Phases of matter are determined by the attractive forces between molecules.
      1. In gases, attractive forces are very weak.
      2. In liquids, attractive forces are strong.
      3. In solids, forces are so strong that atoms are held in place.
   B. During changes of phase, also known as changes of state, heat is either absorbed or released.
      1. Every change of state is characterized by a free-energy change, ΔG.
         a. ΔG consists of an enthalpy term and an entropy term.
         b. The enthalpy term is a measure of the heat absorbed or released during a phase change.
         c. The entropy change is a measure of the change in molecular disorder.
      2. At the temperature where a change of phase occurs, two states are in equilibrium.
      3. At the change from solid to liquid, two phases are at equilibrium at the melting point.
      4. At the change from liquid to gas, two phases are at equilibrium at the boiling point.
II. Gases (Sections 8.2–8.10).
   A. The kinetic–molecular theory explains the behavior of gases (Section 8.2).
      1. A gas consists of a great many molecules moving about with no attractive forces.
      2. The amount of space that molecules occupy is much smaller than the space between molecules.
      3. The energy of the molecules is related to Kelvin temperature.
      4. When molecules collide, their total kinetic energy is conserved.
      5. A gas that obeys all these behaviors is an ideal gas.
   B. Pressure (Sections 8.3).
      1. Pressure is defined as force per unit area.
      2. Units of pressure are mmHg, Pascal (in the SI system), atmosphere, and pounds per square inch (psi).
      3. Gas pressure can be measured by using a barometer or a manometer.
   C. Gas laws (Sections 8.4–8.10).
      1. Boyle's law (for a fixed amount of gas at constant T) (Section 8.4).
         a. The pressure of a gas is inversely proportional to its volume.
         b. $P_1V_1 = P_2V_2$.
      2. Charles's law (for a fixed amount of gas at constant P) (Section 8.5).
         a. The volume of a gas is directly proportional to its temperature in K.
         b. $V_1/T_1 = V_2/T_2$.
      3. Gay-Lussac's law (for a fixed amount of gas at constant V) (Section 8.6).
         a. Pressure is directly proportional to temperature in K.
         b. $P_1/T_1 = P_2/T_2$.
      4. Combined gas law (Section 8.7).
            $P_1V_1/T_1 = P_2V_2/T_2$ for a fixed amount of gas.
      5. Avogadro's law (at constant T and P) (Section 8.8).
         a. The volume of a gas is directly proportional to its molar amount at constant T and P.
         b. $V_1/n_1 = V_2/n_2$.
         c. Standard temperature and pressure = 273.15 K and 1 atm.
         d. Standard molar volume of a gas = 22.4 L.

6. Ideal gas law (Section 8.9).
   $PV = nRT$, where R is a gas constant.
7. Dalton's law of partial pressure (Section 8.10).
   a. Mixtures of gases behave the same as a pure gas.
   b. The partial pressure of a gas in a mixture is the same as the gas would have if it were alone.
III. Intermolecular forces (Section 8.11).
   A. Intermolecular forces are the forces that act between molecules.
   B. In an ideal gas, intermolecular forces are unimportant.
   C. Three types of intermolecular forces are important in liquids and solids.
      1. Dipole–dipole forces occur when the positive end of a polar molecule is attracted to the negative end of a second molecule.
      2. London forces.
         a. Short-lived polarity in molecules causes a temporary attraction between molecules.
         b. London forces increase with increasing molecular weight and vary with molecular shape.
      3. Hydrogen bonding.
         a. Hydrogen bonds occur between a hydrogen atom bonded to an electronegative atom (O, N, F) and an unshared electron pair of a second electronegative atom.
         b. In hydrogen bonds, the hydrogen atom is partially bonded to two different electronegative atoms.
         c. Hydrogen bonds can be quite strong, and hydrogen bonding is responsible for elevated boiling points.
IV. Liquids and solids (Sections 8.12–8.15).
   A. Liquids (Section 8.12–8.13).
      1. Evaporation occurs when molecules near the surface of a liquid escape into the gaseous state.
         a. When molecules are in the gaseous state, they obey gas laws.
      2. The contribution of the partial pressure of the escaped gas to the total pressure is known as vapor pressure.
         a. Vapor pressure rises with increasing temperature.
      3. The normal boiling point of a liquid is at 760 mmHg.
         a. The boiling point rises or falls with atmospheric pressure.
      4. Viscosity and surface tension are properties of liquids.
         a. Viscosity is a liquid's resistance to flow.
         b. Surface tension is the resistance of a liquid to spread out.
      5. Water is a unique liquid (Section 8.13).
         a. Water has very high specific heat, high heat of vaporization, and strong hydrogen bonding.
         b. Solid water is less dense than liquid water.
   B. Solids (Section 8.14).
      1. A crystalline solid has atoms, molecules, or ions rigidly held in an orderly arrangement.
         a. Categories of crystalline solids include ionic solids, molecular solids, covalent network solids, and metallic solids.
      2. Particles in an amorphous solid do not have an orderly arrangement.
   C. Changes of phase (Section 8.15).
      1. The heat needed to completely melt a solid is the heat of fusion.
      2. The heat needed to completely vaporize a liquid is the heat of vaporization.

Solutions to Chapter 8 Problems

8.1   (a) The change of state from liquid to gas is disfavored by ΔH (positive sign) but is favored by ΔS (large positive value).

(b) $\Delta G = \Delta H - T\Delta S : \Delta H = +9.72$ kcal/mol; $\Delta S = +26.1$ cal/(mol · K); $T = 373$ K

$$T\Delta S = 373\text{ K} \times \frac{26.1\text{ cal}}{\text{mol K}} \times \frac{1\text{ kcal}}{10^3\text{ cal}} = \frac{9.74\text{ kcal}}{\text{mol}}$$

$\Delta G = 9.72$ kcal/mol $- 9.74$ kcal/mol $= -0.02$ kcal/mol

(c) For the change from gas to liquid, $\Delta H = -9.72$ kcal/mol and $\Delta S = -26.1$ cal/(mol·K)

8.2   Use the appropriate conversion factor from Section 8.3.

$$220\text{ mmHg} \times \frac{1\text{ atm}}{760\text{ mmHg}} = 0.29\text{ atm}$$

$$220\text{ mmHg} \times \frac{14.7\text{ psi}}{760\text{ mmHg}} = 4.3\text{ psi}$$

$$220\text{ mmHg} \times \frac{101{,}325\text{ Pa}}{760\text{ mmHg}} = 29{,}000\text{ Pa}$$

8.3   The pressure of the gas inside the manometer is greater than atmospheric pressure because the mercury level is higher in the open arm of the manometer than in the closed end. Since atmospheric pressure is 750 mmHg and since the difference in mercury levels in the manometer arm is 250 mmHg, the pressure of the gas inside the manometer is 750 mm + 250 mm = 1000 mmHg.

8.4   If the variables in the problem are pressure and volume, Boyle's law must be used.

Solution: $P_1 \times V_1 = P_2 \times V_2$

$$V_2 = \frac{P_1 \times V_1}{P_2} = \frac{(90\text{ atm})(5.0\text{ L})}{(1.0\text{ atm})} = 450\text{ L}$$

Ballpark check: Since the pressure is reduced by almost 100 times, the volume must increase by almost 100 times, from 5 L to 500 L.

The ballpark solution and the detailed solution agree.

8.5   *Solution:* $P_1 \times V_1 = P_2 \times V_2$

$$P_2 = \frac{P_1 \times V_1}{V_2} = \frac{(4.0\text{ atm})(3.2\text{ L})}{(10.0\text{ L})} = 1.3\text{ atm}$$

Ballpark check: Since the volume increases by three times, the pressure must decrease by the same amount, from 4.0 atm to 1.3 atm.

At a volume of 0.20 L: $\quad P_2 = \dfrac{P_1 \times V_1}{V_2} = \dfrac{(4.0\text{ atm})(3.2\text{ L})}{(0.20\text{ L})} = 64\text{ atm}$

8.6 Charles's law is used to calculate volume or temperature changes when pressure and quantity remain constant.

Solution:

$$\frac{V_1}{T_1} = \frac{V_2}{T_2}$$

$$V_2 = \frac{V_1 \text{ x } T_2}{T_1} = \frac{(0.30 \text{ L})(250 \text{ K})}{273 \text{ K}} = 0.27 \text{ L}$$

Ballpark check: Since the temperature decreases by about 10%, the volume must also decrease by about 10%, from 0.30 L to around 0.27 L.

At 525°C (798 K): $\quad V_2 = \dfrac{V_1 \text{ x } T_2}{T_1} = \dfrac{(0.30 \text{ L})(798 \text{ K})}{273 \text{ K}} = 0.88 \text{ L}$

8.7 Use Gay-Lussac's law when pressure and temperature vary, and volume and quantity are unchanged. Don't forget to change temperature from °C to K.

Solution:

$$\frac{P_1}{T_1} = \frac{P_2}{T_2}$$

$$P_2 = \frac{P_1 \text{ x } T_2}{T_1} = 30 \text{ psi x } \frac{318 \text{ K}}{288 \text{ K}} = 33 \text{ psi}$$

Ballpark check: Since the temperature increase is about 10%, the pressure increase is also expected to be approximately 10%.

8.8 In this problem, *P*, *V*, and *T* vary.

$$\frac{P_1 V_1}{T_1} = \frac{P_2 V_2}{T_2}; \qquad P_1 = 752 \text{ mmHg}; \; T_1 = 295 \text{ K}; \; V_1 = 275 \text{ L}$$

$$P_2 = 480 \text{ mmHg}; \; T_2 = 241 \text{ K}; \; V_2 = \text{?}$$

$$V_2 = \frac{P_1 V_1 T_2}{P_2 T_1} = \frac{(752 \text{ mmHg})(275 \text{ L})(241 \text{ K})}{(480 \text{ mmHg})(295 \text{ K})} = 352 \text{ L}$$

8.9 The temperature increase [from 18 °C (291 K) to 50 °C (323 K)] increases the volume by about 10%. The pressure increase (from 1 atm to 2 atm) decreases the volume by half. The resulting balloon volume should be somewhat more than half the original volume, as represented by balloon (a).

8.10 Use Avogadro's Law; the quantity on the left side of the equation is the standard molar volume of a gas, 22.4 L/mol.

$$\frac{V_1}{n_1} = \frac{V_2}{n_2}$$

$$n_2 = \frac{V_2 \times n_1}{V_1} = 1.00 \times 10^5 \text{ L CH}_4 \times \frac{1.0 \text{ mol}}{22.4 \text{ L}} = 4.46 \times 10^3 \text{ mol CH}_4$$

The same container could also hold 4.46×10^3 moles of CO_2.

$$4.46 \times 10^3 \text{ mol CH}_4 \times \frac{16.0 \text{ g CH}_4}{1 \text{ mol CH}_4} = 7.14 \times 10^4 \text{ g CH}_4$$

$$4.46 \times 10^3 \text{ mol CO}_2 \times \frac{44.0 \text{ g CO}_2}{1 \text{ mol CO}_2} = 1.96 \times 10^5 \text{ g CO}_2$$

Ballpark Check: Since one mole of a gas occupies 22.4 L at STP, a 100,000 L container holds 100,000/22.4 moles, or about 4500 moles. Thus, the ballpark solution and the exact solution agree.

8.11 $PV = nRT$; $P = nRT/V$

$$n = 3.2 \text{ g} \times \frac{1 \text{ mol}}{44.0 \text{ g}} = 0.073 \text{ mol}; \quad R = 0.0821 \frac{\text{L} \cdot \text{atm}}{\text{mol} \cdot \text{K}}$$

$$T = 20°\text{C} = 293 \text{ K}; \quad V = 350 \text{ mL} = 0.35 \text{ L}$$

$$P = \frac{0.073 \text{ mol} \times \dfrac{0.0821 \text{ L} \cdot \text{atm}}{\text{mol} \cdot \text{K}} \times 293 \text{ K}}{0.35 \text{ L}} = 5.0 \text{ atm}$$

8.12 $PV = nRT$; $n = PV/RT$

$$P = 150 \text{ atm}; \quad V = 180 \text{ L He}; \quad R = 0.0821 \frac{\text{L} \cdot \text{atm}}{\text{mol} \cdot \text{K}} ; \quad T = 25°\text{C} = 298 \text{ K}$$

$$n = \frac{150 \text{ atm} \times 180 \text{ L He}}{0.0821 \dfrac{\text{L} \cdot \text{atm}}{\text{mol} \cdot \text{K}} \times 298 \text{ K}} = 1.1 \times 10^3 \text{ mol He}$$

$$1.1 \times 10^3 \text{ mol He} \times \frac{4.0 \text{ g}}{1 \text{ mol He}} = 4.4 \times 10^3 \text{ g He}$$

8.13 We can use the ideal gas law to compare the volumes of two gases: Since the piston is moveable, $P = 1$ atm in all cases.

(a) The increase in temperature increases the volume to 450/300 = 3/2 of the original volume, and the decrease in amount decreases the volume to 0.200/0.300 = 2/3 of the original value. Since 3/2 x 2/3 = 1, the two changes exactly cancel, and the final volume is the same as the original volume.

$T_1 = 300$ K; $n_1 = 0.300$ mol; $T_2 = 450$ K; $n_2 = 0.200$ mol; $V_1/V_2 = ?$

$$\frac{V_1}{V_2} = \frac{n_1 T_1 P_2}{n_2 T_2 P_1} = \frac{n_1 T_1}{n_2 T_2}; \quad \frac{V_1}{V_2} = \frac{(0.300 \text{ mol})(300 \text{ K})}{((0.200 \text{ mol})((450 \text{ K})} = 1$$

(b) The decrease in temperature decreases the volume to 200/300 = 2/3 of the original, and the increase in amount increases the volume to 0.400/0.300 = 4/3 of the original volume. Since 2/3 x 4/3 = 8/9, the final volume is a bit less than the original volume.

$T_1 = 300$ K; $n_1 = 0.300$ mol; $T_2 = 200$ K; $n_2 = 0.400$ mol; $V_1/V_2 = ?$

$$\frac{V_1}{V_2} = \frac{(0.300 \text{ mol})(300 \text{ K})}{((0.400 \text{ mol})((200 \text{ K})} = \frac{9}{8}$$ The volume in (b) is 8/9 of the original volume.

$P = 1$ atm (a) (b)

$T = 300$ K $T = 450$ K $T = 200$ K
$n = 0.300$ mol $n = 0.200$ mol $n = 0.400$ mol

8.14 0.98 x 9.5 atm = 9.3 atm He
0.020 x 9.5 atm = 0.19 atm O_2

The partial pressure of oxygen in diving gas (0.19 atm) is approximately equal to the partial pressure of oxygen in air (0.21 atm).

8.15

$$\frac{573 \text{ mmHg}}{760 \text{ mmHg}} \times 100\% = 75.4\% \text{ N}_2; \qquad \frac{100 \text{ mmHg}}{760 \text{ mmHg}} \times 100\% = 13.2\% \text{ O}_2$$

$$\frac{40 \text{ mmHg}}{760 \text{ mmHg}} \times 100\% = 5.3\% \text{ CO}_2; \qquad \frac{47 \text{ mmHg}}{760 \text{ mmHg}} \times 100\% = 6.2\% \text{ H}_2\text{O}$$

8.16 We know from the previous problem that the partial pressure of O_2 in the lungs at atmospheric pressure is 13.2%. Thus, at 265 mmHg,

265 mmHg x 0.132 = 35.0 mmHg

8.17   Drawing (c) best represents the mixture. In (c), the particles act independently of each other in accordance with kinetic–molecular theory, and the mixture is homogeneous.

8.18   Boiling points generally increase with increasing molecular (or atomic) weight because of London dispersion forces.

(a) Kr, Ar, Ne. This series is arranged in order of decreasing boiling point.
(b) Cl_2, Br_2, I_2. This series is arranged in order of increasing boiling point.

8.19   Methyl alcohol (a) and methylamine (c) are capable of hydrogen bonding because each contains a hydrogen atom bonded to an electronegative atom. Ethylene (b) does not form hydrogen bonds.

8.20   (a) *London forces* are the only intermolecular forces between nonpolar ethane molecules, and thus ethane has a low boiling point.
(b) The major intermolecular force between ethyl alcohol molecules is *hydrogen bonding*, which causes ethyl alcohol to be high boiling. Dipole–dipole interactions and London forces are also present but are weaker than hydrogen bonding.
(c) *Dipole–dipole* interactions are the principal forces between ethyl chloride molecules and cause the boiling point of ethyl chloride to be higher than that of ethane. London forces are also present.

8.21   To melt isopropyl alcohol:

$$1.50 \text{ mol } \times \frac{60.0 \text{ g}}{1 \text{ mol}} \times \frac{21.4 \text{ cal}}{1 \text{ g}} \times \frac{1 \text{ kcal}}{10^3 \text{ cal}} = 1.93 \text{ kcal}$$

To boil isopropyl alcohol:

$$1.50 \text{ mol } \times \frac{60.0 \text{ g}}{1 \text{ mol}} \times \frac{159 \text{ cal}}{1 \text{ g}} \times \frac{1 \text{ kcal}}{10^3 \text{ cal}} = 14.3 \text{ kcal}$$

Understanding Key Concepts

8.22

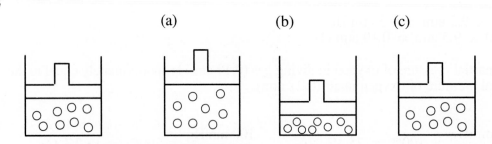

(a)   (b)   (c)

(a) According to Charles's law, the volume of a gas at fixed pressure is directly proportional to its temperature. Since the temperature increases by 50% (from 300 K to 450 K), volume also increases by 50%.
(b) Boyle's law states that the volume of a gas is inversely proportional to its pressure. Doubling the pressure halves the volume.
(c) For changes in both pressure and temperature, the combined gas law states that *PV/T* is constant. Thus, reducing both the pressure and the temperature by one-third leaves the volume unchanged.

8.23   Drawing (c) represents the gas in a sealed container after the temperature has been lowered from 350 K to 150 K. The gas remains a gas, and its volume is unchanged; only pressure is reduced because the molecules are moving slower.

8.24   Drawing (a) shows the sample of water as a solid, its state at 200 K. At 300 K, water is a liquid with a very low vapor pressure (as shown in Figure 8.20), represented by drawing (c).

8.25   At equilibrium, the gases are totally mixed.

8.26   Both sides of the manometer have equal heights because both sides have equal pressure.

8.27   The horizontal parts of the curve represent phase changes.
   (a) Melting point: 10°C
   (b) Boiling point: 75°C
   (c) Heat of fusion: 1.3 kcal/mol (the distance between the two points of the curve at the melting point)
   (d) Heat of vaporization: 7.5 kcal/mol (the distance between the two points of the curve at the boiling point)

8.28 Refer to Problem 8.13 for an approach to solving this problem. Note the quantities that change and those that remain constant; these differ in each part of the problem. Be sure to convert temperature to kelvins.

(a) $\dfrac{V_2}{V_1} = \dfrac{n_2 T_2 P_1}{n_1 T_1 P_2} = \dfrac{T_2}{T_1}; \quad \dfrac{V_2}{V_1} = \dfrac{(323 \text{ K})}{((298 \text{ K})} = 1.08$

(b) $\dfrac{V_2}{V_1} = \dfrac{n_2 T_2 P_1}{n_1 T_1 P_2} = \dfrac{T_2 P_1}{T_1 P_2}; \quad \dfrac{V_2}{V_1} = \dfrac{(448 \text{ K})(0.92 \text{ atm})}{((298 \text{ K})(2.7 \text{ atm})} = 0.51$

(c) $\dfrac{V_2}{V_1} = \dfrac{n_2 T_2 P_1}{n_1 T_1 P_2} = \dfrac{n_2 P_1}{n_1 P_2}; \quad \dfrac{V_2}{V_1} = \dfrac{(0.22 \text{ mol})(0.92 \text{ atm})}{(0.075 \text{ mol})(2.7 \text{ atm})} = 1.0$

(a)	(b)	(c)

$T = 298 \text{ K}$ $\quad$ $T = 323 \text{ K}$ $\quad$ $T = 448 \text{ K}$ $\quad$ $T = 298 \text{ K}$

$n = 0.075 \text{ mol}$ $\quad$ $n = 0.075 \text{ mol}$ $\quad$ $n = 0.075 \text{ mol}$ $\quad$ $n = 0.22 \text{ mol}$

$P = 0.92 \text{ atm}$ $\quad$ $P = 0.92 \text{ atm}$ $\quad$ $P = 2.7 \text{ atm}$ $\quad$ $P = 2.7 \text{ atm}$

8.29 The proportions of each gas in the container:
$P_{\text{red}} + P_{\text{yellow}} + P_{\text{green}} = 600 \text{ mm}$:
red = 6/12 = 1/2;   yellow = 2/12 = 1/6;   green = 4/12 = 1/3
$P_{\text{red}} = 1/2 \times 600 \text{ mmHg} = 300 \text{ mmHg}$;
$P_{\text{yellow}} = 1/6 \times 600 \text{ mmHg} = 100 \text{ mmHg}$;
$P_{\text{green}} = 1/3 \times 600 \text{ mmHg} = 200 \text{ mmHg}$

Gases and Pressure

8.30 One atmosphere is the amount of pressure needed to hold a column of mercury 760 mm high.

8.31 Four common units for measuring pressure: atmosphere (atm), mmHg, pounds per square inch (psi), Pascal (Pa).
$\qquad$ 1 atm = 760 mmHg = 14.7 psi = 101,325 Pa

8.32 (1) A gas consists of many tiny particles moving about at random with no attractive forces between particles.
(2) The amount of space occupied by gas molecules is much smaller than the amount of space between molecules.
(3) The average kinetic energy of gas particles is proportional to Kelvin temperature.
(4) When molecules collide, they spring apart elastically, and their total energy is constant.

8.33 According to the kinetic–molecular theory of gases, gas pressure is due to collisions with the walls of the container. The more collisions, the higher the pressure.

8.34

(a) $1 \text{ atm} \times \dfrac{760 \text{ mmHg}}{1 \text{ atm}} = 760 \text{ mmHg}$

(b) $25.3 \text{ psi} \times \dfrac{760 \text{ mmHg}}{14.7 \text{ psi}} = 1310 \text{ mmHg}$

(c) $7.5 \text{ atm} \times \dfrac{760 \text{ mmHg}}{1 \text{ atm}} = 5.7 \times 10^3 \text{ mmHg}$

(d) $28.0 \text{ in.Hg} \times \dfrac{25.4 \text{mm}}{1 \text{ in.}} = 711 \text{ mmHg}$

(e) $41.8 \text{ Pa} \times \dfrac{760 \text{ mmHg}}{101,325 \text{ Pa}} = 0.314 \text{ mmHg}$

8.35

(a) $440 \text{ mmHg} \times \dfrac{1 \text{ atm}}{760 \text{ mmHg}} = 0.58 \text{ atm}$

(b) $440 \text{ mmHg} \times \dfrac{133.3224 \text{ Pa}}{1 \text{ mmHg}} = 59,000 \text{ Pa}$

8.36   When the level in the arm connected to the container is 176 mm (17.6 cm) lower than the level open to the atmosphere, the pressure in the gas container is greater than atmospheric pressure.

754.3 mmHg + 176 mmHg = 930 mmHg

8.37   When the level in the arm connected to the container is 283 mm (28.3 cm) higher than the level open to the atmosphere, the pressure in the gas container is less than atmospheric pressure.

$283 \text{ mmHg} \times \dfrac{1 \text{ atm}}{760 \text{ mmHg}} = 0.372 \text{ atm}$ 1.021 atm − 0.372 atm = 0.649 atm

Boyle's Law

8.38   Boyle's law: Volume varies inversely with pressure at constant temperature and number of moles, that is, $P_1 V_1 = P_2 V_2$.

8.39   Two assumptions of the KMT explain the behavior of gases described by Boyle's Law. (1) The amount of space occupied by gas particles is much smaller than the space between particles. This allows compression of a gas without interactions between gas molecules. (2) Collisions between gas molecules and between molecules and the wall of a container are elastic. This means that all of the kinetic energy results in gas pressure.

Boyle's law involves an inverse proportionality: Pressure and volume change in opposite directions.

8.40 $P_1 V_1 = P_2 V_2$; $P_1 = 65.0 \text{ mmHg}$; $P_2 = 385 \text{ mmHg}$; $V_1 = 600.0 \text{ mL} = 0.600 \text{ L}$; $V_2 = ?$

$$V_2 = \frac{P_1 V_1}{P_2} = \frac{65.0 \text{ mmHg} \times 0.600 \text{ L}}{385 \text{ mmHg}} = 0.101 \text{ L} = 101 \text{ mL}$$

8.41 $P_1V_1 = P_2V_2$; $P_1 = 1.00$ atm; $P_2 = ?$; $V_1 = 2.85$ L; $V_2 = 1.70$ L

$$P_2 = \frac{P_1V_1}{V_2} = \frac{1.00 \text{ atm} \times 2.85 \text{ L}}{1.70 \text{ L}} = 1.68 \text{ atm}$$

8.42 $P_1V_1 = P_2V_2$; $P_1 = 5.0$ atm; $P_2 = 1.0$ atm; $V_1 = 0.350$ L; $V_2 = ?$

$$V_2 = \frac{P_1V_1}{P_2} = \frac{5.00 \text{ atm} \times 0.350 \text{ L}}{1.00 \text{ atm}} = 1.75 \text{ L}$$

8.43 $P_1V_1 = P_2V_2$; $P_1 = 630$ torr; $V_1 = 1.50$ L; $P_2 = 793$ torr $V_2 = ?$;

$$P_2 = \frac{P_1V_1}{V_2} = \frac{630 \text{ torr} \times 1.50 \text{ L}}{793 \text{ torr}} = 1.19 \text{ L}$$

Charles's Law

8.44   Charles's law: Volume varies directly with temperature at constant pressure and number of moles; that is, $V_1/T_1 = V_2/T_2$.

8.45   An important assumption of the KMT relates to the behavior of gases described by Charles's Law: The average kinetic energy of gas particles is proportional to the Kelvin temperature. This means that the relationship of temperature and volume is linear.

Charles's law involves a direct proportionality: Volume and temperature change in the same direction.

8.46

$$\frac{V_1}{T_1} = \frac{V_2}{T_2}; \qquad V_1 = 960 \text{ L}; \ V_2 = 1200 \text{ L}; \ T_1 = 18 \,°C = 291 \text{ K}; \ T_2 = ?$$

$$T_2 = \frac{V_2T_1}{V_1} = \frac{1200 \text{ L} \times 291 \text{ K}}{960 \text{ L}} = 364 \text{ K} = 91°C$$

8.47

$$\frac{V_1}{T_1} = \frac{V_2}{T_2}; \qquad V_1 = 875 \text{ L}; \ V_2 = 955 \text{ L}; \ T_1 = ? \ ; \ T_2 = 56 \,°C = 329 \text{ K}$$

$$T_1 = \frac{V_1T_2}{V_2} = \frac{875 \text{ L} \times 329 \text{ K}}{955 \text{ L}} = 301 \text{ K} = 28 \,°C$$

8.48

$$\frac{V_1}{T_1} = \frac{V_2}{T_2}; \qquad V_1 = 185 \text{ mL}; \ V_2 = ?; \ T_1 = 38 \,°C = 311 \text{ K}; \ T_2 = 97 \,°C = 370 \text{ K}$$

$$V_2 = \frac{V_1T_2}{T_1} = \frac{185 \text{ mL} \times 370 \text{ K}}{311 \text{ K}} = 220 \text{ mL}$$

8.49

$$\frac{V_1}{T_1} = \frac{V_2}{T_2}; \qquad V_1 = 43.0 \text{ L}; \ V_2 = ?; \ T_1 = 25 \,°C = 298 \text{ K}; \ T_2 = -8 \,°C = 265 \text{ K}$$

$$V_2 = \frac{V_1T_2}{T_1} = \frac{43.0 \text{ L} \times 265 \text{ K}}{298 \text{ K}} = 38.2 \text{ L}$$

Gay-Lussac's Law

8.50 Gay-Lussac's law: Pressure varies directly with temperature at constant volume and number of moles; that is, $P_1/T_1 = P_2/T_2$.

8.51 The assumptions explained for Boyle's Law and Charles's Law explain the behavior of gases under Gay-Lussac's law.

Gay-Lussac's law involves a direct proportionality: Pressure and temperature change in the same direction.

8.52

$$\frac{P_1}{T_1} = \frac{P_2}{T_2}; \qquad P_1 = 0.95 \text{ atm}; \; P_2 = ?; \; T_1 = 25\,°C = 298 \text{ K}; \; T_2 = 117\,°C = 390 \text{ K}$$

$$P_2 = \frac{P_1 T_2}{T_1} = \frac{0.95 \text{ atm x } 390 \text{ K}}{298 \text{ K}} = 1.2 \text{ atm}$$

8.53

$$\frac{P_1}{T_1} = \frac{P_2}{T_2}; \qquad P_1 = 3.85 \text{ atm}; \; P_2 = 18.0 \text{ atm}; \; T_1 = 25\,°C = 298 \text{ K}; \; T_2 = ?$$

$$T_2 = \frac{P_2 T_1}{P_1} = \frac{18.0 \text{ atm x } 298 \text{ K}}{3.85 \text{ atm}} = 1390 \text{ K} = 1120\,°C$$

Combined Gas Law

8.54

$$\frac{P_1 V_1}{T_1} = \frac{P_2 V_2}{T_2}; \qquad \begin{array}{l} P_1 = 760 \text{ mmHg}; \; V_1 = 2.84 \text{ L}; \; T_1 = 273 \text{ K} \\ P_2 = 520 \text{ mmHg}; \; V_2 = 7.50 \text{ L}; \; T_2 = ? \end{array}$$

$$T_2 = \frac{P_2 V_2 T_1}{P_1 V_1} = \frac{520 \text{ mmHg x } 7.50 \text{ L x } 273 \text{ K}}{760 \text{ mmHg x } 2.84 \text{ L}} = 493 \text{ K} = 220\,°C$$

8.55

$$\frac{P_1 V_1}{T_1} = \frac{P_2 V_2}{T_2}; \qquad \begin{array}{l} P_1 = 1.14 \text{ atm}; \; V_1 = 3.50 \text{ L}; \; T_1 = 22.0\,°C = 295 \text{ K} \\ P_2 = 1.20 \text{ atm}; \; V_2 = ?; \; T_2 = 30.0°C = 303 \text{ K} \end{array}$$

$$V_2 = \frac{P_1 V_1 T_2}{T_1 P_2} = \frac{1.14 \text{ atm x } 3.50 \text{ L x } 303 \text{ K}}{295 \text{ K x } 1.20 \text{ atm}} = 3.42 \text{ L}$$

8.56

$$\frac{P_1 V_1}{T_1} = \frac{P_2 V_2}{T_2}; \qquad \begin{array}{l} P_1 = 748 \text{ mmHg}; \; V_1 = 75.4 \text{ mL}; \; T_1 = 23\,°C = 296 \text{ K} \\ P_2 = 760 \text{ mmHg}; \; V_2 = ?; \; T_2 = 0\,°C = 273 \text{ K} \end{array}$$

$$V_2 = \frac{P_1 V_1 T_2}{T_1 P_2} = \frac{748 \text{ mmHg x } 75.4 \text{ mL x } 273 \text{ K}}{296 \text{ K x } 760 \text{ mmHg}} = 68.4 \text{ mL}$$

8.57

$$\frac{P_1V_1}{T_1} = \frac{P_2V_2}{T_2}; \qquad P_1 = 120 \text{ atm}; \ V_1 = 6.80 \text{ L}; \ T_1 = 20 \text{ °C} = 293 \text{ K}$$

$$P_2 = 1.00 \text{ atm}; \ V_2 = ?; \ T_2 = 273 \text{ K}$$

$$V_2 = \frac{P_1V_1T_2}{T_1P_2} = \frac{120 \text{ atm} \times 6.80 \text{ L} \times 273 \text{ K}}{293 \text{ K} \times 1.00 \text{ atm}} = 760 \text{ L}$$

8.58 (a) For one mole of gas, the combined gas law states that P is proportional to T/V, or $P \propto T/V$. Thus, if the temperature doubles and the volume is halved, the new pressure is four times greater than the original pressure:

$$\frac{P_1V_1}{T_1} = \frac{P_2V_2}{T_2}; \qquad V_2 = 0.5V_1; \ T_2 = 2T_1; \ P_2 = ?$$

$$P_2 = \frac{P_1V_1T_2}{T_1V_2} = \frac{P_1V_1 \times 2T_1}{T_1 \times 0.5V_1} = 4\,P_1$$

(b) If the temperature is halved and the volume is doubled, the new pressure is one-fourth the original pressure:

$$\frac{P_1V_1}{T_1} = \frac{P_2V_2}{T_2}; \qquad V_2 = 2V_1; \ T_2 = 0.5T_1; \ P_2 = ?$$

$$P_2 = \frac{P_1V_1T_2}{T_1V_2} = \frac{P_1V_1 \times 0.5T_1}{T_1 \times 2V_1} = 0.25P_1$$

8.59 (a) For one mole of gas, the combined gas law states that V is proportional to T/P, or $V \propto T/P$. Thus, if the pressure is halved and the temperature is doubled, the new volume is four times greater than the original volume.

$$\frac{P_1V_1}{T_1} = \frac{P_2V_2}{T_2}; \qquad P_2 = 0.5P_1; \ T_2 = 2T_1; \ V_2 = ?$$

$$V_2 = \frac{P_1V_1T_2}{T_1P_2} = \frac{P_1V_1 \times 2T_1}{T_1 \times 0.5\,P_1} = 4V_1$$

(b) If both the pressure and the temperature are doubled, the volume remains the same.

$$\frac{P_1V_1}{T_1} = \frac{P_2V_2}{T_2}; \qquad P_2 = 2P_1; \ T_2 = 2T_1; \ V_2 = ?$$

$$V_2 = \frac{P_1V_1T_2}{T_1P_2} = \frac{P_1V_1 \times 2T_1}{T_1 \times 2P_1} = V_1$$

8.60

$$\frac{P_1V_1}{T_1} = \frac{P_2V_2}{T_2}; \qquad P_1 = 775 \text{ mmHg}; \ V_1 = 590 \text{ mL}; \ T_1 = 352 \text{ K}$$

$$P_2 = 800.0 \text{ mmHg}; \ V_2 = ?; \ T_2 = 298 \text{ K}$$

$$V_2 = \frac{P_1V_1T_2}{P_2T_1} = \frac{775 \text{ mmHg x 590 mL x 298 K}}{800.0 \text{ mmHg x 352 K}} = 484 \text{ mL}$$

8.61 In this problem, temperature is constant. First, we find the volume of gas at 1.25 atm and 25 °C.
$P_1V_1 = P_2V_2; \ P_1 = 1850 \text{ atm}; \ P_2 = 1.25 \text{ atm}; \ V_1 = 2.30 \text{ L}; \ V_2 = ?$

$$V_2 = \frac{P_1V_1}{P_2} = \frac{1850 \text{ atm x 2.30 L}}{1.25 \text{ atm}} = 3400 \text{ L}$$

If the cylinder holds 3400 L of helium at 1.25 atm and 25 °C, it can be used to fill
3400 L/1.50 L = 2270 balloons.

Avogadro's Law and Standard Molar Volume

8.62 Avogadro's law states that equal volumes of gases at the same temperature and pressure contain equal numbers of molecules. Since the volume of space taken up by gas molecules is so much smaller than the amount of space between molecules, Avogadro's law is true regardless of the chemical identity of the gas.

8.63 The conditions of STP are 760 mmHg (1 atm) pressure and 273 K temperature.

8.64 A mole of gas at STP occupies 22.4 L.

8.65

$$n_2 = \frac{V_2 \text{ x } n_1}{V_1} = 48.6 \text{ L x } \frac{1.0 \text{ mol}}{22.4 \text{ L}} = 2.17 \text{ mol}$$

8.66 The samples contain equal numbers of molecules. 1.0 L of O_2 weighs more than 1.0 L of H_2 because the molar mass of O_2 is greater than the molar mass of H_2, and equal numbers of moles of both are present.

8.67

$$0.20 \text{ g Cl}_2 \text{ x } \frac{1 \text{ mol Cl}_2}{71 \text{ g Cl}_2} \text{ x } \frac{22.4 \text{ L}}{1 \text{ mol Cl}_2} = 0.063 \text{ L} = 63 \text{ mL}$$

8.68

$$16.5 \text{ L x } \frac{1 \text{ mol}}{22.4 \text{ L}} \text{ x } \frac{16.0 \text{ g CH}_4}{1 \text{ mol CH}_4} = 11.8 \text{ g CH}_4$$

8.69

$$1.75 \text{ g HCN x } \frac{1 \text{ mol}}{27.0 \text{ g HCN}} \text{ x } \frac{22.4 \text{ L}}{1 \text{ mol HCN}} = 1.45 \text{ L HCN at STP}$$

8.70

$$V = 4.0 \text{ m} \times 5.0 \text{ m} \times 2.5 \text{ m} = 50 \text{ m}^3; \ 50 \text{ m}^3 \times \frac{10^3 \text{ L}}{1 \text{ m}^3} = 5.0 \times 10^4 \text{ L}$$

$$\frac{1 \text{ mol}}{22.4 \text{ L}} \times 5.0 \times 10^4 \text{ L} = 2230 \text{ mol gas}$$

$$\frac{0.21 \text{ mol O}_2}{1 \text{ mol gas}} \times 2230 \text{ mol gas} = 470 \text{ mol O}_2$$

$$470 \text{ mol O}_2 \times \frac{32.0 \text{ g O}_2}{1 \text{ mol O}_2} = 15{,}000 \text{ g O}_2 = 15 \text{ kg O}_2$$

8.71

$$\frac{0.79 \text{ mol N}_2}{1 \text{ mol gas}} \times 2230 \text{ mol gas} = 1760 \text{ mol N}_2$$

$$1760 \text{ mol N}_2 \times \frac{28.0 \text{ g N}_2}{1 \text{ mol N}_2} = 49{,}000 \text{ g N}_2 = 49 \text{ kg N}_2$$

The Ideal Gas Law

8.72 The ideal gas law: $PV = nRT$

8.73 The combined gas law can be used to calculate changes in P, V, and T when the amount of gas is fixed. The ideal gas law is valid for any number of moles and uses the ideal gas constant R to calculate any one of the variables P, V, T, and n if the other three are known.

8.74 $PV = nRT$; $n = PV/RT$

For Cl_2: $P = 1.0 \text{ atm}$; $V = 2.0 \text{ L}$; $R = 0.082 \frac{\text{L} \cdot \text{atm}}{\text{mol} \cdot \text{K}}$; $T = 273 \text{ K}$

$$n = \frac{1.0 \text{ atm} \times 2.0 \text{ L}}{0.082 \frac{\text{L} \cdot \text{atm}}{\text{mol} \cdot \text{K}} \times 273 \text{ K}} = 0.089 \text{ mol Cl}_2$$

$$0.089 \text{ mol Cl}_2 \times \frac{71 \text{ g}}{1 \text{ mol Cl}_2} = 6.3 \text{ g Cl}_2$$

For CH_4: $P = 1.5 \text{ atm}$; $V = 3.0 \text{ L}$; $R = 0.082 \frac{\text{L} \cdot \text{atm}}{\text{mol} \cdot \text{K}}$; $T = 300 \text{ K}$

$$n = \frac{1.5 \text{ atm} \times 3.0 \text{ L}}{0.082 \frac{\text{L} \cdot \text{atm}}{\text{mol} \cdot \text{K}} \times 300 \text{ K}} = 0.18 \text{ mol CH}_4$$

$$0.18 \text{ mol CH}_4 \times \frac{16 \text{ g}}{1 \text{ mol CH}_4} = 2.9 \text{ g CH}_4$$

There are more molecules in the CH_4 sample than in the Cl_2 sample. The Cl_2 sample, however, weighs more because the molar mass of Cl_2 is much greater than the molar mass of CH_4.

8.75 As in the preceding problem, use the relationship $n = PV/RT$.

For CO_2: $\quad n = \dfrac{500 \text{ mmHg} \times 2.0 \text{ L } CO_2}{62.4 \dfrac{\text{mmHg} \cdot \text{L}}{\text{mol} \cdot \text{K}} \times 300 \text{ K}} = 0.053 \text{ mol } CO_2$

For N_2: $\quad n = \dfrac{760 \text{ mmHg} \times 1.5 \text{ L } N_2}{62.4 \dfrac{\text{mmHg} \cdot \text{L}}{\text{mol} \cdot \text{K}} \times 330 \text{ K}} = 0.055 \text{ mol } N_2$

The CO_2 sample has slightly fewer molecules. Since the molar mass of CO_2 is much greater than the molar mass of N_2, however, the CO_2 sample weighs more (2.3 g) than the N_2 sample (1.5 g).

8.76

$n = 2.3 \text{ mol He}; \quad T = 294 \text{ K}; \quad V = 1.5 \text{ L}$

$P = \dfrac{nRT}{V} = \dfrac{2.3 \text{ mol He} \times 0.082 \dfrac{\text{L} \cdot \text{atm}}{\text{mol} \cdot \text{K}} \times 294 \text{ K}}{1.5 \text{ L}} = 37 \text{ atm}$

8.77

$n = 3.5 \text{ mol } O_2; \quad P = 1.6 \text{ atm}; \quad V = 27 \text{ L}$

$T = \dfrac{PV}{nR} = \dfrac{1.6 \text{ atm} \times 27 \text{ L}}{3.5 \text{ mol} \times 0.0821 \dfrac{\text{L} \cdot \text{atm}}{\text{mol} \cdot \text{K}}} = 150 \text{ K}$

8.78

$n = 15.0 \text{ g } CO_2 \times \dfrac{1 \text{ mol}}{44 \text{ g}} = 0.341 \text{ mol } CO_2; \quad T = 310 \text{ K}; \quad V = 0.30 \text{ L}$

$P = \dfrac{nRT}{V} = \dfrac{0.341 \text{ mol } CO_2 \times 62.4 \dfrac{\text{mmHg} \cdot \text{L}}{\text{mol} \cdot \text{K}} \times 310 \text{ K}}{0.30 \text{ L}} = 2.2 \times 10^4 \text{ mmHg}$

8.79

$PV = nRT; \quad n = 20.0 \text{ g } N_2 \times \dfrac{1 \text{ mol}}{28.0 \text{ g}} = 0.714 \text{ mol } N_2; \quad V = 4.00 \text{ L}; \quad P = 6.00 \text{ atm}$

$T = \dfrac{PV}{nR} = \dfrac{6.00 \text{ atm} \times 4.00 \text{ L}}{0.714 \text{ mol} \times 0.0821 \dfrac{\text{L} \cdot \text{atm}}{\text{mol} \cdot \text{K}}} = 409 \text{ K} = 136 \,°\text{C}$

8.80

$$n = 18.0 \text{ g O}_2 \text{ x } \frac{1 \text{ mol}}{32.0 \text{ g}} = 0.562 \text{ mol O}_2; \quad T = 350 \text{ K}; \quad P = 550 \text{ mmHg}$$

$$V = \frac{nRT}{P} = \frac{0.562 \text{ mol O}_2 \text{ x } 62.4 \dfrac{\text{mmHg} \cdot \text{L}}{\text{mol} \cdot \text{K}} \text{ x } 350 \text{ K}}{550 \text{ mmHg}} = 22.3 \text{ L O}_2$$

8.81

$$n = \frac{PV}{RT}; \quad P = 2.5 \text{ atm}; \quad V = 0.55 \text{ L}; \quad T = 347 \text{ K}$$

$$= \frac{2.5 \text{ atm x } 0.55 \text{ L}}{0.082 \dfrac{\text{L} \cdot \text{atm}}{\text{mol} \cdot \text{K}} \text{ x } 347 \text{ K}} = 0.048 \text{ moles}$$

Dalton's Law and Partial Pressure

8.82 Partial pressure is the pressure contribution of one component of a mixture of gases to the total pressure.

8.83 Dalton's law of partial pressure says that the total pressure exerted by a gas mixture is the sum of the individual pressures of the components in the mixture.

8.84

$$440 \text{ mmHg x } \frac{1 \text{ atm}}{760 \text{ mmHg}} \text{ x } \frac{160 \text{ mmHg}}{1.0 \text{ atm}} = 93 \text{ mmHg}$$

8.85 If the atmosphere inside the tent consists of 45% oxygen at a pressure of 753 mmHg, then 0.45 x 753 mmHg = 340 mmHg is the partial pressure of oxygen.

Liquids and Intermolecular Forces

8.86 The vapor pressure of a liquid is the partial pressure of the vapor above the liquid.

8.87 At a liquid's normal boiling point, its vapor pressure equals 1 atm (or 760 mmHg).

8.88 Increased pressure raises a liquid's boiling point; decreased pressure lowers a liquid's boiling point.

8.89 A liquid's heat of vaporization is the amount of heat needed to vaporize one gram of the liquid at its boiling point.

8.90 (a) All molecules exhibit London forces, which increase in strength with increasing molecular weight.
(b) Dipole–dipole interactions are important for molecules that are polar.
(c) Hydrogen bonding occurs between an unshared electron pair on an electronegative atom (O, N, or F) and a hydrogen atom bonded to a second electronegative atom (O, N, F).

8.91 Dipole–dipole interactions are most important in compounds that do not exhibit ionic bonding or hydrogen bonding and that have polar covalent bonds. Thus, dipole–dipole interactions are most important only for HCN (b) and CH_3Cl (e). (CCl_4 has polar covalent bonds, but it is symmetrical.)

8.92 Ethanol is higher boiling than dimethyl ether because of hydrogen bonding. Since molecules of ethanol are strongly attracted to each other, the boiling point of ethanol is higher than that of dimethyl ether, whose molecules are held together by weaker dipole–dipole interactions.

8.93 London forces are the major attractive forces for Br_2 and I_2 molecules. Since London forces become stronger with increasing molar mass, the melting point of I_2 is higher than the melting point of Br_2.

8.94

(a) $\dfrac{9.72 \text{ kcal}}{1 \text{ mol } H_2O}$ x 3.00 mol H_2O = 29.2 kcal of heat required.

(b) $\dfrac{9.72 \text{ kcal}}{1 \text{ mol } H_2O}$ x $\dfrac{1 \text{ mol } H_2O}{18.0 \text{ g}}$ x 320 g = 173 kcal of heat is released.

8.95

$\dfrac{159 \text{ cal}}{1 \text{ g isopropyl alcohol}}$ x 190.0 g isopropyl alcohol = 3.02×10^4 cal = 30.2 kcal

Solids

8.96 The atoms in a crystalline solid are arranged in a regular, orderly network. The atoms in an amorphous solid have no regular arrangement.

8.97

Type of Solid	Example
Ionic solid	NaCl, $MgBr_2$
Molecular solid	Ice, sucrose
Covalent network solid	Diamond
Metallic solid	Cu, Fe

8.98

$\dfrac{45.9 \text{ cal}}{1 \text{ g}}$ x $\dfrac{1 \text{ kcal}}{1000 \text{ cal}}$ x $\dfrac{60.0 \text{ g}}{1 \text{ mol}}$ x 1.75 mol = 4.82 kcal

8.99

$\dfrac{630 \text{ cal}}{1 \text{ mol Na}}$ x $\dfrac{1 \text{ kcal}}{1000 \text{ cal}}$ x $\dfrac{1 \text{ mol Na}}{23.0 \text{ g Na}}$ x 262 g Na = 7.18 kcal

Applications

8.100 *Systolic pressure* (the higher number) is the maximum blood pressure developed in the artery just after contraction. *Diastolic pressure* (the lower number) is the minimum pressure that occurs at the end of the heartbeat cycle. A blood pressure reading of 180/110 is an indication of high blood pressure.

8.101 The three most important greenhouse gases are carbon dioxide, water vapor, and methane.

8.102 Increased concentrations of CO_2 in the atmosphere, coupled with an increase in the average global temperature, are evidence for global warming.

8.103

Mineral	Molar mass	Mass of Ca^{2+}	Mass of PO_4^{3-}	Ratio of Ca^{2+}/PO_4^{3-}
$Ca_3(PO_4)_2$	310.2 g	120.2 g	190.0 g	0.632
$Ca_{10}(PO_4)_6(OH)_2$	1004 g	401 g	570 g	0.704

Calcium makes up a larger percent of hydroxyapatite than it does in calcium phosphate.

8.104 The supercritical state of matter is a condition intermediate between liquid and gas, in which there is some space between molecules yet they are too close together to be truly a gas.

8.105 Supercritical CO_2 is nontoxic and nonflammable and can be continuously recycled.

General Questions and Problems

8.106 As the temperature increases, the kinetic energy of gas molecules increases, and the force per unit area that they exert in colliding against the walls of a container increases, thus increasing pressure.

8.107 Two moles of hydrogen react with one mole of oxygen according to the balanced equation. Since equal volumes of gases have equal numbers of moles at STP, 2.5 L of O_2 reacts with 5.0 L of H_2.

8.108 3.0 L of H_2 and 1.5 L of O_2 react completely. At STP, one mole of H_2 occupies 22.4 L. Thus, 3.0 L of hydrogen = 3.0/22.4 or 0.13 mol. This is also the number of moles of H_2O formed.

$$n = 0.13 \text{ mol } H_2O; \quad T = 373 \text{ K}; \quad P = 1.0 \text{ atm}$$

$$V = \frac{nRT}{P} = \frac{0.13 \text{ mol } H_2O \times 0.0821 \frac{L \cdot atm}{mol \cdot K} \times 373 \text{ K}}{1.0 \text{ atm}} = 4.0 \text{ L } H_2O$$

8.109 $PV = nRT$; $P = 1.0$ atm; $V = 0.24$ L; $T = 310$ K

$$n = \frac{PV}{RT} = \frac{1.0 \text{ atm} \times 0.24 \text{ L}}{0.0821 \frac{L \cdot atm}{mol \cdot K} \times 310 \text{ K}} = 0.0094 \text{ mol} = 9.4 \text{ mmol } CO_2$$

8.110

$$0.0094 \text{ mol } CO_2 \times \frac{44.0 \text{ g } CO_2}{1 \text{ mol } CO_2} = 0.41 \text{ g } CO_2$$

$$\frac{0.41 \text{ g } CO_2}{1 \text{ min}} \times \frac{60 \text{ min}}{1 \text{ hr}} \times \frac{24 \text{ hr}}{1 \text{ day}} = \frac{590 \text{ g } CO_2}{\text{day}}$$

8.111 At STP, equal volumes of gases have an equal number of moles. However, O_2 has a greater molecular weight than H_2, and the vessel containing O_2 is heavier.

8.112 $P = 0.975$ atm; $V = 1.6 \times 10^5$ L; $T = 375$ K

$$n = \frac{PV}{RT} = \frac{0.975 \text{ atm } \times 1.6 \times 10^5 \text{ L}}{0.0821 \frac{\text{L} \cdot \text{atm}}{\text{mol} \cdot \text{K}} \times 375 \text{ K}} = 5.07 \times 10^3 \text{ mol}$$

$$\text{Density} = \frac{5.07 \times 10^3 \text{ mol}}{1.6 \times 10^5 \text{ L}} \times \frac{29 \text{ g}}{\text{mol}} = \frac{0.92 \text{ g}}{\text{L}}$$

The air in the balloon is less dense than air at STP (density = 1.3 g/L).

8.113

$$n = \frac{745 \text{ mmHg } \times 14.7 \text{ L}}{62.4 \frac{\text{mmHg} \cdot \text{L}}{\text{mol} \cdot \text{K}} \times 298 \text{ K}} = 0.589 \text{ mol}; \quad \frac{10.0 \text{ g}}{0.589 \text{ mol}} = 17.0 \text{ g/mol}$$

8.114 Divide the molar mass (molecular weight in grams) by 22.4 L to find the density in grams per liter.

Gas	Molecular Weight	Density (g/L) at STP
(a) CH_4	16.0 g/mol	0.714
(b) CO_2	44.0 g/mol	1.96
(c) O_2	32.0 g/mol	1.43

8.115 $n = 1$ mol; $T = 1$ K ; $P = 1 \times 10^{-14}$ mmHg

$$V = \frac{nRT}{P} = \frac{1 \text{ mol } \times 62.4 \frac{\text{mmHg} \cdot \text{L}}{\text{mol} \cdot \text{K}} \times 1 \text{ K}}{1 \times 10^{-14} \text{ mmHg}} = 6 \times 10^{15} \text{ L}$$

$$\text{Density} = \frac{6.022 \times 10^{23} \text{ atoms}}{6 \times 10^{15} \text{ L}} = \frac{1 \times 10^8 \text{ atoms}}{\text{L}}$$

8.116

(a)   (b)

Ethylene glycol   Chloroethane

(c) Ethylene glycol has a higher boiling point than chloroethane because it forms hydrogen bonds.

8.117

(a) $\dfrac{1.0 \text{ atm}}{10 \text{ m}}$ x 25 m = 2.5 atm

(b) For O_2: 0.20 x 2.5 atm = 0.5 atm

For N_2: 0.80 x 2.5 atm = 2.0 atm

8.118 (a) Since the size of a Rankine degree is the same as a Fahrenheit degree, we can use the same conversion factor as we use for °F/°C conversions.

$\dfrac{9°R}{5°C}$ x 273.15°C = 491.67 °R

(b) To calculate the gas constant R, use the ideal gas law at standard temperature and pressure.

$R = \dfrac{PV}{nT}$; P = 1 atm; V = 22.4 L; n = 1 mol; T = 491.67 °R

$R = \dfrac{1 \text{ atm } x \text{ } 22.4 \text{ L}}{1 \text{ mol } x \text{ } 492°R} = 0.0455 \dfrac{L \cdot atm}{mol \cdot °R}$

8.119 (a) 2 C_8H_{18} + 25 O_2 $\longrightarrow$ 16 CO_2 + 18 H_2O

(b) 4.6 x 10^{10} L C_8H_{18} x $\dfrac{0.792 \text{ g}}{1 \text{ mL}}$ x $\dfrac{10^3 \text{ mL}}{1 \text{ L}}$ = 3.6 x 10^{13} g C_8H_{18}

$= 3.6 \text{ x } 10^{10} \text{ kg } C_8H_{18}$

3.6 x 10^{13}g C_8H_{18} x $\dfrac{1 \text{ mol } C_8H_{18}}{114 \text{ g } C_8H_{18}}$ x $\dfrac{16 \text{ mol } CO_2}{2 \text{ mol } C_8H_{18}}$ x $\dfrac{44.0 \text{ g } CO_2}{1 \text{ mol } CO_2}$ = 1.1 x 10^{14} g CO_2

$= 1.1 \text{ x } 10^{11} \text{ kg } CO_2$

(c) To find the volume of CO_2, use the ideal gas law at STP; n can be calculated from the mass of CO_2 that was found in part (b).

$n = 1.1 \text{ x } 10^{14} \text{ g } CO_2 \text{ x } \dfrac{1 \text{ mol } CO_2}{44 \text{ g } CO_2} = 2.5 \text{ x } 10^{12} \text{ mol } CO_2$

$V = \dfrac{nRT}{P} = \dfrac{2.5 \text{ x } 10^{12} \text{ mol } CO_2 \text{ x } 0.0821 \dfrac{L \cdot atm}{mol \cdot K} \text{ x } 273 \text{ K}}{1.0 \text{ atm}} = 5.6 \text{ x } 10^{13} \text{ L } CO_2$

Self-Test for Chapter 8

Multiple Choice

1. Which of the following units would you be least likely to use in a chemical laboratory?
   (a) pascal   (b) pounds per square inch   (c) mmHg   (d) atmosphere

2. A fixed amount of a gas has its temperature and volume doubled. What happens to its pressure?
   (a) increases fourfold   (b) doubles   (c) stays the same   (d) is halved

3. In which of the gas laws is the amount of gas not fixed?
   (a) Boyle's law   (b) Charles's law   (c) Gay-Lussac's law   (d) Avogadro's law

4. Which of the following compounds does not exhibit hydrogen bonding?
   (a) CH_3OCH_3 (b) CH_3OH (c) HF   (d) CH_3NH_2

5. Which of the following compounds is the lowest melting?
   (a) NaI   (b) Au   (c) SiO_2 (d) sugar

6. Which term describes the change of state that occurs when a gas changes to a solid?
   (a) fusion   (b) condensation   (c) deposition   (d) sublimation

7. When does a gas obey ideal behavior?
   (a) at low density   (b) at high pressure   (c) at low temperature   (d) in a large container

8. If 22.0 g of CO_2 has a pressure of 1.00 atm at 300 K, what is its volume?
   (a) 22.4 L   (b) 12.3 L   (c) 11.2 L   (d) 9.5 L

9. What volume does the amount of gas in Problem 8 occupy at STP?
   (a) 22.4 L   (b) 12.3 L   (c) 11.2 L   (d) 9.5 L

10. What is the density of CO_2 gas in g/L at STP if one mole of gas has a volume of 22.4 L?
    (a) 44.0 g/L   (b) 11.0 g/L   (c) 6.4 g/L   (d) 1.96 g/L

Sentence Completion

1. In Boyle's law, the _____ of a gas is inversely proportional to its _____.

2. A liquid has _____ volume and _____ shape.

3. _____ law states that the total pressure of a gas mixture is the sum of the individual pressure of the components in the mixture.

4. A pressure of 760 mmHg and a temperature of 273 K are known as ___ ___ ___ .

5. _____ law says that equal volumes of gases at the same temperature and pressure contain equal numbers of molecules.

6. In a closed container, liquid and vapor are at _____.

7. Units for measuring pressure include _____, _____, _____, and _____.

8. The _____ __ _____ is the heat necessary to melt one gram of a solid at its melting point.

9. In Charles's law, _____ and _____ are kept constant.

10. Gas particles move in straight lines, with energy proportional to _____.

11. The transformation of a substance from one phase to another is known as a _____ ___ _____.

12. A liquid that evaporates readily is said to be _____.

True or False

1. Molecules of ethyl alcohol exhibit hydrogen bonding.

2. All gases are similar in their physical behavior.

3. Molecules of CH_3Cl experience both dipole–dipole interactions and London forces.

4. Doubling the pressure of a gas at constant temperature doubles the volume.

5. $R = 0.082$ L atm/(mol · K) is a value for the gas constant.

6. Atoms in solids have an orderly arrangement.

7. Standard temperature and pressure are 760 mmHg and 273°C.

8. All substances become solids if the temperature is low enough.

9. The atmospheric pressure in Death Valley (282 ft below sea level) is lower than the atmospheric pressure at sea level.

10. The more liquid there is in a closed container, the higher the vapor pressure.

11. Surface tension is a liquid's resistance to flow.

Match each entry on the left with its partner on the right. Use each answer once.

1. $P_1V_1 = P_2V_2$ (a) Avogadro's law

2. Dipole–dipole attraction   (b) Gas constant

3. $P_{\text{total}} = P_{\text{gas 1}} + P_{\text{gas 2}} + ...$ (c) Force per unit area

4. 760 mmHg at 273 K   (d) Charles's law

5. Hydrogen bonding   (e) Occurs between molecules of CH_3Br

6. $V_1/n_1 = V_2/n_2$ (f) STP

7. 0.007500 mmHg   (g) Boyle's law

8. London forces   (h) Occurs between molecules of CH_3OH

9. 62.4 mmHg L/mol K   (i) Ideal gas law

10. $V_1/T_1 = V_2/T_2$ (j) Pascal

11. Pressure   (k) Dalton's law of partial pressure

12. $PV = nRT$ (l) Occurs between molecules of N_2

Chapter 9   Solutions

Chapter Outline

I. Characteristics of solutions (Sections 9.1–9.6).
   A. Mixtures and solutions (Section 9.1).
      1. Mixtures are either heterogeneous or homogeneous.
         a. Heterogeneous mixtures have nonuniform mixing.
         b. Homogeneous mixtures have uniform mixing.
      2. Homogeneous mixtures can be classified by particle size.
         a. In solutions, particles range in size from 0.1 to 2 nm.
         b. In colloids, particles range in size from 2 to 1000 nm.
      3. When a solid is dissolved in a liquid, the liquid is the solvent and the solid is the solute.
   B. The solution process (Sections 9.2–9.3).
      1. Solubility depends on the strength of attraction between solute particles and solvent relative to the attractions in the pure substances.
      2. In predicting solubility, polar solvents dissolve polar substances, and nonpolar solvents dissolve nonpolar substances.
      3. Solvation can be either an exothermic or an endothermic process.
      4. Some ionic compounds attract water to form solid hydrates (Section 9.3).
   C. Solubility (Sections 9.4–9.6).
      1. Solubility is a dynamic process (Section 9.4).
         a. When no more of an added solute will dissolve, the solution is said to be saturated.
         b. In a saturated solution, an equilibrium is established between dissolving and crystallizing.
         c. Two liquids are miscible if they are mutually soluble in all proportions.
      2. The solubility of a substance is the maximum amount of the substance that will dissolve in a solvent.
      3. Effect of temperature on solubility (Section 9.5).
         a. The effect of temperature on the solubility of a solid solute is unpredictable.
         b. A gas is always less soluble as temperature increases.
         c. A solid that is more soluble at high temperature than at low may form a supersaturated solution.
      4. Effect of pressure on solubility (Section 9.6).
         a. Increased pressure makes gas molecules more soluble in a liquid.
         b. Henry's law: $C = kP_{gas}$.
            The solubility of a gas in a liquid is proportional to its partial pressure over the liquid at constant T.
         c. When the partial pressure of a gas changes:
            $$\frac{C_1}{P_1} = \frac{C_2}{P_2} = k \text{ (at constant T)}$$
II. Quantitative relationships in solutions (Sections 9.7–9.10).
   A. Concentration (Section 9.7).
      1. Molarity $= \dfrac{\text{moles of solute}}{\text{volume of solution (L)}}$.
         Molarity can be used as a conversion factor.
      2. weight/volume % concentration [(w/v)%] $= \dfrac{\text{grams of solute}}{\text{mL of solution}} \times 100\%$.

3. volume/volume % concentration $[(v/v)\%] = \dfrac{\text{volume of solute (mL)}}{\text{volume of solution (mL)}} \times 100\%.$

4. parts per million (ppm) $= \dfrac{\text{mass of solute (g)}}{\text{mass of solution (g)}} \times 10^6.$

$$= \dfrac{\text{volume of solute (mL)}}{\text{volume of solution (mL)}} \times 10^6.$$

5. parts per billion (ppb) $= \dfrac{\text{mass of solute (g)}}{\text{mass of solution (g)}} \times 10^9.$

$$= \dfrac{\text{volume of solute (mL)}}{\text{volume of solution (mL)}} \times 10^9.$$

B. Dilution (Section 9.8).
  1. During dilution, the number of moles of solute remains constant, while volume changes.
  2. $M_1 \times V_1 = M_2 \times V_2.$
  3. V_1/V_2 is known as a dilution factor.
C. Equivalents and milliequivalents (Sections 9.9–9.10).
  1. Electrolytes (Section 9.9).
    a. Substances that dissociate completely are strong electrolytes.
    b. Substances that dissociate partially are weak electrolytes.
    c. Molecular substances that don't produce ions are nonelectrolytes.
  2. The concentration of electrolytes is expressed in equivalents (Section 9.10).
    a. 1 equivalent of an ion $= \dfrac{\text{molar mass of the ion}}{\text{number of charges on the ion}}.$
    b. Milliequivalents are useful when measuring ion concentrations in body fluids.
III. Properties of solutions (Sections 9.11–9.13).
  A. Effects of particles in solution—colligative properties (Section 9.11).
    1. Lowering of vapor pressure.
    2. Boiling point elevation.
    3. Freezing point depression.
    4. These effects don't depend on the identity of the particles.
  B. Osmosis (Section 9.12–9.13).
    1. When two solutions of different concentrations are separated by a semipermeable membrane, water passes through to the more concentrated side. This is known as osmosis.
    2. Osmotic pressure can be applied to establish an equilibrium between the rates of forward and reverse passage of water across the membrane.
    3. The osmotic pressure of a solution depends only on the number of particles in solution.
    4. Osmolarity = molarity x number of particles per formula unit.
    5. Two solutions that are isotonic have the same osmolarity.
      a. In cells, a hypotonic solution causes hemolysis.
      b. A hypertonic solution causes crenation.
    6. Dialysis is a process similar to osmosis except that the pores in the membrane allow small solute molecules to pass (Section 9.13).
      a. Hemodialysis is used to cleanse the blood of people whose kidneys malfunction.
      b. Colloidal particles are too large to pass through semipermeable membranes.

Solutions to Chapter 9 Problems

9.1 Orange juice is heterogeneous, and all of the other mixtures are homogeneous, although hand lotion might be heterogeneous in some cases. Apple juice and tea are solutions because they are nonfilterable and transparent to light. Hand lotion is a colloid.

9.2 Remember the rule "like dissolves like."
(a) CCl_4 and H_2O don't form solutions because CCl_4 is nonpolar and H_2O is polar.
(b) Benzene and $MgSO_4$ don't form solutions because $MgSO_4$ is ionic and benzene is nonpolar.
(c), (d) These two pairs of substances form solutions because they are chemically similar.

9.3 Glauber's salt: $Na_2SO_4 \cdot 10H_2O$

9.4 Molar mass of Glauber's salt: 322 g/mol. 322 g of Glauber's salt provides 1.00 mol of sodium sulfate.

9.5 The solubility of KBr at 50°C is approximately 80 g/100 mL.

9.6

$$\frac{C_1}{P_1} = \frac{C_2}{P_2}; P_1 = 760 \text{ mmHg}; C_1 = 0.169 \text{ g/100 mL}; P_2 = 2.5 \times 10^4 \text{ mmHg}; C_2 = ?$$

$$C_2 = \frac{C_1 P_2}{P_1} = \frac{\left(\frac{0.169 \text{ g}}{100 \text{ mL}}\right) \times 2.5 \times 10^4 \text{ mmHg}}{760 \text{ mmHg}} = 5.6 \text{ g } CO_2/100 \text{ mL}$$

9.7

$$\frac{C_1}{P_1} = \frac{C_2}{P_2}; P_1 = 1.00 \text{ atm}; C_1 = 0.169 \text{ g/100 mL}; P_2 = 4.0 \times 10^{-4} \text{ atm}; C_2 = ?$$

$$C_2 = \frac{C_1 P_2}{P_1} = \frac{\left(\frac{0.169 \text{ g}}{100 \text{ mL}}\right) \times 4.0 \times 10^{-4} \text{ atm}}{1.00 \text{ atm}} = 6.8 \times 10^{-5} \text{ g } CO_2/100 \text{ mL}$$

9.8

$$\frac{50.0 \text{ g}}{0.160 \text{ L}} \times \frac{1 \text{ mol}}{337 \text{ g}} = 0.927 \text{ M}$$

9.9

$$\text{moles of solute} = \text{molarity (M)} \times \text{volume} = \frac{\text{mol}}{\text{L}} \times \text{L}$$

(a) $M = \dfrac{0.35 \text{ mol } NaNO_3}{1 \text{ L}}$; $V = 175 \text{ mL} = 0.175 \text{ L}$

$$\text{moles} = \frac{0.35 \text{ mol}}{1 \text{ L}} \times 0.175 \text{ L} = 0.061 \text{ mol } NaNO_3$$

(b) $M = \dfrac{1.4 \text{ mol } HNO_3}{1 \text{ L}}$; $V = 480 \text{ mL} = 0.48 \text{ L}$

$$\text{moles} = \frac{1.4 \text{ mol}}{1 \text{ L}} \times 0.48 \text{ L} = 0.67 \text{ mol } HNO_3$$

9.10   First, find the number of moles of cholesterol in 250 mL of blood:

$$250 \text{ mL} \times \frac{0.0050 \text{ mol cholesterol}}{1000 \text{ mL}} = 0.001\ 25 \text{ mol cholesterol}$$

Next, find the molar mass of cholesterol:

$$(27 \times 12.0 \text{ g/mol C}) + (46 \times 1.0 \text{ g/mol H}) + (16.0 \text{ g/mol O}) = 386.0 \text{ g/mol}$$

Now, convert moles into grams:

$$0.001\ 25 \text{ mol cholesterol} \times \frac{386.0 \text{ g}}{1 \text{ mol}} = 0.48 \text{ g cholesterol}$$

9.11   Molar mass of $CaCO_3$ = 100.0 g

$$0.065 \text{ L} \times \frac{0.12 \text{ mol HCl}}{1 \text{ L}} \times \frac{1 \text{ mol } CaCO_3}{2 \text{ mol HCl}} \times \frac{100.0 \text{ g } CaCO_3}{1 \text{ mol } CaCO_3} = 0.39 \text{ g } CaCO_3$$

9.12   1 dL = 100 mL

$$\frac{8.6 \text{ mg}}{100 \text{ mL}} \times \frac{1 \text{ g}}{1000 \text{ mg}} \times 100\% = 0.0086\% \text{ (w/v) } Ca^{2+}$$

Remember: [(w/v)%] specifies that the weight of solute be expressed in grams.

9.13

$$\frac{23 \text{ g KI}}{350 \text{ mL}} \times 100\% = 6.6\% \text{ (w/v) KI}$$

9.14   (a) A 16% (w/v) solution contains 16 g of solute per 100 mL of solution.

$$125 \text{ mL} \times \frac{16 \text{ g glucose}}{100 \text{ mL}} = 20 \text{ g glucose}$$

(b) A 1.8% (w/v) solution contains 1.8 g of solute per 100 mL of solution.

$$65 \text{ mL} \times \frac{1.8 \text{ g KCl}}{100 \text{ mL}} = 1.2 \text{ g KCl}$$

9.15   A 7.5% (v/v) solution contains 7.5 mL of solute per 100 mL of solution.

$$500 \text{ mL solution} \times \frac{7.5 \text{ mL acetic acid}}{100 \text{ mL solution}} = 38 \text{ mL acetic acid}$$

To prepare the desired solution, measure 38 mL of acetic acid into a 500.0 mL volumetric flask and add water to the 500.0 mL mark.

9.16   (a) 22 mL of ethyl alcohol are needed.

(b) $150 \text{ mL solution} \times \dfrac{12 \text{ mL acetic acid}}{100 \text{ mL solution}} = 18 \text{ mL acetic acid}$

9.17

$$\frac{32 \text{ mg NaF}}{20 \text{ kg solution}} \times \frac{1 \text{ kg}}{10^6 \text{ mg}} \times 10^6 = 1.6 \text{ ppm}$$

9.18 For lead:

$$\frac{0.015 \text{ mg Pb}}{1 \text{ kg solution}} \times \frac{1 \text{ kg}}{10^6 \text{ mg}} \times 10^6 = 0.015 \text{ ppm}$$

$$\frac{0.015 \text{ mg Pb}}{1 \text{ kg solution}} \times \frac{1 \text{ kg}}{10^3 \text{ g}} \times 100 \text{ g} = 0.0015 \text{ mg Pb}$$

For copper:

$$\frac{1.3 \text{ mg Cu}}{1 \text{ kg solution}} \times \frac{1 \text{ kg}}{10^6 \text{ mg}} \times 10^6 = 1.3 \text{ ppm}$$

$$\frac{1.3 \text{ mg Cu}}{1 \text{ kg solution}} \times \frac{1 \text{ kg}}{10^3 \text{ g}} \times 100 \text{ g} = 0.13 \text{ mg Cu}$$

9.19 $M_1 = 12.0 \text{ M};$ $V_1 = 100.0 \text{ mL};$ $V_2 = 500.0 \text{ mL};$ $M_2 = ?$

$$M_2 = M_1 \times \frac{V_1}{V_2} = 12.0 \text{ M} \times \frac{100.0 \text{ mL}}{500.0 \text{ mL}} = 2.40 \text{ M}$$

Ballpark check: Since there is a fivefold dilution, the final molarity is 1/5 of the initial molarity.

9.20 $V_2 = 500.0 \text{ mL};$ $M_2 = 1.25 \text{ M};$ $M_1 = 16.0 \text{ M};$ $V_1 = ?$

$$V_1 = V_2 \times \frac{M_2}{M_1} = 500.0 \text{ mL} \times \frac{1.25 \text{ M}}{16.0 \text{ M}} = 39.1 \text{ mL}$$

Ballpark check: Since the final molarity is about 1/12 the initial molarity, the initial volume is about 1/12 the final volume, or about 40 mL.

9.21 $C_1 = 5.0 \text{ ppm};$ $V_1 = 1.5 \text{ L};$ $C_2 = 0.010 \text{ ppm};$ $V_2 = ?$

$$V_2 = V_1 \times \frac{C_2}{C_1} = 1.5 \text{ L} \times \frac{5.0 \text{ ppm}}{0.01 \text{ ppm}} = 750 \text{ L}$$

9.22

One equivalent = molar mass of ion (g) ÷ number of charges on ion.

Ion	Molar Mass	Charge	Gram Equivalent	Milligram Equivalent
(a) K^+	39.1 g	+1	39.1 g	39.1 mg, or 3.91×10^{-2} g
(b) Br^-	79.9 g	−1	79.9 g	79.9 mg, or 7.99×10^{-2} g
(c) Mg^{2+}	24.3 g	+2	12.2 g	12.2 mg, or 1.22×10^{-2} g
(d) SO_4^{2-}	96.0 g	−2	48.0 g	48.0 mg, or 4.80×10^{-2} g
(e) Al^{3+}	27.0 g	+3	9.0 g	9.0 mg, or 9.0×10^{-3} g
(f) PO_4^{3-}	95.0 g	−3	31.7 g	31.7 mg, or 31.7×10^{-2} g

9.23   One gram equivalent of Mg^{2+} = 12.2 g [Problem 9.21(c)].

$$\frac{g\,Mg^{2+}}{1\,L} = \frac{12\,g\,Mg^{2+}}{1\,Eq} \times \frac{1\,Eq}{1000\,mEq} \times \frac{3.0\,mEq}{1\,L} = \frac{0.036\,g\,Mg^{2+}}{1\,L}$$

$$\frac{0.036\,g\,Mg^{2+}}{L} \times \frac{1000\,mg}{1\,g} \times \frac{1\,L}{1000\,mL} \times 250\,mL = 9.0\,mg\,Mg^{2+}$$

9.24   0.67 mol of $MgCl_2$ in 0.5 kg H_2O yields 2.0 mol solute particles. This is equivalent to 4.0 mol particles in 1.0 kg H_2O, which raise the boiling point by 4.0 x 0.51 °C = 2.0 °C.

Boiling point = 100.0 °C + 2.0 °C = 102.0 °C

9.25   If HF were a strong electrolyte it would dissociate completely, and a solution of 1.0 mol HF would yield 2.0 mol particles, which would elevate the boiling point of water by 2.0 x 0.51 °C = 1.02 °C. Since the observed boiling point elevation is only 0.5 °C, HF must be a weak electrolyte that is only slightly dissociated.

9.26   (a) The red curve represents the pure solvent, because the solvent boils at a lower temperature than the solution.
(b) A liquid boils when its vapor pressure equals atmospheric pressure. The solvent boils at 62 °C, and the solution boils at 69 °C.
(c) One mole of solute raises the boiling point approximately 3.5 °C, and the observed boiling point elevation is approximately 7 °C. Thus, the concentration of the solute is about 2 M.

9.27   Glucose is not an electrolyte. Thus 1.0 mol glucose lowers the freezing point of 1.0 kg H_2O by 1.9 °C.

Freezing point = 0.0 °C – 1.9 °C = –1.9 °C

9.28   A freezing point depression of 1.86 °C is produced by 1 mol of ions in 1 kg of water. Thus, a freezing point depression of 2.8 °C must be produced by 2.8 ÷ 1.86 = 1.5 mol of ions. Since 0.5 mol of the ionic substance produces the freezing point depression expected for 1.5 mol ions, the substance gives three ions when it dissolves.

9.29   Osmolarity = molarity x number of particles.

(a) For 0.35 M KBr, osmolarity = 0.35 M x 2 = 0.70 osmol, since KBr yields two particles (K^+ and Br^-) in solution.

(b) For 0.15 M glucose, osmolarity = 0.15 M x 1 = 0.15 osmol, since glucose yields only one particle in solution. For K_2SO_4, osmolarity = 0.05 M x 3 = 0.15 osmol, since K_2SO_4 provides three particles per mole in solution. Total osmolarity = 0.30 osmol.

9.30 For the oral rehydration solution, osmolarity is equal to the sum of the osmolarities of the individual components. For each of the ionic components, the number of millimoles = the number of mEq, since each ion has one charge. Thus,

$$90 \text{ mM Na}^+ + 20 \text{ mM K}^+ + 110 \text{ mM Cl}^- = 220 \text{ mM ions} = 0.22 \text{ M ions}$$

For glucose:
$$\frac{2.0 \text{ g glucose}}{100 \text{ mL}} \times \frac{1000 \text{ mL}}{1 \text{ L}} \times \frac{1 \text{ mol}}{180 \text{ g glucose}} = 0.11 \text{ M glucose}$$

Osmolarity = molarity x number of particles. In this problem, all components yield one particle in solution.
Osmolarity = 0.22 M + 0.11 M = 0.33 osmol

Understanding Key Concepts

9.31

before equilibrium   at equilibrium

The membrane is permeable to the unshaded spheres but impermeable to the shaded spheres. Solvent (unshaded spheres) passes through the membrane until equilibrium is reached.

9.32 The boiling point of water is elevated by 0.5 °C for every mole of dissolved particles. 1 mol HCl dissolves to form 2 mol particles, which elevate the boiling point of water by 1 °C. Acetic acid exists in solution almost completely as CH_3CO_2H, and 1 mol acetic acid dissolves to form 1 mol particles, which elevate the boiling point of water by only 0.5 °C.

9.33 The same reasoning used in the previous problem applies here. The freezing point of water is depressed by 1.9 °C for every mole of dissolved particles. 1 mol HBr dissociates to form 2 mol ions, which lower the freezing point of water by 3.7 °C, but 1 mol HF is only slightly dissociated and lowers the freezing point by 1.9 °C.

9.34 The lower line on the graph (green) represents the solubility of a gas as a function of temperature. The solubility of a solid may increase or decrease with increasing temperature, but the solubility of a gas *always* decreases when temperature is raised.

9.35

(a)   (b)   (c)

When a beaker of glucose solution (shaded) and a beaker of pure water (unshaded) stand for several days, the liquid levels appear as those pictured in (a). The dissolved glucose particles lower the vapor pressure of water and make evaporation slower.

9.36 Drawing (d) represents the solution that results when 50.0 mL of (a) is withdrawn and diluted by a factor of 4.

9.37 At a given temperature, the vapor pressure of the solution is lower than that of the pure solvent because the dissolved particles in the solution slow evaporation of its solvent. The green curve represents the vapor pressure curve of the solution, and the red curve represents the vapor pressure of a solvent.

Solutions and Solubility

9.38 In a homogeneous mixture (such as tea), mixing is uniform throughout because the particle size is small. In a heterogeneous mixture (such as chicken soup), mixing is nonuniform because particle size is larger.

9.39 A solution is transparent to light; a colloid usually appears murky or opaque.

9.40 The polarity of water enables it to dissolve many ionic solids.

9.41 Water doesn't dissolve motor oil because oil is nonpolar and water is polar.

9.42 Rubbing alcohol (b) and black coffee (d) are solutions.

9.43 All the pairs are miscible.

9.44

$$C_2 = \frac{C_1 P_2}{P_1}; \quad C_1 = 51.8 \text{ g/100 mL}; \quad P_1 = 760.0 \text{ mmHg}; \quad P_2 = 225.0 \text{ mmHg}$$

$$= \frac{(51.8 \text{ g/100 mL}) \times 225.0 \text{ mmHg}}{760.0 \text{ mmHg}} = 15.3 \text{ g/100 mL}$$

9.45

$$C_2 = \frac{C_1 P_2}{P_1}; \quad C_1 = 0.15 \text{ g/100 mL}; \quad P_1 = 760.0 \text{ mmHg} = 1.0 \text{ atm}; \quad P_2 = 4.5 \text{ atm}$$

$$= \frac{(0.15 \text{ g/100 mL}) \times 4.5 \text{ atm}}{1.0 \text{ atm}} = 0.68 \text{ g/100 mL}$$

Concentration and Dilution of Solutions

9.46 Depending on the solubility of the solute in the solvent, a saturated solution may be either dilute or concentrated. If a solute is only slightly soluble in a solvent, a saturated solution will be dilute. If the solute is very soluble in the solvent, a saturated solution will be concentrated. For a highly soluble solute, even a highly concentrated solution may be unsaturated.

9.47 Weight/volume percent concentration [(w/v)%] is defined as the number of grams of solute per 100 mL of solution.

9.48 Molarity (M) is defined as the number of moles of solute per liter of solution.

9.49 Volume/volume percent concentration [(v/v)%] is defined as the volume of solute in 100 mL of solution.

9.50

$$\frac{6.0 \text{ mL ethyl alcohol}}{100.0 \text{ mL solution}} \times 750.0 \text{ mL solution} = 45.0 \text{ mL ethyl alcohol}$$

Add water to 45.0 mL of ethyl alcohol to make a final volume of 750.0 mL.

9.51

$$500.0 \text{ mL solution} \times \frac{0.50 \text{ g B(OH)}_3}{100 \text{ mL solution}} = 2.5 \text{ g B(OH)}_3$$

Dissolve 2.5 g B(OH)$_3$ in water to a final volume of 500.0 mL.

9.52

$$250 \text{ mL solution} \times \frac{0.10 \text{ mol NaCl}}{1000 \text{ mL solution}} \times \frac{58.5 \text{ g NaCl}}{1 \text{ mol NaCl}} = 1.5 \text{ g NaCl}$$

Dissolve 1.5 g NaCl in water to a final volume of 250 mL.

9.53

$$1.50 \text{ L} \times \frac{1000 \text{ mL}}{1 \text{ L}} \times \frac{7.50 \text{ g Mg(NO}_3)_2}{100 \text{ mL solution}} = 113 \text{ g Mg(NO}_3)_2$$

Dissolve 113 g Mg(NO$_3$)$_2$ in water and dilute to 1.50 L.

9.54

(a) $\dfrac{5.8 \text{ g KCl}}{75 \text{ mL}} \times 100 \text{ mL} = 7.7 \text{ g KCl}; \dfrac{7.7 \text{ g KCl}}{100 \text{ mL}} \times 100\% = 7.7\% \text{ (w/v) KCl}$

(b) $\dfrac{15 \text{ g sucrose}}{380 \text{ mL}} \times 100 \text{ mL} = 3.9 \text{ g sucrose}; \dfrac{3.9 \text{ g}}{100 \text{ mL}} \times 100\% = 3.9\% \text{ (w/v) sucrose}$

9.55

$$\frac{90 \text{ mg glucose}}{100 \text{ mL}} \times \frac{1 \text{ g}}{1000 \text{ mg}} = \frac{0.090 \text{ g glucose}}{100 \text{ mL}}; \quad 0.090\% \text{ (w/v) glucose}$$

$$\frac{0.090 \text{ g glucose}}{100 \text{ mL}} \times \frac{1000 \text{ mL}}{1 \text{ L}} \times \frac{1 \text{ mol}}{180 \text{ g glucose}} = 0.005 \text{ M}$$

9.56

(a) $50.0 \text{ mL} \times \dfrac{8.0 \text{ g KCl}}{100 \text{ mL}} = 4.0 \text{ g KCl}$

(b) $200.0 \text{ mL} \times \dfrac{7.5 \text{ g acetic acid}}{100 \text{ mL}} = 15 \text{ g acetic acid}$

9.57

(a) For 0.50 M KCl: $\dfrac{0.50 \text{ mol KCl}}{1 \text{ L}} \times \dfrac{74.6 \text{ g}}{1 \text{ mol}} = \dfrac{37 \text{ g KCl}}{1 \text{ L}} = \dfrac{3.7 \text{ g KCl}}{100 \text{ mL}}$

For 5% (w/v) KCl: $\dfrac{5.0 \text{ g KCl}}{100 \text{ mL}}$

The 5% (w/v) solution is more concentrated.

(b) 2.5% (w/v) $NaHSO_4 = \dfrac{2.5 \text{ g } NaHSO_4}{100 \text{ mL solution}}$

$\dfrac{0.025 \text{ mol } NaHSO_4}{1 \text{ L}} \times \dfrac{120 \text{ g}}{1 \text{ mol}} = \dfrac{3.0 \text{ g } NaHSO_4}{1 \text{ L}} = \dfrac{0.30 \text{ g } NaHSO_4}{100 \text{ mL}}$

The 2.5% (w/v) solution is more concentrated.

9.58

$23 \text{ g KOH} \times \dfrac{100 \text{ mL}}{10.0 \text{ g KOH}} = 230 \text{ mL of a } 10.0\% \text{ (w/v) solution}$

$23 \text{ g KOH} \times \dfrac{1 \text{ mol}}{56.1 \text{ g KOH}} = 0.41 \text{ mol KOH}$

$0.41 \text{ mol KOH} \times \dfrac{1000 \text{ mL}}{0.25 \text{ mol KOH}} = 1600 \text{ mL of } 0.25 \text{ M solution}$

9.59

$\dfrac{3 \text{ g}}{100 \text{ mL}} \times \dfrac{1000 \text{ mL}}{1 \text{ L}} \times \dfrac{1 \text{ mol}}{34 \text{ g}} = 0.9 \text{ M}$

9.60

$\dfrac{10 \text{ mg KCN}}{1 \text{ kg body weight}} \times \dfrac{1 \text{ kg}}{10^6 \text{ mg}} \times 10^6 = 10 \text{ ppm}$

9.61 From Section 9.7 we know that 1 ppb = 1 μg solute/1 L solution. Thus, 15 ppb = 15 μg/L.

$1.0 \text{ μg} \times \dfrac{1 \text{ L}}{15 \text{ μg}} = 0.067 \text{ L}$

9.62

(a) $\dfrac{12.5 \text{ g } NaHCO_3}{0.350 \text{ L}} \times \dfrac{1 \text{ mol}}{84.0 \text{ g}} = 0.425 \text{ M}$

(b) $\dfrac{45.0 \text{ g } H_2SO_4}{0.300 \text{ L}} \times \dfrac{1 \text{ mol}}{98.0 \text{ g}} = 1.53 \text{ M}$

(c) $\dfrac{30.0 \text{ g NaCl}}{0.500 \text{ L}} \times \dfrac{1 \text{ mol}}{58.5 \text{ g}} = 1.03 \text{ M}$

9.63

(a) $0.200 \text{ L} \times \dfrac{0.30 \text{ mol acetic acid}}{1 \text{ L}} = 0.060 \text{ mol acetic acid}$

(b) $1.50 \text{ L} \times \dfrac{0.25 \text{ mol NaOH}}{1 \text{ L}} = 0.38 \text{ mol NaOH}$

(c) $0.750 \text{ L} \times \dfrac{2.5 \text{ mol HNO}_3}{1 \text{ L}} = 1.9 \text{ mol HNO}_3$

9.64

$0.0040 \text{ mol HCl} \times \dfrac{1000 \text{ mL}}{0.75 \text{ mol}} = 5.3 \text{ mL HCl}$

9.65

$1.5 \text{ mg} \times \dfrac{1 \text{ g}}{1000 \text{ mg}} \times \dfrac{100 \text{ mL}}{0.40 \text{ g}} = 0.38 \text{ mL}$

9.66 First, calculate the number of moles of H_2SO_4 spilled:

$0.450 \text{ L} \times \dfrac{0.50 \text{ mol H}_2\text{SO}_4}{1 \text{ L}} = 0.23 \text{ mol H}_2\text{SO}_4$

According to the equation given in the problem, each mole of H_2SO_4 reacts with two moles of $NaHCO_3$. Thus, the 0.23 mol of H_2SO_4 spilled needs to be neutralized with 0.46 mol of $NaHCO_3$.

$0.44 \text{ mol NaHCO}_3 \times \dfrac{84 \text{ g}}{1 \text{ mol}} = 39 \text{ g NaHCO}_3$

9.67

$0.450 \text{ g AgBr} \times \dfrac{1 \text{ mol AgBr}}{187.8 \text{ g}} = 2.40 \times 10^{-3} \text{ mol AgBr}$

According to the equation given, 1 mole of AgBr reacts with 2 moles of $Na_2S_2O_3$. Thus, 2.40×10^{-3} mol AgBr reacts with 4.80×10^{-3} mol $Na_2S_2O_3$. To calculate the volume of 0.0200 M $Na_2S_2O_3$:

$4.80 \times 10^{-3} \text{ mol} \times \dfrac{1000 \text{ mL}}{0.0200 \text{ mol}} = 240 \text{ mL of } 0.0200 \text{ M Na}_2\text{S}_2\text{O}_3$

9.68

20.0% (v/v) means $\dfrac{20.0 \text{ mL concentrate}}{100.0 \text{ mL juice}}$

Thus, $100.0 \text{ mL concentrate} \times \dfrac{100.0 \text{ mL juice}}{20.0 \text{ mL concentrate}} = 500.0 \text{ mL juice}$

Since the final volume of the diluted juice is 500.0 mL, you would have to add 400.0 mL water to the original 100.0 mL of concentrate.

9.69

$$V_2 = V_1 \times \frac{M_1}{M_2}; \ V_1 = 100.0 \text{ mL}; \ M_1 = 0.500 \text{ M}; \ M_2 = 0.150 \text{ M}$$

$$= 100.0 \text{ mL} \times \frac{0.500 \text{ M}}{0.150 \text{ M}} = 333 \text{ mL of } 0.150 \text{ M NaOH solution}$$

100.0 mL of 0.500 M NaOH is diluted with 233 mL water to give 333 mL of 0.150 M NaOH solution.

9.70

$$V_1 = V_2 \times \frac{C_2}{C_1}; \ V_2 = 2.0 \text{ L}; \ C_2 = 75 \text{ ppm}; \ C_1 = 285 \text{ ppm}$$

$$= 2.0 \text{ L} \times \frac{75 \text{ ppm}}{285 \text{ ppm}} = 0.53 \text{ L of } 285 \text{ ppm KNO}_3 \text{ solution}$$

9.71

$$C_2 = C_1 \times \frac{V_1}{V_2}; \ C_1 = 37\% \text{ (w/v)}; \ V_1 = 65 \text{ mL}; \ V_2 = 480 \text{ mL}$$

$$= 37\% \text{ (w/v)} \times \frac{65 \text{ mL}}{480 \text{ mL}} = 5.0\% \text{ (w/v) NaCl}$$

9.72

$$V_2 = V_1 \times \frac{M_1}{M_2}; \ V_1 = 25.0 \text{ mL}; \ M_1 = 12.0 \text{ M}; \ M_2 = 0.500 \text{ M}$$

$$= 25.0 \text{ mL} \times \frac{12.0 \text{ M}}{0.500 \text{ M}} = 600 \text{ mL of } 0.500 \text{ M HCl solution}$$

9.73

$$V_1 = V_2 \times \frac{M_2}{M_1}; \ V_2 = 750.0 \text{ mL}; \ M_1 = 0.100 \text{ M}; \ M_2 = 0.0500 \text{ M}$$

$$= 750.0 \text{ mL} \times \frac{0.0500 \text{ M}}{0.100 \text{ M}} = 375 \text{ mL of } 0.100 \text{ M NaHCO}_3$$

Electrolytes

9.74 An electrolyte is a substance that conducts electricity when dissolved in water.

9.75 Sodium chloride is an example of a strong electrolyte. Glucose is an example of a nonelectrolyte.

9.76 If the concentration of Ca^{2+} is 3.0 mEq/L, there are 3.0 mmol of charges due to calcium per liter of blood. Since calcium has a charge of +2, there are 1.5 mmol of calcium per liter of blood.

9.77   The total anion concentration in the solution must equal the total cation concentration in order to conserve charge. Thus:

[Cations] = [Anions] = 5.0 mEq/L Na^+ + 12.0 mEq/L Ca^{2+} + 2.0 mEq/L K^+ = 19 mEq/L

9.78

$$10\% \text{ (w/v)} = \frac{10 \text{ g KCl}}{100 \text{ mL}}; \quad 30 \text{ mL } \times \frac{10 \text{ g KCl}}{100 \text{ mL}} = 3.0 \text{ g KCl}$$

The molar mass of KCl is 74.6 g/mol. Thus:

$$3.0 \text{ g KCl } \times \frac{1 \text{ mol}}{74.6 \text{ g}} = 0.040 \text{ mol KCl}$$

Since one equivalent equals one mole when an ion has only one charge, there are 0.040 Eq, or 40 mEq, of K^+ in a 30 mL dose.

9.79   One gram-equivalent = molar mass of ion(g) ÷ # of charges on ion:

Ion	Molar mass	Charge	Gram equivalent
(a) Ca^{2+}	40.1 g	2+	20.0 g
(b) K^+	39.1 g	1+	39.1 g
(c) SO_4^{2-}	96.1 g	2–	48.0 g
(d) PO_4^{3-}	95.0 g	3–	31.7 g

9.80   Use the value 100 mEq/L for the concentration of Cl^- in blood:
For Cl^- ion, 100 mEq = 100 mmol = 0.100 mol.

$$1.0 \text{ g } Cl^- \times \frac{1 \text{ mol}}{35.5 \text{ g}} \times \frac{1 \text{ L}}{0.100 \text{ mol}} = 0.28 \text{ L}$$

9.81   For Mg^{2+}, with a molar mass of 24.3 g and a charge of +2, the mass of one equivalent is 24.3 g/2 = 12.2 g, and the mass of 1 milliequivalent is 12.2 mg.

$$\frac{3 \text{ mEq } Mg^{2+}}{1 \text{ L}} \times \frac{12 \text{ mg } Mg^{2+}}{1 \text{ mEq } Mg^{2+}} \times \frac{1 \text{ L}}{1000 \text{ mL}} \times 150.0 \text{ mL} = 5 \text{ mg } Mg^{2+}$$

Properties of Solutions

9.82   0.20 mol NaOH contains 0.40 mol solute particles, and 0.20 mol $Ba(OH)_2$ contains 0.60 mol solute particles. Since $Ba(OH)_2$ produces more solute particles, it produces greater lowering of the freezing point when dissolved in 2.0 kg of water.

9.83   When 0.300 mol KCl dissolves, it produces 0.600 mol particles; when 0.500 mol glucose dissolves, it produces 0.500 mol particles. The solution with more dissolved particles (0.300 mol KCl) has the higher boiling point.

9.84 Methanol has a molar mass of 32.0 g and provides one mole of solute particles per mole of methanol.

$$10.0°C \times \frac{1 \text{ mol}}{1.86°C \times 1 \text{ kg}} \times 5.00 \text{ kg} = 26.9 \text{ mol methanol}$$

$$26.9 \text{ mol} \times \frac{32.0 \text{ g}}{1 \text{ mol}} = 861 \text{ g of methanol needed}$$

9.85 Cane sugar provides one mole of solute particles per mole. The boiling point elevation:

$$\frac{650 \text{ g sugar}}{1.5 \text{ kg H}_2\text{O}} \times \frac{1 \text{ mol}}{342 \text{ g}} \times \frac{0.51 °C \times 1 \text{ kg}}{1 \text{ mol}} = 0.65 °C$$

The boiling point of the resulting solution is $100.0 °C + 0.65 °C = 100.65 °C$.

Osmosis

9.86 The inside of a red blood cell contains dissolved substances and therefore has a higher osmolarity than pure water. Water thus passes through the cell membrane to dilute the cell contents until pressure builds up and the cell eventually bursts.

9.87 If a 0.15 M NaCl solution is isotonic with blood, then the NaCl solution has the same osmolarity as blood. If distilled water is hypotonic with blood, then the water has a lower osmolarity than blood.

9.88

	Solution	Molarity	Number of Particles	Osmolarity
(a)	0.25 M KBr	0.25 M	2	0.50 osmol
	0.20 M Na$_2$SO$_4$	0.20 M	3	0.60 osmol (greater)
(b)	0.30 M NaOH	0.30 M	2	0.60 osmol
	3% (w/v) NaOH	0.75 M	2	1.5 osmol (greater)

9.89 The solution with the higher osmolarity gives rise to the greater osmotic pressure at equilibrium.

For NaCl: $\dfrac{5.0 \text{ g}}{0.350 \text{ L}} \times \dfrac{1 \text{ mol}}{58.5 \text{ g}} \times 2 \text{ particles} = 0.49 \text{ osmol}$

For glucose: $\dfrac{35.0 \text{ g}}{0.400 \text{ L}} \times \dfrac{1 \text{ mol}}{180 \text{ g}} \times 1 \text{ particle} = 0.49 \text{ osmol}$

Both solutions give rise to the same osmotic pressure.

9.90 The molar mass of NaCl is 58.5 g, and each mole of NaCl yields two moles of particles.

$$\frac{270 \text{ g}}{3.8 \text{ L}} \times \frac{1 \text{ mol}}{58.5 \text{ g}} \times 2 \text{ particles} = 2.4 \text{ osmol}$$

9.91   A solution that contains 0.30 osmol KCl is 0.15 M, since KCl produces two particles when dissolved.

$$\frac{74.5 \text{ g}}{1 \text{ mol}} \text{ x } \frac{0.15 \text{ mol}}{1 \text{ L}} \text{ x } \frac{1 \text{ L}}{1000 \text{ mL}} \text{ x } 175 \text{ mL } = 2.0 \text{ g KCl}$$

Approximately 2.0 g KCl are needed.

Applications

9.92   At high altitude, P_{O2} is low, and not enough oxygen is available to cause 100% saturation of hemoglobin. In order to deliver enough oxygen to body tissues, the body compensates by manufacturing more hemoglobin, which drives the hemoglobin equilibrium to the right.

9.93   The major electrolytes in sweat are sodium ion (30–40 mEq/L), potassium ion (5–10 mEq/L), small amounts of metals such as magnesium, and chloride to balance charge (35–50 mEq/L).

9.94   In addition to fluid replacement, sports drinks provide electrolytes to replenish those lost during exercise, they furnish soluble complex carbohydrates for slow-release energy, and they may contain vitamins to protect cells from damage.

9.95   An enteric coating on a medication is a polymeric material that isn't digested by stomach acid but passes into the intestine, where it dissolves in the more basic intestinal environment and releases the medication.

General Questions and Problems

9.96

(a) $0.18 \text{ x } 5.0 \text{ atm } \text{ x } \dfrac{760 \text{ mmHg}}{1.0 \text{ atm}} = 680 \text{ mmHg}$

(b) $\dfrac{C_1}{P_1} = \dfrac{C_2}{P_2}$; $P_1 = 760 \text{ mmHg}$; $C_1 = 2.1 \text{ g/100 mL}$; $P_2 = 680 \text{ mmHg}$; $C_2 = ?$

$$= \frac{(2.1 \text{ g/100 mL}) \text{ x } 680 \text{ mmHg}}{760 \text{ mmHg}} = 1.9 \text{ g/100 mL}$$

9.97

$$\frac{2.1 \text{ g}}{100 \text{ mL}} \text{ x } \frac{1 \text{ mol}}{32 \text{ g}} \text{ x } \frac{1000 \text{ mL}}{1 \text{ L}} = 0.66 \text{ M at } 1.0 \text{ atm}$$

Solubility = 0.59 M at 680 mmHg

9.98   Molar mass of uric acid ($C_5H_4N_4O_3$) = 168 g.

(a) (w/v)%: $\dfrac{0.067 \text{ g}}{1 \text{ L}} = \dfrac{0.0067 \text{ g}}{100 \text{ mL}}$; $\dfrac{0.0067 \text{ g}}{100 \text{ mL}} \text{ x } 100\% = 0.0067\% \text{ (w/v)}$

(b) ppm: One L of water weighs 1 kg. Thus

$$\frac{0.067 \text{ g}}{1 \text{ L}} = \frac{0.067 \text{ g}}{1 \text{ kg}} \text{ x } \frac{1 \text{ kg}}{1000 \text{ g}}; \frac{0.067 \text{ g}}{1000 \text{ g}} \text{ x } 10^6 = 67 \text{ ppm}$$

(c) $\dfrac{0.067 \text{ g}}{1 \text{ L}} \times \dfrac{1 \text{ mol}}{168 \text{ g}} = 0.000\ 40 \text{ M} = 4.0 \times 10^{-4} \text{ M}$

9.99

$5.0\% \text{ (w/v)} = \dfrac{5.0 \text{ g CaCl}_2}{100 \text{ mL}}; \quad \dfrac{5.0 \text{ g CaCl}_2}{100 \text{ mL}} \times 5.0 \text{ mL} = 0.25 \text{ g CaCl}_2$

$0.25 \text{ g CaCl}_2 \times \dfrac{1 \text{ mol}}{111 \text{ g}} = 0.0023 \text{ mol CaCl}_2 = 0.0023 \text{ mol Ca}^{2+}$

$0.0023 \text{ mol Ca}^{2+} \times \dfrac{2 \text{ Eq}}{1 \text{ mol}} = 0.0046 \text{ Eq Ca}^{2+} = 4.6 \text{ mEq Ca}^{2+}$

9.100 $M_1 = 16 \text{ M}, \quad M_2 = 0.20 \text{ M}, \quad V_2 = 750 \text{ mL}$

$V_1 = V_2 \times \dfrac{M_2}{M_1} = 750 \text{ mL} \times \dfrac{0.20 \text{ M}}{16 \text{ M}} = 9.4 \text{ mL HNO}_3$

9.101

(a) $13.0 \text{ mL} \times \dfrac{0.0100 \text{ mol}}{1000 \text{ mL}} = 1.30 \times 10^{-4} \text{ mol I}_2$

According to the equation, one mole of I_2 reacts with one mole of $C_6H_8O_6$. Thus, the 25.0 mL sample contains 1.30×10^{-4} mol $C_6H_8O_6$.

$\dfrac{1.30 \times 10^{-4} \text{ mol}}{25.0 \text{ mL}} \times \dfrac{1000 \text{ mL}}{1 \text{ L}} = 0.005\ 20 \text{ M} = 5.20 \text{ mM}$

(b) Molar mass of $C_6H_8O_6 = 176$ g.

$\dfrac{176 \text{ g}}{1 \text{ mol}} \times \dfrac{0.005\ 20 \text{ mol}}{1 \text{ L}} \times \dfrac{1000 \text{ mg}}{1 \text{ g}} = \dfrac{915 \text{ mg ascorbic acid}}{1 \text{ L}}$

$60 \text{ mg} \times \dfrac{1 \text{ L}}{915 \text{ mg ascorbic acid}} \times \dfrac{1000 \text{ mL}}{1 \text{ L}} = 66 \text{ mL juice}$

9.102–9.103

Component	Mass	Molar Mass	Molarity	Osmolarity
(a) NaCl	8.6 g	58.5 g	0.147 M	0.294 osmol
(b) KCl	0.30 g	74.6 g	0.0040 M	0.0080 osmol
(c) CaCl₂	0.33 g	111 g	0.0030 M	0.0090 osmol
			Total:	0.31 osmol

Ringer's solution (0.31 osmol) is approximately isotonic with blood plasma (0.30 osmol).

9.104

$$\frac{10 \text{ mg}}{5.0 \text{ L}} \times \frac{1 \text{ L}}{1000 \text{ mL}} \times \frac{1 \text{ g}}{1000 \text{ mg}} \times 100\% = 0.0002\% \text{ (w/v)}$$

9.105 For quantities expressed in parts per million, both the solute and solvent must be expressed in the same units. In this problem, both quantities are expressed in grams. The mass of statin drug is 10 mg = 10×10^{-3} g. The density of blood is 1.05 g/mL.

$$\frac{1.05 \text{ g}}{1 \text{ mL}} \times \frac{1000 \text{ mL}}{1 \text{ L}} \times 5.0 \text{ L} = 5.2 \times 10^3 \text{ g}$$

$$\text{ppm} = \frac{\text{mass of solute (g)}}{\text{mass of solvent (g)}} \times 10^6 = \frac{10 \times 10^{-3}\text{g}}{5.2 \times 10^3\text{g}} \times 10^6 = 1.9 \text{ ppm}$$

9.106

$$0.080\% \text{ (v/v)} = \frac{0.080 \text{ mL}}{100 \text{ mL}} = \frac{0.80 \text{ mL}}{1 \text{ L}}; \frac{0.80 \text{ mL}}{1 \text{ L}} \times 5.0 \text{ L} = 4.0 \text{ mL alcohol}$$

9.107

(a)

(b) $\frac{51.8 \text{ g}}{1 \text{ L}} \times \frac{1 \text{ mol}}{17.0 \text{ g}} = 3.05 \text{ mol/L}$

9.108 (a) $CoCl_2(s) + 6 H_2O(g) \rightleftharpoons CoCl_2 \cdot 6H_2O(s)$

(b) Molar mass of $CoCl_2 \cdot 6H_2O$ = 238 g

$$2.50 \text{ g CoCl}_2 \times \frac{1 \text{ mol CoCl}_2 \cdot 6 \text{ H}_2\text{O}}{238 \text{ g}} \times \frac{6 \text{ mol H}_2\text{O}}{1 \text{ mol CoCl}_2 \cdot 6 \text{ H}_2\text{O}} \times \frac{18.0 \text{ g H}_2\text{O}}{1 \text{ mol H}_2\text{O}} = 1.13 \text{ g H}_2\text{O}$$

9.109 $BaCl_2(aq) + Na_2SO_4(aq) \longrightarrow BaSO_4(s) + 2 NaCl(aq)$

According to the balanced equation, one mole of $BaCl_2$ reacts with one mole of Na_2SO_4.

$$\text{\# moles Na}_2\text{SO}_4 = \frac{0.200 \text{ mol}}{1 \text{ L}} \times 0.0350 \text{ L} = 0.007 \text{ 00 mol} = \text{\# moles BaCl}_2$$

$$0.007 \text{ 00 mol BaCl}_2 \times \frac{1 \text{ L}}{0.150 \text{ mol}} = 0.0467 \text{ L} = 46.7 \text{ mL BaCl}_2$$

$$0.007 \text{ 00 mol} \times \frac{233.3 \text{ g}}{1 \text{ mol}} = 1.63 \text{ g BaSO}_4$$

9.110 (a) If 36.0 % of TCA is dissociated, the solution consists of 0.360 mol TCA anions, 0.360 mol H^+ cations, and 0.640 mol undissociated TCA, for a total of 1.360 mol ions and molecules in 1 kg water.

(b) The freezing point of water is depressed by 2.53 °C, resulting in a final temperature of 97.5 °C.

$$1.36 \text{ mol } \times \frac{1.86 \text{ °C}}{1 \text{ mol}} = 2.53 \text{ °C}$$

Self-Test for Chapter 9

Multiple Choice

1. 50 mL of a 1.0 M NaOH solution is diluted to 1.0 L. What is the dilution factor?
   (a) 1/50   (b) 1/20   (c) 1/10   (d) 1/2

2. Which of the following will not speed up the rate of solution of a solid?
   (a) stirring   (b) heating   (c) grinding the solid into powder   (d) increasing pressure on the solution

3. To make up 500 mL of a 5% (v/v) solution of methanol (CH_3OH; molar mass = 32 g) in water:
   (a) Dilute 25 mL of CH_3OH with water to a volume of 500 mL.
   (b) Dilute 5 mL of CH_3OH with water to a volume of 500 mL.
   (c) Add 32 g of CH_3OH to 500 g of water.
   (d) Add 25 mL of CH_3OH to 500 mL of water.

4. Which solution has the greatest osmolarity?
   (a) 0.2 M $CaCl_2$ (b) 0.3 M Na_3PO_4 (c) 0.5 M NaCl   (d) 0.8 M glucose

5. Which of the following is a colloid?
   (a) wine   (b) maple syrup   (c) milkshake   (d) salad oil

6. How many mL of a 12.0 M HCl solution are needed to make 1.0 L of 0.10 M HCl?
   (a) 120 mL   (b) 83 mL   (c) 50 mL   (d) 8.3 mL

7. Which of the following properties do not depend on the number of particles in solution?
   (a) boiling point elevation   (b) osmotic pressure   (c) heat of solution   (d) freezing point depression

8. How many grams of NaOH are needed to make 300 mL of a 0.3 M solution?
   (a) 40 g   (b) 12 g   (c) 3.6 g   (d) 1.0 g

9. How many moles of glucose are present in 250 mL of a 0.25 M solution?
   (a) 0.0625 mol   (b) 0.1 mol   (c) 0.25 mol   (d) 1.0 mol

10. How many mL of a 0.20 M solution of NaF contain 2.1 g of NaF?
    (a) 500 mL   (b) 250 mL   (c) 100 mL   (d) 50 mL

Sentence Completion

1. Two liquids soluble in each other are said to be _____.

2. An ___ ____ is the amount of an ion in grams that contains Avogadro's number of charges.

3. A weight/volume solution can be made up in a piece of glassware called a _____ _____.

4. According to Henry's law, the _____ of a gas varies with its _____ _____.

5. Two solutions that have the same osmolarity are _____.

6. Compounds that attract water from the atmosphere are called _____.

7. The formula used for calculating dilutions is _____.

8. Milk is an example of a _____.

9. _____ and _____ _____ _____ can pass through a dialysis membrane.

10. A solution that has reached its solubility limit is said to be _____.

11. An example of a nonelectrolyte is _____.

12. A solution that is hypotonic with respect to blood has a _____ osmolarity than blood plasma.

True or False

1. A solute is the liquid used to dissolve a substance.

2. It is possible to have a solution of a solid in a solid.

3. In making a volume/volume percent solution, one liquid is added to 100 mL of the other liquid.

4. All ionic compounds are soluble in water.

5. A solution of 0.10 M Na_3PO_4 has a greater osmolarity than a solution of 0.15 M NaCl.

6. Weight/weight percent is a useful way to express concentration.

7. In carrying out a dilution, the number of moles of solute remains constant.

8. The solubility of most substances increases with temperature.

9. A colloid differs from a solution in its ability to transmit light.

10. A blood cell undergoes crenation when placed in distilled water.

11. Particles dissolved in water lower the boiling point of water.

12. The amount of gas dissolved in a liquid increases with increasing pressure.

Match each entry on the left with its partner on the right.

1. Osmotic membrane   (a) Muddy water

2. V_1/V_2 (b) Molarity x number of particles

3. Solution   (c) Conducts electricity in water

4. Equivalent   (d) Vinegar

5. Suspension   (e) Crystalline compound that holds water

6. Dialysis membrane   (f) Dilution factor

7. Osmolarity   (g) Butter

8. Hypotonic   (h) Permeable only to water

9. Colloid   (i) A solution of lower osmolarity than another

10. Crenation   (j) Formula weight/number of charges

11. Hydrate   (k) Permeable to water and small molecules

12. Electrolyte   (l) Happens to cell in hypertonic solution

Chapter Outline

I. Introduction to acids and bases (Sections 10.1–10.5).
  A. Definition of acids and bases (Sections 10.1, 10.3).
    1. Arrhenius definition (Section 10.1).
      a. Acids donate H^+ ions in solution.
      b. Bases donate OH^- ions in solution.
      c. Acid + base —> salt + H_2O.
    2. Brønsted–Lowry definition (Section 10.3).
      a. A Brønsted–Lowry acid is a proton donor (an H_3O^+ donor).
        Some acids can donate more than one proton.
      b. A Brønsted–Lowry base is a proton acceptor.
        The base may be negatively charged or neutral.
      c. An acid–base reaction is one in which a proton is transferred.
      d. Products of acid–base reactions are also acids and bases.
        In the reaction $HA + B: —> A^- + BH^+$
        i. HA and A^- are an acid–conjugate base pair.
        ii. B: and BH^+ are a base–conjugate acid pair.
  B. Many common substances are acids or bases (Section 10.2).
  C. Water as acid and a base (Section 10.4).
    1. Water can act both as an acid and a base.
    2. Substances that can act as both acids and bases are amphoteric.
II. Acid/base strength (Sections 10.5–10.10).
  A. Strong/weak acids and bases (Section 10.5).
    1. Strong acids and bases are 100% dissociated in water.
    2. Weak acids and bases are less than 100% dissociated in solution.
    3. The stronger the acid, the weaker the conjugate base.
      The weaker the acid, the stronger the conjugate base.
    4. An acid–base proton transfer always favors formation of the weaker acid.
  B. Acid dissociation constants (Section 10.6).
    1. K_a is a measure of the degree to which an acid HA dissociates to H_3O^+ and A^-.
    2. K_a values for weak acids are much less than 1.
    3. Donation of each successive H^+ ion from a polyprotic acid becomes successively more difficult.
    4. Most organic acids have K_a near 10^{-5}.
  C Dissociation of H_2O (Section 10.7).
    1. $K_w = [H_3O^+][OH^-] = 1.00 \times 10^{-14}$ at 25°C.
    2. This relationship is true for any aqueous solution.
    3. Thus, we can calculate $[H_3O^+]$ or $[OH^-]$ for any aqueous solution.
  D. Measuring acidity (Sections 10.8–10.10).
    1. pH (Sections 10.8–10.9).
      a. A pH of < 7 indicates acidity; a pH of > 7 indicates basicity.
      b. pH is the negative logarithm of $[H_3O^+]$.
      c. The pH scale is logarithmic.
      d. pH can be computed with a calculator.
    2. In the laboratory, pH can be measured with indicators or a pH meter (Section 10.10).

III. Buffers (Sections 10.11–10.12).
   A. Characteristics of buffers (Section 10.11).
      1. A buffer is the solution of a weak acid and its salt (or a weak base and its salt) at similar concentration.
      2. When a small amount of acid or base is added to a buffered solution, pH changes very little.
      3. The effective pH range of a buffer solution is determined by the K_a of the acid or base.
         a. A buffer solution works best when [HA] is close in value to [A$^-$].
         b. A buffer solution works best when [HA] and [A$^-$] are approximately ten times greater than the amount of acid or base added.
      4. The Henderson–Hasselbalch equation (pH = pK_a + log ([A$^-$]/[HA]) is useful in buffer calculations. (pK_a = –log K_a)
   B. Buffers in the body (Section 10.12).
      1. The carbonate/bicarbonate buffer system is the major regulator of the pH of body fluids.
         a. An increase of [CO_2] makes blood more acidic.
         b. A decrease in [CO_2] makes blood less acidic.
         c. The acidity of blood is regulated by
            i. A reservoir of excess HCO_3^- that keeps pH fluctuations small.
            ii Change of breathing rate.
            iii. The kidneys.
         d. This regulation prevents alkalosis (pH greater than 7.45) and acidosis (pH lower than 7.35).
      2. The phosphate system and proteins are two other buffer systems in the body.
IV. Equivalents of acids and bases (Sections 10.13–10.15).
   A. Normality (Section 10.14).
      1. An equivalent of acid or base $= \dfrac{\text{molar mass}}{\text{number of H}^+ \text{ or OH}^- \text{ produced}}$.
      2. One equivalent of acid neutralizes one equivalent of base.
      3. Normality $= \dfrac{\text{equivalents of acid or base}}{\text{liters of solution}}$.
      4. Normality = (molarity of acid or base) x (number of H$^+$ or OH$^-$ produced).
   B. Common acid–base reactions (Section 10.14).
      1. Acid + hydroxide ion —> water + salt.
      2. Acid + carbonate or bicarbonate —> water + salt + CO_2.
      3. Acid + ammonia —> ammonium salt.
   C. Titration (Section 10.15).
      1. Titration is used to determine the acid or base concentration of a solution.
      2. In titration, a known volume of a solution of unknown acid or base concentration completely reacts with a solution of known concentration.
      3. The volume of solution of known concentration is measured, and the concentration of the unknown is calculated.
V. Acidity and basicity of salt solutions (Section 10.16).
   A. The salt of a strong base and a strong acid is neutral in solution.
   B. The salt of a strong base and a weak acid is basic in solution.
   C. The salt of a weak base and a strong acid is acidic in solution.
   D. The pH of the salt of a weak base and a weak acid can be predicted only if K_a values are known.

Solutions to Chapter 10 Problems

10.1 HCO_2H (a) and H_2S (b) are Brønsted–Lowry acids because they have protons to donate.

10.2 SO_3^{2-} (a) and F^- (c) are Brønsted–Lowry bases because they can be proton acceptors.

10.3   (a) The conjugate acid of HS^- is H_2S.
   (b) The conjugate acid of PO_4^{3-} is HPO_4^{2-}.
   (c) The conjugate base of H_2CO_3 is HCO_3^-.
   (d) The conjugate base of NH_4^+ is NH_3.

10.4

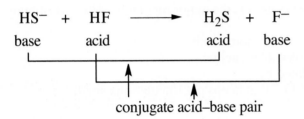

10.5   Water acts as an acid when it reacts to form OH^-; water acts as a base when it reacts to form H_3O^+.

Water as an acid: (b) $F^-(aq) + H_2O(l) \rightleftharpoons HF(aq) + OH^-(aq)$

Water as a base: (a) $H_3PO_4(aq) + H_2O(l) \rightleftharpoons H_2PO_4^-(aq) + H_3O^+(aq)$

   (c) $NH_4^+(aq) + H_2O(l) \rightleftharpoons NH_3(aq) + H_3O^+(aq)$

10.6   In Table 10.1, the stronger acid is listed *higher* in the table than the weaker acid.

Stronger acids: (a) NH_4^+ (b) H_2SO_4 (c) H_2CO_3

10.7   In Table 10.1, the stronger base is listed *lower* in the table than the weaker base.

Stronger bases: (a) F^- (b) OH^-

10.8

$$\underset{\text{acid}}{HPO_4^{2-}(aq)} + \underset{\text{base}}{OH^-(aq)} \rightleftharpoons \underset{\text{base}}{PO_4^{3-}(aq)} + \underset{\text{acid}}{H_2O(l)}$$

conjugate acid–base pair

From Table 10.1, we see that OH^- is a stronger base than PO_4^{3-} and that HPO_4^{2-} is a stronger acid than H_2O. Thus, the forward direction of the equilibrium is favored.

$$\underset{\substack{\text{stronger acid} \quad \text{stronger base}}}{HPO_4^{2-}(aq) + OH^-(aq)} \rightleftharpoons \underset{\substack{\text{weaker base} \quad \text{weaker acid}}}{PO_4^{3-}(aq) + H_2O(l)}$$

10.9   Remember that an electrostatic potential map shows the most electron-rich area of the molecule as red and the least electron-rich area as blue. In alanine, the $-NH_3^+$ group is the most electron-poor, and thus its hydrogens are the most acidic.

10.10   Citric acid is stronger because it has a larger value for K_a, indicating a larger $[H_3O^+]$.

10.11   (a) Beer is slightly acidic. Since $1 \times 10^{-14} = [H_3O^+][OH^-]$,

$$[OH^-] = \frac{K_w}{[H_3O^+]} = \frac{1.0 \times 10^{-14}}{3.2 \times 10^{-5}} = 3.1 \times 10^{-10} \text{ M}$$

(b) Ammonia is basic.

$$[OH^-] = \frac{K_w}{[H_3O^+]} = \frac{1.0 \times 10^{-14}}{3.1 \times 10^{-12}} = 3.2 \times 10^{-3} \text{ M}$$

10.12   A solution with pH = 5 has a greater $[H_3O^+]$ because its pH is a smaller number, indicating a greater concentration of $[H_3O^+]$. The solution with pH = 9 has a greater $[OH^-]$.

10.13   (a) If $[H_3O^+] = 1 \times 10^{-5}$ M, then pH = 5

(b) If $[OH^-] = 1 \times 10^{-9}$ M, then,

$$[H_3O^+] = \frac{1 \times 10^{-14}}{1 \times 10^{-9}} = 1 \times 10^{-5} \text{ M; pH} = 5$$

10.14   (a) For pH = 13, $[H_3O^+] = 1 \times 10^{-13}$ M
(b) For pH = 3, $[H_3O^+] = 1 \times 10^{-3}$ M
(c) For pH = 8, $[H_3O^+] = 1 \times 10^{-8}$ M

The solution of pH = 3 is most acidic, and the solution of pH = 13 is most basic.

10.15   pH $= -\log [H_3O^+]$; $[H_3O^+] = 1 \times 10^{-4}$; $\log [H_3O^+] = -4$; $-\log [H_3O^+] = -(-4) = 4$

The pH of a 1×10^{-4} M solution of HNO_3 is 4.

10.16

Solution	pH	Acidic/Basic	$[H_3O^+]$
(a) Saliva	6.5	acidic	3×10^{-7} M
(b) Pancreatic juice	7.9	basic	1×10^{-8} M
(c) Orange juice	3.7	acidic	2×10^{-4} M
(d) Wine	3.5	acidic	3×10^{-4} M

Least acidic ⟶ Pancreatic juice   Saliva   Orange juice   Wine ⟶ Most acidic

10.17 Use a calculator to determine pH.

(a) $[H_3O^+] = 5.3 \times 10^{-9}$ mol/L: pH = 8.28
(b) $[H_3O^+] = 8.9 \times 10^{-6}$ mol/L: pH = 5.05

10.18 $[H_3O^+] = 2.5 \times 10^{-3}$, since HCl is a strong acid. As in the previous problem, use the EE key and the log key on your calculator, and take the negative value of the log.
    $[H_3O^+] = 2.5 \times 10^{-3}$; pH = $-\log (2.5 \times 10^{-3}) = -(-2.60) = 2.60$

10.19 Refer to Worked Examples 10.13 and 10.14 in the text.
When 0.020 mol of HNO_3 is added, the HF concentration increases from 0.100 M to 0.120 M, and the F^- decreases from 0.120 M to 0.100 M because of the reaction:

$$F^-(aq) + HNO_3(aq) \longrightarrow HF(aq) + NO_3^-(aq)$$

$$pH = pK_a + \log \frac{[A^-]}{[HA]} = 3.46 + \log \frac{[0.100]}{[0.120]} = 3.46 - 0.08 = 3.38$$

10.20

$$NH_4^+(aq) + H_2O(aq) \rightleftharpoons H_3O^+(aq) + NH_3(aq)$$

$$pH = pK_a + \log \frac{[NH_3]}{[NH_4^+]} = 9.25 + \log \frac{[0.080]}{[0.050]} = 9.25 + 0.20 = 9.45$$

10.21 You can see that there are nine HCN molecules and six CN^- molecules in the figure.

$$pH = pK_a + \log \frac{[CN^-]}{[HCN]} = 9.31 + \log \frac{[6]}{[9]} = 9.31 - 0.18 = 9.13$$

10.22–10.23

Sample	Mass	Molar Mass	# of ions*	Gram Equivalent	# of Eq	Normality of 300.0 mL
(a) HNO_3	5.0 g	63.0 g	1	63.0 g	0.079	0.26 N
(b) $Ca(OH)_2$	12.5 g	74.1 g	2	37.0 g	0.338	1.13 N
(c) H_3PO_4	4.5 g	98.0 g	3	32.7 g	0.14	0.47 N

*The "number of ions" refers to the number of H^+ or OH^- ions produced for each mole of acid or base in solution.

10.24 $3 HCl(aq) + Al(OH)_3(aq) \longrightarrow 3 H_2O(l) + AlCl_3(aq)$

$2 HCl(aq) + Mg(OH)_2(aq) \longrightarrow 2 H_2O(l) + MgCl_2(aq)$

10.25 (a) $2 KHCO_3(aq) + H_2SO_4(aq) \longrightarrow 2 H_2O(l) + 2 CO_2(g) + K_2SO_4(aq)$

(b) $MgCO_3(aq) + 2 HNO_3(aq) \longrightarrow H_2O(l) + CO_2(g) + Mg(NO_3)_2(aq)$

10.26 $2 NH_3(aq) + H_2SO_4(aq) \longrightarrow (NH_4)_2SO_4(aq)$

10.27

10.28 First, write the balanced equation for the neutralization reaction:

$$HCl(aq) + NaOH(aq) \longrightarrow H_2O(l) + NaCl(aq)$$

We see from this equation that one mole of base is needed to neutralize each mole of acid.

$$\text{Moles HCl} = 58.4 \text{ mL} \times \frac{1 \text{ L}}{1000 \text{ mL}} \times \frac{0.250 \text{ mol NaOH}}{1 \text{ L}} \times \frac{1 \text{ mol HCl}}{1 \text{ mol NaOH}}$$

$$= 0.0146 \text{ mol HCl}$$

$$\frac{0.0146 \text{ mol HCl}}{20.0 \text{ mL}} \times \frac{1000 \text{ mL}}{1 \text{ L}} = 0.730 \text{ M HCl}$$

10.29 $2 \text{ NaOH}(aq) + H_2SO_4(aq) \longrightarrow 2 H_2O(l) + Na_2SO_4(aq)$

Notice that two moles of base are needed to neutralize one mole of acid.

$$\text{Moles NaOH} = 50.0 \text{ mL} \times \frac{1 \text{ L}}{1000 \text{ mL}} \times \frac{0.200 \text{ mol H}_2SO_4}{1 \text{ L}} \times \frac{2 \text{ mol NaOH}}{1 \text{ mol H}_2SO_4}$$

$$= 0.0200 \text{ mol NaOH}$$

$$0.0200 \text{ mol NaOH} \times \frac{1 \text{ L}}{0.150 \text{ mol}} = 0.133 \text{ L NaOH} = 133 \text{ mL NaOH}$$

10.30 $2 \text{ KOH}(aq) + H_2SO_4(aq) \longrightarrow 2 H_2O(l) + Na_2SO_4(aq)$

$$\text{Moles KOH} = 16.1 \text{ mL} \times \frac{1 \text{ L}}{1000 \text{ mL}} \times \frac{0.150 \text{ mol H}_2SO_4}{1 \text{ L}} \times \frac{2 \text{ mol KOH}}{1 \text{ mol H}_2SO_4}$$

$$= 0.004 \ 83 \text{ mol KOH}$$

$$\frac{0.004 \ 83 \text{ mol}}{0.0215 \text{ L}} = 0.225 \text{ M KOH}$$

10.31 The salt of a weak acid and a strong base produces a basic solution, the salt of a strong acid and a weak base produces an acidic solution, and the salt of a strong acid and a strong base is neutral.

Salt	Cation is from	Anion is from	Solution is
(a) K_2SO_4	strong base (KOH)	strong acid(H_2SO_4)	neutral
(b) Na_2HPO_4	strong base (NaOH)	weak acid ($H_2PO_4^-$)	basic
(c) MgF_2	strong base ($Mg(OH)_2$)	weak acid (HF)	basic
(d) NH_4Br	weak base (NH_3)	strong acid (HBr)	acidic

Understanding Key Concepts

10.32

(a)

$$HCO_3^- + H_2O \longrightarrow CO_3^{2-} + H_3O^+$$
acid   base   base   acid

(b)

$$HCO_3^- + HF \longrightarrow H_2CO_3 + F^-$$
base   acid   acid   base

10.33 (a) The reaction of HF with OH^- is represented by outcome (2). One OH^- reacts with each HF to produce three F^- anions, and nine OH^- anions are left over.
   (b) The reaction of H_2SO_3 with OH^- is represented by outcome (3). Two OH^- ions react with each H_2SO_3 molecule to produce three SO_3^{2-} anions, and six OH^- anions are left over.
   (c) The reaction of H_3PO_4 with OH^- is represented by outcome (1). Three OH^- anions react with each H_3PO_4 molecule to produce three PO_4^{3-} anions, and three OH^- anions are left over.

10.34 In both molecules, the most acidic hydrogen (deepest blue) is bonded to oxygen. Acetic acid is more acidic because its hydrogen is more positively polarized and less tightly held.

10.35 (a) The acid in the first picture (1) is the weakest because it is the least dissociated.
   (b) The acid in the second picture (2) is the strongest acid because all molecules of the acid are dissociated
   (c) The acid in the first picture (1) has the smallest value of K_a because it is the weakest acid.

10.36 (a) Picture (3) represents a weak diprotic acid, which has dissociated slightly to form the HA^- anion.
   (b) Picture (1) represents an impossible situation. H_2A dissociates stepwise to form HA^-. Only when virtually all H_2A has dissociated to form HA^- is A^{2-} formed by dissociation of HA^-.

10.37 The titration reaction uses up 2/3 of the 1.0 M solution in the buret. Since the solution in the buret is 1.0 M, the solution in the flask must be 0.67 M.

Acids and Bases

10.38 In water, HBr dissociates almost completely. Water acts as a base to accept a proton, and a solution of H_3O^+ and Br^- results.

10.39 In water, CH_3CO_2H dissociates only to the extent of about 1%. Water acts as a base, yielding a solution of CH_3CO_2H, along with smaller amounts of H_3O^+ and $CH_3CO_2^-$.

10.40 In water, KOH dissociates completely to yield K^+ and OH^- ions.

10.41 In water, NH_3 remains largely unreacted, but a small amount acts as a base and accepts a proton from water to yield NH_4^+ and OH^- ions.

10.42 A monoprotic acid, such as HCl, has only one proton to donate, whereas a diprotic acid, such as H_2SO_4, has two protons to donate.

10.43 H^+ represents a proton, but the species H^+ is too reactive to exist in solution. Instead, the proton reacts with water to form H_3O^+.

10.44 Strong acids: (a) $HClO_4$; (e) HI

10.45 Weak bases: (a) NH_3; (c) HPO_4^{2-}; (e) CN^-

Brønsted–Lowry Acids and Bases

10.46 Brønsted–Lowry acids: (a) HCN; (d) H_2CO_3; (f) $CH_3NH_3^+$
Brønsted–Lowry base: (b) $CH_3CO_2^-$
Neither: (c) $AlCl_3$; (e) Mg^{2+}

10.47 Base and conjugate acid are pairs, as are acid and conjugate base.

(a) $CO_3^{2-}(aq)$ + HCl(aq) $\longrightarrow$ $HCO_3^-(aq)$ + $Cl^-(aq)$
    base   acid   conjugate acid   conjugate base

(b) $H_3PO_4(aq)$ + $NH_3(aq)$ $\longrightarrow$ $H_2PO_4^-(aq)$ + $NH_4^+(aq)$
    acid   base   conjugate base   conjugate acid

(c) $NH_4^+(aq)$ + $CN^-(aq)$ $\rightleftharpoons$ $NH_3(aq)$ + HCN(aq)
    acid   base   conjugate base   conjugate acid

(d) HBr(aq) + $OH^-(aq)$ $\longrightarrow$ $H_2O(l)$ + $Br^-(aq)$
    acid   base   conjugate acid   conjugate base

(e) $H_2PO_4^-(aq)$ + $N_2H_4(aq)$ $\rightleftharpoons$ $HPO_4^{2-}(aq)$ + $N_2H_5^+(aq)$
    acid   base   conjugate base   conjugate acid

10.48 Base   (a) $ClCH_2CO_2^-$ (b) C_5H_5N (c) SeO_4^{2-} (d) $(CH_3)_3N$
Conjugate $ClCH_2CO_2H$ $C_5H_5NH^+$ $HSeO_4^-$ $(CH_3)_3NH^+$
acid

10.49 Acid   (a) HCN   (b) $(CH_3)_2NH_2^+$ (c) H_3PO_4 (d) $HSeO_3^-$
Conjugate CN^- $(CH_3)_2NH$ $H_2PO_4^-$ SeO_3^{2-}
base

10.50 $HCO_3^-(aq) + HCl(aq) \longrightarrow H_2O(l) + CO_2(g) + Cl^-(aq)$

$HCO_3^-(aq) + NaOH(aq) \longrightarrow H_2O(l) + Na^+(aq) + CO_3^{2-}(aq)$

$H_2PO_4^-(aq) + HCl(aq) \longrightarrow H_3PO_4(aq) + Cl^-(aq)$

$H_2PO_4^-(aq) + NaOH(aq) \longrightarrow HPO_4^{2-}(aq) + H_2O(l) + Na^+(aq)$

10.51 The stronger acid and weaker base are conjugate pairs, as are the stronger base and weaker acid. The reaction to form weaker base and weaker acid is favored.

(a) $HCl(aq) + PO_4^{3-}(aq) \rightleftharpoons HPO_4^{2-}(aq) + Cl^-(aq)$
   stronger acid stronger base   weaker acid   weaker base

(b) $CN^-(aq) + HSO_4^-(aq) \rightleftharpoons HCN(aq) + SO_4^{2-}(aq)$
   stronger base   stronger acid   weaker acid   weaker base

(c) $HClO_4(aq) + NO_2^-(aq) \rightleftharpoons HNO_2(aq) + ClO_4^-(aq)$
   stronger acid   stronger base   weaker acid   weaker base

(d) $HF(aq) + CH_3O^-(aq) \rightleftharpoons CH_3OH(aq) + F^-(aq)$
   stronger acid   stronger base   weaker acid   weaker base

10.52 $2\,HCl(aq) + CaCO_3(s) \longrightarrow H_2O(l) + CO_2(g) + CaCl_2(aq)$

10.53 (a) $LiOH(aq) + HNO_3(aq) \longrightarrow H_2O(l) + LiNO_3(aq)$

(b) $BaCO_3(aq) + 2\,HI(aq) \longrightarrow H_2O(l) + CO_2(g) + BaI_2(aq)$

(c) $H_3PO_4(aq) + 3\,KOH(aq) \longrightarrow 3\,H_2O(l) + K_3PO_4(aq)$

(d) $Ca(HCO_3)_2(aq) + 2\,HCl(aq) \longrightarrow 2\,H_2O(l) + 2\,CO_2(g) + CaCl_2(aq)$

(e) $Ba(OH)_2(aq) + H_2SO_4(aq) \longrightarrow 2\,H_2O(l) + BaSO_4(s)$

Acid and Base Strength: K_a and pH

10.54 For the reaction: $HA(aq) + H_2O(l) \rightleftharpoons H_3O^+(l) + A^-(aq)$

$$K = \frac{\left[H_3O^+\right]\left[A^-\right]}{\left[HA\right]\left[H_2O\right]}$$

Since $[H_2O]$ has no effect on the equilibrium, we define a new constant:

$$K_a = K\left[H_2O\right] = \frac{\left[H_3O^+\right]\left[A^-\right]}{\left[HA\right]}$$

10.55

$$\left[H_3O^+\right] = \frac{K_a\left[HA\right]}{\left[A^-\right]}$$

10.56 K_w is the product of the molar concentrations of H_3O^+ and OH^- in any aqueous solution and is numerically equal to 1.0×10^{-14} at 25°C.

$$K_a = \frac{[H_3O^+][OH^-]}{[H_2O]}; \quad K_a[H_2O] = K_w = [H_3O^+][OH^-]$$

10.57 The quantity pH is defined as the negative logarithm of the molar H_3O^+ concentration. For example, if $[H_3O^+] = 1.0 \times 10^{-3}$ M, then pH = 3.

10.58 A solution of 0.10 M HCl is 100% dissociated; $[H^+] = [HCl] = 0.10$, and pH = 1. A solution of 0.10 M CH_3CO_2H is only partially dissociated, and its pH is expected to be higher than 1.0.

10.59 $CH_3CO_2H(aq) + H_2O(l) \rightleftharpoons CH_3CO_2^-(g) + H_3O^+(aq)$

$[H_3O^+] = $ antilog $(-2.88) = 1.3 \times 10^{-3}$. 1.3% of acetic acid is dissociated.

10.60 $H_3PO_4(aq) + H_2O(l) \rightleftharpoons H_2PO_4^-(aq) + H_3O^+(aq)$

$$K_a = \frac{[H_2PO_4^-][H_3O^+]}{[H_3PO_4]}$$

$H_2PO_4^-(aq) + H_2O(l) \rightleftharpoons HPO_4^{2-}(aq) + H_3O^+(aq)$

$$K_a = \frac{[HPO_4^{2-}][H_3O^+]}{[H_2PO_4^-]}$$

$HPO_4^{2-}(aq) + H_2O(l) \rightleftharpoons PO_4^{3-}(aq) + H_3O^+(aq)$

$$K_a = \frac{[PO_4^{3-}][H_3O^+]}{[HPO_4^{2-}]}$$

10.61 (a) HF is slightly stronger.   (b) HSO_4^- is a stronger acid.
(c) $H_2PO_4^-$ is a stronger acid.   (d) CH_3CO_2H is slightly stronger.

10.62 The stronger base appears lower in the "Base" column of Table 10.1.
(a) OH^-; (b) NO_2^-; (c) OH^-; (d) CN^-; (e) HPO_4^{2-}

10.63 The most acidic solution (see Table 10.1) has the lowest pH.
Lowest pH   *Highest pH*
$HSO_4^- < HF < HCO_2H < H_2CO_3 < NH_4^+$

10.64 Urine (pH = 7.9) is weakly basic, since solutions with pH greater than 7.0 are basic. The $[H_3O^+] = 1.3 \times 10^{-8}$

10.65 Because the pH of a 0.10 M HCN solution is lower than 7.0, the solution is acidic. If HCN were a strong acid, the pH of the 0.10 M solution would be 1. Thus, HCN is a weak acid.

10.66 The concentration of HCl in gastric juice is approximately 1×10^{-2} M.

10.67 For spinal fluid, $[H_3O^+] = 4 \times 10^{-8}$ M.

10.68 $[H_3O^+] = 10^{-pH}$. Since, in this problem, $[H_3O^+] = 0.10$ M $= 1.0 \times 10^{-1}$ M, the pH = 1.00. The pH of an 0.10 M solution of KOH is 13.00.

10.69 pOH = 14 − pH

Substance:	urine	HCN	gastric juice	spinal fluid
pOH:	6.1	8.8	12	6.6

10.70, 10.71

		$[H_3O^+]$	pH	$[OH^-]$	pOH
(a)	Egg white	2.5×10^{-8} M	7.60	4×10^{-7}	6.40
(b)	Apple cider	5.0×10^{-4} M	3.30	2.0×10^{-11}	10.70
(c)	Ammonia	2.3×10^{-12} M	11.64	4.3×10^{-3}	2.36

Ammonia is least acidic and apple cider is most acidic.

10.72
(a) pH = 4; $[H_3O^+] = 1 \times 10^{-4}$ M $[OH^-] = 1 \times 10^{-10}$ M
(b) pH = 11; $[H_3O^+] = 1 \times 10^{-11}$ M $[OH^-] = 1 \times 10^{-3}$ M
(c) pH = 0; $[H_3O^+] = 1$ M $[OH^-] = 1 \times 10^{-14}$ M
(d) pH = 1.38; $[H_3O^+] = 4.2 \times 10^{-2}$ M $[OH^-] = 2.4 \times 10^{-13}$ M
(e) pH = 7.96; $[H_3O^+] = 1.1 \times 10^{-8}$ M $[OH^-] = 9.1 \times 10^{-7}$ M

10.73 0.12 × 0.10 M = 0.012 M H_3O^+. $[H_3O^+] = 1.2 \times 10^{-2}$

$$\left[OH^-\right] = \frac{K_w}{\left[H_3O^+\right]} = \frac{1.0 \times 10^{-14}}{1.2 \times 10^{-2}} = 8.3 \times 10^{-13} \text{ M}$$

pH = 1.92

Buffers

10.74 A buffer is composed of a weak acid and its conjugate base. Any added H_3O^+ can react with the conjugate base and be neutralized, and any added OH^- can react with the acid. In either case, the ratio of acid to conjugate base changes only slightly, and the pH of a buffered solution remains nearly constant.

10.75 $CH_3CO_2H + CH_3CO_2^- Na^+$ is a better buffer than $HNO_3 + NaNO_3$ because acetic acid is a weak acid and acetate ion is its conjugate base. Nitric acid is a strong acid, and nitrate ion is nonbasic. Thus, the nitric acid/sodium nitrate mixture is not a buffer and can't control pH.

10.76

(a) $pH = pK_a + \log\dfrac{\left[CH_3CO_2^-\right]}{\left[CH_3CO_2H\right]} = 4.74 + \log\dfrac{[0.100]}{[0.100]} = 4.74$

(b) $CH_3CO_2^- Na^+(aq) + HNO_3(aq) \longrightarrow CH_3CO_2H(aq) + NaNO_3(aq)$.
The added acid is neutralized by sodium acetate.

$CH_3CO_2H(aq) + OH^-(aq) \longrightarrow CH_3CO_2^-(aq) + H_2O(l)$
The added base is neutralized by acetic acid.

10.77 At a specific pH, the most effective buffer is composed of a solution of an acid whose K_a is close to the desired $[H_3O^+]$ and the salt of that acid. Buffer system (b), whose acid (NH_4^+) has a $K_a = 5.6 \times 10^{-10}$, is the best buffer to use.

10.78

$$pH = pK_a + \log \frac{[CN^-]}{[HCN]} = 9.31 + \log \frac{[0.150]}{[0.200]} = 9.31 - 0.12 = 9.19$$

10.79 Use the formula in the previous problem. Adding 0.020 mol HCl to 1.00 L of the solution in Problem 10.78 changes the value of [HCN] to 0.220 M and the value of [CN⁻] to 0.130 M.

$$pH = pK_a + \log \frac{[CN^-]}{[HCN]} = 9.31 + \log \frac{[0.130]}{[0.220]} = 9.31 - 0.23 = 9.08$$

If 0.020 mol NaOH is added to 1.00 L of the HCN/NaCN buffer system, the concentrations change to [HCN] = 0.180 M and [CN⁻] = 0.170 M.

$$pH = pK_a + \log \frac{[CN^-]}{[HCN]} = 9.31 + \log \frac{[0.170]}{[0.180]} = 9.31 - 0.02 = 9.29$$

10.80

$$pH = pK_a + \log \frac{[NH_3]}{[NH_4^+]} = 9.25 + \log \frac{[0.10]}{[0.15]} = 9.25 - 0.18 = 9.07$$

10.81 A solution with equal amounts of NH_4^+ and NH_3 has a pH of 9.25. If 0.025 moles of NaOH are added to the solution, $[NH_4^+]$ decreases to 0.125 M, $[NH_3]$ increases to 0.125, the base/acid ratio is 1.00, and the solution has pH = 9.25.

Concentrations of Acid and Base Solutions

10.82 An equivalent of an acid or base is its formula weight in grams divided by the number of H_3O^+ or OH^- ions it produces.

10.83 The normality of an acid or base solution is a measure of concentration expressed in number of equivalents per liter of solution.

10.84–10.85
Grams needed for 500 mL of 0.15 N solution are found by multiplying the gram equivalent by 0.075 (0.500 L x 0.15 N).

Sample	Molar Mass	# of H^+ or OH^-	Gram Equivalent	Grams needed for 500 mL of 0.15 N soln.
(a) HNO_3	63.0 g	1	63.0 g	4.72 g
(b) H_3PO_4	98.0 g	3	32.7 g	2.45 g
(c) KOH	56.1 g	1	56.1 g	4.21 g
(d) $Mg(OH)_2$	58.3 g	2	29.2 g	2.19 g

10.86 Since a 0.0050 N solution of any acid has 0.0050 equivalents per liter, 25 mL of a 0.0050 N KOH solution is needed to neutralize 25 mL of either 0.0050 N H_2SO_4 or 0.0050 N HCl.

10.87 Normality = molarity x number of H^+ ions produced.
(a) 0.12 M x 2 H^+ = 0.24 N
(b) 0.12 M x 3 H^+ = 0.36 N

10.88 (a) 0.25 mol $Mg(OH)_2$ x 2 Eq/mol = 0.50 Eq $Mg(OH)_2$

(b) Molar mass of $Mg(OH)_2$ = 58.3 g;   1 Eq $Mg(OH)_2$ = 29.2 g

$$2.5 \text{ g } Mg(OH)_2 \text{ x } \frac{1 \text{ Eq}}{29.2 \text{ g}} = 0.086 \text{ Eq } Mg(OH)_2$$

(c) Molar mass of CH_3CO_2H = 60.0 g;   1 Eq CH_3CO_2H = 60.0 g

$$15 \text{ g } CH_3CO_2H \text{ x } \frac{1 \text{ Eq}}{60 \text{ g}} = 0.25 \text{ Eq } CH_3CO_2H$$

10.89

Molar mass of $C_6H_5O_7H_3$ = 192.0 g; 1 Eq $C_6H_5O_7H_3$ = $\dfrac{192.0 \text{ g}}{1 \text{ mol}}$ x $\dfrac{1 \text{ mol}}{3 \text{ Eq}}$ = 64.0 g

$$\frac{64.0 \text{ g}}{1 \text{ Eq}} \text{ x } \frac{1 \text{ Eq}}{1000 \text{ mEq}} \text{ x } 152 \text{ mEq} = 9.73 \text{ g}$$

10.90 Molar mass of $Ca(OH)_2$ = 74.1 g; 1 Eq $Ca(OH)_2$ = 37.0 g

$$\frac{5.0 \text{ g}}{0.500 \text{ L}} \text{ x } \frac{1 \text{ mol}}{74.1 \text{ g}} = 0.13 \text{ M}; \frac{0.13 \text{ mol}}{1 \text{ L}} \text{ x } \frac{2 \text{ Eq}}{1 \text{ mol}} = \frac{0.26 \text{ Eq}}{1 \text{ L}} = 0.26 \text{ N}$$

10.91 Molar mass of $C_6H_5O_7H_3$ = 192 g; 1 Eq $C_6H_5O_7H_3$ = 64.0 g

$$\frac{25 \text{ g}}{0.800 \text{ L}} \text{ x } \frac{1 \text{ mol}}{192 \text{ g}} = 0.16 \text{ M}; \frac{0.16 \text{ mol}}{1 \text{ L}} \text{ x } \frac{3 \text{ Eq}}{1 \text{ mol}} = \frac{0.48 \text{ Eq}}{1 \text{ L}} = 0.48 \text{ N}$$

10.92 $HCl(aq) + NaOH(aq) \longrightarrow H_2O(l) + NaCl(aq)$

One mole of HCl is needed to neutralize one mole of NaOH.

$$\text{Moles HCl} = 22.4 \text{ mL} \text{ x } \frac{0.12 \text{ mol NaOH}}{1 \text{ L}} \text{ x } \frac{1 \text{ L}}{1000 \text{ mL}} \text{ x } \frac{1 \text{ mol HCl}}{1 \text{ mol NaOH}}$$

$$= 0.0027 \text{ mol HCl}$$

$$\frac{0.0027 \text{ mol HCl}}{12 \text{ mL}} \text{ x } \frac{1000 \text{ mL}}{1 \text{ L}} = 0.23 \text{ M HCl}$$

10.93 $Ba(OH)_2(aq) + 2 HNO_3(aq) \longrightarrow 2 H_2O(l) + Ba(NO_3)_2(aq)$

Moles HNO_3 = 15.0 mL x $\dfrac{0.12 \text{ mol Ba(OH)}_2}{1 \text{ L}}$ x $\dfrac{1 \text{ L}}{1000 \text{ mL}}$ x $\dfrac{2 \text{ mol HNO}_3}{1 \text{ mol Ba(OH)}_2}$

= 0.0036 mol HNO_3

0.0036 mol HNO_3 x $\dfrac{1 \text{ L}}{0.085 \text{ mol}}$ x $\dfrac{1000 \text{ mL}}{1 \text{ L}}$ = 42 mL HNO_3

10.94 $2 KOH(aq) + H_2SO_4(aq) \longrightarrow 2 H_2O(l) + K_2SO_4(aq)$

0.0150 L H_2SO_4 x $\dfrac{0.0250 \text{ mol H}_2SO_4}{1 \text{ L H}_2SO_4}$ x $\dfrac{2 \text{ mol KOH}}{1 \text{ mol H}_2SO_4}$ = 0.00075 mol KOH

$\dfrac{0.00075 \text{ mol NaOH}}{0.010 \text{ L NaOH}}$ = 0.075 M

10.95 V_1 x $N_1 = V_2$ x N_2; V_1 = 35.0 mL; N_1 = 0.100 N; V_2 = 21.5 mL

$N_2 = \dfrac{V_1 \text{ x } N_1}{V_2} = \dfrac{35.0 \text{ mL x } 0.100 \text{ N}}{21.5 \text{ mL}}$ = 0.163 N

Applications

10.96 (a) The pH of stomach acid ranges from 2 to 3.

(b) $NaHCO_3(aq) + HCl(aq) \longrightarrow CO_2(g) + H_2O(l) + NaCl(aq)$

(c) Molarity of acid at pH of 1.8 = 0.016 M

$\dfrac{0.016 \text{ mol HCl}}{1 \text{ L}}$ x 0.0150 L = 0.000 24 mol HCl

0.000 24 mol HCl x $\dfrac{1 \text{ mol antacid}}{1 \text{ mol HCl}}$ x $\dfrac{84.0 \text{ g}}{1 \text{ mol antacid}}$ = 0.020 g = 20 mg

10.97 Gastric juice is the most acidic body fluid, and pancreatic juice is the most basic.

10.98 Bicarbonate reacts with excess H_3O^+ to form H_2CO_3, which goes on to produce H_2O and CO_2 (which is exhaled). This reaction removes H_3O^+ from the blood stream and lowers the serum $[H^+]$, raising pH.

10.99 If the pH is 7.4, the ratio of bicarbonate to carbonate is 20 to 1, and the log of this ratio is 1.3. For a change of –0.1 pH units, the log is 1.2 and the ratio is 16 to 1. A change of +0.1 changes the log to 1.4 and the ratio to 25 to 1. In this range, the carbonate/bicarbonate buffer system is not particularly effective in maintaining constant pH.

10.100 pH of rain = 5.6; $[H_3O^+] = 3 \text{ x } 10^{-6}$ M

10.101 (a) $[H_3O^+]$ = 0.03 M

(b) 25 L x $\dfrac{0.03 \text{ mol}}{1 \text{ L}}$ x $\dfrac{63 \text{ g}}{1 \text{ mol}}$ = 47 g, or approximately 50 g HNO_3

General Questions and Problems

10.102 Citric acid reacts with sodium bicarbonate to release CO_2 bubbles:

$$C_6H_5O_7H_3(aq) + 3\ NaHCO_3(aq) \longrightarrow C_6H_5O_7Na_3(aq) + 3\ H_2O(l) + 3\ CO_2(g)$$

Sodium bicarbonate is the antacid.

10.103 $2\ NaOH(aq) + H_2SO_4(aq) \longrightarrow 2\ H_2O(l) + Na_2SO_4(aq)$

0.040 L H_2SO_4 x $\dfrac{0.10 \text{ mol } H_2SO_4}{1 \text{ L } H_2SO_4}$ x $\dfrac{2 \text{ mol NaOH}}{1 \text{ mol } H_2SO_4}$ = 0.0080 mol NaOH

0.0080 mol NaOH x $\dfrac{1000 \text{ mL NaOH}}{0.50 \text{ mol NaOH}}$ = 16 mL NaOH

10.104

Both 50 mL of a 0.20 N HCl solution and 50 mL of a 0.20 acetic acid solution contain the same number of moles of acid – 0.010 moles. Because HCl is a strong acid, it is almost completely dissociated in water, and the H_3O^+ concentration approaches 0.20 M. Acetic acid, however, is a weak acid that is only slightly dissociated, and the H_3O^+ concentration is much lower – around 0.002 M. Since the HCl solution has a higher H_3O^+ concentration, it has a lower pH.

10.105

(a) pH = pK_a – log $\dfrac{\left[H_2PO_4^-\right]}{\left[HPO_4^{2-}\right]}$ or pK_a = pH + log $\dfrac{\left[HPO_4^{2-}\right]}{\left[H_2PO_4^-\right]}$

(b) Using the second of the above expressions:

7.40 = 7.21+ log $\dfrac{\left[HPO_4^{2-}\right]}{\left[H_2PO_4^-\right]}$; 0.19 = log $\dfrac{\left[HPO_4^{2-}\right]}{\left[H_2PO_4^-\right]}$ = 1.55

A 3/2 ratio of $HPO_4^{2-}/H_2PO_4^-$ maintains the optimum blood pH.

10.106 $2\ HCl(aq) + Ca(OH)_2(aq) \longrightarrow 2\ H_2O(l) + CaCl_2(aq)$

0.140 L HCl x $\dfrac{0.150 \text{ mol HCl}}{1 \text{ L HCl}}$ x $\dfrac{1 \text{ mol Ca(OH)}_2}{2 \text{ mol HCl}}$ = 0.0105 mol $Ca(OH)_2$

$\dfrac{0.0105 \text{ mol Ca(OH)}_2}{30.0 \text{ mL Ca(OH)}_2}$ x $\dfrac{1000mL}{1 \text{ L}}$ = 0.35 M $Ca(OH)_2$

10.107

Both (a), NaF and HF, and (c), NH_4Cl and NH_3 are effective buffer systems. The NaF/HF system is a solution of a weak acid and the salt of its anion. The NH_4Cl/NH_3 system is a solution of a weak base and the salt of its cation. Neither (b) nor (d) are buffer systems because $HClO_4$ and HBr are both strong acids.

The pH of each buffer solution, when the acid and its conjugate base (or the base and its conjugate acid) are of equal concentration, equals the pK_a of the acid. For (a), pH = 3.46; for (c), pH = 9.25.

10.108

(a) $NH_4^+(aq)$ + $OH^-(aq)$ $\longrightarrow$ $NH_3(g)$ + $H_2O(l)$
$\quad$ acid $\qquad\qquad$ base $\qquad\qquad\qquad$ conjugate base $\quad$ conjugate acid

(b) $PV = nRT$; $P = 755$ mmHg; $V = 2.86$ L; $T = 333$ K; $R = \dfrac{62.4 \text{ mmHg·L}}{\text{mol · K}}$

$$n = \frac{PV}{RT} = \frac{755 \text{ mmHg x } 2.86 \text{ L}}{\dfrac{62.4 \text{ mmHg · L}}{\text{mol · K}} \text{ x } 333 \text{ K}} = 0.104 \text{ mol } NH_3$$

0.104 mol x $\dfrac{53.5 \text{ g}}{1 \text{ mol}}$ = 5.56 g NH_4Cl

10.109

(a) $CaO(aq)$ + $SO_2(g)$ $\longrightarrow$ $CaSO_3(s)$

(b) 1 kg SO_2 x $\dfrac{1 \text{ mol } SO_2}{64 \text{ g } SO_2}$ x $\dfrac{1 \text{ mol } SO_2}{1 \text{ mol CaO}}$ x $\dfrac{56 \text{ g CaO}}{1 \text{ mol CaO}}$ = 0.9 kg CaO

10.110

(a) $\quad Na_2O(aq)$ + $H_2O(l)$ $\longrightarrow$ 2 NaOH(aq)

(b) 1.55 g Na_2O x $\dfrac{1 \text{ mol } Na_2O}{62.0 \text{ g } Na_2O}$ x $\dfrac{2 \text{ mol NaOH}}{1 \text{ mol } Na_2O}$ = 0.0500 mol NaOH

$\dfrac{0.0500 \text{ mol NaOH}}{500.0 \text{ mL}}$ x $\dfrac{1000 \text{ mL}}{1 \text{ L}}$ = 0.100 M NaOH; pH = 13.00

(c) 0.0500 mol NaOH x $\dfrac{1 \text{ mol HCl}}{1 \text{ mol NaOH}}$ x $\dfrac{1 \text{ L}}{0.0100 \text{ mol HCl}}$ = 5.00 L HCl

Self-Test for Chapter 10

Multiple Choice

1. What volume of 0.10 M H_2SO_4 will neutralize 30 mL of 0.05 M $Ca(OH)_2$?
    (a) 30 mL   (b) 15 mL   (c) 10 mL   (d) 6.0 mL

2. Which of the following salts is acidic in solution?
    (a) NH_4Br (b) NaBr   (c) NH_4CN (d) NaCN

3. KCN is the salt of a:
    (a) strong acid and strong base   (b) strong acid and weak base   (c) weak acid and strong base
    (d) weak acid and weak base

4. A solution has a pH of 9. What is the value of $[OH^-]$?
    (a) 5   (b) 10^{-9} (c) 9   (d) 10^{-5}

5. Which of the following is a diprotic acid?
    (a) CH_3CO_2H (b) $Ba(OH)_2$ (c) H_2SO_3 (d) H_3PO_4

6. Look at Table 10.2 and decide which base is a weaker base than F^-:
    (a) $H_2PO_4^-$ (b) HCO_3^- (c) CN^- (d) NH_3

7. Which of the following substances turns phenolphthalein red?
    (a) urine   (b) milk of magnesia   (c) blood   (d) coffee

8. Which of the following bases is an Arrhenius base?
    (a) NaOH   (b) $Ca_3(PO_4)_2$ (c) NH_3 (d) LiF

9. In the reaction $Mg(OH)_2(aq) + 2\ HBr(aq) \longrightarrow 2\ H_2O(l) + MgBr_2(aq)$, what is the conjugate acid of $Mg(OH)_2$?
    (a) HBr   (b) H_2O (c) $MgBr_2$ (d) can't tell

10. How many water molecules are produced in the balanced neutralization reaction of $H_3PO_4 + Mg(OH)_2$?
    (a) 2   (b) 3   (c) 4   (d) 6

Sentence Completion

1. One _____ of an acid reacts with one _____ of a base.

2. Phenolphthalein turns _____ in basic solution.

3. H_2CO_3 is a _____ acid.

4. The anion of a weak acid is a _____ base.

5. _____ is the splitting apart of an acid into a proton and an anion.

6. An Arrhenius base yields _____ when dissolved in water.

7. _____ is the reaction of an acid with a base.

8. _____ is the measure of a solution's acidity.

9. To completely neutralize 10.0 mL of 1.0 M H_3PO_4, you need _____ mL of 1.0 M NaOH.

10. CH_3CO_2H and $CH_3CO_2^-$ are known as a _____ acid–base pair.

11. The buffer system of blood is the _____ / _____ system.

12. Substances that can act as either acids or bases are _____.

True or False

1. 30.0 mL of 0.10 M H_2SO_4 is neutralized by 30.0 mL of 0.10 M NaOH.

2. A change of one pH unit is a tenfold change in $[H_3O^+]$.

3. H_2SO_4 / HSO_4^- is a good buffer system.

4. All bases are negatively charged.

5. Bicarbonate ion neutralizes more acid than carbonate ion.

6. If the pH of a solution is 7.0, $[OH^-] = 10^{-7}$.

7. Water can act as both an acid and a base.

8. According to the Brønsted definition, an acid is a substance that dissolves in water to give H_3O^+ ions.

9. Ammonia reacts with an acid to yield ammonium hydroxide.

10. Whether an acid or a base is strong or weak depends on its percent dissociation in water.

11. The reaction $H_2O + H_2PO_4^- \longrightarrow H_3O^+ + HPO_4^{2-}$ proceeds in the direction written.

12. One equivalent of $Ca(OH)_2$ equals 37 g.

Match each entry on the left with its partner on the right.

1. Strong acid

2. 1 M HCl

3. $[H_3O^+] = 10^{-8}$

4. Alkalosis

5. K_w

6. Weak base

7. Strong base

8. Salt

9. $[H_3O^+] = 10^{-6}$

10. Weak acid

11. 1 M H_3PO_4

12. Acidosis

(a) $[H_3O^+]$ $[OH^-]$

(b) Cl^-

(c) pH = 6

(d) HCl

(e) 1 N acid

(f) CH_3CO_2H

(g) $[OH^-] = 10^{-6}$

(h) Blood pH lower than 7.35

(i) $CH_3CO_2^-$

(j) Na_2SO_4

(k) 3 N acid

(l) Blood pH higher than 7.35

Chapter 11   Nuclear Chemistry

Chapter Outline

I. Introduction to radioactivity (Sections 11.1–11.3).
 A Nuclear reactions (Section 11.1).
  1. A nuclear reaction occurs when a nuclide spontaneously changes to a different nuclide.
  2. Nuclear reactions differ from chemical reactions in several ways.
   a. Nuclear reactions produce different elements.
   b. Different isotopes have the same behavior in chemical reactions but different behavior in nuclear reactions.
   c. The rate of a nuclear reaction is unaffected by a change in temperature.
   d. A nuclear reaction is the same whether an atom is in a compound or is elemental.
   e. The energy change in a nuclear reaction is immense.
 B. The discovery and nature of radioactivity (Section 11.2).
  1. Radioactivity was discovered by Becquerel and the Curies.
  2. Three types of radiation may be emitted:
   a. α radiation: He^{2+} nuclei with low penetrating power.
   b. β radiation: electrons (e^-) with medium penetrating power.
   c γ radiation: high-energy light waves with very high penetrating power.
 C. Stable and unstable isotopes (Section 11.3).
  1. All elements have radioactive isotopes.
  2. Most radioisotopes are made in particle accelerators: These are known as artificial radioisotopes.
  3. Radioisotopes have the same chemical properties as their nonradioactive isotopes.
II. Nuclear decay (Sections 11.4–11.7).
 A. Nuclear emissions (Section 11.4).
  1. Alpha emission.
     After α emission, the atomic number of the resulting isotope decreases by 2, and the mass number decreases by 4.
  2. Beta emission.
   a. In β emission, a neutron decomposes to a proton and an electron.
   b. The electron is emitted, and the proton is retained.
   c. The atomic number of the resulting isotope increases by 1, and the mass number is unchanged.
  3. Gamma (γ) emission.
     Gamma (γ) emission usually accompanies α or β emission and doesn't affect either mass number or atomic number.
  4. Positron emission.
   a. Positron emission occurs when a proton is converted to a neutron and an ejected positron (positive electron).
   b. The mass number of the nucleus is unchanged, but the atomic number decreases by 1
  5. Electron capture (EC).
   a. EC occurs when a nucleus captures an electron from the surrounding electron cloud, converting a proton into a neutron.
   b. The mass number of the nucleus is unchanged, but the atomic number decreases by 1.

B. Half-life (Section 11.5).
    1. Half-life is the amount of time it takes for half of a sample of a radioisotope to decay.
    2. Half-life doesn't depend on the amount of sample or on temperature.
    3. Each half-life sees the decay of half of what remains of the sample.
C. Radioactive decay series (Section 11.6).
    Some heavy radioisotopes undergo a series of disintegrations until a nonradioactive product is reached.
D. Ionizing radiation (Section 11.7).
    1. Ionizing radiation is any high-energy radiation that can create reactive ions when it collides with a chemical compound.
    2. Ionizing radiation converts molecules into highly reactive ions.
    3. Ionizing radiation can injure the body.
        a. Gamma and X radiation are more harmful when radiation comes from outside the body.
        b. Alpha and β radiation are more dangerous when emitted from within the body.
    4. The intensity of radiation decreases with the square of the distance from the source.
III. Detecting radiation (Sections 11.8–11.9).
A. Devices for detecting radiation (Section 11.8).
    1. Photographic film badges.
    2. Geiger counter.
    3. Scintillation counter.
B. Units of radiation (Section 11.9).
    1. The *curie* measures the number of disintegrations per second.
    2. The *roentgen* measures the intensity of radiation.
    3. The *rad* measures the energy absorbed per gram of tissue.
    4. The *rem* and the *sievert* measure tissue damage.
IV. Artificial transmutation (Section 11.10).
A. Artificial transmutation occurs when nuclei are bombarded with high-energy particles.
B. After bombardment, a new nucleus is produced.
C. The transuranium elements were all produced via artificial transmutation.
V. Nuclear fission and nuclear fusion (Section 11.11).
A. Nuclear fission.
    1. Nuclear fission occurs when a heavy nucleus fragments after bombardment by a small particle, such as a neutron.
    2. The large amounts of energy released are due to mass-to-energy conversions and are measured by $E = mc^2$.
    3. Many different fission products can result from one bombardment.
    4. In some cases, bombardment with one neutron can cause production of more than one neutron, in addition to fragmentation.
        a. This is called a chain reaction.
        b. If the bombarded sample weighs more than a critical mass, a nuclear explosion can result.
        c. A controlled fission reaction can be used to produce energy.
B. Nuclear fusion.
    1. If two light nuclei are made to collide, a nuclear fusion reaction occurs that produces a combined nucleus plus energy.
    2. Nuclear fusion reactions occur in stars.

Solutions to Chapter 11 Problems

11.1 For α emission, subtract 2 from the atomic number of radon and 4 from the mass number:

$$^{222}_{86}\text{Rn} \rightarrow {}^{4}_{2}\text{He} + {}^{218}_{84}?$$

Then look in the periodic table for the element with atomic number 84:

$$^{222}_{86}\text{Rn} \rightarrow {}^{4}_{2}\text{He} + {}^{218}_{84}\text{Po}$$

11.2 Add 4 to the mass number of radon-222 to calculate the isotope of radium:

$$^{226}_{88}\text{Ra} \rightarrow {}^{4}_{2}\text{He} + {}^{222}_{86}\text{Rn}$$

11.3

$$^{14}_{6}\text{C} \rightarrow {}^{0}_{-1}\text{e} + ?$$

The mass number of the product element stays the same, but the atomic number increases by 1, to 7. Looking in the periodic table, we find that ^{14}N is the element formed:

$$^{14}_{6}\text{C} \rightarrow {}^{0}_{-1}\text{e} + {}^{14}_{7}\text{N}$$

11.4

(a) $^{3}_{1}\text{H} \rightarrow {}^{0}_{-1}\text{e} + {}^{3}_{2}\text{He}$ (b) $^{210}_{82}\text{Pb} \rightarrow {}^{0}_{-1}\text{e} + {}^{210}_{83}\text{Bi}$ (c) $^{20}_{9}\text{F} \rightarrow {}^{0}_{-1}\text{e} + {}^{20}_{10}\text{Ne}$

11.5 For positron emission, the atomic number decreases by 1, but the mass number stays the same.

(a) $^{38}_{20}\text{Ca} \rightarrow {}^{0}_{1}\text{e} + {}^{38}_{19}\text{K}$ (b) $^{118}_{54}\text{Xe} \rightarrow {}^{0}_{1}\text{e} + {}^{118}_{53}\text{I}$ (c) $^{79}_{37}\text{Rb} \rightarrow {}^{0}_{1}\text{e} + {}^{79}_{36}\text{Kr}$

11.6 As in positron emission, the atomic number decreases by 1 and the mass number stays unchanged in electron capture.

(a) $^{62}_{30}\text{Zn} + {}^{0}_{-1}\text{e} \rightarrow {}^{62}_{29}\text{Cu}$ (b) $^{110}_{50}\text{Sn} + {}^{0}_{-1}\text{e} \rightarrow {}^{110}_{49}\text{In}$ (c) $^{81}_{36}\text{Kr} + {}^{0}_{-1}\text{e} \rightarrow {}^{81}_{35}\text{Br}$

11.7 Table 11.2 shows the changes brought about by various radioactive decay patterns. Only β emission produces a change of +1 to the atomic number and a decrease in the number of neutrons. The original element was indium ($Z = 49$), and tin ($Z = 50$) is the decay product.

$$^{120}_{49}\text{In} \rightarrow {}^{0}_{-1}\text{e} + {}^{120}_{50}\text{Sn}$$

11.8 $17{,}000 \div 5730 = 2.97$, or approximately 3 half-lives.

The percentage of $^{14}_{6}\text{C}$ is (1/2) x (1/2) x (1/2) x 100% = 12.5% of the original sample.

11.9 Find the point on the graph that represents 50% of the sample remaining. Locate the time that corresponds to this point; this is the half-life – 3 days.

11.10

$$\frac{I_1}{I_2} = \frac{d_2^2}{d_1^2} : I_1 = 250 \text{ units}; I_2 = 25 \text{ units}; d_1^2 = (4.0 \text{ m})^2 = 16 \text{ m}^2; d_2^2 = ?$$

$$d_2^2 = \frac{d_1^2 \times I_1}{I_2} = \frac{16 \text{ m}^2 \times 250 \text{ units}}{25 \text{ units}} = 160 \text{ m}^2$$
$$d_2 = 13 \text{ m}$$

11.11

$$\frac{5 \text{ mrem}}{270 \text{ mrem}} \times 100\% = 1.9\%$$

The annual dose of radiation for most people will increase by approximately 2%.

11.12

$$\frac{175 \text{ } \mu\text{Ci}}{\text{dose}} \times \frac{1 \text{ mL}}{44 \text{ } \mu\text{Ci}} = \frac{4.0 \text{ mL}}{\text{dose}}$$

11.13

$$^{241}_{95}\text{Am} \rightarrow {}^{4}_{2}\text{He} + {}^{237}_{93}\text{Np}$$

11.14

$$^{241}_{95}\text{Am} + {}^{4}_{2}\text{He} \rightarrow 2 {}^{1}_{0}\text{n} + {}^{243}_{97}\text{Bk}$$

11.15

$$^{40}_{18}\text{Ar} + {}^{1}_{1}\text{H} \rightarrow {}^{1}_{0}\text{n} + {}^{40}_{19}\text{K}$$

11.16

$$^{235}_{92}\text{U} + {}^{1}_{0}\text{n} \rightarrow 2 {}^{1}_{0}\text{n} + {}^{137}_{52}\text{Te} + {}^{97}_{40}\text{Zr}$$

Understanding Key Concepts

11.17 After one half-life, the sample would consist of eight $^{28}_{13}\text{Al}$ atoms and eight $^{28}_{12}\text{Mg}$ atoms. After two half-lives, the remaining eight $^{28}_{12}\text{Mg}$ atoms would have decayed to four $^{28}_{13}\text{Al}$ atoms, producing the outcome shown in the picture.

11.18

$$^{28}_{12}\text{Mg} \rightarrow {}^{0}_{-1}\text{e} + {}^{28}_{13}\text{Al}$$

11.19

● Aluminum-28

○ Magnesum-28

11.20 The illustrated isotope, with six protons and eight neutrons, is $^{14}_{6}\text{C}$.

11.21 The shorter arrows represent β emission because they show the decomposition of a neutron with an accompanying one-unit increase in atomic number.
The longer arrows represent α emission because they indicate a decay that results in the loss of two protons and two neutrons (α particle).

11.22

$$^{241}_{94}\text{Pu} \rightarrow {}^{241}_{95}\text{Am} \rightarrow {}^{237}_{93}\text{Np} \rightarrow {}^{233}_{91}\text{Pa} \rightarrow {}^{233}_{92}\text{U}$$

11.23 The isotope can decay by either positron emission or electron capture since the atomic number decreases by 1 but the mass number remains the same.

$$^{148}_{69}\text{Tm} \rightarrow {}^{0}_{1}\text{e} + {}^{148}_{68}\text{Er} \quad \text{or} \quad {}^{148}_{69}\text{Tm} + {}^{0}_{-1}\text{e} \rightarrow {}^{148}_{68}\text{Er}$$

11.24 The half-life is approximately 3.5 years.

11.25 The curve doesn't represent nuclear decay. According to the curve, half of the sample has decayed after 5 days. Half of the remaining sample should have decayed after 10 days, but on this curve the second half-life is shown at 13 days. A decay curve should approach zero after six half-lives, but this curve shows 10% activity remaining at that time.

Radioactivity

11.26 A substance is said to be radioactive if it emits radiation by decay of an unstable nucleus.

11.27

Radiation	Particle Produced	Atomic Number	Mass Number	Penetrating Power
α emission	$^{4}_{2}\text{He}$	decreases by 2	decreases by 4	low
β emission	$^{0}_{-1}\text{e}$	increases by 1	unchanged	medium
γ emission	none	unchanged	unchanged	high
positron emission	$^{0}_{1}\text{e}$	decreases by 1	unchanged	medium
electron capture	$^{0}_{-1}\text{e}$ (captured, not emitted)	decreases by 1	unchanged	high

11.28

Nuclear Reaction	Chemical Reaction
Involves change in an atom's nucleus	Involves change in an atom's outer-shell electrons
Usually produces a different element	Never produces a different element
Different isotopes have different behavior in a nuclear reaction	Different isotopes have the same behavior in a chemical reaction
Rate is unaffected by a change in temperature or by a catalyst	Rate changes with a change in temperature or by using a catalyst
Rate is the same, whether the atom is in a compound or uncombined	
Energy change is millions of times larger for a nuclear reaction	

11.29 Transmutation is the change of one element into another brought about by nuclear decay.

11.30 The symbol for an α particle is ^4_2He.

11.31 The symbol for a β particle is $^0_{-1}\text{e}$, and the symbol for a positron is ^0_1e.

11.32 Outside of the body, gamma radiation has the highest penetrating power, and α radiation has the lowest penetrating power.

11.33 When ionizing radiation strikes a molecule, a high-energy reactive ion with an odd number of electrons is produced. This reactive ion immediately reacts with other chemical compounds, creating other reactive fragments that can cause further reactions.

11.34 Ionizing radiation causes cell damage by breaking bonds in DNA. The resulting damage may lead to mutation, cancer, or cell death.

11.35 Background radiation may arise from naturally occurring radioactive isotopes or from cosmic rays.

11.36 A neutron in the nucleus decomposes to a proton and an electron, which is emitted as a β particle.

11.37 An α particle is a helium nucleus, ^4_2He; a helium atom is a helium nucleus plus two electrons.

Nuclear Decay and Transmutation

11.38 A nuclear equation is balanced if the number of nucleons is the same on both sides and if the sums of the charges on the nuclei and on any other elementary particles are the same on both sides.

11.39 A transuranium element is an element with an atomic number greater than 92. It is produced by bombardment of a slightly lighter element with high-energy particles.

11.40 For an atom emitting an α particle, the atomic number decreases by 2, and the mass number decreases by 4.
For an atom emitting a β particle, the atomic number increases by 1, and the mass number is unchanged.

11.41 For an atom emitting a γ ray, both atomic number and mass number are unchanged.
For an atom emitting a positron, the atomic number decreases by 1, and the mass number is unchanged

11.42 In nuclear fission, bombardment of a nucleus causes fragmentation in many different ways to yield a large number of smaller fragments. Normal radioactive decay of a nucleus produces an atom with a similar mass and yields a predictable product.

11.43 Bombardment of a $^{235}_{92}$U nucleus with one neutron produces three neutrons, which, on collision with three more $^{235}_{92}$U nuclei yield nine neutrons, and so on. Because the reaction is self-sustaining, it is known as a chain reaction.

11.44

(a) $^{35}_{16}$S $\rightarrow$ $^{0}_{-1}$e + $^{35}_{17}$Cl
(b) $^{24}_{10}$Ne $\rightarrow$ $^{0}_{-1}$e + $^{24}_{11}$Na

(c) $^{90}_{38}$Sr $\rightarrow$ $^{0}_{-1}$e + $^{90}_{39}$Y

11.45

(a) $^{190}_{78}$Pt $\rightarrow$ $^{4}_{2}$He + $^{186}_{76}$Os
(b) $^{208}_{87}$Fr $\rightarrow$ $^{4}_{2}$He + $^{204}_{85}$At

(c) $^{245}_{96}$Cm $\rightarrow$ $^{4}_{2}$He + $^{241}_{94}$Pu

11.46

(a) $^{109}_{47}$Ag + $^{4}_{2}$He $\rightarrow$ $^{113}_{49}$In
(b) $^{10}_{5}$B + $^{4}_{2}$He $\rightarrow$ $^{13}_{7}$N + $^{1}_{0}$n

11.47

(a) $^{140}_{55}$Cs $\rightarrow$ $^{0}_{-1}$e + $^{140}_{56}$Ba
(b) $^{248}_{96}$Cm $\rightarrow$ $^{4}_{2}$He + $^{244}_{94}$Pu

11.48

(a) $^{235}_{92}$U + $^{1}_{0}$n $\rightarrow$ $^{160}_{62}$Sm + $^{72}_{30}$Zn + 4$^{1}_{0}$n

(b) $^{235}_{92}$U + $^{1}_{0}$n $\rightarrow$ $^{87}_{35}$Br + $^{146}_{57}$La + 3$^{1}_{0}$n

11.49

(a) $^{126}_{50}$Sn $\rightarrow$ $^{0}_{-1}$e + $^{126}_{51}$Sb
(b) $^{210}_{88}$Ra $\rightarrow$ $^{4}_{2}$He + $^{206}_{86}$Rn

(c) $^{76}_{36}$Kr + $^{0}_{-1}$e $\rightarrow$ $^{76}_{35}$Br

11.50

$^{198}_{80}$Hg + $^{1}_{0}$n $\rightarrow$ $^{198}_{79}$Au + $^{1}_{1}$H

A proton is produced in addition to gold-198.

11.51

$^{59}_{27}$Co + $^{1}_{0}$n $\rightarrow$ $^{60}_{27}$Co

$^{60}_{27}$Co $\rightarrow$ $^{0}_{-1}$e + $^{60}_{28}$Ni

11.52 The four α decays result in a loss of 16 nucleons from the mass number and a reduction of 8 in atomic number. The β decay results in a gain of 1 in atomic number and no change in mass number. The parent isotope, which has seven more protons and a mass 16 units greater than bismuth-212, is thorium-228.

11.53

$$^{209}_{83}Bi + ^{58}_{26}Fe \rightarrow ^{266}_{109}Mt + ^{1}_{0}n \quad \text{A neutron is also produced.}$$

Half-Life

11.54 If strontium-90 has a half-life of 28.8 years, half of a given quantity of strontium-90 will have decayed after 28.8 years.

11.55 1/2 x 1/2 x 100% = 25%. 25% of the original radioactivity remains in a sample after 2 half-lives. For 3 half-lives: 1/2 x 1/2 x 1/2 x 100% = 12.5%. For 4 half-lives: 1/2 x 1/2 x 1/2 x 1/2 x 100% = 6.25%. The amount remaining after 3 1/2 half-lives is between 6.25% and 12.5% but closer to 12.5% than 6.25%.

11.56 365 ÷ 120 = 3.04, or approximately 3 half-lives.

$$0.050 \text{ g} \times (0.5)^3 = 0.050 \times 0.125 = 0.0062 \text{ g}$$

Approximately 0.006 grams of $^{75}_{34}Se$ will remain after a year.

11.57 After 7 half-lives, 99% of any sample will have decayed. Since the half-life of $^{75}_{34}Se$ is approximately 0.33 year, 99% of the sample will have disintegrated in 7 x 0.33 = 2.3 years.

11.58 If the half-life of mercury-97 is 64.1 hours,
7 days = 168 hours ; 168/64.1 = 2.6, or approximately 3 half-lives
30 days = 720 hours ; 720/64.1 = approximately 11 half-lives
5.0 ng x $(0.5)^3$ = approx. 1 ng of mercury-197 remains after 7 days.
5.0 ng x $(0.5)^{11}$ = approx. 2×10^{-3} ng of mercury-197 remains after 30 days.

11.59

(a) $^{198}_{79}Au \rightarrow ^{0}_{-1}e + ^{198}_{80}Hg$

(b) $\dfrac{3.75 \text{ mCi}}{30.0 \text{ mCi}} = 0.125 = 3.00$ half lives; 3.00×2.695 days = 8.09 days

(c) $\dfrac{1.0 \text{ mCi}}{1 \text{ kg}} \times 70.0 \text{ kg} = 70 \text{ mCi}$

Measuring Radioactivity

11.60 The inside walls of a Geiger counter tube are negatively charged, and a wire in the center is positively charged. Radiation ionizes argon gas inside the tube, which creates a conducting path for current between the wall and the wire. The current is detected, and the Geiger counter makes a clicking sound.

11.61 A film badge is protected from light exposure, but exposure to other radiation causes the film to get cloudy. Photographic development of the film and comparison with a standard allows the amount of exposure to be calculated.

11.62 In a scintillation counter, a phosphor emits a flash of light when struck by radiation. The number of flashes are counted and converted to an electrical signal.

11.63 Rems indicate the amount of tissue damage from any type of radiation, and allow comparisons between equivalent doses of different types of radiation to be made.

11.64 According to Table 11.6, any amount of radiation above 25 rems produces detectable effects in humans.

11.65 (1) curie   (c) Number of disintegrations per second
(2) rem   (b) Amount of tissue damage
(3) rad   (d) Amount of radiation per gram of tissue
(4) roentgen   (a) Ionizing intensity of radiation

11.66

$$28 \text{ mCi} \times \frac{1 \text{ mL}}{15 \text{ mCi}} = 1.9 \text{ mL}$$

11.67

$$68 \text{ kg} \times \frac{180 \text{ } \mu\text{Ci}}{1 \text{ kg}} \times \frac{1 \text{ mCi}}{10^3 \text{ } \mu\text{Ci}} \times \frac{1 \text{ mL}}{6.5 \text{ mCi}} = 1.9 \text{ mL}$$

11.68

$$\frac{I_1}{I_2} = \frac{d_2^2}{d_1^2}; \quad I_1 = 300 \text{ rem}; \quad d_1^2 = (2.0 \text{ m})^2 = 4.0 \text{ m}^2; \quad d_2^2 = (25.0 \text{ m})^2 = 625 \text{ m}^2; \quad I_2 = ?$$

$$I_2 = \frac{d_1^2 \times I_1}{d_2^2} = \frac{4.0 \text{ m}^2 \times 300 \text{ rem}}{625 \text{ m}^2} = 1.9 \text{ rem}$$

11.69

$$\frac{I_1}{I_2} = \frac{d_2^2}{d_1^2}; \quad I_1 = 650 \text{ rem}; \quad I_2 = 25 \text{ rem}; \quad d_1^2 = 1.0 \text{ m}^2; \quad d_2^2 = ?$$

$$d_2^2 = \frac{d_1^2 \times I_1}{I_2} = \frac{1.0 \text{ m}^2 \times 650.0 \text{ rem}}{25 \text{ rem}} = 26 \text{ m}^2$$

$$d_2 = 5.1 \text{ m}$$

Applications

11.70 (1) *In vivo procedures* take place inside the body and assess the functioning of organs or body systems. Determination of whole-blood volume using chromium-51 is an example.
(2) *Therapeutic procedures* are used to kill diseased tissue. For example, irradiation of a tumor with cobalt-60 is a treatment for cancer.
(3) In *boron neutron capture therapy (BNCT)*, boron-containing drugs are administered to a cancer patient and are concentrated in the tumor, which is then irradiated with a neutron beam. The boron captures a neutron and undergoes transmutation to produce a lithium nucleus and an alpha particle, which kills the tumor.

11.71 The total sample dose is 2.0 mL x 1.25 μCi = 2.5 μCi. The calculated blood volume:

$$2.5 \ \mu Ci \ \ x \ \frac{1.0 \ mL}{2.6 \ x \ 10^{-4} \ \mu Ci} \ \ x \ \frac{1 \ L}{1000 \ mL} \ = 9.6 \ L$$

11.72 The purpose of food irradiation is to kill harmful microorganisms by exposing food to ionizing radiation, which destroys the genetic material of the microorganisms.

11.73 Gamma rays from cobalt-60 are used to treat food.

11.74 The body-imaging techniques CT and PET are noninvasive and yield a large array of images that can be processed by computer to produce a three-dimensional image of an organ.

11.75 MRI imaging does not involve radiation and produces images that have greater contrast than those from CT and PET scans.

11.76 Only living organisms can incorporate atmospheric $^{14}CO_2$. In organisms that are still alive, the ratio of $^{14}C/^{12}C$ is constant, but after death the ratio of $^{14}C/^{12}C$ decreases. By measuring the ratio, it is possible to determine the age of the sample.

11.77 It takes 3 half-lives for radiation to decay to one-eighth of its original value.
3 x 5715 years = 17,100 years old.

General Questions and Problems

11.78 Nuclear reactions occur spontaneously, and no substance can "react with" radioactive emissions to neutralize them.

11.79 A film badge is more useful for measuring radiation exposure over a period of time. Scintillation counters and Geiger counters are more useful for measuring a current source of radiation.

11.80

(a) $^{99}_{42}Mo \ \rightarrow \ ^{0}_{-1}e \ + \ ^{99}_{43}Tc$ ^{99}Mo decays to Tc-99*m* by β emission.

(b) $^{98}_{42}Mo \ + \ ^{1}_{0}n \ \rightarrow \ ^{99}_{42}Mo$

11.81 24 hours ÷ 6.01 hours = approx. 4 half-lives. 15 μCi x $(0.5)^4$ = 0.94 μCi

11.82

(a) $^{238}_{94}Pu \ \rightarrow \ ^{4}_{2}He \ + \ ^{234}_{92}U$

(b) The metal case serves as a shield to protect the wearer from α radiation.

11.83

(a) $^{24}_{11}Na \rightarrow ^{0}_{-1}e + ^{24}_{12}Mg$

(b) 50 hr ÷ 15 hr = 3.3 half-lives. $(0.5)^3$ = 0.125. Somewhat less than 12.5% of the original sodium-24 remains after 50 hrs.

11.84 Embryos and fetuses are particularly susceptible to the effects of radiation because their rate of cell division is high.

11.85 This question illustrates the relative dangers of internal radiation and external radiation. Alpha and beta radiation, because of their short penetrating distance, are dangerous inside the body. You can put the alpha cookie in your pocket, but don't try this with the beta cookie, which might damage sensitive genetic material—hold it your hand (wearing gloves). The gamma cookie, with a large penetrating distance, can probably be eaten because the radiation will pass through the body before it can cause damage. Throw away the neutron cookie.

11.86 Nuclear fusion produces few radioactive by-products, and the deuterium fuel used is abundant and inexpensive. Drawbacks include providing high enough temperatures and holding materials long enough for nuclei to react.

11.87

(a) $^{162}_{75}Re \rightarrow ^{4}_{2}He + ^{158}_{73}Ta$ (b) $^{188}_{74}W \rightarrow ^{0}_{-1}e + ^{188}_{75}Re$

11.88

(a) $^{253}_{99}Es + ^{4}_{2}He \rightarrow ^{256}_{101}Md + ^{1}_{0}n$ (b) $^{250}_{98}Cf + ^{11}_{5}B \rightarrow ^{257}_{103}Lr + 4\,^{1}_{0}n$

11.89

$^{238}_{92}U + ^{1}_{0}n \rightarrow 2\,^{0}_{-1}e + ^{239}_{94}Pu$

11.90

$^{10}_{5}B + ^{1}_{0}n \rightarrow ^{7}_{3}Li + ^{4}_{2}He$

11.91

$^{232}_{90}Th \rightarrow ^{208}_{82}Pb + 6\,^{4}_{2}He + 4\,^{0}_{-1}e$

The 24-amu loss in mass in going from $^{232}_{90}Th$ to $^{208}_{82}Pb$ is due to the emission of six α particles, which also account for the reduction in atomic number from 90 to 78. The emission of four β particles increases the atomic number from 78 to 82 and yields $^{208}_{82}Pb$.

11.92 Alpha particles are used for the bombardment.

$^{238}_{92}U + 3\,^{4}_{2}He \rightarrow ^{246}_{98}Cf + 4\,^{1}_{0}n$

Self-Test for Chapter 11

Multiple Choice

1. Bombardment of a uranium-235 atom with a neutron produces three neutrons, which can go on to bombard three more U-235 atoms. How many neutrons are produced after the fourth cycle?
   (a) 12   (b) 36   (c) 81   (d) 108

2. The product of the α emission of $^{146}_{62}Sm$ is:
   (a) $^{146}_{63}Eu$ (b) $^{144}_{61}Pm$ (c) $^{144}_{60}Nd$ (d) $^{142}_{60}Nd$

3. A half-inch-thick piece of plastic blocks 50% of radiation. How much radiation passes through a one-inch-thick piece of plastic?
   (a) 50%   (b) 25%   (c) 12%   (d) 0%

4. The *curie* measures:
   (a) amount of radioactivity   (b) ionizing intensity of radiation   (c) amount of radiation absorbed   (d) tissue damage

5. A sample of a radionuclide has a half-life of 40 days. How much radioactivity remains after 160 days?
   (a) 25%   (b) 12.5%   (c) 6.25%   (d) 0%

6. How many disintegrations per second does one microcurie of a sample emit?
   (a) 3.7×10^{10} (b) 3.7×10^{7} (c) 3.7×10^{6} (d) 3.7×10^{4}

7. If a person standing 100 m from a radiation source approaches to within 10 m of the source, how much does the intensity of the radiation change?
   (a) increases by a hundredfold   (b) increases tenfold   (c) stays the same   (d) decreases tenfold

8. Artificial transmutation was probably used to produce which one of the following radionuclides?
   (a) $^{238}_{92}U$ (b) $^{210}_{82}Pb$ (c) $^{60}_{27}Co$ (d) $^{239}_{94}Pu$

9. Which of the following radioisotopes is not medically useful?
   (a) $^{131}_{53}I$ (b) $^{14}_{6}C$ (c) $^{24}_{11}Na$ (d) $^{60}_{27}Co$

10. In an experiment by the Curies, aluminum-27 was bombarded with α particles. If each aluminum-27 atom captured one α particle and emitted one neutron, what other atom was produced?
    (a) $^{29}_{13}Al$ (b) $^{28}_{14}Si$ (c) $^{30}_{15}P$ (d) $^{31}_{15}P$

Sentence Completion

1. The change of one element to another is called _____.

2. _____ _____ causes the most tissue damage.

3. A chemical compound tagged with a radioactive atom can be used as a _____.

4. All people are exposed to _____ radiation.

5. A nuclear equation is balanced when the number of _____ is the same on both sides of the equation.

6. The age of a sample can be determined by measuring the amount of _____ it contains.

7. The _____ is a unit for measuring the number of radioactive disintegrations per second.

8. In _____ _____, an atom is split apart by neutron bombardment to give small fragments.

9. People who work around radiation sources wear _____ _____ for detection of radiation.

10. PET and CT are techniques for _____ _____.

11. Very light elements release large amounts of energy when they undergo _____ _____.

12. The _____ _____ is the size of a radioactive sample that is needed for a nuclear reaction to be self-sustaining.

True or False

1. If a sample has a half-life of 12 days, it will have decayed completely in 24 days.

2. X rays are considered to be ionizing radiation.

3. The ratio of carbon-14 to carbon-12 in the atmosphere is constant.

4. Pierre and Marie Curie discovered radioactivity.

5. A β particle travels at nearly the speed of light.

6. An α particle travels at nearly the speed of light.

7. The product of β emission has an atomic number 1 amu smaller than the starting material.

8. A nuclear power plant can undergo a nuclear explosion in an accident.

9.   The rad is the unit most commonly used in medicine to measure radiation dosage.

10.   Radiation causes injury by ionizing molecules.

11.   Most of the known radioisotopes are naturally occurring.

12.   Many isotopes undergo nuclear fission.

Match each entry on the left with its partner on the right.

1.   Rutherford   (a) α particle

2. $^{245}_{96}Cm$ (b) Used in cancer therapy

3. $t_{1/2}$ (c) Discovered radioactivity

4. $^{0}_{-1}e$ (d) Neutron

5.   Becquerel   (e) Used for archeological dating

6. $^{90}_{38}Sr$ (f) Discovered α and β particles

7. $^{1}_{0}n$ (g) Natural radioactive element that undergoes fission

8.   P. and M. Curie   (h) Discovered radium

9. $^{60}_{27}Co$ (i) Transuranium element

10. $^{4}_{2}He$ (j) Component of radioactive waste

11. $^{14}_{6}C$ (k) β particle

12. $^{235}_{92}U$ (l) Half-life

Chapter Outline

I. Introduction to organic chemistry (Sections 12.1–12.5).
  A. The nature of organic molecules (Section 12.1).
    1. Carbon always forms four bonds.
    2. Almost all of the bonds in organic molecules are covalent.
      a. These bonds are polar covalent bonds when carbon forms a bond to an element on the far left of the periodic table.
      b. Carbon can form multiple bonds by sharing more than two electrons.
    3. Organic molecules have specific three-dimensional shapes.
    4. In addition to hydrogen, oxygen and nitrogen are often present in organic molecules.
    5. Organic molecules are low-melting and low-boiling, relative to inorganic compounds.
    6. Organic molecules are usually insoluble in water and don't conduct electricity.
  B. Functional groups (Section 12.2).
    1. A functional group is an atom or group of atoms that has a characteristic reactivity.
    2. The chemistry of organic molecules is determined by functional groups.
    3. Functional groups fall into three categories.
      a. Hydrocarbons.
      b. Compounds with C–X single bonds, where X is electronegative.
      c. Compounds with C=O double bonds.
  C. Structures of organic molecules: alkane isomers (Sections 12.3–12.4).
    1. When hydrocarbons contain more than three carbons, there is more than one way to arrange the carbon atoms.
      a. Some alkanes are straight-chain alkanes.
      b. Other alkanes are branched.
    2. Compounds with the same formula but different orders of connecting the carbon atoms are called constitutional isomers.
      a. Constitutional isomers have different structures and different properties.
    3. Drawing structures (Section 12.4).
      a. Condensed structures are simpler to draw than structural formulas.
        i. In condensed structures, C—H and C—C single bonds are implied rather than drawn.
        ii. Vertical bonds are often shown for clarity.
        iii. Occasionally, parentheses are used to show a row of —CH$_2$— groups.
      b. In line structures C and H don't appear.
        i Each C–C bond is represented as a line
        ii. The beginning or end of a line represents a carbon atom.
        iii. Any atom other than C or H must be shown.
  D. The shapes of organic molecules (Section 12.5).
    1. The groups around a C—C bond are free to assume an infinite number of conformations.
    2. Molecules adopt the least crowded conformation.
    3. Two structures with identical connections between atoms are identical, no matter how they are drawn.
II. Alkanes (Sections 12.6–12.8).
  A. Naming alkanes (Section 12.6).
    1. Straight-chain alkanes.
      a. Count the carbons.
      b. Find the root name.
      c. Add -ane to the root name.

  2. Alkyl groups.
    a. Remove a hydrogen from an alkane and replace -ane with -yl.
    b. More than one alkyl group can be formed from some alkanes.
      i. Isopropyl and propyl are the two groups that can be formed from propane.
      ii. Four groups can be formed from butane.
      iii. Alkyl groups can be substituents on a straight chain.
  3. Substitution patterns.
    a. Primary carbon: $R–CH_3$.
    b. Secondary carbon: $R–CH_2–R'$.
    c. Tertiary carbon:

$$R'$$
$$|$$
$$R–CH–R$$

    d. Quaternary carbon:

  4. Naming branched-chain alkanes.
    a. Name the main chain by finding the longest continuous chain of carbons and naming it.
    b. Number the carbons in the main chain, starting from the end nearer the first branch point.
    c. Identify and number each branching substituent according to its point of attachment to the main chain.
    d. Write the name as a single word.
 B. Properties of alkanes (Section 12.7).
  1. The boiling points and melting points of alkanes increase with the number of carbons.
  2. Alkanes are insoluble in water but are soluble in nonpolar organic solvents.
  3. Alkanes are colorless and odorless.
  4. Alkanes are flammable.
  5. Alkanes with four or fewer carbons are gases, those from C_5 to C_{15} are liquids, and those with more than 15 carbons are solids.
 C. Reactivity of alkanes (Section 12.8).
  1. Alkanes are very unreactive.
  2. Reactions that alkanes undergo:
    a. Combustion: alkane $+ O_2 —> CO_2 + H_2O$.
    b. Halogenation: alkane $+ X_2 —>$ halogenated alkane $+ HCl$.
III. Cycloalkanes (Sections 12.9–12.10).
 A. Properties of cycloalkanes (Section 12.9).
  1. Cycloalkanes contain rings of carbon atoms.
  2. Cyclopropane and cyclobutane are more reactive than other cycloalkanes.
  3. Cyclohexane exists in a chairlike conformation.
  4. Cycloalkanes have properties similar to those of acyclic alkanes.
  5. Free rotation is not possible around the carbon–carbon bonds of a cycloalkane ring.
 B. Drawing and naming cycloalkanes (Section 12.10).
  1. Drawing cycloalkanes.
    a. The cycloalkane ring is represented as a polygon.
  2. Naming cycloalkanes.
    a. Use the cycloalkane as the parent.
    b. Number the substituents.
      i. Start numbering at the group that has alphabetical priority.
      ii. Proceed around the ring to give to the second group the lowest possible number.

Solutions to Chapter 12 Problems

12.1

(a)

$CH_3-\overset{\overset{\displaystyle H}{|}}{C}-\overset{\overset{\displaystyle O}{\|}}{C}-OH$
$\underset{\displaystyle OH}{|}$

carboxylic acid

alcohol

Lactic acid

(b)

$H_2C=C-\overset{\overset{\displaystyle O}{\|}}{C}-O-CH_3$
$\underset{\displaystyle CH_3}{|}$

C—C double bond   ester

Methyl methacrylate

(c)

aromatic ring   amine   carboxylic acid

Phenylalanine

12.2

(a)

$H-\overset{\overset{\displaystyle H}{|}}{\underset{\underset{\displaystyle H}{|}}{C}}-\overset{\overset{\displaystyle O}{\|}}{C}-H$

an aldehyde

(b)

$H-\overset{\overset{\displaystyle H}{|}}{\underset{\underset{\displaystyle H}{|}}{C}}-\overset{\overset{\displaystyle H}{|}}{\underset{\underset{\displaystyle H}{|}}{C}}-\overset{\overset{\displaystyle O}{\|}}{C}-OH$

a carboxylic acid

12.3

$H-\overset{\overset{\displaystyle H}{|}}{\underset{\underset{\displaystyle H}{|}}{C}}-\overset{\overset{\displaystyle H}{|}}{\underset{\underset{\displaystyle H}{|}}{C}}-\overset{\overset{\displaystyle H}{|}}{\underset{\underset{\displaystyle H}{|}}{C}}-\overset{\overset{\displaystyle H}{|}}{\underset{\underset{\displaystyle H}{|}}{C}}-\overset{\overset{\displaystyle H}{|}}{\underset{\underset{\displaystyle H}{|}}{C}}-\overset{\overset{\displaystyle H}{|}}{\underset{\underset{\displaystyle H}{|}}{C}}-\overset{\overset{\displaystyle H}{|}}{\underset{\underset{\displaystyle H}{|}}{C}}-H$ C_7H_{16} Heptane

12.4 There are eight branched-chain heptanes:

12.5

(a)

CH₃CH₂CH₂CH₂CH₃

Pentane

(b)

$$CH_3$$
$$CH_3CHCH_2CH_3$$

2-Methylbutane

(c)

$$CH_3$$
$$CH_3CCH_3$$
$$CH_3$$

2,2-Dimethylpropane

12.6 *Step 1:* Find the longest carbon chain and draw this "backbone" as a zigzag line.
Step 2: Add groups to the appropriate carbons, remembering that atoms other than carbon and hydrogen must be indicated.

	Condensed Structure	*Line-bond Backbone*	*Line-bond Structure*
(a)	CH₂CH₃ CH₃CHCCH₂CH₂CH₃ 1 6 CH₂OH		
(b)	CH₂CH₃ CH₃ CH₃CHCHCH₂CHCH₃ 1 6 CH₃CHCH₂CH₃		

(c)

Notice that it is sometimes necessary to change the direction of a group to keep two groups from bumping into each other.

12.7 Reverse the steps in the previous problem.
Step 1: Draw a chain of carbons and hydrogens that is the same length as the longest chain in the line structure.
Step 2: Add condensed groups to the condensed backbone.

Line Structure	*Condensed Backbone*	*Condensed Structure*

(a)

(b)

12.8 All three structures have the same molecular formula (C_7H_{16}). Structures (a) and (c) are identical.

12.9 To solve this problem in a systematic way, use the following method:

(a) Draw the isomer of C_8H_{18} having no branches:

$$CH_3CH_2CH_2CH_2CH_2CH_2CH_2CH_3$$

(b) Draw the C_7H_{16} isomer having no branches, and replace one of the $-CH_2-$ hydrogens with a $-CH_3$. There are three different isomers:

(c) Continue with the C_6, C_5, and C_4 isomers having no branches, and replace the different kinds of hydrogens with $-CH_3$ or $-CH_2CH_3$ groups, making sure that you don't draw the same isomer.

$$CH_3CH_2CH_2CH_2\underset{\underset{CH_3}{|}}{\overset{\overset{CH_3}{|}}{C}}CH_3 \qquad CH_3CH_2CH_2\underset{\underset{CH_3}{|}}{\overset{\overset{CH_3}{|}}{CH}}CHCH_3 \qquad CH_3CH_2\overset{\overset{CH_3}{|}}{CH}CH_2\overset{\overset{CH_3}{|}}{CH}CH_3$$

$$CH_3\overset{\overset{CH_3}{|}}{CH}CH_2CH_2\overset{\overset{CH_3}{|}}{CH}CH_3 \qquad CH_3CH_2CH_2\underset{\underset{CH_3}{|}}{\overset{\overset{CH_3}{|}}{C}}CH_2CH_3 \qquad CH_3CH_2\underset{\underset{CH_3}{|}}{\overset{\overset{CH_3}{|}}{CH}}CHCH_2CH_3$$

$$CH_3CH_2CH_2\overset{\overset{CH_2CH_3}{|}}{CH}CH_2CH_3$$

$$CH_3CH_2\underset{\underset{H_3C\;CH_3}{|\;\;|}}{\overset{\overset{CH_3}{|}}{CH}}CCH_3 \qquad CH_3\overset{\overset{CH_3}{|}}{CH}CH_2\underset{\underset{CH_3}{|}}{\overset{\overset{CH_3}{|}}{C}}CH_3 \qquad CH_3CH_2\underset{\underset{CH_3}{|}}{\overset{\overset{CH_3}{|}}{C}}-\overset{\overset{CH_3}{|}}{CH}CH_3$$

$$CH_3\overset{\overset{CH_3}{|}}{CH}\underset{\underset{CH_3}{|}}{\overset{\overset{CH_3}{|}}{CH}}CHCH_3 \qquad CH_3CH_2\underset{\underset{CH_3}{|}}{\overset{\overset{CH_2CH_3}{|}}{CH}}CHCH_3 \qquad CH_3CH_2\underset{\underset{CH_3}{|}}{\overset{\overset{CH_2CH_3}{|}}{C}}CH_2CH_3 \qquad CH_3\underset{\underset{CH_3}{|}}{\overset{\overset{CH_3}{|}}{C}}-\underset{\underset{CH_3}{|}}{\overset{\overset{CH_3}{|}}{C}}CH_3$$

Line structures:

12.10

(a)

```
        7    8                                      ← 2-methyl group
       CH2—CH3                          CH3
        |                                |
→ CH3—CH—CH2—CH2—CH2—CH—CH3
      6    5    4    3    2    1 ↖
6-methyl group                          longest chain—an octane
              2,6-Dimethyloctane
```

(b)

```
                    CH2—CH3 ←——— 3-ethyl group
                     |
CH3—CH2—CH2—CH2—C—CH2—CH3 ←——— longest chain—a heptane
  7    6    5    4   3|   2    1
                    CH2—CH3 ←— 3-ethyl group
              3,3-Diethylheptane
```

12.11 To answer this problem, draw the straight-chain hydrocarbon corresponding to the parent name, and replace —H's with the groups indicated.

(a)
```
            p CH3
              |
CH3CH2CH2CHCH2CH3
 p   s    s   t  s   p
```
3-Methylhexane

(b)
```
                    p CH3
                    t |
CH3CH2CH2CH2CHCHCH2CH3
 p   s    s    s  | t  s   p
                  p CH3
```
3,4-Dimethyloctane

(c)
```
   p CH3  p CH3
     |      |
CH3CHCH2CCH3
 p   t   s  ↗| p
           q   p CH3
```
2,2,4-Trimethylpentane

Where p = primary, s = secondary, t = tertiary, and q = quaternary

12.12 There are many answers to this question. For example,

(a)
```
    CH3
     |
CH3CHCH3
     t
```
2-Methylpropane

(b)
```
    CH3          CH3
     |            |
CH3CHCH2CH2CCH3
     t           |q
                CH3
```
2,2,5-Trimethylhexane

12.13

(a)

2,2-Dimethylpentane

(b)

2,3,3-Trimethylpentane

12.14

$$2\ CH_3CH_3\ +\ 7\ O_2\ \longrightarrow\ 4\ CO_2\ +\ 6\ H_2O$$

12.15

Six different mono- and disubstitution products can be formed from the reaction of propane with chlorine.

12.16

(a)

1-Ethyl-4-methylcyclohexane

The parent ring is a cyclohexane. The two substituents are an ethyl group and a methyl group. The ethyl group receives the smaller number because it has alphabetical priority.

(b)

1-Ethyl-3-isopropylcyclopentane

The parent ring is a cyclopentane. The two substituents are an ethyl group and an isopropyl group. The ethyl group receives the smaller number because it has alphabetical priority.

12.17

(a)

1,1-Diethylcyclohexane

(b)

1,3,5-Trimethylcycloheptane

12.18

Propylcyclohexane

Understanding Key Concepts

12.19

(a)

12 hydrogens

(b)

10 hydrogens

(c)

8 hydrogens

12.20

(a)

(b)

12.21 In a line drawing, a carbon is assumed to be at the intersection of lines.

(a)

(b)

12.22

(a)

(b)

12.23

(a)

2,3-Dimethylpentane

(b)

2,5-Dimethylhexane

12.24

(a)   (b)

1,1-Dimethylcyclopentane   Isopropylcyclobutane

12.25 In one of the isomers (b), the methyl groups are on the same side of the ring, and in the other isomer (a), they are on opposite sides.

(a)   (b)

Organic Molecules and Functional Groups

12.26 If you look at the periodic table you will see that carbon belongs to group 4A, whose elements can form four bonds. Because carbon is in the middle of the periodic table, these bonds are covalent, and because it is in period 2, these bonds are strong. Consequently, carbon is unique in that it can form four strong bonds to other elements and to other carbon atoms, making possible a great many different compounds.

12.27 Functional groups are groups of atoms within a molecule that have a characteristic chemical behavior. They are important because most of the chemistry of organic compounds is determined by functional groups. The reactivity of a functional group is similar in all compounds in which it occurs.

12.28 Most organic compounds don't dissolve in water because they are nonpolar. They don't conduct electricity because they are covalent, not ionic.

12.29 There are several ways you might tell water and hexane apart. One way is to put a small amount of each sample in a test tube. The two liquids don't mix, and the less dense hexane remains on top. Alternatively, you might add a small amount of NaCl to each liquid. The salt dissolves in water but not in hexane.

12.30 A polar covalent bond is a covalent bond in which electrons are shared unequally, being more attracted to one atom than the other. For example, the electrons in the C—Br bond of bromomethane are attracted more strongly to the electronegative bromine than to carbon.

12.31 There are many possible answers to this question. For example,

(a)   (b)   (c)   (d)

Ethanol   Methylamine   Acetic acid   Diethyl ether

12.32

(a)

sulfonamide   amide

* = amine
# = double bond

Viagra

aromatic ring

ether

(b)

carboxylic acid

ester

aromatic ring

Aspirin

12.33

(a)

alcohol

C–C double bonds

Vitamin A

(b)

aromatic ring

* = amine
# = double bond

amide

Ambien

12.34 There are many possible answers to each of these questions. For example,

(a)

$CH_3CH_2CH_2CCH_3$

ketone

(b)

$CH_3CH_2CH_2C-OCH_2CH_3$

ester

(c)

H_2N-CH_2C-OH

amine
carboxylic acid

12.35

(a)

amide

(b)

aldehyde

(c)

aromatic ether

Alkanes and Isomers

12.36 For two compounds to be isomers, they must have the same molecular formula but different structures.

12.37 Compounds with the formulas C_5H_{10} and C_4H_{10} are not isomers because they don't have the same molecular formulas.

12.38 A primary carbon is bonded to one other carbon; a secondary carbon is bonded to two other carbons; a tertiary carbon is bonded to three other carbons; and a quaternary carbon is bonded to four other carbons.

12.39 A compound can't have a quintary carbon because carbon forms only four bonds, not five.

12.40 There are many possible answers to this question and the following question. For example,

(a)

2,3-Dimethylbutane

(b)

Cyclopentane

12.41

(a)

2,2-Dimethylpropane

(b)

2-Isopropyl-1,4-dimethylcyclohexane

12.42

$CH_3CH_2CH_2OH$

$CH_3CH_2-O-CH_3$

12.43 There are several possible answers to this question. For example,

(a) $CH_3CH_2NH_2$ (b) ☐ $CH_3CH=CHCH_3$ (c) $CH_3\overset{\overset{\displaystyle O}{\|}}{C}-H$ (d) $H-\overset{\overset{\displaystyle O}{\|}}{C}-OH$, $\overset{\overset{\displaystyle O}{\|}}{\underset{H}{C}}{\diagdown}OH$

12.44

(a)

$CH_3CH_2CH_2CH_2OH$ $CH_3CH_2\overset{\overset{\displaystyle OH}{|}}{C}HCH_3$ $CH_3\overset{\overset{\displaystyle CH_3}{|}}{C}HCH_2OH$ $CH_3\overset{\overset{\displaystyle OH}{|}}{\underset{\underset{\displaystyle CH_3}{|}}{C}}CH_3$

(b)

$CH_3CH_2CH_2NH_2$ $CH_3\overset{\overset{\displaystyle NH_2}{|}}{C}HCH_3$ $CH_3CH_2\overset{\overset{\displaystyle H}{|}}{N}CH_3$ $CH_3\overset{\overset{\displaystyle CH_3}{|}}{N}CH_3$

(c)

$CH_3CH_2CH_2\overset{\overset{\displaystyle O}{\|}}{C}CH_3$ $CH_3CH_2\overset{\overset{\displaystyle O}{\|}}{C}CH_2CH_3$ $CH_3\overset{\overset{\displaystyle O}{\|}}{\underset{\underset{\displaystyle CH_3}{|}}{C}}HCCH_3$

12.45

(a)

$CH_3CH_2CH_2CH_2\overset{\overset{\displaystyle O}{\|}}{C}-H$ $CH_3CH_2\overset{\overset{\displaystyle O}{\|}}{\underset{\underset{\displaystyle CH_3}{|}}{C}}HC-H$ $CH_3\overset{\overset{\displaystyle CH_3}{|}}{C}H\overset{\overset{\displaystyle O}{\|}}{C}H_2C-H$ $CH_3\overset{\overset{\displaystyle H_3C}{|}}{\underset{\underset{\displaystyle H_3C}{|}}{C}}-\overset{\overset{\displaystyle O}{\|}}{C}-H$

(b)

$CH_3CH_2\overset{\overset{\displaystyle O}{\|}}{C}-OCH_3$ $CH_3\overset{\overset{\displaystyle O}{\|}}{C}-OCH_2CH_3$ $H\overset{\overset{\displaystyle O}{\|}}{C}-OCH_2CH_2CH_3$ $H\overset{\overset{\displaystyle O}{\|}}{C}-O\overset{\overset{\displaystyle CH_3}{|}}{C}HCH_3$

(c)

$CH_3CH_2CH_2\overset{\overset{\displaystyle O}{\|}}{C}-OH$ $CH_3\overset{\overset{\displaystyle O}{\|}}{\underset{\underset{\displaystyle CH_3}{|}}{C}}HC-OH$

Remember that the C=O group of an aldehyde is found only at the end of a chain, and the C=O group of a ketone must occur in the middle.

12.46

(a)

CH$_3$CH$_2$CH$_3$ and   CH$_3$CH$_2$ are identical.
                                            |
                                           CH$_3$

(b)

CH$_3$—N—CH$_3$ and   CH$_3$CH$_2$—N—H   are isomers.
       | |
       H   H

(c)

CH$_3$CH$_2$CH$_2$—O—CH$_3$ and   CH$_3$CH$_2$CH$_2$—C̈—CH$_3$ are unrelated.

(where the second structure has O double-bonded:

$$CH_3CH_2CH_2-\overset{\overset{\displaystyle O}{\|}}{C}-CH_3$$)

(d)

$$CH_3-\overset{\overset{\displaystyle O}{\|}}{C}-CH_2CH_2\overset{\overset{\displaystyle CH_3}{|}}{C}HCH_3 \quad \text{and} \quad CH_3CH_2-\overset{\overset{\displaystyle O}{\|}}{C}-CH_2CH_2CH_2CH_3 \quad \text{are isomers.}$$

(e)

$$CH_3CH=CHCH_2CH_2-O-H \quad \text{and} \quad CH_3CH_2\overset{\overset{\displaystyle}{|}}{C}H-\overset{\overset{\displaystyle O}{\|}}{C}-H \quad \text{are isomers.}$$

(with CH$_3$ below the CH)

12.47

(a)

The first two structures are identical; the third is an isomer.

(b)

$$\overset{\overset{\displaystyle CH_3}{|}}{CH_3CHCHCH_3} \qquad \overset{\overset{\displaystyle CH_3}{|}}{CH_3CHCHCH_3} \qquad \overset{\overset{\displaystyle CH_3}{|}}{CH_2CHCH_2CH_3}$$
$$\ \ \ \ \ |\ \ \ \ \ \qquad\qquad \ \ \ \ \ |\ \ \ \ \ \qquad\qquad \ \ \ \ \ |$$
$$\ \ \ \ \ Br\ \ \ \ \ \qquad\qquad \ \ \ \ \ Br\ \ \ \ \ \qquad\qquad \ \ \ \ \ Br$$

The first two structures are identical; the third is an isomer.

12.48 All three structures have a carbon atom with five bonds.

(a)   (b)   (c)

CH$_3$=CHCH$_2$CH$_2$OH   CH$_3$CH$_2$CH=CCH$_3$ CH$_2$CH$_2$CH$_2$C≡CCH$_3$

(with O double bond on the C in (b), and CH$_3$ branch on (c))

↑   ↗   ↑   ↗

5 bonds   5 bonds   3 bonds   5 bonds

12.49

a. The carbon lettered "a" has five bonds.
b. The chlorine–carbon bond should be a single bond.

Naming Alkanes

12.50

(a)

CH_2CH_3
|
$CH_3CH_2CH_2CH_2CHCHCH_2CH_3$
|
CH_3

4-Ethyl-3-methyloctane

(b)

CH_3CHCH_3
|
$CH_3CH_2CH_2CHCH_2CHCH_3$
|
CH_2CH_3

5-Isopropyl-3-methyloctane

(c)

CH_3 CH_3
| |
$CH_3CCH_2CH_2CH_2CHCH_3$
|
CH_3

2,2,6-Trimethylheptane

(d)

$CH_2CH_2CH_2CH_3$
|
$CH_3CH_2CH_2CCH_3$
|
CH_3CHCH_3

4-Isopropyl-4-methyloctane

(e)

CH_3 CH_3
| |
$CH_3CCH_2CCH_3$
| |
CH_3 CH_3

2,2,4,4-Tetramethylpentane

(f)

CH_3CH_2 CH_3
| |
$CH_3CH_2CCH_2CH$
| |
CH_3CH_2 CH_3

4,4-Diethyl-2-methylhexane

(g)

CH_3
|
$CH_3(CH_2)_7C$—CH_3
|
CH_3

2,2-Dimethyldecane

12.51

$CH_3CH_2CH_2CH_2CH_2CH_3$
Hexane

CH_3
|
$CH_3CH_2CH_2CHCH_3$
2-Methylpentane

CH_3
|
$CH_3CH_2CHCH_2CH_3$
3-Methylpentane

CH_3
|
$CH_3CH_2CCH_3$
|
CH_3
2,2-Dimethylbutane

CH_3
|
$CH_3CHCHCH_3$
|
CH_3
2,3-Dimethylbutane

12.52

(a)

$$H_3C \quad C(CH_3)_3$$
$$CH_3CH_2C—CHCHCH_2CH_3$$
$$CH_3 \quad CH_3$$

4-*tert*-Butyl-3,3,5-trimethylheptane

(b)

$$CH_3 \quad CH_3$$
$$CH_3CHCH_2CHCH_3$$

2,4-Dimethylpentane

(c)

$$H_3C \quad CH_2CH_3$$
$$CH_3CH_2CHCCH_2CH_2CH_2CH_3$$
$$CH_2CH_3$$

4,4-Diethyl-3-methyloctane

(d)

$$CH_3CHCH_3 \quad CH_3$$
$$CH_3CHCCH_2CH_2CHCHCH_2CH_3$$
$$H_3C \quad CH_3 \quad CH_3$$

3-Isopropyl-2,3,6,7-tetramethylnonane

(e)

3-Isobutyl-1-isopropyl-5-methylcycloheptane

(f)

1,1,3-Trimethylcyclopentane

12.53

(a)

1,1-Dimethylyclopropane

(b)

1,2,3,4-Tetramethylcyclopentane

(c)

4-*tert*-Butyl-1,1-dimethylcyclohexane

(d)

Cycloheptane

(e)

1,3,5-Triisopropylcyclohexane

(f)

1,3,5,7-Tetramethylcyclooctane

12.54

(a)

1-Ethyl-3-methylcyclobutane

(b)

1,1,3,3-Tetramethylcyclopentane

(c)

1-Ethyl 3-propylcyclohexane

(d)

4-Butyl-1,1,2,2-tetramethylcyclopentane

12.55

(a)

Isobutylcyclooctane

(b)

1,2-Diethyl-3-methylcyclopropane

(c)

2-Ethyl-1-methyl-3-propylcyclopentane

12.56

	Structure	*Error*

(a)

$$CH_3CCH_2CH_2CH_3$$
with CH_3 above and CH_3 below the second carbon

2,2-Dimethylpentane

The prefix *di-* must appear when two substituents are the same.

(b)

$$CH_3CHCH_2CHCH_3$$
with CH_3 and CH_3 above

2,4-Dimethylpentane

You must choose the longest carbon chain as the parent name.

(c)

$$CH_3CHCH_2-$$
with CH_3 above, attached to cyclobutane

Isobutylcyclobutane

This compound is an alkyl-substituted cycloalkane. Choose the cycloalkane as the parent name.

12.57   *Structure*   *Error*

(a)

$$CH_2CH_3$$
$$|$$
$$CH_3CH_2CHCH_3$$

3-Methylpentane

The longest carbon chain is a pentane and should be used as the root name.

(b)

$$CH_3CHCH_3$$
$$|$$
$$CH_3CH_2CH_2CCH_3$$
$$|$$
$$CH_3$$

2,3,3-Trimethylhexane

The longest carbon chain is a hexane and should be used as the root name.

(c)

2-Ethyl-1,1-dimethylcyclopentane

The substituents should be given the lowest possible numbers. The prefix *di*- should be used when two substituents are the same.

(d)

$$CH_3 \quad CH_2CH_3$$
$$| \qquad |$$
$$CH_3CCH_2CCH_2CH_3$$
$$| \qquad |$$
$$CH_3 \quad CH_3$$

4-Ethyl-2,2,4-trimethylhexane

Numbering must start from the end nearer the first substituent.

(e)

4-Ethyl-1,2-dimethylcyclohexane

Substituents must be cited in alphabetical order (prefixes are not used for alphabetizing).

(f)

$$CH_2CH_3$$
$$|$$
$$CH_3CHCH_2CHCH_3$$
$$|$$
$$CH_2CH_3$$

3,5-Dimethylheptane

The longest carbon chain is a heptane and should be used as the root name.

(g)

$$CH_3CH_2 \quad CH_3 \quad CH_3$$
$$| \qquad | \qquad |$$
$$CH_3CH_2CH_2C —— C —— CCH_2CH_2CH_2CH_3$$
$$| \qquad | \qquad |$$
$$CH_3CH_2 \quad CH_3 \quad CH_3$$

4,4-Diethyl-5,5,6,6-tetramethyldecane

The prefixes *tetra*- and *di*- must be included in the name. Substituents must be cited in alphabetical order. Numbering must start from the end nearer to the first substituent.

12.58

$$CH_3CH_2CH_2CH_2CH_2CH_2CH_3$$

Heptane

$$\overset{\displaystyle CH_3}{\underset{\displaystyle |}{CH_3CH_2CH_2CH_2CHCH_3}}$$

2-Methylhexane

$$\overset{\displaystyle CH_3}{\underset{\displaystyle |}{CH_3CH_2CH_2CHCH_2CH_3}}$$

3-Methylhexane

$$CH_3CH_2CH_2\overset{\displaystyle CH_3}{\underset{\displaystyle CH_3}{C}}CH_3$$

2,2-Dimethylpentane

$$CH_3CH_2\overset{\displaystyle H_3C \ \ CH_3}{CHCHCH_3}$$

2,3-Dimethylpentane

$$\overset{\displaystyle CH_3 \ \ CH_3}{CH_3CHCH_2CHCH_3}$$

2,4-Dimethylpentane

$$CH_3CH_2\overset{\displaystyle CH_3}{\underset{\displaystyle CH_3}{C}}CH_2CH_3$$

3,3-Dimethylpentane

$$\overset{\displaystyle CH_2CH_3}{CH_3CH_2CHCH_2CH_3}$$

3-Ethylpentane

$$CH_3CH\overset{\displaystyle CH_3 \ \ CH_3}{-}C\overset{}{CH_3}$$
$$\underset{\displaystyle CH_3}{}$$

2,2,3-Trimethylbutane

12.59

Cyclohexane

Methylcyclopentane

1,2-Dimethylcyclobutane

1,1-Dimethylcyclobutane

1,3-Dimethylcyclobutane

Ethylcyclobutane

Propylcyclopropane

Isopropylcyclopropane

1-Ethyl-1-methylcyclopropane

1-Ethyl-2-methylcyclopropane

1,1,2-Trimethyl-
cyclopropane

1,2,3-Trimethylcyclopropane

Reactions of Alkanes

12.60

$$CH_3CH_2CH_3 + 5\ O_2 \longrightarrow 3\ CO_2 + 4\ H_2O$$

12.61

$$2\ C_8H_{18} + 25\ O_2 \longrightarrow 16\ CO_2 + 18\ H_2O$$

12.62

$$CH_3CH_2\underset{\underset{CH_3}{|}}{\overset{\overset{CH_3}{|}}{C}}CH_3 + Cl_2 \xrightarrow{\text{light}} CH_3CH_2\underset{\underset{CH_3}{|}}{\overset{\overset{CH_3}{|}}{C}}CH_2Cl + CH_3\underset{\underset{CH_3}{|}}{\overset{\overset{Cl\ \ CH_3}{|\ \ |}}{CHC}}CH_3 + ClCH_2CH_2\underset{\underset{CH_3}{|}}{\overset{\overset{CH_3}{|}}{C}}CH_3$$

12.63

$$CH_3CH_2\underset{\underset{CH_3}{|}}{\overset{\overset{CH_3}{|}}{C}}CH_3 + Br_2 \xrightarrow{\text{light}} CH_3CH_2\underset{\underset{CH_3}{|}}{\overset{\overset{CH_3}{|}}{C}}CHBr_2 + CH_3CH_2\underset{\underset{CH_3}{|}}{\overset{\overset{CH_2Br}{|}}{C}}CH_2Br + CH_3\underset{\underset{CH_3}{|}}{\overset{\overset{Br\ \ CH_3}{|\ \ |}}{CHC}}CH_2Br$$

$$+\ BrCH_2CH_2\underset{\underset{CH_3}{|}}{\overset{\overset{CH_3}{|}}{C}}CH_2Br + CH_3\underset{\underset{Br\ \ CH_3}{|\ \ |}}{\overset{\overset{Br\ \ CH_3}{|\ \ |}}{C-C}}CH_3 + BrCH_2\underset{\underset{CH_3}{|}}{\overset{\overset{Br\ \ CH_3}{|\ \ |}}{CHC}}CH_3 + Br_2CHCH_2\underset{\underset{CH_3}{|}}{\overset{\overset{CH_3}{|}}{C}}CH_3$$

Applications

12.64 It is important to know the shape of a molecule because minor differences in shape can cause differences in chemical behavior and physiological activity.

12.65 Natural gas consists of $C_1 - C_4$ hydrocarbons and is a gas at room temperature. Petroleum consists of other alkanes, some of which are very high boiling.

12.66 Branched-chain hydrocarbons burn more efficiently than straight-chain alkanes in an internal combustion engine.

General Questions and Problems

12.67–12.68

(a)

p = primary
s = secondary
t = tertiary
q = quaternary

Testosterone

(b)

amide   ester

m = methyl
p = primary
s = secondary
t = tertiary
q = quaternary

carboxylic acid

amine

Aspartame

aromatic ring

12.69 Because carbon forms only four bonds, the largest number of hydrogens that can be bonded to three carbons is eight.

C_3H_8

12.70 Since "like dissolves like," lipstick, which is composed primarily of hydrocarbons, is more soluble in the hydrocarbon petroleum jelly than in water.

12.71

(a)

monobromination product

(b)

dibromination products

12.72 Pentane has a higher boiling point than neopentane because London forces, which must be overcome in boiling, are greater for linear than for more spherical or nonlinear compounds with the same number of carbons.

12.73 Other structures are also possible.

(a)

$CH_3CH_2CH_2C-H$ with O double bonded to C

(b)

$CH_3CH_2CH=CHCH_2I$

(c)

(d)

$CH_3CH=CHCH=CH_2$

Self-Test for Chapter 12

Multiple Choice

1. Which of the following functional groups doesn't contain a carbon–oxygen double bond?
   (a) ether   (b) aldehyde   (c) ketone   (d) ester

2. In which of the following alkanes are carbons not tetrahedral?
   (a) ethane   (b) propane   (c) cyclopropane   (d) cyclohexane

3. How many products can result from chlorination of ethane? (Include products with more than one chlorine.)
   (a) 2   (b) 4   (c) 6   (d) 9

4. How many branched-chain isomers of C_6H_{14} are there?
   (a) 2   (b) 3   (c) 4   (d) 5

5. Which of the following condensed structures doesn't represent a cycloalkane?
   (a) C_3H_6 (b) C_4H_{10} (c) C_5H_{10} (d) C_6H_{12}

6.

$$CH_3CH_2\overset{\overset{\displaystyle CH_3}{|}}{C}CH_2\overset{\overset{\displaystyle CH_3}{|}}{C}HCH_3$$
$$\underset{\underset{\displaystyle CH_2CH_3}{|}}{}$$

   The correct name for the above structure is:
   (a) 3-ethyl-3,5-dimethylhexane   (b) 3-methyl-3-*sec*-butylpentane
   (c) 2,4-dimethyl-4-ethylhexane   (d) 4-ethyl-2,4-dimethylhexane

7. How many secondary carbons are in the structure shown in Problem 6?
   (a) 1   (b) 2   (c) 3   (d) 4

8. Which of the following structures is incorrectly drawn?

   (a)
   $$CH_3CH_2\overset{\overset{\displaystyle CH_3CH_2CH_2}{|}}{C}CH_2CH_2\overset{\overset{\displaystyle CH_3}{|}}{\underset{\underset{\displaystyle CH_3}{|}}{C}}CH_3$$

   (b)
   $$CH_3\overset{\overset{\displaystyle CH_3}{|}}{\underset{\underset{\displaystyle CH_3}{|}}{C}}CH_2CH_2\overset{\overset{\displaystyle CH_2CH_2CH_3}{|}}{C}HCH_3$$

   (c)
   $$CH_3CH_2\overset{\overset{\displaystyle CH_3}{|}}{C}HCH_2\overset{\overset{\displaystyle CH_3}{|}}{C}HCH_3$$

   (d)
   $$CH_3CH_2CH_2\overset{\overset{\displaystyle CH_3}{|}}{C}H\overset{\overset{\displaystyle CH_3}{|}}{\underset{\underset{\displaystyle CH_3}{|}}{C}}HCH_3$$

9. How many moles of O_2 are necessary for the complete combustion of one mole of C_6H_{12}?
   (a) 4   (b) 6   (c) 9   (d) 10

10. Which alkyl group has a quaternary carbon when part of a hydrocarbon?
    (a) *tert*-butyl   (b) isobutyl   (c) *sec*-butyl   (d) butyl

Sentence Completion

1. C_{20} to C_{36} alkanes are known as _____.

2. Alkynes are compounds that contain _____ bonds.

3. Alcohols and ethers are functional groups that contain _____.

4. Mixtures of hydrocarbons can be separated by _____.

5. A _____ _____ is a shorthand way of drawing a chemical structure.

6. A _____ carbon is bonded to four other carbons.

7. Organic compounds generally have _____ melting points than inorganic compounds.

8. Cycloalkanes are compounds that contain carbon atoms joined in a _____.

9. Organic molecules are named by the _____ system.

10. Compounds with the same formula but different structures are called _____.

11. _____ is the reaction of an alkane with oxygen.

12. A straight-chain alkane is _____ boiling than a branched-chain alkane.

True or False

1. Cyclohexane and hexane are isomers.

2. A molecule with the formula C_5H_{12} can have the root name pentane, butane, or propane.

3. A cyclohexane ring is flat.

4. The correct name of the following alkane is 1,3-dimethylpentane.

$$
\begin{array}{cc}
CH_3 & CH_3 \\
| & | \\
\end{array}
$$
$$
CH_3CH_2CHCH_2CH_2
$$

5. The compound 2,3-dimethylbutane has only primary and tertiary carbons.

6. Acyclic alkanes and cycloalkanes have similar chemical reactivity.

7. The C—Cl bond in CH_3Cl is ionic.

8. The compound 1,4-dimethylcyclohexane is correctly named.

9. Alkanes with one to four carbons exist as gases at room temperature.

10. Compounds with many functional groups are more reactive than compounds with few functional groups.

11. 2-Methylpentane and 3-methylpentane have nearly identical boiling points.

12. At room temperature, an alkane exists in a single conformation.

Match each entry on the left with its partner on the right.

1. RCH=O   (a) Contains polar covalent bonds

2. C_5H_{12} (b) Butyl group

3. $CH_3CH(CH_3)_2$ (c) Ketone

4. $CH_3CH_2CH_2CH_3$ (d) Natural gas

5. $CH_3CH_2CH_2-$ (e) Formula of methylcyclobutane

6. $R_2C=O$ (f) Branched-chain alkane

7. CH_2Cl_2 (g) An alkene

8. $C_{30}H_{62}$ (h) Propyl group

9. C_5H_{10} (i) Aldehyde

10. $CH_3CH_2CH_2CH_2-$ (j) Formula of 2-methylbutane

11. $CH_3CH=CH_2$ (k) A solid

12. CH_4 (l) Straight-chain alkane

Answers to Self Tests

Chapter One

Multiple choice: 1. b 2. d 3. b 4. d 5. a 6. a 7. c 8. b
Sentence completion: 1. nonmetallic 2. physical 3. Bi 4. condenses 5. mass and volume
6. liquid 7. pure substance 8. chemical formulas 9. malleable 10. carbon, hydrogen, oxygen
and nitrogen
True/false: 1. T 2. T 3. T 4. F (physical methods) 5. F (seven atoms) 6. T 7. F (Ag)
8. T 9. F (a gas) 10. T

Chapter Two

Number questions: 1. (a) micrometer (b) deciliter (c) megagram (d) liter (e) nanogram
2. (a) kL (b) pg (c) cm (d) hL 3. (a) 5 (b) 2 (c) 1 (d) exact (e) 3, 4, 5 or 6
4. (a) 7.03×10^{-5} g; 3 sig. fig. (b) $1.371\ 00 \times 10^5$ m; 4, 5,or 6 sig. fig. (c) 1.1×10^{-2} L; 2 sig.
fig. (d) $1.837\ 100\ 8 \times 10^7$ mm; 8 sig. fig. 5. (a) 8.07×10^2 L (b) 4.77×10^6 people
(c) 1.27×10^{-3} g (d) 1.04×10^4 μm 6. (a) 0.564 lb (b) 0.417 m (c) 7.6 L (d) 85.4 in.
(e) 95°F (f) 25°C (g) 5.92 fl oz (h) 6.17×10^{-3} oz 7. 31 cal 8. 217 g
Multiple choice: 1. b 2. d 3. b 4. a 5. c 6. d 7. b 8. c 9. c 10. a
Sentence completion : 1. kilogram, meter, cubic meter, Kelvin 2. number, unit 3. specific
heat 4. nano- 5. 3 6. 1 lb/454 g 7. calorie, joule 8. factor-label 9. Specific gravity
10. Celsius, Kelvin
True/false: 1. F (specific gravity is unitless) 2. T 3. F (three sig. fig.) 4. F (0.9464 L/1 qt.)
5. T 6. F 7. F 8. T 9. F 10. T
Matching: 1. e 2. j 3. g 4. i 5. h 6. l 7. f 8. k 9. c 10. a 11. d 12. b

Chapter Three

Multiple choice: 1. c 2. b 3. a 4. c 5. d 6. d 7. a 8. b 9. d 10. d 11. a 12. b
Sentence completion: 1. p 2. dalton 3. protons, neutrons 4. atomic number 5. shells
6. group 7. 13 8. subatomic particles 9. isotopes 10. 18 11. quantized
True/false: 1. T 2. F (5.486×10^{-4} amu) 3. F 4. T 5. F (atomic number indicates only
protons) 6. F (They're less reactive.) 7. F (in the same group) 8. T 9. T 10. F (Subshells can
contain 2,6,10 ·· electrons.) 11. T 12. F
Matching: 1. h 2. e 3. k 4. a 5. j 6. l 7. c 8. b 9. i 10. d 11. g 12. f

Chapter Four

Multiple choice: 1. d 2. a 3. d 4. c 5. a 6. b 7. b 8. d 9. b 10. d
Sentence completion: 1. Ionization energy 2. potassium phosphate 3. 2 4. polyatomic
5. simplest 6. 8 7. base 8. Hydroxyapatite 9. crystalline 10. 4A or 5A
True/false: 1. F (It forms only Zn^{2+}.) 2. T 3. F (energy needed to form an ion) 4. T 5. F
(ions formed may be H^+, $H_2PO_4^-$, and HPO_4^{2-}.) 6. F (Solutions of ions conduct electricity.) 7. F
8. T 9. T 10. F (group 8A) 11. T 12. F
Matching: 1. e 2. l 3. k 4. a 5. h 6. j 7. i 8. b 9. f 10 g 11. d 12. c

Chapter Five

Multiple choice: 1. c 2. d 3. b 4. c 5. a 6. a 7. d 8. b 9. d 10. a
Sentence completion: 1. electronegative 2. biomolecule 3. covalent 4. $C\equiv C$, $C\equiv N$
5. diatomic 6. planar trigonal 7. *d* 8. triple 9. Binary 10. organic 11. condensed
True/false: 1. T 2. T 3. F 4. F (valence electrons) 5. F (It's planar.) 6. F (covalent compounds) 7. T 8. F 9. F (Some bent molecules have bond angles that are approx. 109.5°.)
10. T 11. T
Matching: 1. h 2. j 3. f 4. a 5. k 6. i 7. e 8. c 9. b 10. g 11. d 12. l

Chapter Six

Multiple choice: 1. a 2. a 3. c 4. b 5. d 6. c 7. c 8. b 9. a 10. d
Sentence completion: 1. coefficients 2. precipitate 3. spectator 4. aqueous 5. molar mass
6. percent yield 7. reactants 8. +3 9. reducing 10. neutralization
True/false: 1. F (It has the same number of atoms.) 2. T 3. T 4. F 5. T 6. F (Molar mass is the conversion factor.) 7. F 8. F (The mole ratio is 1/2.) 9. T 10. T
Matching: 1. h 2. f 3. k 4. a 5. i 6. c 7. j 8. b 9. g 10. l 11. d 12. e

Chapter Seven

Multiple choice: 1. c 2. b 3. d 4. d 5. b 6. a 7. c 8. a 9. d 10. d
Sentence completion: 1. 1 2. conservation of energy 3. catalyst 4. reversible 5.
endothermic 6. equilibrium-constant expression 7. temperature, pressure, catalyst
8. metabolism 9. Reaction rate 10. collide
True/false: 1. F (produced) 2. F (At equilibrium, the ratio of concentrations is constant.) 3. T
4. T 5. F (The size of E_{act} and ΔH are unrelated.) 6. F (not always true for biochemical reactions) 7. T 8. F (Catalysts lower the height of the energy barrier.) 9. F (At equilibrium, the rate of the forward reaction equals the rate of the reverse reaction.) 10. T
Matching: 1. c 2. j 3. l 4. i 5. a 6. k 7. b 8. f 9. d 10. e 11. g 12. h

Chapter Eight

Multiple choice: 1. b 2. c 3. d 4. a 5. d 6. c 7. a 8. b 9. c 10. d
Sentence completion: 1. pressure, volume 2. definite, indefinite 3. Dalton's 4. standard
temperature and pressure 5. Avogadro's 6. equilibrium 7. atmosphere, Pascal, mm Hg,
pounds per square inch 8. heat of fusion 9. number of atoms, volume 10. temperature
11. change of state 12. volatile
True/false: 1. T 2. F (Only ideal gases have similar physical behavior.) 3. T 4. F (Doubling pressure halves the volume.) 5. T 6. F (only true in crystals) 7. F (273 K) 8. T 9. F (higher)
10. F (Vapor pressure doesn't depend on quantity of liquid.) 11. F (viscosity)
Matching: 1. g 2. e 3. k 4. f 5. h 6. a 7. j 8. l 9. b 10. d 11. c 12. i

Chapter Nine

Multiple choice: 1. b   2. d   3. a   4. b   5. c   6. d   7. c   8. c   9. a   10. b
Sentence completion: 1. miscible   2. gram equivalent   3. volumetric flask   4. solubility, partial pressure   5. isotonic   6. hygroscopic   7. $M_1 \times V_1 = M_2 \times V_2$ 8. colloid   9. solvent, small solute molecules   10. saturated   11. glucose   12. lower
True/false: 1. F (solvent)   2. T   3. F (A quantity of the second liquid is added to make 100 mL of solution.)   4. F   5. T   6. F (Weight/weight percent is rarely used.)   7. T   8. F (Effect of temperature is unpredictable.)   9. T (It also differs with respect to particle size.)   10. F (hemolysis)   11. F (raise)   12. T
Matching: 1. h   2. f   3. d   4. j   5. a   6. k   7. b   8. i   9. g   10. l   11. e   12. c

Chapter Ten

Multiple choice: 1. b   2. a   3. c   4. d   5. c   6. c   7. b   8. a   9. b   10. d
Sentence completion: 1. equivalent   2. red   3. diprotic   4. strong   5. Dissociation   6. OH^- ions   7. Neutralization   8. pH   9. 30.0 mL   10. conjugate   11. carbonate/bicarbonate   12. amphoteric
True/false: 1. F (60 mL of 0.1 M NaOH)   2. T   3. F (H_2SO_4 is a strong acid.)   4. F   5. F   6. T   7. T   8. F (According to this definition, an acid donates H^+.)   9. F (Ammonia yields ammonium ion, plus the anion of the acid.)   10. T   11. F   12. T
Matching: 1. d   2. e   3. g   4. l   5. a   6. b   7. i   8. j   9. c   10. f   11. k   12. h

Chapter Eleven

Multiple choice: 1. c   2. d   3. c   4. a   5. c   6. d   7. a   8. d   9. b   10. c
Sentence completion: 1. transmutation   2. Gamma radiation   3. tracer   4. background   5. nucleons   6. ^{14}C 7. curie   8. nuclear fission   9. film badges   10. body imaging   11. nuclear fusion   12. critical mass
True/false: 1. F (3/4 will have decayed after 24 days.)   2. T   3. T   4. F (Becquerel)   5. T   6. F   7. F (Atomic number increases by 1.)   8. F (Hazards are due to emissions of radiation.)   9. F (The rem is more common.)   10. T   11. F (Most are synthetic.)   12. F
Matching: 1. f   2. i   3. l   4. k   5. c   6. j   7. d   8. h   9. b   10. a   11. e   12. g

Chapter Twelve

Multiple choice: 1. a   2. c   3. d   4. c   5. b   6. d   7. c   8. a   9. c   10. a
Sentence completion: 1. paraffins   2. triple   3. oxygen   4. distillation   5. condensed structure   6. quaternary   7. lower   8. ring   9. IUPAC   10. isomers   11. Combustion   12. higher
True/false: 1. F (They have different molecular formulas.)   2. T   3. F (It's puckered.)   4. F (3-Methylhexane)   5. T   6. T   7. F (It's polar covalent.)   8. T   9. T   10. F (Reactivity depends on the nature of the functional groups.)   11. T   12. F
Matching: 1. i   2. j   3. f   4. l   5. h   6. c   7. a   8. k   9. e   10. b   11. g   12. d